Ralph J. Fessenden
University of Montana

and Joan S. Fessenden

ORGANIC CHEMISTRY

 *Willard Grant Press*
Boston, Massachusetts

© **Copyright 1979 by Willard Grant Press**
Statler Office Building, 20 Providence Street
Boston, Massachusetts 02116

Willard Grant Press is a division of Wadsworth, Inc.

Third printing: August 1980

Library of Congress Cataloging in Publication Data

Fessenden, Ralph J
     Organic chemistry.

     Includes index.
     1. Chemistry, Organic.   I.   Fessenden, Joan S., joint
author.   II.   Title.
QD251.2.F49   547   78-23768
ISBN 0-87150-724-2

Production supervised by David Chelton under the direction of Michael Michaud.

Text design by David Chelton in collaboration with Michael Michaud and the staff of Willard Grant Press. Text composition in Monophoto Times Roman by Composition House Limited. Technical art by J & R Services. Cover design by John Servideo. Printed and bound by Rand McNally & Co.

Preface

To the beginning student, organic chemistry often appears to be a bewildering collection of unrelated structures, names, reactions, and mechanisms. This impression, of course, is false; but if students are to sort out these complexities, they must be able to distinguish between basic concepts and the extensions of these concepts. They must also be able to recognize the interrelationships between the various organic reactions. Therefore, a textbook should be more than just a source of information. It must guide the students and supply the framework for their learning. This is what we have attempted to provide in this book.

We have tried to explain each new topic and reaction thoroughly. Formulas and equations are annotated with explanatory notes. New reactions are compared and contrasted with reactions previously introduced. "Electron-pushing" mechanisms are shown wherever feasible. Each chapter is liberally supplied with worked-out sample problems and study problems for student solution. Chapter summaries are provided to reinforce the important points and to show similarities among groups of reactions.

In overall organization, our approach has been to develop first the concepts of structure and bonding and then discuss reactions and reaction mechanisms. Explanation of a few other points will point out why.

Introductory Material. Teaching organic chemistry was a rather simple affair 25 years ago. The traditional order of presentation was structural isomerism and nomenclature, followed by reactions. Today, in addition to these subjects, we must teach molecular orbital theory, stereochemistry, spectroscopy, and mechanisms, not to mention new reactions.

The inclusion of these new topics can impose a heavy "front load" of introductory material. We have made a special attempt to keep this to a minimum. Even so, we cannot, in good conscience, present a reaction and its mechanism on page 1. It is more important that the student first get a firm grasp on structure and bonding. These are the topics stressed in the first four chapters.

Chapters 1 and 2 are primarily reviews of atomic and molecular structure, along with electronegativity, hydrogen bonding, acid–base reactions, and molecular orbitals, presented for the most part in a graphical way. We have included the bonding of some simple nitrogen and oxygen compounds as a way of introducing the concept of functional groups. A brief introduction to resonance theory is also presented here.

The student's introduction to structural isomerism and nomenclature comes in Chapter 3. Besides describing the nomenclature of alkanes, we briefly introduce the naming of a few other classes of compounds that will be encountered early in the book. Chapter 4, "Stereochemistry," contains more on structure: geometric isomerism, conformation, and chirality.

Organic Reactions. Since all of organic chemistry is interrelated, instructors must decide where and how to introduce organic reactions. If they start with free-radical halogenation, will this reaction assume the position of highest importance in the student's mind? Will such an approach place undue emphasis on hydrocarbon chemistry? We believe the answer to both these questions is "Yes." Therefore, our approach is to begin in Chapter 5 with the substitution and elimination reactions of alkyl halides (S_N2, S_N1, E1, and E2). This is followed by free-radical halogenation in Chapter 6.

There are several reasons why we introduce reactions and reaction mechanisms in this way instead of with the more traditional free-radical chlorination of methane.

(1) Reactions involving pairs of electrons are more common in organic chemistry than those involving unpaired electrons.

(2) The S_N2 reaction is a one-step reaction with a single transition state, and thus is ideal for introducing transition-state diagrams and reaction kinetics.

(3) The S_N2 reaction, as well as the S_N1, E1, and E2 reactions that follow, allows us to apply the stereochemical principles just covered in Chapter 4.

(4) The presentation of the S_N1 reaction is a logical extension of the S_N2 reaction; therefore, steric hindrance and carbocations can be discussed early in the course.

(5) Substitution and elmination reactions are excellent vehicles for introducing organic syntheses, and they lend themselves much better to beginning laboratory experiments than do free-radical reactions.

Alcohols, Chapter 7, follow the two chapters on alkyl halides because of the similarities in the substitution and elimination reactions of these two groups of compounds. After pausing in the presentation of organic reactions to introduce spectroscopy in Chapter 8, we continue with the chemistry of alkenes and alkynes (Chapter 9), benzene (Chapter 10), and carbonyl compounds (Chapters 11–13). The remaining chapters in the text are of more specialized interest. They may be included or omitted, in whole or in part, or presented in a different order as the instructor desires or has time for.

Throughout this text, our approach to reactions has been to show the similarities of the reactions of a particular group of compounds. For this reason. most reactions and their mechanisms are introduced in the sections on *reactions* of a class of compounds, instead of in the *preparation* section. Consequently, our preparation sections, such as 7.4 and 7.5 (preparations of alcohols and ethers), tend to be reviews of previously learned material. Although we feel these sections are good reinforcement, it is possible to delete them or present them elsewhere in your own presentation.

Spectroscopy.   Spectroscopy is discussed as early as we think feasible—
Chapter 8. By this time, the student has a working knowledge of structure, a few
functional groups, and a few reactions. However, those who wish to do so may
cover the spectroscopy chapter right after Chapter 4, as soon as the students are
familiar with organic structures.

We have included only infrared and nuclear magnetic resonance spectroscopy in Chapter 8 because of their importance in structure determination.
Sufficient background in the principles behind infrared and nmr spectroscopy is
presented so that students can appreciate why spectra and structures are related,
but the emphasis is on structure. Wherever appropriate after Chapter 8, we have
inserted sections on the infrared and nmr characteristics of the compound classes
being discussed. Structure-determination problems involving infrared and nmr
spectra are included at the ends of many of these later chapters.

Ultraviolet and mass spectra are covered in Chapter 20. Our only reason for
having two separate chapters on spectroscopy is to get the students quickly back
into reaction chemistry. Both of these techniques can be presented along with infrared and nmr spectra if the instructor wishes. Ultraviolet and mass spectroscopy are designed to stand alone. One or both can be introduced whenever
you think desirable.

Problems.   We are firm believers in problem solving as an important part
of learning organic chemistry, and we have included more than 1100 unsolved
problems in the text. Within each chapter, a number of worked-out sample problems are included to illustrate the approach to problem solving and to provide
further information. Often these sample problems are followed directly by study
problems with answers at the end of the book. Many of these study problems are
designed to relate previous material to the present discussion. Others are designed
to test students on their mastery of new material.

The problems at the end of each chapter are of two types: drill problems and
thought problems. Although their order of presentation tends to follow the
chapter organization, they are graded in difficulty. The last several problems in
each chapter should challenge even the best students. The *Study Guide with Solutions* that accompanies this text contains the answers to the chapter-end problems
and also provides further explanation where appropriate.

Nomenclature.   Many chemists think the time is overdue to switch from
trivial names of organic compounds to systematic names. We agree. However,
any issue of *Chemical and Engineering News* or any chemical catalog makes
heavy use of trivial nomenclature. To be able to speak the language of chemists, a
student needs to know that "acetone" and "propanone" are synonymous.
Because of the present unsettled state of nomenclature, we have emphasized the
IUPAC system, but we have not used it exclusively. Also used are some trivial
names that are part of every organic chemist's vocabulary; for example, acetone
and *t*-butyl chloride.

Our presentation of naming begins with a brief survey of systematic
nomenclature in Chapter 3. The names presented there are those that the student
will encounter again in chapters immediately following. The nomenclature for
each class of compound is then discussed in more detail in later chapters. An appendix is included for those who wish additional material or a quick source of
reference.

Synthesis. Opinions vary widely among instructors as to how much synthesis should be presented to students in an introductory course. Our formal discussions of organic synthesis are set off in separate sections and can therefore easily be emphasized or de-emphasized. These include Sections 5.12 (one-step syntheses); 7.18 (multistep syntheses); 10.12 (syntheses from benzene); and Chapter 14 (syntheses using enolates and enamines).

Topics of Specialized Interest. Organic chemistry lends itself to many fascinating sidelights. Unfortunately, what is of particular interest to one instructor may be of no interest to another. Although many authors have chosen to group topics of specialized interest into separate chapters, we prefer not to. Instead these subjects are placed where they follow logically from previous material. In this book, for example, electrocyclic reactions and polymers are found toward the end of Chapter 9 on alkenes and alkynes. In almost all cases, specialized topics will be found in separate sections so that they may be dealt with as the instructor deems best.

What sort of special-interest topics are included? Generally, ours fall into one of two categories: *organic chemistry for organic chemists* (e.g., electrocyclic reactions, polymers, carbenes, the cyclization of squalene) or *organic chemistry as it relates to the biological sciences* (e.g., the role of imines in transamination reactions, metabolism of ethanol, acetylcoenzyme A as an alkylating agent).

Bio-organic material. Many students in the introductory organic course are majoring in biological fields. Therefore, numerous sections and problems that are biological in nature have been included. We have selected material that is appropriate to the chemistry under discussion and that requires application of organic logic. Our intention is to show the close relationship between organic chemistry and the biological sciences.

Acknowledgments

A book of this magnitude requires the help of many people. We are indebted to the reviewers of the various drafts of the manuscript as it progressed from crude copy to its final form. First, we thank those who helped us formulate our ideas of topics to be included: James M. Bobbitt (Univ. of Connecticut); Harland D. Embree (San Jose State Univ.); John A. Katzenellenbogen (Univ. of Illinois); Robert R. Winkler (Ohio Univ.); and many others.

Second, we thank those who reviewed portions of the manuscript: Richard Field and Fred Shafizadeh (both of the Univ. of Montana); Kurt Loening (Chemical Abstracts); Richard Bozak (California State Univ., Hayward); Slayton Evans (Univ. of North Carolina, Chapel Hill); David Garin (Univ. of Missouri, St. Louis); Jack E. Leonard (Texas A & M Univ.); and Charles H. Stammer (Univ. of Georgia).

Third, we thank our colleagues who reviewed a complete draft of the manuscript in detail: John P. Idoux (Florida Technological Univ.); Edwin M. Kaiser (Univ. of Missouri, Columbia); Philip W. Le Quesne (Northeastern Univ.); Yorke E. Rhodes (New York Univ.); Martin A. Schwartz (Florida State Univ.); and Leroy G. Wade (Colorado State Univ.).

We are especially grateful to James O. Schreck (Univ. of Northern Colorado) and Boris Weinstein (Univ. of Washington), who critiqued *more than one draft* of the manuscript, a monumental undertaking!

The manuscript for this book has been used in the sophomore organic chemistry course here at the University of Montana for two years. The students have been extremely helpful (and maybe eager) in pointing out rough spots and errors.

Only someone who has typed a manuscript for an organic chemistry textbook can truly appreciate what this task entails! Therefore, we acknowledge our typists: Jackie Dunston, Karen Kougioulis, Susan Pirrong, Dianne Wilcoxson, and Carrie Avshalomov.

Our gratitude also goes to the people at Willard Grant Press: Arthur Weber, who kindled our initial enthusiasm; David Chelton, who has done an excellent job of putting the final manuscript into book form; and, most of all, our editor Bruce Thrasher. His interest, his encouragement, his patience, and his advice made this book possible.

Ralph J. Fessenden
Joan S. Fessenden

University of Montana
Missoula, Montana

Contents

Atoms and Molecules— A Review

Around 1850, organic chemistry was defined as **the chemistry of compounds that come from living things**—hence the term *organic*. This definition was well-outgrown by about 1900. By that time, chemists were synthesizing new organic compounds in the laboratory, and many of these new compounds had no link with any living thing. Today, organic chemistry is defined as **the chemistry of the compounds of carbon**. This definition too is not entirely correct, because a few carbon compounds, such as carbon dioxide, sodium carbonate, and potassium cyanide, are considered to be inorganic. We accept this definition, however, because all organic compounds do contain carbon.

Carbon is but one element among many in the periodic table. What is so unique about carbon that its compounds justify a major subdivision in the study of chemistry? The answer is that carbon atoms can be covalently bonded to other carbon atoms and to atoms of other elements in a wide variety of ways, leading to an almost infinite number of different compounds. These compounds range in complexity from the simple compound methane (CH_4), the major component of natural gas and marsh gas, to the quite complex nucleic acids, the carriers of the genetic code in living systems.

A knowledge of organic chemistry is indispensable to many scientists. For example, because living systems are composed primarily of water and organic compounds, almost any area of study concerned with plants, animals, or micro-organisms depends on the principles of organic chemistry. These areas of study include medicine and the medical sciences, biochemistry, microbiology, agriculture, and many others. However, these are not the only fields that depend on organic chemistry. Plastics and synthetic fibers are also organic compounds. Petroleum and natural gas consist mostly of compounds of carbon and hydrogen that have been formed by the decomposition of plants. Coal is a mixture of elemental carbon combined with compounds of carbon and hydrogen.

Where do we start? The cornerstone of organic chemistry is the covalent bond. Before we discuss the structure, nomenclature, and reactions of organic compounds in detail, we will first review some aspects of atomic structure and bonding (Chapter 1) and then the molecular orbital theory of covalent bonding (Chapter 2) as these topics apply to organic compounds.

Section 1.1

Electron Structure of the Atom

The most important elements to organic chemists are carbon, hydrogen, oxygen, and nitrogen. These four elements are in the first two periods of the periodic table and their electrons are all found in the two electron shells closest to the nucleus. Consequently, our discussion of the electron structures of atoms will center mainly on elements with electrons only in these two electron shells.

Each electron shell is associated with a certain amount of energy. Electrons close to the nucleus are more attracted by the protons than are electrons farther away. Therefore, the closer an electron is to the nucleus, the lower is its energy. The electron shell closest to the nucleus is the one of lowest energy, and an electron in this shell is said to be at the **first energy level**. Electrons in the second shell, at the **second energy level**, are of higher energy than those in the first shell. Electrons in the third shell, at the **third energy level**, are of higher energy yet.

A.   Atomic Orbitals

We cannot accurately determine the position of an electron relative to the nucleus of an atom. Instead, we must rely upon quantum theory to describe the most likely location of an electron. Each electron shell of an atom is subdivided into **atomic orbitals**, an atomic orbital being a region in space where the probability of finding an electron of a specific energy content is high (90–95%). **Electron density** is another term used to describe the probability of finding an electron in a particular spot; a higher electron density means a greater probability, while a lower electron density means a lesser probability.

The first electron shell contains only the spherical 1s orbital. The probability of finding a 1s electron is highest in this sphere. The second shell, which is slightly farther from the nucleus than the first shell, contains one 2s orbital and three 2p orbitals. The 2s orbital, like the 1s orbital, is spherical.

Figure 1.1 shows a graph of electron density in the 1s and 2s orbitals as a function of distance from the nucleus. It may be seen from the graph that the 1s and 2s orbitals do not have sharply defined surfaces, but rather the electron density increases and decreases over a range of distances from the nucleus. The result is that the 1s and 2s orbitals overlap each other.

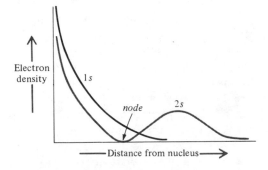

Figure 1.1.   Graphic relationship between the 1s and 2s atomic orbitals.

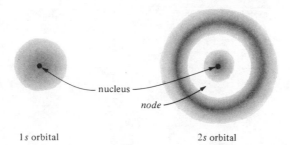

1s orbital   2s orbital

Figure 1.2. Pictorial representations of the 1s and 2s atomic orbitals.

The electron density–distance curve for the 2s orbital reveals two areas of high electron density separated by a zero point. This zero point is called a **node**, and represents a region in space where the probability of finding an electron (the 2s electron in this case) is very small. All orbitals except the 1s orbital have nodes. Pictorial representations of the 1s and 2s orbitals are shown in Figure 1.2.

The second energy level also contains three 2p atomic orbitals. The 2p orbitals are at a slightly greater distance from the nucleus than the 2s orbital and are of slightly higher energy. The p orbitals are shaped rather like dumbbells; each p orbital has two lobes separated by a node (a nodal plane in this case) at the nucleus (see Figure 1.3).

A sphere (an s orbital) is nondirectional; that is, it appears the same when viewed from any direction. This is not the case with a p orbital, which can assume different orientations around the nucleus. The three 2p orbitals are at *right angles* to each other—this orientation allows maximum distance between the electrons in the three p orbitals and thus minimizes repulsions between electrons in different p orbitals. The mutually perpendicular p orbitals are sometimes designated p_x, p_y, and p_z. The subscript letters refer to the x, y, and z axes that may be drawn through pictures of these p orbitals, as in Figure 1.3.

Since the three 2p orbitals are equivalent in shape and in distance from the nucleus, they have equal energies. Orbitals that have the same energy, such as the three 2p orbitals, are said to be **degenerate**.

The third electron shell contains one 3s orbital, three 3p orbitals, and also five 3d orbitals. The numbers of atomic orbitals at each of the first three energy levels are summarized in Table 1.1.

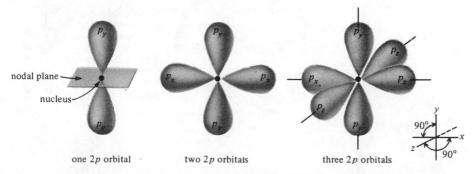

nodal plane

nucleus

one 2p orbital   two 2p orbitals   three 2p orbitals

Figure 1.3. The shapes and orientations of the 2p orbitals.

Table 1.1.   *Atomic Orbitals in the First Three Energy Levels*

Energy level	Atomic orbitals
1	$1s$
2	$2s$ $2p_x$ $2p_y$ $2p_z$
3	$3s$ $3p_x$ $3p_y$ $3p_z$ plus five $3d$

B.   Filling the Orbitals

Electrons have spin, which can be either clockwise or counterclockwise. The spin of a charged particle gives rise to a small magnetic field, or **magnetic moment**, and two electrons rotating in opposite directions have *opposite magnetic moments*. The repulsion between the negative charges of two electrons with opposite spin is minimized by the opposite magnetic moments, allowing two such electrons to become *paired* within an orbital. For this reason, any orbital can hold a maximum of two electrons, but those electrons must be of opposite spin. Because of the number of orbitals at each energy level (one at the first energy level, four at the second, and nine at the third), the first three energy levels can hold up to two, eight, and 18 electrons, respectively.

The **aufbau principle** (German, "building up") states that as we progress from hydrogen (atomic number 1) to atoms of successively higher atomic number, orbitals become filled with electrons in such a way that the *lowest-energy orbitals are filled first*. A hydrogen atom has its single electron in a $1s$ orbital. The next element, helium (atomic number 2), has its second electron also in the $1s$ orbital. The two electrons in this orbital are paired.

A description of the electron structure for an element is called its **electron configuration**. The electron configuration for H is $1s^1$, which means one electron (superscript 1) in the $1s$ orbital. For He, the electron configuration is $1s^2$, meaning *two* electrons (superscript 2) in the $1s$ orbital. Lithium (atomic number 3) has two electrons in the $1s$ orbital and one electron in the $2s$ orbital; its electron configuration is $1s^2$ $2s^1$.

Table 1.2.   *Electron Configurations of the Elements in Periods 1 and 2*

Element	Atomic number	Electron configuration
H	1	$1s^1$
He	2	$1s^2$
Li	3	$1s^2$ $2s^1$
Be	4	$1s^2$ $2s^2$
B	5	$1s^2$ $2s^2$ $2p^1$
C	6	$1s^2$ $2s^2$ $2p^2$
N	7	$1s^2$ $2s^2$ $2p^3$
O	8	$1s^2$ $2s^2$ $2p^4$
F	9	$1s^2$ $2s^2$ $2p^5$
Ne	10	$1s^2$ $2s^2$ $2p^6$

The electron configurations for the first- and second-period elements are shown in Table 1.2. In carbon and the succeeding elements, each $2p$ orbital receives one electron before any $2p$ orbital receives a second electron. This is an example of **Hund's rule**: In filling the orbitals, pairing of two electrons in degenerate orbitals does not occur until each degenerate orbital contains one electron. Therefore, carbon has an electron configuration of $1s^2\ 2s^2\ 2p_x^1\ 2p_y^1$.

Atomic Radius

The **radius of an atom** is the distance from the center of the nucleus to the outermost electrons. The atomic radius is determined by measuring the **bond distance** (the distance between nuclei) in a covalent compound such as Cl—Cl or H—H and dividing by two. Therefore, atomic radii are often called **covalent radii**. Values for atomic radii are usually given in Angstroms (Å), where 1 Å = 10^{-8} cm.

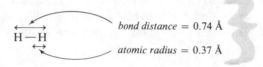

H—H   bond distance = 0.74 Å
       atomic radius = 0.37 Å

Atomic radii vary depending on the extent of attraction between the nucleus and its electrons. The greater the attraction, the smaller is the atomic radius. What factors affect this attraction? The most important factors are the *number of protons in the nucleus* and *the number of shells containing electrons*.

A nucleus with a greater number of protons has a greater attraction for its electrons, including the outermost electrons. Consider the elements of the second row of the periodic table (lithium to fluorine). An atom of any of these elements has electrons in only the first two electron shells. As we progress stepwise from lithium to fluorine, a proton is added to the nucleus. At each step, the nucleus has a greater attraction for the electrons, and the atomic radius decreases (refer to Figure 1.4, page 6).

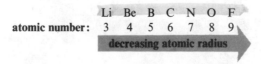

	Li	Be	B	C	N	O	F
atomic number:	3	4	5	6	7	8	9

decreasing atomic radius

As we proceed from top to bottom within a group in the periodic table, the number of electron shells increases, and therefore so does the atomic radius.

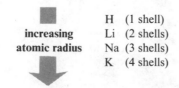

increasing atomic radius

H   (1 shell)
Li   (2 shells)
Na   (3 shells)
K   (4 shells)

H 0.37						
Li 1.225	**Be** 0.889	**B** 0.80	**C** 0.771	**N** 0.74	**O** 0.74	**F** 0.72
Na 1.572	**Mg** 1.364	**Al** 1.248	**Si** 1.173	**P** 1.10	**S** 1.04	**Cl** 0.994
						Br 1.142
						I 1.334

Figure 1.4. Atomic radii (in Angstroms, Å) of some of the elements.

In organic chemistry, atoms are bonded together in close proximity to one another by covalent bonds. We will find the concept of atomic radii useful in estimating the attractions and repulsions between atoms and in discussing covalent bond strengths.

Section 1.3

Electronegativity

Electronegativity is a measure of the ability of an atom to attract its outer electrons. Since it is the outer electrons of an atom that are used for bonding, electronegativity is useful for predicting and explaining chemical reactivity. Like the atomic radius, electronegativity is affected by the number of protons in the nucleus and by the number of shells containing electrons. A greater number of protons means a greater positive nuclear charge, and thus an increased attraction for the bonding electrons. Therefore, electronegativity increases as we go from left to right in a given period of the periodic table.

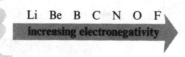

Li Be B C N O F
increasing electronegativity

Attractions between oppositely charged particles decrease with increasing distance between the particles. Thus, electronegativity decreases as we proceed from top to bottom in a given group of the periodic table because the bonding electrons are at a greater distance from the nucleus.

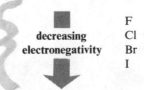

decreasing
electronegativity

F
Cl
Br
I

The **Pauling scale** (Figure 1.5) is a numerical scale of electronegativities. This scale is derived from bond-energy calculations for different elements joined by covalent bonds. In the Pauling scale, fluorine, the most electronegative element, has an electronegativity value of 4. Lithium, which has a low electronegativity, has a value of 1. An element with a very low electronegativity (such as lithium) is sometimes called an **electropositive** element. Carbon has an intermediate electronegativity value of 2.5.

H 2.1						
Li 1.0	**Be** 1.5	**B** 2.0	**C** 2.5	**N** 3.0	**O** 3.5	**F** 4.0
Na 0.9	**Mg** 1.2	**Al** 1.5	**Si** 1.8	**P** 2.1	**S** 2.5	**Cl** 3.0
						Br 2.8
						I 2.5

Figure 1.5.   Electronegativities of some elements (Pauling scale).

Section 1.4

Introduction to the Chemical Bond

Because of their different electron structures, atoms can become bonded together in molecules in different ways. In 1916, G. N. Lewis and W. Kössel advanced the following theories:

(1)   An **ionic bond** results from the transfer of electrons from one atom to another.

(2)   A **covalent bond** results from the sharing of a pair of electrons by two atoms.

(3)   Atoms transfer or share electrons so as to gain a **noble-gas electron configuration**. This configuration is usually eight electrons in the outer shell, which is the electron configuration of neon and argon. This theory is called the **octet rule**.

The ionic bond is formed by electron transfer. One atom donates one or more of its outermost, or bonding, electrons to another atom or atoms. The atom that loses electrons becomes a positive ion, or **cation**. The atom that gains the electrons becomes a negative ion, or **anion**. The ionic bond is the resulting electrostatic attraction between these oppositely charged ions. We may illustrate electron transfer by using dots to represent the bonding electrons.

$$Na\cdot + \cdot\ddot{\underset{\cdot\cdot}{Cl}}: \longrightarrow Na:\ddot{\underset{\cdot\cdot}{Cl}}: \quad or \quad Na^+ \ Cl^-$$

A covalent bond is the sharing of a pair of bonding electrons between two atoms. Shared electrons result from the merging of the atomic orbitals into shared orbitals called **molecular orbitals**, a topic that we will discuss in Chapter 2. For now, we will use dots to represent bonding electrons. With the dot formulas, called **Lewis formulas**, we can easily count electrons and see that the atoms attain noble-gas configurations: two electrons (helium configuration) for hydrogen and eight electrons for most other atoms.

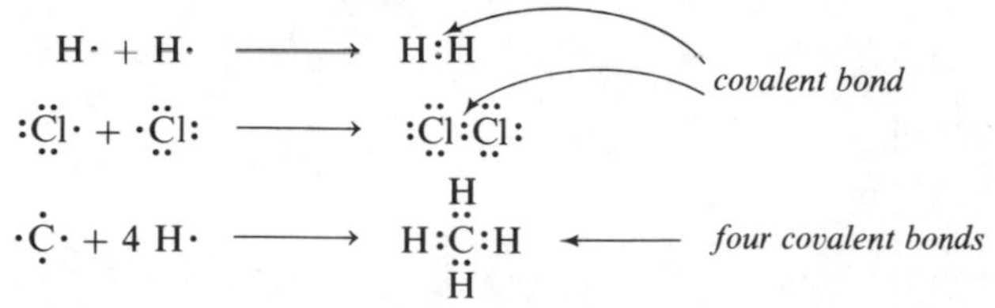

The sharing of one pair of electrons between two atoms is called a **single bond**. Two atoms can share two pairs or even three pairs of electrons; these multiple bonds are called **double bonds** and **triple bonds**, respectively.

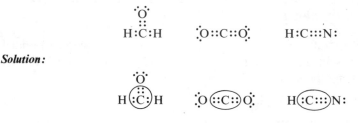

Sample Problem

Circle the eight bonding electrons associated with the carbon atom in each of the following structures:

$$ \overset{\displaystyle \cdot \cdot}{\underset{\displaystyle \cdot \cdot}{O}} $$
$$ H\!:\!\overset{..}{C}\!:\!H \qquad \cdot\overset{..}{O}::C::\overset{..}{O}\cdot \qquad H\!:\!C\!:::\!N\!: $$

Solution:

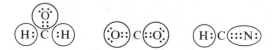

Sample Problem

For the structures in the preceding problem, circle the two electrons associated with each hydrogen atom and the eight electrons associated with each oxygen and nitrogen atom.

Solution:

When do atoms form ionic bonds and when do they form covalent bonds? Ionic bonds are formed when the electronegativity difference between two atoms is large (greater than about 1.7). For example, a sodium atom (electronegativity

0.9), with little attraction for its bonding electron, readily loses this electron to a chlorine atom (electronegativity 3.0). On the other hand, the electronegativity difference between two carbon atoms is zero; between carbon and hydrogen, only 0.4; and between carbon and chlorine, 0.5. Because carbon has an electro-negativity of 2.5, intermediate between the extremes of high and low electro-negativity, it almost never forms ionic bonds with other elements. Instead, *carbon forms covalent bonds with other carbon atoms and with atoms of other elements.*

A. Valence

The **valence** of an atom is the number of electrons that the atom loses, gains, or shares. In a covalent molecule, the valence of each atom is the number of co-valent bonds that the atom forms. Carbon has four bonding electrons and forms four covalent bonds to attain an octet. Therefore, we say that carbon has a valence of four. Table 1.3 lists typical valences of elements commonly found in organic compounds.

$$
\begin{array}{ccc}
\underset{\substack{\text{valence}\\\text{of 4}}}{\cdot \overset{\cdot}{\text{C}} \cdot} & + & \underset{\substack{\text{valence}\\\text{of 1}}}{4\ \text{H} \cdot} & \longrightarrow & \overset{\displaystyle \text{H}}{\underset{\displaystyle \text{H}}{\text{H} : \overset{..}{\underset{..}{\text{C}}} : \text{H}}}
\end{array}
$$

$$
\begin{array}{ccc}
\underset{\substack{\text{valence}\\\text{of 4}}}{\cdot \overset{\cdot}{\text{C}} \cdot} & + & \underset{\substack{\text{valence}\\\text{of 1}}}{4\ : \overset{..}{\underset{..}{\text{Cl}}} \cdot} & \longrightarrow & \overset{\displaystyle : \overset{..}{\underset{..}{\text{Cl}}} :}{\underset{\displaystyle : \overset{..}{\underset{..}{\text{Cl}}} :}{: \overset{..}{\underset{..}{\text{Cl}}} : \overset{..}{\underset{..}{\text{C}}} : \overset{..}{\underset{..}{\text{Cl}}} :}}
\end{array}
$$

Table 1.3. *Most Common Valence of Some Elements Typically Encountered in Organic Compounds*

Element	Valence
H	1
C	4
O	2
N	3
Cl	1
I	1
Br	1

For simple structures, we can often deduce the Lewis formula for a compound of known composition from valence rules alone.

Sample Problem

Give the Lewis formulas for H_2O and C_2H_6.

Solution:

(1)   Determine the number of valence electrons of each atom: H = 1;   O = 6;   C = 4.

(2)   Draw the skeleton of the molecule following the rules of valence: H can form one covalent bond; O can form two; and C can form four,

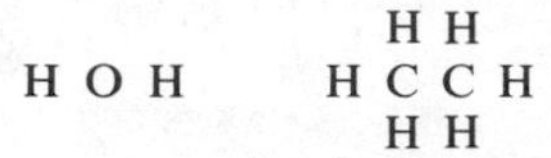

$$\begin{array}{cc} & \text{H H} \\ \text{H O H} & \text{H C C H} \\ & \text{H H} \end{array}$$

(3)   Distribute the valence electrons in such a way that each H has two electrons and each other atom has an octet.

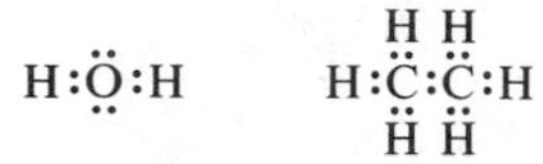

$$\begin{array}{cc} & \text{H H} \\ \text{H:}\overset{..}{\text{O}}\text{:H} & \text{H:}\overset{..}{\text{C}}\text{:}\overset{..}{\text{C}}\text{:H} \\ & \text{H H} \end{array}$$

Sample Problem

Give the Lewis formula for C_3H_8 and two Lewis formulas for C_2H_6O.

Solution:

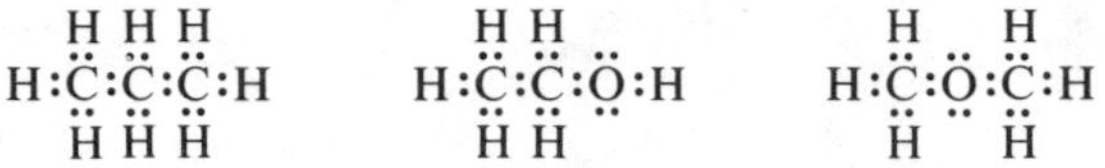

$$\begin{array}{ccc} \text{H H H} & \text{H H} & \text{H \quad H} \\ \text{H:}\overset{..}{\text{C}}\text{:}\overset{..}{\text{C}}\text{:}\overset{..}{\text{C}}\text{:H} & \text{H:}\overset{..}{\text{C}}\text{:}\overset{..}{\text{C}}\text{:}\overset{..}{\text{O}}\text{:H} & \text{H:}\overset{..}{\text{C}}\text{:}\overset{..}{\text{O}}\text{:}\overset{..}{\text{C}}\text{:H} \\ \text{H H H} & \text{H H} & \text{H \quad H} \end{array}$$

STUDY PROBLEM

1.1   Each of the following structures contains a double or triple bond. Give the Lewis formulas.

(a) Cl_2CO (b) C_2Cl_4

B.   Formal Charge

In some structures, the rules of valence do not seem to be followed. One such case occurs when one atom in a molecule provides both electrons for a covalent bond.

$$\overset{\overset{..}{\text{O}}\text{:}}{\underset{}{\text{H:}\overset{..}{\text{O}}\text{:N::}\overset{..}{\text{O}}\text{:}}} \quad both\ e^-\ from\ N$$

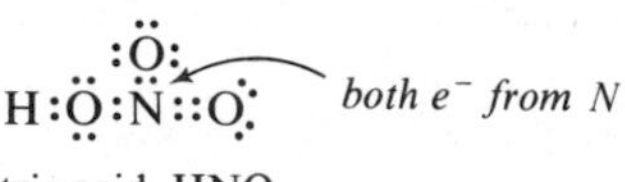

nitric acid, HNO_3

If one atom provides both electrons for a covalent bond, the bond is called a **coordinate covalent bond**. In such a case, some atoms within the covalent structure carry a positive or negative charge called a **formal charge**. In the coordinate covalent bond, the donating atom has a formal charge of $+1$, and the accepting atom has a formal charge of -1. Since both charges are found within the same structure, the opposite charges cancel, and the molecule as a whole may have no net ionic charge. (If the charges do not cancel, the structure represents an ion with a net ionic charge.)

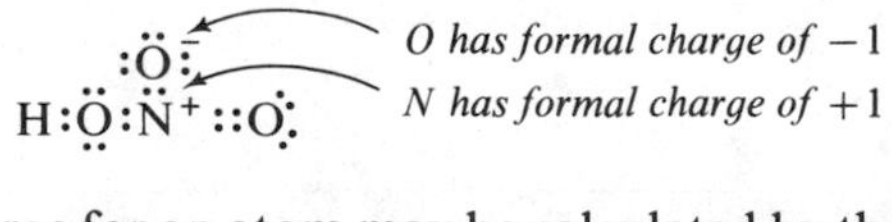

$$\begin{array}{l} :\overset{..}{\text{O}}\text{:} \\ \text{H:}\overset{..}{\text{O}}\text{:N}^+\text{::}\overset{..}{\text{O}}\text{:} \end{array} \quad \begin{array}{l} O\ has\ formal\ charge\ of\ -1 \\ N\ has\ formal\ charge\ of\ +1 \end{array}$$

The formal charge for an atom may be calculated by the following equation:

formal charge = (number of valence e^- in a neutral atom)

$-\frac{1}{2}$ (number of shared e^-) $-$ (number of unshared e^-)

Example: Using the formula, we can calculate the formal charges on N and each O in HNO_3. (H does not carry a formal charge in covalent molecules.)

$$H:\ddot{O}:N::\ddot{O}:$$

no. of valence e^- for N = 5

$\frac{1}{2}$(no. of shared e^- for N) = 4

no. of unshared e^- for N = 0

formal charge for N = $5 - 4 - 0 = +1$

For each O, the same technique is used.

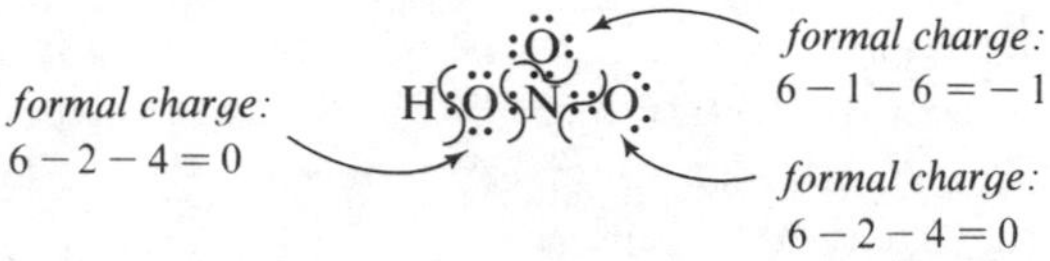

formal charge:
$6 - 1 - 6 = -1$

formal charge:
$6 - 2 - 4 = 0$

formal charge:
$6 - 2 - 4 = 0$

Some other examples of calculation of formal charge follow:

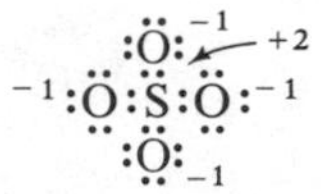

for S: $6 - 4 - 0 = +2$

for each O: $6 - 1 - 6 = -1$

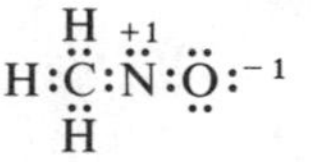

for C: $4 - 4 - 0 = 0$

for N: $5 - 2 - 2 = +1$

for O: $6 - 1 - 6 = -1$

STUDY PROBLEM

1.2   Calculate the formal charge on each atom in the following structures:

(a) 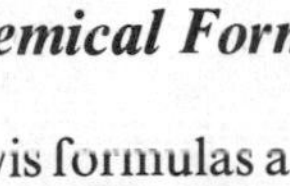 $H:\ddot{O}:\ddot{N}::\ddot{O}:$

(b) 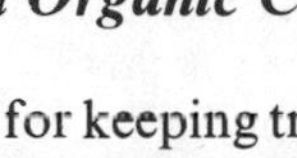 $H:\ddot{C}::N::\ddot{N}:$ with H above C

(c) $H:\ddot{C}:\ddot{O}:\ddot{S}:\ddot{O}:H$ with H's and O's

---

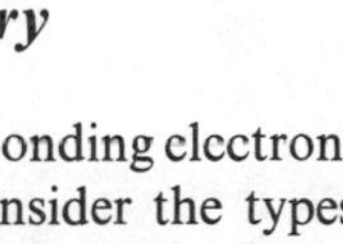

Section 1.5

Chemical Formulas in Organic Chemistry

Lewis formulas are useful for keeping track of bonding electrons, but organic chemists rarely use true Lewis formulas. Let us consider the types of chemical formula that are more frequently encountered.

An **empirical formula** tells us the types of atoms and their numerical ratio in a molecule. For example, a molecule of ethane contains carbon and hydrogen atoms in a ratio of 1 to 3; the empirical formula is CH_3. A **molecular formula** tells us the actual number of atoms in a molecule, not simply the ratio. The molecular formula for ethane is C_2H_6. A **structural formula** shows the *structure* of a molecule—that is, the order of attachment of the atoms. In order to explain or predict chemical reactivity, we need to know the structure of a molecule; therefore, structural formulas are the most useful of the different types of formula.

CH₃   C₂H₆

$$CH_3 \qquad\qquad C_2H_6 \qquad\qquad H{-}\underset{\underset{H}{|}}{\overset{\overset{H}{|}}{C}}{-}\underset{\underset{H}{|}}{\overset{\overset{H}{|}}{C}}{-}H$$

empirical formula   molecular formula   structural formula
for ethane   for ethane   for ethane

A. Structural Formulas

Lewis formulas are one type of structural formula. However, chemists usually represent a covalent structure by using a dash for each shared pair of electrons, and rarely show unshared pairs of bonding electrons. Formulas with dashes for bonds are called **valence-bond formulas**. In this text, we will also refer to them as **complete structural formulas**.

H:H becomes H—H

:C̈l:C̈l: becomes Cl—Cl

$$H{:}\overset{\overset{H}{..}}{\underset{\underset{H}{..}}{C}}{:}H \quad \text{becomes} \quad H{-}\underset{\underset{H}{|}}{\overset{\overset{H}{|}}{C}}{-}H$$

$$\overset{H}{\underset{H}{.}}{:}C{::}C{:}\overset{H}{\underset{H}{.}} \quad \text{becomes} \quad \overset{H}{\underset{H}{\diagdown}}C{=}C\overset{\diagup H}{\diagdown H}$$

Although unshared pairs of electrons are not usually shown in valence-bond formulas, we will sometimes show these electrons when we want to emphasize their role in a chemical reaction.

All represent the same molecule:

$$H{:}\underset{\underset{H}{\ddot{}}}{\overset{..}{N}}{:}H \quad \text{or} \quad H{-}\underset{\underset{H}{|}}{N}{-}H \quad \text{or} \quad H{-}\underset{\underset{H}{|}}{\overset{..}{N}}{-}H$$

—— unshared pair of e⁻

Give the valence-bond formula for each of the following Lewis formulas:

$$H{:}\overset{\overset{H}{..}}{\underset{\underset{H}{}}{C}}{:}\overset{..}{\underset{..}{O}}{:}\overset{\overset{H}{..}}{\underset{\underset{H}{}}{C}}{:}H \qquad\qquad H{:}\overset{\overset{H}{}}{\underset{\underset{H}{}}{C}}{:}\overset{\overset{H}{}}{\underset{\underset{H}{}}{C}}{:}\overset{..}{\underset{..}{O}}{:}H$$

Solution:

$$H{-}\underset{\underset{H}{|}}{\overset{\overset{H}{|}}{C}}{-}O{-}\underset{\underset{H}{|}}{\overset{\overset{H}{|}}{C}}{-}H \qquad\qquad H{-}\underset{\underset{H}{|}}{\overset{\overset{H}{|}}{C}}{-}\underset{\underset{H}{|}}{\overset{\overset{H}{|}}{C}}{-}O{-}H$$

B. *Condensed Structural Formulas*

Complete structural formulas are frequently condensed to shorter, more convenient formulas. **In condensed structural formulas,** bonds are not always shown, and atoms of the same type bonded to one other atom are grouped together. The structure of a molecule is still evident from a condensed structural formula as long as the rules of valence are taken into consideration.

$$
\begin{array}{ccc}
 & & \text{H } \text{H} \\
 & & | \quad | \\
\text{CH}_3\text{CH}_3 & \text{is the condensed structural formula for} & \text{H}-\text{C}-\text{C}-\text{H} \\
 & & | \quad | \\
 & & \text{H } \text{H}
\end{array}
$$

$$
\begin{array}{ccc}
 & & \text{H } \text{H} \\
 & & | \quad | \\
\text{CH}_3\text{CH}_2\text{OH} & \text{is the condensed structural formula for} & \text{H}-\text{C}-\text{C}-\text{O}-\text{H} \\
 & & | \quad | \\
 & & \text{H } \text{H}
\end{array}
$$

Sample Problem

Write (a) the complete structural formula (showing all bonds as dashes), and (b) the condensed structural formula, for each of the following Lewis formulas:

$$
\begin{array}{cc}
\text{H H} & \text{H H H} \\
\text{H}\!:\!\ddot{\text{C}}\!:\!\ddot{\text{C}}\!:\!\ddot{\text{Cl}}\!: & \text{H}\!:\!\ddot{\text{C}} : \text{C} : \ddot{\text{C}}\!:\!\text{H} \\
\text{H H} & \text{H } :\!\ddot{\text{Cl}}\!: \text{H}
\end{array}
$$

Solution:

$$
\begin{array}{cc}
\text{H } \text{H} & \text{H } \text{H } \text{H} \\
| \quad | & | \quad | \quad | \\
\text{(a)} \quad \text{H}-\text{C}-\text{C}-\text{Cl} & \text{H}-\text{C}-\text{C}-\text{C}-\text{H} \\
| \quad | & | \quad | \quad | \\
\text{H } \text{H} & \text{H } \text{Cl } \text{H}
\end{array}
$$

(b) $\text{CH}_3\text{CH}_2\text{Cl}$ $\text{CH}_3\text{CHClCH}_3$

Structural formulas may be condensed even further if a molecule has two or more identical groups of atoms. In these cases, parentheses are used to include a repetitive group of atoms. The subscript following the parentheses indicates the number of times the entire group is found at that position in the molecule.

$$
\begin{array}{ccc}
 & & \text{CH}_3 \\
 & & | \\
(\text{CH}_3)_2\text{CHOH} & \text{is the same as} & \text{CH}_3-\text{C}-\text{OH} \\
 & & | \\
 & & \text{H}
\end{array}
$$

$$
\begin{array}{ccc}
 & & \text{CH}_3 \\
 & & | \\
(\text{CH}_3)_3\text{CCl} & \text{is the same as} & \text{CH}_3-\text{C}-\text{Cl} \\
 & & | \\
 & & \text{CH}_3
\end{array}
$$

$\text{CH}_3(\text{CH}_2)_3\text{CH}_3$ is the same as $\text{CH}_3\text{CH}_2\text{CH}_2\text{CH}_2\text{CH}_3$

For the sake of clarity, double or triple bonds are usually shown in a condensed structural formula.

$CH_2=CH_2$ is the same as

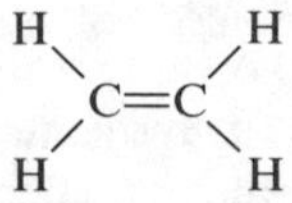

$$\begin{array}{c} H \\ \diagdown \\ \end{array} C=C \begin{array}{c} H \\ \diagup \\ \end{array}$$

$CH_3CH=CH_2$ is the same as

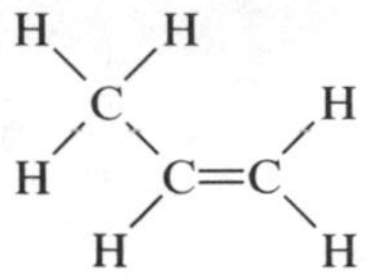

$CH_3C\equiv CH$ is the same as $H-\overset{H}{\underset{H}{C}}-C\equiv C-H$

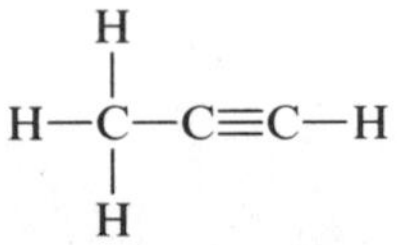

$CH_3\overset{O}{\overset{\|}{C}}CH_2CH_3$ is the same as $H-\overset{H}{\underset{H}{C}}-\overset{O}{\overset{\|}{C}}-\overset{H}{\underset{H}{C}}-\overset{H}{\underset{H}{C}}-H$

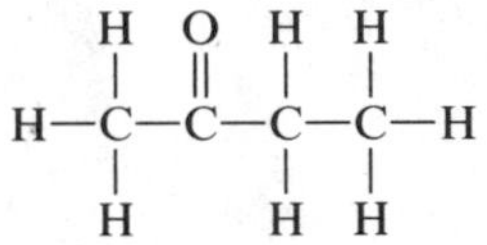

STUDY PROBLEM

1.3 For each of the following formulas, write a more condensed formula:

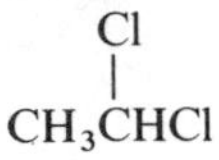

(a) 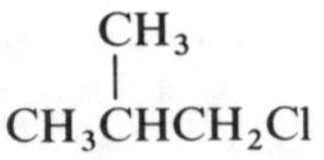 $CH_3\overset{CH_3}{\underset{|}{C}}HCH_2Cl$ (b) $CH_3\overset{Cl}{\underset{|}{C}}HCl$ (c) $CH_3CH_2CH_2CH_2\overset{Cl}{\underset{|}{C}}HCH_2Cl$

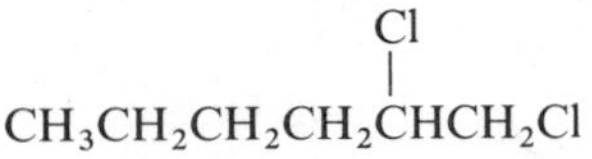

(d) 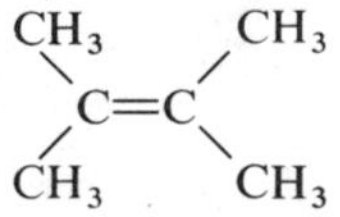 $\overset{CH_3}{\underset{CH_3}{}}C=C\overset{CH_3}{\underset{CH_3}{}}$

C. Cyclic Compounds and Polygon Formulas

A compound such as $CH_3CH_2CH_2CH_3$ is said to have its carbon atoms connected in a chain. Carbon atoms can be joined together in rings as well as in chains; a compound containing one or more rings is called a **cyclic compound**.

Cyclic structures are usually represented by **polygon formulas**, which are another type of condensed structural formula. For example, a triangle is used to represent a three-membered ring, while a hexagon is used for a six-membered ring.

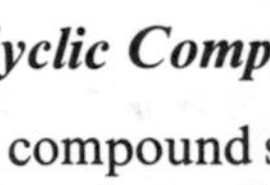

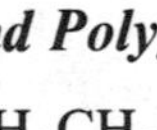

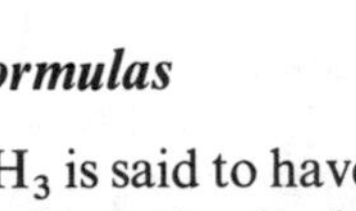

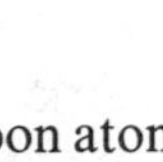

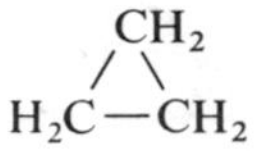

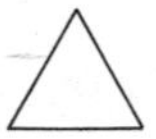

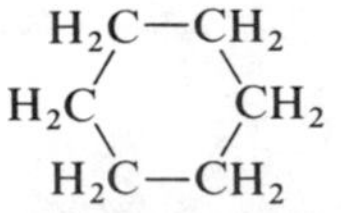

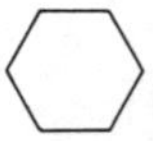

In polygon formulas, a corner represents a carbon atom along with its hydrogens; the sides of the polygon represent the bonds joining the carbons. If an atom or group other than hydrogen is attached to a carbon of the ring, the number of hydrogens at that position is reduced accordingly.

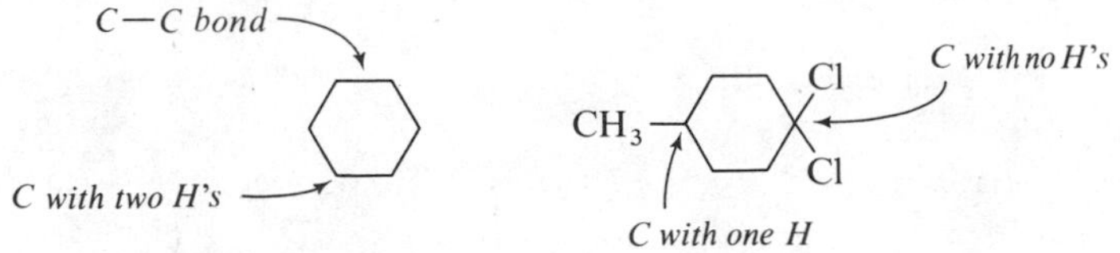

Rings can contain atoms other than carbon; these atoms and any hydrogens attached to them must be indicated in the polygon formula. Double bonds must also be indicated.

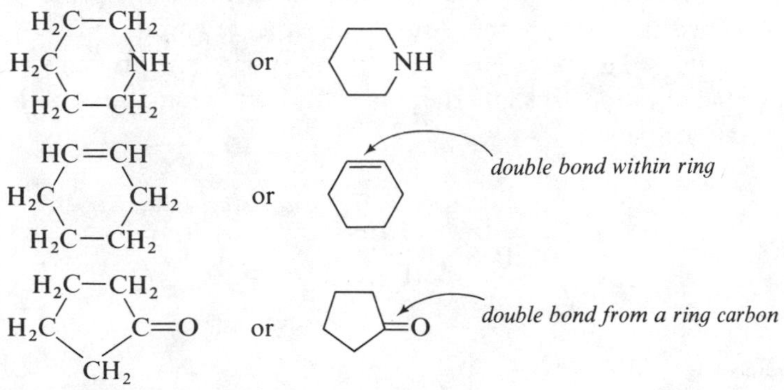

STUDY PROBLEMS

1.4 Draw the complete structural formulas for the following structures, showing each C, each H, and each bond.

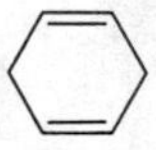

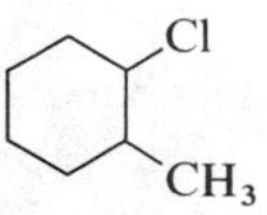

1.5 Draw polygon formulas for the following structures:

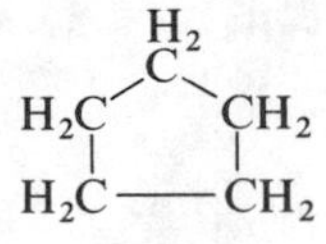

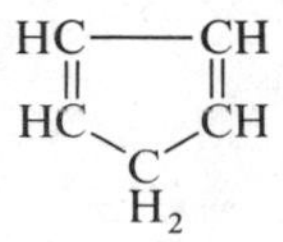

Section 1.6

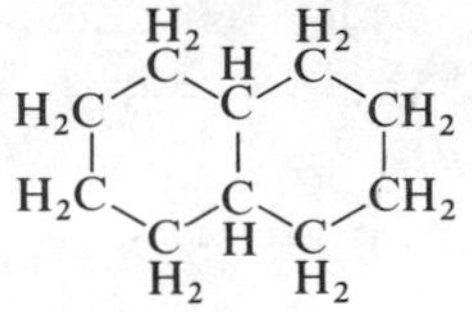

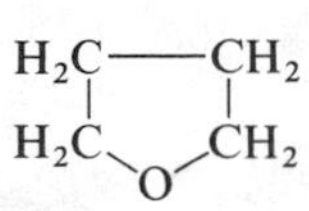

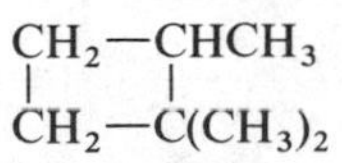

Bond Distances and Bond Angles

We have discussed how we represent covalent compounds. Now let us consider some of the properties of covalent bonds. The distance that separates the nuclei of two covalently bonded atoms is called the **bond distance**. Covalent bond distances, which can be measured experimentally, range from 0.74 Å to 2 Å.

If there are more than two atoms in a molecule, the bonds form an angle, called the **bond angle**. Bond angles vary from about 60° up to 180°.

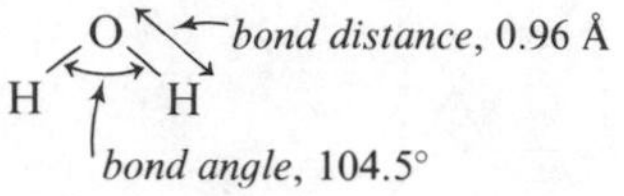

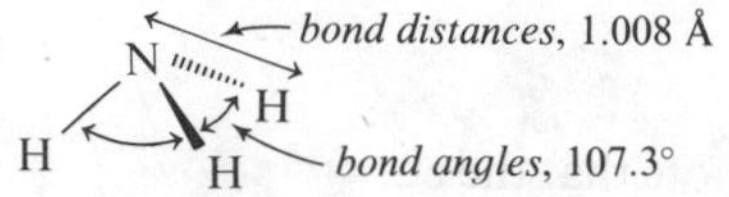

Most organic structures contain more than three atoms, and are three-dimensional rather than two-dimensional. The preceding structural formula for ammonia (NH_3) illustrates one technique for representing a three-dimensional structure. A line bond (—) represents a bond in the plane of the paper. The solid wedge (——) represents a bond coming out of the paper toward the viewer; the H at the wide end of the solid wedge is in front of the paper. The broken wedge (∙∙∙∙∙∙∙∙) represents a bond pointing back into the paper; the H at the small end of the broken wedge is behind the paper.

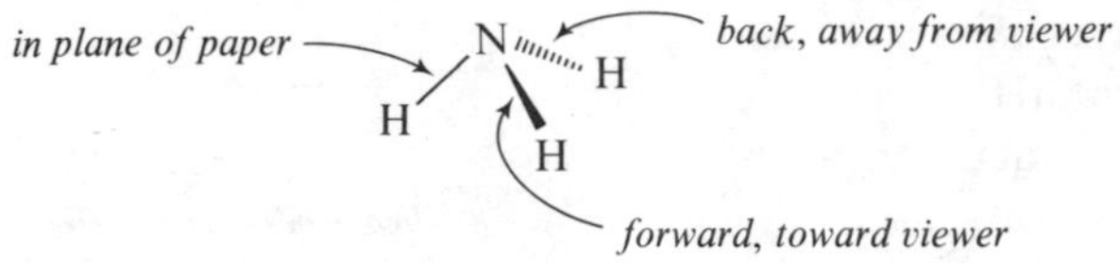

Section 1.7

Bond Dissociation Energy

When atoms become bonded together as molecules, energy is liberated (usually as heat or light). Thus, for a molecule to be dissociated into its atoms, energy must be supplied.

There are two ways a bond may dissociate. One way is by **heterolytic cleavage** (Greek *hetero*, "different"), in which both bonding electrons are retained by one of the atoms. The result of heterolytic cleavage is a pair of ions.

We use a curved arrow (⌢) in these equations to show the direction in which the pair of bonding electrons moves during bond breakage. In the heterolytic cleavage of HCl or H_2O, the bonding electrons are transferred to the more electronegative Cl or O.

The other process by which a bond may dissociate is **homolytic cleavage** (Greek *homo*, "same"). In this case, each atom involved in the covalent bond receives one electron from the original shared pair. Electrically neutral atoms or groups of atoms result.

Homolytic cleavage:

$$H\!\!\frown\!\!\frown\!\!H \longrightarrow H\cdot + H\cdot$$

$$H\!\!\frown\!\!\frown\!\!Cl \longrightarrow H\cdot + Cl\cdot$$

$$H_3C\!\!\frown\!\!\frown\!\!H \longrightarrow H_3C\cdot + H\cdot$$

Note that the curved arrows in these equations have only half an arrowhead. This type of arrow ($\curvearrowright$), called a fishhook, is used to show the direction of shift of *one* electron, whereas the curved arrow with a complete head ($\curvearrowright$) is used to show the direction of shift of a *pair* of electrons.

Another new symbol is the single dot, as in Cl·. This dot stands for a lone, unshared, unpaired electron. Other outer electrons are ignored in this symbolism. The symbol Cl· really means :$\ddot{C}l\cdot$. An atom such as H· or a group of atoms such as $H_3C\cdot$ that contains an unpaired electron is called a **free radical**. Free radicals are usually electrically neutral; therefore, there are no electrostatic attractions between free radicals, as there are between ions. Also, free radicals are usually of high energy and consequently are unstable and very reactive.

Homolytic cleavage is more useful than heterolytic cleavage in determining the energies required for bond dissociations because calculations are not complicated by ionic attractions between the products. From measurements of the components of dissociating gases at high temperatures, the **change in enthalpy** ΔH (change in heat content, or energy) has been calculated for a large number of bond dissociations. For the reaction $CH_4 \rightarrow CH_3\cdot + H\cdot$, ΔH equals 104 kcal/mole. In other words, to cleave one hydrogen atom from each carbon atom in one mole of CH_4 requires 104 kcal. This value (104 kcal/mole) is the **bond dissociation energy** for the $H_3C—H$ bond.

The bond dissociation energies for several types of bonds are listed in Table 1.4. To break a more stable bond requires a higher energy input. For example, cleavage of HF to H· and F· (135 kcal/mole) is difficult compared with cleavage of the O—O bond in hydrogen peroxide, HOOH (35 kcal/mole).

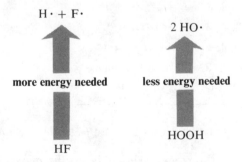

Note in Table 1.4 that atoms joined by multiple bonds require more energy for dissociation than the same atoms joined by single bonds. (CH≡CH, 200 kcal/mole, versus $CH_3—CH_3$, 88 kcal/mole.) Also note that other parts of a molecule may affect the bond dissociation energy:

$$H_3C\!\!\frown\!\!\frown\!\!H + 104\,kcal/mole \xrightarrow{\text{more difficult}} H_3C\cdot + H\cdot$$

$$(CH_3)_3C\!\!\frown\!\!\frown\!\!H + 91\,kcal/mole \xrightarrow{\text{easier}} (CH_3)_3C\cdot + H\cdot$$

Table 1.4. Selected Bond Dissociation Energies (in kcal/mole)

Miscellaneous bonds		C—H bonds		C—Cl bonds		C—C bonds	
H—H	104	CH_3—H	104	CH_3—Cl	83.5	CH_3—CH_3	88
N≡N	226	CH_3CH_2—H	98	CH_3CH_2—Cl	81.5	CH_2=CH_2	146
F—F	37	$(CH_3)_2$CH—H	94.5	$(CH_3)_2$CH—Cl	81	CH≡CH	200
Cl—Cl	58	$(CH_3)_3$C—H	91	$(CH_3)_3$C—Cl	78.5		
Br—Br	46	CH_2=CH—H	103	CH_2=CH—Cl	84		
I—I	36						
H—F	135						
H—Cl	103						
H—Br	87						
H—I	71						
HO—OH	35						

Bond dissociation energies allow a chemist to calculate relative stabilities of compounds and to predict (to an extent) the courses of chemical reactions. For example, one reaction we will discuss later in this text is the chlorination of methane, CH_4:

$$CH_4 + Cl_2 \longrightarrow CH_3Cl + HCl$$

Will this reaction be **exothermic** (releasing energy) or **endothermic** (requiring energy)? We may break down the reaction into its component parts and calculate from the individual bond dissociation energies whether or not energy will be liberated. The greater the amount of energy liberated, the more favorable is the reaction. (Note that in these equations, $+\Delta H$ indicates energy put into a reaction, while $-\Delta H$ indicates energy that is liberated.)

	ΔH
Cl—Cl + 58 kcal/mole $\longrightarrow$ Cl· + Cl·	+ 58 kcal/mole
H_3C—H + 104 kcal/mole $\longrightarrow$ H_3C· + H·	+ 104 kcal/mole
H_3C· + Cl· $\longrightarrow$ H_3C—Cl + 83.5 kcal/mole	− 83.5 kcal/mole
H· + Cl· $\longrightarrow$ H—Cl + 103 kcal/mole	− 103 kcal/mole

net reaction:

$Cl_2 + CH_4 \longrightarrow CH_3Cl + HCl + 24.5$ kcal/mole   net $\Delta H = -24.5$ kcal/mole

We calculate that this reaction should be exothermic. When we run this reaction in the laboratory, we find that it is indeed exothermic.

STUDY PROBLEM

1.6 Using bond dissociation energies from Table 1.4, predict which of the following reactions liberates more energy:

(a) $(CH_3)_3CH + Cl_2 \longrightarrow (CH_3)_3CCl + HCl$

(b) $CH_4 + Cl_2 \longrightarrow CH_3Cl + HCl$

Section 1.8

Polar Covalent Bonds

Atoms with equal or nearly equal electronegativities form covalent bonds in which both atoms exert equal or nearly equal pulls on the bonding electrons. This type of covalent bond is called a **nonpolar bond**. In organic molecules, carbon–carbon bonds and carbon–hydrogen bonds are the most common types of nonpolar bond.

Some compounds containing nonpolar covalent bonds:

$$H\!-\!H \qquad N\!\equiv\!N \qquad H\!-\!\overset{\displaystyle H}{\underset{\displaystyle H}{C}}\!-\!H \qquad H\!-\!\overset{\displaystyle H}{\underset{\displaystyle H}{C}}\!-\!\overset{\displaystyle H}{\underset{\displaystyle H}{C}}\!-\!H \qquad \overset{H}{\underset{H}{}}\!\!C\!=\!C\!\!\overset{H}{\underset{H}{}}$$

In covalent compounds like H_2O, HCl, CH_3OH, or $H_2C\!=\!O$, one atom has a substantially greater electronegativity than the others. The more electronegative atom has a greater attraction for the bonding electrons—not enough of an attraction for the atom to break off as an ion, but enough so that this atom takes the larger share of electron density. The result is a **polar covalent bond**, a bond with an uneven distribution of electron density. The degree of polarity of a bond depends partly on the difference in electronegativities of the two atoms bonded together and partly on other factors, such as the size of the atoms. We may think of chemical bonds as a continuum from nonpolar covalent bonds to ionic bonds. Within this continuum, we speak of the increasing **ionic character** of the bonds.

$$H\!-\!H \qquad CH_3\!-\!O\!-\!CH_3 \qquad H\!-\!O\!-\!H \qquad H\!-\!Cl \qquad Na^+ \; Cl^-$$

increasing ionic character of bonds ⟶

The distribution of electrons in a polar molecule may be symbolized by **partial charges**: $\delta+$ (partial positive) and $\delta-$ (partial negative). Another way of representing the different electron densities within a molecule is by a crossed arrow ($\longmapsto$) that points from the partially positive end of a molecule to the partially negative end.

$$\overset{\delta+}{H}\!-\!\overset{\delta-}{Cl} \quad \text{or} \quad \overset{\longmapsto}{H\!-\!Cl} \qquad\qquad \underset{\delta+}{CH_3}\overset{\overset{\delta-}{O}}{\diagdown}\underset{\delta+}{CH_3} \quad \text{or} \quad CH_3\overset{O}{\diagdown}CH_3$$

STUDY PROBLEM

1.7 Show by both partial charges and a crossed arrow the polarity of the following compounds:

(a) CH_3Br and   (b) $CH_3\overset{\displaystyle O}{\overset{\displaystyle \|}{C}}OH$

A.   Bond Moments

If a polar bond, such as an O—H bond, is subjected to an electric field, the bond feels a certain amount of "turning force." This force is simply the push of the electric field to align the bond in the field. A more polar bond feels more force than a less polar bond. The **bond moment**, a measure of the polarity of a bond, may be calculated from the value of the force felt by that bond.

The bond moment is defined as $e \times d$, where e is the charge (in electrostatic units) and d is the distance between the charges (in Å), and is reported in units called *Debyes* (D). Bond moments range from 0.4 D for the nonpolar C—H bond to 3.5 D for the highly polar C≡N bond (see Table 1.5). The bond moment for a particular bond is relatively constant from compound to compound.

Table 1.5.   Bond Moments for Selected Covalent Bonds

Bond[a]	Bond moment, D	Bond[a]	Bond moment, D
H—C	0.4	C—Cl	1.46
H—N	1.31	C—Br	1.38
H—O	1.51	C—I	1.19
C—N	0.22	C=O	2.3
C—O	0.74	C≡N	3.5
C—F	1.41		

[a] In each case, the more positive atom is on the left.

B.   Dipole Moments

The **dipole moment** μ is the *vector sum of the bond moments* in a molecule. Because vector addition takes into account the direction as well as the magnitude of the bond moments, the dipole moment is a measure of the polarity of the molecule as a whole.

The dipole moments for a few organic compounds are listed in Table 1.6. Note that the dipole moment of CCl_4 is zero, even though each C—Cl bond has a moment of 1.46 D. The reason for this apparent anomaly is that the CCl_4 molecule is *symmetrical*; in the vector addition, the bond moments cancel and result in a vector sum of zero. Carbon dioxide is another molecule with bond moments but no dipole moment. Again, this is a case of a symmetrical molecule in which the bond moments cancel. On the other hand, the bond moments of a water molecule

Table 1.6.   Dipole Moments of Selected Compounds

Compound	Dipole moment, D	Compound	Dipole moment, D
H_2O	1.84	CH_3OCH_3	1.3
NH_3	1.46		
CH_3Cl	1.86	$\overset{\displaystyle O}{\overset{\|}{CH_3CH}}$	2.7
CCl_4	0		
CO_2	0	$\overset{\displaystyle O}{\overset{\|}{CH_3CCH_3}}$	2.8

do not cancel, and water has a dipole moment. From this observation, we can deduce that the water molecule is not symmetrical. Dipole moments can thus be used to help determine molecular geometry.

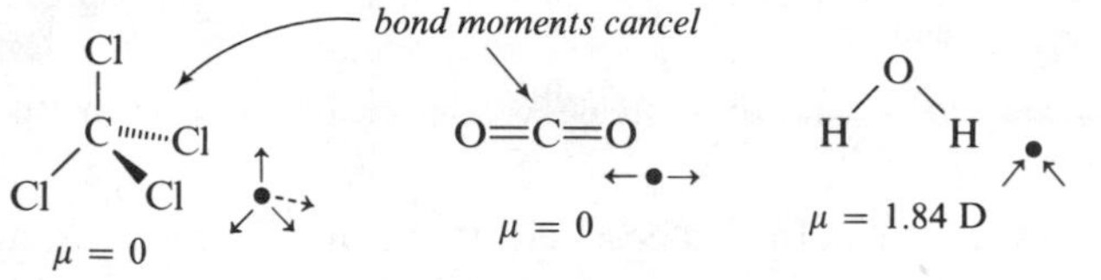

STUDY PROBLEMS

1.8   Which of the indicated bonds is more polar?

(a) CH_3—NH_2 or CH_3—OH (b) CH_3—OH or CH_3O—H
(c) CH_3—Cl or CH_3—OH

1.9   Use a crossed arrow to show the approximate direction of the bond moment (if any) of the double or triple bond in each of the following structures:

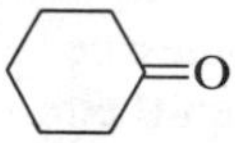

Section 1.9

Attractions Between Molecules

A.   Dipole–Dipole Interactions

Except in a highly dispersed gas, molecules attract and repel each other. These attractions and repulsions arise primarily from molecular dipole–dipole interactions. For example, in the liquid state, molecules of CH_3I can either attract or repel each other, depending on the orientation of the molecules. Two CH_3I molecules are attracted to each other because of the attraction between the partially negative iodine of one molecule and the partially positive carbon of the other molecule.

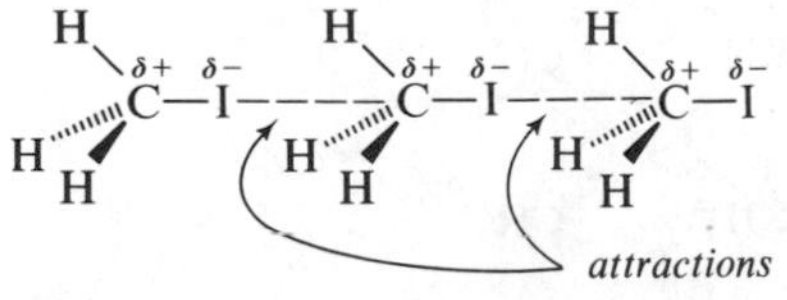

When the iodine ends of two CH_3I molecules approach closely, the two molecules repel each other.

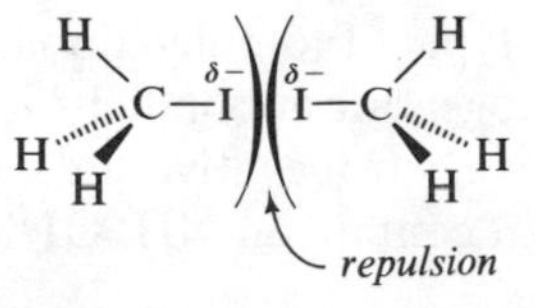

Nonpolar molecules are attracted to each other by weak dipole–dipole interactions called **London forces**. London forces arise from dipoles *induced* in

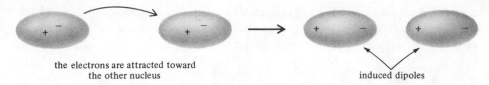

the electrons are attracted toward
the other nucleus

induced dipoles

Figure 1.6.   Nonpolar molecules can induce dipoles in each other.

one molecule by another. In this case, electrons of one molecule are weakly attracted to a nucleus of a second molecule; then the electrons of the second molecule are repelled by the electrons of the first. The result is an uneven distribution of electrons and an induced dipole. Figure 1.6 depicts how an induced dipole can occur.

The various dipole–dipole interactions (attractive and repulsive) are collectively called **van der Waals forces**. The distances between molecules have an important effect on the strength of van der Waals forces. The distance at which attraction is greatest is called the **van der Waals radius**. If two atoms approach each other more closely than this distance, repulsions develop between the two nuclei and between the two sets of electrons. When the distance between two molecules becomes larger than the van der Waals radius, the attractive forces between the molecules decrease.

Continuous-chain molecules, such as $CH_3CH_2CH_2CH_2CH_3$, can align themselves in zigzag chains, enabling the atoms of different molecules to assume positions that match the van der Waals radii. Maximal van der Waals attractions can develop between such long-chain molecules. Branched molecules cannot approach one another closely enough for all the atoms to assume optimal van der Waals distances. Because more energy is necessary to overcome van der Waals attractions and to free molecules from the liquid state, continuous-chain compounds have higher boiling points than branched compounds of the same molecular weight and otherwise similar structures.

$$CH_3 \underset{CH_2}{\overset{CH_2}{\diagdown}} \underset{CH_2}{\underset{\diagup}{}} \overset{CH_2}{\underset{CH_2}{\diagup}} CH_3$$

bp 36°C

$$CH_3-\underset{\underset{CH_3}{|}}{\overset{\overset{CH_3}{|}}{C}}-CH_3$$

$$CH_3-\underset{\underset{CH_3}{|}}{\overset{\overset{CH_3}{|}}{C}}-CH_3$$

bp 9.5°C

B.   Hydrogen Bonding

An especially strong type of dipole–dipole interaction occurs between molecules containing a hydrogen atom bonded to nitrogen, oxygen, or fluorine. Each of these latter elements is electronegative and has unshared bonding electrons. Some typical compounds that contain an NH, OH, or FH bond are:

$$H-\underset{\underset{H}{|}}{\overset{..}{O}}: \qquad CH_3-\underset{\underset{H}{|}}{\overset{..}{O}}: \qquad H-\underset{\underset{H}{|}}{\overset{..}{N}}-H \qquad CH_3-\underset{\underset{H}{|}}{\overset{..}{N}}-H \qquad H-\overset{..}{\underset{..}{F}}:$$

In the liquid state, the molecules of any one of these compounds have strong attractions for one another. A partially positive hydrogen atom of one molecule is attracted to the unshared pair of electrons of the electronegative atom of another molecule. This attraction is called a **hydrogen bond**.

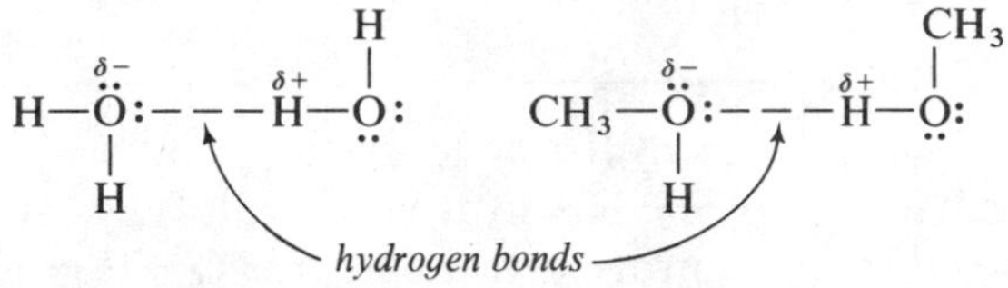

$$\overset{\delta-}{H-O}: - - \overset{\delta+}{H-O}: \qquad CH_3-\overset{\delta-}{O}: - - \overset{\delta+}{H-O}:$$

hydrogen bonds

Compounds or groups containing only carbon and hydrogen cannot undergo hydrogen bonding. As an example, consider methane, CH_4. Methane cannot undergo hydrogen bonding for two reasons:

(1) Because the CH bond is nonpolar, a CH_4 molecule does not have a partially positive H.
(2) The carbon atom in CH_4 has no unshared electrons to attract a hydrogen atom.

The dissociation energy of a hydrogen bond is only 5–10 kcal/mole, much lower than the bond dissociation energy of a typical covalent bond (80–100 kcal/mole) but substantially stronger than most dipole–dipole attractions. The reason for this difference is the size of the atoms involved. A hydrogen atom is small compared to other atoms and can occupy a position very close to the unshared electrons of an electronegative atom. A strong electrostatic attraction results. Atoms larger than hydrogen cannot occupy positions so near to each other; consequently, dipole–dipole attractions between other atoms are weaker.

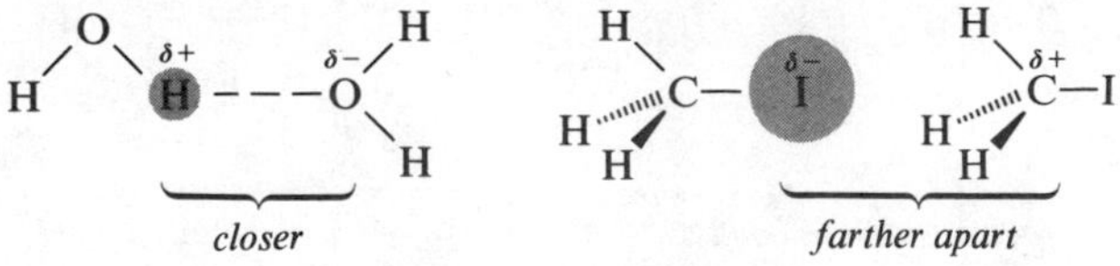

closer   *farther apart*

Sample Problem

Show the hydrogen bonding between two molecules of $CH_3CH_2NH_2$.

Solution:

(1) Look for one or more partially positive hydrogens.

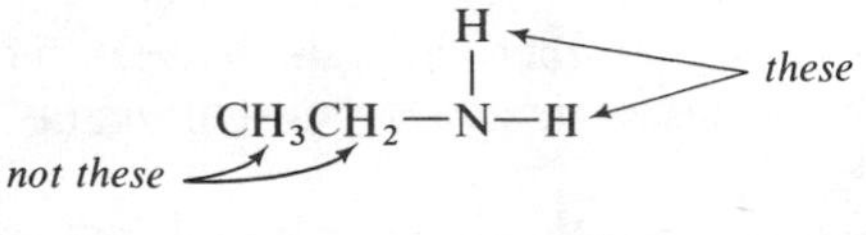

$$CH_3CH_2-\overset{H}{N}-H$$

these

not these

(2) Look for an electronegative atom (N, O, or F) with unshared electrons.

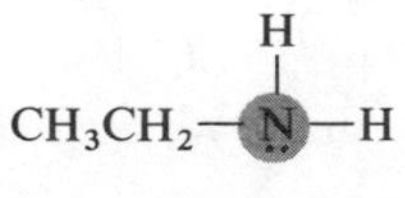

$$CH_3CH_2-\overset{H}{N}-H$$

(3)   Draw two molecules with a hydrogen bond between one partially positive H and the N of the other molecule. (You need not show the unshared electrons here.)

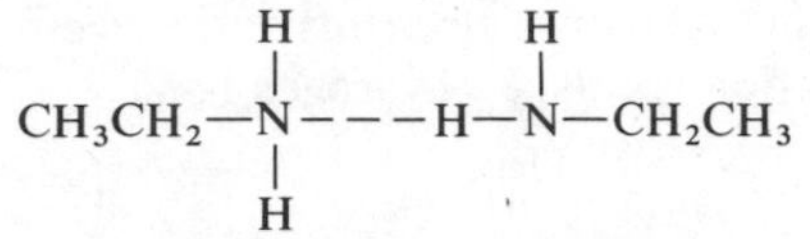

$$
\begin{array}{ccc}
& \overset{\displaystyle H}{|} & \overset{\displaystyle H}{|} \\
CH_3CH_2\!-\!N\!-\!-\!-\!H\!-\!N\!-\!CH_2CH_3 \\
& \underset{\displaystyle H}{|} &
\end{array}
$$

Hydrogen bonds are not all the same strength. An $O\!-\!-\!-\!HO$ hydrogen bond is stronger than an $N\!-\!-\!-\!HN$ hydrogen bond. Why is this true? Oxygen is more electronegative than nitrogen; therefore, the $O\!-\!H$ group is more polar and has a more positive H. This more positive H is more strongly attracted by a negative center.

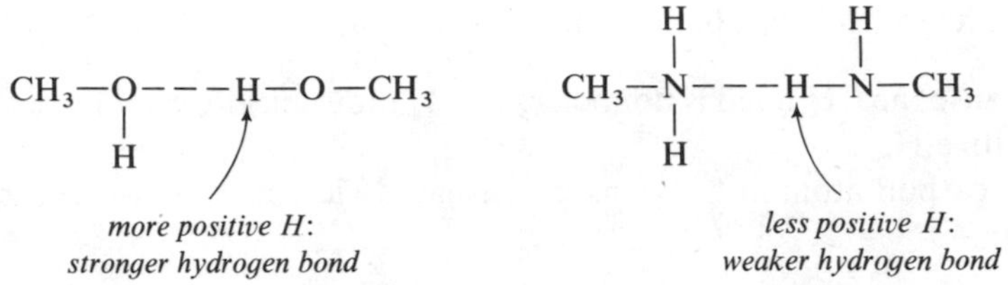

$$
\begin{array}{cccc}
& & & \overset{\displaystyle H}{|} \qquad\quad \overset{\displaystyle H}{|} \\
CH_3\!-\!\underset{\displaystyle H}{\overset{}{O}}\!-\!-\!-\!H\!-\!O\!-\!CH_3 & & & CH_3\!-\!\underset{\displaystyle H}{\overset{}{N}}\!-\!-\!-\!H\!-\!N\!-\!CH_3
\end{array}
$$

more positive H: *less positive H:*
stronger hydrogen bond   *weaker hydrogen bond*

Hydrogen bonds may form between two different compounds, such as between CH_3OH and H_2O or between CH_3NH_2 and H_2O. In these cases, there is often more than one possibility for hydrogen bonding. The following structures show two types of hydrogen bond between CH_3NH_2 and H_2O. (In a mixture of these two compounds, hydrogen bonds can also form between two molecules of H_2O and between two molecules of CH_3NH_2.)

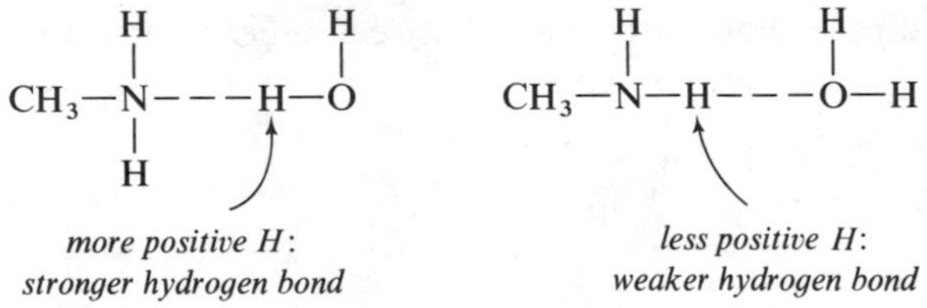

$$
\begin{array}{cccc}
\overset{\displaystyle H}{|} \qquad\quad \overset{\displaystyle H}{|} & & & \overset{\displaystyle H}{|} \qquad\quad \overset{\displaystyle H}{|} \\
CH_3\!-\!\underset{\displaystyle H}{\overset{}{N}}\!-\!-\!-\!H\!-\!O & & & CH_3\!-\!N\!-\!H\!-\!-\!-\!O\!-\!H
\end{array}
$$

more positive H: *less positive H:*
stronger hydrogen bond   *weaker hydrogen bond*

Table 1.7 shows the amount of energy needed to break some different types of hydrogen bond. Note that the $OH\!-\!-\!-\!N$ hydrogen bond is the strongest of the group. Because nitrogen is less electronegative than oxygen, its electrons are more loosely held and more easily attracted by another atom. The combination of nitrogen's loose electrons and the more positive hydrogen of an OH group leads to a quite strong hydrogen bond.

C.   *Effects of Hydrogen Bonding*

Hydrogen bonds are rather like glue between molecules. Although a single hydrogen bond by itself is weak, all the molecules taken together may form a great many hydrogen bonds.

For all substances, boiling points increase with molecular weight because of increased van der Waals attractions. However, a hydrogen-bonded compound has a *higher boiling point* than would be predicted from molecular weight alone. For a hydrogen-bonded liquid to be volatilized, additional energy must be supplied for breaking all the intermolecular hydrogen bonds.

Table 1.7. Approximate Dissociation Energies of Some Hydrogen Bonds

Type of hydrogen bond	Approximate dissociation energy (kcal/mole)
—O—H— — —:N—	7
—O—H— — —:O—	5
—N—H— — —:N—	3
—N—H— — —:O—	2

Ethanol (CH_3CH_2OH) and dimethyl ether (CH_3OCH_3) have the same molecular weight. Ethanol has a much higher boiling point than does dimethyl ether—ethanol is a liquid at room temperature while dimethyl ether is a gas. The difference in boiling points between these two compounds can be directly attributed to the fact that ethanol molecules are joined by hydrogen bonds, while dimethyl ether molecules cannot form hydrogen bonds among themselves.

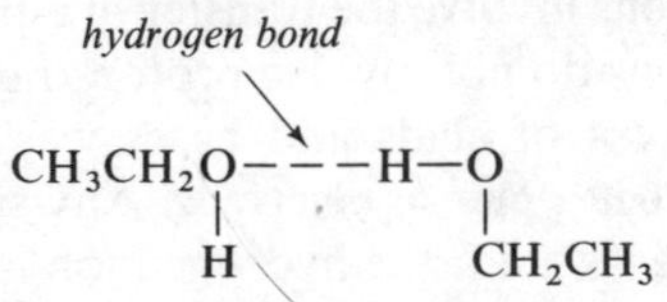

hydrogen bond

CH_3CH_2O— — —H—O

H CH_2CH_3

ethanol
bp 78.5°

no H to form a hydrogen bond

CH_3—O—CH_3

dimethyl ether,
bp −23.6°

Solubility of covalent compounds in water is another property affected by hydrogen bonding. A compound that can form hydrogen bonds with water tends to be far more soluble in water than a compound that cannot. Sugars, such as glucose, contain many —OH groups and are quite soluble in water. Hexane, however, cannot form hydrogen bonds and cannot break the existing hydrogen bonds in water; therefore, hexane is water-insoluble.

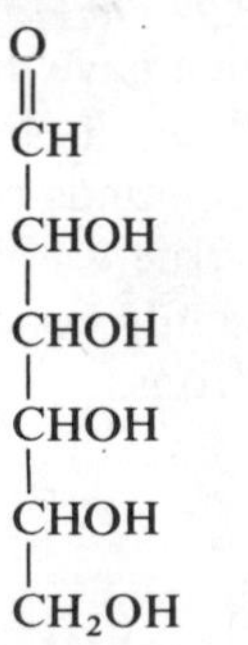

$$
\begin{array}{cc}
\overset{\displaystyle O}{\underset{\displaystyle \|}{}} & \\
CH & CH_3 \\
| & | \\
CHOH & CH_2 \\
| & | \\
CHOH & CH_2 \\
| & | \\
CHOH & CH_2 \\
| & | \\
CHOH & CH_2 \\
| & | \\
CH_2OH & CH_3 \\
\end{array}
$$

glucose   hexane

soluble in water   *insoluble in water*

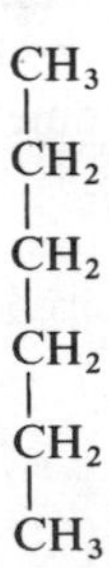

STUDY PROBLEM

1.10 Show all the types of hydrogen bond (if any) that would be found in:

    (a) liquid $CH_3CH_2CH_2NH_2$ (b) a solution of CH_3OH in H_2O

    (c) liquid $CH_3CH_2OCH_2CH_3$ (d) a solution of CH_3OCH_3 in H_2O

Section 1.10

Acids and Bases

According to the Brønsted–Lowry concept of acids and bases, an **acid** is a substance that can **donate a hydrogen ion**; two examples of Brønsted–Lowry acids are HCl and HNO_3. A **base** is defined as a substance that can **accept a hydrogen ion**; OH^- and NH_3 are examples.

A hydrogen ion is electron-deficient, and a base has an unshared pair of bonding electrons. Reaction between a hydrogen ion and a base results in bonding between the two.

$$H^+ + :\ddot{O}H^- \rightleftharpoons H-\ddot{O}H$$

$$H^+ + :NH_3 \rightleftharpoons H-\overset{+}{N}H_3$$

Although many acid–base reactions involve the transfer of a proton from an acid to a base, some acid–base reactions do not involve proton transfer. For this reason, the more general Lewis concept of acids and bases was developed. A **Lewis acid** is a substance that can **accept a pair of electrons**. Any species with an electron-deficient atom can act as a Lewis acid; the hydrogen ion is a Lewis acid. Most Lewis acids other than H^+ that we will encounter in this text are anhydrous metal salts (for example, $ZnCl_2$, $FeCl_3$, and $AlBr_3$).

A reaction involving a Lewis acid:

$$FeBr_3 + :\ddot{B}r-\ddot{B}r: \rightleftharpoons FeBr_4^- + \ddot{B}r:^+$$

A **Lewis base** is a substance that can **donate a pair of electrons**. Examples of Lewis bases are NH_3 and ^-OH, both of which have unshared pairs of electrons. (Most Lewis bases are bases by the Brønsted–Lowry theory as well.)

Let us now consider some organic compounds that act as acids and bases. **Amines** are a class of organic compounds structurally similar to ammonia; an amine contains a nitrogen atom that is covalently bonded to one or more carbon atoms and that has an unshared pair of electrons.

Some common amines:

$$CH_3-\ddot{N}-H \quad\quad CH_3-\ddot{N}-H \quad\quad CH_3-\ddot{N}-CH_3$$
$$\quad\quad\ |\quad\quad\quad\quad\quad\quad\ |\quad\quad\quad\quad\quad\quad\ |$$
$$\quad\quad H \quad\quad\quad\quad\quad CH_3 \quad\quad\quad\quad CH_3$$

Amines, like ammonia, are weak bases and undergo reversible reactions with acids or with water.

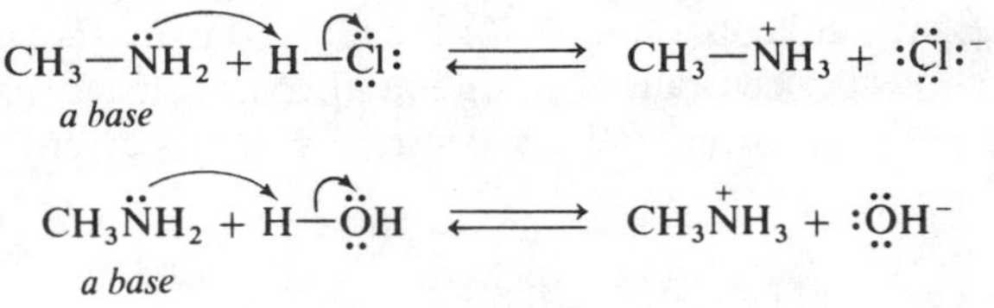

$$CH_3-\overset{\frown}{\ddot{N}H_2} + H-\overset{\curvearrowleft}{\ddot{C}l}: \rightleftharpoons CH_3-\overset{+}{N}H_3 + :\ddot{C}l:^-$$
$$\textit{a base}$$

$$CH_3\ddot{N}H_2 + H-\overset{\frown}{\ddot{O}H} \rightleftharpoons CH_3\overset{+}{N}H_3 + :\ddot{O}H^-$$
$$\textit{a base}$$

An organic compound containing a **carboxyl group** ($-CO_2H$) acts as a weak acid. Compounds that contain carboxyl groups are called **carboxylic acids**. Acetic acid, CH_3CO_2H, is an example. One of the reasons for the acidity of carboxylic acids is the polarity of the O—H bond.

The carboxyl group ($-CO_2H$):

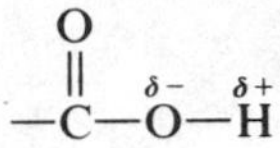

$$\overset{\displaystyle O}{\overset{\|}{-C}}-\overset{\delta-}{O}-\overset{\delta+}{H}$$

In water solution, the hydrogen ion is removed from the carboxyl group in a reversible reaction, and the carboxylate anion is formed.

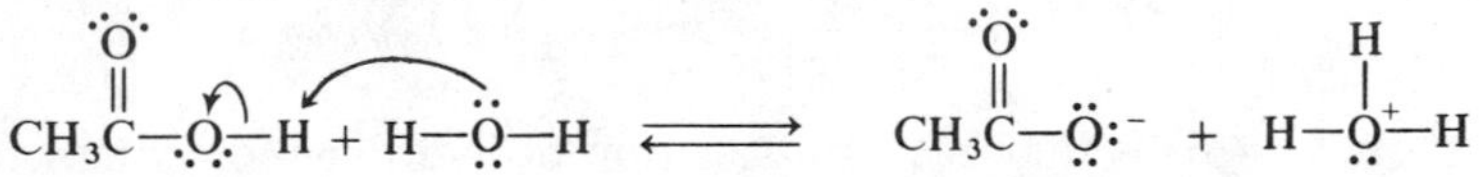

$$CH_3\overset{\overset{\displaystyle \cdot\ddot{O}\cdot}{\|}}{C}-\ddot{\underset{..}{O}}-H + H-\ddot{O}-H \rightleftharpoons CH_3\overset{\overset{\displaystyle \cdot\ddot{O}\cdot}{\|}}{C}-\ddot{\underset{..}{O}}:^- + H-\overset{\overset{\displaystyle H}{|}}{\underset{..}{O}}{}^+-H$$

acetic acid	acetate ion
a carboxylic acid	*a carboxylate ion*

STUDY PROBLEMS

1.11 Which of the following compounds or ions acts as an acid and which acts as a base in H_2O?

(a) $^-NH_2$

(b) $CH_3CH_2CH_2\overset{\overset{\displaystyle O}{\|}}{C}OH$

(c) $^-OCH_2CH_3$

(d) 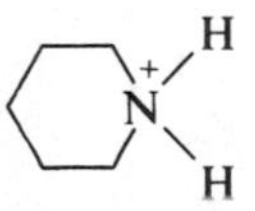 ⬡$\overset{+}{N}\overset{H}{\underset{H}{<}}$

(e) 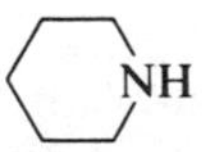 ⬡NH

1.12 Complete the following equations for acid–base reactions:

(a) $CH_3CH_2CO_2H + H_2O \rightleftharpoons$

(b) 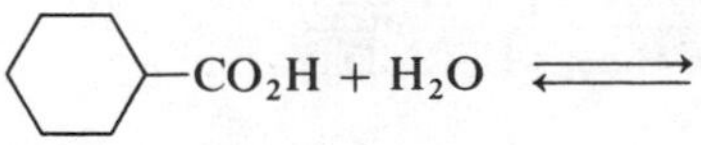 ⬡$-CO_2H + H_2O \rightleftharpoons$

(c) $(CH_3)_2NH + H_2O \rightleftharpoons$

(d) 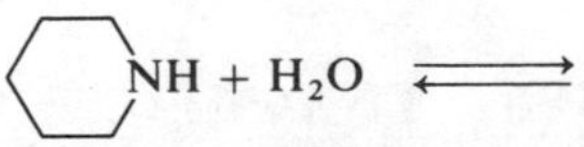 ⬡$NH + H_2O \rightleftharpoons$

A. Acidity Constants

A chemical reaction has an **equilibrium constant** K that reflects how far the reaction proceeds toward completion. For the ionization of a weak acid, this constant is called an **acidity constant** K_a. An equilibrium constant is determined by the following general equation, with concentration values given in molarity, M:

$$K = \frac{\text{concentrations of products in } M}{\text{concentrations of reactants in } M}$$

For acetic acid:

$$CH_3CO_2H \rightleftharpoons CH_3CO_2^- + H^+$$

$$K_a = \frac{[CH_3CO_2^-][H^+]^*}{[CH_3CO_2H]}$$

where $[H^+]$ = concentration of H^+
$[CH_3CO_2^-]$ = concentration of $CH_3CO_2^-$
$[CH_3CO_2H]$ = concentration of CH_3CO_2H

The more ionized a weak acid is, the larger is the value for K_a because the values in the numerator are larger. *A stronger acid has a larger K_a value.*

$$K_a = \frac{[H^+][\text{anion}]}{[\text{nonionized acid}]} \quad \begin{matrix}\text{as numerator increases,}\\ K_a \text{ increases}\end{matrix}$$

Just as pH is the negative logarithm of hydrogen ion concentration, pK_a is the negative logarithm of K_a. We will use pK_a values in this text for comparison of acid strength. (The K_a values and pK_a values for some carboxylic acids are given in Table 1.8.)

$$pH = -\log[H^+]$$

$$pK_a = -\log K_a$$

Examples: If $K_a = 10^{-3}$, then $pK_a = 3$

If $K_a = 10^2$, then $pK_a = -2$

---

* More correctly, the *activity*, or *effective concentration*, should be used, rather than molarity. Since activities of ions approach their molarities in dilute solution, molarity may be used for the sake of simplicity. In addition, the equilibrium expression should contain the hydrogen acceptor, water:

$$CH_3CO_2H + H_2O \rightleftharpoons CH_3CO_2^- + H_3O^+$$

$$K_a' = \frac{[CH_3CO_2^-][H_3O^+]}{[CH_3CO_2H][H_2O]}$$

For all practical purposes, the molar concentration of water remains fixed at 55.5. This constant factor is generally grouped with the equilibrium constant K_a, and the $[H_3O^+]$ term is simplified to $[H^+]$.

$$K_a = K_a'[H_2O] = \frac{[CH_3CO_2^-][H_3O^+]}{[CH_3CO_2H]} = \frac{[CH_3CO_2^-][H^+]}{[CH_3CO_2H]}$$

Table 1.8. *Acidity Constants and* pK_a *Values for Some Carboxylic Acids*

Formula	K_a	pK_a
HCO_2H	17.5×10^{-5}	3.75
CH_3CO_2H	1.75×10^{-5}	4.75
$CH_3CH_2CO_2H$	1.34×10^{-5}	4.87
$CH_3CH_2CH_2CO_2H$	1.54×10^{-5}	4.81

Sample Problem

Calculate the pK_a of an acid with K_a equal to 136×10^{-5}.

Solution:

$$p K_a = -\log K_a$$
$$= -\log(136 \times 10^{-5})$$
$$= -\log(1.36 \times 10^{-3})$$
$$= -(\log 1.36 - 3)$$
$$= 3 - \log 1.36$$
$$= 3 - 0.133 \quad \longleftarrow \quad \text{from log table, slide}$$
$$\text{rule, or calculator}$$
$$= 2.87$$

As K_a gets larger (stronger acid), pK_a gets smaller. *The smaller the value for* pK_a, *the stronger the acid.*

K_a:	10^{-10}	10^{-5}	10^{-1}	10^2
pK_a:	10	5	1	−2

increasing acid strength →

B. Basicity Constants

The reversible reaction of a weak base with water, like the reaction of a weak acid with water, results in a small but constant concentration of ions at equilibrium. The **basicity constant** K_b is the equilibrium constant for this reaction. As in the case of K_a, the value for $[H_2O]$ is included in K_b in the equilibrium expression.

$$NH_3 + H_2\ddot{O} \rightleftharpoons NH_4^+ + :\ddot{O}H^-$$

$$K_b = \frac{[NH_4^+][OH^-]}{[NH_3]}$$

$$pK_b = -\log K_b$$

With an increase in base strength, the value for K_b increases and the pK_b value decreases. *The smaller the value for* pK_b, *the stronger the base.*

K_b:	10^{-10}	10^{-7}	10^{-5}
pK_b:	10	7	5

increasing base strength →

Table 1.9.   *Basicity Constants and* pK_b *Values for*
Ammonia and Some Amines

Formula	K_b	pK_b
NH_3	1.79×10^{-5}	4.75
CH_3NH_2	45×10^{-5}	3.34
$(CH_3)_2NH$	54×10^{-5}	3.27
$(CH_3)_3N$	6.5×10^{-5}	4.19

STUDY PROBLEMS

1.13   List the following compounds in order of increasing basicity (weakest first). See Table 1.9 for pK_b values.

(a) NH_3 (b) CH_3NH_2 (c) $(CH_3)_2NH$

1.14   List the following anions in order of increasing basicity:

(a) CH_3O^-, $pK_b = -1.5$;   (b) $CH_3CO_2^-$, $pK_b = 9.25$;   (c) Cl^-, $pK_b = 21$.

SUMMARY

The probable location (relative to the nucleus) of an electron with a particular energy is called the **atomic orbital**. The first electron shell (closest to the nucleus, lowest energy) contains only the spherical 1s orbital. The second shell (higher energy) contains a spherical 2s orbital and three mutually perpendicular, two-lobed 2p orbitals. Any orbital can hold a maximum of two paired (opposite spin) electrons.

The **atomic radius** equals half the distance between nuclei bonded by a non-polar covalent bond, such as in H—H. The atomic radius increases as we go down any group in the periodic table and decreases as we go from left to right across a period. **Electronegativity** is a measure of the pull of the nucleus on the outer electrons. It decreases as we go down any group and increases as we go from left to right in the periodic table.

A chemical bond results from electron transfer (**ionic bond**) or electron sharing (**covalent bond**). The number of bonds an atom can form (the **valence**) is determined by the number of bonding electrons. Carbon has four bonding electrons and forms four covalent bonds.

An **empirical formula** tells us the *relative number* of different atoms in a molecule, and the **molecular formula** tells us the *actual number* of different atoms in a covalent molecule.

$$C_2H_5 \qquad C_4H_{10}$$

empirical   *molecular*
formula   *formula*

In **structural formulas**, which show the structures of molecules, pairs of electrons may be represented by dots or by lines. Unshared bonding electrons are not always shown in structural formulas.

$$
\begin{array}{ccc}
\overset{\displaystyle H}{\underset{\displaystyle \overset{..}{H}\ \overset{..}{H}}{H:\overset{..}{C}:\overset{..}{N}:H}} &
\overset{\displaystyle H}{\underset{\displaystyle H\ \ H}{H—\overset{|}{C}—\overset{|}{N}—H}} &
CH_3NH_2
\end{array}
$$

Lewis formula   *complete*   *condensed*
structural formula   *structural formula*

An atom may share two, four, or six electrons with another atom—that is, two atoms may be joined by a **single bond**, a **double bond**, or a **triple bond**.

single bond ⟶   *double bond*
triple bond ⟶ $H—C{\equiv}C—\overset{\displaystyle H}{\overset{|}{C}}{=}CH_2$

A **formal charge** arises from a **coordinate covalent bond**, a bond in which both electrons are supplied by one atom.

$$CH_3—\overset{+}{N}\underset{\cdot\overset{..}{O}\cdot^-}{\overset{\displaystyle \overset{..}{O}\cdot}{}}$$

both e$^-$ from N

The **bond distance** is the distance between nuclei of covalently bonded atoms. The **bond angle** is the angle between two covalent bonds in a molecule. The **bond dissociation energy** (ΔH in the following equation) is the amount of energy needed to effect **homolytic cleavage** of a covalent bond.

$$H_3C\text{—}H \longrightarrow H_3C\cdot + H\cdot \quad \Delta H = +104 \text{ kcal/mole.}$$

A **polar covalent bond** is a covalent bond between atoms with substantially different electronegativities. The **bond moment** is the measure of the polarity of the bond. The **dipole moment** is the measure of the polarity of the entire molecule.

Dipole–dipole attractions between molecules (**van der Waals attractions**) are generally well under 5 kcal/mole except for **hydrogen bonds** (attractions between a partially positive H and an unshared pair of electrons of N, O, or F), which require 5–10 kcal/mole for their dissociation. Hydrogen bonding leads to an increase in boiling point and water solubility of a compound.

A **Brønsted–Lowry acid** is a substance that can donate H^+; a **Brønsted–Lowry base** is a substance that can accept H^+. A **Lewis acid** is a substance that can accept electrons; a **Lewis base** is a substance that can donate a pair of electrons.

Brønsted–Lowry acids: HCl, CH_3CO_2H *Lewis acids:* H^+, $FeCl_3$
Brønsted–Lowry bases: ^-OH, NH_3 *Lewis bases:* ^-OH, NH_3

The strength of a weak acid or a weak base is reported as K_a (or pK_a) or as K_b (or pK_b), respectively. A stronger acid has a larger value for K_a (and a smaller pK_a); a stronger base has a larger K_b (and a smaller pK_b).

anion

$$K_a = \frac{[H^+][A^-]}{[HA]} \quad \text{and} \quad pK_a = -\log K_a$$

$$K_b = \frac{[\overset{+}{B}H][OH^-]}{[B]} \quad \text{and} \quad pK_b = -\log K_b$$

base

STUDY PROBLEMS

1.15 Without referring to the text, give the electron configurations (for example, $1s^2\,2s^1$) for:

(a) carbon (atomic no. 6)   (b) silicon (14)
(c) phosphorus (15)   (d) sulfur (16)

1.16 Which atomic orbitals contain the *bonding* electrons of carbon?

1.17 If an atom used p atomic orbitals to form single covalent bonds with two hydrogen atoms, what would be the expected bond angle?

1.18 Which element in each of the following lists has the largest atomic radius? (Do not refer to the text, but make your prediction on the basis of relative locations in the periodic table.) (a) Si, C, O; (b) B, C, F; (c) H, C, O.

1.19 Which element in each of the following lists is the most electronegative? (Refer to Figure 1.5.)

(a) C, H, O   (b) C, H, N   (c) C, H, Mg   (d) C, Cl, O

1.20 Which of the following compounds would you expect to have (1) *an ionic bond*; (2) *a covalent bond*; or (3) *both ionic and covalent bonds*?

(a) CH_3CO_2Na (b) CH_3I (c) LiOH   (d) CH_3ONa
(e) CH_3OH (f) $Mg(OH)Br$ (g) H_2S (h) $CHCl_3$

1.21 Without referring to the text, give the valences for the elements in period 2.

1.22 What is the expected *maximum* number of covalent bonds that an atom of any second-period element could form? Why?

1.23 Give the *Lewis formula* for each of the following structures:

(a)
```
    H  H  H  H
    |  |  |  |
H — C— C— C— C —H
    |  |  |  |
    H  H  H  H
```
(b)
```
    H        H        H
    |        |        |
H — C ———— C ———— C —H
    |        |        |
    H     H—C—H      H
             |
             H
```

(c) $CH_3CHCH(CH_3)_2$ (with Cl below the first CH)
       |
       Cl

(d) H_2O_2

(e)
```
        O
       / \
  H_2C—CH_2
```

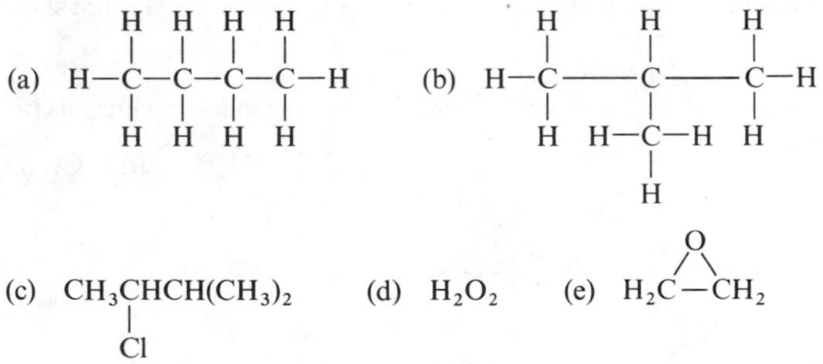

1.24 Calculate the formal charges of all atoms except H in each of the following structures:

(a)
```
      :Ö:
       |
CH_3—S—Cl
       |
      :O:
```

(b)
```
      CH_3
       |
CH_3—C—N̈—Ö:
       |     ··
      CH_3
```

(c) $CH_3—C\equiv N:$

(d)
```
     :O:
      ||
CH_3C—Ö:⁻
      ··
```

(e)
```
      ··   ··
CH_3—N̈—Ö—H
      |
      H
```

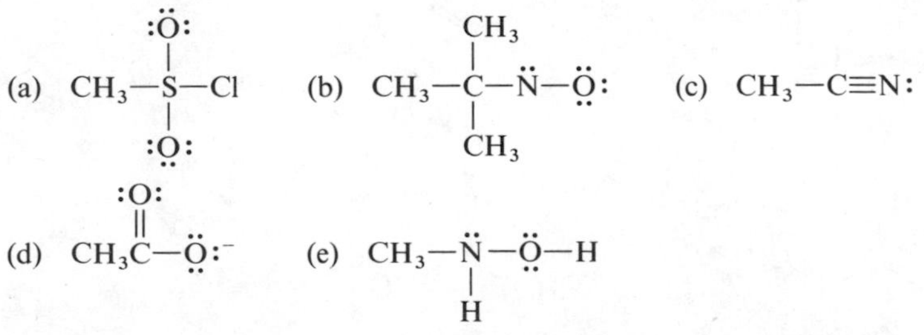

1.25 Give the *complete structural formula* (showing each atom and using lines for bonds) for each of the following condensed formulas:

(a) $(CH_3)_2CHCHBrCH_3$ (b) $(CH_3)_2CHCNHCH(CH_3)CH=CH_2$ (with O double-bonded above C)

(c) $(CH_3)_2C=C(CH_3)C\equiv CCH_3$

1.26 Write the *condensed structural formula* for each of the following structures:

(a) 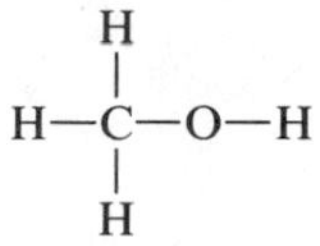 H—C—O—H (with H above and below C)

(b) H—C—C—N (with H's)

(c) H:C:N:C:H (with H's)

1.27 Write the *molecular formula* for each of the following structural formulas:

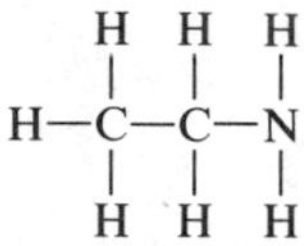

(a) 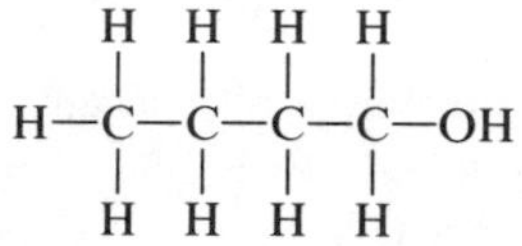 H—C—C—C—C—OH (with H's)

(b) H—C—C—C—C—H (with H's and OH)

(c) H—C—C—C—H (with branches)

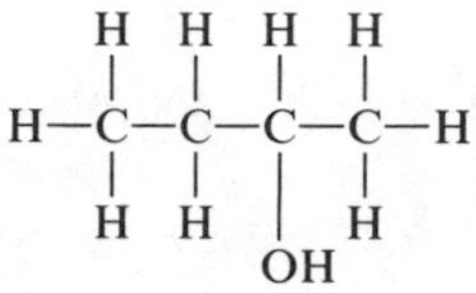

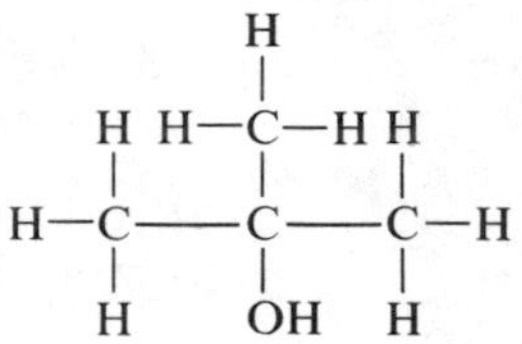

(d) 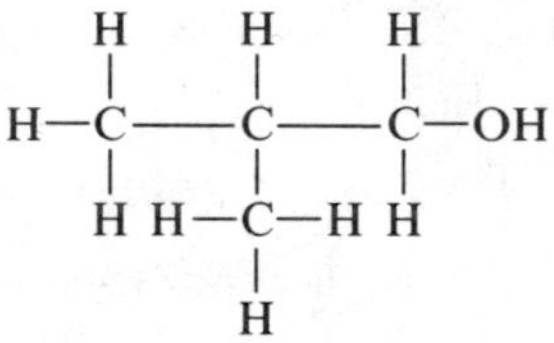 H—C—C—C—OH (with branches)

1.28 Give the *complete structural formula* for each of the following compounds:

(a) $H_2C=CHCH=CHCN$ (b) CH_3COCH_3

(c) CH_3CO_2H (d) $OHCCH_2CHO$

(*Hint:* Each structure contains at least one double or triple bond that is not shown. Use rules of valence to find these.)

1.29 Show any *unshared pairs of valence electrons* (if any) in the following formulas:

(a) CH_3NH_2 (b) $(CH_3)_3N$ (c) $(CH_3)_3NH^+$ (d) CH_3OH

(e) $(CH_3)_3COH$ (f) $CH_2=CH_2$ (g) $H_2C=O$

1.30 Draw a polygon formula for each of the following cyclic structures:

(a) 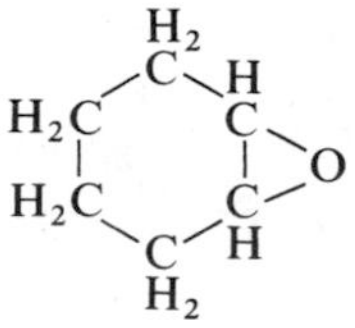 (cyclic structure with H₂C, CH, O)

(b) 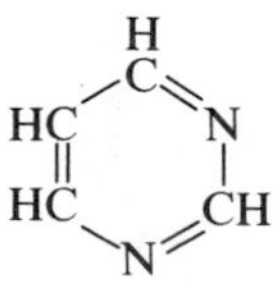 (cyclic structure with HC, N, CH)

(c) 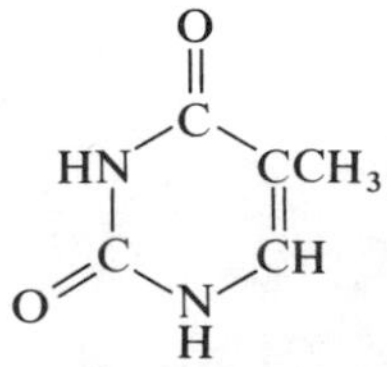 (cyclic structure with HN, C, O, CCH₃)

(d) 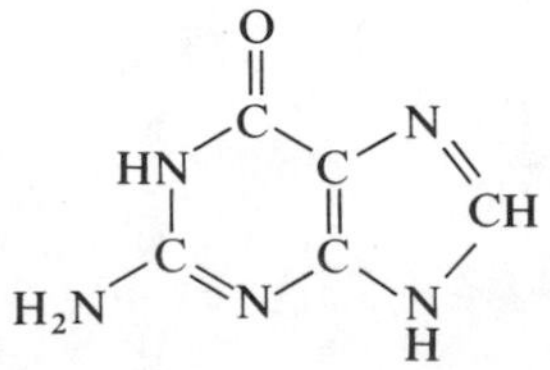 (cyclic structure with HN, C, N, CH, H₂N)

1.31 Convert each of the following polygon formulas to a complete structural formula, showing each atom and each bond. Show also any unshared pairs of valence electrons.

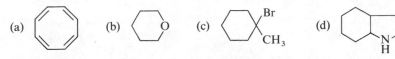

1.32 Draw the polygon and the structural formulas for a carbon ring system containing:

(a) six ring carbons and a double bond;
(b) five ring carbons and a carbonyl group (C=O) in the ring.

1.33 The bond dissociation energy for the carbon–halogen bond of CH_3—F is 108 kcal/mole; for CH_3—Cl, it is 83.5 kcal/mole; for CH_3—Br, it is 70 kcal/mole; and for CH_3—I, it is 56 kcal/mole. Calculate the net ΔH for each of the following reactions:

(a) $CH_4 + F_2 \longrightarrow CH_3F + HF$
(b) $CH_4 + Cl_2 \longrightarrow CH_3Cl + HCl$
(c) $CH_4 + Br_2 \longrightarrow CH_3Br + HBr$
(d) $CH_4 + I_2 \longrightarrow CH_3I + HI$

1.34 Write chemical equations for (1) the *homolytic cleavage*, and (2) the *heterolytic cleavage*, of each of the following compounds at the indicated bond. (Apply your knowledge of electronegativities in the heterolytic cleavages.)

(a) CH_3CH_2—Cl   (b) H—OH   / (c) H—NH_2
(d) CH_3—OH   (e) CH_3O—H

1.35 Circle the most electronegative element in each of the following structures, and show the direction of polarization of its bond(s):

$$O$$
$$\parallel$$
(a) CH_3OH (b) CH_3CCH_3
(c) FCH_2CO_2H (d) $(CH_3)_2NCH_2CH_2OH$

1.36 Which is the positive end and which is the negative end of the dipole in each of the following bonds?

(a) C—Mg   (b) C—Br   (c) C—O
(d) C—Cl   (e) C—H   (f) C—B

1.37 Arrange each of the following series of compounds in order of increasing polarity (least polar first):

(a) $CH_3CH_2CH_2NH_2$, $CH_3CH_2CH_3$, $CH_3CH_2CH_2OH$;
(b) $CH_3CH_2CH_2Br$, $CH_3CH_2CH_2I$, $CH_3CH_2CH_2Cl$.

1.38 Arrange the following compounds in order of increasing ionic character (least ionic first): (a) CH_4; (b) HBr; (c) LiCl.

1.39 Which of the following compounds can form hydrogen bonds with other molecules of its own kind?

(a) $(CH_3)_2NH$ (b) $CH_3CH_2OCH_2CH_2OH$

$$O$$
$$\parallel$$
(c) CH_3COH (d) $CH_3OCH_2CH_2OCH_3$

1.40 Draw structures to show the hydrogen bonding (if any) you would expect in the following compounds:

(a) CH_3CH_2OH (b) $CH_3CH_2OCH_3$ (c) CH_3CH_2F (d) $(CH_3)_3N$

1.41 Which of the following compounds would form hydrogen bonds with itself? With water?

(a) $CH_3CH_2CH_2OH$ (b) $CH_3\overset{\overset{O}{\|}}{C}CH_3$ (c) $CH_3\underset{\underset{CH_3}{|}}{C}HCH_3$

(d) $(CH_3)_2CHOCH_3$ (e) 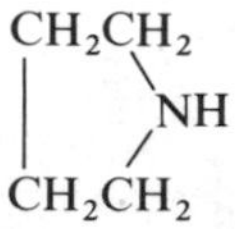 $\begin{array}{c} CH_2CH_2 \\ | \quad \diagdown \\ \quad \quad NH \\ | \quad \diagup \\ CH_2CH_2 \end{array}$

1.42 Show all types of hydrogen bond in an aqueous solution of $(CH_3)_2NH$. Which is the strongest hydrogen bond?

1.43 Complete the following equations for acid–base reactions:

(a) $CH_3O^- + H_2O \rightleftharpoons$

(b) $CH_3NH_2 + HCl \rightleftharpoons$

(c) 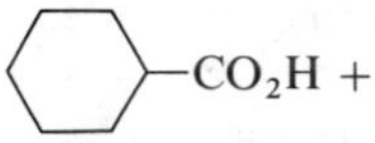 ⬡$-CO_2H + OH^- \rightleftharpoons$

(d)  ⬡$NH + H^+ \rightleftharpoons$

(e) $CH_3CO_2^- + H^+ \rightleftharpoons$

(f) $CH_3NH_2 + CH_3\overset{\overset{O}{\|}}{C}OH \rightleftharpoons$

1.44 Calculate the pK_a of each of the following acids, and arrange in order of increasing acidity (weakest acid first):

	Structure	K_a
(a)	CH_3CO_2H	1.75×10^{-5}
(b) 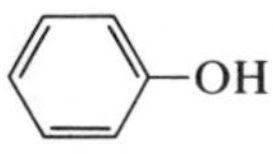	⬡$-OH$	1.0×10^{-10}
(c) 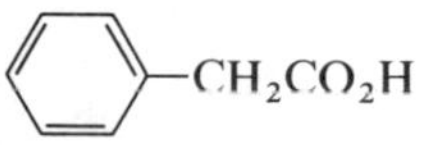	⬡$-CH_2CO_2H$	5.2×10^{-5}
(d)	CH_3CH_2OH	$\sim 10^{-16}$
(e)	CH_3CH_3	$\sim 10^{-43}$

1.45 Calculate the pK_b of the following bases, and arrange in order of increasing base strength:

Structure	K_b
(a) $CH_3\overset{\displaystyle O}{\overset{\|}{C}}NH_2$	4.3×10^{-14}
(b) ⟨⟩—NH_2	4.3×10^{-10}
(c) $(CH_3)_3CNH_2$	6.8×10^{-4}
(d) morphine (page 766)	1.6×10^{-6}

1.46 What element corresponds with each of the following electron configurations?

(a) $1s^2\ 2s^2\ 2p^6\ 3s^1$ (b) $1s^2\ 2s^2\ 2p^6\ 3s^2\ 3p^5$ (c) $1s^2\ 2s^2\ 2p^6$

1.47 From the electron configurations, which pairs of elements would you expect to exhibit similar chemical behavior?

(a) $1s^2\ 2s^1$ and $1s^2\ 2s^2$
(b) $1s^2\ 2s^1$ and $1s^2\ 2s^2\ 2p^6\ 3s^2\ 3p^6\ 4s^1$
(c) $1s^2\ 2s^1$ and $1s^2\ 2s^2\ 2p^6\ 3s^1$

1.48 If you mix equal volumes of equimolar solutions of NaBr and LiCl, you will obtain the same solution as a similar mixture prepared from LiBr and NaCl. Why? Would this be true for solutions of CH_3Cl + NaBr, and CH_3Br + NaCl? Why?

1.49 Lead(IV) chloride, $PbCl_4$, is a liquid at room temperature (mp $-15°$), while lead(II) chloride, $PbCl_2$, is a high-melting solid (mp 501°). What do these properties suggest about the bonding in these two compounds?

1.50 Assign the proper ionic charge to each of the following ions:

(a) $:C\equiv N:$ (b) $:C\equiv CH$ (c) $H-\overset{..}{O}-\overset{\displaystyle |}{\underset{\displaystyle H}{C}}-H$ (d) $CH_3\overset{..}{O}:$

1.51 None of the following compounds contain double bonds. Can you devise a condensed structural formula for each? More than one answer may be possible. (Remember the valences.)

(a) C_3H_6; (b) C_2H_4O; (c) C_4H_8O.

1.52 Calculate the heats of reaction for:

(a) $CH_3CH_3 + Cl_2 \longrightarrow CH_3CH_2Cl + HCl$;
(b) $CH_3CH_3 + Br_2 \longrightarrow CH_3CH_2Br + HBr$.

Which reaction liberates more energy? (The bond dissociation energy for CH_3CH_2-Br is 68 kcal/mole. See Table 1.4, page 18, for others.)

1.53 Considering the electronegativities of the atoms involved, which reaction in each of the following pairs is the more reasonable?

(a) $CH_3OH \longrightarrow CH_3O^- + H^+$
     $CH_3OH \longrightarrow CH_3O^+ + H^-$

(b) $(CH_3)_2CHBr \longrightarrow (CH_3)_2\overset{+}{C}H + Br^-$
     $(CH_3)_2CHBr \longrightarrow (CH_3)_2\overset{-}{C}H + Br^+$

(c) $CH_3CH_2Li \longrightarrow CH_3\overset{-}{C}H_2 + Li^+$
     $CH_3CH_2Li \longrightarrow CH_3\overset{+}{C}H_2 + Li^-$

1.54 BF_3 has a dipole moment of zero. Suggest a shape for the BF_3 molecule.

1.55 Arrange the following compounds according to increasing solubility in water, least soluble first:

$$\overset{\displaystyle O}{\overset{\displaystyle \|}{}}$$

(a) CH_3COH (b) CH_3CH_3 (c) $CH_3CH_2OCH_2CH_3$

1.56 Diethyl ether, $CH_3CH_2OCH_2CH_3$, and 1-butanol, $CH_3CH_2CH_2CH_2OH$, are equally soluble in water, but the boiling point of 1-butanol is 83° higher than that of diethyl ether. What explanation can you give for these observations?

1.57 In the following reactions, which of the reactants is the Lewis acid and which is the Lewis base?

(a) $(CH_3)_3CCl + AlCl_3 \rightleftharpoons (CH_3)_3C^+ + AlCl_4^-$

(b) $(CH_3)_3C^+ + CH_2{=}CH_2 \rightleftharpoons (CH_3)_3CCH_2\overset{+}{C}H_2$

1.58 Indicate the most likely position of attack by a Lewis acid on each of the following structures:

(a)  HNNH   (b) 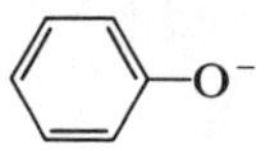 ⟨◯⟩—O⁻   (c) CH_3OH

Orbitals and Their Role in Covalent Bonding

In Chapter 1, we took a brief look at atomic orbitals and at covalent bonding. In this chapter, we will discuss the **molecular orbital theory of covalent bonding.** We will see that the molecular orbital theory can be used to explain why different covalent molecules have different shapes and why some covalent bonds are more reactive than others. A knowledge of molecular orbitals is indispensable because the differences in the shapes and in the bonds of molecules lead to differences in chemistry—whether in a flask in the laboratory or in the cells of an animal.

Properties of Waves

Until 1923, chemists assumed that electrons were nothing more than negatively charged particles whirling about the atomic nuclei. In 1923, Louis de Broglie, a French graduate student, proposed the revolutionary idea that electrons have properties of waves as well as properties of particles. De Broglie's proposal met with skepticism at first, but his idea was the seed that grew into today's quantum-mechanical concept of electron motion.

Quantum mechanics is a mathematical subject. For our understanding of covalent bonds, we need only the results of quantum-mechanical studies, rather than the mathematical equations themselves. With this in mind, let us survey some of the basic concepts of wave motion as they pertain to the current theories of covalent bonds.

We will begin with some simple **standing waves** (Figure 2.1), the type of wave that occurs when you pluck a string, like a guitar string, that is fixed at both ends. This type of wave exhibits motion in only one dimension. By contrast, the standing waves caused by beating the head of a drum are two-dimensional, and the wave system of an electron is three-dimensional. The height of a standing wave is its **amplitude**, which may be up (positive value) or down (negative value) in relation to the resting position of the string. (Note that the + or − sign of amplitude is a mathematical sign, not an electrical charge.) A position on the wave at which the amplitude is zero is called a **node**, and is a position on the guitar string that does not move as the string vibrates.

Two standing waves can be either **in phase** or **out of phase** in reference to each other. Intermediate states in which waves are only partially in phase are also

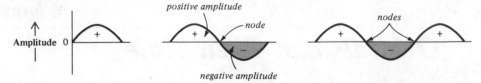

Figure 2.1. Some standing waves of a vibrating string with fixed ends (negative amplitudes shaded).

possible. We can illustrate these terms by two wave systems on two identical vibrating strings. If the positive and negative amplitudes of the two waves correspond to each other, the two waves are *in phase*. If the mathematical signs of the amplitudes are opposite, the waves are *out of phase* (see Figure 2.2).

If two in-phase waves on the same string overlap, they **reinforce** each other. The reinforcement is expressed by addition of the mathematical functions of the same sign describing the waves. Conversely, a pair of overlapping waves that are out of phase **interfere** with each other. The process of interference is represented by addition of two mathematical functions of opposite sign. Complete interference

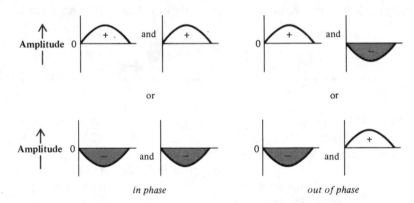

Figure 2.2. Two standing waves may be either in phase or out of phase.

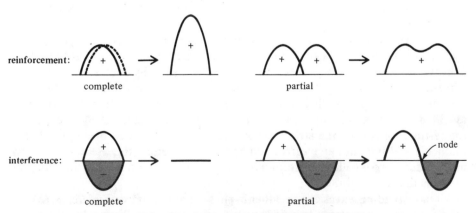

Figure 2.3. Reinforcement and interference of waves.

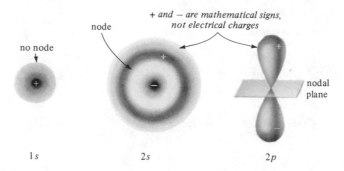

Figure 2.4.   The $1s$, $2s$, and $2p$ orbitals with their signs of amplitude.

results in the cancelling of one wave by another. Partial overlap of two out-of-phase waves gives rise to a node. Figure 2.3 illustrates reinforcement and interference.

Although a three-dimensional electron wave system is more complicated than a one-dimensional string system, the principles are similar. Each atomic orbital of an atom behaves as a wave function and may have a positive or negative amplitude. If the orbital has both positive and negative amplitudes, it has a node. Figure 2.4 depicts the $1s$, $2s$, and $2p$ orbitals, including their signs of amplitude and their nodes.

One atomic orbital may overlap an atomic orbital of another atom. When the overlapping orbitals are in phase, the result is reinforcement and a **bonding molecular orbital**. On the other hand, interaction between atomic orbitals that are out of phase results in interference, creating a node between the two nuclei. Interference leads to **antibonding molecular orbitals**. We will expand upon these definitions of bonding and antibonding orbitals in Section 2.2B.

Section 2.2

Bonding in Hydrogen

Hydrogen (H_2) is the simplest molecule. We will look at the covalent bond of H_2 in some detail because many features of this bond are similar to those of more complex covalent bonds.

Let us consider two isolated hydrogen atoms, each with one electron in a $1s$ atomic orbital. As these two atoms begin bond formation, the electron of each atom becomes attracted by the nucleus of the other atom, as well as by its own nucleus. When the nuclei are at a certain distance from each other (the bond distance, 0.74 Å for H_2), the atomic orbitals merge, or overlap, to reinforce each other and form a bonding molecular orbital. This molecular orbital encompasses both hydrogen nuclei and contains two paired electrons (one from each H). Both electrons are now equally attracted to both nuclei. Because a large portion of the electron density of this new orbital is located between the two nuclei, repulsions between the nuclei are minimized. This molecular orbital results in the covalent bond between the two hydrogen atoms in H_2 (see Figure 2.5).

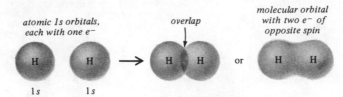

*atomic 1s orbitals,
each with one e⁻*

overlap

*molecular orbital
with two e⁻ of
opposite spin*

1s   1s   or

Figure 2.5.   The formation of the molecular orbital in H_2.

A.   The Sigma Bond

The molecular orbital that bonds the two hydrogen atoms together is *cylindrically symmetrical*—that is, symmetrical around a line, or axis, joining the two nuclei. Think of the axis as an axle, and rotate the orbital around this axis. If the appearance of the orbital is not changed by the rotation, the orbital is symmetrical around that axis (see Figure 2.6).

Any molecular orbital that is symmetrical around the axis connecting the nuclei is called a **sigma (σ) molecular orbital**; the bond is a **sigma bond**. The bond in H_2 is only one of many sigma bonds we will encounter. (We will also encounter molecular orbitals that are not sigma orbitals—that is, orbitals that are not symmetrical around their nuclear axes.)

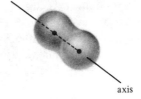

Figure 2.6.   The sigma bond of hydrogen is symmetrical around the axis joining the two nuclei.

axis

B.   The Bonding Orbital and the Antibonding Orbital

When a pair of waves overlap, they either reinforce each other or interfere with each other. Addition of two in-phase 1s atomic orbitals of two H atoms results in reinforcement and the σ bonding molecular orbital, with a high electron density between the bonded nuclei.

If two waves are out of phase, they interfere with each other. Interference of two out-of-phase atomic orbitals of two hydrogen atoms gives a molecular orbital with a *node between the nuclei*. In this molecular orbital, the probability of finding an electron between the nuclei is *very low*. Therefore, this particular molecular orbital gives rise to a system where the two nuclei are not shielded by the pair of electrons, and the nuclei repel each other. Because of the nuclear repulsion, this system is of *higher energy* than the system of two independent H atoms. This higher-energy orbital is the **antibonding orbital**, in this case, a σ* orbital (the * meaning "antibonding"). Figure 2.7 compares the shapes of the σ and σ* orbitals for H_2.

The energy of the H_2 molecule with two electrons in the σ bonding orbital is *lower* by 104 kcal/mole than the combined energy of two separate hydrogen atoms.

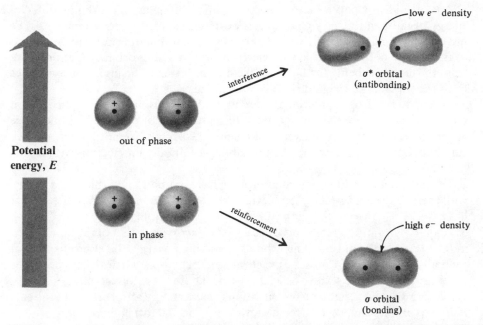

Figure 2.7. Reinforcement and interference of two 1*s* orbitals. (The + and − refer to phases of the wave functions, not electrical charges.)

The energy of the molecule with electrons in the σ* antibonding orbital, on the other hand, is *higher* than that of two separate hydrogen atoms. These relative energies may be represented by the following diagram:

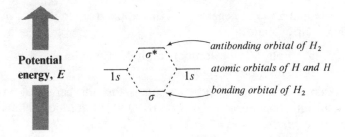

A molecular orbital, like an atomic orbital, can hold no electrons, one electron, or two paired electrons. The two electrons in a hydrogen molecule go into the lowest-energy orbital available, the σ bonding orbital. In the following diagram, we use a pair of arrows (one pointing up and one pointing down) to represent a pair of electrons of opposite spin.

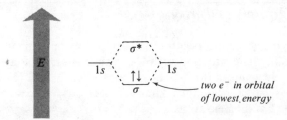

We said in Chapter 1 that electrons in different atomic orbitals differ in energy because of the varying distances of these electrons from the nucleus. The higher energy of a molecule with electrons in an antibonding orbital (compared to the energy of the molecule with electrons in a bonding orbital) does not arise from the electrons being farther from the nuclei. Instead, the higher energy arises from the presence of the node between the nuclei.

For the hydrogen molecule, the σ and σ^* orbitals are in the same general region of space. Although two particles of matter cannot occupy the same space at the same time, two orbitals may. Remember, orbitals are not matter, but are simply regions of space where the probability of finding an electron with a particular energy is high.

Almost all bonding molecular orbitals have antibonding orbitals associated with them. In each case, a molecule with electrons in a bonding molecular orbital has a *lower energy* than the energy of the nonbonded atoms, and a molecule with electrons in an antibonding orbital has a *higher energy* than that of the nonbonded atoms. Because the antibonding orbitals are of high energy, the electrons are not generally found there. Almost all the chemistry in this text will deal with molecules in the **ground state**, the state in which the electrons are in the lowest-energy orbitals. However, we will encounter a few situations where energy absorbed by a molecule is used to promote an electron from a low-energy orbital to a higher-energy orbital. A molecule is said to be in an **excited state** when one or more electrons are not in the orbital of lowest energy.

Section 2.3

Some General Features of Bonding and Antibonding Orbitals

Let us summarize some general rules that apply to all molecular orbitals, not only the molecular orbitals of H_2:

(1) Any orbital (molecular or atomic) can hold a maximum of two electrons, which must be of opposite spin.

(2) The number of molecular orbitals equals the number of atomic orbitals that went into their formation. (For H_2, two $1s$ atomic orbitals yield two molecular orbitals: σ and σ^*.)

(3) In the filling of molecular orbitals with electrons, the lowest-energy orbitals are filled first. If two orbitals are degenerate (of equal energies), each gets one electron before either is filled.

Section 2.4

Hybrid Orbitals of Carbon

When a hydrogen atom becomes part of a molecule, it uses its $1s$ atomic orbital for bonding. The situation with the carbon atom is somewhat different. Carbon has two electrons in the $1s$ orbital; consequently, the $1s$ orbital is a filled orbital that is not used for bonding. The four electrons at the *second energy level* of carbon are the bonding electrons.

There are four atomic orbitals at the second energy level: one $2s$ and three $2p$ orbitals. However, carbon does not use these four orbitals in their pure states for bonding. Instead, carbon blends, or **hybridizes**, its four second-level atomic orbitals in one of three different ways for bonding:

(1) sp^3 **hybridization,** used when carbon forms four single bonds.

$$\text{—} sp^3 \text{ carbons} \text{—}$$

$$
\begin{array}{ccc}
& H & \\
& | & \\
H\text{—}C\text{—}H & \\
& | & \\
& H &
\end{array}
\qquad
\begin{array}{cc}
H & H \\
| & | \\
H\text{—}C\text{—}C\text{—}H \\
| & | \\
H & H
\end{array}
$$

(2) sp^2 **hybridization,** used when carbon forms a double bond.

$$sp^2 \text{ carbons}$$

$$
\begin{array}{ccc}
H & & H \\
\diagdown & & \diagup \\
& C\text{=}C & \\
\diagup & & \diagdown \\
H & & H
\end{array}
$$

(3) sp **hybridization,** used when carbon forms a triple bond.

$$H\text{—}C\text{≡}C\text{—}H \qquad sp \text{ carbons}$$

Why does a carbon atom form compounds with hybrid orbitals rather than with unhybridized atomic orbitals? The answer is that hybridization gives stronger bonds because of greater overlap, and therefore results in more-stable, lower-energy molecules. As we discuss each type of hybridization, note that the *shape* of each hybrid orbital is favorable for maximum overlap with an orbital of another atom. Also note that the *geometries* of the three types of hybrid orbital allow attached groups to be as far from each other as possible, thus minimizing their repulsions for each other.

A. sp^3 *Hybridization*

In methane (CH_4), the carbon atom has four equivalent bonds to hydrogen. Each C—H bond has a bond distance of 1.09 Å and a bond dissociation energy of 104 kcal/mole. The bond angle between each C—H bond is 109.3°. From this experimental evidence alone, it is evident that carbon does not form bonds by means of one s atomic orbital and three p atomic orbitals. If that were the case, the four C—H bonds would not all be equivalent.

According to present-day theory, these four equivalent bonds arise from complete hybridization of the four atomic orbitals (one $2s$ orbital and three $2p$ orbitals) to yield four equivalent sp^3 orbitals. The sp^3 orbitals have equal energies – slightly higher than that of the $2s$ orbitals, but slightly lower than that of the $2p$ orbitals. Each of the sp^3 orbitals contains one electron for bonding.

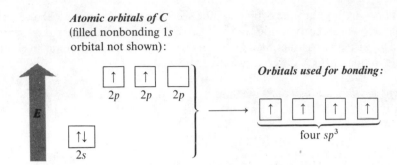

Atomic orbitals of C
(filled nonbonding 1s
orbital not shown):

Orbitals used for bonding:

The preceding diagram is called an **orbital diagram**. Each box in the diagram represents an orbital. The relative energies of the various orbitals are signified by the vertical positions of the boxes within the diagram. Electrons are represented by arrows, and the direction of electron spin is indicated by the direction of the arrow.

The sp^3 orbital, which results from a blend of the 2s and 2p orbitals, is shaped rather like a bowling pin: it has a large lobe and a small lobe (of opposite amplitude) with a node at the nucleus. Figure 2.8 shows one isolated sp^3 orbital. The small end of the hybrid orbital is not used for bonding because overlap of the large end with another orbital gives more complete overlap and results in a stronger bond.

Four sp^3-hybrid orbitals surround the carbon nucleus. Because of repulsions between electrons in different orbitals, these sp^3 orbitals lie as far apart from each other as possible while still extending away from the same carbon nucleus—that is, the four orbitals point toward the corners of a regular tetrahedron (Figure 2.8). This geometry gives idealized bond angles of 109.3°. An sp^3 carbon atom is often referred to as a **tetrahedral carbon atom** because of the geometry of its bonds.

When an sp^3 carbon atom forms bonds, it does so by overlapping each of its four sp^3 orbitals (each with one electron) with orbitals from four other atoms (each orbital in turn containing one electron). In methane (Figures 2.9 and 2.10), each sp^3 orbital of carbon overlaps with a 1s orbital of hydrogen. Each of the resultant sp^3–s molecular orbitals is symmetrical around the axis passing through the nuclei of the carbon and the hydrogen. The covalent bonds between C and H in methane, like the H—H covalent bond, are sigma bonds.

Ethane (CH_3CH_3) contains two sp^3 carbon atoms. These two carbon atoms form a C—C sigma bond by the overlap of one sp^3 orbital from each carbon (sp^3–sp^3 sigma bond). Each carbon atom has three remaining sp^3 orbitals, and each of these overlaps with a 1s orbital of a hydrogen atom to form a C—H sigma bond. Each carbon atom in ethane is tetrahedral (see Figures 2.11 and 2.12).

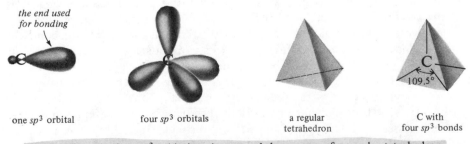

the end used for bonding

one sp^3 orbital   four sp^3 orbitals   a regular tetrahedron   C with four sp^3 bonds

Figure 2.8.   The four sp^3 orbitals point toward the corners of a regular tetrahedron.

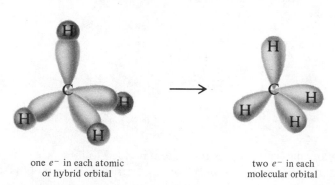

one e^- in each atomic
or hybrid orbital

two e^- in each
molecular orbital

Figure 2.9. Formation of C—H sigma bonds in methane, CH_4. (The small lobes of the sp^3 orbitals are not shown.)

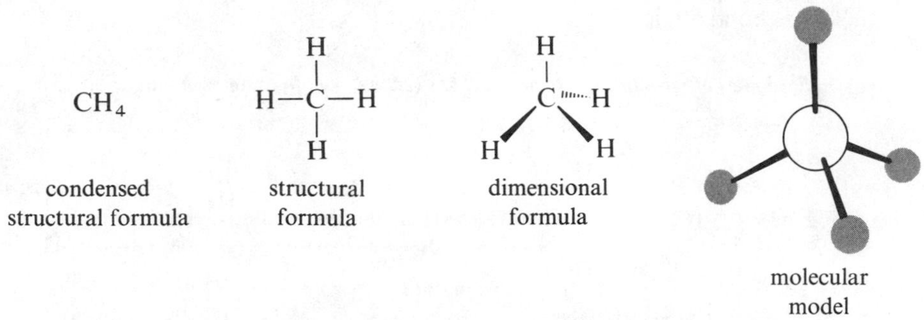

CH_4

condensed
structural formula

structural
formula

dimensional
formula

molecular
model

Figure 2.10. Some different ways of representing methane.

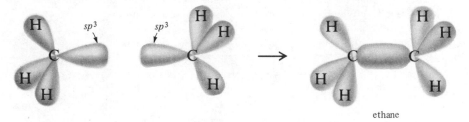

ethane

Figure 2.11. Formation of the sp^3–sp^3 sigma bond in ethane, CH_3CH_3.

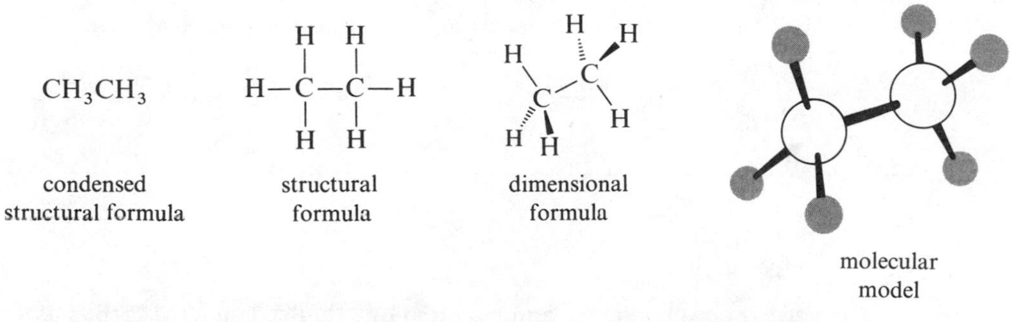

CH_3CH_3

condensed
structural formula

structural
formula

dimensional
formula

molecular
model

Figure 2.12. Some different ways of representing ethane.

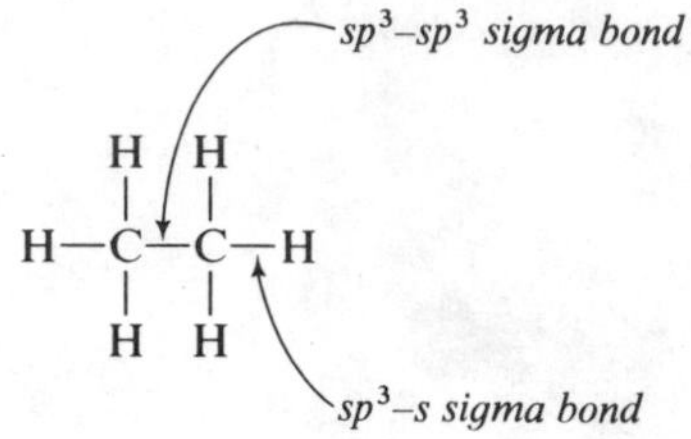

$sp^3–sp^3$ *sigma bond*

$$H \overset{\displaystyle H}{\underset{\displaystyle H}{-C-}} \overset{\displaystyle H}{\underset{\displaystyle H}{C-}} H$$

$sp^3–s$ *sigma bond*

In any molecule, any carbon atom bonded to four other atoms is in the sp^3-hybrid state, and the four bonds from that carbon are sigma bonds. When carbon is bonded to four other atoms, the sp^3 hybridization allows maximum overlap and places the four attached atoms at the maximum distances from each other. If possible, the sp^3 bond angles are 109.5°; however, other factors, such as dipole–dipole repulsions or the geometry of a cyclic compound, can cause deviations from this ideal bond angle.

Examples of structures with sp^3 carbons (each C has four sigma bonds):

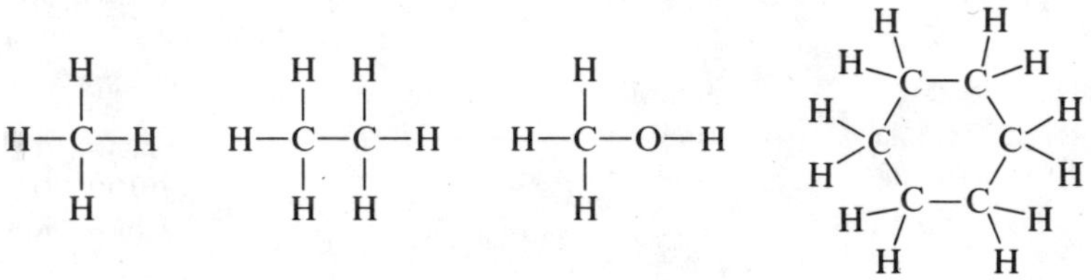

Sample Problem

Give the complete structural formula (showing all atoms and bonds) for propane ($CH_3CH_2CH_3$). Which types of orbitals overlap to form each bond?

Solution:

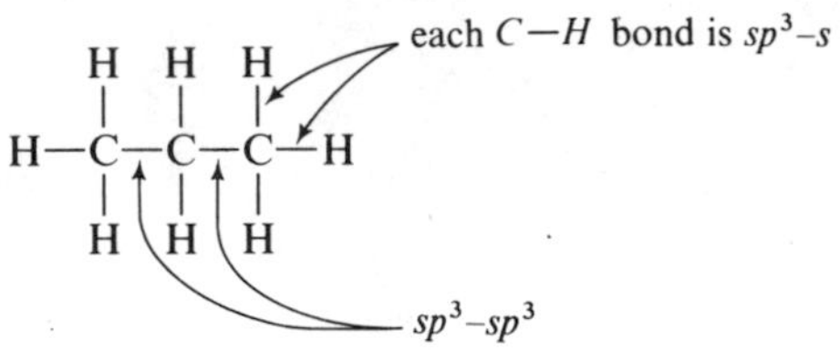

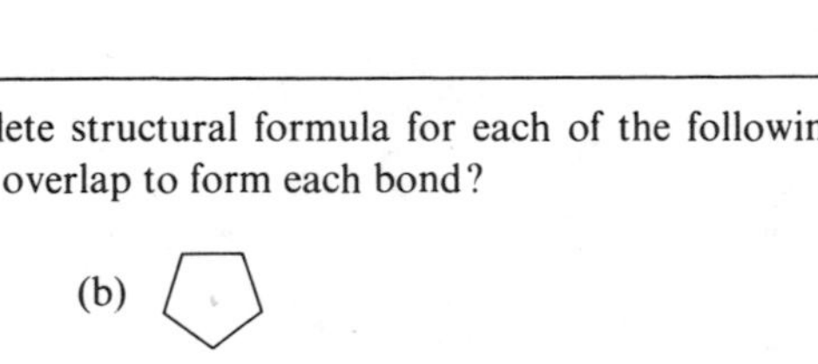

each $C—H$ bond is $sp^3–s$

$sp^3–sp^3$

STUDY PROBLEM

2.1   Write the complete structural formula for each of the following compounds. Which types of orbitals overlap to form each bond?

(a) $(CH_3)_3CH$ (b) ⬠

B. sp^2 *Hybridization*

When carbon is bonded to another atom by a double bond, the carbon atom is in the sp^2-hybrid state.

Examples of compounds with sp² carbons:

$$\begin{array}{c} H \\ \diagdown \\ \diagup \\ H \end{array} C=C \begin{array}{c} H \\ \diagup \\ \diagdown \\ H \end{array} \qquad \begin{array}{c} H \\ \diagdown \\ \diagup \\ H \end{array} C=O$$

ethylene   formaldehyde

To form sp^2 bonding orbitals, carbon hybridizes its $2s$ orbital with only two of its $2p$ orbitals. One p orbital remains unhybridized on the carbon atom. Because three atomic orbitals are used to form the sp^2 orbitals, three sp^2-hybrid orbitals result. Each sp^2 orbital has a shape similar to that of an sp^3 orbital and contains one electron that can be used for bonding.

The three sp^2 orbitals around a carbon nucleus lie as far apart from one another as possible—that is, the sp^2 orbitals lie in a plane with angles of 120° (ideally) between them. An sp^2 carbon atom is said to be a **trigonal** (triangular) carbon. Figure 2.13 shows a carbon atom with three sp^2 orbitals and the one unhybridized p orbital, which is perpendicular to the sp^2 plane.

In ethylene ($CH_2{=}CH_2$), two sp^2 carbons are joined by a sigma bond formed by the overlap of one sp^2 orbital from each carbon atom. (This sigma bond is one of the bonds of the double bond.) Each carbon atom still has two sp^2 orbitals left for bonding with hydrogen. (Each carbon atom also has a p orbital, which is not shown in the following structure.)

Planar sigma-bond structure of ethylene (p orbitals not shown):

$$\begin{array}{c} H \\ \diagdown \\ \diagup \\ H \end{array} \overset{121°}{C{-}C} \begin{array}{c} H \\ \diagup \\ \diagdown \\ H \end{array} 118°$$

a trigonal carbon; three sp^2 orbitals in a plane with 120° angles between them

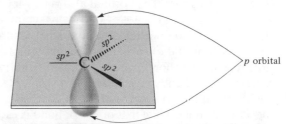

p orbital at a right angle to the plane

Figure 2.13. Carbon in the sp^2-hybrid state.

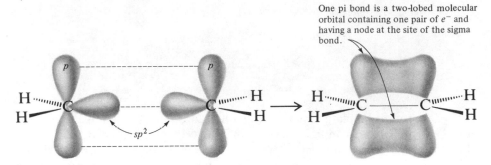

One pi bond is a two-lobed molecular orbital containing one pair of e^- and having a node at the site of the sigma bond.

Figure 2.14. Formation of the sp^2–sp^2 sigma bond and the p–p pi bond in ethylene, CH_2=CH_2.

What of the remaining p orbital on each carbon? Each p orbital has two lobes, one above the plane of the sigma bonds and the other (of opposite amplitude) below the plane. Each p orbital contains one electron. If these p electrons become paired in a bonding molecular orbital, then the energy of the system is lowered. Since the p orbitals lie side by side in the ethylene molecule, the *ends* of the orbitals cannot overlap, as they do in sigma-bond formation. Rather, the two p orbitals overlap their *sides* (see Figure 2.14). The result of this side-to-side overlap is the **pi (π) bond**—a bonding molecular orbital joining the two carbons and located above and below the plane of the sigma bonds. The pi bond is the second bond of the double bond.

Any carbon atom that is bonded to three other atoms is in the sp^2-hybrid state. In stable compounds, the p orbital on the sp^2 carbon must overlap with a p orbital of an adjacent atom, which can be another carbon atom or an atom of some other element.

sp^2 carbons

C.   Some Features of the Pi Bond

Each p orbital of a pi bond has two lobes and has a node at the nucleus. It is not surprising that the pi orbital also is two-lobed and has a node. Unlike a sigma orbital, a pi orbital is not cylindrically symmetrical. However, just like any molecular orbital, a pi orbital can hold a maximum of two paired electrons.

A $2p$ orbital of carbon is of slightly higher energy than an sp^2 orbital. For this reason, a pi bond, which is formed from two $2p$ orbitals, has slightly higher energy and is slightly less stable than an sp^2–sp^2 sigma bond. The bond dissociation energy of the sigma bond of ethylene's carbon–carbon double bond is estimated to be 95 kcal/mole, while that of the pi bond is estimated to be only 68 kcal/mole.

The more-exposed pi electrons are more vulnerable to external effects than are electrons in sigma bonds. The pi bond is polarized more easily—we might say that the pi electrons are more mobile. The pi electrons are more easily promoted

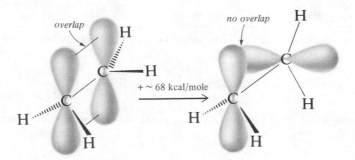

Figure 2.15.   The portion of a molecule surrounding a pi bond is held in a planar structure unless enough energy is supplied to break the pi bond.

to an excited state. Also, they are more readily attacked by an outside atom or molecule. What does this vulnerability mean in terms of the chemistry of pi-bonded compounds? In a molecule, the pi bond is a site of chemical reactivity.

Another property of the pi bond of ethylene is that its geometry holds the molecule in a rigid shape. For the carbon atoms to rotate around their bonds, the pi bond must first be broken (see Figure 2.15). In chemical reactions, molecules may have sufficient energy (about 68 kcal/mole) for this bond to break. In a flask at room temperature, however, molecules do not have enough energy for this bond breakage to occur. (Approximately 20 kcal/mole is the maximum energy available to molecules at room temperature.) The significance of the rigidity of pi bonds will be discussed in Chapter 4.

In a structural formula, the double bond is indicated by two identical lines. Keep in mind that the double bond is not simply two identical bonds, but that the double line represents one strong sigma bond and one weak pi bond.

Sample Problem

What type of overlap (sp^3-s, for example) is present in each bond of $CH_3CH{=}CH_2$? What is each bond angle (approximately)?

Solution:

STUDY PROBLEMS

2.2   Give the complete structural formula for each of the following compounds. Indicate which types of orbitals are used to form each bond.

(a) $CH_2{=}C(CH_3)_2$ (b) $CH_2{=}CHCH{=}CH_2$ (c)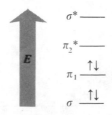

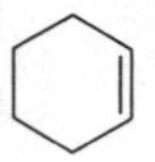

2.3   For compound (b) in Problem 2.2, draw the structure showing the pi bonds with its correct geometry in reference to the sigma bonds. (Use lines to represent the sigma bonds.)

D.   *The Bonding and Antibonding Orbitals of Ethylene*

The carbon–carbon sigma bond in ethylene results from overlap of two sp^2 orbitals. Because *two* sp^2 orbitals form this bond, *two* molecular orbitals result. The other molecular orbital, arising from interference between the two sp^2 orbitals, is the antibonding σ^* orbital. This antibonding orbital is similar to the σ^* orbital of hydrogen; it has a node between the two carbon nuclei and is of high energy. The two electrons of the C—C sigma bond in ethylene are usually found in the lower-energy σ orbital.

In the pi bond joining the two carbons of ethylene, each carbon atom contributes one p orbital for a total of two p orbitals; therefore, two pi molecular orbitals result. One of these is the π bonding orbital that arises from the overlap of two in-phase p orbitals. The other orbital is the π^* antibonding orbital, which arises from interference between two p orbitals of opposite phase. These two orbitals are frequently designated π_1 for the bonding orbital and π_2^* for the antibonding orbital. Some molecules contain several π orbitals, which we number in order of increasing energy; the subscript numbers are useful for differentiating the π orbitals. (We do not usually use subscript numbers for σ orbitals because σ^* orbitals are usually of minor importance to the organic chemist.)

Figure 2.16 shows the orbital representations of the π_1 and π_2^* orbitals of ethylene. Note that besides the node at the σ-bond site, the π_2^* orbital has an additional node *between the two carbon nuclei*. A minimum of the pi electron density is located between the nuclei in this orbital; thus, the π_2^* orbital is of higher energy than the π_1 orbital. In the ground state of ethylene, the pi electrons are found in the lower-energy π_1 orbital.

The following diagram comparing energies of the σ, σ^*, π_1, and π_2^* orbitals shows that the σ^* orbital is of higher energy than the π_2^* orbital. The amount of energy required to promote an electron from the σ orbital to the σ^* orbital is therefore greater than the energy required to promote a π electron to the π^* orbital.

Ground state of C=C in ethylene:

$$
\begin{array}{ll}
\sigma^* & \underline{\quad\quad} \\[1em]
\pi_2^* & \underline{\quad\quad} \\[1em]
\pi_1 & \underline{\uparrow\downarrow} \\[1em]
\sigma & \underline{\uparrow\downarrow}
\end{array}
$$

E

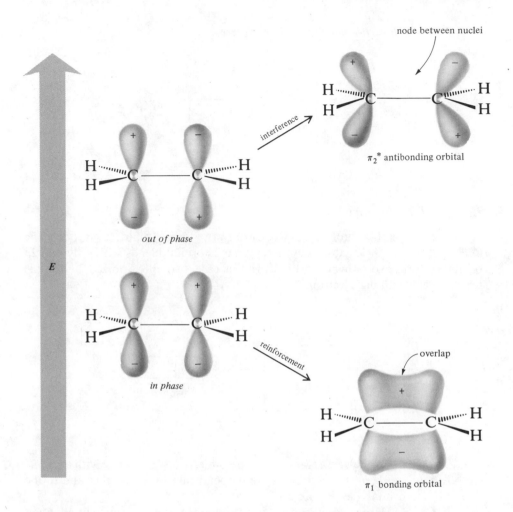

Figure 2.16. The π_1 bonding orbital and the π_2^* antibonding orbital of ethylene. (The + and − refer to phases of the wave function, not electrical charges.)

Why is more energy required to promote a σ electron than a π electron? Sigma bonding electrons are found close to the nucleus and, for the most part, directly between the nuclei. Promotion of one of these sigma electrons results in severe nuclear repulsion. However, the π bonding electrons are farther from the nucleus. Promotion of one of these pi electrons does not result in such severe nuclear repulsions. (Also, when a pi electron is promoted, the nuclei are still shielded from each other by σ bonding electrons.)

Because of the large amount of energy required to promote a sigma electron, electron transitions of the $\sigma \rightarrow \sigma^*$ type are rare and relatively unimportant to the organic chemist. However, $\pi \rightarrow \pi^*$ electron transitions, which require less energy, are important. For example, $\pi \rightarrow \pi^*$ transitions are responsible for vision, a topic that will be mentioned in Chapter 20, and for the energy capture needed for photosynthesis.

Two possible excited states of C=C *in ethylene:*

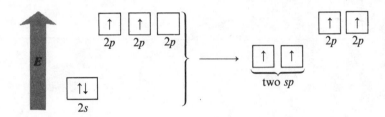

$\sigma \to \sigma^*$, higher ΔE ...... $\pi_1 \to \pi_2^*$, lower ΔE

E.   sp Hybridization

When a carbon atom is joined to only two other atoms, as in acetylene (CH≡CH), its hybridization state is *sp*. One 2*s* orbital blends with only one 2*p* orbital to form two *sp*-hybrid orbitals. In this case, two unhybridized 2*p* orbitals remain, each with one electron.

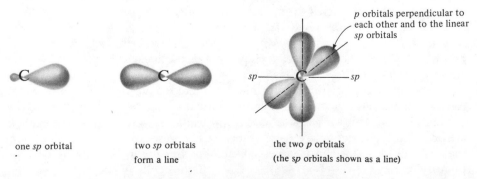

The two *sp* orbitals lie as far apart as possible, in a straight line with an angle of 180° between them. The *p* orbitals are perpendicular to each other and to the line of the *sp* orbitals (see Figure 2.17).

In CH≡CH, the two carbon atoms are joined by an *sp–sp* sigma bond. Each carbon is also bonded to a hydrogen atom by an *sp–s* sigma bond. The two *p* orbitals of one carbon then overlap with the two *p* orbitals of the other carbon to form *two* pi bonds. One pi bond is above and below the line of the sigma bonds, as shown in Figure 2.18; the other pi bond is located in front and back.

Figure 2.17.   Carbon in the *sp*-hybrid state.

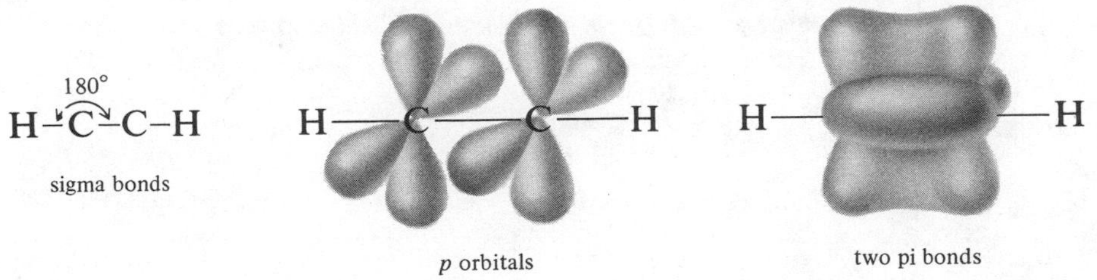

Figure 2.18. Bonding in acetylene, CH≡CH.

As you might guess, the chemical reactions of a compound containing a triple bond are not too different from those of a compound containing a double bond. Instead of one pi bond, there are two.

one σ bond, two pi bonds

$$H-C\equiv C-H \qquad CH_3-C\equiv C-H \qquad H-C\equiv N$$

STUDY PROBLEM

2.4 What type of overlap is present in each bond of $CH_3-C\equiv CH$? What are the approximate bond angles?

F. Effects of Hybridization on Bond Distances

A $2s$ orbital is of slightly lower energy than a $2p$ orbital. On the average, $2s$ electrons are found closer to the nucleus than $2p$ electrons. For this reason, a hybrid orbital with a greater proportion of s character is of lower energy and is closer to the nucleus than a hybrid orbital with less s character.

An sp-hybrid orbital is one-half s and one-half p; we may say that the sp orbital has 50% s character and 50% p character. At the other extreme is the sp^3 orbital, which has only one-fourth, or 25%, s character.

	hybridization of carbon	percent s character
CH≡CH	sp	50
$CH_2=CH_2$	sp^2	$33\frac{1}{3}$
CH_3CH_3	sp^3	25

Because the sp orbital contains more s character, it is closer to its nucleus; it forms shorter and stronger bonds than the sp^3 orbital. The sp^2 orbital is intermediate between sp and sp^3 in its s character and in the length and strength of the bonds it forms.

Table 2.1 shows the differences in bond distances among the three C—C and C—H bond types. Note that the sp–s C—H bond in CH≡CH is the shortest,

Table 2.1.　*Effect of Hybridization on Bond Distance*

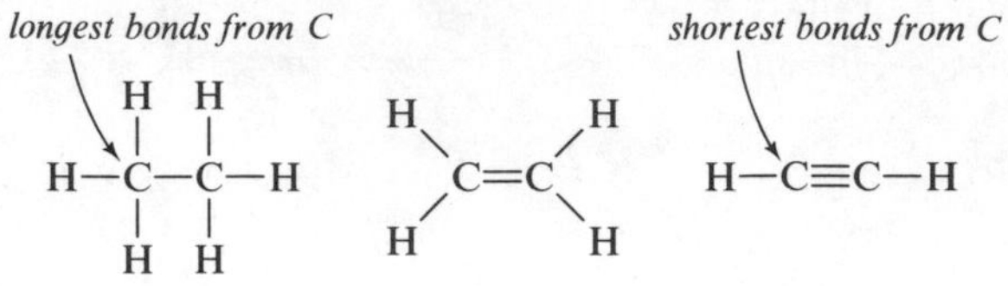

	longest bonds from C		shortest bonds from C
percent s character:	25	$33\frac{1}{3}$	50
C—C bond length:	1.54 Å	1.34 Å	1.20 Å
C—H bond length:	1.09 Å	1.08 Å	1.06 Å

while the sp^3–s C—H bond is the longest. We see an even wider variation in the C—C bonds because these bond distances are affected by the *number* of bonds joining the carbon atoms as well as by the hybridization of the carbon atoms.

STUDY PROBLEM

2.5 For each of the following structures, list the numbered bonds in order of increasing bond distance (shortest bond first):

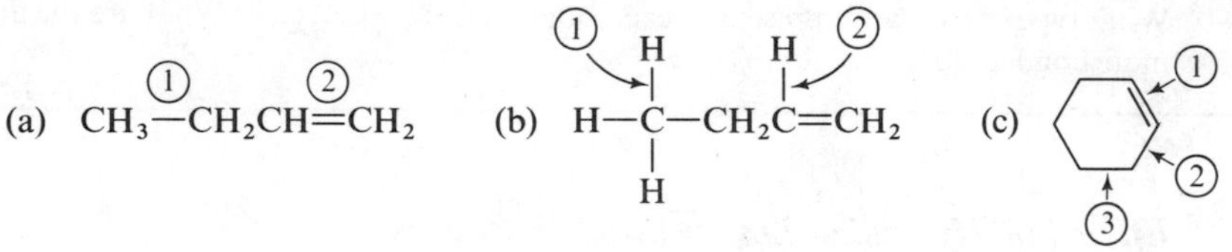

G.　Summary of the Hybrid Orbitals of Carbon

(1) When a carbon atom is bonded to *four other atoms*, the bonds from the carbon atom are formed from four equivalent sp^3 orbitals. The sp^3 carbon is **tetrahedral**.

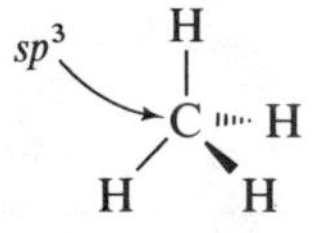

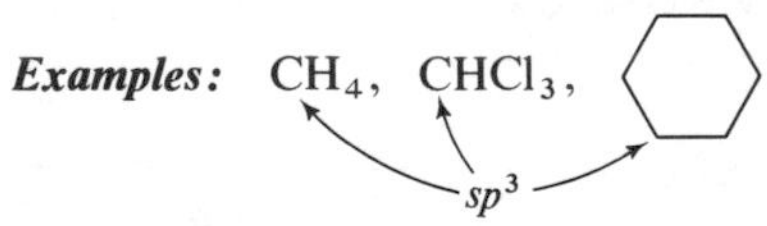

(2) When carbon bonds to *three other atoms*, the bonds from the carbon atom are formed from three equivalent sp^2 orbitals with one p orbital remaining. The sp^2 orbitals form three sigma bonds; the p orbital forms a pi bond. The sp^2 carbon is **trigonal**.

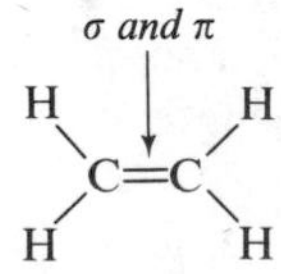

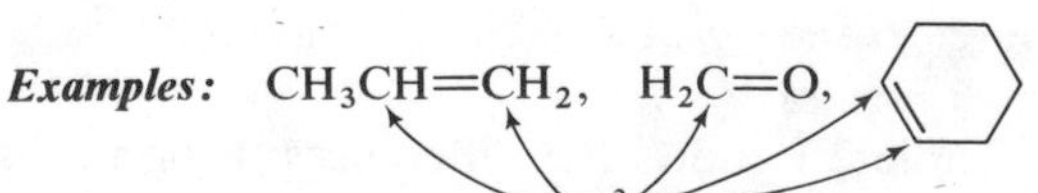

(3) When carbon bonds to *two other atoms*, the bonds from the carbon atom are formed from two equivalent *sp* bonds, with two *p* orbitals remaining. The two *p* orbitals overlap with two *p* orbitals of another atom to form two pi bonds. The *sp* orbitals form two equivalent and **linear** sigma bonds.

$$one \ \sigma, \ two \ \pi$$
$$\downarrow$$
$$H-C\equiv C-H$$
$$linear$$

Examples: $CH_3C\equiv CH, \ HC\equiv N$
$$sp$$

Section 2.5

Functional Groups

Although sp^3-sp^3 carbon–carbon bonds and sp^3-s carbon–hydrogen bonds are common to almost all organic compounds, surprisingly, these bonds do not usually play the major role in organic reactions. For the most part, it is the presence of either pi bonds or other atoms in an organic structure that confers reactivity. A site of chemical reactivity in a molecule is called a **functional group**. A pi bond or an electronegative (or electropositive) atom in an organic molecule can lead to chemical reaction; either one of these is considered a functional group or part of a functional group.

Some functional groups (circled):

$$CH_3 \ CH\!=\!C \ H_2 \qquad CH_3CH_2 \ NH_2 \qquad CH_3CH_2 \ OH$$

STUDY PROBLEM

2.6   Circle the functional groups in the following structures:

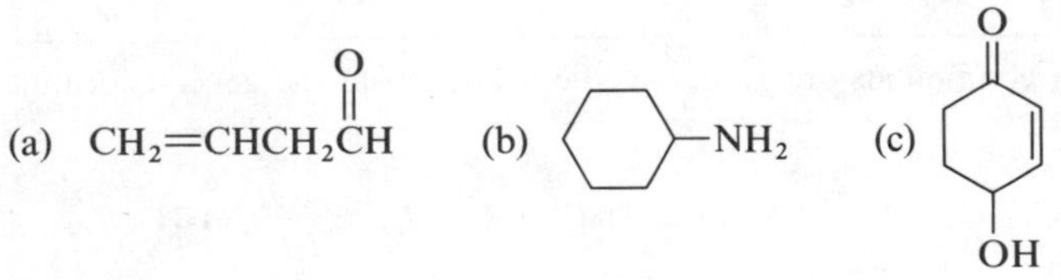

(a) $CH_2\!=\!CHCH_2\overset{\overset{\displaystyle O}{\|}}{C}H$ (b) 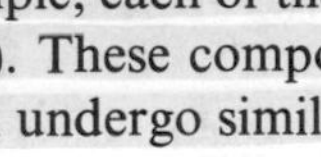 ⬡—NH_2 (c)

A series of compounds with the same functional group tend to undergo the same chemical reactions. For example, each of the following series of compounds contains a **hydroxyl group** (—OH). These compounds all belong to the class of compounds called **alcohols**, and all undergo similar reactions.

Some alcohols:

$$CH_3CH_2OH \qquad (CH_3)_3COH \qquad ⬡\!-\!OH$$

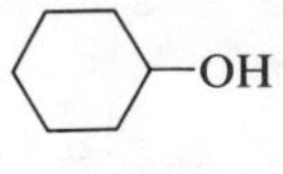

Because of the similarities in reactivity among compounds with the same functional group, it is frequently convenient to use a general formula for a series of compounds. We usually use R— to represent an **alkyl group**, a group that contains only sp^3 carbon atoms plus hydrogens. By this technique, we may represent an

Table 2.2.   Some Functional Groups and Compound Classes

Functional group		Class of compound	
Structure	Name	General structure	Class name
C=C	double bond	$R_2C=CR_2$	alkene
C≡C	triple bond	$RC≡CR'^a$	alkyne
—NH_2	amino group	RNH_2	amine
—OH	hydroxyl group	ROH	alcohol
—OR	alkoxyl group	$R'OR^a$	ether

a R′ refers to an alkyl group that may be the same as or different from R.

alcohol as ROH. Table 2.2 shows some functional groups and some classes of compounds with generalized formulas.

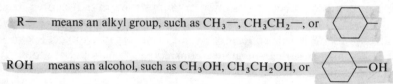

R—   means an alkyl group, such as CH_3—, CH_3CH_2—, or

ROH   means an alcohol, such as CH_3OH, CH_3CH_2OH, or —OH

Sample Problem

The following compounds are all **amines**. Give a general formula for an amine.

$$CH_3NH_2 \qquad CH_3CH_2NH_2 \qquad (CH_3)_2CHCH_2NH_2$$

Solution: RNH_2

STUDY PROBLEM

2.7   The following compounds are all **carboxylic acids**. Write the general formula for a carboxylic acid.

$$CH_3CO_2H \qquad CH_3CH_2CH_2CO_2H \qquad \text{⬡}—CO_2H$$

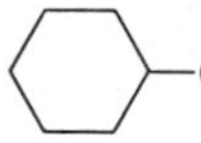

Section 2.6

Hybrid Orbitals of Nitrogen

Many important functional groups in organic compounds contain nitrogen or oxygen. Electronically, nitrogen is similar to carbon, and the atomic orbitals of nitrogen hybridize in a manner very similar to those of carbon:

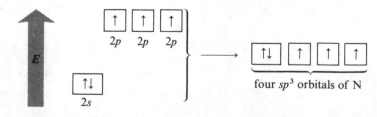

four sp^3 orbitals of N

As these orbital diagrams show, nitrogen can hybridize its four second-level atomic orbitals to four equivalent sp^3 bonding orbitals. However, note one important difference between nitrogen and carbon. While carbon has four electrons to distribute in four sp^3 orbitals, nitrogen has five electrons to distribute in four sp^3 orbitals. One of the sp^3 orbitals of nitrogen is filled with a pair of electrons, and nitrogen can form compounds with only three covalent bonds to other atoms.

A molecule of ammonia contains an sp^3 nitrogen atom bonded to three hydrogen atoms. An amine molecule has a similar structure: an sp^3 nitrogen atom bonded to one or more carbon atoms. In either ammonia or an amine, the nitrogen has one orbital filled with a pair of unshared electrons.

Some amines:

$$CH_3\ddot{N}H_2 \qquad (CH_3)_3\ddot{N}$$

General terms for amines:

$$RNH_2, \quad R_2NH, \quad or \quad R_3N$$

Figure 2.19 shows the geometry and the filled orbitals of ammonia and two amines: the similarities in structure are evident in this figure.

The unshared pair of electrons in the filled orbital on the nitrogen of ammonia and amines allows these compounds to act as bases. When an amine is treated with an acid, these unshared electrons are used to form a sigma bond with the acid. The product is an **amine salt**.

$$CH_3-\underset{\underset{CH_3}{|}}{\overset{}{\ddot{N}}}-CH_3 + HCl \longrightarrow CH_3-\underset{\underset{CH_3}{|}}{\overset{\overset{H}{|}}{N^+}}-CH_3 \ Cl^-$$

an amine *an amine salt*

By analogy with carbon, we would expect the H—N—H bond angle in NH_3 to be 109.5°. Experiments have shown that this is not so; the bond angles in NH_3 are 107.3°. Some chemists believe that the bond angles are compressed by the large size of the filled orbital with its unshared electrons. (Since the electrons in this filled orbital are attracted to only one nucleus rather than to two nuclei, they

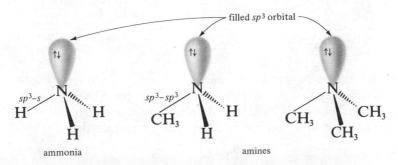

Figure 2.19. Bonding in ammonia and in two amines.

are less tightly held; therefore, the filled orbital is larger than an N—H sigma orbital.) When atoms other than hydrogen are bonded to an sp^3 nitrogen, the bond angles are observed to be closer to the tetrahedral angle of 109.5° because of repulsions between these larger groups.

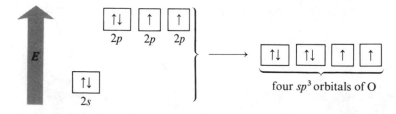

Like carbon, nitrogen is also found in organic compounds in the sp^2- and sp-hybrid states. Again, the important difference between nitrogen and carbon is that one of the orbitals of nitrogen is filled with a pair of unshared electrons.

$$CH_3CH{=}\overset{\cdot\cdot}{N}\diagdown_{CH_3} \qquad\qquad CH_3CH_2C{\equiv}N\colon$$

STUDY PROBLEM

2.8 Give the complete structural formula for each of the following compounds and tell which types of orbitals overlap to form each bond:

(a) $(CH_3)_2NCH_2NH_2$ (b) $\underset{\displaystyle \quad}{H_2N\overset{\displaystyle NH}{\overset{\displaystyle \|}{C}}NHCH_2CN}$

Section 2.7

Hybrid Orbitals of Oxygen

Like carbon and nitrogen, oxygen forms bonds with sp^3-hybrid orbitals. Because oxygen has six bonding electrons, it forms two covalent bonds and has two filled orbitals.

Water is an example of a compound containing an sp^3 oxygen. The bond angle in water is measured to be 104.5°, not the idealized 109.5°. It is believed that the size of the filled orbitals with unshared electrons compresses the H—O—H bond angle, just as the filled orbital in ammonia compresses the H—N—H bond angles.

There are a number of classes of organic compounds that contain sp^3 oxygen atoms. For the present, let us consider just two, alcohols and ethers.

A.   Alcohols

An **alcohol** is a compound that contains an oxygen atom bonded to an sp^3 carbon atom and a hydrogen atom. The bonding in an alcohol is directly analogous to the bonding in water—the oxygen is sp^3 hybridized and has two pairs of unshared electrons. The geometries of a molecule of water and of molecules of two alcohols are shown in Figure 2.20.

HOH	CH_3OH	CH_3CH_2OH	ROH
water	methanol	ethanol	*general term for an alcohol*

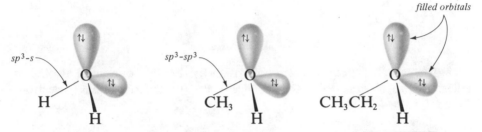

Figure 2.20.   Bonding in water and in the alcohols CH_3OH and CH_3CH_2OH.

B.   Ethers

An **ether** is a compound that contains an sp^3 oxygen bonded to *two carbon atoms*. The structure of an ether is directly analogous to that of water or an alcohol except that both hydrogen atoms of H_2O have been replaced by alkyl groups. The oxygen in an ether is sp^3 hybridized and has two pairs of unshared electrons.

$CH_3OCH_2CH_3$	CH_3OCH_3	ROR'
methyl ethyl ether	dimethyl ether	*general term for an ether*

The functional group in an ether (—OR) is called an **alkoxyl group**. (This term is analogous to *hydroxyl* for —OH.) In methyl ethyl ether, either CH_3O or OCH_2CH_3 may be considered the alkoxyl group.

STUDY PROBLEMS

2.9   Draw the structure of dimethyl ether to show the geometry around the oxygen. Indicate the unshared electrons as we have done for the alcohols in Figure 2.20.

2.10   Circle the alkoxyl groups in the following structures:

(a) ⬡—OCH_3 (b) [ring structure with O]

C. Carbonyl Compounds

The **carbonyl group** (C=O) contains an sp^2 carbon atom connected to an oxygen atom by a double bond. It is tempting to think that a carbonyl oxygen is in the sp^2-hybrid state just as the carbonyl carbon is; however, chemists are not truly sure of the hybridization of a carbonyl oxygen.

The geometry of a carbonyl group is determined by the sp^2 carbon. The carbonyl group is *planar* around the trigonal sp^2 carbon. The carbon–oxygen bond contains a pair of *exposed pi electrons*. The oxygen also has *two pairs of unshared electrons*. Figure 2.21 shows the geometry of a carbonyl group.

The carbonyl group:

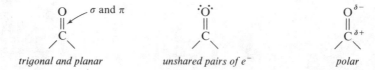

trigonal and planar   unshared pairs of e^- polar

The carbonyl group is more polar than the C—O group in an alcohol or ether. The probable reason for this enhanced polarity is that the mobile pi electrons

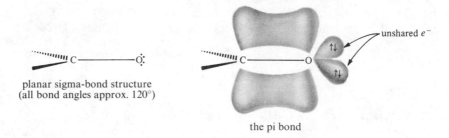

planar sigma-bond structure
(all bond angles approx. 120°)

the pi bond

Figure 2.21. Bonding in the carbonyl group.

Table 2.3. *Some Classes of Carbonyl Compounds*

Functional group		Class of compound	
Structure	Name	General structure	Class name
O‖—CH	aldehydo group	O‖ RCH, or RCHO	aldehyde
O‖—C—	keto group	O‖ RCR′	ketone
O‖—COH	carboxyl group	O‖ RCOH, RCO$_2$H, or RCOOH	carboxylic acid
O‖—COR	ester, or carbalkoxyl, group	O‖ R′COR, R′CO$_2$R, or R′COOR	ester

are more easily drawn toward the electronegative oxygen than are the C—O sigma electrons.

The carbonyl group itself is not considered to be a functional group; rather, it is part of a variety of functional groups. The functional group and class of compound are determined by the other atoms bonded to the carbonyl carbon. If one of the atoms bonded to the carbonyl carbon is a hydrogen, then the compound is an **aldehyde**. If two carbons are bonded to the carbonyl carbon, then the compound is a **ketone**. A few classes of carbonyl compounds are shown in Table 2.3.

Sample Problem

Classify each of the following compounds as an aldehyde, a ketone, a carboxylic acid, or an ester:

(a) ⬡—CO_2H (b) $CH_3CH_2\overset{O}{\overset{\|}{C}}H$ (c) ⬡—$\overset{O}{\overset{\|}{C}}CH_3$

(d) $CH_3\overset{O}{\overset{\|}{C}}OCH_3$ (e) $CH_3\overset{O}{\overset{\|}{C}}CH_2\overset{O}{\overset{\|}{C}}OH$ (f) $H\overset{O}{\overset{\|}{C}}CH_2\overset{O}{\overset{\|}{C}}OCH_3$

Solution: (a) carboxylic acid; (b) aldehyde; (c) ketone; (d) ester; (e) ketone and carboxylic acid; (f) aldehyde and ester.

STUDY PROBLEMS

2.11 Write condensed structural formulas for four-carbon compounds that contain: (a) an aldehydo group; (b) a keto group; (c) a carboxyl group; (d) an ester group; (e) an aldehydo and a keto group; (f) a carboxyl group and an ester group.

2.12 Which of the following compounds are esters? Which are ethers?

(a) $CH_3O\overset{O}{\overset{\|}{C}}CH_3$ (b) $CH_3CH_2OCH_2CH_3$ (c) [ring with O]

(d) [ring lactone]   (e) ⬡—OCH_3 (f) $CH_3\overset{O}{\overset{\|}{C}}O$—⬡

Conjugated Double Bonds

An organic molecule may contain more than one functional group. In most polyfunctional compounds, each functional group is independent of another; however, this is not always the case. Let us consider some compounds with more than one carbon–carbon double bond.

There are two principal ways double bonds can be positioned in an organic molecule. Two double bonds coming from adjacent atoms are called **conjugated double bonds.**

Orbitals and Covalent Bonding

Conjugated double bonds:

$$CH_2{=}CH{-}CH{=}CH_2$$

adjacent carbon atoms

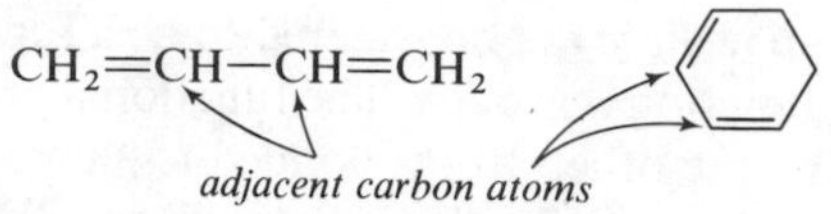

Double bonds joining atoms that are not adjacent are called **isolated**, or **nonconjugated**, double bonds.

Isolated double bonds:

$$CH_2{=}CH{-}CH_2{-}CH{=}CH_2$$

carbon atoms are not adjacent

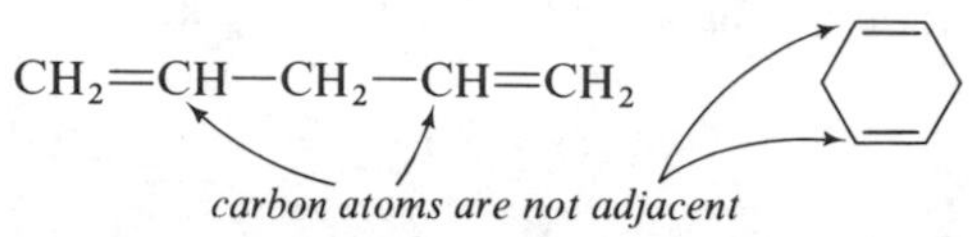

A compound may contain several double bonds in conjugation, and the same compound may contain isolated double bonds as well.

$$CH_2{=}CH{-}CH{=}CH{-}CH{=}CHCH_2CH_2CH{=}CH_2$$

conjugated   *isolated*

STUDY PROBLEMS

2.13 Vitamin A_1 has the structure shown below. How many conjugated double bonds does it contain?

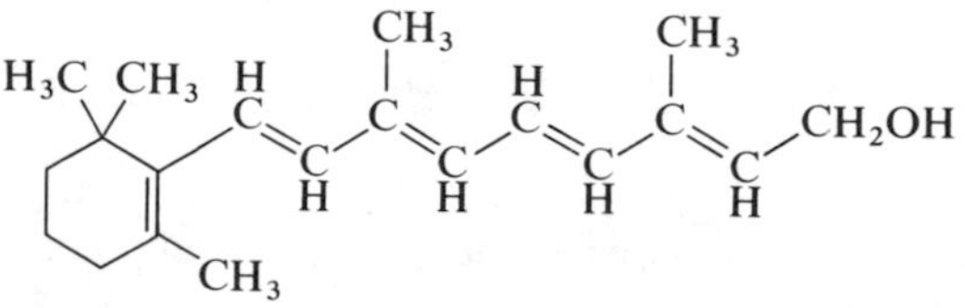

2.14 Draw the structure of an eight-carbon compound that has (a) three conjugated double bonds; (b) two conjugated double bonds and one isolated double bond; and (c) three isolated double bonds.

Isolated double bonds behave independently; each double bond undergoes reaction as if the other were not present. Conjugated double bonds, on the other hand, are not independent of each other; there is electronic interaction between them. Let us choose the simplest of the conjugated systems, $CH_2{=}CH{-}CH{=}CH_2$, called 1,3-butadiene, to discuss this phenomenon. Figure 2.22 illustrates the *p*-orbital overlap in 1,3-butadiene.

We have numbered the carbon atoms of 1,3-butadiene in Figure 2.22 for reference. There are two pairs of *p* orbitals that form two pi bonds: one pi bond between carbons 1 and 2, and one pi bond between carbons 3 and 4. However, the *p* orbitals of carbons 2 and 3 are also adjacent, and *partial overlap* of these *p* orbitals occurs. Although most of the pi-electron density is located between carbons 1–2 and 3–4, some pi-electron density is also found between carbons 2–3.

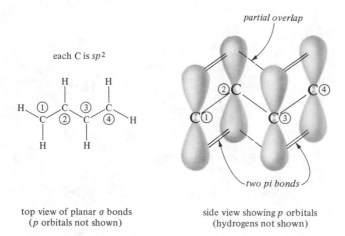

top view of planar σ bonds   side view showing *p* orbitals
(*p* orbitals not shown)   (hydrogens not shown)

Figure 2.22. The *p*-orbital picture of 1,3-butadiene, $CH_2{=}CH{-}CH{=}CH_2$.

We use a number of terms to describe this pi-bond interaction in conjugated systems. We may say that there is **partial *p*-orbital overlap** between the central carbons. We may also say that the bond between carbons 2 and 3 in 1,3-butadiene has **partial double-bond character**. Yet another way of describing the system is to say that the pi electrons are **delocalized**, which means that the pi-electron density is distributed over a somewhat larger region within the molecule. By contrast, **localized electrons** are restricted to two nuclei; nonconjugated pi bonds have localized pi electrons.

STUDY PROBLEMS

2.15 Draw the *p* orbitals of each of the following compounds, using lines to show pi-bond overlap and dotted lines to show partial overlap, as we have done in Figure 2.22.

(a) $CH_2{=}CHCH_2CH{=}CHCH{=}CH_2$ (b)

2.16 Write the structure of a four-carbon compound that has a keto group in conjugation with a carbon–carbon double bond.

Section 2.9

Benzene

Benzene (C_6H_6) is a cyclic compound with six carbon atoms joined in a ring. Each carbon atom is sp^2 hybridized, and the ring is planar. Each carbon atom has one hydrogen atom attached to it, and each carbon atom also has an unhybridized *p* orbital perpendicular to the plane of the sigma bonds of the ring. Each of these six *p* orbitals can contribute one electron for pi bonding (see Figure 2.23).

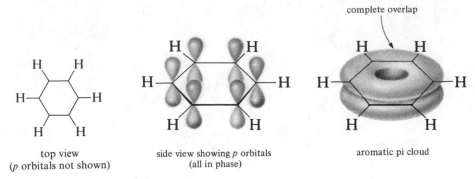

Figure 2.23.   The structure of benzene, C_6H_6.

With six *p* electrons, benzene should contain three pi bonds. We could draw three pi bonds in the ring one way (formula **A**), or we could draw them another way (formula **B**). However, we might also wonder—could this type of *p*-orbital system lead to *complete* delocalization of all six *p* electrons (formula **C**) instead of just partial delocalization?

sigma-bond structure
(Each C is sp^2 and
has one *p* electron.)

placement of pi bonds
(The circle represents complete delocalization.)

It is known that all carbon–carbon bond distances in benzene are the same, 1.40 Å. All six bonds are longer than C—C double bonds, but shorter than C—C single bonds. If the benzene ring contained three localized double bonds separated by three single bonds, the bonds would be of different lengths. The fact that all the carbon–carbon bonds in the benzene ring have the same length suggests that the benzene ring does not contain alternating single and double bonds.

From the bond distances plus a body of other evidence that we will present in later chapters, chemists have concluded that benzene is a symmetrical molecule and that each of the six ring bonds is like each of the other ring bonds. Instead of alternating double and single bonds, the six pi electrons are *completely delocalized* in a cloud of electronic charge shaped rather like a pair of donuts. This cloud of pi electrons is called the **aromatic pi cloud** of benzene. Figure 2.23 depicts the lowest-energy bonding orbital of benzene, the one commonly used to represent the aromatic pi cloud. For most purposes in this text, we will use a hexagon with a circle inside it to represent benzene; the circle represents the aromatic pi cloud.

Benzene is just one member of a class of **aromatic compounds**, compounds that contain aromatic pi clouds. Historically, the term "aromatic" derives from

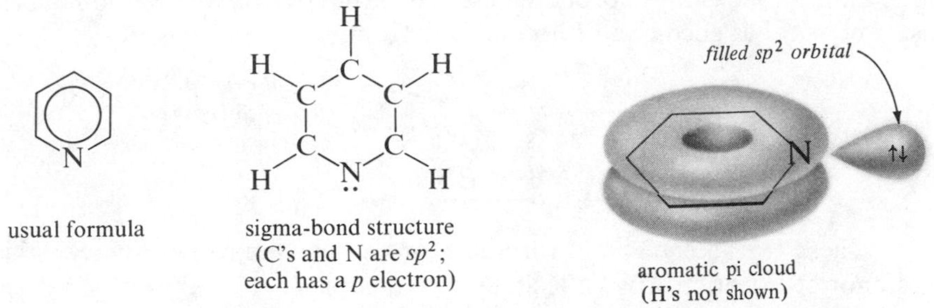

Figure 2.24. The structure of pyridine, C_5H_5N.

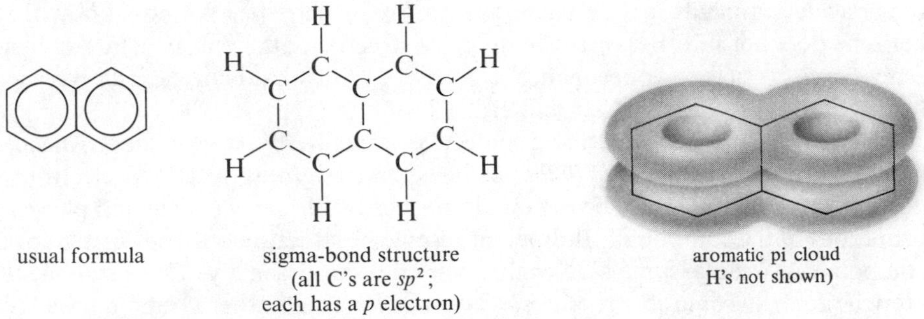

usual formula

sigma-bond structure
(C's and N are sp^2;
each has a p electron)

aromatic pi cloud
(H's not shown)

filled sp^2 orbital

Figure 2.25. The structure of naphthalene, $C_{10}H_8$.

usual formula

sigma-bond structure
(all C's are sp^2;
each has a p electron)

aromatic pi cloud
H's not shown)

the fact that many of these compounds have distinctive odors. We will discuss aromatic compounds in detail in Chapters 10 and 16. Here, let us mention two more aromatic compounds that we will encounter earlier in the text. One of these is pyridine, which contains a nitrogen atom in the ring. The other is naphthalene, which contains two fused benzene rings (benzene rings that share two carbon atoms in common). The structures of these compounds are shown in Figures 2.24 and 2.25.

Resonance

Methane (CH_4) and ethylene ($CH_2\!=\!CH_2$) are examples of organic compounds with structures that may reasonably be described using single valence-bond formulas (that is, using lines for pairs of bonding electrons). In each case, a line joining two atomic symbols represents a covalent bond between two atoms.

Benzene is an example of an organic compound that cannot be accurately represented by a single valence-bond formula. The delocalization of the pi electrons results in a system in which the pi electrons encompass more than two atoms. Classical valence-bond notation does not cover this circumstance. (The circle in the hexagon representing the aromatic pi cloud in benzene is a fairly recent addition to organic symbolism.) In order to describe the pi-electron distribution in benzene using classical valence-bond formulas, *two* formulas must be used.

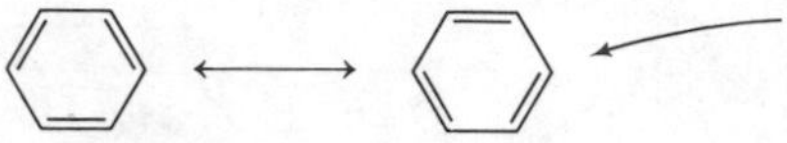

resonance structures for benzene
(*Kekulé formulas*)

the real structure is
a composite of these
two resonance structures

These two valence-bond formulas for benzene are called **Kekulé structures** in honor of Friedrich August Kekulé, who first proposed them in 1872. Kekulé's original proposal was brilliant, but unfortunately incorrect. His idea was that the two structures for benzene shifted back and forth so fast that neither could be isolated independently of the other. The two Kekulé structures were said to be in **resonance** with each other; for this reason, the Kekulé structures are also called the **resonance symbols**, or **resonance structures**, for benzene. We now know that benzene does not shift between two different structures; the real structure of benzene is in between the two resonance structures. We say that benzene is a **resonance hybrid** of the two resonance structures.

Whenever we can describe a molecular structure by two or more valence-bond formulas that differ *only in the positions of the electrons* (usually pi electrons), none of these formulas will be in complete accord with the chemical and physical properties of the compound. If different resonance structures can be written for a compound, we can assume a delocalization of electron density. These statements are true for all aromatic structures, as well as for some other structures we will mention shortly.

The real structure of naphthalene is a composite of the resonance structures:

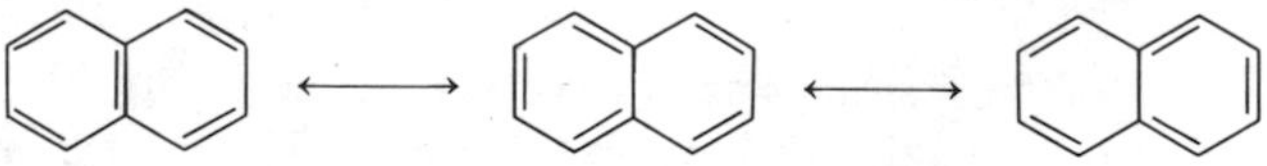

The real structure of pyridine is a composite of the resonance structures:

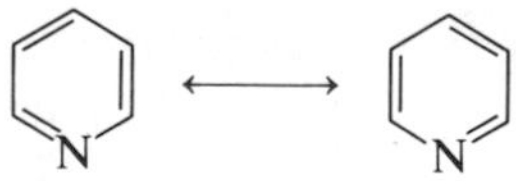

The important thing to keep in mind is that resonance symbols are not *true* structures; the true structure is a composite of all the resonance symbols. Many chemists have made the analogy that a rhinoceros (a real animal) might be described as a resonance hybrid of a unicorn (imaginary) and a dragon (imaginary). A rhinoceros does not shift back and forth from unicorn to dragon, but is simply an animal with characteristics of both a unicorn and a dragon.

To show that two or more formulas represent resonance structures (imaginary) and not real structures in equilibrium, we use a double-headed arrow ($\leftrightarrow$). By contrast, we indicate an equilibrium by *two* arrows ($\rightleftarrows$).

Resonance: rhinoceros: unicorn $\longleftrightarrow$ dragon
        (*real*)   (*imaginary*)

benzene: $\longleftrightarrow$

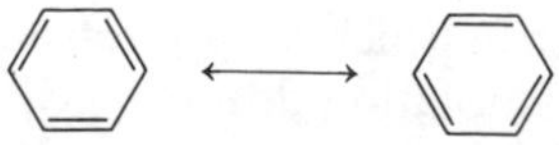

      (*real*)   (*imaginary*)

Equilibrium: $\qquad 2\,H_2O \;\rightleftharpoons\; H_3O^+ + OH^-$

$\qquad\qquad\qquad$ (*real*) $\qquad\qquad$ (*real*) $\quad$ (*real*)

Aromatic compounds are not the only compounds for which single valence-bond formulas are inadequate. The **nitro group** ($-NO_2$) is a group of atoms that we can best describe using resonance structures. A single valence-bond structure for the nitro group shows two types of N—O bond. However, it is known that the two N—O bonds are identical. Two valence-bond structures are needed; the true structure of the NO_2 group is somewhere in between the two. Resonance structures for nitromethane, CH_3NO_2, are shown below. To show that the bonds from the nitrogen to the oxygens in the NO_2 group are the same, some chemists represent the nitro group with dotted lines for the partial double bonds. (Figure 2.26 shows the *p*-orbital overlap that leads to identical N—O bonds.)

Resonance structures for nitromethane:

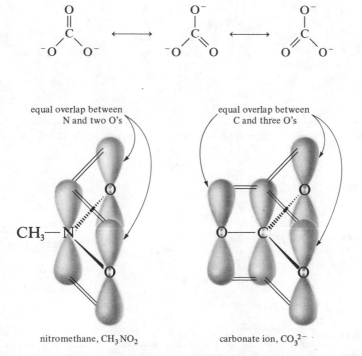

The **carbonate ion** ($CO_3{}^{2-}$) is an ion that cannot be represented by a single valence-bond structure. Each C—O bond in the carbonate ion is the same length (see Figure 2.26). We must use *three* resonance structures to describe the real structure.

Figure 2.26. The *p*-orbital overlap in the nitro group and in the carbonate ion. (The unshared electrons on oxygen are not shown here.)

A. Electron Shifts

In a series of resonance symbols, we often show shifts of pi-bond electrons by small curved arrows. The value of electron-shift arrows is that they allow us to progress systematically from one resonance symbol to another. These electron shifts are purely artificial because the pi electrons do not truly shift, but are de-localized. Note that electron-shift arrows may be drawn only to an *adjacent atom* or an *adjacent bond position*.

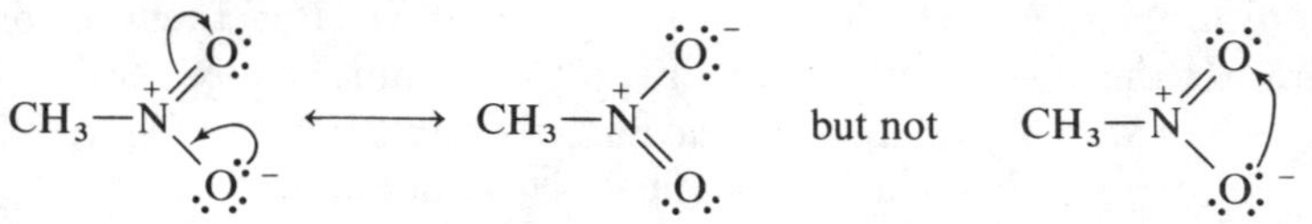

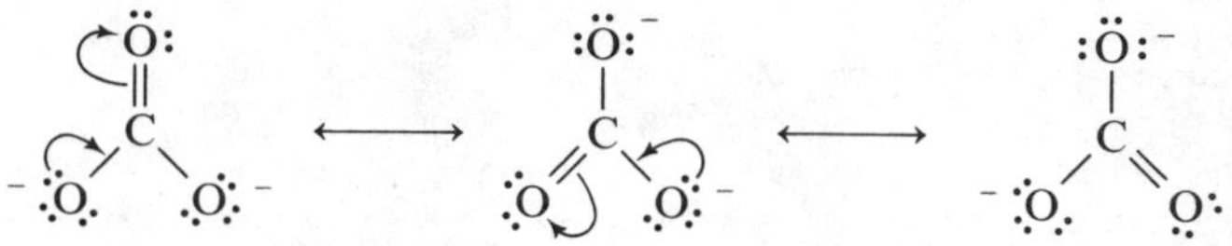

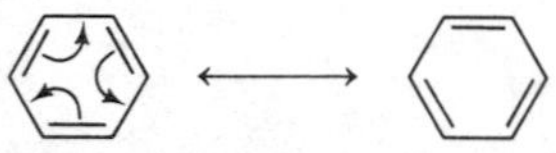

When using electron-shift arrows, we must pay special attention to valence rules. An atom of the period-2 elements can accommodate a maximum of eight valence electrons. For purposes of keeping track of these electrons, it is often advisable to show the unshared electrons in resonance structures.

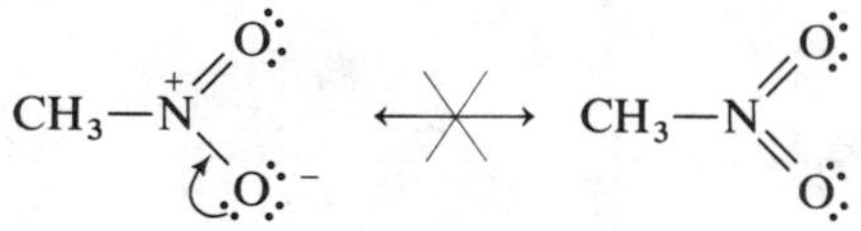

not possible: N cannot accommodate ten e⁻

Sample Problem

Write resonance structures with electron-shift arrows for pyrimidine and for the acetate ion, $CH_3CO_2^-$.

pyrimidine

Solution:

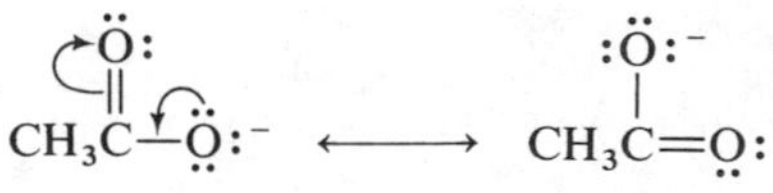

STUDY PROBLEM

2.17 The nitrate ion, NO_3^-, contains three equivalent N—O bonds. Write resonance structures for the nitrate ion.

B. *Major and Minor Contributors*

In each example we have shown so far, the bonding has been the same in each resonance symbol. When the bonding is the same, the resonance structures are of equal energy and are equivalent to each other. *Equivalent resonance structures contribute equally to the real structure.*

Resonance structures for a compound or ion may not all contribute equally to the real structure. Consider the following example:

lower energy, major contributor   *higher energy, minor contributor*

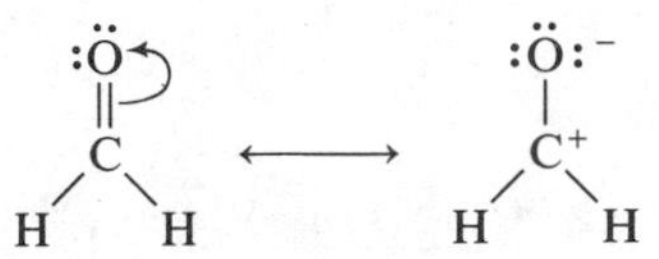

formaldehyde

This pair of resonance structures for formaldehyde shows one structure (on the left) in which all atoms have an octet of valence electrons and no charge separation. This resonance structure is of lower energy than the right-hand structure, in which the carbon atom has only six electrons surrounding it and the carbon–oxygen bond has a charge separation.

The lower-energy structure is more like the real structure than is the higher-energy structure. We say that the left-hand structure is a *more important resonance structure*, or a *major contributor* to the real structure, while the right-hand structure is a *less important resonance structure*, or a *minor contributor*. (This is similar to saying that a rhinoceros is like a dragon with just a little unicorn thrown in.)

Formaldehyde is like H—C—H with a small amount of H—C—H thrown in.

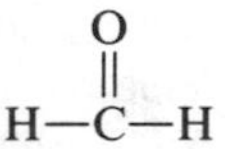

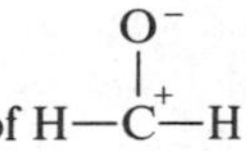

STUDY PROBLEM

2.18   Which of the following resonance structures is the major contributor to the real structure?

$$CH_3C{=}CH{-}CH_2 \longleftrightarrow CH_3C{-}CH{=}CH_2 \longleftrightarrow CH_3C{-}CH{=}CH_2$$

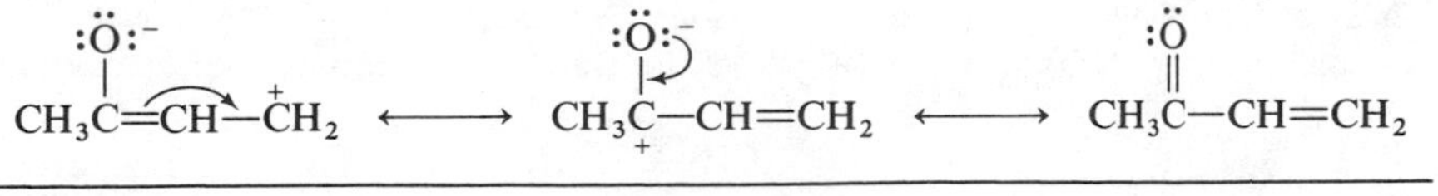

C. *Rules for Writing Resonance Structures*

We will encounter resonance structures frequently in the coming chapters. Let us summarize the rules for writing resonance structures:

(1)   *Only electrons* (*not atoms*) *may be shifted*, and they may be shifted only to adjacent atoms or bond positions.

(2)   Resonance structures in which an atom carries more than its quota of electrons (eight for the period-2 elements) are not contributors to the real structure.

(3)   The more important resonance structures show each atom with a complete octet and as little charge separation as possible.

$$CH_3\overset{+}{N}\begin{smallmatrix}\ddot{O}:\\ \\\ddot{O}:^-\end{smallmatrix} \longleftrightarrow CH_3\overset{2+}{N}\begin{smallmatrix}\ddot{O}:^-\\ \\\ddot{O}:^-\end{smallmatrix}$$

more important because	*less important because*
each atom has an octet	*N has only six electrons*

D.   Resonance Stabilization

If a structure is a resonance hybrid of two or more resonance structures, *the energy of the real structure is lower than that of any single resonance structure.* The real structure is said to be **resonance-stabilized**. In most cases, the energy difference is slight, but for aromatic systems, like benzene or naphthalene, the energy difference is substantial. (The reasons for aromatic stabilization will be discussed in Chapter 10.)

The hypothetical structure $\begin{smallmatrix}O\\||\\^-O^{\diagup}{}^{C}{}_{\diagdown}O^-\end{smallmatrix}$ is of higher energy than $\begin{smallmatrix}O^{\delta-}\\|\\{}_{\delta^-}O^{\diagup}{}^{C}{}_{\diagdown}O^{\delta-}\end{smallmatrix}$

The hypothetical structure ⬡ is of substantially higher energy than ⬡

The reason for the energy differences between hypothetical resonance structures and the real structure of a compound is not entirely understood. Chemists believe part of the reason is that a delocalized electron is attracted to more than one nucleus. It is generally true that a system with delocalization of electrons or of electronic charge is of lower energy and of greater stability than a system with localized electrons or electronic charge.

Sample Problem

Which of the following compounds are resonance-stabilized? (*Note*: Because the bonding electrons of sulfur are in the third energy level, it can accommodate more than eight electrons.)

(a) $CH_3CH_2CH_3$ (b) $\begin{smallmatrix}H\\ \\H\end{smallmatrix}C=C\begin{smallmatrix}CH_3\\ \\H\end{smallmatrix}$ (c) $CH_3O-\overset{\overset{\displaystyle O}{||}}{\underset{\underset{\displaystyle O}{||}}{S}}-O^-$

Solution: (a) is not resonance-stabilized because it contains no pi electrons.
(b) is not resonance-stabilized because there is no position in the molecule where the pi electrons can be delocalized.
(c) is resonance-stabilized:

$$CH_3O\overset{:\ddot{O}:^-}{\underset{\overset{||}{\ddot{O}:}}{\overset{|}{S}}}=\ddot{O}: \longleftrightarrow CH_3O\overset{\overset{\ddot{O}}{||}}{\underset{\overset{||}{\ddot{O}:}}{S}}\ddot{O}:^- \longleftrightarrow CH_3O\overset{\overset{\ddot{O}}{||}}{\underset{\overset{|}{:\ddot{O}:^-}}{S}}=\ddot{O}:$$

SUMMARY

A covalent bond is the result of two atomic orbitals overlapping to form a lower-energy **bonding molecular orbital** in which two electrons are paired.

The four atomic orbitals of C undergo **hybridization** in bond formation:

*sp*³ **hybridization:**   four equivalent single bonds (*tetrahedral*).

*sp*² **hybridization:**   three equivalent single bonds (*trigonal*) plus one un-hybridized *p* orbital.   1 π bond

sp **hybridization:**   two equivalent single bonds (*linear*) plus two unhybridized *p* orbitals.   2 π bonds

Overlap of a hybrid orbital with an orbital of another atom (end-to-end overlap) results in a **sigma bond**. Overlap of a *p* orbital with a parallel *p* orbital of another atom (side-to-side overlap) results in a **pi bond**.

$$
\begin{array}{ccc}
 & \sigma \text{ and } \pi & \sigma \text{ and two } \pi \\
\end{array}
$$

$$
\underset{sp^3,\ all\ \sigma}{\begin{array}{c} \text{H} \quad \text{H} \\ | \quad | \\ \text{H—C—C—H} \\ | \quad | \\ \text{H} \quad \text{H} \end{array}}
\qquad
\underset{sp^2}{\begin{array}{c} \text{H} \qquad \text{H} \\ \text{C=C} \\ \text{H} \qquad \text{H} \end{array}}
\qquad
\underset{sp}{\text{H—C≡C—H}}
$$

Each bonding molecular orbital has an **antibonding molecular orbital** associated with it. Antibonding orbitals are of higher energy than either bonding orbitals or the atomic orbitals that went into their formation. In the ground state, molecules have their electrons in the lowest-energy orbitals, usually the bonding orbitals.

A **functional group** is a *site of chemical reactivity* in a molecule and arises from a *pi bond* or from *differences in electronegativity* between bonded atoms. A double or triple bond is a functional group. The following compounds are examples of other compounds with functional groups:

$$
\underset{an\ amine}{\text{R}\ddot{\text{N}}\text{H}_2}
\qquad\qquad
\underset{an\ alcohol}{\text{R}\ddot{\text{O}}\text{H}}
\qquad\qquad
\underset{an\ ether}{\text{R}\ddot{\text{O}}\text{R}'}
$$

$$
\underset{an\ aldehyde}{\overset{\overset{\displaystyle\ddot{\text{O}}}{\|}}{\text{RCH}}}
\qquad\qquad
\underset{a\ ketone}{\overset{\overset{\displaystyle\ddot{\text{O}}}{\|}}{\text{RCR}'}}
\qquad\qquad
\underset{a\ carboxylic\ acid}{\overset{\overset{\displaystyle\ddot{\text{O}}}{\|}}{\text{RC}\ddot{\text{O}}\text{H}}}
$$

Pi bonds extending from adjacent carbon atoms are called **conjugated double bonds**. In the case of benzene and other aromatic compounds, complete delocalization of pi electrons results in the **aromatic pi cloud**.

$$
\text{CH}_2\text{=CH—CH=CH}_2
$$

some pi-electron density here   *pi electrons completely delocalized*

Resonance symbols may be used to show delocalization of *p* electrons.

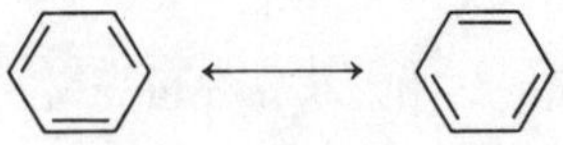

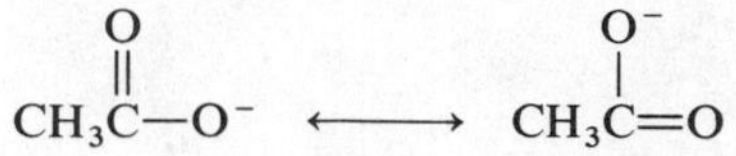

$$
\bigcirc \longleftrightarrow \bigcirc \qquad
\underset{\text{}}{CH_3\overset{O}{\overset{\|}{C}}-O^-} \longleftrightarrow \underset{\text{}}{CH_3\overset{O^-}{\overset{|}{C}}=O}
$$

If all resonance symbols are not equivalent, the lowest-energy resonance symbol is the **major contributor**.

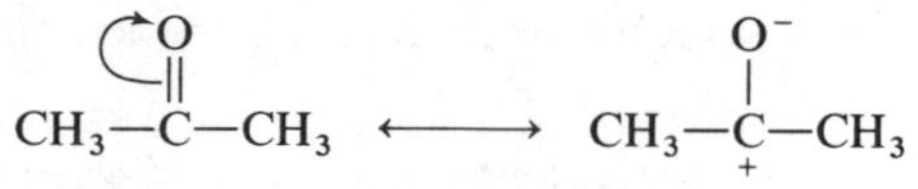

$$
\underset{\text{major contributor}}{CH_3-\overset{O}{\overset{\|}{C}}-CH_3} \longleftrightarrow CH_3-\overset{O^-}{\underset{+}{\overset{|}{C}}}-CH_3
$$

Delocalization of pi electrons in a molecule, or of electronic charge in an ion, results in a slight increase in the stability of the system. However, for aromatic compounds, the increase in stability is substantial.

STUDY PROBLEMS

2.19 Do the following structures represent the same or different compounds? Explain.

2.20 Which of the following molecular formulas could represent a real compound?

(a) C_2H_7 (b) C_3H_6 (c) C_3H_8 (d) C_4H_9

2.21 Draw a carbon atom with two p orbitals. What hybrid orbitals are present on this carbon?

2.22 Draw an orbital picture for each of the following compounds. (Use lines for sigma orbitals.)

(a) $(CH_3)_2CHCH(CH_3)_2$ (b) $(CH_3)_2C{=}C(CH_3)_2$ (c) $CH_3C{\equiv}CCH_3$

2.23 Indicate the hybridization of each carbon in the following structures:

(a) $(CH_3)_3CH$ (b)  ⬠   (c) 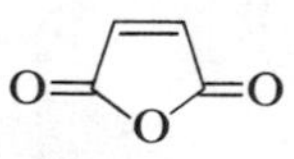 O=⬠=O

(d) $CH_2{=}CHC{\equiv}CH$

2.24 In each of the following structures, do the pair of indicated carbon atoms lie in the same plane or not?

(a) 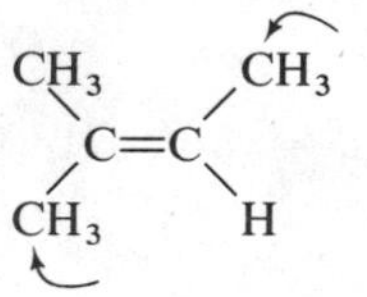   (b) 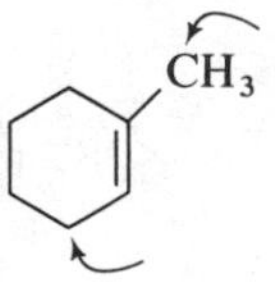   (c)

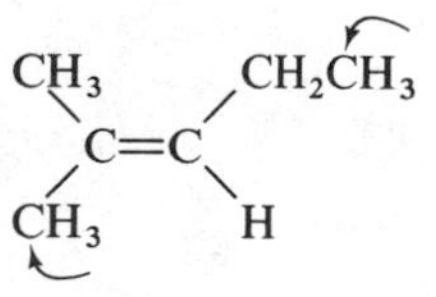

2.25 What would be the expected *sigma-bond angles* in the following structures?

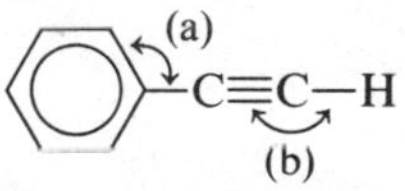

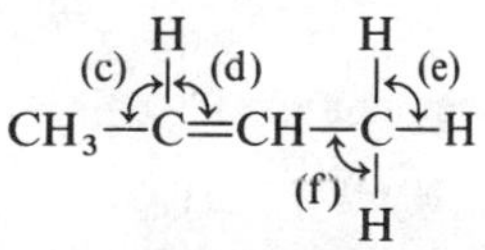

2.26 What type of orbital overlap (e.g., $s{-}sp^3$) is present in each bond in each of the following compounds?

(a) 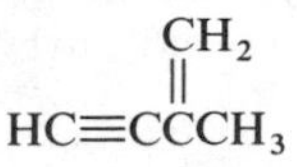 $HC{\equiv}CCH_3$ (with CH_2 double-bonded)   (b) $CH_3OCH_2CH_3$ (c)

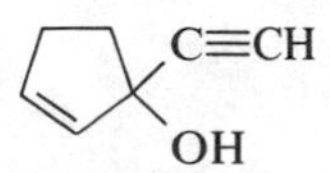

(d) $(CH_3)_2NH$

2.27 Draw an orbital picture for each of the following formulas. Indicate the types of orbital from each atom, and show any filled orbitals. (Use lines for sigma orbitals.)

(a) H_3O^+ (b) HCN   (c) OH^- (d)

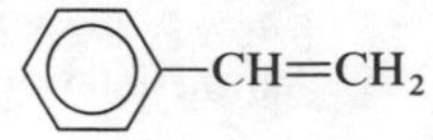

(e) NH_2NH_2 (f) $(CH_3)_4N^+$ (g) $^-OCH_3$

2.28 The molecular-orbital diagram that follows is for the carbon–carbon double bond in cyclohexene.

cyclohexene

σ^* ——
$\pi_2{}^*$——
π_1 ——
σ ——

E

(a) Indicate by arrows which orbitals contain the double-bond electrons when cyclohexene is in the ground state.
(b) Absorption of ultraviolet light by a double bond results in the promotion of an electron to a higher-energy orbital. Which electron transition requires the least energy when cyclohexene goes to an excited state?

2.29 In each of the following structures, which of the indicated bonds (1 or 2) is the shorter one?

(a) 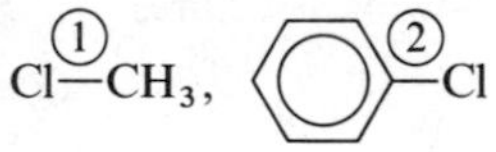 Cl—①CH₃, ②Cl (benzene)

(b) 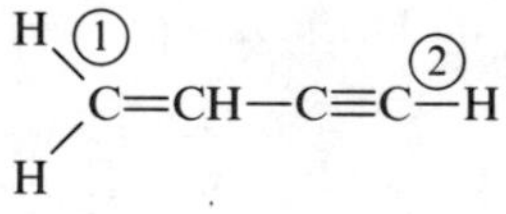 $\underset{H}{\overset{H}{C}}=CH-C\equiv C-H$ ① ②

(c) (cyclohexyl)—①CH₃, (phenyl)—②CH₃

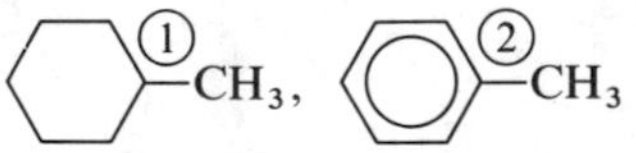

(d) 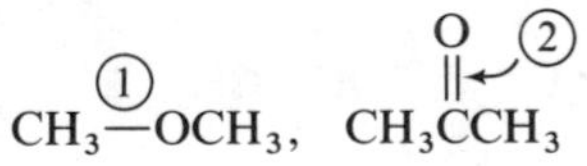 CH_3—①OCH_3, $CH_3\overset{O}{\overset{\|}{C}}CH_3$ ②

2.30 Show by electron dots any unshared electrons in the following structures:

(a) CH_3Cl (b) CH_3NH_2 (c)  (pyridine, N)   (d) $CH_3\overset{O}{\overset{\|}{C}}OH$

(e) 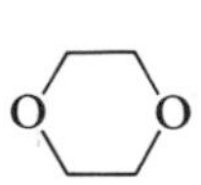 O⎯O (dioxane ring)   (f) CH_3NHCH_3 (g) $CH_3\overset{O}{\overset{\|}{C}}NH_2$

2.31 Which compound of each pair is more polar?

(a) CH_3CH_2OH, CH_3OCH_3 (b) CH_3OCH_3, $(CH_3)_2C=O$
(c) CH_3NH_2, $(CH_3)_3N$ (d) CH_3CH_3, CH_3CH_2Cl

2.32 Piperazine is the drug of choice for treatment of patients with roundworms or pinworms. Draw the complete structural formula, showing each atom and using a line for each covalent bond. Indicate unshared electron pairs by dots. What is the hybridization of each ring atom?

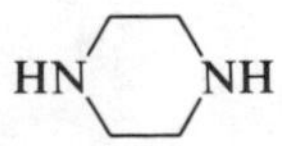

piperazine

2.33 Circle the functional groups in the following structures:

(a) $CH_3\overset{\overset{\textstyle O}{\|}}{C}H$ (b) $CH_3\overset{\overset{\textstyle O}{\|}}{C}CH_2CH_3$ (c) $CH_3CH{=}CH\overset{\overset{\textstyle O}{\|}}{C}OCH_3$

2.34 Which of the following compounds contains a pi bond?

(a) CH_3CH_2CHO (b) CH_3CH_2OH (c) $CH_3CH_2CO_2CH_3$

2.35 Circle and name each functional group in the following structures:

(a) 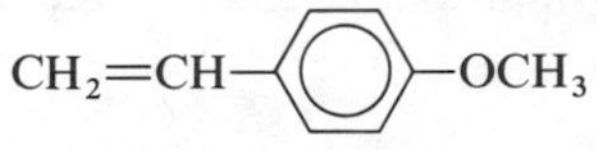 $CH_2{=}CH{-}\!\!\bigcirc\!\!{-}OCH_3$ (b) 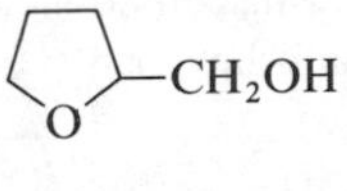 ⬠O⟩$-CH_2OH$ (c) 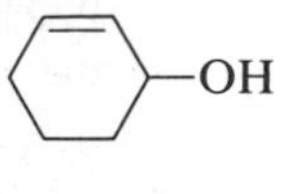 ⬡$-OH$

(d) 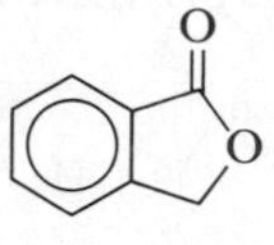 (bicyclic lactone structure with O and O)   (e) $CH_3\overset{\overset{\textstyle NH_2}{|}}{C}HCO_2H$

(f) 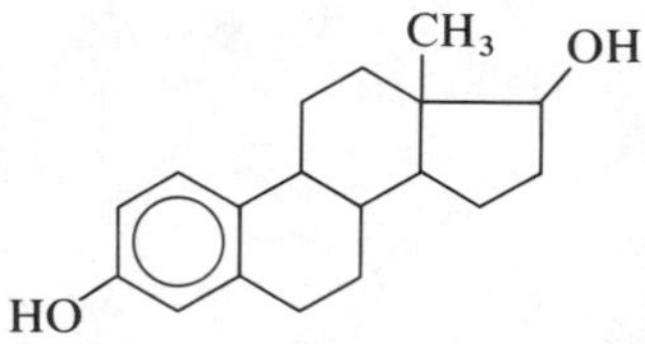 (steroid structure with CH_3, OH, HO)
estradiol
(*a female hormone*)

(g) 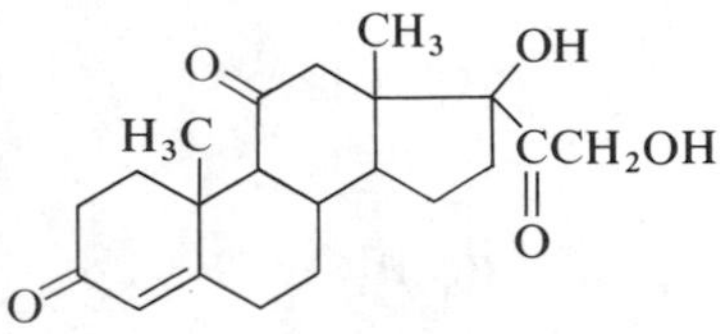 (steroid structure with O, CH_3, OH, H_3C, $\overset{\overset{\textstyle }{}}{C}CH_2OH$ with O)
cortisone
(*an adrenal steroid
used to treat arthritis*)

2.36 Give a general formula, using R and R′, for each of the following compounds. (*Example*: $CH_3OH = ROH$.)

(a) 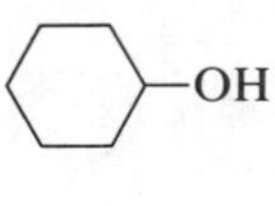 ⬡$-OH$ (b) $CH_3CH_2CH_2\overset{\overset{\textstyle O}{\|}}{C}OCH_3$ (c) $CH_3CH_2NHCH_3$

(d) 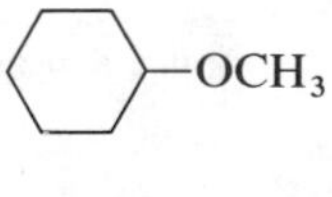 ⬡$-OCH_3$

2.37 Label each of the following compounds as an aldehyde, a ketone, an ester, or a combination of these:

(a) $CH_3CH_2\overset{\overset{\textstyle O}{\|}}{C}OCH_3$ (b) 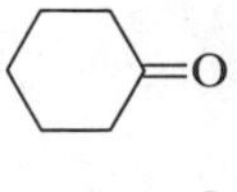 ⬡$={O}$ (c) 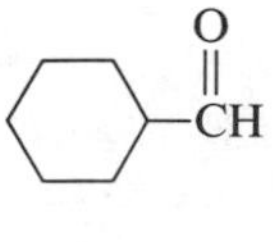 ⬡$-\overset{\overset{\textstyle O}{\|}}{C}H$

(d) 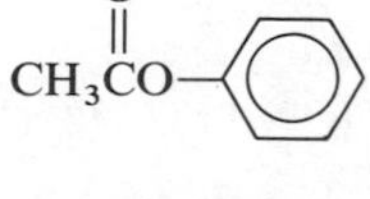 $CH_3\overset{\overset{\textstyle O}{\|}}{C}O{-}\!\!\bigcirc$ (e) 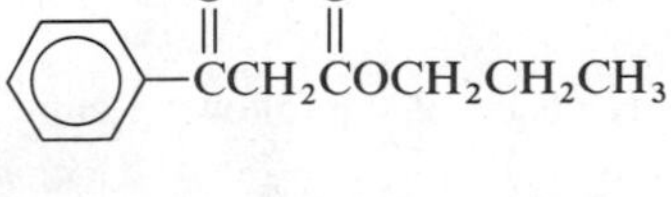 $\bigcirc\!\!{-}\overset{\overset{\textstyle O}{\|}}{C}CH_2\overset{\overset{\textstyle O}{\|}}{C}OCH_2CH_2CH_3$

2.38 Give a three-carbon structure to illustrate each of the following compound types:
(a) alkene; (b) alkyne; (c) ether; (d) alcohol; (e) amine; (f) ketone; (g) aldehyde; (h) carboxylic acid; (i) ester.

2.39 Redraw each structure to emphasize the carbonyl group:

(a) $CH_3CH_2CH_2CO_2H$ (b) 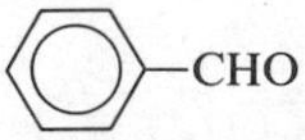   (c)

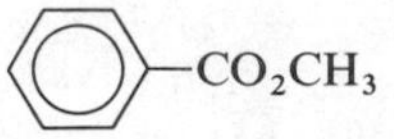

2.40 Write a condensed structural formula for each of the following compounds. (There may be more than one answer.)

(a) an ester, $C_8H_8O_2$ (b) a cyclic alcohol, $C_6H_{12}O$
(c) an alkene, C_5H_{10} (d) an aldehyde, C_3H_6O

2.41 Group the following compounds according to those which might be expected to exhibit similar chemical behavior:

(a) CH_3CH_2OH (b)    (c) $HOCH_2CH_2OH$

(d) CH_3CH_3 (e) CH_3CH_2Cl (f) 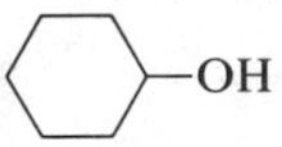 ⬡—OH

(g) CH_3CH_2Br (h) $CH_3CH_2OCH_2CH_3$ (i) 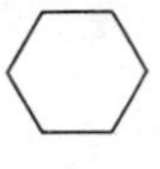 ⬡

(j) $CH_3CH_2CH_2CH_3$

2.42 Give the structure of a five-carbon compound with (a) two double bonds in conjugation; (b) two isolated double bonds. (More than one answer may be possible.)

2.43 In the following structure for cyclohexanone, (a) show the placement of a C—C double bond in conjugation with the carbonyl group, and (b) indicate the hybridization of each carbon atom in the structure with the C—C double bond.

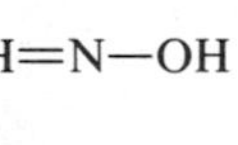

⬡=O

cyclohexanone

2.44 Tell whether each of the following pairs of structures are resonance symbols or compounds (or ions) in equilibrium:

(a) CH_3CO_2H and $CH_3CO_2^- + H^+$

(b) $CH_3CH_2N{=}O$ and $CH_3CH{=}N{-}OH$

(c) $CH_3\overset{\displaystyle O}{\overset{\|}{C}}CH_2^-$ and $CH_3\overset{\displaystyle O^-}{\overset{|}{C}}{=}CH_2$

(d) $CH_3\overset{+}{C}HCH{=}CH_2$ and $CH_3CH{=}CH\overset{+}{C}H_2$

2.45 Indicate whether each of the following compounds contains *conjugated* pi bonds or *isolated* pi bonds:

(a)   (b) ⬡⬡   (c) ⬡

(d) 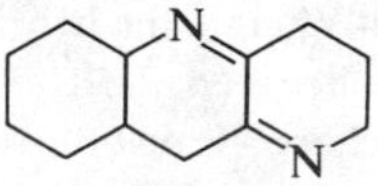 (e) CH≡CCHO (f) CH$_2$=CHCH$_2$CHO

2.46 Which of the following pairs of structures are resonance structures of each other?

(a) 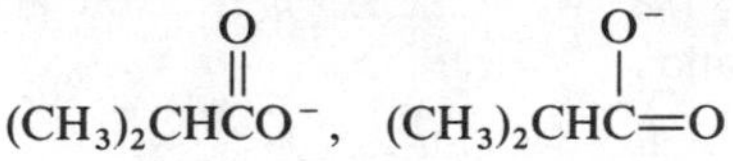 (CH$_3$)$_2$CHCO$^-$, (CH$_3$)$_2$CHC=O   (b) 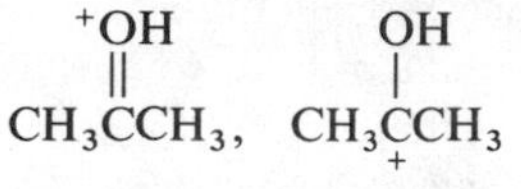 CH$_3$CCH$_3$, CH$_3$CCH$_3$

(c) 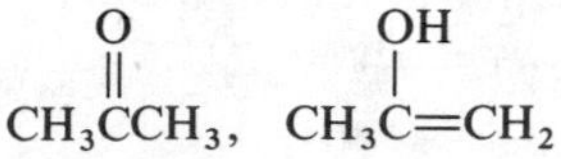 CH$_3$CCH$_3$, CH$_3$C=CH$_2$ (d)

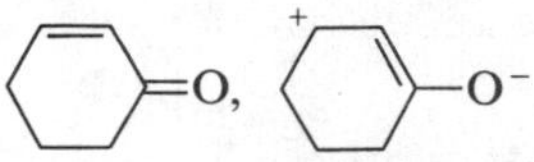

(e) CH$_2$=C=O, CH≡C—OH

(f) CH$_2$=CHCH=CHCH$_2$, CH$_2$CH=CHCH=CH$_2$

2.47 Give the important resonance contributors for each of the following structures:

(a) 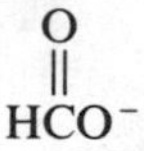 HCO$^-$ (b) 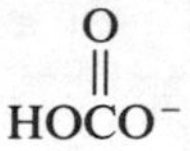 HOCO$^-$ (c) 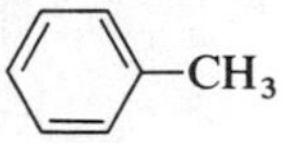 —CH$_3$

2.48 Which of the following resonance structures would be the major contributor to the real structure?

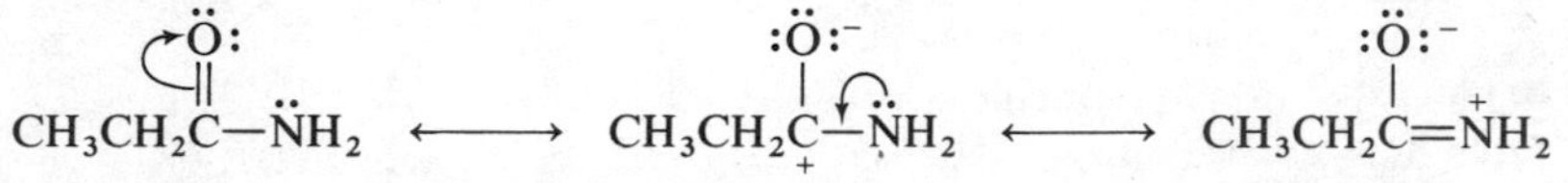

CH$_3$CH$_2$C—NH$_2$ ⟷ CH$_3$CH$_2$C—NH$_2$ ⟷ CH$_3$CH$_2$C=NH$_2$

  (a)   (b)   (c)

2.49 Write the important Kekulé structures for each of the following aromatic compounds. (*Hint*: First, determine the number of pi electrons. Second, determine the number of double bonds formed by this number of pi electrons. Third, follow the rules of valence and distribute the double bonds in as many ways as possible.)

(a) 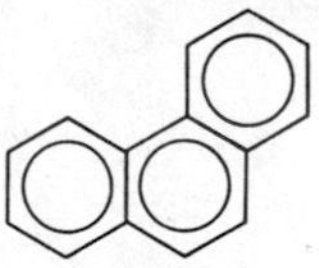   (b)

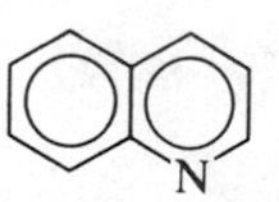

2.50 Which of the following resonance symbols would contribute *least* to the stability of each structure?

(a) 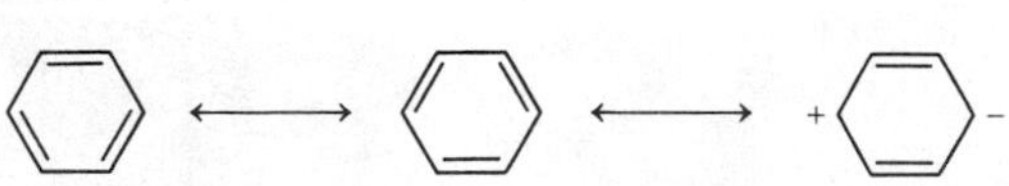 ⟷   ⟷

(b) 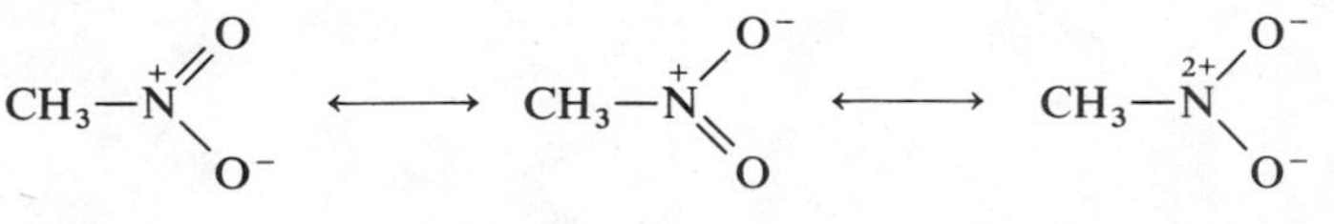 CH$_3$—N ⟷ CH$_3$—N ⟷ CH$_3$—N

(c) 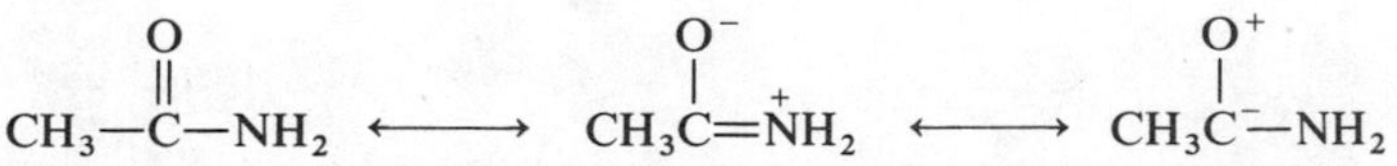 CH$_3$—C—NH$_2$ ⟷ CH$_3$C=NH$_2$ ⟷ CH$_3$C—NH$_2$

2.51 *Allene* has the following structure: $CH_2\!\!=\!\!C\!\!=\!\!CH_2$.   (a) What is the hybridization of each carbon?   (b) What would be the expected angle between the two pi bonds? (c) Are the two pi bonds conjugated?   (d) Can electronic charge be delocalized throughout both pi bonds?

2.52 The O—C—O bond angle in CO_2 is $180°$. Write the Lewis structure and draw the *p*-orbital picture. What is the hybridization of the carbon?

2.53 *Guanidines* and *amidines* are classes of compounds that react as bases. Draw the resonance structures for the conjugate acids—that is, the cations.

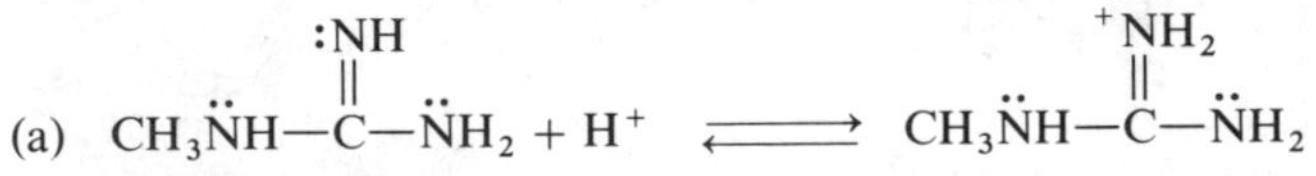

(a) $CH_3\ddot{N}H\!-\!\overset{\overset{\displaystyle :NH}{\|}}{C}\!-\!\ddot{N}H_2 + H^+ \;\;\rightleftarrows\;\; CH_3\ddot{N}H\!-\!\overset{\overset{\displaystyle ^+NH_2}{\|}}{C}\!-\!\ddot{N}H_2$

     a guanidine

(b) $CH_3\!-\!\overset{\overset{\displaystyle :NH}{\|}}{C}\!-\!\ddot{N}H_2 + H^+ \;\;\rightleftarrows\;\; CH_3\!-\!\overset{\overset{\displaystyle ^+NH_2}{\|}}{C}\!-\!\ddot{N}H_2$

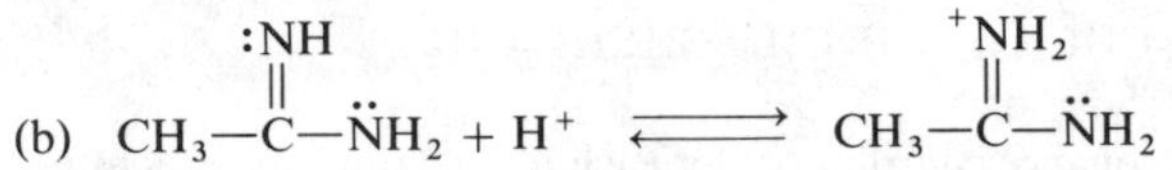

     an amidine

2.54 What is the electron distribution in the bonding and in the antibonding orbitals of $H_2{}^+$ and $H_2{}^-$?

2.55 *Triplet methylene* is a very unstable species with the formula $:CH_2$. The H—C—H bond angle is $180°$. Draw the orbital picture (using lines for sigma bonds). Indicate the hybridization state of the carbon atom.

2.56 Draw the orbital structures (using lines for sigma bonds) for (a) N_2 and (b) $CH_2\!\!=\!\!C\!\!=\!\!O$.

2.57 Draw four additional resonance structures for the following anion:

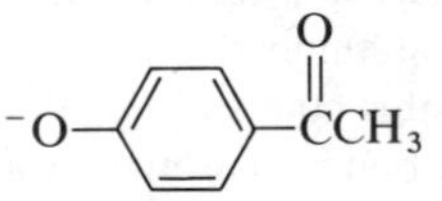

Chapter 3

Structural Isomerism, Nomenclature, and Alkanes

In Chapter 2, we discussed the bonding of several compounds that contain only carbon and hydrogen. A compound containing only these two elements is called a **hydrocarbon**. Methane (CH_4), ethylene ($CH_2 = CH_2$), and benzene (C_6H_6) are all examples of hydrocarbons.

Hydrocarbons with only sp^3 carbon atoms (that is, only single bonds) are called **alkanes** (or **cycloalkanes** if the carbon atoms are joined in rings). Some typical alkanes are methane, ethane (CH_3CH_3), propane ($CH_3CH_2CH_3$), and butane ($CH_3CH_2CH_2CH_3$). All these alkanes are gases that are found in petroleum deposits and used as fuels. Gasoline is primarily a mixture of alkanes. At the end of this chapter, we will discuss some of these aspects of hydrocarbon chemistry.

Alkanes and cycloalkanes are said to be **saturated hydrocarbons**, meaning "saturated with hydrogen." These compounds do not undergo reaction with hydrogen. Compounds containing pi bonds are said to be **unsaturated**; under the proper reaction conditions, they undergo reaction with hydrogen to yield saturated products.

Saturated hydrocarbons:

$$CH_4 + H_2 \longrightarrow \text{no reaction}$$

methane
an alkane

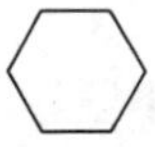

$$\text{(hexagon)} + H_2 \longrightarrow \text{no reaction}$$

cyclohexane
a cycloalkane

Unsaturated hydrocarbons:

$$CH_2 = CH_2 + H_2 \xrightarrow{\text{Ni catalyst}} CH_3CH_3$$

ethylene   ethane

$$CH_3C \equiv CH + 2\ H_2 \xrightarrow{\text{Ni catalyst}} CH_3CH_2CH_3$$

propyne   propane

$$\text{(benzene ring)} + 3\ H_2 \xrightarrow[\text{heat, pressure}]{\text{Ni catalyst}} \text{(hexagon)}$$

benzene   cyclohexane

In this chapter, we will discuss primarily alkanes and cycloalkanes—the saturated hydrocarbons. Because saturated hydrocarbons lack a true functional group, their chemistry is not typical of most organic compounds; however, these compounds provide the carbon skeletons of organic compounds that do contain functional groups. Therefore, saturated hydrocarbons are an excellent vehicle for introducing the variations in the structures of organic compounds and the naming of organic compounds.

Section 3.1

Structural Isomers

Variations in structures of organic compounds arise from the number and types of atoms in the molecules of a compound. Variations in structure also arise from *the order in which the atoms are attached to each other in a molecule*. For example, we can write two different structural formulas for the molecular formula C_2H_6O. As we saw in Section 1.9C, these two structural formulas represent two different compounds. Dimethyl ether (bp $-23.6°C$) is a gas that has been used as a refrigerant and as an aerosol propellant. Ethanol (bp $78.5°$) is a liquid that is used as a solvent and in alcoholic beverages.

$$CH_3OCH_3 \qquad\qquad CH_3CH_2OH$$

dimethyl ether   ethanol

a gas at room temperature   *a liquid at room temperature*

Two or more different compounds that have the same molecular formula are called **isomers** of each other. If the compounds with the same molecular formula have their atoms attached in different orders, they have different structures and are said to be **structural isomers** of each other. (We will encounter other types of isomerism later.) Dimethyl ether and ethanol are examples of a pair of structural isomers.

Alkanes that contain three or fewer carbons have no isomers. In each case, there is only one possible way in which the atoms can be arranged.

No isomers: CH_4 CH_3CH_3 $CH_3CH_2CH_3$

methane   ethane   propane

The four-carbon alkane (C_4H_{10}) has two possibilities for arrangement of the carbon atoms. As the number of carbon atoms increases, so does the number of isomers. The molecular formula C_5H_{12} represents three structural isomers; C_6H_{14} represents five; and $C_{10}H_{22}$ represents 75!

Structural isomers for C_4H_{10}:

$$\begin{array}{ccc} & & CH_3 \\ & & | \\ CH_3CH_2CH_2CH_3 & & CH_3CHCH_3 \end{array}$$

butane, bp $-0.5°$ methylpropane, bp $-12°$

a continuous-chain alkane   *a branched-chain alkane*

Write the structures for the three structural isomers of C_5H_{12}.

Solution:

(a) $CH_3CH_2CH_2CH_2CH_3$ (b) $CH_3CH_2CHCH_3$ (c) CH_3CCH_3

with (b) having CH_3 below, and (c) having CH_3 above and CH_3 below.

You might have listed $CH_3CHCH_2CH_3$. This structure is the same as (b). (with CH_3 below)

Different positions of attachment of a functional group in a molecule also lead to structural isomerism. The alcohols 1-propanol and 2-propanol are structural isomers with slightly different properties. The alkenes 1-butene and 2-butene are also structural isomers with different properties.

$$CH_3CH_2CH_2OH$$
1-propanol
bp 97°

$$CH_3CHCH_3$$ (with OH above)
2-propanol
bp 82°

$$CH_2=CHCH_2CH_3$$
1-butene
bp −6.3°

$$CH_3CH=CHCH_3$$
2-butene
bp 3.7°

STUDY PROBLEMS

3.1 Draw a structural isomer for

(a) CH_3CH_2CHCH (with O double bond above CH, and CH_3 below)   and   (b) 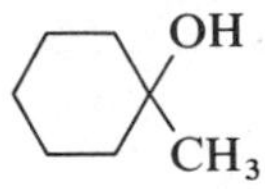 (cyclohexane ring with OH and CH_3)

(There is more than one answer for each.)

3.2 For each of the following compounds, write the structural formula of an isomer that has a *different functional group*. (There may be more than one correct answer.)

(a) $HCOCH_3$ (with O double bond above C)   (b) (cyclohexane ring)—OCH_3 (c) $CH_3CH_2CCH_2CH_3$ (with O double bond above C)

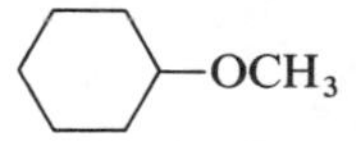

Example: An isomer of $CH_3CH_2CH_2OH$ that has a different functional group is $CH_3OCH_2CH_3$, but not $(CH_3)_2CHOH$, which is an isomer with the *same* functional group.

A. Isomers or Not?

Molecules can move around in space and twist and turn in "snake-like motion," as Kekulé once described it. (Kekulé, you will recall, was the chemist who proposed a structure for benzene.) We may write the same structure on paper in a number of ways. The *order of attachment* of the atoms is the factor that determines if two structural formulas represent isomers or the same compound. For example, all the following formulas show the same order of attachment of atoms; they all represent the same compound and do not represent isomers.

All represent the same compound:

$$\underset{\displaystyle CH_3CH_2CHCH_3}{\overset{\displaystyle OH}{\overset{|}{}}} \qquad \underset{\displaystyle CH_3CHOH}{\overset{\displaystyle CH_3CH_2}{}} \qquad \underset{\displaystyle \overset{\displaystyle CH_3CH_2}{\underset{\displaystyle CH_3}{\diagdown}}}{CHOH} \qquad \underset{\displaystyle CH_3CHCH_2CH_3}{\overset{\displaystyle OH}{\overset{|}{}}}$$

Sample Problem

Which of the following pairs of formulas represent isomers and which represent the same compound?

(a) $\underset{\displaystyle CH_3CHCHCl_2}{\overset{\displaystyle Cl}{\overset{|}{}}}$ and $\underset{\displaystyle Cl_2CHCHCH_3}{\overset{\displaystyle Cl}{\overset{|}{}}}$ (b) ⬡ and ⬡

(c) Cl—⬡—Cl and ⬡ (with Cl, Cl substituents)

(d) $\underset{\displaystyle (CH_3)_3CCHCH_3}{\overset{\displaystyle OH}{\overset{|}{}}}$ and $(CH_3)_3CCH_2CH_2OH$

Solution: (c) and (d) represent pairs of structural isomers. In (a) and (b) the structures are oriented differently, but the order of attachment of the atoms is the same; therefore, the formulas in (a) and (b) represent the same compound.

B.   A Ring or Unsaturation?

Given a molecular formula for a hydrocarbon, we can often deduce a reasonable amount of information about its structure. For example, all acyclic (noncyclic) alkanes have the general formula C_nH_{2n+2}, where n = the number of carbon atoms in the molecule. Propane ($CH_3CH_2CH_3$, or C_3H_8) has three carbon atoms ($n = 3$). The number of hydrogen atoms in propane is $2n + 2$, or eight. Try the formula on the following alkanes:

$$CH_4 \qquad \underset{\displaystyle CH_3CHCH_3}{\overset{\displaystyle CH_3}{\overset{|}{}}} \qquad \underset{\displaystyle CH_3CH_2CH_2CHCH_3}{\overset{\displaystyle CH_3}{\overset{|}{}}}$$

The presence of a ring or a double bond reduces the number of hydrogens in the formula by two for each double bond or ring; that is, a compound with the general formula C_nH_{2n} contains either one double bond or one ring.

$$CH_3CH_2CH_2CH_3 \qquad CH_3CH_2CH{=}CH_2 \qquad \square$$
$$C_4H_{10} \qquad\qquad\qquad C_4H_8 \qquad\qquad\qquad C_4H_8$$
$$C_nH_{2n+2} \qquad\qquad\qquad C_nH_{2n} \qquad\qquad\qquad C_nH_{2n}$$

A compound with the general formula C_nH_{2n-2} might have one triple bond, two rings, two double bonds, or one ring plus one double bond.

Three of many possible structural isomers for C_8H_{14}:

$$CH_3(CH_2)_5C\equiv CH$$

one triple bond   two rings   one double bond and one ring

STUDY PROBLEM

3.3   What can you deduce about the possible structures represented by each of the following molecular formulas?

(a) $C_{16}H_{34}$ (b) $C_{10}H_{20}$ (c) C_5H_8

Section 3.2

How Organic Nomenclature Developed

In the middle of the 19th century, the structures of many organic compounds were unknown. At that time, compounds were given names that were illustrative of their origins or their properties. Some compounds were named after friends or relatives of the chemists who first discovered them. For example, HCO_2H is a carboxylic acid that at one time was obtained from the distillation of red ants. This acid was given the name *formic acid* from the Latin *formica*, which means "ants." The name *barbituric acid* (and hence the common drug classification *barbiturates*) comes from the woman's name Barbara. These names are both called **trivial names**, or **common names**. In many respects, these trivial names are like nicknames; both these compounds have more formal (but seldom-used) names.

Faced with the specter of an unlimited number of organic compounds, each with its own quaint name, organic chemists in the late 19th century decided to systematize organic nomenclature to correlate the names of compounds with their structures. The system of nomenclature that has been developed is called the **Geneva system** or the **IUPAC system**. The term *Geneva* comes from the fact that the first nomenclature conference was held in Geneva, Switzerland. The initials IUPAC stand for the *International Union of Pure and Applied Chemistry*, the organization responsible for the continued development of organic nomenclature.

In the next section, we will present a brief survey of the IUPAC nomenclature system along with some frequently used trivial names. In future chapters we will expand our discussion of nomenclature as it becomes necessary. A more complete outline of organic nomenclature is presented in the appendix.

Section 3.3

A Survey of Organic Nomenclature

A.   *Continuous-Chain Alkanes*

The IUPAC system of nomenclature is based upon the idea that the structure of an organic compound can be used to derive its name and, in turn, that a unique structure can be drawn for each name. The foundations of the IUPAC system are

Table 3.1. *The First Ten Continuous-Chain Alkanes*

Number of carbons	Structure	Name
1	CH_4	methane
2	CH_3CH_3	ethane
3	$CH_3CH_2CH_3$	propane
4	$CH_3(CH_2)_2CH_3$	butane
5	$CH_3(CH_2)_3CH_3$	pentane
6	$CH_3(CH_2)_4CH_3$	hexane
7	$CH_3(CH_2)_5CH_3$	heptane
8	$CH_3(CH_2)_6CH_3$	octane
9	$CH_3(CH_2)_7CH_3$	nonane
10	$CH_3(CH_2)_8CH_3$	decane

the names of the continuous-chain alkanes. The structures and names of the first ten continuous-chain alkanes are shown in Table 3.1.

The compounds in Table 3.1 are arranged so that each compound differs from its neighbors by only a methylene (CH_2) group. Such a grouping of compounds is called a **homologous series**, and the compounds in such a list are called **homologs**.

From Table 3.1, we may see that all the alkane names end in **-ane**, which is the IUPAC ending denoting a saturated hydrocarbon. The first parts of the names of the first four alkanes (methane through butane) are derived from the traditional trivial names. The higher alkane names are derived from Greek or Latin numbers; for example, pentane is from *penta*, "five."

Let us briefly consider the derivations of the names for the first four alkanes. *Methane* (CH_4) is named after methyl alcohol (CH_3OH). *Methyl*, in turn, is a combination of the Greek words *methy* (wine) and *hyle* (wood). Methyl alcohol may be prepared by heating wood in the absence of air. Even today, this alcohol is sometimes referred to as wood alcohol.

The name *ethane* (CH_3CH_3) is derived from the Greek word *aithein*, which means "to kindle or blaze." Ethane is quite flammable. The name for *propane* ($CH_3CH_2CH_3$) is taken from the trivial name for the three-carbon carboxylic acid, propionic acid ($CH_3CH_2CO_2H$). *Propionic* is a combination of the Greek *proto* (first) and *pion* (fat). Propionic acid is the first (or lowest-molecular-weight) carboxylic acid to exhibit properties of fatty acids, which are acids that can be obtained from fats. *Butane* ($CH_3CH_2CH_2CH_3$) is named after butyric acid—the odorous component of rancid butter (Latin *butyrum*, "butter").

B.   Cycloalkanes

Cycloalkanes are named according to the number of carbon atoms in the ring, with the prefix **cyclo-** added.

cyclopentane   cyclohexane   cyclooctane

C.   Side Chains

When alkyl groups or functional groups are attached to an alkane chain, the continuous chain is called the **root**, or **parent**. The groups are then designated in the name of the compound by prefixes and suffixes on the name of the parent.

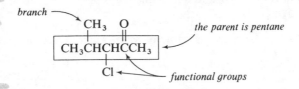

A side chain, or branch, is an alkyl group branching from a parent chain. A continuous-chain alkyl group is named after its own alkane parent with the **-ane** ending changed to **-yl**. (CH_4 is methane: therefore, the CH_3- group is the *methyl group*. CH_3CH_3 is ethane; therefore, the CH_3CH_2-group is the *ethyl group*.) The names for the first five continuous-chain alkyl groups are listed in Table 3.2.

Table 3.2.   The First Five Continuous-Chain Alkyl Groups

Structure	Name
CH_3-	methyl
CH_3CH_2-	ethyl
$CH_3CH_2CH_2-$	propyl
$CH_3(CH_2)_2CH_2-$	butyl
$CH_3(CH_2)_3CH_2-$	pentyl

How is the name of a side chain incorporated into the name of a compound? To illustrate the technique, we will use hexane as the parent. If there is a methyl group on the second carbon of the hexane chain, the compound is named 2-methylhexane; *2-* for the position of attachment on the parent, *methyl* for the branch at this position, *hexane* for the parent. Methylhexane is one word.

$$CH_3 \qquad \text{methyl at position 2}$$
$$CH_3CHCH_2CH_2CH_2CH_3$$
$$① \quad ② \quad ③ \quad ④ \quad ⑤ \quad ⑥$$

2-methylhexane

Sample Problem

Why is the following compound *not* named 1-methylhexane? What is its correct name?

$$CH_2CH_2CH_2CH_2CH_2CH_3$$
$$CH_3$$

Solution: The structure contains a continuous chain of seven carbons; it is called *heptane*.

The general procedure to be followed in naming branched alkanes follows:

(1) Number the carbon atoms in the longest continuous chain, starting at the end closer to the position of the branch so that the prefix number will be as low as possible. (The longest continuous chain in an alkane is the parent, even if the chain is not shown in a straight line.)

(2) Identify the branch and its position.

(3) Attach the number and the name of the branch to the name of the parent.

Sample Problem
_____

Name the following compound:

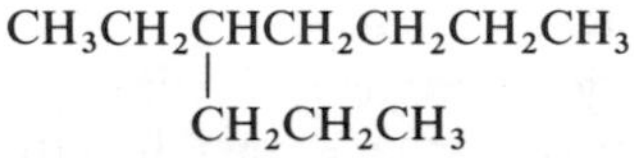

$$CH_3CH_2CHCH_2CH_2CH_2CH_3$$
$$|$$
$$CH_2CH_2CH_3$$

Solution: The longest continuous chain is eight carbons. The parent is *octane.*

numbering:

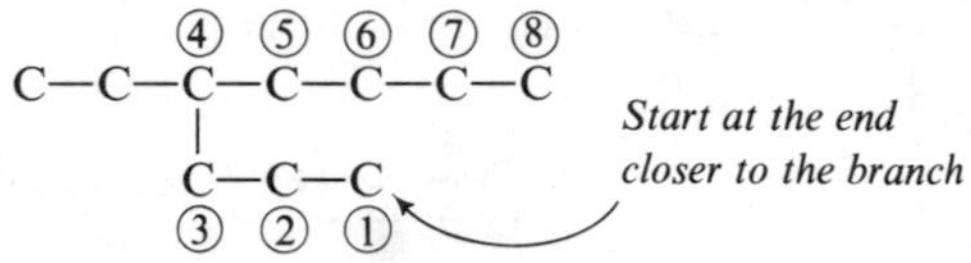

$$\overset{④}{C}—\overset{⑤}{C}—\overset{⑥}{C}—\overset{⑦}{C}—\overset{⑧}{C}$$

C—C—C—C—C—C—C   *Start at the end*
$$|$$ *closer to the branch*
$$\underset{③}{C}—\underset{②}{C}—\underset{①}{C}$$

alkyl group: ethyl at carbon 4

name: 4-ethyloctane

Sample Problem
_____

Write the structure for 3-methylpentane.

Solution: *the parent chain:*   C—C—C—C—C   (pentane)

numbering: $\underset{①}{C}—\underset{②}{C}—\underset{③}{C}—\underset{④}{C}—\underset{⑤}{C}$

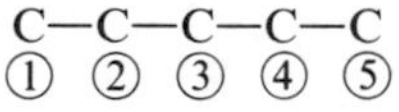

$$CH_3$$
$$|$$
the alkyl group: C—C—C—C—C   (3-methyl)

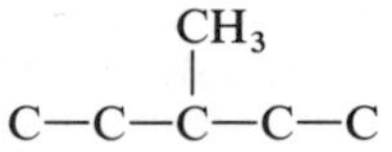

add the hydrogens (each carbon must have four bonds):

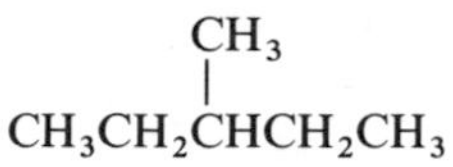

$$CH_3$$
$$|$$
$$CH_3CH_2CHCH_2CH_3$$

Sample Problem
_____

Name the following structure. In this name, a prefix number is not needed. Why not?

$$(CH_3)_2CHCH_2CH_3$$

Solution: Methylbutane. A prefix number is not needed because there is only one methyl-butane:

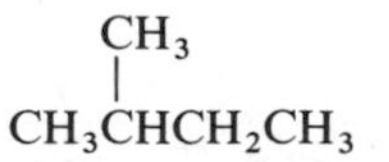

$$CH_3$$ $$CH_3$$
$$|$$ $$|$$
$$CH_3CHCH_2CH_3$$ is the same as $$CH_3CH_2CHCH_3$$

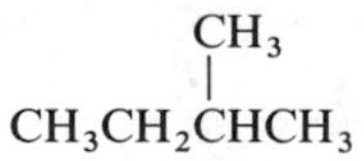

The only other place to attach the methyl group would be on an end carbon; however, this compound is pentane, not methylbutane:

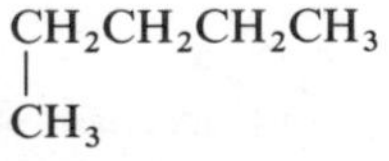

$$CH_2CH_2CH_2CH_3$$
$$|$$
$$CH_3$$

D. Branched Side Chains

An alkyl group may be branched, rather than a continuous chain. The following examples show branched side chains on a cyclohexane ring and on a heptane chain, respectively.

$$\text{(cyclohexane ring)}-\overset{\overset{\displaystyle CH_3}{|}}{CH}CH_2CH_3 \qquad\qquad CH_3CH_2CH_2\overset{\overset{\displaystyle CH_3CHCH_3}{|}}{CH}CH_2CH_2CH_3$$

Common branched groups have specific names. For example, the two propyl groups are called the **propyl group** and the **isopropyl group**.

$$CH_3CH_2CH_2- \qquad\qquad \overset{\overset{\displaystyle CH_3}{|}}{CH_3CH}-$$

propyl (or *n*-propyl)   isopropyl

To emphasize that a side chain is *not* branched, a prefix *n*- (for *normal-*) is often used. (The *n*- is redundant since the absence of a prefix also indicates a continuous chain.) The prefix iso- (from *isomeric*) is used to indicate a methyl branch at the end of the alkyl side chain.

A four-carbon side chain has four structural possibilities. The **butyl**, or ***n*-butyl**, group is the continuous-chain group. The **isobutyl group** has a methyl branch at the end of the chain. These two butyl groups are named similarly to the propyl groups.

methyl branch at end

$$CH_3CH_2CH_2CH_2- \qquad\qquad \overset{\overset{\displaystyle CH_3}{|}}{CH_3CH}CH_2-$$

butyl (or *n*-butyl)   isobutyl

The ***secondary*-butyl group** (abbreviated *sec*-butyl) has two carbons bonded to the head (attaching) carbon. The ***tertiary*-butyl group** (abbreviated *tert*-butyl or *t*-butyl) has three carbons attached to the head carbon.

two C's on head carbon   *three C's on head carbon*

$$CH_3CH_2\overset{\overset{\displaystyle CH_3}{|}}{CH}- \qquad\qquad CH_3-\overset{\overset{\displaystyle CH_3}{|}}{\underset{\underset{\displaystyle CH_3}{|}}{C}}-$$

sec-butyl   t-butyl

Sample Problem

Name the following compounds:

(a) (cyclohexane ring)$-\overset{\overset{\displaystyle CH_3}{|}}{CH}CH_2CH_3$ (b) $CH_3CH_2CH_2\overset{\overset{\displaystyle CH_3CHCH_3}{|}}{CH}CH_2CH_2CH_3$

Solution: (a) *sec*-butylcyclohexane;   (b) 4-isopropylheptane

STUDY PROBLEM

3.4   Give structures for (a) *n*-propylcyclohexane; (b) isobutylcyclohexane; and (c) 4-*t*-butyloctane.

E.   Multiple Branches

If two or more branches are attached to a parent chain, more prefixes are added to the parent name. The prefixes are placed alphabetically, each with its number indicating the position of attachment to the parent.

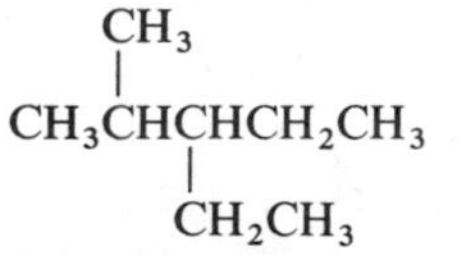

$$CH_3CHCHCH_2CH_3 \qquad CH_3CH_2CCH_2CH_2CH_3$$

3-ethyl-2-methylpentane 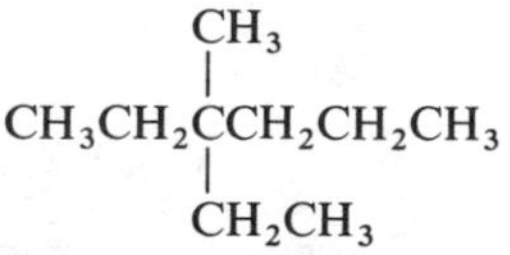   3-ethyl-3-methylhexane

If two or more substituents on a parent are the same (such as two methyl groups or three ethyl groups), these groups are consolidated in the name. For example, *dimethyl* means "two methyl groups" and *triethyl* means "three ethyl groups." The prefixes (*di-*, *tri-*, etc.) that denote number are listed in Table 3.3.

Table 3.3.   *Prefixes for Naming Multiple Substituents*

Number	Prefix
2	di-
3	tri-
4	tetra-
5	penta-
6	hexa-

In a name, the *di-* or *tri-* prefix is preceded by position numbers. If *di* is used, two numbers are required; if *tri* is used, three numbers must be present. Note the use of commas and hyphens in the following examples:

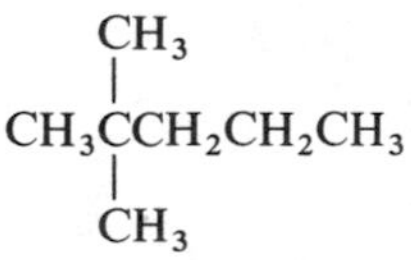

$$CH_3CCH_2CH_2CH_3$$

2,2-dimethylpentane 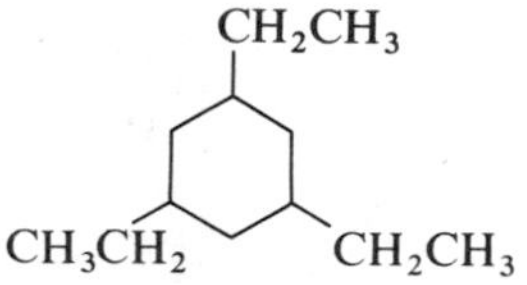   1,3,5-triethylcyclohexane

Sample Problem

Name the following compounds:

(a) 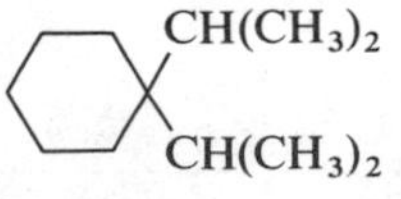   (b) 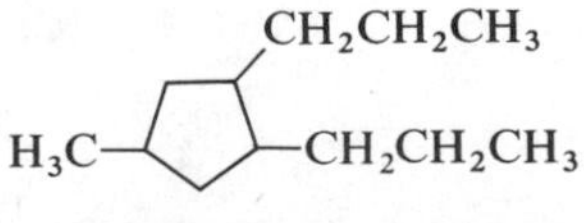 H₃C—

$$\text{(c)} \quad CH_3CH_2CH_2\overset{\overset{\displaystyle CH(CH_3)_2}{\displaystyle |}}{C}H\overset{}{C}H\underset{\underset{\displaystyle CH(CH_3)_2}{\displaystyle |}}{}CH_2CH_2CH_2CH_3$$

Solution: (a) 1,1-diisopropylcyclohexane; (b) 4-methyl-1,2-dipropylcyclopentane; (c) 4,5-diisopropylnonane. (We number a ring so that the prefix numbers are as low as possible. We alphabetize *dipropyl* as *propyl*.)

F. Other Prefix Substituents

Like alkyl branches, a few functional groups are named as prefixes to the parent name. Some of these groups and their prefix names are listed in Table 3.4.

Table 3.4. Some Substituents Named as Prefixes

Substituents	Prefix name
—NO$_2$	nitro-
—F	fluoro-
—Cl	chloro-
—Br	bromo-
—I	iodo-

The rules governing the use of these prefixes are identical to those for the alkyl groups except that the parent is the longest continuous chain *containing the functional group*. The position of the functional group is specified by a number (as low as possible), and identical groups are preceded by *di-* or *tri-*.

$$\text{CH}_3\text{CH}_2\overset{\overset{\displaystyle NO_2}{\displaystyle |}}{C}H\overset{\overset{\displaystyle Br}{\displaystyle |}}{C}H_2CH_2 \qquad\qquad CH_3-\overset{\overset{\displaystyle Cl}{\displaystyle |}}{\underset{\underset{\displaystyle Cl}{\displaystyle |}}{C}}-\overset{\overset{\displaystyle Cl}{\displaystyle |}}{\underset{\underset{\displaystyle Cl}{\displaystyle |}}{C}}-CH_3$$

1-bromo-3-nitropentane   2,2,3,3-tetrachlorobutane

STUDY PROBLEM

3.5   Give structures for (a) 1,1,2-trichloroethane, and (b) 1,2-dichloro-4-nitrocyclohexane.

G. Alkenes and Alkynes

In IUPAC nomenclature, carbon–carbon unsaturation is always designated by a change in the *ending* of the parent name. As we have indicated, if the parent hydrocarbon contains no double or triple bonds, the suffix **-ane** is used. If a double bond is present, the -**ane** ending is changed to -**ene**; the general name for a hydrocarbon with a double bond is **alkene**. A triple bond is indicated by -**yne**; a hydrocarbon containing this group is an **alkyne**.

$$CH_3CH_3 \qquad CH_2{=}CH_2 \qquad HC{\equiv}CH$$

ethane	ethene	ethyne
an alkane	*an alkene*	*an alkyne*

When the parent contains four or more carbons, a prefix number must be used to indicate the position of the double or triple bond. The chain is numbered so as to *give the double or triple bond as low a number as possible*, even if a prefix group must then receive a higher number. Only a single number is used for each double and triple bond; it is understood that the double or triple bond *begins at this numbered position and goes to the carbon with the next higher number*. Thus, a prefix number 2 means the double or triple bond is between carbons 2 and 3, not between carbons 2 and 1.

C=C starts at carbon 1   *C=C starts at carbon 2*

$$CH_2{=}CHCH_2CH_3 \qquad CH_3CH{=}CHCH_3$$

1-butene   2-butene

a branch precedes the name

$$CH_3$$
$$|$$
$$CH_3CHCH_2CH_2C{\equiv}CH$$

5-methyl-1-hexyne

If a structure contains more than one double or triple bond, the name becomes slightly more complex. The following example of a **diene**, a compound with two double bonds, shows the placement of the numbers and the *di*. (Note that an *a* is inserted before *di* to ease the pronunciation.)

$$CH_2{=}CHCH{=}CH_2$$

1,3-butadiene

two double bonds

four C's

Sample Problem

Name the following compounds:

(a) $(CH_3)_2CHCH_2CH_2CH{=}CH_2$ (b) $CH_2{=}CHCH{=}CHCH{=}CH_2$
(c) $CH{\equiv}CC{\equiv}CH$

Solution: (a) 5-methyl-1-hexene   (b) 1,3,5-hexatriene   (c) 1,3-butadiyne

STUDY PROBLEMS

3.6   Name the following compounds:

(a) $CH_3CH{=}CH_2$ (b) ⬡   (c) ⬡

3.7   Give structures for   (a) cyclopentene, and   (b) 1,3-pentadiyne.

Table 3.5. *Names of Some Common Alkenes and Alkynes*

Structure	IUPAC name	Trivial name
$CH_2\!=\!CH_2$	ethene	ethylene
$CH_3CH\!=\!CH_2$	propene	propylene
$\underset{\displaystyle CH_2\!=\!\overset{\textstyle \|}{C}CH\!=\!CH_2}{CH_3}$	2-methyl-1,3-butadiene	isoprene
$CH\!\equiv\!CH$	ethyne	acetylene

Some alkenes and alkynes are frequently referred to by their trivial names. We have listed a few of these trivial names in Table 3.5.

H. Alcohols

In the IUPAC system, the name of an alcohol (ROH) is the name of the parent hydrocarbon with the final **-e** changed to **-ol**. Prefix numbers are used when necessary; the hydroxyl group (—OH) receives the lowest prefix number possible.

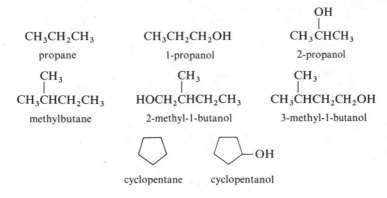

		OH
$CH_3CH_2CH_3$	$CH_3CH_2CH_2OH$	$CH_3\overset{\displaystyle \|}{C}HCH_3$
propane	1-propanol	2-propanol

CH_3	CH_3	CH_3
$CH_3\overset{\displaystyle \|}{C}HCH_2CH_3$	$HOCH_2\overset{\displaystyle \|}{C}HCH_2CH_3$	$CH_3\overset{\displaystyle \|}{C}HCH_2CH_2OH$
methylbutane	2-methyl-1-butanol	3-methyl-1-butanol

cyclopentane   cyclopentanol

STUDY PROBLEM

3.8   (a)   Name the following compound:

$$\underset{\displaystyle CH_3CH_2CH_2\overset{\textstyle \|}{C}HCH_3}{OH}.$$

(b)   Give the structure for 3-methyl-1-cyclohexanol.

I. Aldehydes

Because an aldehyde (RCHO) contains a carbonyl group bonded to a hydrogen atom, the aldehyde group must be at the beginning of a carbon chain. The aldehyde carbon is considered carbon 1; therefore, no number is used in the name to indicate the position. The ending of an aldehyde name is **-al**.

O	O	CH_3 O
$\|\|$	$\|\|$	$\|$ $\|\|$
—CH	CH_3CH_2CH	CH_3CHCH_2CH
	③ ② ①	
the aldehydo group	propanal	3-methylbutanal

J. Ketones

A keto group, by definition, cannot be at the beginning of a carbon chain. Therefore, except for propanone and a few other simple ketones, a prefix number is necessary. The chain should be numbered to give the carbonyl group the lowest possible number. The ending for a ketone name is **-one**.

$$
\underset{\textit{the keto group}}{-\overset{\displaystyle O}{\overset{\|}{C}}-} \qquad \underset{\textit{propanone}}{CH_3\overset{\displaystyle O}{\overset{\|}{C}}CH_3} \qquad \underset{\textit{3-methyl-2-hexanone}}{\underset{\underset{\displaystyle CH_3}{|}}{CH_3\overset{\displaystyle O}{\overset{\|}{C}}CHCH_2CH_2CH_3}}
$$

K. Carboxylic Acids

A carboxyl group, like an aldehyde group, must be at the beginning of a carbon chain and again contains the first carbon atom (carbon-1). Again, a number is not needed in the name. The ending for a carboxylic acid name is **-oic acid**.

$$
\underset{\textit{the carboxyl group}}{-\overset{\displaystyle O}{\overset{\|}{C}}OH} \qquad \underset{\textit{ethanoic acid}}{\underset{②\quad①}{CH_3\overset{\displaystyle O}{\overset{\|}{C}}OH}} \qquad \underset{\textit{5,5-dimethylhexanoic acid}}{\underset{\underset{\displaystyle CH_3}{|}}{CH_3\overset{\overset{\displaystyle CH_3}{|}}{C}CH_2CH_2CH_2\overset{\displaystyle O}{\overset{\|}{C}}OH}}
$$

STUDY PROBLEM

3.9 Write structures and names for an aldehyde, a ketone, and a carboxylic acid, each containing four carbons in a continuous chain.

L. Esters

An ester is similar to a carboxylic acid, but the acidic hydrogen has been replaced by an alkyl group.

$$
\underset{\textit{a carboxylic acid}}{CH_3\overset{\displaystyle O}{\overset{\|}{C}}O-H} \qquad \underset{\textit{an ester}}{CH_3\overset{\displaystyle O}{\overset{\|}{C}}O-CH_3} \longleftarrow R \text{ instead of } H
$$

The name of an ester consists of two words: (1) the name of the ester alkyl group, and (2) the name of the carboxylic acid with the **-ic acid** ending changed to **-ate**. (The ester alkyl group is always the group attached to the oxygen, while the carboxylic acid portion is always that portion containing the carbonyl group.)

$$
\textit{from ethanoic acid} \longrightarrow \underset{\textit{methyl ethanoate}}{CH_3\overset{\displaystyle O}{\overset{\|}{C}}O-CH_3} \longleftarrow \textit{methyl group}
$$

Name the following ester: $CH_3CH_2CH_2\overset{\overset{\displaystyle O}{\|}}{C}OCH_2CH_3$

Solution:

Step 1:   the ester alkyl group = ethyl
Step 2:   the acid = butanoic acid
Step 3:   the name = ethyl butanoate

STUDY PROBLEM

3.10   Write the structure for cyclohexyl hexanoate.

M. *Benzene Compounds*

The benzene ring is considered a parent in the same way that a continuous-chain alkane is. Alkyl groups, halogens, and the nitro group are named as prefixes to benzene.

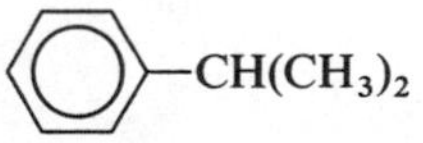

isopropylbenzene 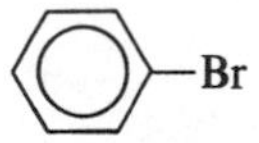   bromobenzene 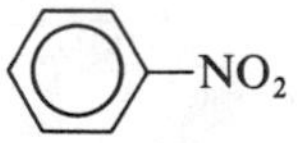   nitrobenzene

When a benzene ring is attached to an alkane chain with a functional group or to an alkane chain of seven or more carbon atoms, benzene is considered a substituent instead of a parent. The name for a benzene substituent is **phenyl**.

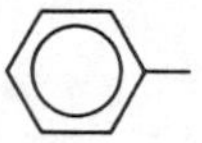

the phenyl group   2-phenyl-1-ethanol 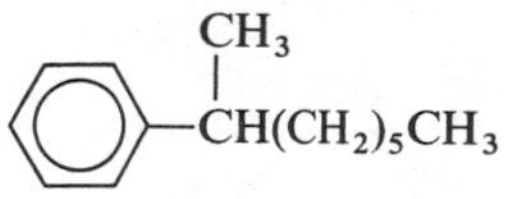   2-phenyloctane
(C_6H_5—)

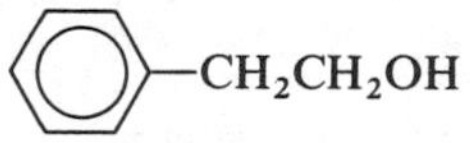

N. *Conflicts in Numbering*

A structure that has more than one type of substituent can sometimes be numbered in more than one way. Should the name for $ClCH_2CH{=}CH_2$ be 1-chloro-2-propene or 3-chloro-1-propene? To cover such situations, a *system of priorities* for prefix numbers has been developed (Table 3.6); the higher-priority substituent receives the lower number. (A more complete list of nomenclature priorities is found in Table A8 in the appendix.)

From Table 3.6, we can see that a double bond is higher in priority than Cl. When numbering a carbon chain, we give the double bond the lowest possible number. The name of $ClCH_2CH{=}CH_2$ is therefore 3-chloro-1-propene, and not

Table 3.6.   Nomenclature Priorities of Selected Functional Groups

	Partial structure	Name
	—CO$_2$H	-oic acid
	$\overset{\displaystyle O}{\overset{\displaystyle \|}{—CH}}$	-al
increasing priority	$\overset{\displaystyle O}{\overset{\displaystyle \|}{—C—}}$	-one
	—OH	-ol
	$\overset{\displaystyle \diagdown}{\diagup}C{=}C\overset{\displaystyle \diagup}{\diagdown}$	-ene
	R—, C$_6$H$_5$—, Cl—, Br—, —NO$_2$, etc.	prefix substituents

1-chloro-2-propene. Similarly, the following compounds are numbered to give the higher-priority groups the lower prefix numbers.

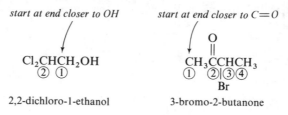

start at end closer to OH

Cl$_2$CHCH$_2$OH
② ①

2,2-dichloro-1-ethanol

start at end closer to C=O

$$CH_3\overset{\displaystyle O}{\overset{\displaystyle \|}{C}}CHCH_3$$
① ② ③ ④
Br

3-bromo-2-butanone

STUDY PROBLEM

3.11 Name each of the following compounds:

(a) (CH$_3$)$_2$CHCH$_2$CH=CHCH$_3$

(b) CH$_3$CH$_2$$\overset{\displaystyle O}{\overset{\displaystyle \|}{C}}CH_2CH_2CH_2NO_2$

Section 3.4

Alkanes

Most organic compounds have a portion of their structures composed of carbon atoms and hydrogen atoms. A fat is one example of an organic compound with ester groups and with long hydrocarbon chains, which may be alkyl or alkenyl (containing a double bond).

CH$_2$O$\overset{\displaystyle O}{\overset{\displaystyle \|}{C}}$(CH$_2$)$_{14}CH_3$

CHO$\overset{\displaystyle O}{\overset{\displaystyle \|}{C}}$(CH$_2$)$_{14}CH_3$ *long hydrocarbon chains*

CH$_2$O$\overset{\displaystyle O}{\overset{\displaystyle \|}{C}}$(CH$_2$)$_7$CH=CH(CH$_2$)$_7CH_3$

a typical animal fat

Early chemists did not know the molecular structure of a fat, but they did know that many compounds containing long hydrocarbon chains behave similarly to fats. (For example, most of these compounds are water-insoluble and are less dense than water.) For this reason, compounds with hydrocarbon chains are referred to as **aliphatic compounds** (Greek *aleiphatos*, "fat"). (The term *aliphatic compound* is usually contrasted to *aromatic compound*, such as benzene or a substituted benzene.)

Some aliphatic compounds:

$$CH_3$$
$$|$$
$$CH_3CHCH{=}CH_2 \qquad CH_3CH_2CH_2OH \qquad CH_3CH_2NHCH_2CH_3$$

Some of the physical and chemical properties of an aliphatic compound arise from the alkyl part of its molecules. Therefore, much of what we have to say about alkanes and cycloalkanes is true for other organic compounds as well. Of course, the properties of a compound are also greatly determined by any functional groups that may be present. For example, a hydroxyl group in a molecule leads to hydrogen bonding and a large change in physical properties. Ethane (CH_3CH_3) is a gas at room temperature, while ethanol (CH_3CH_2OH) is a liquid.

A. Physical Properties of Alkanes

The alkanes are nonpolar compounds. As a result, the attractive forces between molecules are weak. The continuous-chain alkanes through butane are gases at room temperature, while the C_5 to C_{17} alkanes are liquids (see Table 3.7). The alkanes with 18 or more carbon atoms are solids.

The boiling point of a compound depends, in part, on the amount of energy needed by the molecules of that compound to escape from the liquid into the vapor phase. The boiling points of the compounds of a homologous series, such as the alkanes in Table 3.7, increase by about 30° for each additional methylene (CH_2) group. This increase in boiling point is due principally to an increase in the van der Waals attractions between longer and longer molecules. Other homologous series show similar effects.

$$CH_3I \qquad CH_3CH_2I \qquad CH_3CH_2CH_2I$$

iodomethane   iodoethane   1-iodopropane
bp 43°   bp 72°   bp 102°

As we mentioned in Section 1.9A, branching in the hydrocarbon portion of a molecule lowers the boiling point from the expected value because of interference

Table 3.7. Boiling Points of Some Alkanes

Structure	Bp, °C	Structure	Bp, °C
CH_4	−162	$CH_3(CH_2)_4CH_3$	69
CH_3CH_3	−88.5	$CH_3(CH_2)_5CH_3$	98
$CH_3CH_2CH_3$	−42	$CH_3(CH_2)_6CH_3$	126
$CH_3(CH_2)_2CH_3$	0	$CH_3(CH_2)_7CH_3$	151
$CH_3(CH_2)_3CH_3$	36	$CH_3(CH_2)_8CH_3$	174

with van der Waals attractions between the molecules in the liquid state.

$$CH_3CH_2CH_2CH_2CH_3 \qquad \underset{\underset{\text{methylbutane}}{\displaystyle CH_3CHCH_2CH_3}}{\overset{\displaystyle CH_3}{|}} \qquad \underset{\underset{\text{dimethylpropane}}{\displaystyle CH_3}}{\overset{\displaystyle CH_3}{\underset{|}{\overset{|}{CH_3CCH_3}}}}$$

pentane   methylbutane
bp 36°   bp 28°
dimethylpropane
bp 9.5°

Because they are nonpolar, alkanes are soluble in nonpolar or slightly polar solvents such as other alkanes, diethyl ether ($CH_3CH_2OCH_2CH_3$), or benzene. The solubility arises from van der Waals attractions between the solvent and the solute. Alkanes are insoluble in water (Section 1.9C).

All the alkanes have densities less than that of water, a fact easy to remember because we know that gasoline and motor oil (which are principally alkanes) float on water.

B.   Chemical Properties of Alkanes

The alkanes and cycloalkanes are chemically unreactive compared to organic compounds with functional groups. For example, many organic compounds undergo reaction with strong acids, bases, oxidizing agents, or reducing agents. Alkanes and cycloalkanes generally do not undergo reaction with these reagents. Because of their lack of reactivity, alkanes are sometimes referred to as **paraffins** (Latin *parum affinis*, "slight affinity").

There are two principal reactions of alkanes that we will discuss in this text. One is the *reaction with halogens*, such as chlorine gas. We will present this reaction in detail in Chapter 6. The other important reaction of alkanes is *combustion*. The remainder of this chapter will be concerned primarily with the combustion of alkanes and their use as a source of energy.

Halogenation: $CH_4 + Cl_2 \xrightarrow{\text{ultraviolet light}} CH_3Cl + HCl$

methane   chloromethane

$$CH_3CH_2CH_3 + Br_2 \xrightarrow{\text{ultraviolet light}} \underset{\text{2-bromopropane}}{\overset{\displaystyle Br}{\underset{|}{CH_3CHCH_3}}} + HBr$$

Combustion: $CH_4 + 2\ O_2 \xrightarrow{\text{spark}} CO_2 + 2\ H_2O$

carbon dioxide

$$CH_3CH_2CH_3 + 5\ O_2 \xrightarrow{\text{spark}} 3\ CO_2 + 4\ H_2O$$

C.   Combustion

Combustion is the process of burning—that is, the rapid reaction of a compound with oxygen. Combustion is accompanied by the release of light and heat, two forms of energy that man has sought since he first built a fire and found that it kept him warm. Although we will present the subject of combustion under the heading of alkanes, keep in mind that almost all organic compounds can burn.

Combustion of organic mixtures, such as wood, is not always a simple conversion to CO_2 and H_2O. Rather, combustion is the result of a large number of complex reactions. One type of reaction that occurs is **pyrolysis**, the thermal fragmentation of large molecules into smaller molecules in the absence of oxygen. (How pyrolysis occurs will be discussed in Chapter 6.) Pyrolysis of large molecules in wood, for example, yields smaller gaseous molecules that then react with oxygen above the surface of the wood. This reaction with oxygen gives rise to the flames. On the surface of the wood, a slow, but very hot, oxidation of the carbonaceous residue takes place. Most of the heat from a wood or coal fire results from this slow oxidation, rather than from the actual flames.

Complete combustion is the conversion of a compound to CO_2 and H_2O. If the oxygen supply is insufficient for complete combustion, **incomplete combustion** occurs. Incomplete combustion leads to carbon monoxide or sometimes carbon as carbon black or soot.

Incomplete combustion:

$$2\ CH_3CH_2CH_3 + 7\ O_2 \longrightarrow \quad 6\ CO \quad + 8\ H_2O$$
$$\text{carbon}$$
$$\text{monoxide}$$

$$CH_3CH_2CH_3 + 2\ O_2 \longrightarrow \quad 3\ C \quad + 4\ H_2O$$
$$\text{carbon}$$

D. Heat of Combustion

The energy released when a compound is oxidized completely to CO_2 and H_2O is called the **heat of combustion** ΔH. Under controlled laboratory conditions, ΔH may be measured. (As we described in Section 1.7, the value for ΔH is negative when energy is liberated because the molecules have lost energy.)

$$CH_4 \quad + 2\ O_2 \longrightarrow CO_2 + 2\ H_2O + 213 \text{ kcal/mole}$$
$$\text{methane}$$

$$2\ CH_3CH_2CH_2CH_3 + 13\ O_2 \longrightarrow 8\ CO_2 + 10\ H_2O + 688 \text{ kcal/mole}$$
$$\text{butane}$$

Values for heats of combustion (Table 3.8) depend primarily upon the number of carbon and hydrogen atoms in a molecule. In a homologous series, the energy liberated increases by about 157 kcal/mole for each additional methylene group.

Table 3.8. *Heats of Combustion for Some Hydrocarbons*

Name	$-\Delta H$, kcal/mole	Name	$-\Delta H$, kcal/mole
methane	213	cyclopropane	500
ethane	373	cyclobutane	656
propane	531	cyclopentane	794
butane	688	cyclohexane	944

The heat of combustion of a compound may also reflect unusual bonding characteristics. For example, cyclohexane has a ΔH of -944 kcal/mole, or -157 kcal per methylene group, the same value observed for open-chain alkanes. However, cyclopropane has a ΔH of -167 kcal per methylene group, a higher value than that for an open-chain alkane. (See Section 4.4A.)

$$\bighexagon + 9\,O_2 \longrightarrow 6\,CO_2 + 6\,H_2O + 157 \text{ kcal/mole per } CH_2 \text{ group}$$
cyclohexane

$$2\,\triangle + 9\,O_2 \longrightarrow 6\,CO_2 + 6\,H_2O + 167 \text{ kcal/mole per } CH_2 \text{ group}$$
cyclopropane

Section 3.5

The Hydrocarbon Resources

Natural gas, which is 60–90% methane depending on its source, has been formed by the anaerobic decay (decay in the absence of air) of plants. The other components of natural gas are ethane and propane, along with nitrogen and carbon dioxide. Natural gas found in the Texas panhandle and in Oklahoma also is a source of helium. Deposits of natural gas are usually found with petroleum deposits.

Petroleum has been formed by the decay of plants and animals, probably of marine origin. Crude petroleum, called *crude oil*, is a complex mixture of aliphatic and aromatic compounds, including sulfur and nitrogen compounds (1–6%). In fact, over 500 compounds have been detected in a single sample of petroleum. The actual composition varies from deposit to deposit.

Because of its complexity, crude oil itself is not very useful. Separating the crude oil into useful components is called **refining**. The first step in refining is a fractional distillation, called **straight-run distillation**. The fractions that are collected are listed in Table 3.9.

Table 3.9.   Fractions of Straight-Run Distillation

Boiling range	Number of carbons	Name	Use
under 20°C	1–4	gas fraction	heating fuel
30–60°	5–6	petroleum ether	solvent
60–100°	6–7	ligroin	solvent
40–205°	5–10	gasoline	automobile fuel
175–325°	12–18	kerosene	jet fuel
275–350°	over 12	gas oil	furnace oil, diesel fuel

Residue: (1) Volatile oils: lubricating oils, paraffin wax, and petroleum jelly. (2) Nonvolatile material: asphalt and petroleum coke.

The gasoline fraction of straight-run distillation is too scanty for the needs of our automobile-oriented society, and straight-run gasoline is usually of poor quality. To increase both quantity and quality of the gasoline fraction, the higher-boiling fractions are subjected to *cracking* and *reforming*.

Catalytic cracking is the process of heating the high-boiling material under pressure in the presence of a catalyst (finely divided, acid-washed aluminum silicate clay). Under these conditions, large molecules are cracked, or broken, into smaller fragments.

Steam cracking is a technique for converting alkanes to alkenes, and **catalytic reforming** converts aliphatic compounds to aromatic compounds. The alkenes and aromatics formed in these cracking and reforming procedures are used as starting materials for making plastics and other synthetic organic compounds. The following represents just a sample of the many reactions that can occur in cracking and refining.

$$CH_3CH_2CH_2CH_2CH_3 + CH_2\!\!=\!\!CH_2$$

$$\text{pentane} \qquad\qquad \text{ethylene}$$

$$CH_3CH_2CH_2CH_2CH_2CH_2CH_3$$

$$\text{heptane}$$

$$\bigcirc\!\!-\!\!CH_3 + 4\ H_2$$

toluene
(methylbenzene)

The high-compression engines in automobiles are relatively efficient for their weight, but in these engines continuous-chain hydrocarbons burn unevenly and cause knocking, the ticking noise heard when a car accelerates uphill. Knocking decreases the power output of the engine and decreases the life of the engine through wear and tear. Quality automobile fuels contain branched alkanes and aromatic compounds, which burn more evenly than continuous-chain compounds. Fortunately, cracking procedures provide both branched alkanes and aromatics.

At one time, isooctane (a trivial name) was the alkane with the best anti-knock characteristics for automobile engines, and heptane was the poorest. These two compounds were used to develop an octane rating of petroleum fuels.

$$\overset{\displaystyle CH_3\ \ CH_3}{\underset{\displaystyle CH_3}{\overset{|\quad\ \ |}{CH_3CCH_2CHCH_3}}} \qquad\qquad CH_3(CH_2)_5CH_3$$

"isooctane"   heptane
(2,2,4-trimethylpentane)

To rate the quality of a gasoline, the fuel is compared with a mixture of isooctane and heptane and given an **octane number**. An octane number of 100 means that the gasoline is equivalent in burning characteristics to pure isooctane. Gasoline with an octane number of 0 is equivalent to pure heptane. An octane number of 75 is given to gasoline that is equivalent to a mixture of 75% isooctane and 25% heptane.

Additives are also added to gasoline to decrease engine knock and thus to increase octane ratings. The best-known additive is *Ethyl fluid*, which contains approximately 60% tetraethyllead; 25% 1,2-dibromoethane; and 10% 1,2-dichloroethane. The halogenated hydrocarbons are essential for conversion of the lead to the volatile lead bromide, which is removed from the cylinder in the exhaust.

$(CH_3CH_2)_4Pb$	$BrCH_2CH_2Br$	$ClCH_2CH_2Cl$
tetraethyllead	1,2-dibromoethane	1,2-dichloroethane
	(ethylene dibromide)	(ethylene dichloride)

A gasoline engine puts forth a variety of pollutants: unburned hydrocarbons, carbon monoxide, and nitrogen oxides. The presence of tetraethyllead in the gasoline adds lead compounds to the list of pollutants. Catalytic converters have been installed in many automobiles to convert nonoxidized and partially oxidized compounds to more-highly oxidized and acceptable forms of exhaust. For example, a catalytic converter oxidizes unburned hydrocarbons and carbon monoxide to carbon dioxide and water. The platinum catalyst used in these converters is "poisoned" (made nonfunctional) by lead compounds; therefore, leaded gasoline cannot be used in cars equipped with catalytic converters.

Coal is formed by the bacterial decomposition of plants under varying degrees of pressure. Coal is classified by its carbon content: anthracite, or hard coal, contains the highest carbon content, followed by bituminous (soft) coal, lignite, and, finally, peat.

When coal is subjected to heat and distillation in the absence of air, a process called **destructive distillation**, three crude products result: *coal gas* (the noncondensable distillate), *coal tar* (the condensable distillate), and *coke* (the residue). Coal gas and coke are both useful fuels. Coke is used primarily in the manufacture of steel and to a limited extent for the synthesis of acetylene. This acetylene synthesis involves fusing coke and calcium oxide (obtained by heating limestone). The resulting calcium carbide yields acetylene when it is treated with water.

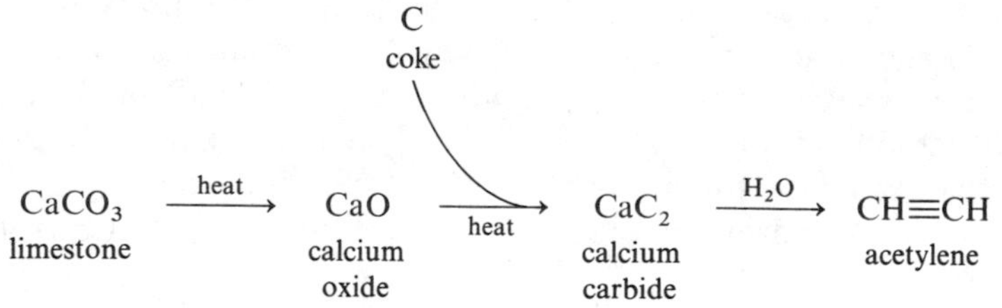

Coal tar is valuable as a source of organic chemicals. Destructive distillation converts the organic compounds in crude coal to a variety of aromatic compounds, which are widely used in fuels, as solvents, and as starting materials for the synthesis of other organic compounds.

Some of the aromatic compounds found in coal tar:

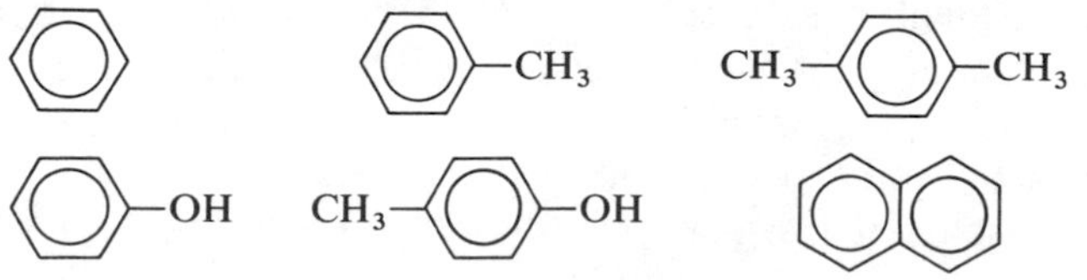

The coal reserves of the world are more extensive than the petroleum and natural gas reserves. Combustible gas can be made from coal in a process called

coal gasification. Thus, coal can provide an alternate source of gaseous fuel when our natural gas supplies become depleted.

One coal gasification technique is a high-temperature reaction between coal and steam. The gas released is a medium-quality fuel containing CO_2 and the combustible gases CO and H_2. Alternatively, the CO and H_2 can be separated from the mixture and subjected to a catalytic combination to yield methane, a high-quality fuel.

$$\text{coal} + H_2O \xrightarrow{\text{heat}} CO_2 + CO + H_2$$

$$CO + 3\,H_2 \xrightarrow{\text{catalyst}} CH_4 + H_2O$$

Direct hydrogenation of coal with hydrogen gas also yields methane. An economical source of hydrogen is a limiting factor in this synthesis of methane.

$$\text{coal} + H_2 \longrightarrow CH_4$$

SUMMARY

Compounds with the same molecular formula, but different structures (order of attachment of the atoms), are **structural isomers** of each other.

The **IUPAC system of nomenclature** is based on the names of the *continuous-chain alkanes* as parents. If a hydrocarbon chain forms a ring, the prefix *cyclo-* is added to the alkane name. Branches and functional groups are indicated in a name by prefixes or suffixes.

The longest continuous chain containing the functional group (if any) is the parent. The chain is numbered from the end nearer to the branches or functional groups. (The functional group of highest priority, as listed in Table 3.6, receives the lowest number.) Positions of substitution on the chain are then specified by these numbers.

$$
\text{1,4-dichloro-4-methyl-2-pentene:}\quad
\underset{\underset{CH_3}{|}}{\overset{\overset{Cl}{|}}{\underset{(5)}{CH_3}\underset{(4)}{C}\underset{(3)}{CH}=\underset{(2)}{CH}\underset{(1)}{CH_2}Cl}}
$$

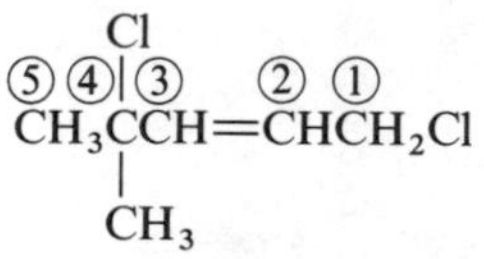

The principal reactions of alkanes are **halogenation** and **combustion**. The **heat of combustion** of an alkane (or other compound) is the result of a decrease in bond energies between the original compound and the products $CO_2 + H_2O$. Petroleum and coal tar are chief sources of hydrocarbons, both for fuels and for the chemical industry.

STUDY PROBLEMS

3.12 Which of the following compounds are unsaturated?

(a) 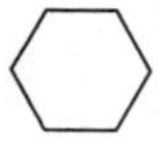   (b)    (c)

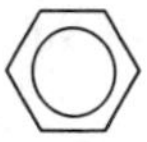

(d) $CH_3CH_2CH{=}CH_2$ (e) $CH_3CH_2CH_2OH$ (f) CH_3CH_2CHO

(g) CH_3CN

3.13 Give the structures for all possible structural isomers of   (a) C_3H_8O, and   (b) C_3H_7Cl.

3.14 Which of the following structures can have no structural isomers?

(a)    (b) $BrCH_2CH_2Br$ (c) CH_3OH

(d) $\overset{\overset{O}{\|}}{H\overset{}{C}H}$ (e) $ClCH_2Br$ (f) $\overset{\overset{O}{\|}}{H\overset{}{C}OH}$

3.15 Which of the following pairs of compounds represent structural isomers?

(a) $CH_3CH_2CH_2CH_2CH_2OH$, $CH_3\overset{\overset{CH_3}{|}}{\underset{\underset{CH_3}{|}}{C}}CH_2CH_2OH$

(b) 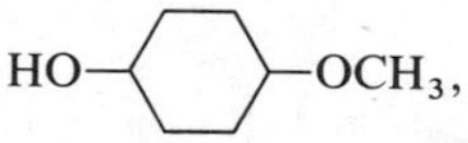 HO—⟨ ⟩—OCH_3, CH_3O—⟨ ⟩—OH

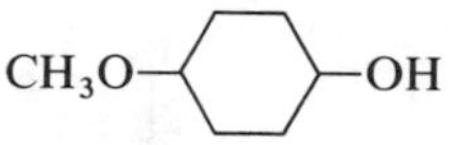

(c) $(CH_3)_3CCl$, $CH_3\overset{\overset{CH_3}{|}}{\underset{\underset{CH_2Cl}{|}}{C}H}$

(d) $CH_3CH_2\overset{}{\underset{\underset{\underset{CH_2OH}{|}}{\underset{CH_2}{|}}}{C}H}CH_3$, $CH_3CH_2\overset{\overset{OH}{|}}{\underset{\underset{CH_3}{|}}{C}H}CH_2CH_2$

(e) $CH_3\overset{\overset{OH}{|}}{C}HCH_2CH_3$, $CH_3CH_2\overset{\overset{OH}{|}}{C}HCH_3$

(f) 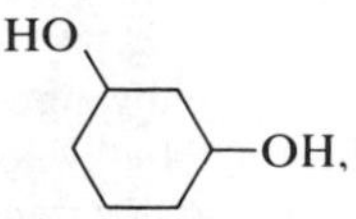 , —OH,

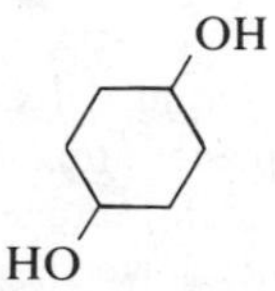

3.16   Give the structures as indicated:

(a)   five structural isomers for C_6H_{14}
(b)   all the isomeric alcohols for $C_4H_{10}O$
(c)   all the isomeric amines for $C_4H_{11}N$
(d)   all the structural isomers for C_3H_6BrCl
(e)   all the structural isomers for C_4H_6

3.17   In the following list of structures, which are structural isomers of each other, and which are the same compound?

(a) $CH_3CCl_2CH_2CH_3$
(b) $CH_3CH(CH_2Cl)CH_2CH_3$

(c) $CH_3C(CH_3)_2CH_2CH_2OH$
(d) $CH_3CHClCH_2CH_3$

(e) $CH_2ClCH(CH_3)CH_2CH_3$
(f) $CH_3CHClCHClCH_3$

3.18   What is the molecular formula and the general formula (e.g., C_nH_{2n}) for each of the following compounds?

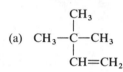

(a) CH_3-C-CH_3

(b)

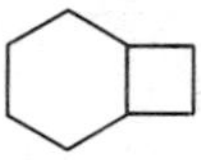

(c) $CH_2{=}CHCH{=}CHCH_2CH(CH_3)_2$
(d)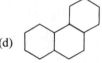

3.19   Write the formula of one structural isomer for each of the following compounds:

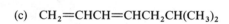

(a) 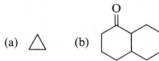   (b)   (c) 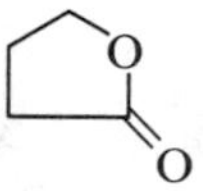   (d)

3.20   For each of the following compounds, write the structural formula of an isomer that has a different functional group (see Problem 3.2, page 83).

(a)    (b) $HOCH_2\overset{\overset{\displaystyle O}{\|}}{C}H$ (c) $H\overset{\overset{\displaystyle O}{\|}}{C}CH_2CH_3$ (d) $CH_3CH{=}CH_2$

3.21   Arrange the following structures into an homologous series:

(a) $CH_3CH_2CH_2CH_2CH_2OH$
(b) CH_3OH
(c) $CH_3CH_2CH_2OH$

(d) CH_3CH_2OH
(e) $CH_3CH_2CH_2CH_2OH$

3.22   Write structural formulas for an homologous series of alkyl bromides (monobromo-alkanes) from C_5 to C_{10}.

3.23   Give the condensed structural (or polygon) formula of each of the following compounds: (a) 2,2-dimethyloctane; (b) 3,4-diethylheptane; (c) 2,4-dimethyl-4-ethylnonane; (d) 1,3-diisopropylcyclohexane; (e) *sec*-butylcyclopentane; (f) *t*-butylbenzene; (g) iso-butylcycloheptane; (h) 1-methyl-3-pentylcyclohexane; (i) 4-isopropylheptane.

3.24 Write the IUPAC name for each of the following compounds:

(a) $(CH_3CH_2)_2CHCH_2CH_3$

(b) $(CH_3)_2CHCH(CH_3)_2$

(c)

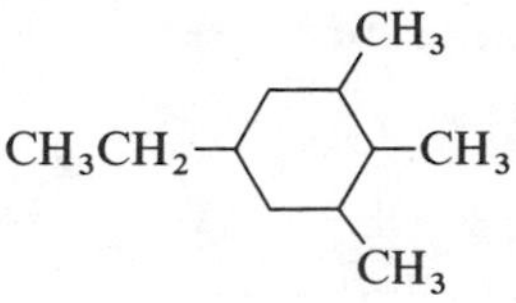

(d) 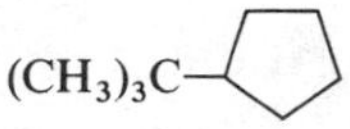 $(CH_3)_3C$—

(e) $CH_3CH_2CH_2C(CH_3)_2CH_2C(CH_3)_3$

3.25 Each of the following names is *incorrect*. Give a more suitable name in each case. (a) 3-propylpentane; (b) 6-methyloctane; (c) *t*-butylmethane; (d) 3-methyl-3-ethyl-4-methyldecane.

3.26 Write a structure for each of the following compounds:

(a) a six-carbon ketone with a methyl branch
(b) a six-carbon continuous-chain ketone
(c) a six-carbon cyclic ketone with a methyl branch
(d) a six-carbon cyclic ketone with no branches

3.27 Draw structures for five-membered carbon rings with the following branches: (a) propyl; (b) isopropyl; (c) butyl; (d) isobutyl; (e) *sec*-butyl; (f) *t*-butyl; (g) cyclobutyl; (h) pentyl.

3.28 Circle and name the functional groups in the following structures:

(a) $CH_2{=}CHCHC{\equiv}CCH(CH_3)_2$ with OH

(b)

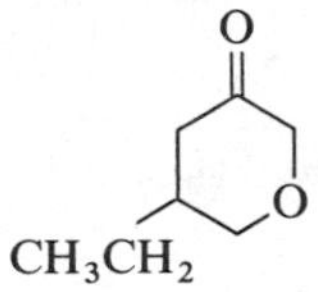

(c) $BrCH_2C{-}COH$ with two O double bonds

(d)

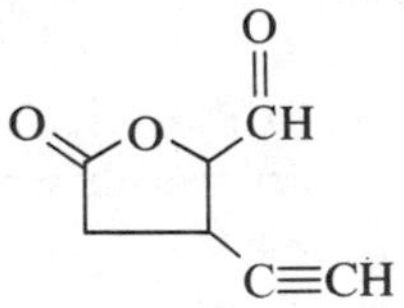

3.29 Give structures for all the structural isomers of C_8H_{18} with names that end in pentane. (*Hint*: There are six.)

3.30 Give structures for all the monochloro isomers of the following alkanes: (a) pentane; (b) cyclopentane; (c) 2,2-dimethylbutane; (d) 2,2-dimethylpropane.

3.31 Write an IUPAC name for each of the following structures:

(a)

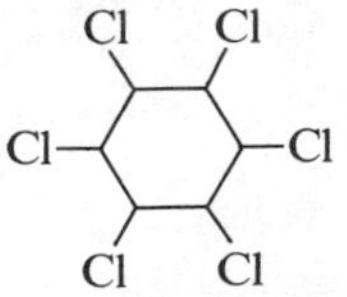

(b) $CH_2ClCHCl_2$

(c) $(CH_3)_2CBrCCl(CH_3)_2$

(d) CH_3NO_2

(e) $(CH_3CH_2)_2CBrCH_2CH(CH_3)CH(CH_3)CCl_3$

Structural Isomerism, Nomenclature, and Alkanes

3.32   Write the formula for each of the following names: (a) 1-bromo-1,2-diphenylpropane;   (b) hexachloroethane;   (c) 2-iodo-1-octanol;   (d) 1,1-dichloro-3-methylcyclohexane.

3.33   Give IUPAC names for each of the following compounds:

   (a) $CH_3CH_2CH=CHCH_3$ (b) $(CH_3)_2C=CHCH_3$

   (c) 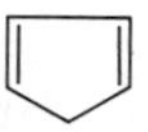   (d) $CH_2=CHC=CHCH=CH_2$
                                            with CH_3 above the third carbon

   (e) $CH_3C\equiv CCH_3$ (f) $Cl_2C=CHCl$

   (g) 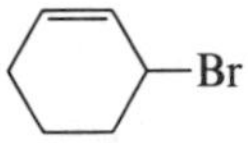   —Br

3.34   Give the IUPAC name and structure for   (a) a continuous-chain seven-carbon aldehyde;   (b) a two-carbon carboxylic acid that contains two Cl atoms;   (c) a continuous-chain, nine-carbon ketone that is symmetrical (the carbonyl group is in the center).

3.35   Write the IUPAC name for each of the following structures:

   (a) CH_3CHCO_2H with CH_3 below   (b) $CH_3CHCO_2CH_2CH_3$ with Cl above

3.36   Write a structure for each of the following compounds: (a) isopropyl propanoate;   (b) 3-methyl-4,4-diethyloctanal;   (c) 1-cyclohexyl-1-ethanol.

3.37   Predict the heat of combustion for octane. (Refer to Table 3.8.)

3.38   Of each of the following pairs of structural isomers, which would you expect to have the higher boiling point: (a) hexane or 2,2-dimethylbutane?   (b) 2-butene or methylpropene?   (c) 1-pentanol or 2,2-dimethyl-1-propanol?

3.39   Methanol is often added to automobile gas tanks in the winter to prevent the gas line from freezing. The freezing point of gasoline is somewhere around $-50°C$, far below the temperature of any anticipated cold spell. Suggest: (a) why a gas line might freeze, and (b) how methanol could help prevent this.

3.40   Gram for gram, which would be the most efficient fuel, propane or cyclopropane?

3.41   A chemist determines that a compound with the molecular formula C_4H_8O is a ketone. What are the possible structures for this compound?

3.42   An alcohol with no carbon–carbon double bonds has the formula C_4H_8O. What are the possible structures?

3.43   What are the possible structures for a carboxylic acid with the molecular formula $C_4H_8O_2$?

3.44 A four-carbon compound contains an aldehyde group and a carboxyl group. What are two possible structures for this compound?

3.45 A compound with the formula $C_4H_6O_2$ contains at least one carbonyl group. The compound does not contain a hydroxyl group, an alkoxyl group (in an ether or ester), or a carbon–carbon double bond. The compound is not acidic. What are the possible structures for this compound?

Chapter 4

Stereochemistry

Stereochemistry is the study of molecules in three dimensions—that is, how atoms in a molecule are arranged in space relative to one another. The three aspects of stereochemistry that will be covered in this chapter are:

(1) **Geometric isomers:** how rigidity in a molecule can lead to isomerism;

(2) **Conformations of molecules:** the shapes of molecules and how they can change;

(3) **Chirality of molecules:** how the right- or left-handed arrangement of atoms around a carbon atom can lead to isomerism.

It is often difficult to visualize a three-dimensional molecule from a two-dimensional illustration. Therefore, in our discussions of stereochemistry here and in subsequent chapters, we strongly urge you to use a set of molecular models.

Section 4.1

Geometric Isomerism in Alkenes

In Chapter 3, we defined structural isomers as compounds with the same molecular formula but with different orders of attachment of their atoms. Structural isomerism is only one type of isomerism. **Geometric isomerism** is a type of isomerism that results from rigidity in molecules and occurs in only two classes of compounds: *alkenes* and *cyclic compounds*.

Molecules are not quiet, static particles. They move, spin, rotate, and flex. Atoms and groups attached only by sigma bonds can rotate so that the overall shape of a molecule is in a state of continuous change. However, groups attached by a double bond cannot rotate around the double bond without the pi bond being broken. The amount of energy needed to break a pi bond (68 kcal/mole) is not available to molecules at room temperature. Because of the rigidity of a pi bond, groups attached to pi-bonded carbons are fixed in space relative to one another.

We usually write the structure for an alkene as if the sp^2 carbon atoms and the atoms attached to them are all in the plane of the paper. In this representation, we can visualize one lobe of the pi bond as being in front of the paper and the other lobe of the pi bond as being underneath the paper, behind the front lobe (see Figure 4.1).

In Figure 4.1, we show a structure with two Cl atoms (one on each sp^2 carbon) on one side of the pi bond and two H atoms on the other side. Because the

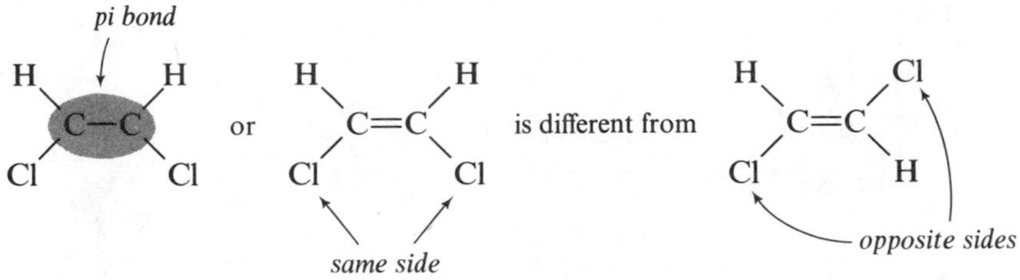

Figure 4.1. The groups attached to sp^2 carbons are fixed in relation to one other.

double bond is rigid, this molecule is not readily interconvertible with the compound in which the Cl atoms are on opposite sides of the pi bond.

Two groups on the *same side of the pi bond* are said to be **cis** (Latin, "on the side"). Groups on the *opposite sides* are said to be **trans** (Latin, "across"). Note how the *cis* or *trans* designation is incorporated into the name.

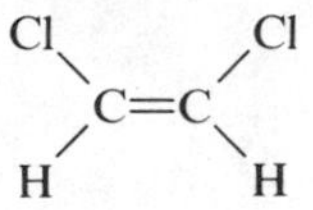

cis-1,2-dichloroethene
bp 60°

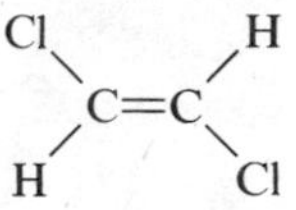

trans-1,2-dichloroethene
bp 48°

The *cis*- and *trans*-1,2-dichloroethenes have different physical properties (such as boiling points); they are different compounds. However, these two compounds are not structural isomers because the order of attachment of the atoms and the location of the double bond are the same in each compound. This pair of isomers falls into the general category of **stereoisomers**: different compounds that have the same structure, but differ in the *arrangement of the atoms in space*. This pair of isomers falls into a more specific category of **geometric isomers** (also called *cis*, *trans*-isomers): stereoisomers that differ by groups being on the same side or on opposite sides of a site of rigidity in a molecule.

The requirement for geometric isomerism in alkenes is that each carbon atom involved in the pi bond have two different groups attached to it, such as H and Cl, or CH_3 and Cl. If one of the carbons of the double bond has two identical groups, such as two H atoms or two CH_3 groups, then geometric isomerism is not possible. (We urge you to make molecular models and verify for yourself this requirement of geometric isomerism.)

Geometric isomers:

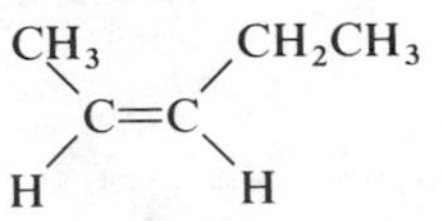

cis-2-pentene

and

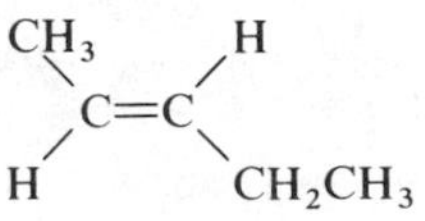

trans-2-pentene

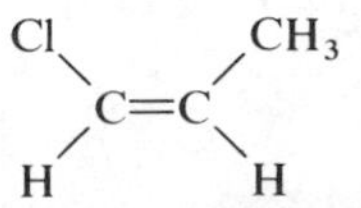

cis-1-chloro-1-propene

and

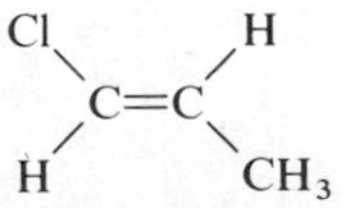

trans-1-chloro-1-propene

Not geometric isomers:

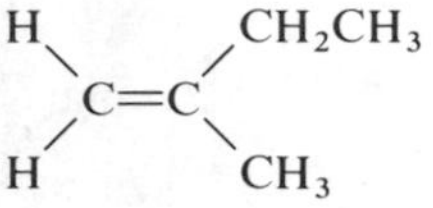

$$H\!\!\diagdown \atop H \diagup C\!\!=\!\!C\diagup^{CH_2CH_3} _{\diagdown CH_3} \quad \text{is the same as} \quad H\!\!\diagdown \atop H \diagup C\!\!=\!\!C\diagup^{CH_3} _{\diagdown CH_2CH_3}$$

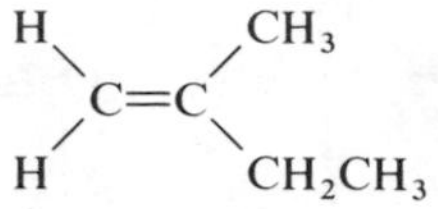

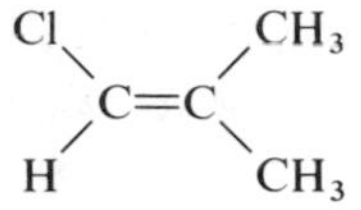

$$Cl\!\!\diagdown \atop H \diagup C\!\!=\!\!C\diagup^{CH_3} _{\diagdown CH_3} \quad \text{is the same as} \quad H\!\!\diagdown \atop Cl \diagup C\!\!=\!\!C\diagup^{CH_3} _{\diagdown CH_3}$$

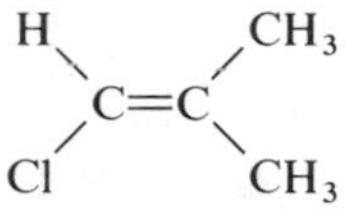

Sample Problem

Label each of the following pairs of structures as *structural isomers* of each other, as *geometric isomers* of each other, or as the *same compound*:

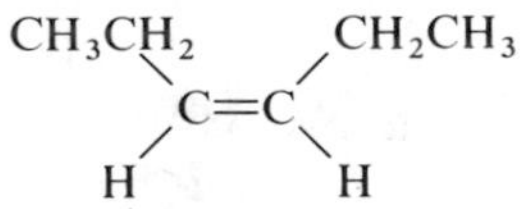

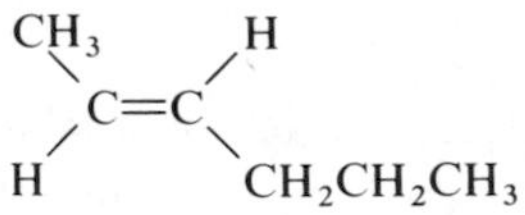

(a) 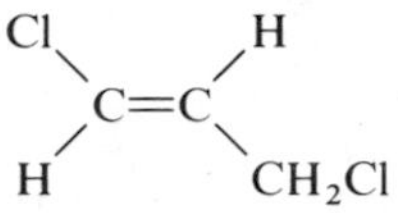 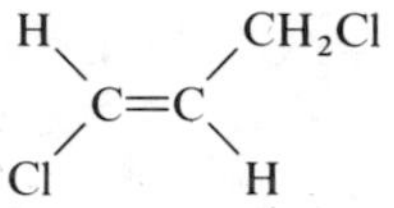 $Cl\!\!\diagdown \atop H \diagup C\!\!=\!\!C\diagup^{H} _{\diagdown CH_2Cl} \qquad H\!\!\diagdown \atop Cl \diagup C\!\!=\!\!C\diagup^{CH_2Cl} _{\diagdown H}$

(b) $CH_3CH_2\!\!\diagdown \atop H \diagup C\!\!=\!\!C\diagup^{CH_2CH_3} _{\diagdown H} \qquad CH_3\!\!\diagdown \atop H \diagup C\!\!=\!\!C\diagup^{H} _{\diagdown CH_2CH_2CH_3}$

(c) $H\!\!\diagdown \atop CH_2=CH \diagup C\!\!=\!\!C\diagup^{H} _{\diagdown CH_3} \qquad CH_2=CH\!\!\diagdown \atop H \diagup C\!\!=\!\!C\diagup^{H} _{\diagdown CH_3}$

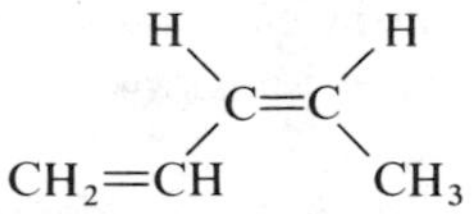

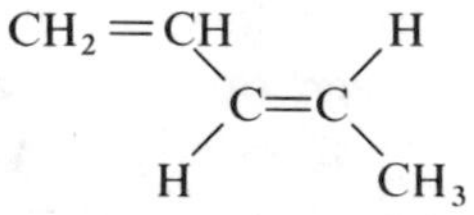

Solution:

(a) *same compound* (H's *trans* to each other in each);
(b) *structural isomers* (position of double bond is different; each structural isomer has a geometric isomer);
(c) *geometric isomers* (the first is *cis*; the second is *trans*).

Sample Problem

Why does the dry-cleaning solvent trichloroethene ($Cl_2C\!=\!CHCl$) *not* have geometric isomers?

Solution: Reversing any two groups in the structure does not give a different isomer. For geometric isomers to exist, there must be two different groups attached to each carbon of the double bond.

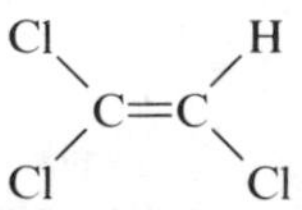

$$Cl\!\!\diagdown \atop Cl \diagup C\!\!=\!\!C\diagup^{H} _{\diagdown Cl} \quad \text{is the same as} \quad Cl\!\!\diagdown \atop Cl \diagup C\!\!=\!\!C\diagup^{Cl} _{\diagdown H}$$

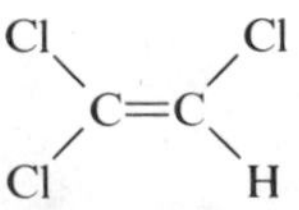

Sample Problem

Is geometric isomerism around a triple bond possible?

Solution: No. The groups attached to an *sp* carbon lie in a line. There is no "same side" or "opposite side."

A.   (E) and (Z) System of Nomenclature

When there are three or four different groups attached to the carbon atoms of a double bond, a pair of geometric isomers exists, but it is sometimes difficult to assign *cis* or *trans* designations to the isomers.

$$Br \diagdown \qquad \diagup F$$
$$C{=}C$$
$$I \diagup \qquad \diagdown Cl$$

cis or *trans*?

In our example, we can say that Br and Cl are *trans* to each other, or that I and Cl are *cis* to each other. However, we cannot name the structure in its entirety as being either the *cis* or the *trans* isomer. Because of the ambiguity in cases of this type, a more general system of isomer assignment has been devised, called the **(E) and (Z) system**. In practice, geometric isomers are named by the *cis* and *trans* system if possible; the *(E)* and *(Z)* system is generally used only for those compounds that cannot be designated *cis* or *trans*.

The *(E)* and *(Z)* system is based on an assignment of priorities (not to be confused with nomenclature priorities) to the atoms or groups attached to each carbon of the double bond. If the higher-priority atoms or groups are on *opposite sides* of the pi bond, the isomer is *(E)*. If the higher-priority groups are on the *same side*, the isomer is *(Z)*. (The letter *E* is from the German *entgegen*, "across"; the letter *Z* is from the German *zusammen*, "together.")

If the two atoms on each double-bond carbon are different, priority is based on the atomic numbers of the single atoms directly attached to the double-bond carbons. *Higher atomic number means a higher priority.* In our example, I has a larger atomic number than does Br; I is of higher priority. On the other carbon of the double bond, Cl is of higher priority than F.

	F	Cl	Br	I
atomic number:	9	17	35	53

increasing priority →

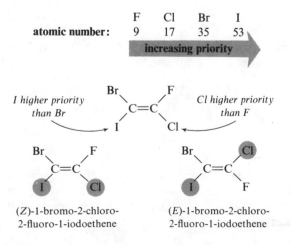

(Z)-1-bromo-2-chloro-   (E)-1-bromo-2-chloro-
2-fluoro-1-iodoethene   2-fluoro-1-iodoethene

Sample Problem

Is the following structure (*E*) or (*Z*)?

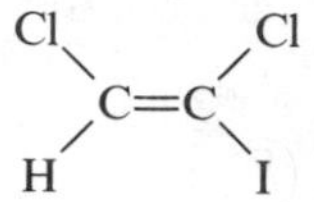

$$\underset{H}{\overset{Cl}{\diagdown}}C=C\underset{I}{\overset{Cl}{\diagup}}$$

Solution: On one carbon of the double bond, the Cl has a higher priority than H. On the other carbon, I is of higher priority than Cl. The higher-priority atoms are on opposite sides; the isomer is (*E*). Its name is (*E*)-1,2-dichloro-1-iodoethene.

Sample Problem

Name the following compound by the (*E*) and (*Z*) system:

$$\underset{CH_3}{\overset{H}{\diagdown}}C=C\underset{Cl}{\overset{CH_2CH_2CH_3}{\diagup}}$$

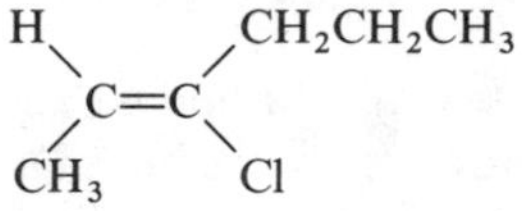

Solution: The left-hand carbon of the double bond has an H and a C attached to it; the C has the higher priority. The right-hand carbon has a Cl and a C attached to it; the Cl has a higher priority. (Look at the *single atoms* directly attached to the double-bond carbon: C, and not the entire —CH₂CH₂CH₃ group.) The higher-priority atoms are on the same side. The compound is named (*Z*)-3-chloro-2-hexene.

STUDY PROBLEM

4.1 Name the following compound by the (*E*) and (*Z*) system:

$$\underset{H}{\overset{F}{\diagdown}}C=C\underset{Cl}{\overset{CH_2CH_3}{\diagup}}$$

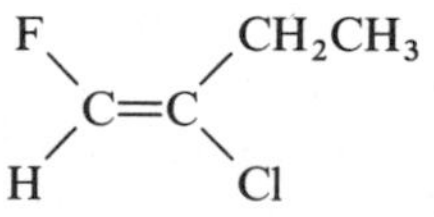

B. Sequence Rules

Determination of priorities by atomic number alone cannot handle all cases. For example, how would we name the following compound by the (*E*) and (*Z*) system?

$$\underset{H}{\overset{CH_3}{\diagdown}}C=C\underset{CH_3}{\overset{CH_2CH_3}{\diagup}}$$

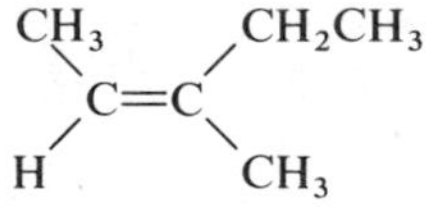

To handle such a case, and others like it, a set of *sequence rules* to determine order of priority has been developed. These priority rules form the basis of the **Cahn–Ingold–Prelog nomenclature system,** named in honor of the chemists who developed the system.

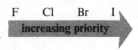

(1) If the atoms in question are different, the sequence order is by atomic number, with the atom of highest atomic number receiving the highest priority.

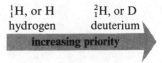

(2) If two isotopes of the same element are present, the isotope of *higher mass* receives the higher priority.

$^1_1$H, or H $\quad$ $^2_1$H, or D
hydrogen $\qquad$ deuterium

increasing priority

(3) If two atoms are identical, the atomic numbers of the *next atoms* are used for priority assignment. If these atoms also have identical atoms attached to them, priority is determined at the first point of difference along the chain. The atom that has attached to it an atom of higher priority has the higher priority. (Do not use the sums of the atomic numbers, but look for the single atom of highest priority.)

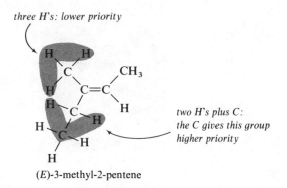

(E)-3-methyl-2-pentene

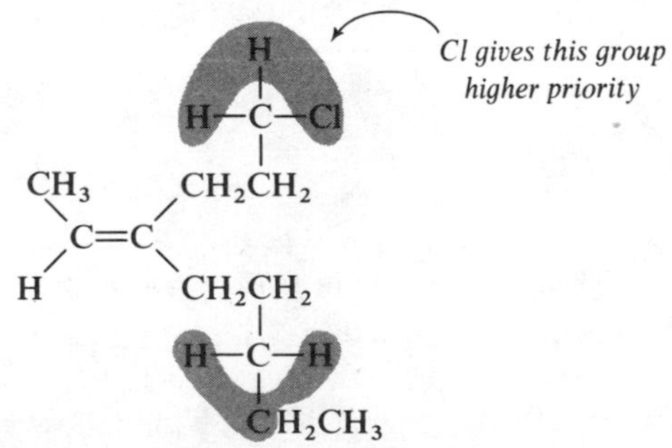

(Z)-6-chloro-3-pentyl-2-hexene

(4)   Atoms attached by double or triple bonds are given single-bond *equivalencies* so that they may be treated like single-bonded groups in determining priority. Each doubly bonded atom is duplicated (or triplicated for triple bonds), a process better seen in examples.

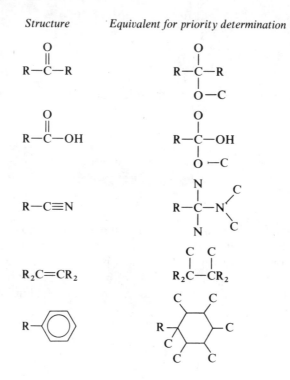

| | *Structure* | *Equivalent for priority determination* |

By this rule, we obtain the following priority sequence:

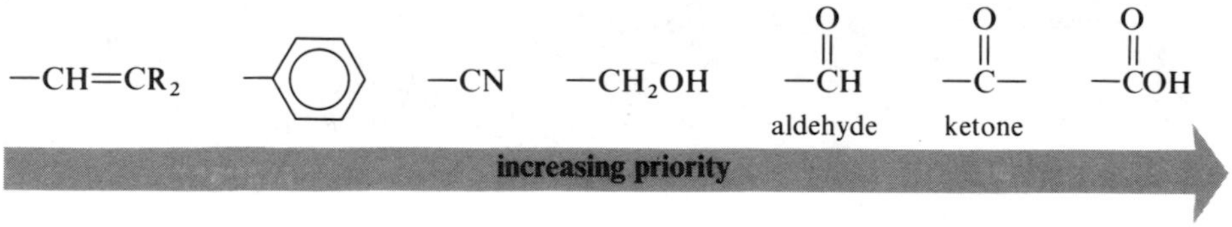

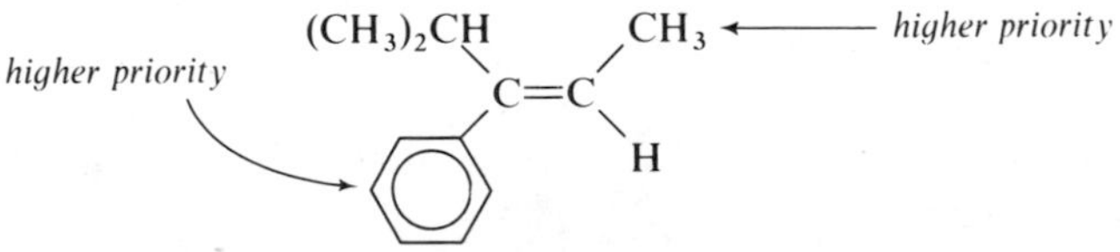

$-CH{=}CR_2$ ⬡ $-CN$ $-CH_2OH$ $-\overset{\overset{\displaystyle O}{\|}}{C}H$ aldehyde $-\overset{\overset{\displaystyle O}{\|}}{C}-$ ketone $-\overset{\overset{\displaystyle O}{\|}}{C}OH$

increasing priority →

(E)-4-methyl-3-phenyl-2-pentene

Sample Problem

List the following atoms or groups in order of increasing priority (lowest priority first):

$-NH_2$, $-H$, $-CH_3$, $-Cl$.

Solution: Increasing atomic number of the attached atom (N, H, C, Cl) gives increasing priority: H, CH_3, NH_2, Cl

Sample Problem

List the order of priority of the following groups (lowest to highest):

$$-CO_2H \quad -CO_2CH_3 \quad -CH_2OH \quad -OH \quad -H$$

Solution: Following the sequence rules: $-H, -CH_2OH, -CO_2H, -CO_2CH_3, -OH$

Sample Problem

Which group is of higher priority, the *n*-butyl group or the isobutyl group?

Solution: The first carbon is the same in each (two H's and one C attached).

$$-CH_2CH_2CH_2CH_3 \qquad -CH_2CH(CH_3)_2$$

Therefore, we proceed to the second carbon and we find that the isobutyl group is of higher priority.

The *n*-butyl group has one C and two H's at the first point of difference.

The isobutyl group has two C's and one H at the first point of difference.

STUDY PROBLEM

4.2 Tell whether each of the following compounds is (*E*) or (*Z*):

(a)
$$\begin{array}{c} D \\ \diagdown \\ H \end{array} C = C \begin{array}{c} H \\ \diagup \\ D \end{array}$$

(b)
$$\begin{array}{c} CH_3 \\ \diagdown \\ H \end{array} C = C \begin{array}{c} CH_2CH_3 \\ \diagup \\ CH_3 \end{array}$$

(c)
$$\begin{array}{c} Cl \\ \diagdown \\ H \end{array} C = C \begin{array}{c} CH_2CH_3 \\ \diagup \\ CH(CH_3)_2 \end{array}$$

(d)
$$\begin{array}{c} O \\ \parallel \\ CH_3C \\ \diagdown \\ ClCH_2 \end{array} C = C \begin{array}{c} O \\ \parallel \\ CCH_3 \\ \diagup \\ Cl \end{array}$$

Section 4.2

Geometric Isomerism in Cyclic Compounds

We have seen how restricted rotation around a double bond can lead to geometric isomerism. Let us now consider restricted rotation in cyclic compounds.

Atoms joined in a ring are not free to rotate around the sigma bonds of the ring. Rotation around the ring sigma bonds would require that attached atoms or groups pass through the center of the ring. Van der Waals repulsions prevent this from happening unless the ring contains ten or more carbon atoms. The most common rings in organic compounds are five- and six-membered rings; therefore, we will concentrate our discussion on rings of six and fewer carbon atoms.

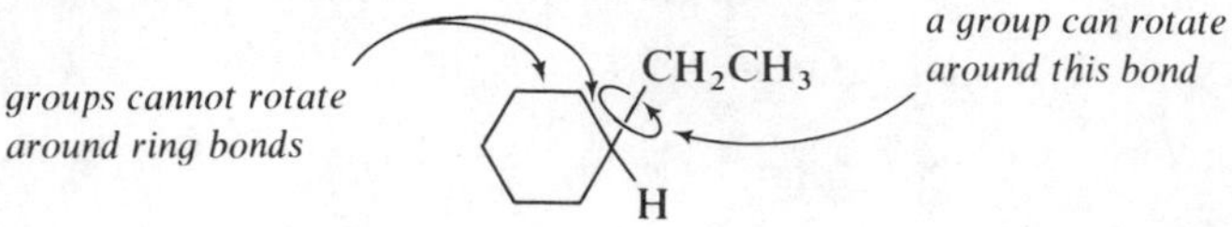

For the moment, we will assume that the carbon atoms of a cyclic structure such as cyclohexane form a plane. (While this is not strictly correct, as we will see later in this chapter, it is often convenient to assume that they do lie in a plane.) For the present discussion, we will view the plane of the ring as being almost horizontal. The edge of the ring projected toward us is shaded more heavily.

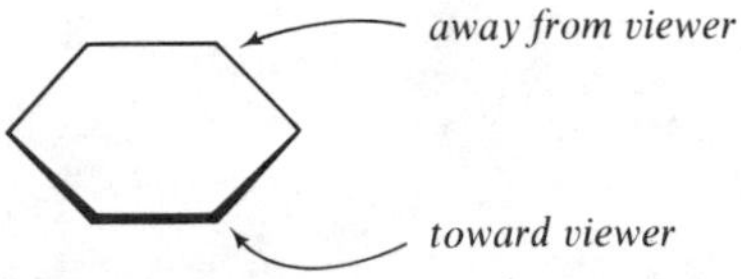

Each carbon atom in the cyclohexane ring is joined to its neighboring ring carbon atoms and also to two other atoms or groups. The bonds to these two other groups are represented by vertical lines. A group attached to the top of a vertical line is said to be *above the plane of the ring*, and the group attached to the bottom of a vertical line is said to be *below the plane of the ring*.

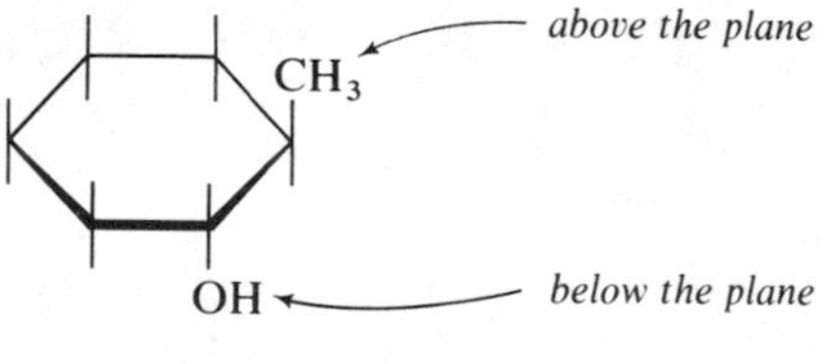

In this symbolism, hydrogen atoms attached to the ring and their bonds are not always shown.

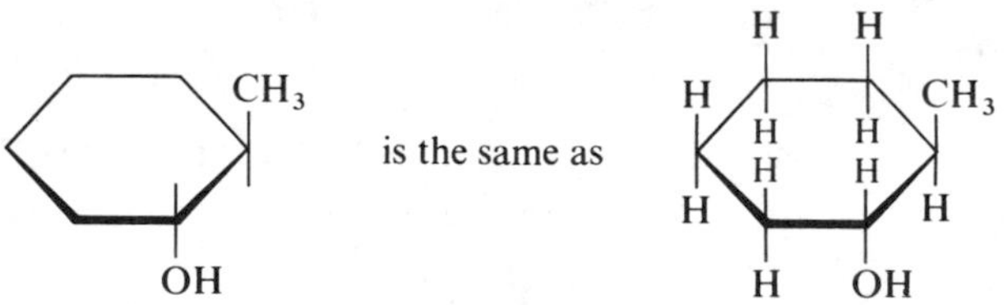

Another way of showing how groups are attached to the ring is by using a broken wedge to indicate a group below the plane of the ring, and a solid line bond to represent a group above the plane.

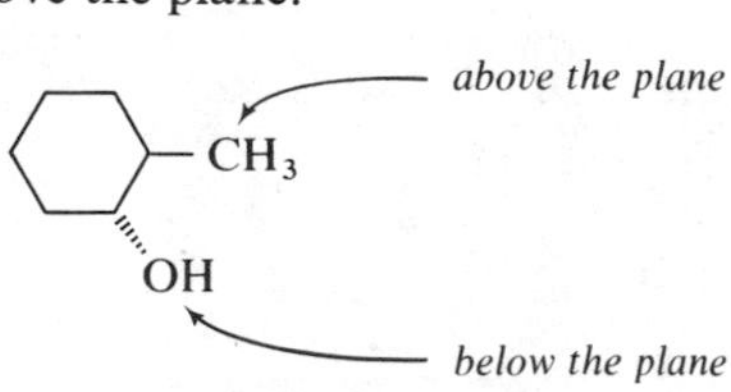

Descriptions of substituents as being "above the plane" or "below the plane" are correct for only a particular representation of a structure. A molecule can be flipped over in space and the descriptions reversed.

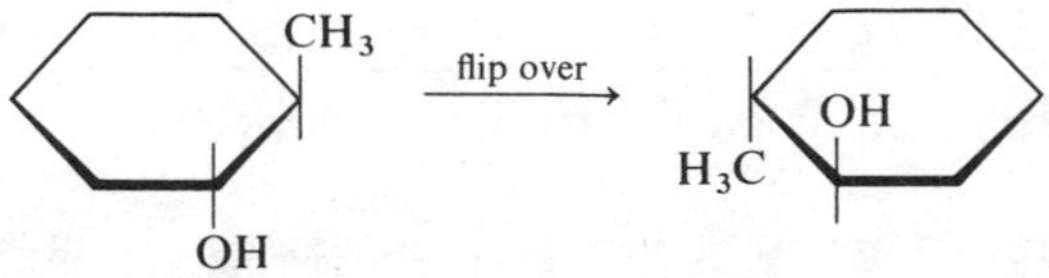

The important point is that, in all of the preceding formulas, the methyl group and the hydroxyl group are on *opposite sides* of the plane of the ring. When the two groups are on opposite sides of the ring, they are *trans*; when they are on the same side, they are *cis*. These designations are directly analogous to *cis* and *trans* in alkenes. The *cis*- and *trans*-compounds are geometric isomers of each other, just as *cis*- and *trans*-alkenes are.

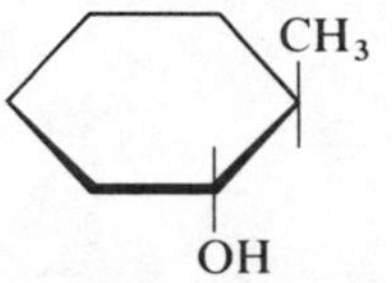

trans-2-methyl-1-cyclohexanol

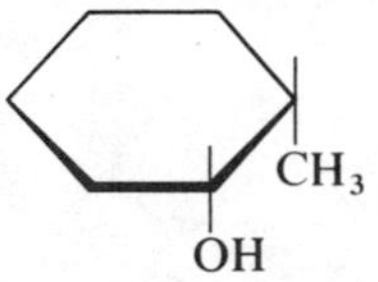

cis-2-methyl-1-cyclohexanol

The following compounds are other examples of geometric isomers of cyclic compounds:

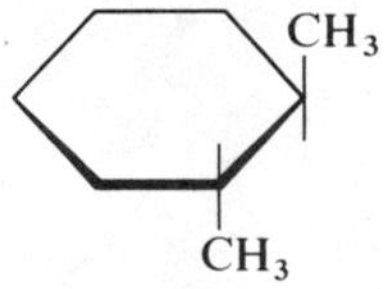

trans

and

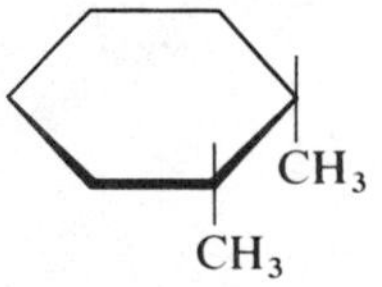

cis

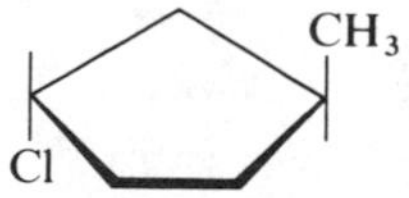

trans

and

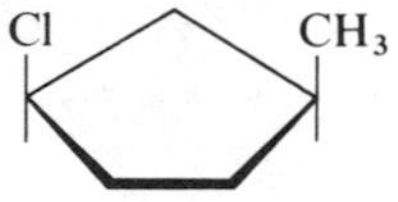

cis

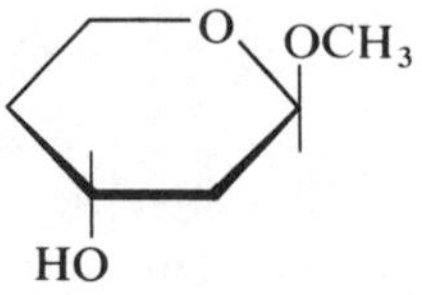

trans

and

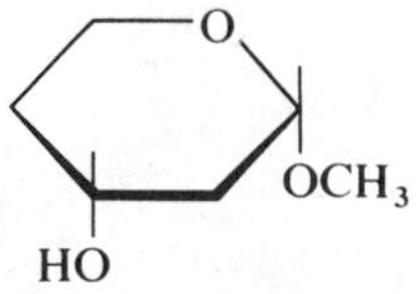

cis

Sample Problem

Tell whether each of the following compounds is *cis*, *trans*, or neither:

(a) 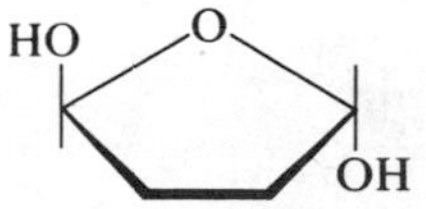

(b) 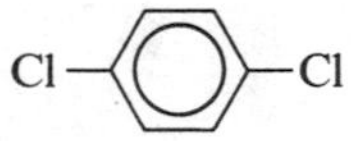

(c) 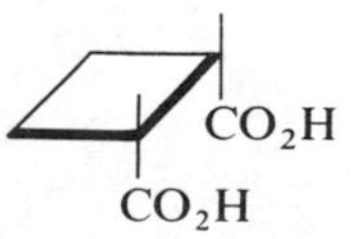

Solution: (a) *trans*; (b) neither (because the benzene ring and its substituents are in the same plane, the substituents cannot be up or down); (c) *cis*.

STUDY PROBLEM

4.3 Give formulas for the geometric isomers of 2-isopropyl-5-methyl-1-cyclohexanol (commonly called *menthol*), which is used in cigarettes and throat lozenges.

Section 4.3

Conformations of Open-Chain Compounds

In open-chain compounds, groups attached by sigma bonds can rotate around these bonds. Therefore, the atoms in an open-chain molecule can assume a variety of positions in space relative to each other. Ethane is a small molecule, but even ethane can assume different arrangements in space, called **conformations**.

To represent conformations, we will use two types of formula: the **ball-and-stick formula** and the **Newman projection**. (We suggest that you use models. See Figure 4.2 for comparisons of these formulas with models.)

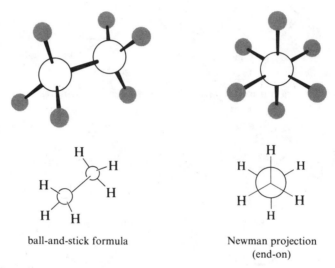

ball-and-stick formula   Newman projection
                                  (end-on)

Figure 4.2. Comparisons of molecular models of ethane with a ball-and-stick formula and a Newman projection.

A ball-and-stick formula is a three-dimensional representation of the molecular model of a compound (see Figure 4.2). The Newman projection is an end-on view of only *two carbon atoms* in the molecule. The bond joining these two carbons is hidden. The three bonds attached to the front carbon appear to go to the center of the projection, and the three bonds of the rear carbon are only partially shown.

bonds from the   *bonds from the*   *Newman projection*
front carbon   *rear carbon*   *for CH_3CH_3*

Newman projections may be drawn for molecules with more than two carbon atoms. Because only two carbon atoms at a time may be shown in the projection, more than one Newman projection may be drawn for a molecule. For example, we can show two Newman projections for 3-chloro-1-propanol.

Looking at carbons 1 and 2:

OH
| ①CH₂
| ②CH₂
| ③CH₂Cl
3-chloro-1-propanol

ball-and-stick

Newman

Looking at carbons 2 and 3:

OH
| ①CH₂
| ②CH₂
| ③CH₂Cl

ball-and-stick

Newman

Because of rotation around its sigma bonds, a molecule can assume any number of conformations. However, certain conformations are more stable than others. These preferred conformations are called **conformers**. Conformers are not isomers because they are interconvertible—they are only different spatial orientations of the same molecule.

In our formulas of ethane and 3-chloro-1-propanol, we have shown the **staggered conformers**, in which the hydrogen atoms or the attached groups are as far apart from one another as possible. Because the C—C bond can undergo rotation, the hydrogen atoms might also be **eclipsed**, or as close as possible, one behind the other in the Newman projection. We will show them not quite eclipsed so that you can see them. (Figure 4.3 also shows molecular models in staggered and eclipsed conformations.)

staggered   *eclipsed*

The rotation around sigma bonds is often called **free rotation**, but it is not entirely free. The eclipsed conformation of ethane is about 3 kcal/mole less stable

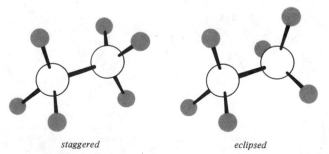

staggered   *eclipsed*

Figure 4.3. Molecular models showing the staggered and eclipsed conformations of ethane.

(of higher energy) than the staggered conformer because of repulsions between the hydrogen atoms. To undergo rotation from a staggered to an eclipsed conformation, a mole of ethane molecules would require 3 kcal. Since this amount of energy is readily available to molecules at room temperature, the rotation can occur easily; this is why the different conformations are not isomers. However, even though the conformations of ethane are interconvertible at room temperature, at any given time we would expect a greater percentage of ethane molecules to be in the staggered conformation because of its lower energy. A diagram showing the ebb and flow in potential energy with rotation around the C—C bond in ethane is presented in Figure 4.4.

Butane ($CH_3CH_2CH_2CH_3$), like ethane, can exist in eclipsed and staggered conformations. In butane, there are two relatively large methyl groups attached to the center two carbons. Viewing butane from the center two carbons, the presence of these methyl groups gives rise to two types of staggered conformation that differ in the positions of the methyl groups in relation to each other. The staggered conformation in which the methyl groups are at the maximum distance

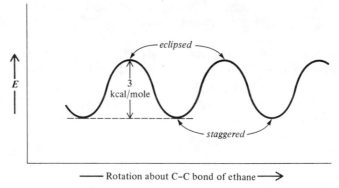

Figure 4.4.   Energy changes involved in rotation around the carbon–carbon sigma bond of ethane.

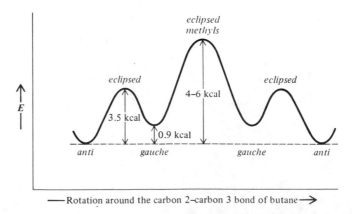

Figure 4.5.   Energy relations (in kcal/mole) of the different conformations of butane.

apart is called the ***anti*** conformation (Greek *anti*, "against"). The staggered conformations in which the methyl groups are closer are called ***gauche*** conformations (French *gauche*, "left" or "crooked"). Newman projections for one-half a complete rotation follow.

Partial rotation around the carbon 2–carbon 3 bond of butane (rear carbon rotating):

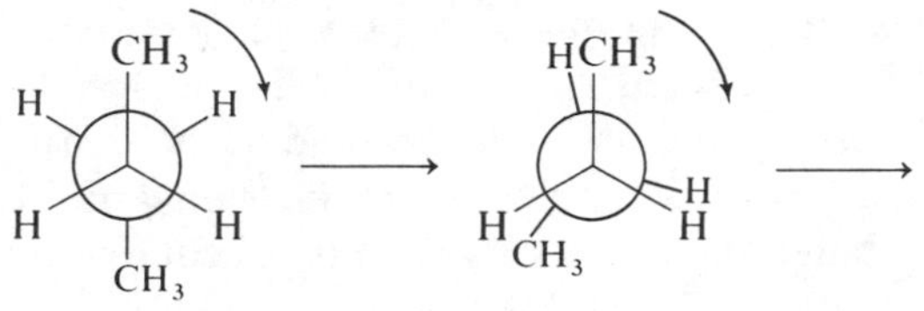

anti
(*lowest energy*)   eclipsed

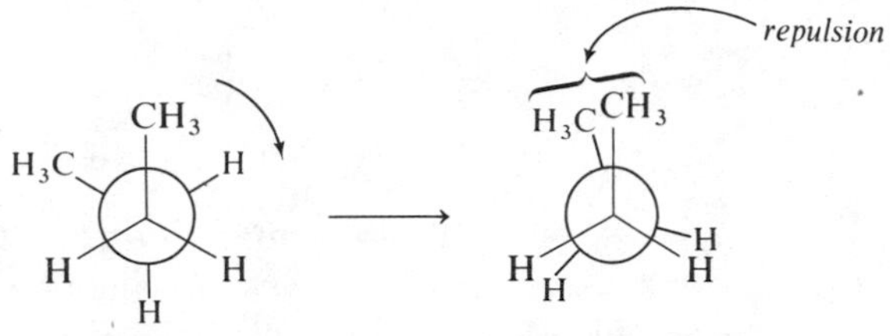

gauche   eclipsed methyls
(*highest energy*)

The larger the groups attached to two carbon atoms, the greater is the energy difference between the molecule's conformations. It takes more energy to push two bulky groups together than two small groups. While it takes only 3 kcal/mole for ethane to rotate from staggered to eclipsed, it takes 4–6 kcal/mole for butane to rotate from *anti* to the conformation in which the methyls are eclipsed. The energy relationships of the complete rotation around the carbon 2–carbon 3 bond of butane are shown in Figure 4.5.

Sample Problem

Draw Newman projections for the *anti* and *gauche* conformers of 1,2-dichloroethane.

Solution:

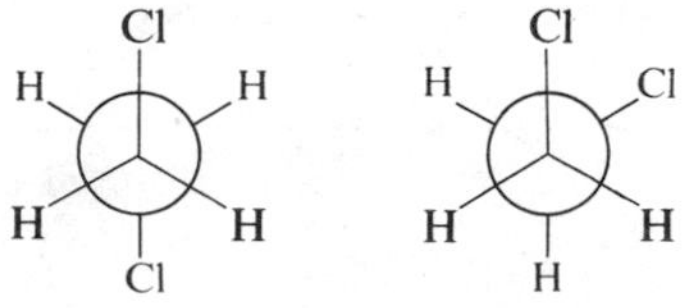

anti   gauche

STUDY PROBLEM

4.4 Draw Newman projections for the *anti* and *gauche* conformations of (a) 1-bromo-2-chloroethane, and (b) 3-hydroxypropanoic acid.

Section 4.4

Shapes of Cyclic Compounds

A. Ring Strain

In 1885, Adolf von Baeyer, a German chemist, theorized that cyclic compounds form planar rings. Baeyer further theorized that all cyclic compounds except for cyclopentane would be "strained" because their bond angles are not close to the tetrahedral angle of 109.5°. He proposed that, because of the abnormally small bond angles of the ring, cyclopropane and cyclobutane would be more reactive than an open-chain alkane. According to Baeyer, cyclopentane would be the most stable ring system (because its bond angles are closest to tetrahedral), and then reactivity would increase again starting with cyclohexane.

Bond angles according to Baeyer:

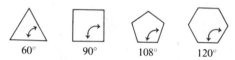

Baeyer's theory was not entirely correct. Cyclohexane and larger-sized rings are not more reactive than cyclopentane. We now know that cyclohexane is not a flat ring with bond angles of 120°, but rather a puckered ring with bond angles close to 109°, the normal sp^3 bond angles.

bond angles ~109°

However, there is indeed what we call **ring strain** in the smaller ring systems. Cyclopropane is the most reactive of the cycloalkanes. Its heat of combustion is higher per CH_2 group than that of other alkanes (Table 4.1; also see Section 3.4D).

Table 4.1.   Strain Energies from Heat of Combustion Data

	$-\Delta H$ per $CH_2{}^a$	Strain energy per $CH_2{}^b$	Strain energy, total[c]
cyclopropane	167 kcal/mole	10 kcal/mole	30 kcal/mole
cyclobutane	164	7	28
cyclopentane	159	2	10
cyclohexane	157	0	0

[a] $-\Delta H$/mole divided by number of CH_2 groups.

[b] The difference between (1) the value of $-\Delta H/CH_2$ for that compound, and (2) the value for cyclohexane, the assumption being that cyclohexane is not strained.

[c] Strain energy/CH_2 × number of CH_2 groups.

When treated with hydrogen gas, cyclopentane does not react, but cyclopropane undergoes ring opening.

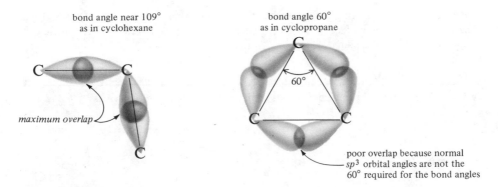

Today we would say that the sp^3 orbitals of the carbon atoms in cyclopropane cannot undergo complete overlap with each other because the bond angles of cyclopropane are geometrically required to be 60° (see Figure 4.6). The ring sigma bonds of cyclopropane are of higher energy than sp^3 sigma bonds that have the normal tetrahedral angle. The cyclopropane bonds are more easily broken than most other C—C sigma bonds and, in comparable reactions, more energy is released.

Figure 4.6. Maximum overlap cannot be achieved between the ring carbon atoms in cyclopropane.

Cyclobutane is less reactive than cyclopropane but more reactive than cyclopentane. Following along reasonably with Baeyer's theory, the cyclopentane ring is stable and is far less reactive than the three- and four-membered rings.

With cyclohexane and larger rings, Baeyer's predictions fail. Cyclohexane and rings larger than cyclohexane are found in puckered conformations rather than as flat rings, and are not particularly reactive. Larger rings are not commonly found in naturally occurring compounds, as are five- and six-membered rings. Baeyer felt the rarity was due to ring strain. We now realize that the rarity of larger rings is not due primarily to unusually high bond energies. Instead, the scarcity of these compounds arises from the decreasing probability that the ends of longer molecules will find each other to undergo reaction and form a ring. (The problem is one of *entropy*, or randomness, and not one of *enthalpy*.)

Sample Problem

Considering ring sizes, which of the following compounds would you expect to suffer from substantial amounts of ring strain?

(a) 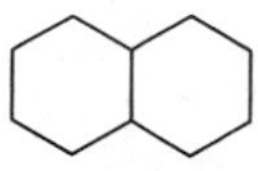 decalin

(b) 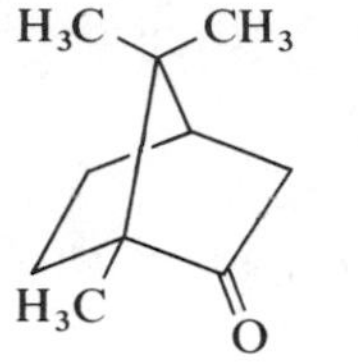 camphor

(c) 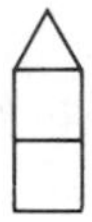 apartmenthousane

(d)  cubane

Solution:

(a) has only six-membered rings: little or no strain.
(b) has two five-membered rings (or a six- and a five-, depending on your point of view): little strain.
(c) has two four- and one three-membered ring: strained.
(d) has four-membered rings: strained.

Sample Problem

Would you expect the benzene ring to be flat or puckered?

Solution: The benzene ring is flat because the carbon atoms are sp^2 (not sp^3) hybridized. The normal positioning of sp^2 bonds is planar and with angles of 120° between them, corresponding to a regular planar hexagon.

STUDY PROBLEM

4.5 Which of the following compounds contains one or more strained rings?

(a) 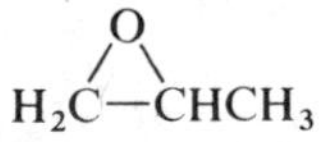 $H_2C-CHCH_3$
propylene oxide

(b) 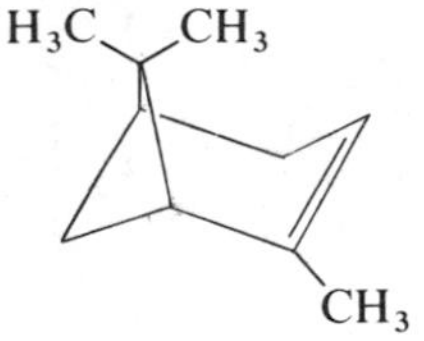 α-pinene
in turpentine

(c) 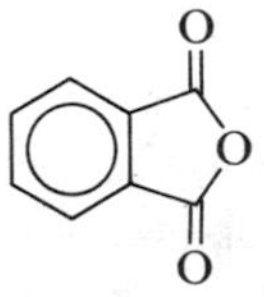 phthalic anhydride

(d) 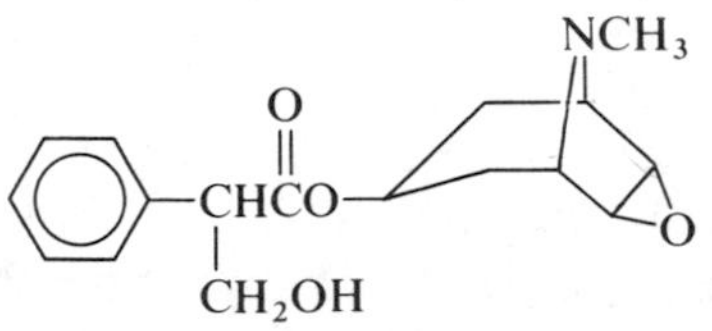 scopolamine
a preoperative anesthetic

B. *Ring Puckering and Hydrogen–Hydrogen Repulsions*

If the cyclohexane ring were flat, all the hydrogen atoms on the ring carbons would be eclipsed. In the puckered conformer that we have shown, however, all the hydrogens are staggered. The energy of this puckered conformer of cyclohexane is lower than the energy of flat cyclohexane, both because of more-favorable sp^3 bond angles and also because of fewer hydrogen–hydrogen repulsions.

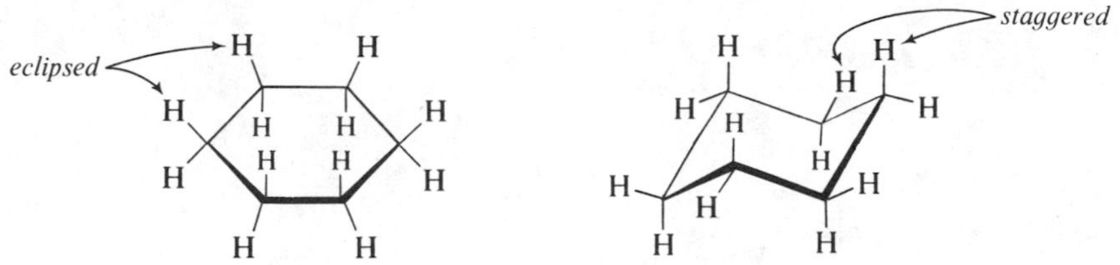

flat   *puckered*

What of the other cyclic compounds? Cyclopentane would have near-optimal bond angles (108°) if it were flat, but cyclopentane also is slightly puckered so that the hydrogen atoms attached to the ring carbons are staggered. Cyclobutane (flat bond angles of 90°) also is puckered, even though the puckering causes more-strained bond angles. Cyclopropane must be planar; geometrically, three points (or three carbon atoms) define a plane. The hydrogen atoms in cyclopropane necessarily are eclipsed.

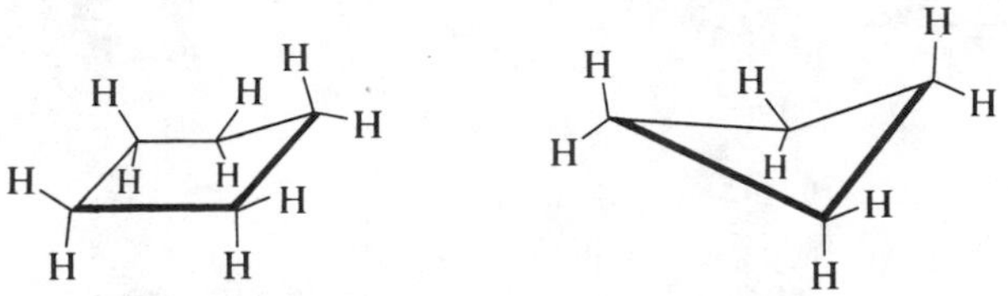

envelope form
of cyclopentane   *butterfly form*
of cyclobutane

Section 4.5

The Conformers of Cyclohexane

The cyclohexane ring, either alone or in fused-ring systems (ring systems that jointly share carbon atoms), is the most important of all the ring systems. In this section, we will study the conformations of cyclohexane and substituted cyclohexanes. In Chapter 19, we will discuss the conformations of fused-ring systems.

There are many shapes that a cyclohexane ring can assume, and one single cyclohexane molecule is in a continuous state of flexing into different shapes. (Molecular models are invaluable for showing the relationships between the various conformations.) We have so far shown the **chair form** of cyclohexane. Some other shapes the cyclohexane molecule can assume are as follows:

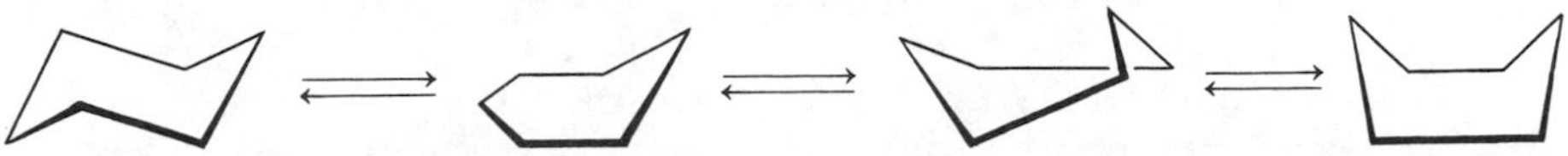

chair   *half-chair*   *twist-boat*   *boat*

None of these other conformations has the favorable, staggered-hydrogen structure of the chair form. The eclipsing of hydrogens, as in the boat form, adds

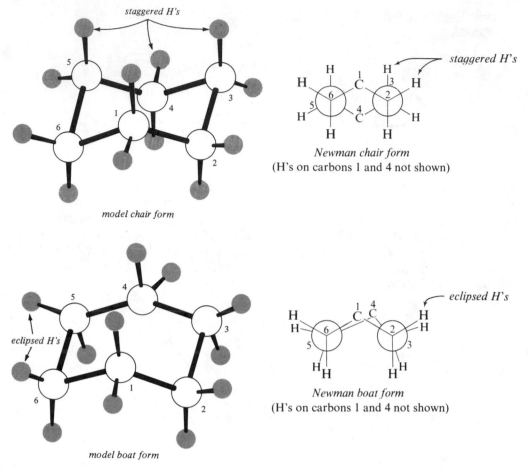

staggered H's

model chair form

Newman chair form
(H's on carbons 1 and 4 not shown)

eclipsed H's

model boat form

staggered H's

eclipsed H's

Newman boat form
(H's on carbons 1 and 4 not shown)

Figure 4.7. Molecular models and Newman projections of the chair and boat forms of cyclohexane.

to the energy of the molecule. Figure 4.7 shows models and Newman projections of the chair form and boat form; the staggered and eclipsed hydrogens are apparent in these representations.

The energy requirements for the interconversion of the different conformations of cyclohexane are shown in Figure 4.8. We can see that the chair form has the lowest energy, while the half-chair (which has an almost-planar structure) has the highest energy. At any given time, we would expect most cyclohexane molecules to be in the chair form. Indeed, it has been calculated that about 99.9% of cyclohexane molecules are in the chair form at any one time.

Equatorial and Axial Substituents.   The carbon atoms of the chair form of cyclohexane roughly form a plane. For purposes of discussion, an axis may be drawn perpendicular to this plane. These operations are shown in Figure 4.9.

Each ring carbon of cyclohexane is bonded to two hydrogen atoms. The bond to one of these hydrogens is in the rough plane of the ring; this hydrogen atom is

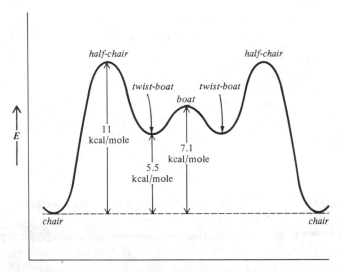

Figure 4.8.   Relative potential energies of the conformations of cyclohexane.

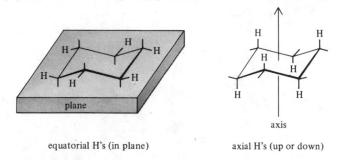

Figure 4.9.   The equatorial and axial hydrogens of cyclohexane.

called the **equatorial hydrogen**. The bond to the other hydrogen atom is parallel to the axis; this is the **axial hydrogen**. Each of the six carbon atoms of cyclohexane has one equatorial and one axial hydrogen atom. (Again, refer to Figure 4.9.) In the flipping and reflipping between the conformers, axial becomes equatorial, while equatorial becomes axial.

A methyl group is bulkier than a hydrogen atom. When the methyl group in methylcyclohexane is in the axial position, the methyl group and axial hydrogens on the ring repel each other. Interactions between axial groups are called **axial–axial interactions**. When the methyl group is in the equatorial position, the repulsions are minimized. Thus, the energy of the conformer with an equatorial methyl is lower. At room temperature, about 95% of methylcyclohexane molecules are in the conformation in which the methyl group is equatorial.

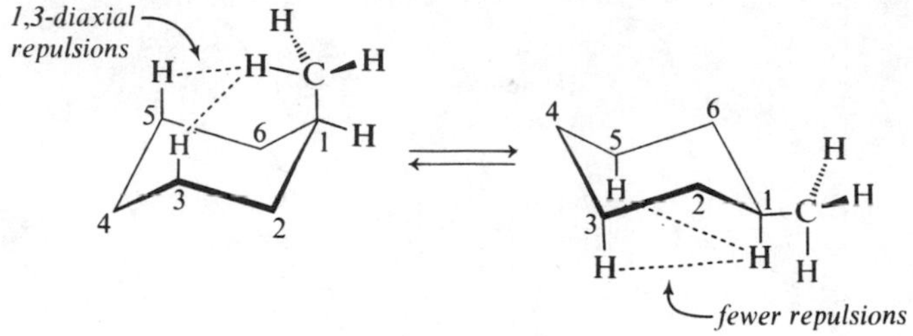

The bulkier the group, the greater is the energy difference between a pair of axial and equatorial conformers. In other words, a cyclohexane ring with a bulky substituent is more likely to have that group in the equatorial position. When the size of the substituent group reaches *t*-butyl, the difference in energies between the conformers becomes quite large. *t*-Butylcyclohexane is often said to be "frozen" in the conformation in which the *t*-butyl group is equatorial. The ring is not truly frozen, but the energy difference (5.6 kcal/mole) between the equatorial and the axial positions of the *t*-butyl group means that only 1 in 10,000 molecules has the *t*-butyl group in an axial position.

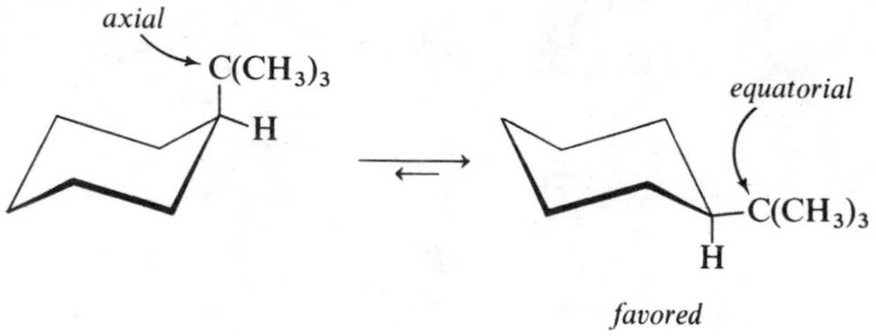

favored

B. *Disubstituted Cyclohexanes*

Two groups substituted on a cyclohexane ring may be either *cis* or *trans*. The *cis*- and *trans*-disubstituted rings are geometric isomers and are not interconvertible at room temperature; however, either isomer may assume a variety of conformations. For example, consider some chair forms of *cis*-1,2-dimethylcyclohexane.

Some different representations of cis-1,2-dimethylcyclohexane,

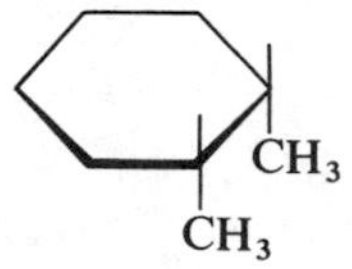

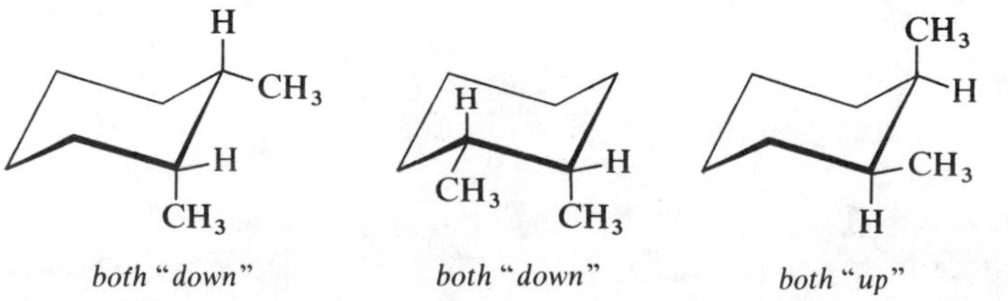

| both "down" | both "down" | both "up" |

Because this is the *cis*-isomer, the methyl groups must both be on the same side of the ring, regardless of the conformation. In each chair conformation that we can draw, one methyl is axial and the other is equatorial. For any *cis*-1,2-disubstituted cyclohexane, one substituent must be axial and the other substituent must be equatorial. (Refer back to Figure 4.9 or use molecular models and verify this statement for yourself.)

When *cis*-1,2-dimethylcyclohexane changes from one chair conformer to the other, the two methyl groups reverse their equatorial–axial status. The energies of the two conformers are equal because their structures and bonding are identical. Therefore, this compound exists primarily as a 50 : 50 mixture of these two chair-form conformers.

Conformers of cis-1,2-dimethylcyclohexane:

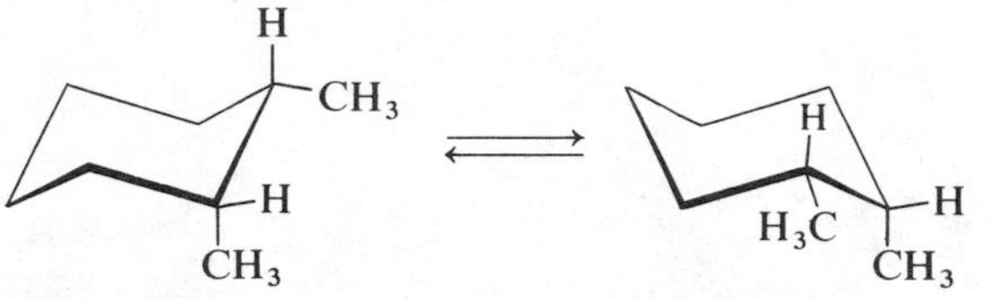

axial, equatorial (or *a,e*)   *equatorial, axial* (or *e, a*)

In *trans*-1,2-dimethylcyclohexane, the methyl groups are on *opposite* sides of the ring. In the chair form of the *trans*-isomer, one group must be attached to an "uppermost" bond, while the other is attached to a "lowermost" bond.

Some different representations of trans-1,2-dimethylcyclohexane,

up CH$_3$ *up*   H

down   *down*

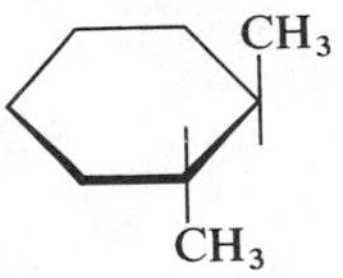

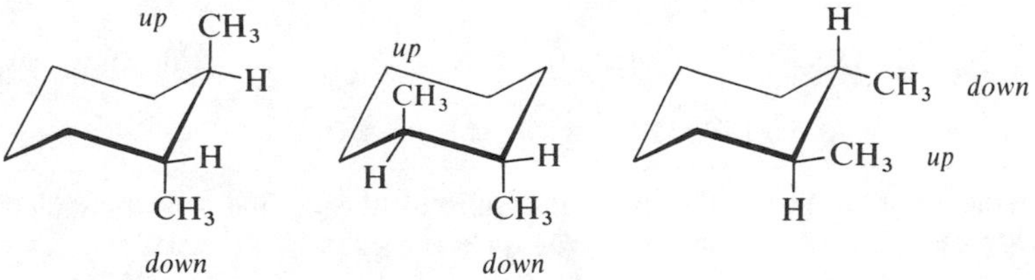

No matter how the two adjacent *trans* groups are shown, they are *both axial* (*a, a*) or they are *both equatorial* (*e, e*). There is no way for two groups to be *trans* and 1,2 on the chair form of cyclohexane without assuming either the *a,a* or the *e,e* conformation.

Conformers of trans-1,2-dimethylcyclohexane:

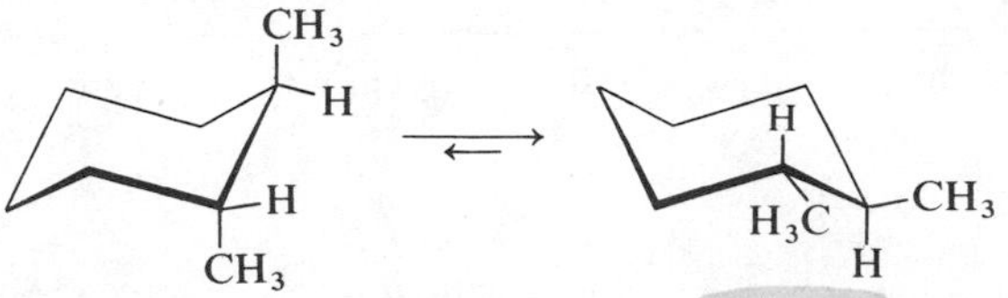

a,a   *e,e favored*

A single methyl group on a cyclohexane ring assumes the equatorial position preferentially. *Two* methyl groups on a cyclohexane ring also assume the equatorial positions preferentially, if possible. In *trans*-1,2-dimethylcyclohexane, the *e,e* conformer is the preferred conformer and is of lower energy than the *a,a* conformation. The *trans e,e* conformer is also of lower energy (by 1.87 kcal/mole) than either conformer of the *cis*-compound, which must be *a,e* or *e,a*.

In the case of a 1,2-disubstituted cyclohexane, the *trans*-isomer is more stable than the *cis*-isomer because both substituents can be equatorial. However, when the two substituents are 1,3 to each other on a cyclohexane ring, the *cis*-isomer is more stable than the *trans*-isomer. The reason is that both substituents in the *cis*-1,3-isomer can be equatorial. In the *trans*-1,3-isomer, one group must be axial.

cis-1,3-dimethylcyclohexane:

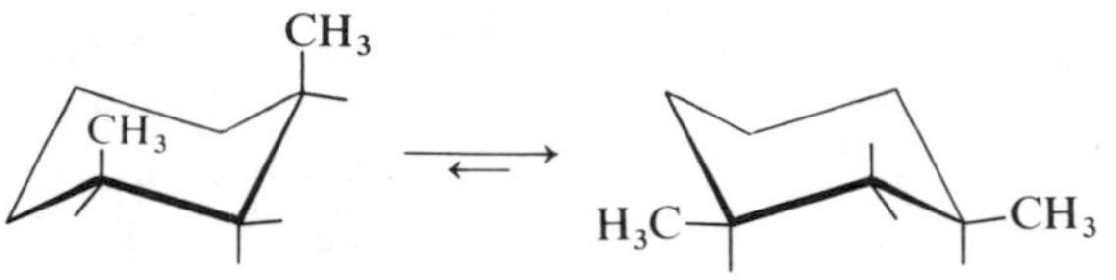

trans-1,3-dimethylcyclohexane:

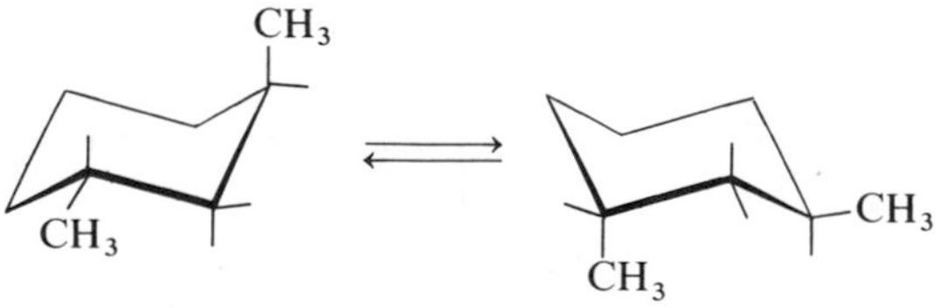

Sample Problem

What are the possible equatorial–axial relationships for the *cis*- and *trans*-1,4-dimethylcyclohexanes? In each case, which conformer is of lower energy?

Solution: cis-1,4:   *a,e*;   *e,a*
                    trans-1,4:   *a,a*;   *e,e*

The *cis*-conformers are of equal energy. The *e,e trans*-conformer is of lower energy than the *a,a trans*-conformer (and of lower energy than either *cis*-conformer).

STUDY PROBLEM

4.6   Label each of the following disubstituted rings as *cis* or *trans* and as *a,a*; *e,e*; or *a,e*:

(c) Cl—, —Cl

(d) —CH$_3$, CH$_3$

(e) Br—, H$_3$C—

(f) CH$_2$CH$_3$, OH

Section 4.6

Chirality of Molecules

A. *Symmetry*

We usually think of symmetry as a similarity of form on either side of a dividing line or plane; however, there are several types of symmetry. Three types that are used in various contexts in this book are:

(1) **symmetry around a point**, such as is found in a sphere or an *s* orbital;

(2) **symmetry around an axis, or line**, such as is found in a sigma bond, a nail, or an automobile tire;

(3) **symmetry in regards to a plane**, such as is found in a cup or a cube.

It is primarily the *plane of symmetry* that interests us here. To be considered symmetrical in relation to a plane, an object must be divisible by at least one hypothetical plane into *equal and mirror-reflective halves*. In Figure 4.10, note the plane of symmetry through the ball. The ball has an infinite number of planes of symmetry. The cube has nine planes of symmetry (do not forget diagonal planes). The cup has only one plane of symmetry.

Any object with at least one plane of symmetry can be *superimposed on its mirror image*. For example, hold a plain cup up to a mirror. With a bit of imagination, you can merge the cup into its mirror image point for point; the cup and its mirror image are superimposable (see Figure 4.11).

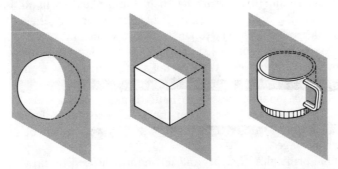

Figure 4.10. Planes of symmetry through various objects.

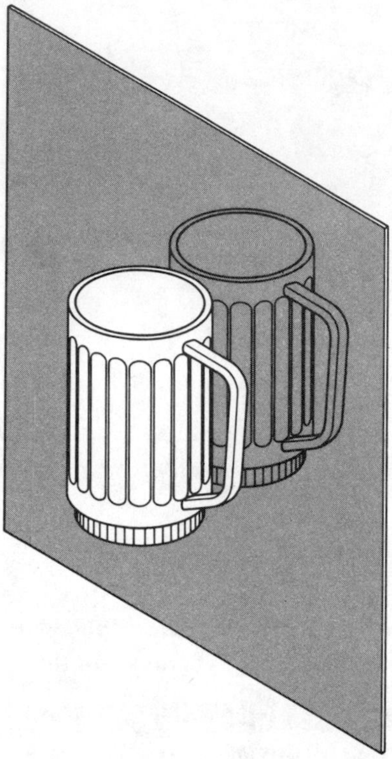

Figure 4.11. An object with a plane of symmetry is superimposable on its mirror image.

mirror

STUDY PROBLEMS

4.7   Which of the following objects is symmetrical with respect to a plane?   (a) a fork; (b) a kitchen chair;   (c) a sock;   (d) a glove

4.8   Which of the preceding objects could be superimposed on its mirror image?

B.   Chirality

Consider your right hand. There is no plane of symmetry that can be placed through your hand; your hand cannot be superimposed on its mirror image. If you hold your right hand up to a mirror, the image looks like a left hand. If you do not have a mirror handy, hold your hands with palms facing together—you can see that they are mirror images. Try to superimpose your hands (*both palms down*); you cannot do it (see Figure 4.12). This right- and left-handedness is also encountered in shoes and gloves. (Try wearing a left-handed glove on a right hand!)

Any object that *cannot be superimposed on its mirror image* is said to be **chiral** (Greek *cheir*, "handedness"). A hand, a glove, and a shoe—all are chiral objects, and their chirality arises from the lack of a plane of symmetry. Conversely, a cup and a cube are **achiral** (not chiral) objects; these can be superimposed on their mirror images.

The same principles of right- and left-handedness also apply to molecules. *A molecule that has a plane of symmetry is achiral and can be superimposed upon its*

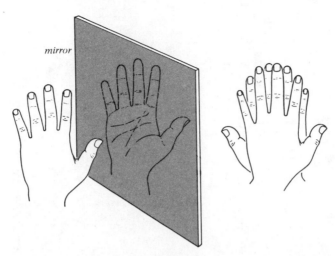

Figure 4.12. An object without a plane of symmetry is usually chiral and cannot be superimposed on its mirror image.

*mirror image. A molecule that does not have a plane of symmetry is usually chiral;
it cannot be superimposed upon its mirror image.* Figures 4.13 and 4.14 show an
achiral molecule and a chiral molecule, respectively.

An achiral molecule and its superimposable mirror image are the same
compound; they are not isomers. But a chiral molecule is not superimposable on
its mirror image; this molecule and its mirror image represent a pair of stereoisomers called **enantiomers**. A pair of enantiomers is simply a pair of molecules
that are *nonsuperimposable mirror images.*

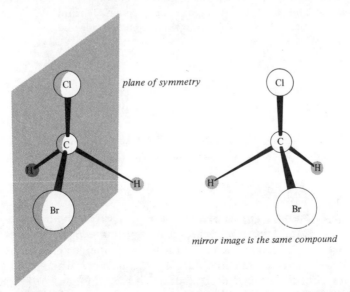

Figure 4.13. A molecule with a carbon atom that has two identical substituents (H, in this
case) has a plane of symmetry; it is achiral and can be superimposed upon its
mirror image. (Try it with models.)

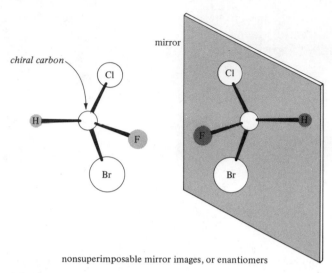

Figure 4.14. A molecule that does not have a plane of symmetry is usually chiral and not superimposable on its mirror image. (Try it with models.)

Sample Problem

The following molecule is not chiral. Why not?

Solution: Even though this molecule has no plane of symmetry, it is superimposable on its mirror image and is therefore achiral. It is thus an exception to the rule that no plane of symmetry leads to chirality. (Flip the structure top side to bottom side to see that it is superimposable on its mirror image.)

not a plane
of symmetry   *mirror image*

C.   Chiral Carbon Atoms

The most common structural feature that gives rise to chirality in molecules is that the molecule contains an sp^3 carbon atom with *four different groups* attached to it. If a molecule contains one carbon with four different groups attached, the molecule has no plane of symmetry. Such a molecule is chiral and exists as a pair of enantiomers. For this reason, a carbon atom with four different groups attached is a center of chirality in a molecule. Such a carbon is usually called a *chiral carbon atom* (although, technically, it is the molecule and not the carbon atom that is chiral).

In deciding whether groups attached to a carbon are identical or different, we look at each entire group attached to the carbon in question, not just the atoms bonded directly to that carbon.

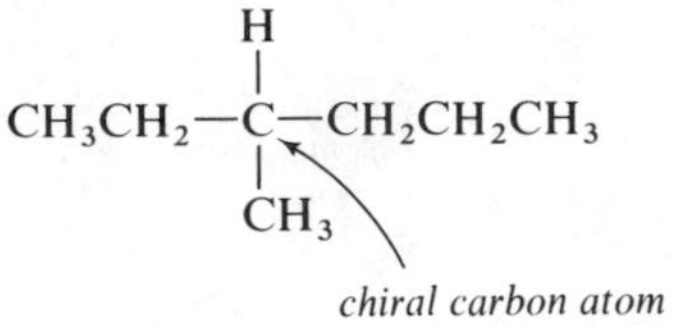

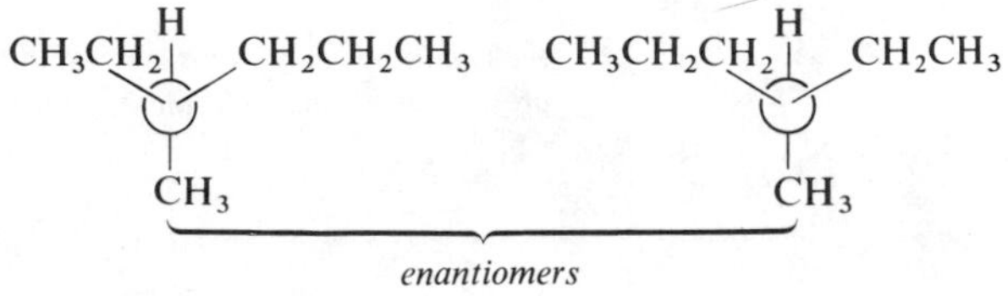

$$
CH_3CH_2-\overset{\overset{\displaystyle H}{|}}{\underset{\underset{\displaystyle CH_3}{|}}{C}}-CH_2CH_2CH_3
$$

chiral carbon atom

$$
CH_3CH_2 \underset{CH_3}{\diagdown} CH_2CH_2CH_3 \qquad CH_3CH_2CH_2 \underset{CH_3}{\diagdown} CH_2CH_3
$$

enantiomers

Chiral carbon atoms are often starred for emphasis. Star the chiral carbons in the following structures:

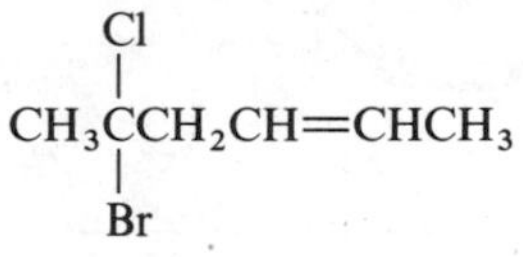

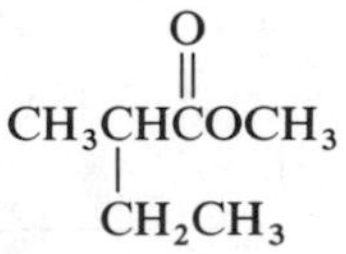

$$
CH_3\overset{\overset{\displaystyle Cl}{|}}{\underset{\underset{\displaystyle Br}{|}}{C}}CH_2CH{=}CHCH_3
\qquad
CH_3\overset{\overset{\displaystyle O}{\|}}{\underset{\underset{\displaystyle CH_2CH_3}{|}}{CHCOCH_3}}
$$

Solution:

$$
CH_3^*\overset{\overset{\displaystyle Cl}{|}}{\underset{\underset{\displaystyle Br}{|}}{C}}CH_2CH{=}CHCH_3
\qquad
CH_3\overset{\overset{\displaystyle O}{\|}}{\underset{\underset{\displaystyle CH_2CH_3}{|}}{\overset{*}{C}HCOCH_3}}
$$

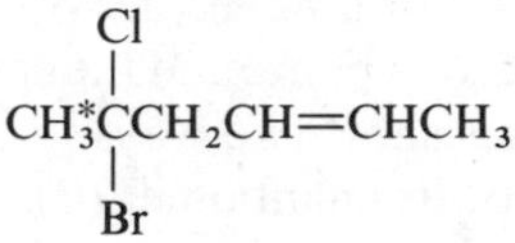

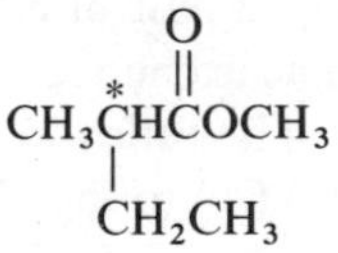

STUDY PROBLEM

4.9 Star the chiral carbons (if any) in the following structures:

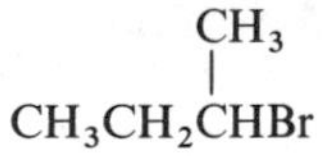

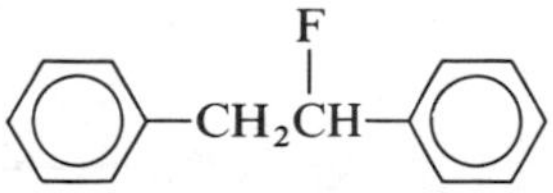

(a) $CH_3\overset{\overset{\displaystyle CH_3}{|}}{C}HBr$
(b) $CH_3CH_2\overset{\overset{\displaystyle CH_3}{|}}{C}HBr$
(c) $\bigcirc{-}CH_2\overset{\overset{\displaystyle F}{|}}{C}H{-}\bigcirc$

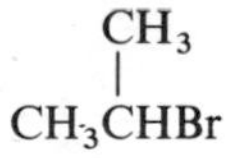

One of the following molecules is chiral, and one is achiral. Which is the chiral molecule?

(a) (b)

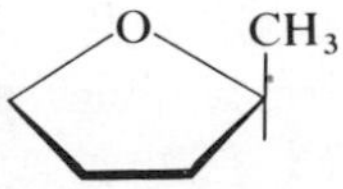

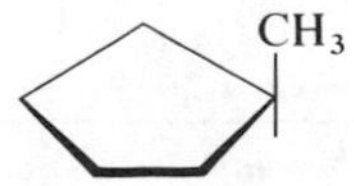

Solution: The ring carbon with the methyl group in (a) is a chiral center because it has four different groups attached: CH_3, H, O, and CH_2; therefore, the structure in (a) is chiral. The corresponding carbon in (b) has two identical groups; it is achiral.

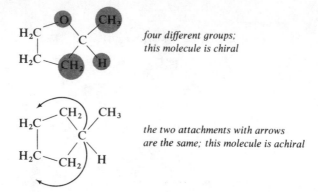

four different groups; this molecule is chiral

the two attachments with arrows are the same; this molecule is achiral

STUDY PROBLEM

4.10 Star any chiral carbon atoms in the following formulas:

(a)

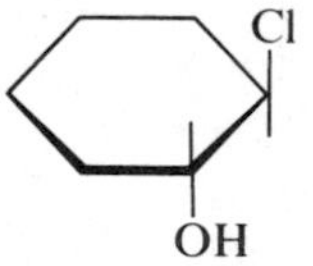

(b)

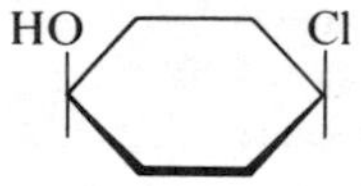

Drawing structures of a pair of enantiomers for a molecule with one chiral carbon is relatively easy. The exchange of any two groups around the chiral carbon results in the enantiomer. The following examples show two ways to convert the formula for one compound (A) to the formula for its enantiomer (B).

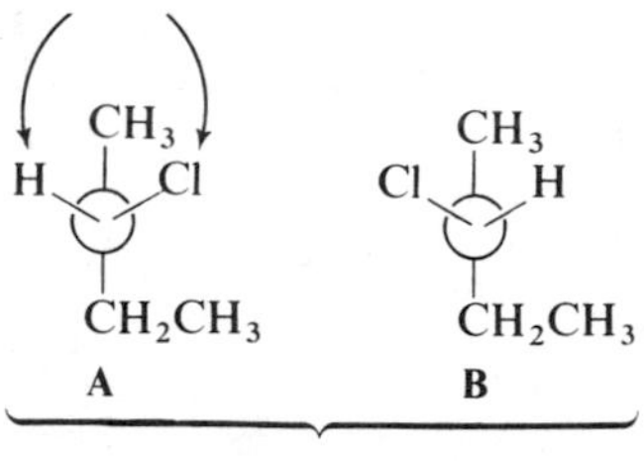

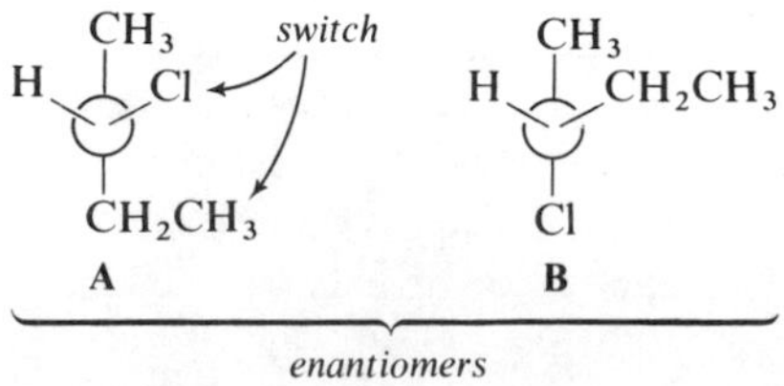

STUDY PROBLEM

4.11   Give the formulas for both enantiomers of each of the following compounds:

(a) 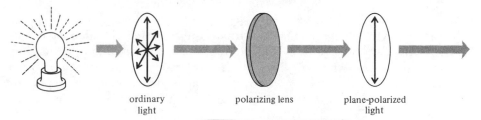   (b) $CH_3CH_2CHCH_3$

Rotation of Plane-Polarized Light

Because the structures (order of attachment of atoms) of a pair of enantiomers are the same, almost all of their physical and chemical properties are the same. For example, consider a pair of enantiomers. Each pure enantiomer has the same melting point and the same boiling point. Only two sets of properties are different for a single pair of enantiomers:

(1)   reactions with other chiral molecules (discussed in Sections 15.9 and 18.14B);
(2)   direction of rotation of the plane of vibration of plane-polarized light (a discussion of which follows).

Ordinary light travels in waves, and the waves are at right angles to the direction of travel. **Plane-polarized light** is light in which all wave vibrations have been filtered out except for those in one plane. The plane polarization is effected by passing ordinary light through a crystal of calcite ($CaCO_3$) or a polarizing lens. (The same principle is used in Polaroid sunglasses.) Figure 4.15 shows a simplified diagram of the plane polarization of light.

ordinary   polarizing lens   plane-polarized
light   light

Figure 4.15.   The plane polarization of light.

If plane-polarized light is passed through a solution containing a single enantiomer, the plane of vibration of the light is *rotated* either to the right or to the left (see Figure 4.16, page 140). The rotation of plane-polarized light is referred to as **optical rotation**. A compound that rotates the plane of vibration of plane-polarized light is said to be **optically active**. For this reason, enantiomers are sometimes referred to as **optical isomers**.

A **polarimeter** is an instrument designed for polarizing light and then showing the angle of rotation of the plane of vibration of the plane-polarized light by an optically active compound. The amount of rotation depends on (1) the structure of the molecules; (2) the temperature; (3) the wavelength; and (4) the number of molecules in the path of the light.

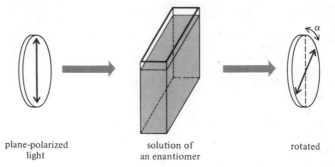

plane-polarized   solution of   rotated
light   an enantiomer

Figure 4.16.   The plane of vibration of plane-polarized light is rotated by a single enantiomer.

Specific rotation is the rotation by 1.00 gram of sample in 1.00 ml of solution in a tube with a path length of 1.00 decimeter (dm), at a specified temperature and wavelength. The commonly used wavelength is 589.3 nm (the *D* line of sodium), obtained from a sodium lamp as the light source. The specific rotation for a compound (at 20°, for example) may be calculated from the observed rotation by the following formula:

$$[\alpha]_D^{20} = \frac{\alpha}{lc}$$

where $[\alpha]_D^{20}$ = specific rotation of sodium *D* line at 20°
α = observed rotation at 20°
l = cell length in dm (1.0 dm = 10 cm)
c = concentration of sample solution in g/ml

The fact that some compounds rotate the plane of vibration of plane-polarized light was discovered in 1815 by French physicist Jean-Baptiste Biot. But it was Louis Pasteur who in 1848 made the momentous discovery that there are two types of sodium ammonium tartrate crystals and that these two types are mirror images of each other. (We will discuss the structure of tartaric acid in Section 4.9C.)

Pasteur painstakingly separated the "left-handed" crystals from the "right-handed" crystals with a pair of tweezers. Imagine his amazement when he found that (1) a solution of the original mixture of crystals did not rotate plane-polarized light; (2) a solution of left-handed crystals did rotate plane-polarized light; and (3) a solution of right-handed crystals also rotated plane-polarized light to exactly the same extent, but in the opposite direction. Pasteur's experiment and later experiments of innumerable other scientists lead us to the following conclusions:

(1)   A pair of pure enantiomers each rotates the plane of vibration of plane-polarized light the same number of degrees, but in the opposite directions (one to the left; one to the right).

(2)   A mixture of equal parts of a pair of enantiomers does not rotate plane-polarized light.

A. Some Terms Used in Discussing Optical Rotation

Glyceraldehyde is the trivial name for 2,3-dihydroxypropanal. Glyceraldehyde has a chiral center at carbon 2 and therefore exists as a pair of enantiomers.

$$
\begin{array}{c}
\overset{O}{\underset{\parallel}{}} \\
\textcircled{1}\text{CH} \\
| \\
\textcircled{2}\text{CHOH} \\
| \\
\textcircled{3}\text{CH}_2\text{OH}
\end{array}
$$

chiral carbon

glyceraldehyde

The enantiomer of glyceraldehyde (or one enantiomer of any enantiomeric pair) that rotates plane-polarized light to the *right* is said to be **dextrorotatory** (Latin *dexter*, "right"). Its mirror image, which rotates plane-polarized light to the *left*, is said to be **levorotatory** (Latin *laevus*, "left"). The direction of rotation is specified in the name by ($+$) for dextrorotatory and ($-$) for levorotatory. (In older literature, *d* for dextrorotatory and *l* for levorotatory are sometimes encountered.)

(+)-glyceraldehyde
$[\alpha]_D^{20} = +8.7°$

(−)-glyceraldehyde
$[\alpha]_D^{20} = -8.7°$

A mixture of equal parts of any pair of enantiomers is called a **racemic mixture**, or **racemic modification**. A racemic mixture may be indicated in the name by the prefix ($\pm$). Racemic glyceraldehyde is thus called ($\pm$)-glyceraldehyde. (The term *racemic* comes from the Latin *racemis*, "a bunch of grapes." The reason for this unusual derivation is that *racemic* was first used to describe racemic tartaric acid, which was isolated as a by-product of wine-making.)

(+)-glyceraldehyde + (−)-glyceraldehyde = ($\pm$)-glyceraldehyde
$[\alpha]_D^{20} = +8.7°$ $\qquad$ $[\alpha]_D^{20} = -8.7°$ $\qquad$ $[\alpha]_D^{20} = 0$

a racemic mixture

A racemic mixture does not rotate plane-polarized light because the rotation by each enantiomer is cancelled by the equal and opposite rotation of the other. An achiral compound does not rotate plane-polarized light because each of its molecules has a plane of symmetry. A solution of either a racemic mixture or of an achiral compound is said to be **optically inactive**, but the causes of the optical inactivity are different.

The physical separation of a racemic mixture into pure enantiomers is called the **resolution**, or **resolving**, of the racemic mixture. Pasteur's separation of racemic sodium ammonium tartrate was a resolution of that mixture. It is a very rare occurrence for enantiomers to crystallize separately; therefore, the method that

Pasteur used cannot be considered as a general method of resolution. The usual method is to subject the racemic mixture to a reaction with a pure enantiomeric reagent and then separate the reaction products. Discussion of this type of separation will be deferred to Chapter 15.

In most laboratory reactions, a chemist uses achiral or racemic starting materials and obtains achiral or racemic products. Therefore, often we will ignore the chirality (or lack of it) in reactants or products in future chapters. On the other hand, we will also discuss many reactions in which stereochemistry is quite important.

As opposed to laboratory reactions, most biological reactions start with chiral reactants and lead to chiral products. These biological reactions are possible because of biological catalysts called **enzymes**, which are chiral. Enzymes will be mentioned frequently in this text; their structures and catalytic action will be discussed in Chapter 18. Most biological reactions are **stereospecific reactions**, reactions in which stereoisomeric reactants yield different products. Part of the reason that biological reactions are stereospecific is that reacting molecules must fit correctly on chiral enzyme surfaces. Although one chiral molecule may match the enzyme, its enantiomer may not. (See Figure 18.6, page 860, for a pictorial representation of this "matching.")

Section 4.8

Relative and Absolute Configuration

The order of arrangement of four groups around a chiral carbon atom is called the **absolute configuration** around that carbon. (Do not confuse configuration with *conformation*, which is a shape arising from rotation around bonds.) A pair of enantiomers have opposite configurations.

opposite configurations around carbon 2

A molecule of glyceraldehyde has one chiral carbon and exists in two enantiomeric forms: $(+)$- and $(-)$-glyceraldehyde. But which formula represents the dextrorotatory enantiomer, and which represents the levorotatory one? Until 1951, chemists did not know! Prior to that time, it was known that $(+)$-glyceraldehyde and $(-)$-glyceric acid (2,3-dihydroxypropanoic acid) have the same configuration around carbon 2, even though they rotate plane-polarized light in opposite directions. But it was not known whether the —OH at carbon 2 was to the right or to the left in the two formulas as we have drawn them.

(−)-glyceric acid   (+)-glyceraldehyde

same configuration, but is the −OH on the right (as shown) or on the left?

Even though chemists did not know the absolute configurations of (−)-glyceric acid and other optically active compounds, they could speak of **relative configurations** of these compounds. Usually, the configurations of optically active compounds were related to (+)-glyceraldehyde. The relative configurations were said to be either the same as, or opposite from, the configuration of (+)-glyceraldehyde.

To make structures and formulas easier to work with, it was decided in the late 19th century to assume that (+)-glyceraldehyde had the following absolute configuration:

(+)-glyceraldehyde: and not

In 1951, x-ray diffraction studies by J. M. Bijvoet at the University of Utrecht in Holland showed that the original assumption was correct. (+)-Glyceraldehyde does indeed have the absolute configuration that chemists had been using for 60 years. If the early chemists had guessed wrong, the chemical literature would have been in a state of confusion—all pre-1951 articles would show configurations the *reverse* of those in more modern articles. The original assumption was indeed a lucky guess!

The direction of rotation of plane-polarized light by a particular enantiomer is a physical property. The absolute configuration of a particular enantiomer is a characteristic of its molecular structure. There is no simple relationship between the absolute configuration of a particular enantiomer and its direction of rotation of plane-polarized light. As we have said, the enantiomer of glyceric acid with the same absolute configuration as (+)-glyceraldehyde is levorotatory, not dextrorotatory.

A. Assignment of Configuration: The (R) and (S) System

We have shown how the direction of rotation of plane-polarized light can be indicated by (+) or (−). However, a system is also needed to indicate the absolute configuration—that is, the actual arrangement of groups around a chiral center. This system is the **(R) and (S) system**. The letter (R) comes from the Latin *rectus*, "right," while (S) comes from the Latin *sinister*, "left." Any chiral carbon atom has either an (R) configuration or an (S) configuration; therefore, one enantiomer is (R) and the other is (S). A racemic mixture may be designated (R)(S), meaning a mixture of the two.

To assign an (*R*) or (*S*) configuration to a chiral carbon:

(1) Rank the four groups (or atoms) attached to the chiral carbon in order of priority by the Cahn–Ingold–Prelog sequence rules (page 115–116).

(2) Project the molecule with the group of *lowest priority* in the rear.

(3) Select the group of *highest priority* and *draw a curved arrow to the group of next highest priority.*

(4) If this arrow is *clockwise*, the configuration is (*R*). If the arrow is *counter-clockwise*, the configuration is (*S*).

Let us illustrate the use of this procedure by assigning (*R*) and (*S*) to the enantiomers of 1-bromo-1-chloroethane.

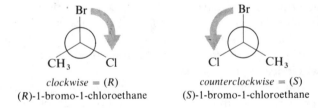

enantiomers of 1-bromo-1-chloroethane

(1) Rank the four groups. In the case at hand, the order of priority of the four atoms by atomic number is Br (highest), Cl, C, H (lowest).

(2) Draw projections with the lowest-priority atom (H) in the rear. (This atom is hidden behind the carbon atom in the projections below.)

(3) Draw an arrow from highest priority (Br) to second-highest priority (Cl).

(4) Assign (*R*) and (*S*).

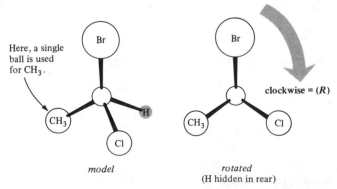

Placing a structure in the correct position for an (*R*) or (*S*) assignment is easily done with a molecular model. Construct the model, grasp the group of

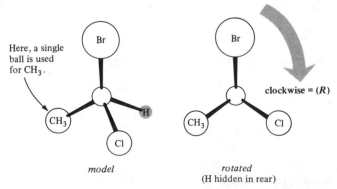

Figure 4.17.   Using a molecular model to determine (*R*) or (*S*) configuration.

lowest priority with one hand, and turn the model so that the remaining three groups face you. Determine if the structure is (R) or (S) in the usual way. (See Figure 4.17.)

Sample Problem

Name the following compound, including an (R) or (S) designation.

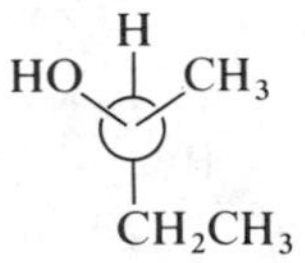

$$HO \underset{CH_2CH_3}{\overset{H}{\underset{|}{C}}} CH_3$$

Solution:

(1) order of priority: OH (highest), CH_2CH_3, CH_3, H (lowest)

(2) projection with H in rear:

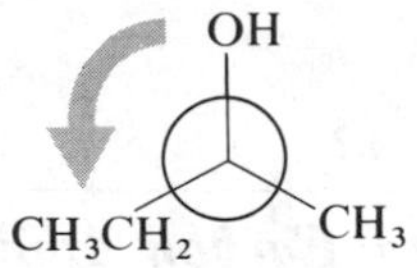

$$CH_3CH_2 \qquad \overset{OH}{\diagup\!\!\!\diagdown} \qquad CH_3$$

(3) counterclockwise = (S)

(4) name: (S)-2-butanol

Sample Problem

Draw the structure of (R)-($-$)-2-butanol.

Solution:

(1) Draw the formula of the compound without regard to configuration of the chiral carbon.

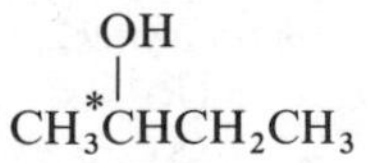

$$\overset{OH}{\underset{|}{CH_3\overset{*}{C}HCH_2CH_3}}$$

(2) Assign the priorities around the chiral carbon: OH (highest), CH_2CH_3, CH_3, H (lowest).

(3) Draw the projection with the lowest-priority group (H) in the rear. Place the remaining groups in such a way that from OH to CH_2CH_3 is clockwise for the (R) configuration.

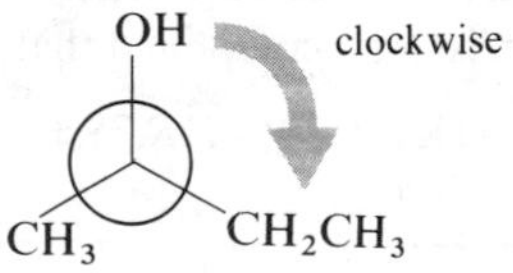

$$\overset{OH}{\underset{CH_3 \qquad CH_2CH_3}{}} \quad clockwise$$

(4) Redraw the structures as a ball-and-stick or dimensional formula. (Models make this task easier.)

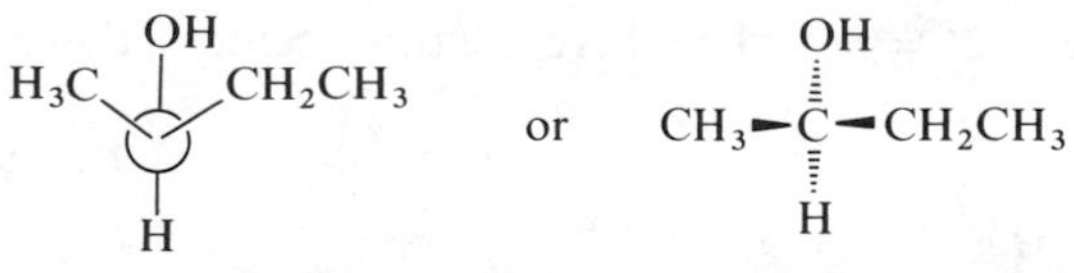

$$H_3C \underset{H}{\overset{OH}{\underset{|}{C}}} CH_2CH_3 \qquad \text{or} \qquad CH_3 \blacktriangleright \overset{OH}{\underset{H}{C}} \blacktriangleleft CH_2CH_3$$

Note that in the solution of this problem, the sign of rotation in the name is not used. The ($-$) is the indication of direction of rotation of plane-polarized light, a physical property of (R)-2-butanol, and is not used in determining its configuration.

STUDY PROBLEMS

4.12   Assign each of the following molecules an (R) or (S) configuration:

(a)
```
      CHO
   H  |  OH
      \ /
       O
       |
      CH₂OH
```

(b)
```
       Br
  H₃C  |  D
      \ /
       O
       |
       H
```

(c)
```
            H
  CH₃CH₂  |  CH₃
        \ /
         O
         |
        NH₂
```

(d)
```
          H
  H₃C  |  CO₂H
      \ /
       O
       |
      NH₂
```

4.13   Give formulas for   (a) (R)-3-bromoheptane, and   (b) (S)-2-pentanol, that show the absolute configurations around the chiral carbons.

Section 4.9

More Than One Chiral Carbon Atom

Our discussion up to the present time has been limited to compounds that have only one chiral center, but compounds can have more than one such center. Consider a compound with two different chiral carbons. Each of these two chiral centers can be either (R) or (S): consequently, there are four different ways that these configurations can be arranged within a molecule. A molecule with two different chiral centers can therefore have four different stereoisomers.

chiral center 1	chiral center 2	total configuration
(R)	(R)	(1R,2R)
(R)	(S)	(1R,2S)
(S)	(R)	(1S,2R)
(S)	(S)	(1S,2S)

Sample Problem

How many stereoisomers could exist for a compound that has three different chiral centers?

Solution: eight: (1R,2R,3R);   (1R,2R,3S);   (1R,2S,3R);   (1R,2S,3S);   (1S,2R,3R); (1S,2R,3S);   (1S,2S,3R);   (1S,2S,3S).

The *maximum number of optical isomers* for a compound is 2^n, where n is the number of chiral centers. If there are two chiral centers, then there can be up to four stereoisomers ($2^2 = 4$); when there are three centers, there can be up to eight stereoisomers ($2^3 = 8$).

STUDY PROBLEM

4.14   What is the maximum number of stereoisomers for each of the following compounds? (a) 1,2-dibromo-1-phenylpropane; (b) 1,2-dibromo-2-methyl-1-phenylpropane; (c) 2,3,4,5-tetrahydroxypentanal

A. (*R*) and (*S*) System for a Compound with Two Chiral Carbon Atoms

To assign (*R*) or (*S*) configurations to two chiral carbon atoms in one molecule, we consider each chiral carbon atom separately.

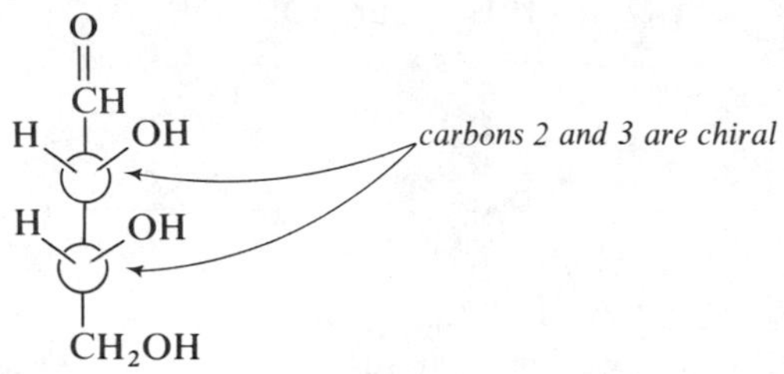
O
CH
H
OH
H
OH
CH2OH
carbons 2 and 3 are chiral

For carbon 2:

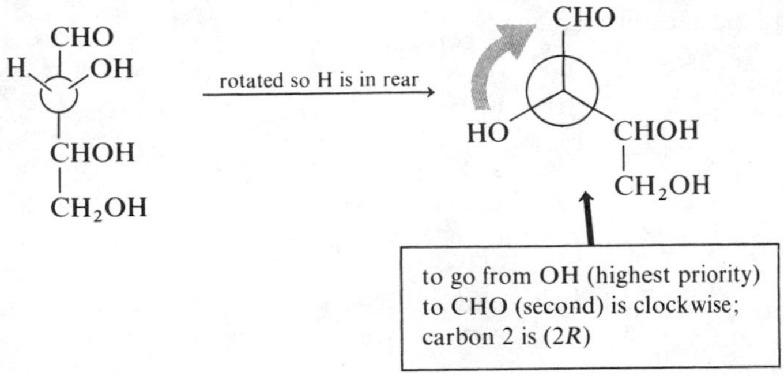
CHO
H
OH
CHOH
CH2OH
rotated so H is in rear
CHO
HO
CHOH
CH2OH
to go from OH (highest priority) to CHO (second) is clockwise; carbon 2 is (2R)

For carbon 3:

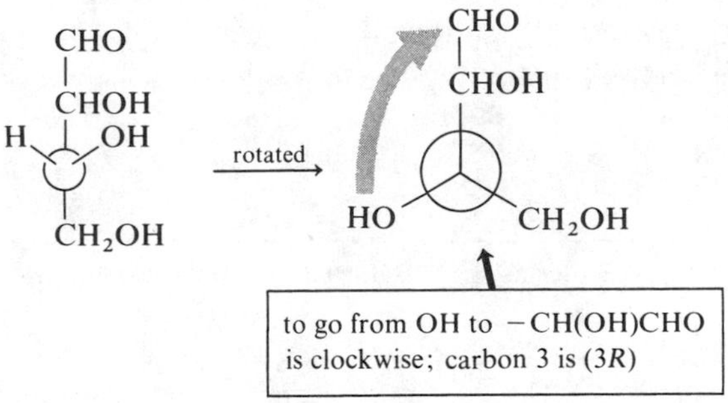
CHO
CHOH
H
OH
CH2OH
rotated
CHO
CHOH
HO
CH2OH
to go from OH to −CH(OH)CHO is clockwise; carbon 3 is (3R)

The name for the above compound is therefore (2*R*,3*R*)-2,3,4-trihydroxybutanal. This compound is a sugar; its trivial name is (2*R*,3*R*)-erythrose. Note that the numbers and letters in one set of parentheses refer to the configurations around two different chiral centers in one molecule. Contrast this notation with (*R*)(*S*), which means a racemic mixture.

B. Diastereomers

When a molecule has more than one chiral carbon, not all of the optical isomers are enantiomers. By definition, enantiomers (mirror images) come in pairs.

The four stereoisomers of 2,3,4-trihydroxybutanal:

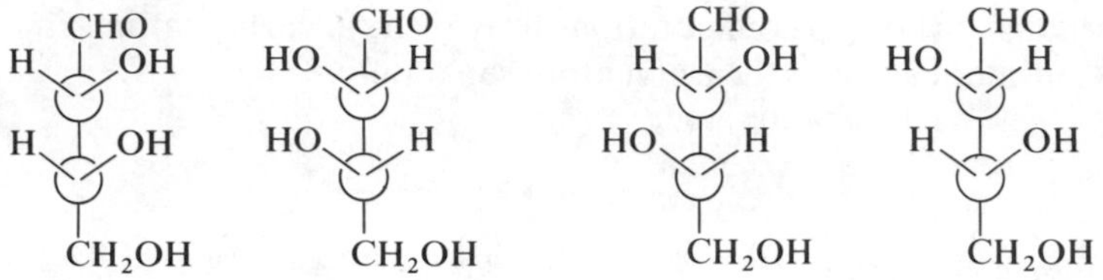

(2R,3R)	(2S,3S)	(2R,3S)	(2S,3R)

enantiomers   *enantiomers*

Note that the (2R,3R)- and (2S,3S)-stereoisomers are enantiomers. The (2R,3S)- and (2S,3R)-stereoisomers are also enantiomers. However, the (2S,3S)- and (2R,3S)-stereoisomers are *not* enantiomers. (What other nonenantiomeric pairings can be arranged?) Any pair of stereoisomers that are not enantiomers are called **diastereomers**, or **diastereoisomers**. Thus the (2S,3S)- and (2R,3S)-stereo-isomers are diastereomers.

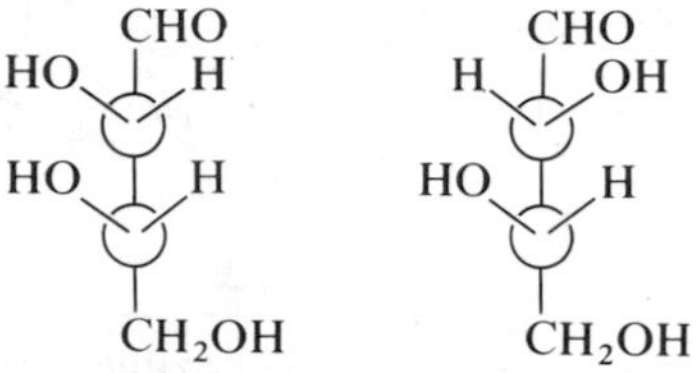

a pair of diastereomers:
stereoisomers that are not enantiomers

A pair of enantiomers have identical physical and chemical properties except for reactions with other chiral molecules and for the direction of rotation of plane-polarized light. Diastereomers, however, are chemically and physically different. They have different melting points, different solubilities, and often undergo chemical reactions in a different fashion.

Sample Problem

Identify each pair of molecules as *structural isomers*, *enantiomers*, or *diastereomers*.

(a)

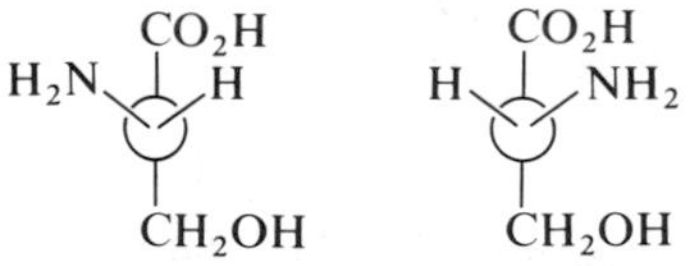

(b)

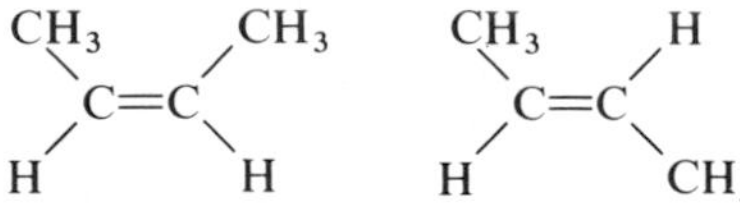

(c)

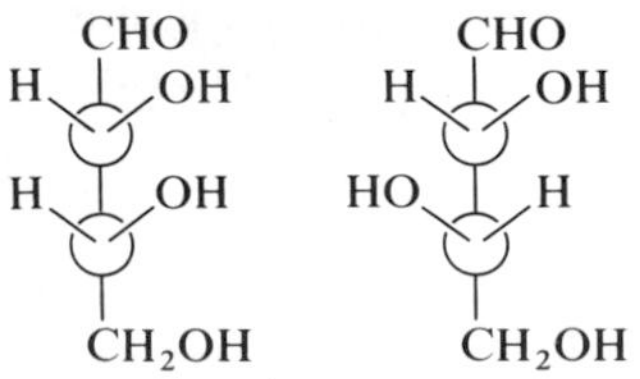

(d)

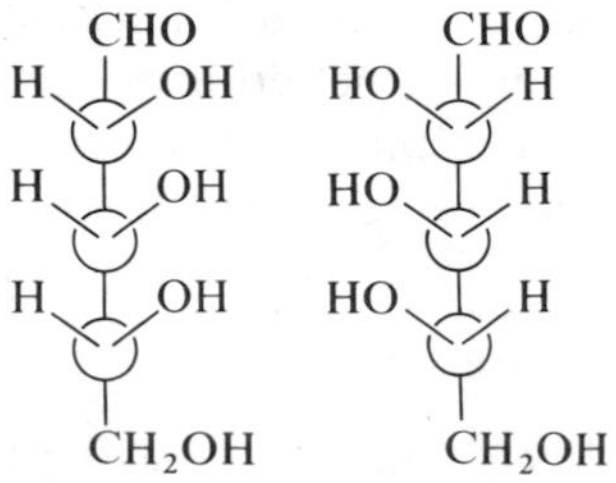

Solution: (a) and (d) are enantiomers. (b) and (c) are diastereomers.

C.   Meso Compounds

A compound with n chiral centers can have a maximum of 2^n stereoisomers, but it may not have that many. The reason is that, in certain compounds with more than one chiral center, there can be an internal plane of symmetry that renders an apparent pair of enantiomers superimposable. If two molecules are superimposable, the two are identical and are not stereoisomers of each other.

Consider a pair of structures (A and B) with two chiral carbon atoms. At first glance, we might assume that A and B are enantiomers.

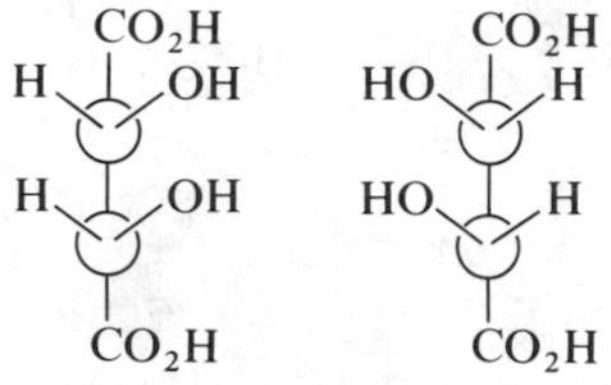

$$\text{A} \qquad\qquad \text{B}$$

Let us take B and rotate it 180° in the plane of the paper. B is identical to A! A and B indeed are mirror images, but the mirror images are superimposable; therefore, A and B are the same compound.

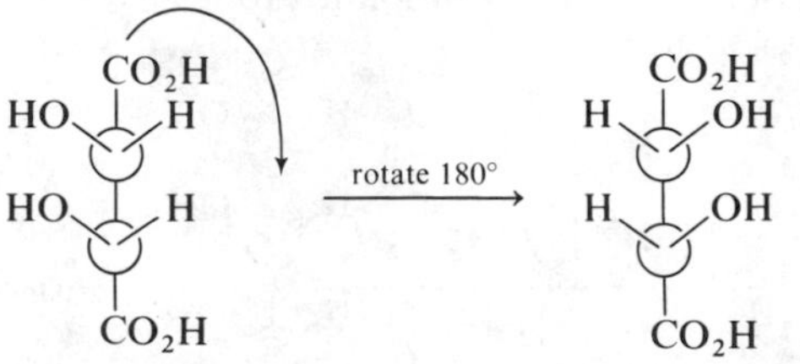

rotate 180°

B   **B** *superimposable on* **A**

Why is it possible that the mirror images of a molecule with two chiral centers are superimposable? The answer is that this isomer has an internal plane of symmetry. The "top" half of the molecule is the mirror image of the "bottom" half. We might say that the two halves of the molecule cancel each other so far as chirality is concerned. Therefore, the molecule as a whole is achiral and does not cause a rotation of plane-polarized light.

A stereoisomer that contains chiral carbons but has an internal plane of symmetry is called a *meso* **form**. The compound we have been discussing here is *meso*-tartaric acid.

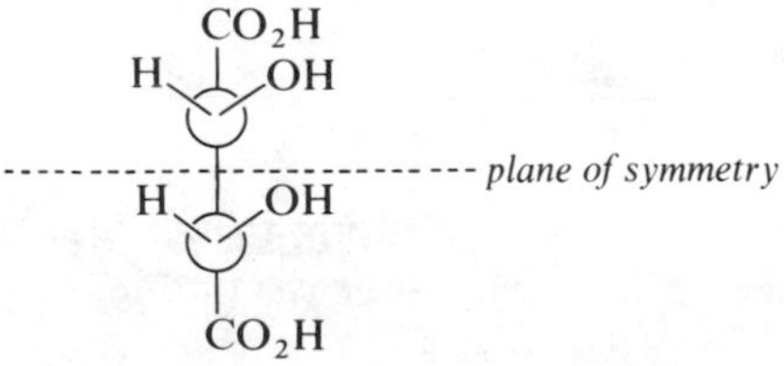

-------------------------------- *plane of symmetry*

meso-tartaric acid

$[\alpha] = 0$

A compound with two chiral carbons can have up to four stereoisomers. For tartaric acid, we have looked at two possibilities, and these two added up to only one isomer, *meso*-tartaric acid. What about the other two stereoisomers of tartaric acid? Do they have an internal plane of symmetry? No, they do not. The top halves are not mirror images of the bottom halves. Rotation of either structure by 180° does not result in the other structure or in the *meso*-isomer. The following two stereoisomers of tartaric acid are enantiomers. They are both optically active and rotate the plane of vibration of plane-polarized light in equal and opposite directions.

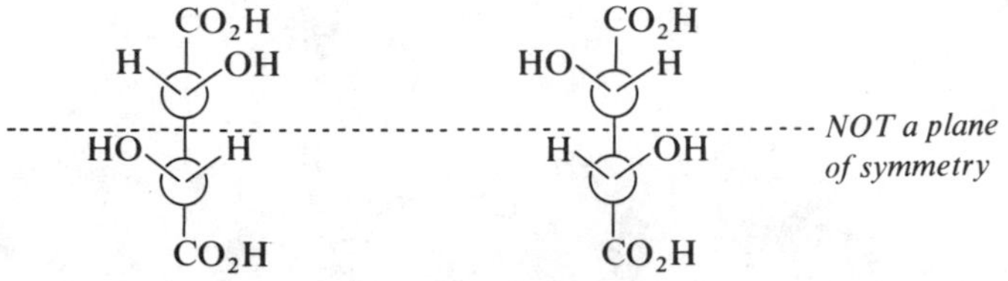

(2R,3R)-(+)-tartaric acid   (2S,3S)-(−)-tartaric acid

What are our conclusions about tartaric acid? Because of the internal plane of symmetry in *meso*-tartaric acid, there is a total of only *three* stereoisomers for tartaric acid, rather than the four stereoisomers predicted by the 2^n rule. These three stereoisomers are a pair of enantiomers and the diastereomeric *meso* form.

The *meso* forms of some other compounds follow:

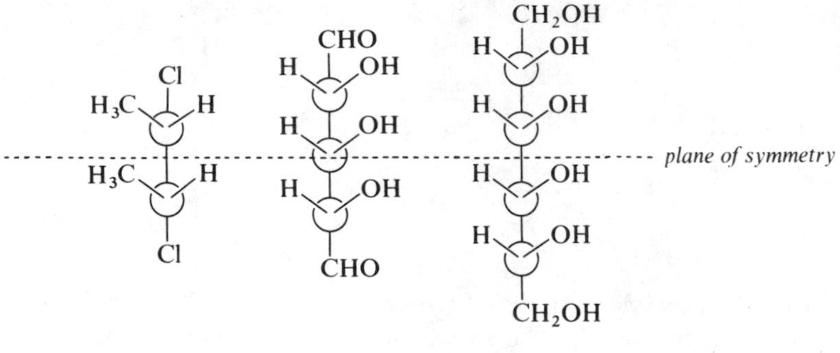

STUDY PROBLEM

4.15 Draw all possible stereoisomers of 2,3-dichlorobutane. Indicate any enantiomeric pairs.

SUMMARY

Stereoisomerism is isomerism resulting from different spatial arrangements of atoms in molecules. **Geometric isomerism**, one form of stereoisomerism, results from groups being *cis* (same side) or *trans* (opposite sides) around a pi bond or on a ring. Geometric isomers of alkenes may also be differentiated by the letter (*E*), opposite sides, or (*Z*), same side.

Rotation of groups around sigma bonds results in different conformations, such as the **eclipsed**, *gauche*, **staggered**, and *anti* conformations. Lower-energy conformers predominate. Conformers are interconvertible at room temperature and therefore are not isomers. A cyclic compound assumes puckered conformations to relieve strain of unfavorable bond angles and, more importantly, to minimize repulsions of substituents. For the cyclohexane ring, the chair-form conformer with substituents **equatorial** instead of **axial** is favored.

A **chiral molecule** is a molecule that is nonsuperimposable on its mirror image. The pair of nonsuperimposable mirror images are called **enantiomers** and represent another type of stereoisomerism. Each member of a pair of enantiomers rotates the plane of vibration of plane-polarized light an equal amount, but in opposite directions. An equimolar mixture of enantiomers, called a **racemic mixture**, is optically inactive.

Chirality usually arises from the presence of a carbon with four different atoms or groups attached to it. The arrangement of these groups around the chiral carbon is called the **absolute configuration** and may be described as (R) or (S).

A molecule with more than one chiral carbon has more stereoisomers than a single enantiomeric pair. Stereoisomers that are not enantiomers are **diastereomers**. If a molecule has more than one chiral center and has an internal plane of symmetry, it is optically inactive and is called a *meso* **form**.

The different types of isomerism may be summarized:

A.   **Structural isomers** differ in order of attachment of atoms:

$$(CH_3)_2CHCH_3 \quad \text{and} \quad CH_3CH_2CH_2CH_3$$

B.   **Stereoisomers** differ in arrangement of atoms in space.

(1)   **Enantiomers:**   nonsuperimposable mirror images

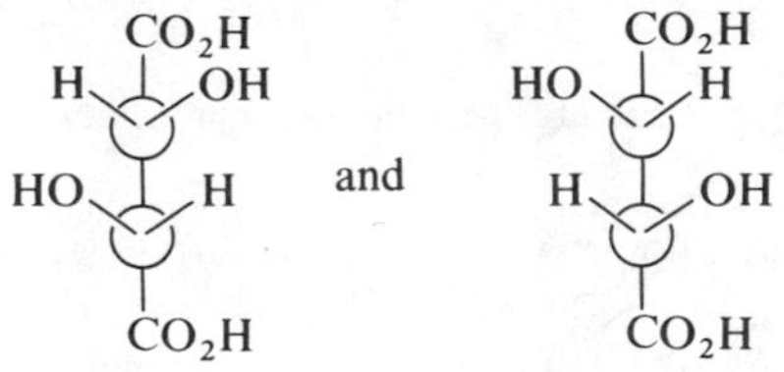

(2)   **Diastereomers:**   nonenantiomeric stereoisomers

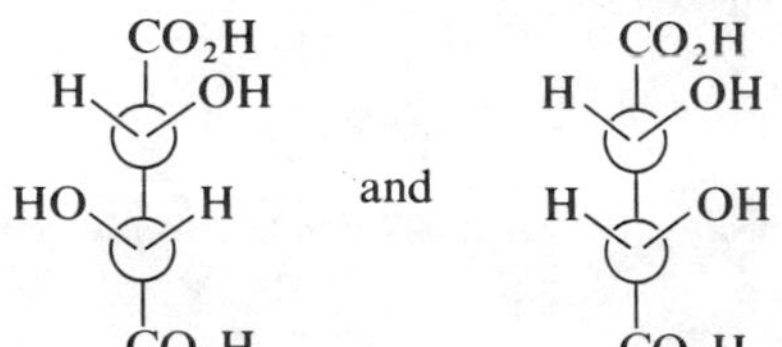

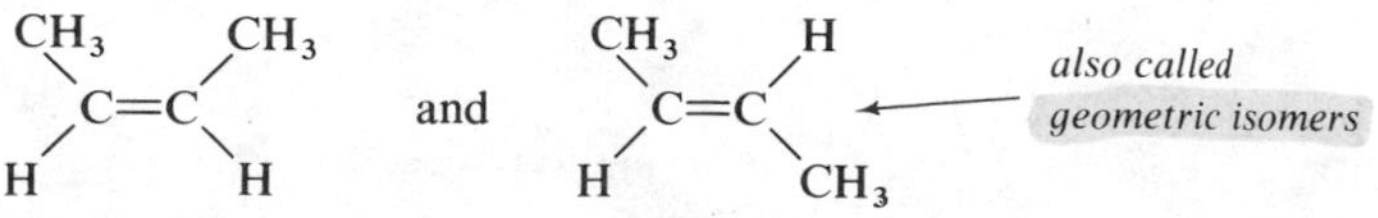

STUDY PROBLEMS

4.16 Give structural formulas for each of the following compounds (both geometric isomers, if any) and label each as *cis*, *trans*, or *no geometric isomer*: (a) 1-hexene; (b) 2-hexene; (c) 2-methyl-1-butene; (d) 1-chloro-2-butene.

4.17 Write structural formulas for the alkenes of molecular formula C_5H_{10} that exhibit geometric isomerism. Show the *cis*- and *trans*-structures.

4.18 Give the structural formulas for the four isomeric butenes (four-carbon alkenes) and name each.

4.19 Which of the following compounds exhibit geometric isomerism?

(a) 1,2-diphenylethene
(b) 1-butene-3-yne, $CH_2{=}CHC{\equiv}CH$
(c) 2-pentene-4-yne, $CH_3CH{=}CHC{\equiv}CH$
(d) 2,3-dimethyl-2-pentene
(e) ethyl 2-butenoate, $CH_3CH{=}CHCO_2CH_2CH_3$

4.20 Assign (*E*) or (*Z*) to each of the following alkenes. (*Note:* $C_6H_5{-}$ = phenyl.)

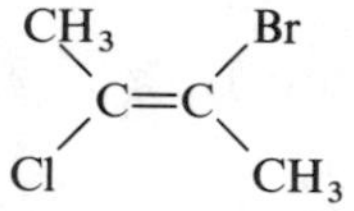

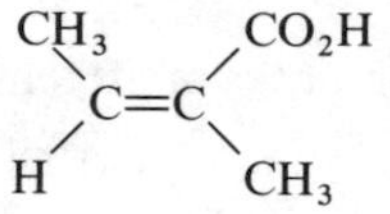

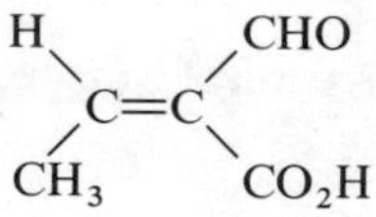

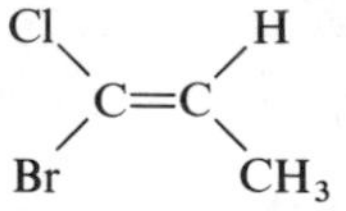

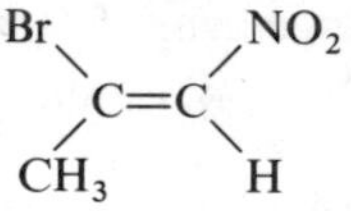

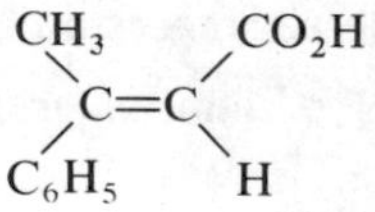

4.21 Draw the structure of each of the following compounds, showing its stereochemistry:

(a) (*E*)-2-chloro-2-butene
(b) (2*Z*,4*Z*)-nonadiene, $CH_3CH{=}CHCH{=}CH(CH_2)_3CH_3$
(c) (*Z*)-2-pentene
(d) (*E*)-2-bromo-1-nitro-2-butene

4.22 Name and give formulas for the geometric isomers of 2,4-hexadiene,

$$CH_3CH{=}CHCH{=}CHCH_3.$$

(Use the *E* and *Z* system.)

4.23 Draw the formulas and label the geometric isomers (if any) for each of the following compounds:

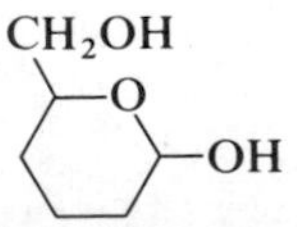

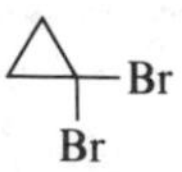

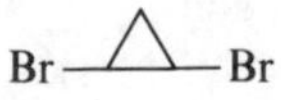

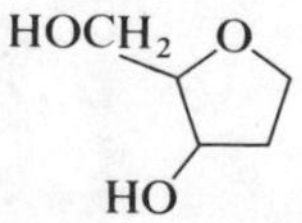

4.24 Give the Newman projections for the *anti* and two eclipsed conformations of 1,2-diiodoethane. Of the two eclipsed conformations, which is of higher energy?

4.25 Give the Newman projection for an *anti* conformer (if any) for each of the following compounds. Use the circled carbons as the center of the Newman projection.

(a) HO₂CCHCH₂CH₂CO₂H (b) HO₂CCHCH₂CH₂CO₂H
         | |
        CH₃   CH₃

(c) HO₂CCHCH₂CH₂CO₂H
         |
        CH₃

4.26 Label each of the following positions as axial or equatorial:

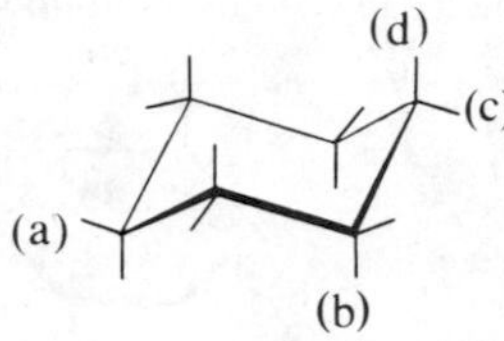

4.27 Which of the following conformations is most stable? (More than one compound is shown.)

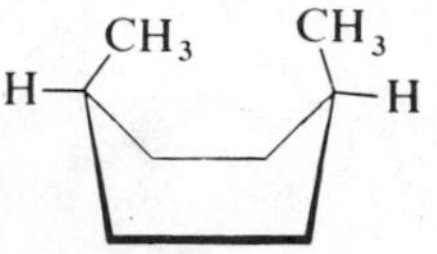

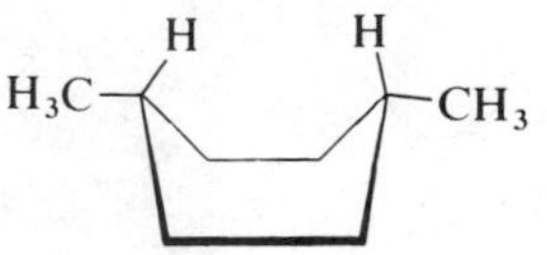

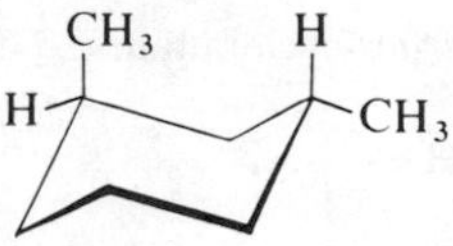

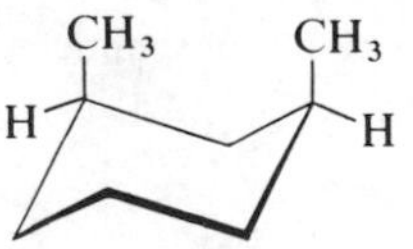

4.28 Which of the following conformations is more stable?

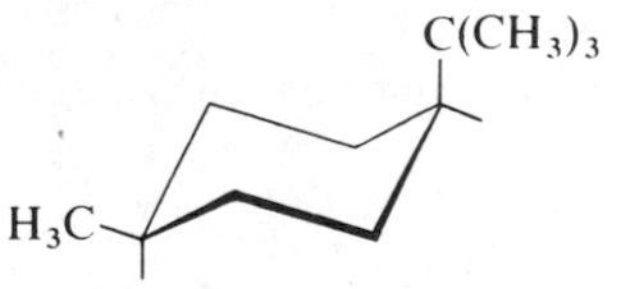

4.29 (a) Why is a *cis*-1,3-disubstituted cyclohexane more stable than the corresponding *trans*-structure?

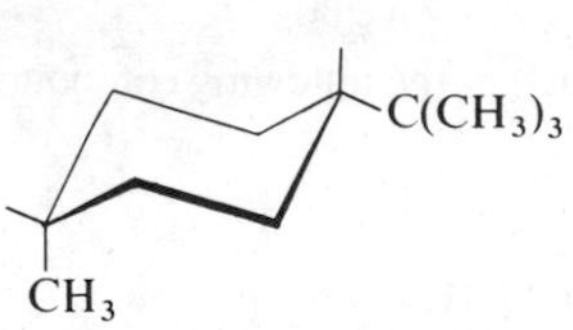

(b) Is the *cis*-1,2-isomer more stable than the *trans*-1,2-disubstituted cyclohexane?

4.30 Draw the following compound in the chair form with all of the ring hydrogen atoms in axial positions:

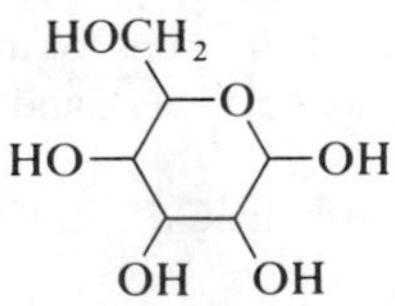

4.31 Give the structure of the preferred conformation of 1-methyl-1-propylcyclohexane.

4.32 Give the structure of the most stable conformer of the more stable isomer of 1,3-di-isopropylcyclohexane.

4.33 Which of the following compounds contain chiral molecules?   (a) 2-methyl-2-phenyl-butane;   (b) 1,2-dibromo-1,2-diphenylpropane.

4.34 Star the chiral carbons (if any):

(a) $(CH_3)_2CHCHBrCH_3$

(b) $CH_3CH_2CH_2\overset{\displaystyle CH_3}{\underset{\displaystyle |}{C}}HOH$

(c) $H_2N\overset{}{\underset{\displaystyle |}{C}}HCO_2H$
$\qquad\quad CH_3$

(d) $CH_3CHBrCHBrCH_2CH_3$

(e) $H_2NCH_2CO_2H$

4.35 Locate one plane of symmetry in each of the following structures:

(a)

(b)

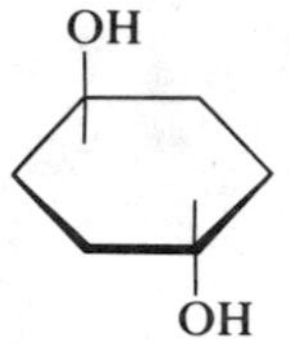

(c)

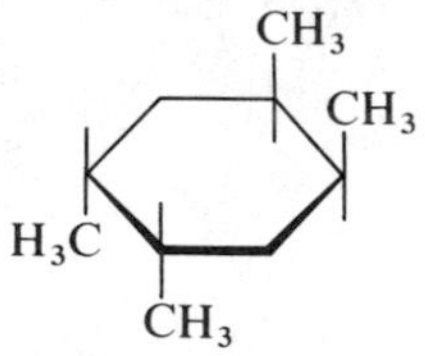

(d)

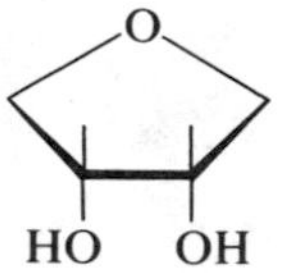

4.36 Locate all possible planes of symmetry for *cis*- and *trans*-cyclobutane-1,3-dicarboxylic acid:

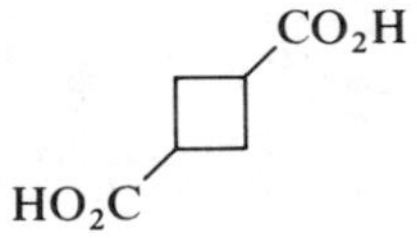

4.37 Show the configuration of the enantiomer of each of the following compounds:

(a)

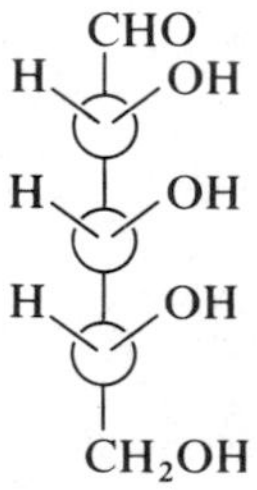

(b)

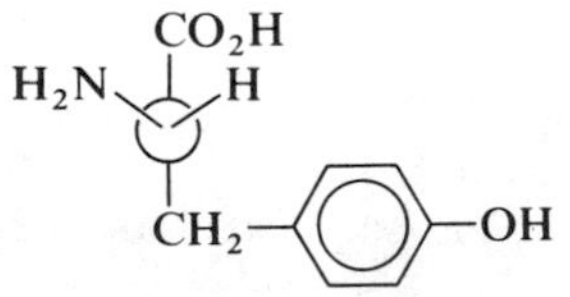

4.38 Give the structures and configurations for all the stereoisomers of five-carbon alcohols (with one OH) that have stereoisomers, and indicate any enantiomeric pairs.

4.39 A carboxylic acid of the formula $C_3H_5O_2Br$ is optically active. What is its structure?

4.40 Give the structure of the lowest-molecular-weight alcohol (containing only C, H, and O) that is chiral.

4.41 Match the compound on the left with its stereoisomer, if any, on the right.

(a)

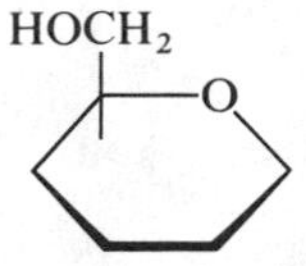

(1)

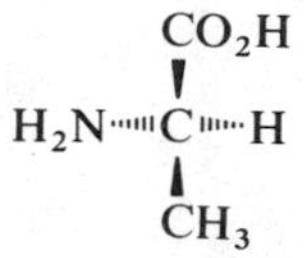

(b)

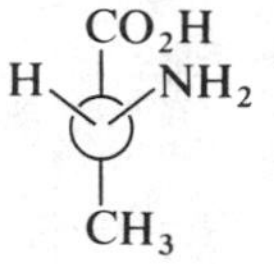

(2)

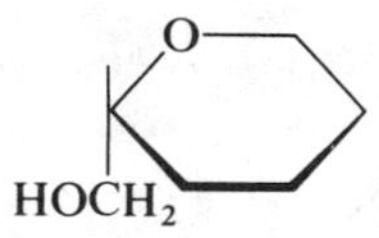

(c)

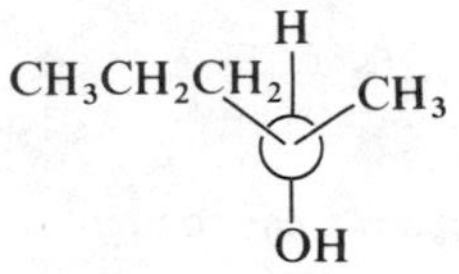

(3)

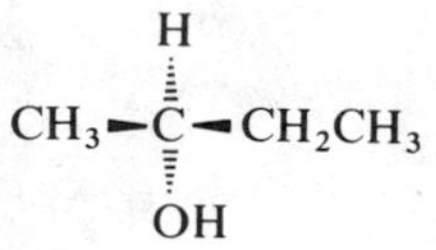

(d)

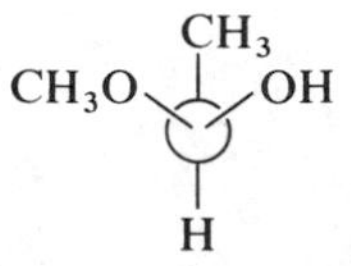

(4)

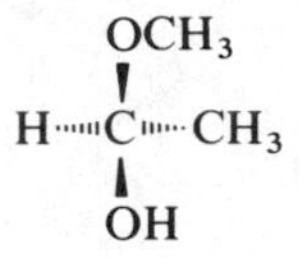

4.42 Which of the following pairs of formulas represent enantiomeric pairs?

(a) 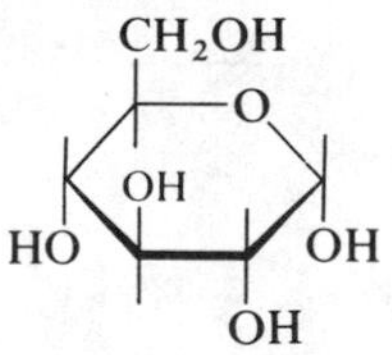 and

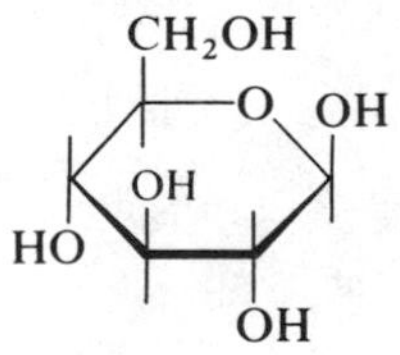

(b) 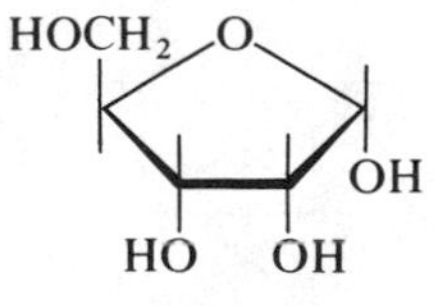 and

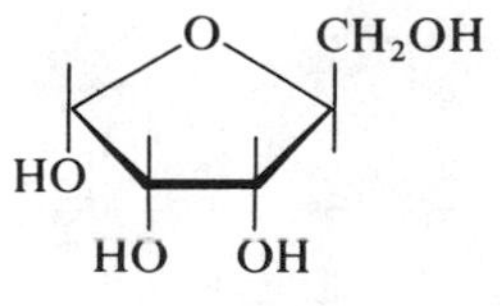

(c) 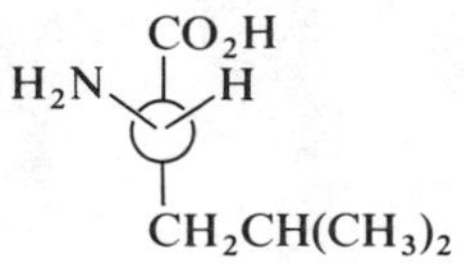 and

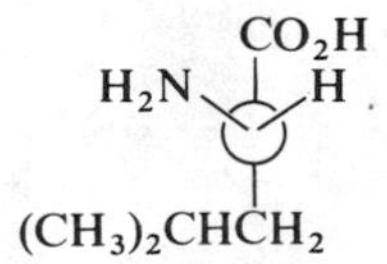

(d) 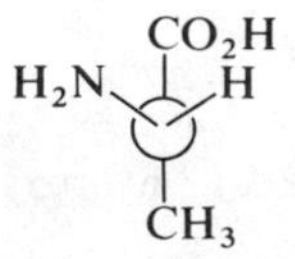 and

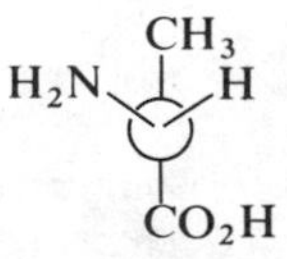

4.43 A pure sample of (S)-2-butanol has an $[\alpha]_D^{25}$ of $+13.5°$. What is the specific rotation of (R)-2-butanol?

4.44 Which of the following formulas represent *meso* compounds?

(a)    (b) 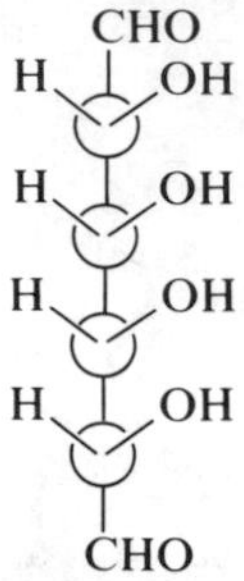   (c)

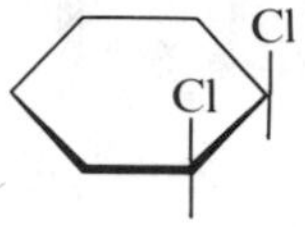

4.45 How many chiral carbons do each of the following compounds contain?

(a) 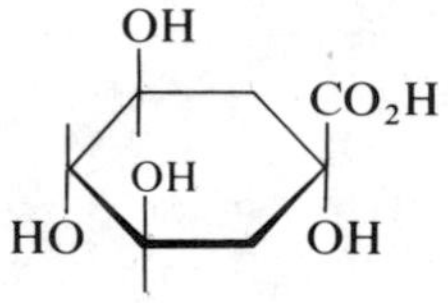   (b)

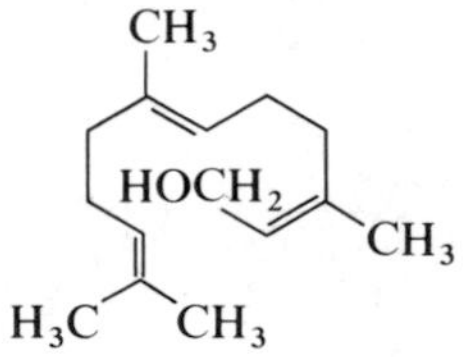

(c) 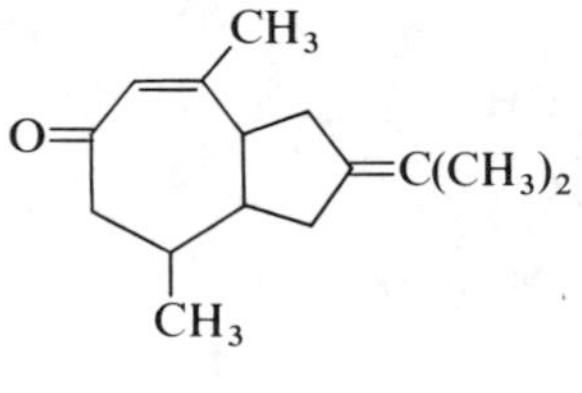   (d) 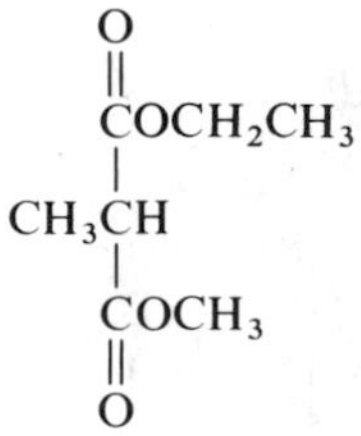 $CH_3\overset{\displaystyle \overset{O}{\|}}{C}H\overset{\displaystyle COCH_2CH_3}{\underset{\displaystyle \underset{O}{\|}}{|}}COCH_3$

(e) 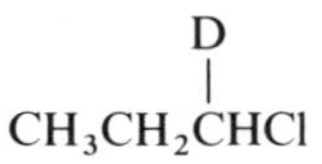 $CH_3CH_2\overset{\displaystyle \overset{D}{|}}{C}HCl$ (f)

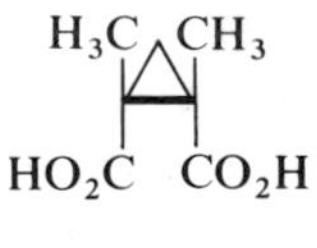

4.46 Draw ball-and-stick formulas for

(a) (R)-2-bromopropanoic acid, and
(b) ethyl (2R,3S)-3-amino-2-iodo-3-phenylpropanoate,

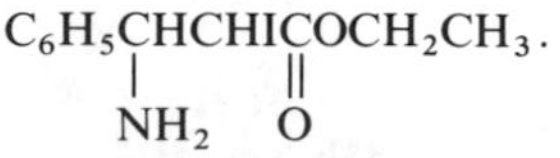

$$C_6H_5\overset{\displaystyle \underset{NH_2}{|}}{C}H\overset{\displaystyle |}{C}HI\overset{\displaystyle \overset{O}{\|}}{C}OCH_2CH_3.$$

4.47 What is the *maximum number* of stereoisomers possible for   (a) 3-hydroxy-2-methyl-butanoic acid, and   (b) 2,4-dimethyl-1-pentanol?

4.48 (a) Which of the following formulas are enantiomers?
(b) Which are diastereomers?
(c) Which is a *meso* form?

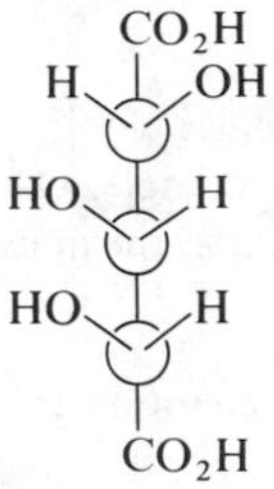

$$\begin{array}{ccc}
\text{I} & \text{II} & \text{III}
\end{array}$$

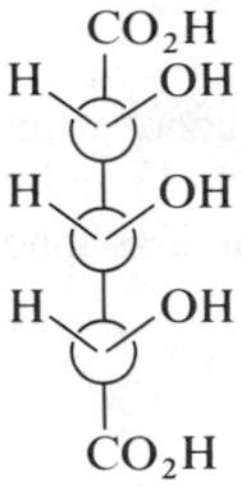

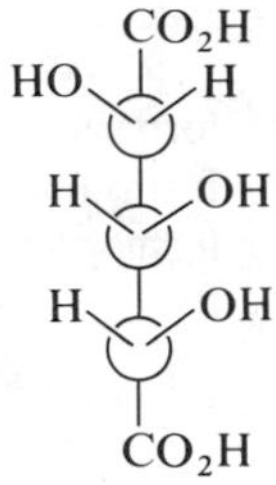

4.49 Give the structures of all possible configurations of 2,3,4-pentanetriol. Indicate enantiomeric pairs. Are there any *meso* forms?

4.50 Draw ball-and-stick formulas for (a) any enantiomeric pairs, (b) a *meso* form, and (c) any diastereomeric pairs for $HO_2CCHBrCH_2CHBrCO_2H$.

4.51 Draw a ball-and-stick formula for (2S,3S)-2,3-dichlorobutanedioic acid,

$$HO_2CCHClCHClCO_2H.$$

4.52 Draw a projection with H in the rear for each of the following formulas. For (c), show a projection for each chiral carbon.

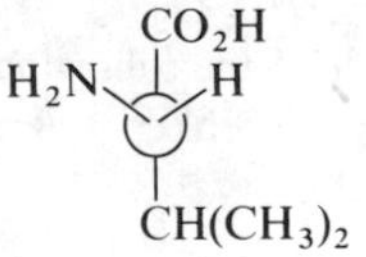

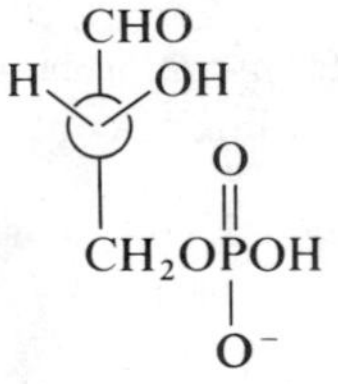

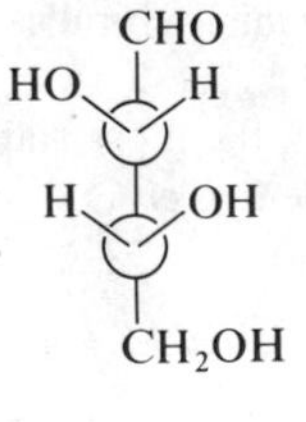

4.53 Assign an (R) or (S) designation to each of the following structures:

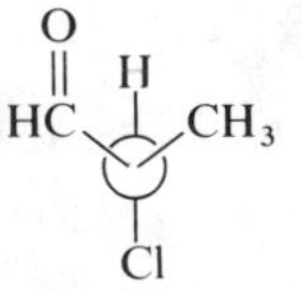

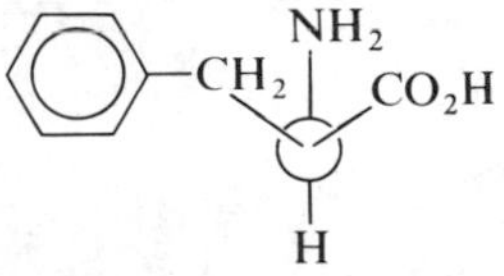

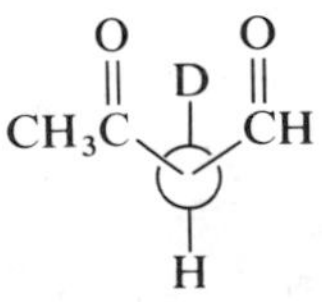

4.54 Assign (R) or (S) to each of the following structures:

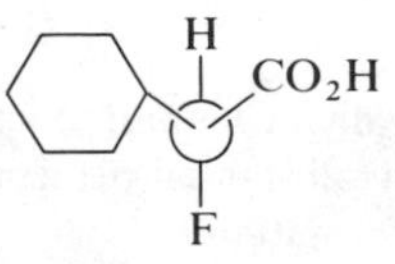

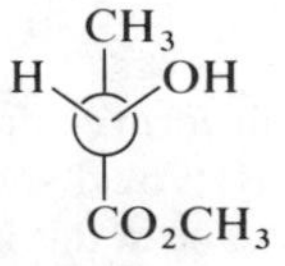

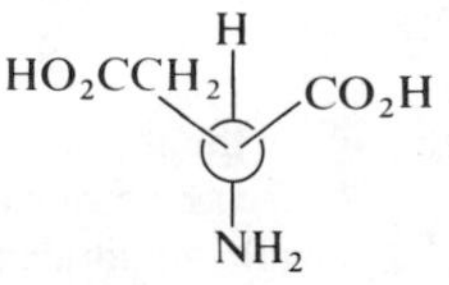

4.55 In the middle of the 19th century, it was proposed that a carbon atom with four groups attached is tetrahedral and not flat or pyramidal. Place yourself in the position of a chemist of that era and answer the following question. In each of the following systems, how many stereoisomers would exist for a compound in which carbon is attached to four different groups?

(a) Carbon forms four planar bonds with bond angles of 90°.
(b) Carbon forms four tetrahedral bonds with bond angles of 109.5°.
(c) Carbon forms regular pyramidal bonds (carbon at the apex).

4.56 In each system in Problem 4.55, how many pairs of enantiomers are possible?

4.57 Enzymes in the liver convert all-*trans*-vitamin A to 11-*cis*-vitamin A. (The geometry around the other double bonds is not changed.) The 11-*cis*-vitamin A is then converted to rhodopsin, which is the receptor of light in the eye. Give the structure of 11-*cis*-vitamin A.

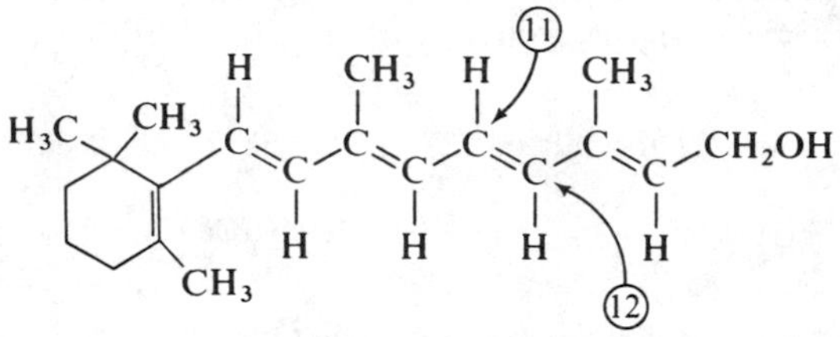

all-*trans*-vitamin A

4.58 How many chiral carbons are there in a molecule of vitamin A? (See Problem 4.57.)

4.59 Draw the most stable chair-form conformation for each of the following structures. (Note that *cis* and *trans* relationships may be deduced by the broken wedges or lack of them.)

(a) 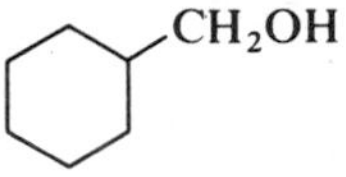   (b) 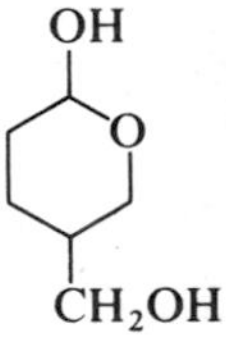   (c)

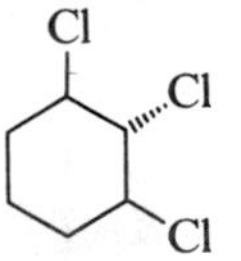

4.60 (a) Give the structure for the most stable conformer of the following menthyl chloride:

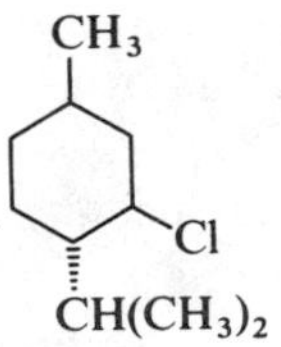

(b) Give the structure of the chair-form conformer in which Cl is *anti* to an H on one of the adjacent carbon atoms. Would you expect a substantial percentage of the menthyl chloride molecules to be in this latter conformation?

4.61 *Inositols* are 1,2,3,4,5,6-hexahydroxycyclohexanes that are found in all cells. *scyllo*-Inositol is the most stable of all the inositols. Draw its structure in the chair form.

4.62 Draw Newman projections of carbons 2 and 3 in the following structures, showing all possible staggered conformations:

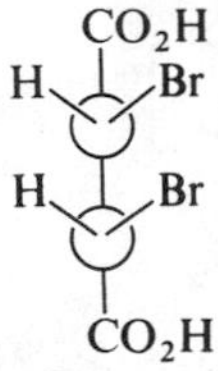

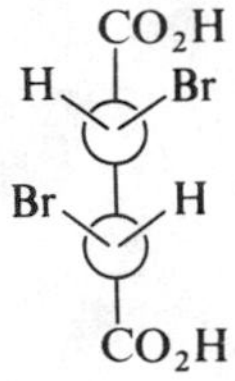

4.63 Give Newman projections for the most stable and the least stable conformations of (1S,2R)-1,2-dibromo-1,2-diphenylethane.

4.64 Draw Newman projections for all stereoisomers of 1-bromo-1,2-diphenylpropane in which the H on carbon 2 and the Br are *anti*.

4.65 Assign (R) and (S) configurations to the stereoisomers of 1-bromo-1,2-diphenylpropane.

4.66 The compound $CH_3CH{=}C{=}CHCH_3$ is of a class called *allenes*. Although this compound has no chiral carbon, it does have a pair of enantiomers. Explain. (*Hint*: Consider the bonding and the resultant geometry. Use models.)

4.67 (S)-2-Iodobutane has an $[\alpha]_D^{24}$ of $+15.9°$. (a) What is the observed rotation at 24° of an equimolar mixture of (R)- and (S)-2-iodobutane? (b) What is the observed rotation (at 24°, 1-dm sample tube) of a solution (1.0 g/ml) of a mixture that is 25% (R)- and 75% (S)-2-iodobutane?

4.68 What is the specific rotation of each of the following solutions at 20°, Na D-line?

(a) 1.00 g of sample is diluted to 5.00 ml. A 3.00-ml aliquot is placed in a tube that is 1.0 cm long. The observed rotation is $+0.45°$.
(b) A 0.20-g sample is diluted to 2.0 ml and placed in a 10-cm tube. The observed rotation is $-3.2°$.

4.69 Each of the following compounds is dissolved in an optically inactive solvent. Which would cause a rotation of the plane of vibration of plane-polarized light?

(a) (2S,3R)-butanediamine, $CH_3CH{-}CHCH_3$;
(b) (2S,3S)-butanediamine;
(c) an equimolar mixture of (a) and (b);
(d) an equimolar mixture of (b) and (2R,3R)-butanediamine;
(e) the principal constituent of oil of balsam (page 895).

4.70 Calculate the specific rotation of   (a) an equimolar mixture of (−)-tartaric acid and *meso*-tartaric acid, and   (b) an equimolar mixture of (−)- and (+)-tartaric acid. (The $[\alpha]_D^{20}$ for (+)-tartaric acid is +12.0°.)

4.71 Which of the following compounds has an enantiomer? [Use models for (b) and (c).]

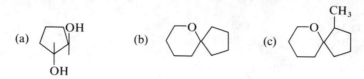

(a)

(b)

(c)

(d)

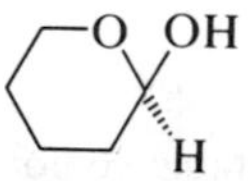

(e)

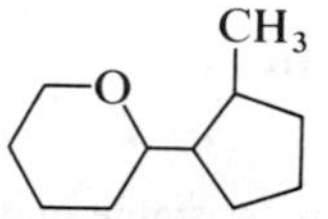

Chapter 5

Alkyl Halides; Substitution and Elimination Reactions

Organohalogen compounds are used extensively in modern society. Some are used as solvents, some as insecticides, and some as intermediates in the synthesis of other organic compounds.

$$ClCH{=}CCl_2$$

trichloroethene
a dry-cleaning solvent

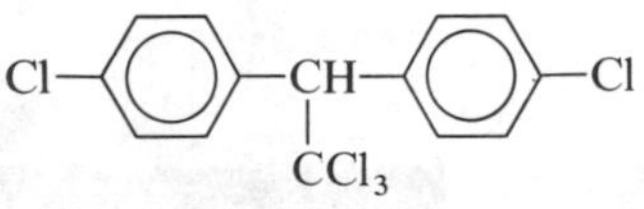

DDT
an insecticide

Most organohalogen compounds are synthetic. Naturally occurring organohalogen compounds are rather rare. Thyroxine, a component of the thyroid hormone thyroglobulin, is a naturally occurring iodine compound. Another naturally occurring organohalogen compound is Tyrian purple, a compound obtained in tiny amounts from a rare species of snail found in Crete. Tyrian purple was used as a dye by the Phoenician royalty and later by the Romans. (We still hear the phrases "royal purple" or "born to the purple.")

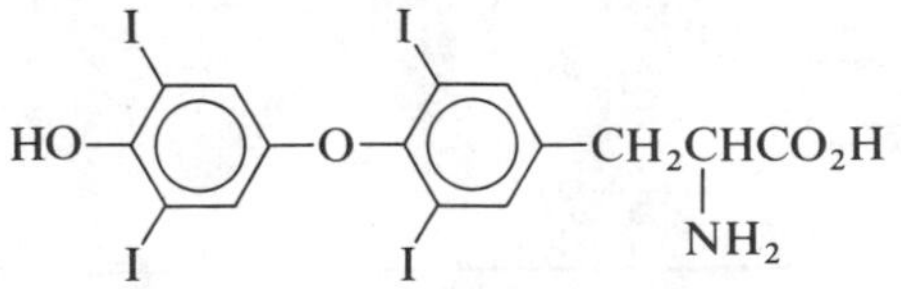

thyroxine

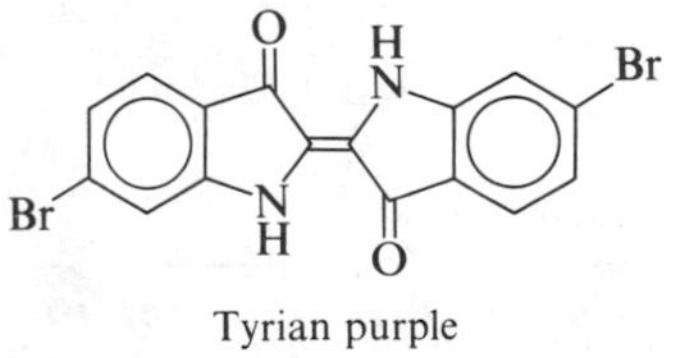

Tyrian purple

As a class of compounds, organohalogen compounds are toxic and should be used with caution. For example, the solvents carbon tetrachloride (CCl_4) and chloroform ($CHCl_3$) both cause liver damage when inhaled in excess. Insecticides that contain halogens (such as DDT) have been widely used in agriculture; however, their use has declined in recent years due to their detrimental effects upon the environment. Certain organohalogen compounds are strong lachrymators—that is, they cause tears to flow profusely.

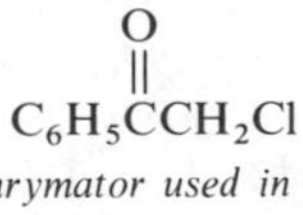

$$\overset{\displaystyle O}{\overset{\displaystyle \|}{C_6H_5CCH_2Cl}}$$

a lachrymator used in Mace

Compounds containing only carbon, hydrogen, and a halogen atom fall into three categories: **alkyl halides**, **aryl halides** (in which a halogen is bonded to a carbon of an aromatic ring), and **vinyl halides** (in which a halogen is bonded to a double-bonded carbon). A few examples follow:

Alkyl halides (RX): CH_3I 〈 〉—Br   〈 ◯ 〉—CH_2Cl

Aryl halides (ArX):   〈 ◯ 〉—Br   〈 ◯◯ 〉—Cl

Vinyl halides: $CH_2{=}CHCl$ $CH_3CH{=}CCH_2CH_3$
                                                              |
                                                             Br

We have already defined R as the general symbol for an alkyl group. In a similar manner, Ar is the general symbol for an aromatic, or **aryl**, group. A halogen atom (F, Cl, Br, or I) may be represented by X. Using these general symbols, an alkyl halide is RX, and an aryl halide such as bromobenzene (C_6H_5Br) is ArX.

A halogen atom in an organic compound is a functional group, a site of chemical reactivity. In this chapter, we will discuss reactions of only the alkyl halides. Aryl halides and vinyl halides do not undergo the reactions that we will present in this chapter, partly because a bond from an sp^2 carbon is stronger than a bond from an sp^3 carbon (Section 2.4F). Because this is the first chapter devoted to compounds containing functional groups, we will also use this chapter as an introduction to organic chemical reactions.

Section 5.1

Bonding in Organohalogen Compounds

The carbon–halogen sigma bond is formed by the overlap of an orbital of the halogen atom and a hybrid orbital of the carbon atom. We cannot be sure of the hybridization of the halogen atom in an organic halide because a halogen forms only one covalent bond and therefore has no bond angle around it. However, carbon uses the same type of hybrid orbital to bond to a halogen atom as it does to bond to a hydrogen atom or to another carbon atom.

A halogen atom is electronegative with respect to carbon; an alkyl halide is polar, as illustrated by the following dipole moments. (Dipole moments were discussed in Section 1.8B.)

Dipole moments of the methyl halides:

	CH_3F	CH_3Cl	CH_3Br	CH_3I
$\mu =$	1.81 D	1.86 D	1.78 D	1.64 D

A carbon atom bonded to a halogen atom has a *partial positive charge*. The positive charge renders this particular carbon atom in an organic molecule susceptible to attack by an anion. As we will see, attack at this positive carbon is part of the general pattern of reactions of alkyl halides.

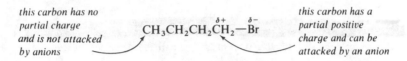

this carbon has no partial charge and is not attacked by anions

$$CH_3CH_2CH_2\overset{\delta+}{CH_2}-\overset{\delta-}{Br}$$

this carbon has a partial positive charge and can be attacked by an anion

Physical Properties of Alkyl Halides

Except for fluorine, halogen atoms have large atomic radii, and thus their outer electrons are diffuse. Halogen atoms do not form strong bonds with hydrogen. For this reason, a halide ion is an extremely weak base. In covalent compounds, such as alkyl halides, the halogen does not undergo hydrogen bonding; the alkyl halides are therefore insoluble in water.

The names, boiling points, and densities of several alkyl halides are listed in Table 5.1. Except for fluorine, halogen atoms are heavy compared to carbon or hydrogen atoms. The increase in molecular weight as halogen atoms are substituted into molecules causes an increase in the boiling point of a compound. Compare, for example, the boiling points of CH_3Cl, CH_2Cl_2, $CHCl_3$, and CCl_4.

Again, because of the mass of a halogen atom, the densities of liquid alkyl halides are generally greater than those of other comparable organic compounds. Whereas most organic compounds are lighter than water (densities less than

Table 5.1.   Physical Properties of Some Halogenated Alkanes

Trivial name	Formula	Bp, °C	Density, g/cc at 20°
methyl chloride	CH_3Cl	−24	gas
methylene chloride	CH_2Cl_2	40	1.34
chloroform	$CHCl_3$	61	1.49
carbon tetrachloride	CCl_4	77	1.60
methyl bromide	CH_3Br	5	gas
methyl iodide	CH_3I	43	2.28

1.0 g/cc), many common alkyl halides are *heavier*; an alkyl halide sinks to the bottom of a container of water rather than floating on top as most organic compounds do.

Section 5.3

Nomenclature and Classification of Alkyl Halides

In the IUPAC system, an alkyl halide is named with a **halo-** prefix.

$$\overset{\overset{\text{Cl}}{|}}{\text{CH}_3\text{CHCH}_2\text{CH}_3}$$

IUPAC: 2-chlorobutane   bromocyclohexane

Many common alkyl halides have trivial **functional-group names**. In these names, the name of the alkyl group is given, followed by the name of the halide.

$$\overset{\overset{\text{Cl}}{|}}{\text{CH}_3\text{CHCH}_2\text{CH}_3}$$

trivial: *sec*-butyl chloride   cyclohexyl bromide

STUDY PROBLEMS

5.1 Give two names for   (a) $(CH_3)_3CI$ and for   (b) $(CH_3)_2CHCl$.

5.2 Write structural formulas for   (a) 1,1-dibromobutane, (b) 3-chloro-1-butene, and (c) 2-fluoro-1-ethanol.

In chemical reactions, the structure of the alkyl portion of an alkyl halide is important. Therefore, we need to differentiate the four types of alkyl halide: **methyl**, **primary**, **secondary**, and **tertiary**.

A **methyl halide** is a structure in which one hydrogen of methane has been replaced by a halogen.

The methyl halides:

CH_3F	CH_3Cl	CH_3Br	CH_3I
methyl fluoride	methyl chloride	methyl bromide	methyl iodide
(fluoromethane)	(chloromethane)	(bromomethane)	(iodomethane)

The *head carbon* of an alkyl halide is the carbon atom bonded to the halogen. A **primary (1°) alkyl halide** (RCH_2X) has *one alkyl group* bonded to the head carbon. In the following examples, the head carbons and their hydrogens are circled.

Primary alkyl halides (one alkyl group attached to head):

$$\text{CH}_3\text{—CH}_2\text{Br} \qquad (\text{CH}_3)_3\text{C—CH}_2\text{Cl}$$

ethyl bromide   neopentyl chloride   (iodomethyl)cyclohexane
(bromoethane)   (1-chloro-2,2-
                       dimethylpropane)

A **secondary (2°) alkyl halide** (R_2CHX) has *two* alkyl groups attached to the head carbon, and a **tertiary (3°) alkyl halide** (R_3CX) has *three* alkyl groups attached to the head carbon. (Note that a halogen attached to a cycloalkane ring must be either secondary or tertiary.)

Secondary alkyl halides (*two alkyl groups attached to head*):

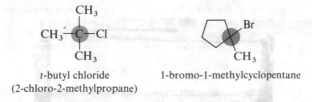

sec-butyl bromide	cyclopentyl chloride
(2-bromobutane)	(chlorocyclopentane)

Tertiary alkyl halides (*three alkyl groups attached to head*):

$$CH_3-\overset{\overset{\displaystyle CH_3}{|}}{\underset{\underset{\displaystyle CH_3}{|}}{C}}-Cl$$

t-butyl chloride	1-bromo-1-methylcyclopentane
(2-chloro-2-methylpropane)	

Sample Problem

Classify each of the following alkyl halides as 1°, 2°, or 3°:

(a) $CH_3\overset{\overset{\displaystyle CH_3}{|}}{C}HCH_2Cl$

(b) [cyclohexane]—Cl

(c) $CH_3\underset{\underset{\displaystyle CH_2CH_2CH_3}{|}}{C}HCl$

(d) [cyclohexane with CH_2CH_3 and Cl]

Solution: (a) 1°; (b) 2°; (c) 2°; (d) 3°

Section 5.4

A Preview of Substitution and Elimination Reactions

A. Substitution Reactions

The head carbon atom of an alkyl halide has a partial positive charge. In solution, this carbon can be attacked by an anion. The result is a **substitution reaction**, a reaction in which one atom, ion, or group is substituted for another.

$$OH^- + CH_3\overset{\delta+}{C}H_2\overset{\delta-}{-}Br \longrightarrow CH_3CH_2-OH + Br^-$$

ethyl bromide	ethanol

$$^-OCH_3 + (CH_3)_2CH-Cl \longrightarrow (CH_3)_2CH-OCH_3 + Cl^-$$

isopropyl chloride	isopropyl methyl ether

In substitution reactions of the alkyl halides, the halogen is called the **leaving group**, a term meaning any group that can be displaced from a carbon atom. In this chapter, we will discuss only the halides as leaving groups; we will introduce other leaving groups as we encounter them in subsequent chapters.

$$\underset{\text{the leaving group}}{:\overset{..}{\underset{..}{O}}H^- + CH_3CH_2-\overset{..}{\underset{..}{B}}r:} \longrightarrow CH_3CH_2-\overset{..}{\underset{..}{O}}H + :\overset{..}{\underset{..}{B}}r:^-$$

the leaving group

these σ-bond electrons leave with the halogen

In substitution reactions of alkyl halides, the iodide ion is the halide most easily displaced, followed by the bromide ion and then the chloride ion. Because the C—F bond is the strongest of the C—X bonds, the fluoride ion is not easily displaced. From a practical standpoint, only Cl, Br, and I are good enough leaving groups to be useful in substitution reactions. For this reason, when we refer to RX, we usually mean alkyl chlorides, bromides, and iodides.

$$RF \quad RCl \quad RBr \quad RI$$
increasing reactivity

The anion or molecule that attacks an alkyl halide in a substitution reaction is called a **nucleophile** (literally, "nucleus lover"), often abbreviated Nu⁻. In our preceding equation, OH⁻ is the nucleophile. A nucleophile is *any species that is attracted to a positive center*. Substitution reactions caused by nucleophiles are called **nucleophilic substitutions**, or **nucleophilic displacements**. A general equation for a nucleophilic substitution reaction of an alkyl halide is:

$$Nu^- + RX \longrightarrow RNu + X^-$$

The opposite of nucleophile is **electrophile** ("electron lover"), or E⁺. An electrophile is *a species that is attracted toward a negative center*—that is, a Lewis acid, such as H⁺. Electrophilic reactions are common in organic chemistry; we will encounter many of these reactions in later chapters. In this chapter, we will be dealing only with the reactions of nucleophiles with alkyl halides.

To be an effective nucleophile in a substitution reaction, the nucleophile generally should be a *stronger base than the leaving group*. For example, OH⁻ displaces the weaker base Cl⁻, but the reverse is not true (Cl⁻ will not displace OH⁻). A few species that are stronger bases than halide ions (and can displace a halide ion from RX) are listed in Table 5.2. We will discuss nucleophiles in more detail in Section 5.11.

$$CH_3O^- + CH_3CH_2Br \longrightarrow CH_3CH_2OCH_3 + Br^-$$
stronger base   methyl ethyl ether   *weaker base*

$$CH_3S^- + CH_3CH_2Br \longrightarrow CH_3CH_2SCH_3 + Br^-$$
stronger base   methyl ethyl sulfide   *weaker base*

$$^-CN + CH_3CH_2Br \longrightarrow CH_3CH_2CN + Br^-$$
stronger base   propanenitrile   *weaker base*

Table 5.2. Some Nucleophiles That Can Displace X⁻ from RX

Nucleophile	Typical reagent	Product
$^-:\ddot{O}H$	NaOH	ROH (an alcohol)
$^-:\ddot{O}R'$	$NaOCH_2CH_3$	ROR' (an ether)
$^-:\ddot{S}R'$	$NaSCH_3$	RSR' (a sulfide)
$^-:C{\equiv}N:$	NaCN	RCN (a nitrile)

Sample Problem

You wish to run a series of nucleophilic substitution reactions with ethyl chloride in ethanol as the solvent. Which of the following laboratory reagents would be useful as nucleophiles?

(a) HCl   (b) NaO—⟨◯⟩   (c) $NaSCH_3$

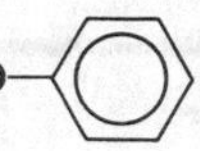

Solution: (b) and (c) both contain nucleophiles that are stronger bases than Cl^-: $^-OC_6H_5$ and $^-SCH_3$. (a) contains H^+ and Cl^-: it would not be useful.

Sample Problem

Give the structures of the substitution products (if any) of the following reactions:

(a) $CH_3CH_2CH_2CH_2I + {}^-CN \longrightarrow$

(b) 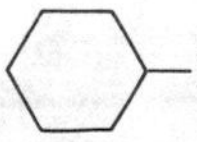   ⟨⬡⟩—Br + $NaSCH_2CH_3 \longrightarrow$

(c) 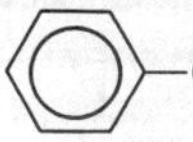   ⟨◯⟩—Cl + $^-OH \longrightarrow$

(d)   Cl—⟨◯⟩—CH_2Cl + $^-OH \longrightarrow$

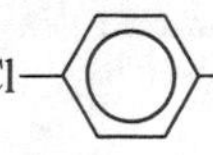

Solution: (a) $CH_3CH_2CH_2CH_2CN$; (b) 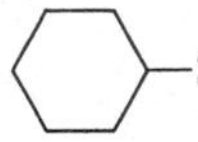 ⟨⬡⟩—SCH_2CH_3; (c) no reaction for an

aryl halide; (d) Cl—⟨◯⟩—CH_2OH

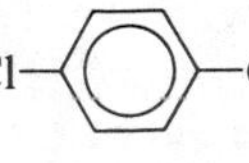

B. Elimination Reactions

Another reaction that can occur when an alkyl halide is treated with a nucleophile or a base is an **elimination reaction**: a reaction in which part of a molecule is eliminated. In an elimination reaction of an alkyl halide, the elements of H and X are lost (usually from adjacent carbon atoms); therefore, these reactions are also called **dehydrohalogenation reactions**. (The prefix *de-* means "minus" or "loss of.") The product of a dehydrohalogenation reaction of an alkyl halide is an alkene.

$$CH_3CH \!\!\! \underset{\substack{\uparrow \\ Br}}{\overset{}{-}} \!\!\! CH_2 \;+\; {}^-OH \;\longrightarrow\; CH_3CH{=}CH_2 \;+\; H_2O \;+\; Br^-$$

isopropyl bromide   propene
                                               (propylene)

$$CH_3 \!\!\! \underset{\substack{| \\ CH_3}}{\overset{\substack{CH_3 \\ |}}{C}} \!\!\! -Cl \;+\; {}^-OH \;\longrightarrow\; CH_3 \!\!\! \underset{\substack{| \\ CH_3}}{\overset{\substack{CH_2 \\ ||}}{C}} \;+\; H_2O \;+\; Cl^-$$

t-butyl chloride   methylpropene
                                               (isobutylene)

Section 5.5

Competing Reactions

Substitution and elimination reactions of alkyl halides are **competing reactions** —that is, one starting material can undergo more than one reaction. The actual products depend on the particular alkyl halide, the nucleophile, the solvent, and other reaction conditions.

Competing reactions can lead to mixtures of products:

$$\underset{\substack{| \\ Br}}{CH_3CHCH_3} \;+\; {}^-OCH_2CH_3 \;\longrightarrow\; \underset{\substack{| \\ OCH_2CH_3}}{CH_3CHCH_3} \;+\; CH_2{=}CHCH_3$$

isopropyl bromide   ethyl isopropyl ether   propene
                                              20%   80%

There are two different types of substitution reaction: S_N2 (meaning *substitution, nucleophilic, bimolecular*) and S_N1 (*substitution, nucleophilic, unimolecular*). There are also two different types of elimination reaction: **E2** (*elimination, bimolecular*) and **E1** (*elimination, unimolecular*). These four reactions are competing, and all four may occur within one reaction flask at the same time. (Because product mixtures are the rule rather than the exception when competing reactions occur, we will not balance most of the organic equations that you will find in this book.) For simplicity, we will discuss each of these four reactions separately, then toward the end of the chapter we will discuss them in relation to each other.

Section 5.6

The S_N2 Reaction

The reaction of ethyl bromide with hydroxide ion to yield ethanol and bromide ion is a typical S_N2 reaction. Virtually any primary alkyl halide undergoes S_N2 reaction with any of the nucleophiles in Table 5.2. Secondary alkyl halides can also undergo S_N2 reactions; however, tertiary alkyl halides do not.

A.   Reaction Mechanism

The detailed description of how a reaction occurs is called a **reaction mechanism**. A reaction mechanism must take into account all known facts. For some reactions, the number of facts known is considerable, and the particular reaction mechanisms are accepted by most chemists. The mechanisms of some other reactions are still quite speculative. The S_N2 reaction is one that has been studied extensively; there is a large amount of data supporting the mechanism that we will present.

For molecules to undergo reaction, they must first collide. Often the orientation of molecules is an important factor in determining whether a reaction will occur. This is true in an S_N2 reaction; therefore, we will discuss first the *stereochemistry* of this type of reaction.

Most collisions between molecules do not result in a reaction; rather, the molecules simply rebound. To undergo reaction, the colliding molecules must contain enough *potential energy* for bond breakage to occur. The potential energy of the molecules may be increased by increasing the kinetic energy of the system (that is, by heating). As the molecules gain kinetic energy and collide more frequently, some of the kinetic energy is converted into potential energy. After we discuss the stereochemistry of an S_N2 reaction, we will return to a discussion of the energy requirements.

B. Stereochemistry of an S_N2 Reaction

In the S_N2 reaction between ethyl bromide and hydroxide ion, the oxygen of the hydroxide ion collides with the rear of the head carbon and displaces the bromide ion.

Overall S_N2 reaction:

rear attack

When a nucleophile collides with the backside of a tetrahedral carbon atom bonded to a halogen, two things occur simultaneously: (1) a new bond begins to form, and (2) the C—X bond begins to break. The process is said to be a one-step, or *concerted*, process. If the potential energy of the two colliding species is high enough, a point is reached where it is energetically more favorable for the new bond to form and the old C—X bond to break. As the reactants are converted to products, they must pass through an in-between state that has maximum potential energy. This state is called the **transition state**, or the **activated complex**. Because the transition state is composed of two particles (Nu^- and RX), the S_N2 reaction is said to be **bimolecular**.

transition state:
maximum potential energy,
equally able to go to reactants
or products

A transition state in any reaction is the fleeting high-energy arrangement of the reactants as they go to products. We cannot isolate a transition state and put it in a flask. The transition state is simply a description of "molecules in a state of transition." We will use square brackets in an equation to show any temporary, nonisolable structure in a reaction. Here, we use brackets to enclose the structure of a transition state. Later on, we will also use brackets to indicate unstable products that undergo further reaction.

For the S_N2 reaction, the transition state involves a temporary rehybridization of the head carbon from sp^3 to sp^2 and finally back to sp^3 again. You may ask how we know this. Our answer is that this is the hybridization that explains the geometry of the transition state: the carbon atom has three planar sp^2 bonds, plus two half-bonds using the p orbital.

As the nucleophile attacks from the rear, the other three groups attached to the carbon flatten out in the transition state, then flip to the other side of the carbon atom, much as an umbrella blowing inside out. (Models would be useful to help you visualize this.) This flipping is called **inversion of configuration**, or **Walden inversion** after the chemist who discovered it.

The existence of inversion of configuration as part of the mechanism of an S_N2 reaction has been beautifully demonstrated by reactions of pure enantiomers of chiral secondary alkyl halides. For example, the reaction of (R)-2-bromopentane with $^-$OH gives exclusively (S)-2-pentanol.

(R)-2-bromopentane (S)-2-pentanol

Most reactions involving chiral centers are carried out with racemic mixtures —that is, equal mixtures of (R) and (S) reactants. In these cases, the products also are racemic mixtures. Even though inversion occurs, we cannot observe the effects because half the molecules go one way and half go the other way.

C. *Energy in an S_N2 Reaction*

We have mentioned that colliding molecules need energy to undergo reaction. We will now look at these energy requirements in more detail.

Molecules moving around in a solution contain a certain amount of potential energy in their bonds and a certain amount of kinetic energy from their movement. Not all molecules in solution have exactly the same amount of potential or kinetic energy; however, we may speak of the *average energy* of the molecules. The energy of the reaction mixture as a whole may be increased by heating the solution, for example. The molecules gain kinetic energy, collide, and exchange some kinetic energy for potential energy.

Before a reaction can begin to occur, some of the colliding molecules and ions in the flask must contain enough energy to reach the transition state upon collision. Reaching the potential-energy level of the transition state is rather like driving an old car to a mountain pass. Does the car have enough energy to make the top? Or will it stall and slide back down the mountain? Once you reach the top, which way do you go—back the way you came or on down the other side? Once you are descending the far side, the choice is easy—you can relax and let the car roll to the bottom.

Figure 5.1 shows an energy diagram for the progress of an S$_N$2 reaction. The potential energy required to reach the transition state forms an energy barrier; it is the point of maximum energy on the graph. For a colliding alkyl halide and nucleophile to reach the transition state, they need a certain minimum amount of energy called the **energy of activation E_{act}**. At the transition state, the molecules find it just as easy to go back to reactants or on to products. But, once over the top, the path of least resistance is that of going to products.

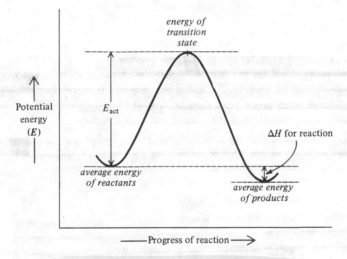

Figure 5.1.   Energy diagram of an S$_N$2 reaction.

Each molecule that undergoes reaction to yield product must pass through the transition state, both structurally and energetically. Since the energies of all the molecules are not the same, a certain amount of time is required for all the molecules present to react. This time requirement gives rise to the **rate of a reaction**, a topic that will be discussed shortly.

The difference between the average potential energy of reactants and that of products is the change in enthalpy ΔH for the reaction. If the energy of the products is less than the energy of the reactants, the overall reaction is *exothermic*: heat is liberated. If the energy of the products is greater, then the reaction is *endothermic*: the reaction absorbs heat rather than liberating it. These relationships are shown in Figure 5.2 (page 172).

Alkyl Halides; Substitution and Elimination Reactions

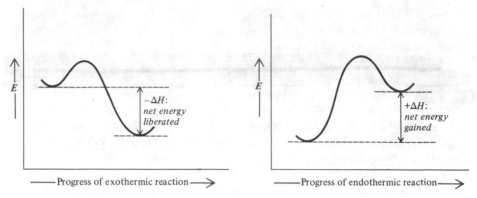

Figure 5.2. Energy diagrams for exothermic and endothermic reactions.

Note that ΔH for the reaction has very little to do with E_{act}. A reaction may be exothermic, yet still have a high energy of activation. For example, the burning of natural gas gives off substantial amounts of heat, but the natural gas must be ignited first. The spark or match supplies the initial E_{act}. The exothermic character of the combustion supplies the E_{act} for further reaction.

D. Rate of an $S_N 2$ Reaction

The rate of a chemical reaction is a measure of how fast the reaction proceeds —how fast reactants are consumed and products are formed. **Reaction kinetics** is the term used to describe the study and measurement of reaction rates.

The rate of a reaction depends on many variables, some of which may be held constant for a given experiment (temperature and solvent, for example). In this chapter, we will be concerned primarily with two variables: (1) the concentrations of the reactants, and (2) the structures of the reactants.

E. Effect of Concentration on Rate

Increasing the concentration of reactants undergoing an $S_N 2$ reaction increases the rate at which products are formed by increasing the frequency of molecular collisions. The rate of an $S_N 2$ reaction is proportional to the concentrations of both reactants. If all other variables are held constant and the concentration of either the alkyl halide or the nucleophile is doubled, the rate of product formation is doubled. If either concentration is multiplied by three, the rate is tripled.

$$Nu^- + RX \longrightarrow RNu + X^-$$

$$S_N 2 \text{ rate} = k\,[RX][Nu^-]$$

In this equation, [RX] and [Nu$^-$] represent the concentrations in moles/liter of the alkyl halide and the nucleophile, respectively. The term k is the proportionality constant, called the **rate constant**, between these concentrations and the measured rate of product formation. The value for k is constant for the same reaction under identical conditions (solvent, temperature, etc.)

Sample Problem

What would be the effect on the rate of the S_N2 reaction of CH_3I with CH_3O^- if the concentrations of *both* reactants were doubled and all other variables were held constant?

Solution: If the concentrations of both CH_3I and CH_3O^- were doubled, the rate would quadruple; the reaction would proceed four times as fast.

Because the rate of an S_N2 reaction is dependent on the concentrations of two particles (RX and Nu$^-$), the rate is said to be **second order**. The S_N2 reaction is said to follow **second-order kinetics**. Not all reactions follow second-order kinetics. We will find that the rate of an S_N1 reaction depends on the concentration of only one particle, and therefore follows first-order kinetics.

F. *Effect of E_{act} on Rate and on Products*

The effect of the energies of activation on the relative rates of reaction may be stated simply: *Under the same conditions, the reaction with the lower E_{act} has a faster rate.* The reason for this relationship is that, if less energy is required for reaction, a greater number of molecules have enough energy to react.

The effect of E_{act} on products is a direct result of relative rates. If one starting material can undergo two different reactions, the reaction with the lower E_{act} proceeds more quickly. *The products of the faster reaction (lower E_{act}) predominate.* Figure 5.3 shows an energy curve of two such reactions of the same starting material.

The E_{act} is the energy of the transition state relative to the reactants. Relative rates of reaction may thus be related to the energies of the transition states. In competing reactions of the same starting material, *the reaction with the lower-energy transition state is the faster reaction.* From Figure 5.3, it is evident that the reaction with the lower-energy transition state has the lower E_{act}.

A species of low potential energy is more stable than one of high energy. Therefore, we can say that *the reaction with a more stabilized transition-state*

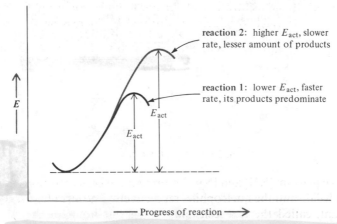

Figure 5.3. In competing reactions of a single starting material, the reaction with the lower E_{act} is the predominant one.

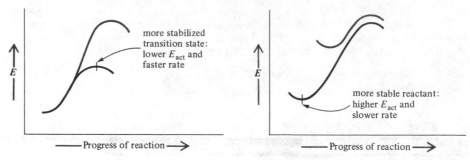

Figure 5.4.   The relationship between rates of reaction and the potential energies of transition
states and reactants.

structure is the faster reaction. Note that (1) a reaction of a lower-energy, more
stable *starting material* may proceed more slowly, but (2) a reaction that goes
through a lower-energy, more stabilized *transition state* proceeds more rapidly.
The important point is that the relative rates of reaction under the same conditions
depend ultimately on the value for E_{act} (see Figure 5.4).

G.   Effect of Structure on Rate

Reaction kinetics provide a valuable tool for exploring the effects of structure upon reactivity. Consider the following two reactions:

(1) $OH^- +$ CH_3Br $\longrightarrow$ $CH_3OH + Br^-$

methyl bromide   methanol
a methyl halide

(2) $OH^- +$ CH_3CH_2Br $\longrightarrow$ $CH_3CH_2OH + Br^-$

ethyl bromide   ethanol
a 1° alkyl halide

Both are S_N2 reactions and both yield alcohols. The two reactions differ only
in the alkyl portion of the alkyl halides. We may ask the following question:
"Does this difference in the alkyl group have an effect upon the rate of the S_N2
reaction?" To answer such a question, the rates of the two reactions are measured
under the same reaction conditions (the same solvent, the same concentrations,
and the same temperature). Then, either the two rate constants (k_1 and k_2) are
determined or, more commonly, the *relative rates* are determined.

$$CH_3Br \xrightarrow{\ OH^-\ } CH_3OH \qquad rate = k_1[CH_3Br][OH^-]$$

$$CH_3CH_2Br \xrightarrow{\ OH^-\ } CH_3CH_2OH \qquad rate = k_2[CH_3CH_2Br][OH^-]$$

$$relative\ rates\ of\ reaction\ of\ CH_3CH_2Br\ compared\ to\ CH_3CH_2Br = \frac{k_1}{k_2}$$

Under the conditions used in this study, methyl bromide undergoes reaction
30 times faster than ethyl bromide. (If it takes one hour for the ethyl bromide
reaction to reach completion, the methyl bromide reaction would take about
1/30 as long, or only two minutes!) We conclude that there is indeed a big difference

Table 5.3.   *Average Relative Rates of Some Alkyl Halides in a Typical S_N2 Reaction*

Alkyl halide	Relative rate
CH_3X	30
CH_3CH_2X	1
$CH_3CH_2CH_2X$	0.4
$CH_3CH_2CH_2CH_2X$	0.4
$(CH_3)_2CHX$	0.03
$(CH_3)_3CX$	~0

in how the methyl and ethyl groups affect the course of the reaction, and that the ethyl bromide reaction has a higher-energy transition state.

In a similar fashion, the relative rates of a variety of S_N2 reactions of alkyl halides have been determined. Table 5.3 shows some average relative rates (compared to ethyl halides) of S_N2 reactions of alkyl halides.

H.   *Steric Hindrance in S_N2 Reactions*

In S_N2 reactions of the alkyl halides listed in Table 5.3, methyl halides show the fastest rate, followed by primary alkyl halides, then secondary alkyl halides. Tertiary alkyl halides do not undergo S_N2 reactions.

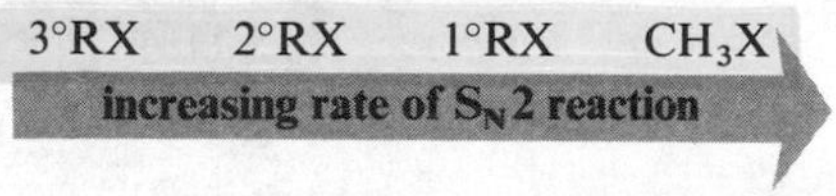

$$3°RX \qquad 2°RX \qquad 1°RX \qquad CH_3X$$

increasing rate of S_N2 reaction

As the number of alkyl groups attached to the head carbon increases ($CH_3X \rightarrow 1° \rightarrow 2° \rightarrow 3°$), the transition state becomes increasingly crowded with atoms. Consider the following examples of reactions of alkyl bromides with the methoxide ion (CH_3O^-) as the nucleophile ($CH_3O^- + RBr \rightarrow CH_3OR + Br^-$):

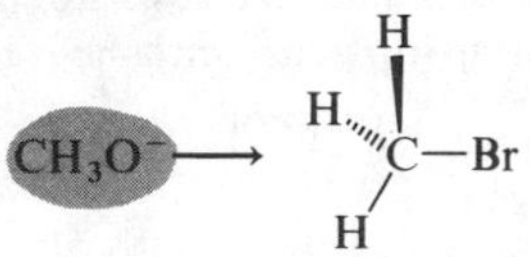

methyl bromide
very fast

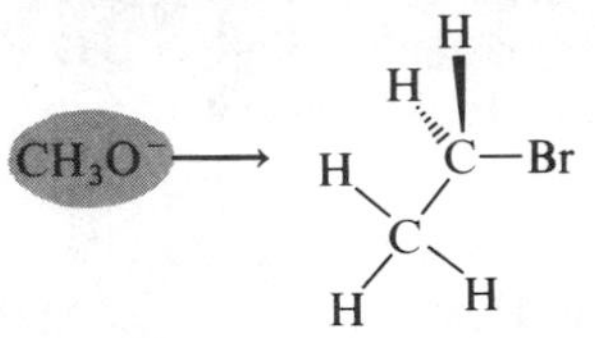

ethyl bromide
moderate rate

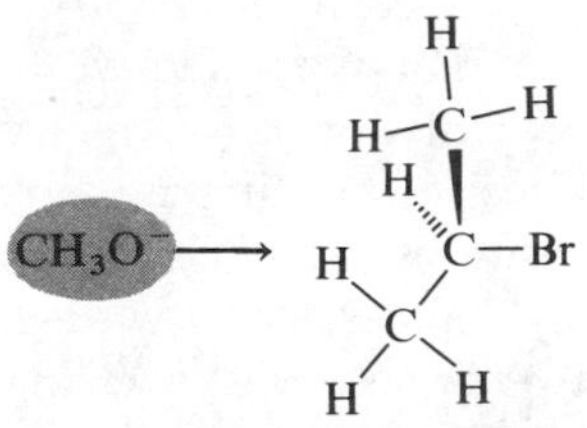

isopropyl bromide
very slow

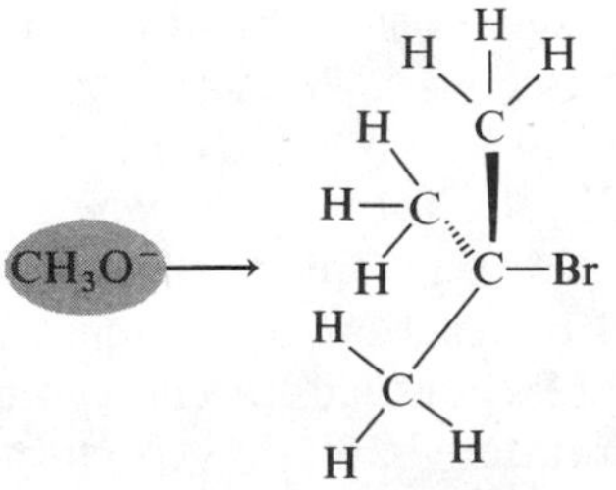

t-butyl bromide
no S_N2 reaction

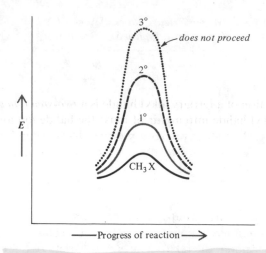

Figure 5.5. Energy diagram for S_N2 reactions of different types of alkyl halides.

Crowding in structures is called **steric hindrance**. When large groups are crowded in a small space, repulsions between groups become severe and therefore the energy of the system is high. The energy of a crowded transition state is higher than that of a transition state with less steric hindrance. For this reason, the rates of reaction become progressively slower in the series methyl, primary, secondary, and tertiary (see Figure 5.5). The energy of the S_N2 transition state of a tertiary alkyl halide is so high relative to other possible reaction paths that the S_N2 reaction does not proceed.

Sample Problem

The rate of S_N2 reaction of neopentyl bromide, $(CH_3)_3CCH_2Br$, with $Na^+ \ ^-OCH_2CH_3$ proceeds about 0.00001 times as fast as the reaction of ethyl bromide. Explain.

Solution: Although neopentyl bromide is a primary alkyl halide, the alkyl group attached to the head carbon atom is very bulky. The steric hindrance in the transition state is considerable. Therefore, the E_{act} is high and the rate is slow.

Section 5.7

The S_N1 Reaction

Because of steric hindrance, *t*-butyl bromide and other tertiary alkyl halides do not undergo S_N2 reactions. Yet, if *t*-butyl bromide is treated with a dilute solution of sodium hydroxide, *t*-butyl alcohol is rapidly formed. (An elimination product is also formed, but we will defer our discussion of elimination reactions until Section 5.9.) Inversion of configuration is not observed in the nucleophilic substitution reactions of enantiomeric tertiary alkyl halides, as it is with secondary alkyl halides; instead, racemic products generally are obtained. A change in the concentration of OH^- has no effect upon the overall rate of the reaction.

The reason for these differences from the S_N2 reaction is that *t*-butyl bromide and other tertiary alkyl halides undergo reaction with nucleophiles by a different pathway from that of primary alkyl halides. Tertiary alkyl halides undergo substitution by an S_N1 reaction path (*substitution, nucleophilic, unimolecular*).

$$(CH_3)_3CBr + OH^- \xrightarrow{S_N1} (CH_3)_3COH + Br^-$$

t-butyl bromide   *t*-butyl alcohol

The S_N1 reaction of a tertiary alkyl halide is a *two-step reaction*. Step 1 is the cleavage of the alkyl halide into a pair of ions: the halide ion and a **carbocation**, an ion in which a carbon atom carries a positive charge. Step 2 is the combining of the carbocation with the nucleophile (OH^-) to yield the product (*t*-butyl alcohol).

Step 1 (slow):

$$(CH_3)_3C-\ddot{B}r: \longrightarrow \left[(CH_3)_3\overset{\delta+}{C} - - - \overset{\delta-}{\ddot{B}r}: \right] \longrightarrow [(CH_3)_3C^+] + :\ddot{B}r:^-$$

t-butyl bromide   *transition state 1*   *unstable carbocation*
                                             intermediate

Step 2 (fast):

$$[(CH_3)_3C^+] + :\ddot{O}H^- \longrightarrow \left[(CH_3)_3\overset{\delta+}{C} - - - \overset{\delta-}{\ddot{O}H} \right] \longrightarrow (CH_3)_3C-\ddot{O}H$$

                                transition state 2   *t*-butyl alcohol

Step 1 in the reaction has a high E_{act} (Figure 5.6); it is the *slow step* in the overall process. Enough energy must be supplied to the tertiary alkyl halide to break the C—X sigma bond and yield the carbocation and the halide ion.

                                     means loss of Br⁻

Step 1: $(CH_3)_3CBr \xrightarrow[\text{slow}]{-Br^-} [(CH_3)_3C^+]$

The carbocation is an **intermediate** in this reaction, a structure that is formed during the reaction, and then undergoes further reaction to products. An intermediate is not a transition state. An intermediate has a finite lifetime; a transition state does not. At the transition state, molecules are undergoing bond-breaking and bond-making. The potential energy of a transition state is a high

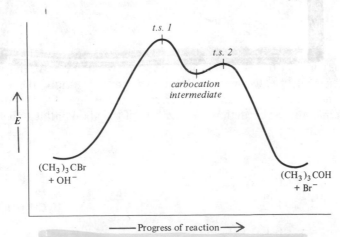

Figure 5.6. Energy diagram for an S_N1 reaction.

point on a potential-energy curve. By contrast, an intermediate is a temporary, reactive product. No bond-breaking or bond-making is occurring in an intermediate. An intermediate is of lower energy than transition states that surround it, but is of higher energy than the final products. The energy diagram in Figure 5.6 shows a dip for the carbocation formation; the dip is not a large one because the carbocation is a high-energy, reactive species.

Step 2 in the reaction is the further reaction of the carbocation with a hydroxide ion. The two combine in a reaction having a low energy of activation— a fast reaction.

Step 2: $[(CH_3)_3C^+]$ $\xrightarrow[\text{fast}]{OH^-}$ $(CH_3)_3COH$

STUDY PROBLEM

5.3 Draw the energy diagram for the following S_N1 reaction. Label all parts and draw the structures for all transition states and intermediates.

$$
\underset{\text{2-chloro-2-methylbutane}}{CH_3CH_2\overset{\overset{\displaystyle CH_3}{|}}{\underset{\underset{\displaystyle CH_3}{|}}{C}}-Cl} + NaOH \longrightarrow \underset{\text{2-methyl-2-butanol}}{CH_3CH_2\overset{\overset{\displaystyle CH_3}{|}}{\underset{\underset{\displaystyle CH_3}{|}}{C}}-OH} + NaCl
$$

A. Stereochemistry of an S_N1 Reaction

A carbocation (or **carbonium ion**, as it is also called) is a carbon atom with only three groups attached, instead of the usual four. Because there are only three. groups, the bonds to these groups lie in a plane, and the angles between the bonds from the positive carbon are approximately 120°. To attain this geometry, the positive carbon is sp^2-hybridized and has an empty p orbital.

empty p orbital

$$
\underset{R}{\overset{R}{\diagdown}}\!\!\!\!\!\!\!\!\!\!\overset{+}{C}-R
$$

sigma-bond angles around C^+ are approximately 120°

Let us consider the S_N1 reaction of a chiral alkyl halide. When (*S*)-3-bromo-3-methylhexane is treated with sodium hydroxide solution, the enantiomeric reactant undergoes *racemization* to yield a racemic mixture of the product alcohol. The first step in this S_N1 reaction is ionization of the alkyl halide to a carbocation and a halide ion:

Step 1:

(*S*)-3-bromo-3-methylhexane   *planar carbocation*

In the second step, OH^- attacks the carbocation to form two alcohols. If the OH^- attacks the empty p orbital from the top side, as we have shown the structure, the carbocation yields the (S)-enantiomer of the alcohol. However, if the OH^- attacks from the bottom side, the (R)-enantiomer is the product. Since there is equal probability of attack from either side, equal amounts of the (R)- and (S)-alcohols are produced.

Step 2:

attack from top

(S)-3-methyl-3-hexanol

attack from bottom

(R)-3-methyl-3-hexanol

Inversion of configuration is not observed in an S_N1 reaction because the intermediate carbocation is planar. A nucleophile can attack either lobe of the empty p orbital—that is, the nucleophile can attack from either side. As the nucleophile becomes bonded to the carbon atom, the hybridization of the carbon atom returns to sp^3. Half the product molecules are inverted from the original configuration, and half the product molecules have the same configuration as the starting material.

B. Rate of an S_N1 Reaction

We mentioned earlier that the rate of an S_N1 reaction does not depend on the concentration of the nucleophile, but is dependent only on the concentration of alkyl halide.

$$S_N1 \text{ rate} = k\,[RX]$$

The reason for this behavior is that the reaction between R^+ and OH^- is very fast, but the concentration of R^+ is very low. The combination of R^+ and OH^- occurs only when a carbocation is formed. Therefore, the rate of the overall reaction is entirely determined by how fast RX can ionize (and OH^- cannot help this process). This ionization step (Step 1 of the overall reaction) is called the **rate-determining step**. In any stepwise reaction, the slowest step is the rate-determining step.

An S_N1 reaction is **first order in rate** because the rate is proportional to the concentration of only one reactant. It is a **unimolecular reaction** because only one particle (RX) is involved in the transition state of the rate-determining step.

Rate-determining step:

$$(CH_3)_3C\!-\!Br \longrightarrow [(CH_3)_3\overset{\delta+}{C}\text{-}\text{-}\text{-}\overset{\delta-}{Br}] \longrightarrow [(CH_3)_3C^+] + Br^-$$

transition state 1
(from one particle)

C.   Relative Reactivities in S_N1 Reactions

Table 5.4 lists the relative rates of some alkyl bromides in a typical S_N1 reaction. Note that a secondary alkyl halide undergoes S_N1 reaction 11.6 times faster than a primary alkyl halide, while a tertiary alkyl halide undergoes S_N1 reaction a million times faster than a primary halide!

Methyl: CH_3Br $+ OH^-$ $\xrightarrow[S_N1]{\text{negligible rate}}$ CH_3OH $+ Br^-$

1°: CH_3CH_2Br $+ OH^-$ $\xrightarrow[S_N1]{\text{negligible rate}}$ CH_3CH_2OH $+ Br^-$

2°: $(CH_3)_2CHBr$ $+ OH^-$ $\xrightarrow[.S_N1]{\text{very slow}}$ $(CH_3)_2CHOH$ $+ Br^-$

3°: $(CH_3)_3CBr$ $+ OH^-$ $\xrightarrow[S_N1]{\text{fast}}$ $(CH_3)_3COH$ $+ Br^-$

The rates at which different alkyl halides undergo S_N1 reaction depend on the relative energies of activation leading to the different carbocations. In this reaction, the energy of the transition state leading to the carbocation is largely determined by the stability of the carbocation, which is already half-formed in the transition state. We say that the transition state has **carbocation character**. Therefore, the reaction leading to a more stabilized, lower-energy carbocation has the faster rate. A tertiary alkyl halide yields a carbocation that is more stabilized than the carbocation from a methyl halide or a primary alkyl halide, and consequently, this reaction has the fastest rate.

Table 5.4.   **Relative Rates of Some Alkyl Bromides in a Typical S_N1 Reaction**

CH_3Br	1.00
CH_3CH_2Br	1.00
$(CH_3)_2CHBr$	11.6
$(CH_3)_3CBr$	1.2×10^6

D.   Stability of Carbocations

A carbocation is unstable and quickly undergoes further reaction. However, we may still speak of *relative stabilities* of carbocations. The different types of carbocation that concern us here are the **methyl cation** (the carbocation resulting from ionization of a methyl halide), **primary carbocations** (from 1° alkyl halides), **secondary carbocations** (from 2° alkyl halides), and **tertiary carbocations** (from 3° alkyl halides). Some examples follow:

$^+CH_3$	$CH_3\overset{+}{C}H_2$	$(CH_3)_2\overset{+}{C}H$	$(CH_3)_3C^+$
methyl	1°	2°	3°

What increases the stability of a positively charged carbon atom? The answer is: anything that can *disperse the positive charge*. In alkyl cations, the principal phenomenon that disperses the positive charge is the **inductive effect**, a term used to describe the attraction of sigma-bond electrons in a molecule or ion by a positive center. In a carbocation, the positive center is the positively charged carbon atom. The electron density of the sigma bonds is shifted toward the positive carbon, and this shift creates a partial positive charge on the next atom in line. We will use arrows in place of line bonds to show the direction of this attraction.

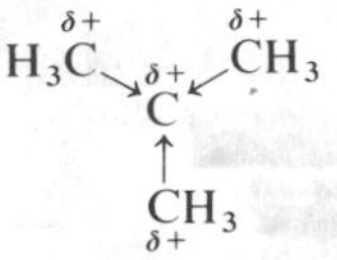

sigma-bond e^- are drawn toward the positive charge

These partial positive charges, in turn, polarize the next sigma bonds. In this way, the positive charge of the carbocation is somewhat dispersed, and the carbocation is stabilized to some extent.

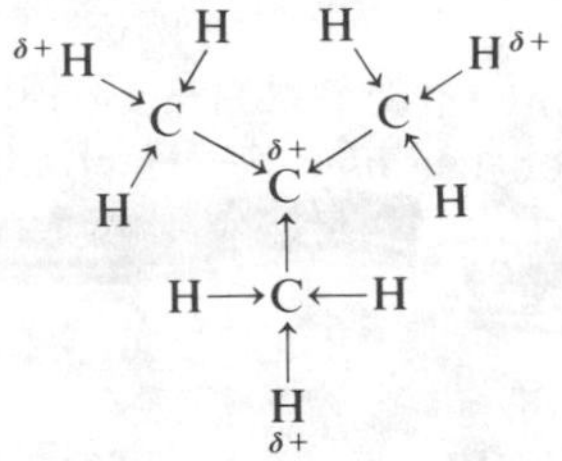

Alkyl groups contain more atoms and electrons than does a hydrogen atom. When there are more alkyl groups attached to a positively charged carbon atom, there are more atoms that can help share the positive charge and help stabilize the carbocation.

$$^+CH_3 \quad\quad CH_3\overset{+}{C}H_2 \quad\quad (CH_3)_2\overset{+}{C}H \quad\quad (CH_3)_3C^+$$

methyl $\quad\quad$ 1° $\quad\quad\quad$ 2° $\quad\quad\quad$ 3°

increasing carbocation stability;
increasing S_N1 rate of RX

STUDY PROBLEM

5.4 List the following carbocations in order of increasing stability (least stable first):

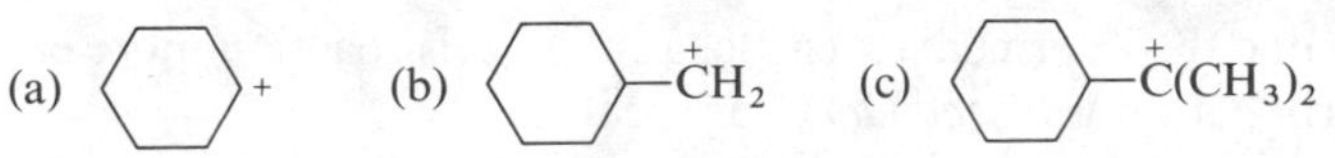

(a) (b) (c)

Another factor that may increase the stability of tertiary carbocations is **steric assistance**. Repulsions between groups in a sterically hindered alkyl halide add energy to the neutral molecule. The groups attached to the head carbon are farther apart in the planar carbocation than in the alkyl halide, and repulsions are

Alkyl Halides; Substitution and Elimination Reactions

minimized. The result is that less energy is needed to form a carbocation from a sterically hindered alkyl halide than from an unhindered alkyl halide.

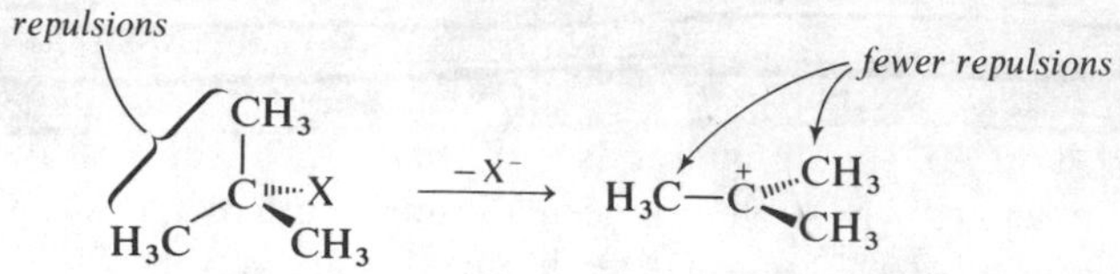

a t-butyl halide   *the t-butyl cation*

Another theory proposed to explain the relative stabilities of carbocations is **hyperconjugation**, the overlap of an sp^3–s orbital (a C—H bond) with the empty p orbital of the positively charged carbon.

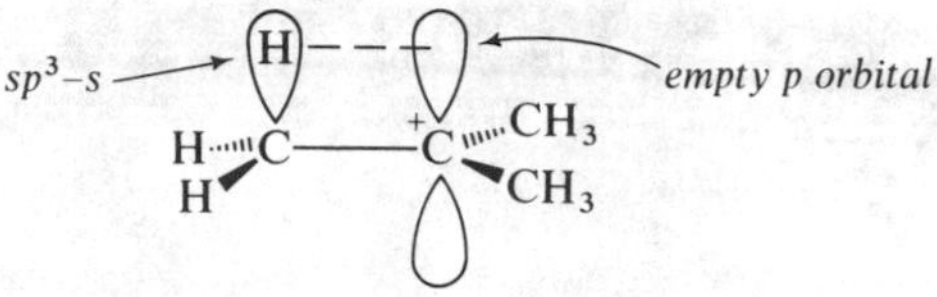

An ethyl cation has only three C—H bonds that can overlap the empty p orbital, but the *t*-butyl cation has *nine* C—H bonds that can help disperse the charge in this fashion. Therefore, a tertiary carbocation is stabilized by a greater dispersal of the positive charge.

E. Rearrangements of Carbocations

The following secondary alkyl chloride can undergo S_N1 reaction with bromide ion as the nucleophile. Instead of the expected product, however, *two* substitution products are observed.

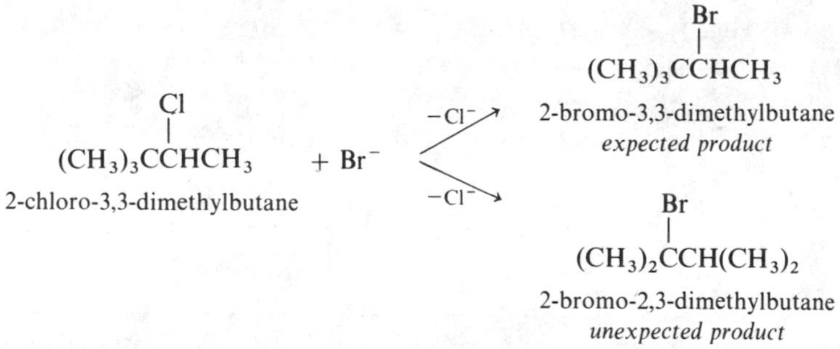

$$Br$$
$$|$$
$$(CH_3)_3CCHCH_3$$
2-bromo-3,3-dimethylbutane
expected product

$$Br$$
$$|$$
$$(CH_3)_2CCH(CH_3)_2$$
2-bromo-2,3-dimethylbutane
unexpected product

2-chloro-3,3-dimethylbutane

Let us examine the intermediate carbocation in this reaction more carefully. The expected carbocation is a *secondary* carbocation.

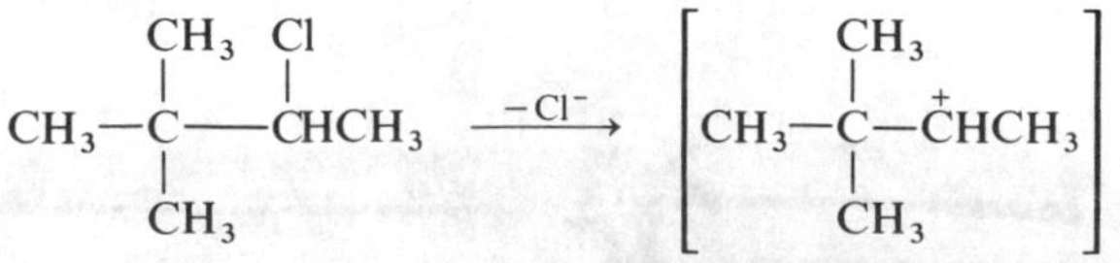

expected carbocation; 2°

A secondary carbocation is of much higher energy than a tertiary carbocation. The energy of this particular carbocation can be lowered by the shift of a methyl group with its bonding electrons from the adjacent carbon atom. The result is the rearrangement of the secondary carbocation to a more stable tertiary carbocation.

1,2-shift of a methyl group:

$$CH_3 - \overset{\overset{\displaystyle CH_3}{|}}{\underset{\underset{\displaystyle CH_3}{|}}{C}} - \overset{+}{C}HCH_3 \longrightarrow CH_3 - \overset{\overset{\displaystyle CH_3}{|}}{\underset{\underset{\displaystyle CH_3}{|}}{\overset{+}{C}}} - CHCH_3$$

        a 2° carbocation   *a more stable 3° carbocation*

The shift of an atom or of a group from an adjacent carbon is called a **1,2-shift**. (The numbers 1,2 used in this context have nothing to do with nomenclature numbers, but refer to the positive carbon and the adjacent atom.) The 1,2-shift of a methyl group is called a **methyl shift**, or a **methide shift**. (The *-ide* suffix is sometimes used because :CH_3 is an anion.)

The presence of both secondary and tertiary carbocations in solution leads to the two observed products, the so-called "normal" product and the **rearrangement product**, a product in which the skeleton or the position of the functional group is different from that of the starting material.

$$[(CH_3)_3\overset{+}{C}CHCH_3] \xrightarrow{\text{Br}^-} (CH_3)_3C\overset{\overset{\displaystyle Br}{|}}{C}HCH_3$$

    2° carbocation   2-bromo-3,3-dimethylbutane

$$[(CH_3)_2\overset{+}{C}CH(CH_3)_2] \xrightarrow{\text{Br}^-} (CH_3)_2C\overset{\overset{\displaystyle Br}{|}}{C}H(CH_3)_2$$

    3° carbocation   2-bromo-2,3-dimethylbutane

If an alkyl group, an aryl group, or a hydrogen atom (each with its bonding electrons) on an adjacent carbon atom can shift and thereby create a more stable carbocation, rearrangement occurs. The following rearrangements exemplify 1,2-shifts and the formation of more-stable carbocations.

A methide shift:

$$CH_3 - \overset{\overset{\displaystyle CH_3}{|}}{\underset{\underset{\displaystyle CH_3}{|}}{C}} - \overset{+}{C}HCH_2CH_3 \longrightarrow CH_3 - \overset{\overset{\displaystyle CH_3}{|}}{\underset{\underset{\displaystyle CH_3}{|}}{\overset{+}{C}}} - CHCH_2CH_3$$

        a 2° carbocation   *a more stable 3° carbocation*

A hydride (H$^-$) shift:

$$CH_3 - \overset{\overset{\displaystyle H}{|}}{\underset{\underset{\displaystyle CH_3}{|}}{C}} - \overset{+}{C}HCH_3 \longrightarrow CH_3 - \overset{\overset{\displaystyle +}{}}{\underset{\underset{\displaystyle CH_3}{|}}{C}} - CH_2CH_3$$

        a 2° carbocation   *a more stable 3° carbocation*

STUDY PROBLEMS

5.5 Although many carbocations can form more-stable carbocations by 1,2-shifts, not all carbocations have structures that can yield more-stable carbocations by rearrangement. Indicate which of the following cations undergoes rearrangement. Show by an arrow the shift of an alkyl group or a hydrogen, and give the structure of the rearranged carbocation.

(a) $CH_3CH_2\overset{+}{C}HCH_3$ (b) $(CH_3)_2CH\overset{+}{C}HCH_2CH_3$

5.6 What S_N1 products would be formed by the following reactants?

$$\underset{\substack{| \\ }}{\overset{Cl}{(CH_3)_2CHCHCH_2CH_3}} + Br^- \longrightarrow$$

Section 5.8

Allyl Halides and Benzyl Halides

Two types of alkyl halide behave differently in S_N1 and S_N2 reactions from the alkyl halides we have been discussing. These are the **allyl halides** and the **benzyl halides**.

$$CH_2{=}CH{-}CH_2{-}$$
the allyl group

$$CH_2{=}CHCH_2Cl$$
allyl chloride
(3-chloro-1-propene)

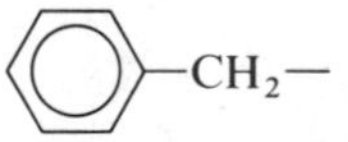

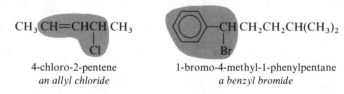
the benzyl group 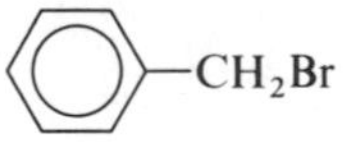   benzyl bromide

An atom or group that is attached to the carbon atom *adjacent to one of the sp^2 carbon atoms* is said to be in the **allylic position** or the **benzylic position**, respectively. The halogen atoms in our previous examples and also in the following examples are in allylic or benzylic positions.

$$CH_3 CH{=}CHCH CH_3$$
$$\underset{Cl}{|}$$

4-chloro-2-pentene
an allyl chloride

$$-CHCH_2CH_2CH(CH_3)_2$$
$$\underset{Br}{|}$$

1-bromo-4-methyl-1-phenylpentane
a benzyl bromide

Sample Problem

Circle the allyl or benzyl halide grouping in each of the following structures. Classify each as also being 1°, 2°, or 3°.

(a) 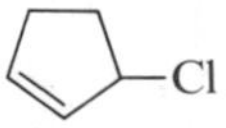 ⬠—Cl   (b) 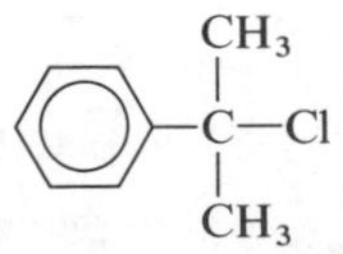 ⬡—$\overset{\overset{\displaystyle CH_3}{|}}{\underset{\underset{\displaystyle CH_3}{|}}{C}}$—Cl   (c) ⬡$=CH_2$, Cl

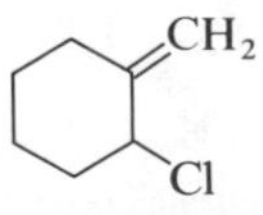

Solution: (a) 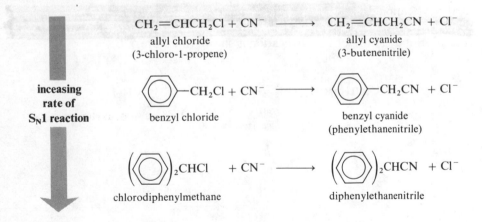 2° (b) 3° (c) 2°

STUDY PROBLEM

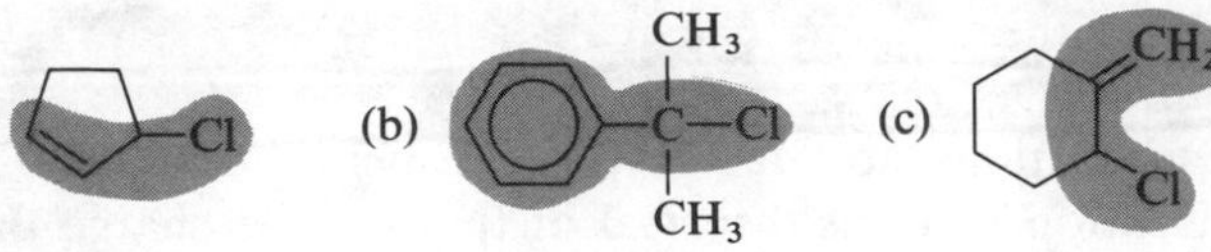

5.7   Circle the benzyl or allyl halide grouping in each of the following structures:

(a) (structure with Br, –CH– and two ring groups)   (b) CH_3– (ring) –Cl

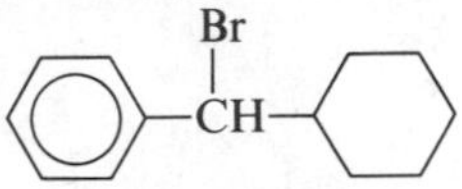

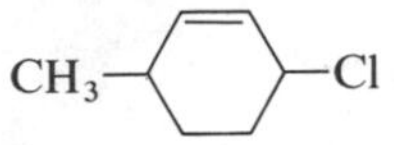

A. S_N1 *Reactions*

Most primary alkyl halides undergo substitution by the S_N2 path exclusively, and do not undergo S_N1 reactions. However, a primary allyl halide or benzyl halide is very reactive in an S_N1 reaction. Table 5.5 lists the relative reactivities of some halides in a typical S_N1 reaction. An allyl halide is more than 30 times more reactive than an ethyl halide. A benzyl halide is almost 400 times as reactive. If *two* phenyl groups are present, the halide is 100,000 times as reactive!

inceasing rate of S_N1 reaction

$$CH_2{=}CHCH_2Cl + CN^- \longrightarrow CH_2{=}CHCH_2CN + Cl^-$$
allyl chloride
(3-chloro-1-propene)
allyl cyanide
(3-butenenitrile)

(benzene)–$CH_2Cl + CN^- \longrightarrow$ (benzene)–$CH_2CN + Cl^-$
benzyl chloride
benzyl cyanide
(phenylethanenitrile)

$(C_6H_5)_2CHCl + CN^- \longrightarrow (C_6H_5)_2CHCN + Cl^-$
chlorodiphenylmethane
diphenylethanenitrile

Table 5.5. *Relative Rates of Some Alkyl Halides in a Typical S_N1 Reaction*

Alkyl halide	Relative rate
CH_3CH_2X	1.0
$CH_2{=}CHCH_2X$	33
$C_6H_5CH_2X$	380
$(C_6H_5)_2CHX$	$\sim 10^5$

The reason for the enhanced reactivity of these two types of halide lies in the *resonance-stabilization of the carbocation and the transition state leading to the carbocation.* Carbocations are stabilized by dispersal of the positive charge. Inductive stabilization involves dispersal of the positive charge through sigma bonds. We have used the inductive effect to explain the relative stabilities of 1°, 2°, and 3° carbocations. Resonance-stabilization involves the dispersal of the positive charge by *pi bonds*.

Let us consider the S_N1 reaction of allyl chloride with OH^-:

Step 1: $CH_2{=}CHCH_2Cl \longrightarrow [CH_2{=}CH\overset{+}{C}H_2] + Cl^-$
                  allyl chloride   allyl cation

Step 2: $[CH_2{=}CH\overset{+}{C}H_2] + OH^- \longrightarrow CH_2{=}CHCH_2OH$
                                              allyl alcohol
                                        (2-propen-1-ol)

Recall from Section 2.10 that structures differing only in the position of pi electrons are resonance structures. If resonance structures can be drawn for a molecule or ion, the resonance hybrid (the real structure) has less energy than if delocalization of electrons or electrical charges could not occur. The two resonance structures for the allyl cation are identical in structure and bonding; therefore, they have the same energy content and contribute equally to the structure of the real allyl cation. Because the allyl cation is resonance-stabilized, the transition state leading to its formation is low and consequently the rate of its reaction is fast. The *p*-orbital picture of the allyl cation is shown in Figure 5.7.

$$[CH_2{=}CH{-}\overset{+}{C}H_2 \longleftrightarrow \overset{+}{C}H_2{-}CH{=}CH_2]$$

resonance structures for the allyl cation
(equal contributors)

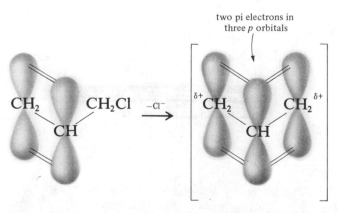

Figure 5.7.   Formation of the allyl cation from allyl chloride.

Both end carbons in the allyl cation have an equal amount of positive charge. Which atom is attacked by the nucleophile? The answer is—either of them! Let us use another allylic system to illustrate this fact. The S_N1 reaction of 1-chloro-2-butene with OH^- leads to two products. These two products arise from attack of OH^- at either of the two partially positive carbon atoms.

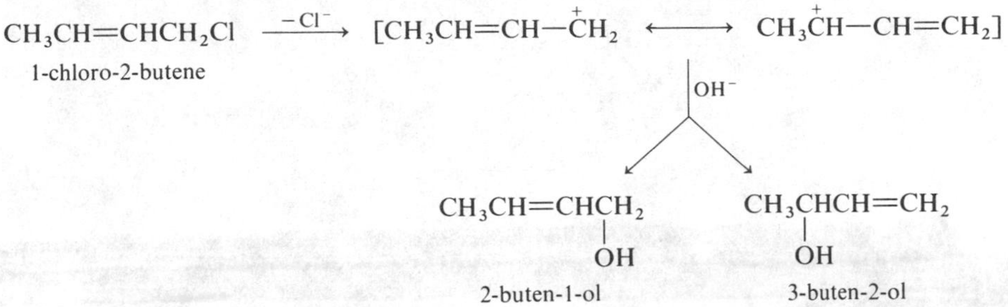

$$CH_3CH=CHCH_2Cl \xrightarrow{-Cl^-} [CH_3CH=CH-\overset{+}{C}H_2 \longleftrightarrow CH_3\overset{+}{C}H-CH=CH_2]$$

1-chloro-2-butene

$$\Big| OH^-$$

$$CH_3CH=CHCH_2 \qquad\qquad CH_3CHCH=CH_2$$
$$\ \ \ \ \ \ \ \ \ \ \ \ \ \ | \qquad\qquad\qquad\quad\ \ \ |$$
$$\ \ \ \ \ \ \ \ \ \ \ \ OH \qquad\qquad\qquad\quad OH$$

2-buten-1-ol   3-buten-2-ol

Benzyl halides also show enhancement of the S_N1 rate because of resonance-stabilization of the transition state leading to the carbocation. In this case, the pi electrons in the aromatic pi cloud of the benzene ring help disperse the charge.

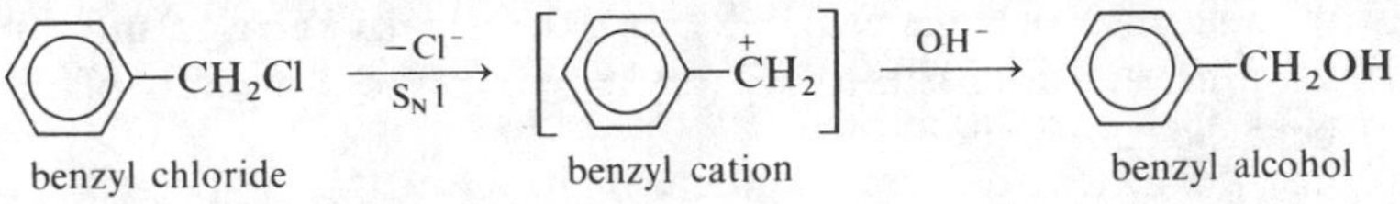

benzyl chloride   benzyl cation   benzyl alcohol

We usually symbolize the aromatic pi cloud of benzene by a circle in the ring. However, in discussions of delocalization of pi electrons, Kekulé formulas are more convenient. With Kekulé formulas, we can count the pi electrons in the ring and readily see which atoms are electron-deficient.

Note the similarity between the resonance structures for the benzyl cation and those for the allyl cation. The benzyl cation has four resonance structures similar to allylic resonance structures.

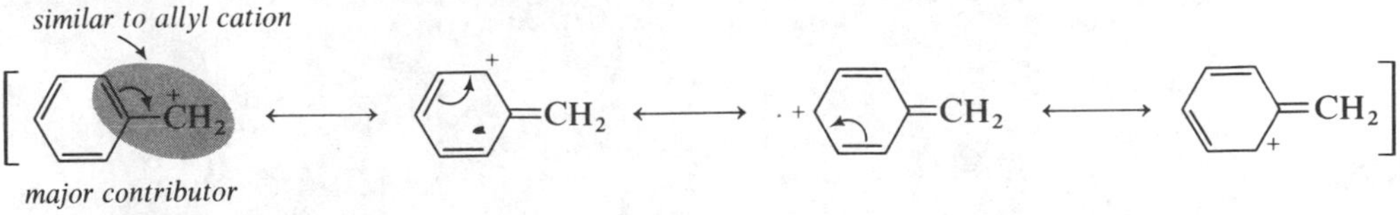

similar to allyl cation

major contributor

The first resonance structure shown is the major contributor because this structure has aromatic stabilization. Therefore, the most positive carbon in the intermediate is the benzyl carbon. This is the carbon attacked by the nucleophile.

most positive carbon,
Nu^- attacks here

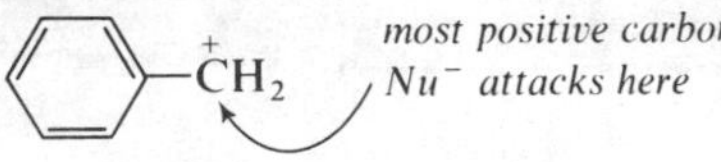

B. S_N2 Reactions

Allyl halides and benzyl halides also undergo S_N2 reactions at faster rates than primary alkyl halides or even methyl halides. Table 5.6 (page 188) lists the average relative rates of some alkyl halides in a typical S_N2 reaction.

Alkyl Halides; Substitution and Elimination Reactions

Table 5.6. *Average Relative S_N2 Rates for Some Alkyl Halides*

Alkyl halide	Relative rate
CH_3X	30
CH_3CH_2X	1
$CH_3CH_2CH_2X$	0.40
$(CH_3)_2CHX$	0.03
$CH_2=CHCH_2X$	40
$C_6H_5CH_2X$	120

The reason for the greater S_N2 reactivity of allyl and benzyl halides is that the allyl pi bond or the aromatic pi cloud reduces the energy of the transition state of an S_N2 reaction. In the transition state, the carbon undergoing reaction changes from the sp^3-hybrid state to the sp^2-hybrid state and has a p orbital. This p orbital forms partial bonds with both the incoming nucleophile and the leaving group. The entire grouping of atoms carries a negative charge. Adjacent p orbitals, as in an allylic or benzylic group, undergo partial overlap with the transitional p orbital. In this way, adjacent p orbitals help delocalize the negative charge and thus lower the energy of the transition state. Figure 5.8 shows the p orbitals of the allylic case; the benzylic case is similar.

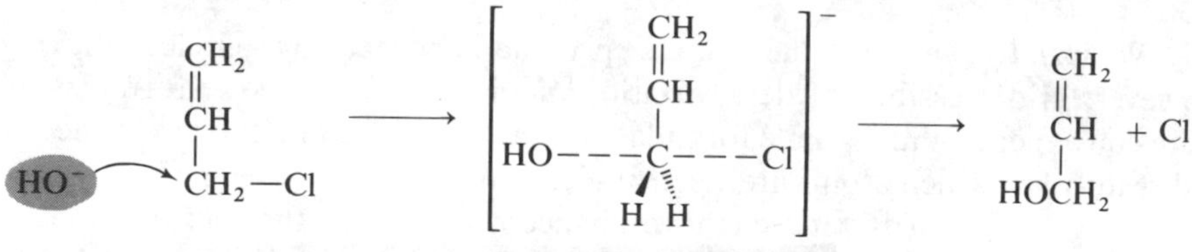

S_N2 transition state

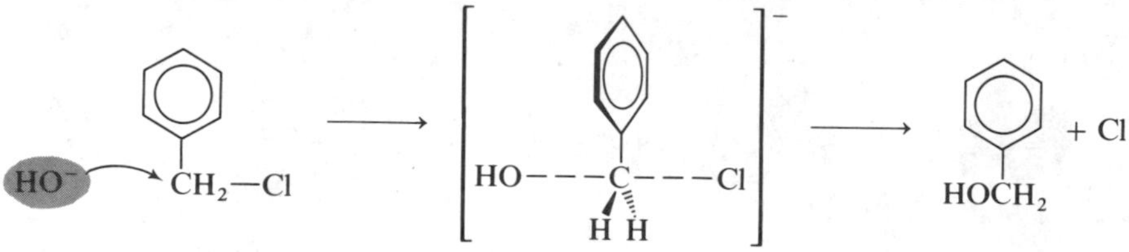

S_N2 transition state

For increased stabilization to occur in either S_N1 or S_N2 reactions of compounds with pi systems, the pi system must be *adjacent* to the reacting carbon. If it is farther away, it cannot overlap and cannot help stabilize the transition state.

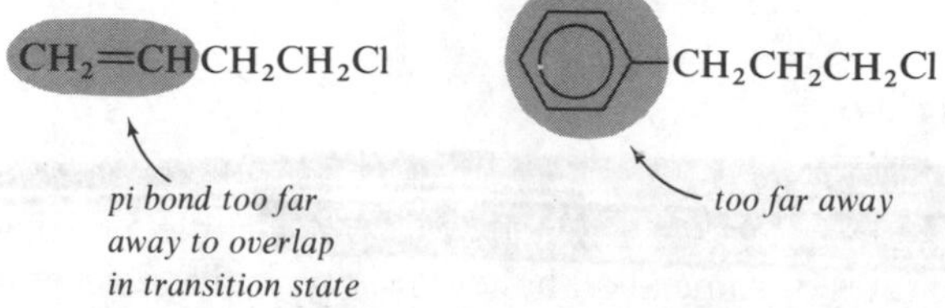

$CH_2=CH CH_2CH_2Cl$ $CH_2CH_2CH_2Cl$

pi bond too far away to overlap in transition state   *too far away*

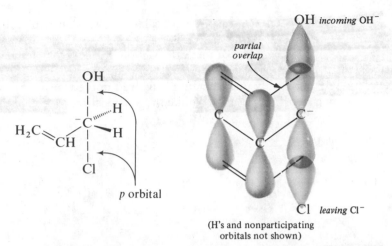

Figure 5.8. The S_N2 transition state of an allyl halide is stabilized by the adjacent pi bond.

Which of the following compounds exhibit enhanced reactivities in S_N1 and S_N2 reactions because of resonance-stabilization or partial *p*-orbital overlap?

(a) $CH_3CH=CHCHBrCH=CH_2$ (b) $CH_3CH=CHCH_2CHBrCH_2CH_3$
(c) $C_6H_5CH=CHCH_2I$ (d) $CH_2=CHCH_2CHBrCH=CH_2$

Solution: (a), (c), (d)

Section 5.9

The E1 Reaction

A carbocation is a high-energy, unstable intermediate that quickly undergoes further reaction. One way a carbocation can reach a stable product is by combining with a nucleophile. This, of course, is the S_N1 reaction. However, there is an alternative: the carbocation can *lose a proton to a nucleophile in an elimination reaction*, an **E1 reaction** in this case, and become an alkene. In elimination reactions, the nucleophile must be a base because it must be able to accept a proton.

Substitution:

$$(CH_3)_3CBr \xrightarrow{-Br^-} [(CH_3)_3C^+] \xrightarrow[S_N1]{OH^-} (CH_3)_3COH$$

*t*-butyl bromide *t*-butyl cation *t*-butyl alcohol

Elimination:

$$(CH_3)_3CBr \xrightarrow{-Br^-} \left[(CH_3)_2\overset{+}{C}-CH_2 \right] \longrightarrow (CH_3)_2C=CH_2 + H_2O$$

*t*-butyl cation methylpropene

Alkyl Halides; Substitution and Elimination Reactions

The first step in an E1 reaction is identical to the first step in an S_N1 reaction: the ionization of the alkyl halide. This is the slow step and thus the rate-determining step of the overall reaction. Like the S_N1 reaction, the E1 reaction shows first-order kinetics, with the rate of the reaction dependent on the concentration of only the alkyl halide. Since only one reactant is involved in the transition state of the rate-determining step, the E1 reaction, like the S_N1 reaction, is unimolecular.

Step 1 (slow):

$$(CH_3)_3C\ddot{B}r\colon \longrightarrow \left[(CH_3)_3\overset{\delta+}{C} - - - \overset{\delta-}{\ddot{B}r}\colon\right] \longrightarrow \left[\begin{array}{c} H_3C_{\cdots\cdots}\\ \overset{+}{C}-CH_3\\ H_3C \end{array}\right] + \colon\ddot{B}r\colon^-$$

transition state 1   carbocation intermediate

In the second step of an elimination reaction, the base removes a proton from a carbon that is *adjacent to the positive carbon*. The electrons of that carbon–hydrogen sigma bond shift toward the positive charge, the adjacent carbon re-hybridizes from the sp^3 state to the sp^2 state, and an alkene is formed.

Step 2 (fast) :

$$\left[\begin{array}{c} H_3C_{\cdots\cdots}\\ \overset{+}{C}-CH_2\\ H_3C \end{array}\!\!\!\!\!\overset{H}{\mid}\right] + \ ^-\colon\ddot{O}H \longrightarrow \left[\begin{array}{c} H\ddot{O}- - -H\\ H_3C_{\cdots\cdots}\ \mid\\ \overset{\delta+}{C}=\!=\!=CH_2\\ H_3C \end{array}\right]$$

transition state 2

$$\longrightarrow \begin{array}{c} H_3C\\ \diagdown\\ C=CH_2 + H_2\ddot{O}\colon\\ \diagup\\ H_3C \end{array}$$

Although an elimination reaction results in the loss of HX from the alkyl halide, HX is not a real product of the reaction. The proton is eliminated by being removed from the carbocation by the base. If the base is OH^-, then water (along with X^-) is the product.

Overall reaction:

$$(CH_3)_3CBr + OH^- \xrightarrow{\text{E1}} (CH_3)_2C=CH_2 + Br^- + H_2O$$

An E1 reaction, like an S_N1 reaction, proceeds through a carbocation intermediate; therefore, it is not surprising that tertiary alkyl halides undergo this reaction more rapidly than primary alkyl halides.

1°RX   2°RX   3°RX
increasing rate of E1 ⟶

A. Mixtures of Alkenes

If *t*-butyl bromide undergoes elimination, there is only one possible alkene product. However, if the alkyl groups around the positive carbon in the carbocation are different, more than one alkene can result. The E1 reaction of 2-bromo-2-methylbutane yields two alkenes because two types of hydrogen atom can be eliminated: a hydrogen from a CH_3 group or a hydrogen from a CH_2 group.

$$CH_3-\underset{\underset{CH_3}{|}}{\overset{\overset{CH_3}{|}}{C}}-Br \xrightarrow{E1} CH_2=C\overset{CH_3}{\underset{CH_3}{\big\backslash}}$$

t-butyl bromide   methylpropene
only possible alkene

$$CH_3CH_2-\underset{\underset{CH_3}{|}}{\overset{\overset{CH_3}{|}}{C}}-Br \xrightarrow{E1} CH_3CH=C(CH_3)_2 + CH_3CH_2\overset{\overset{CH_2}{||}}{C}CH_3$$

2-bromo-2-methylbutane   2-methyl-2-butene   2-methyl-1-butene
two possible alkenes

Different types of carbon and hydrogen atoms in a molecule may be labeled as α, β, and so forth, according to the Greek alphabet. The carbon atom attached to the principal functional group in a molecule is called the **alpha (α) carbon**, and the adjacent carbon is the **beta (β) carbon**. The hydrogens attached to the α carbon are called α hydrogens, while those attached to the β carbon are β hydrogens. In an E1 reaction, it is a β hydrogen that is eliminated. For this reason, E1 reactions are sometimes referred to as **beta (β) eliminations**.

β carbons and hydrogens circled:

$$CH_3CH_2-\underset{CH_3}{\overset{CH_3}{C}}-Br \xrightarrow{-Br^-} CH_3CH_2-\underset{CH_3}{\overset{CH_3}{C^+}}$$

As you can see, there are two types of β hydrogen in the preceding alkyl halide. Elimination of a β hydrogen from either CH_3 group yields one alkene, while elimination of a β hydrogen from the CH_2 group yields the second alkene.

$$CH_3CH_2-\underset{\underset{CH_3}{|}}{\overset{\overset{CH_3}{|}}{C}}-Br \xrightarrow{-Br^-} CH_3CH-\overset{CH_2}{\underset{CH_3}{C^+}}$$

$$\xrightarrow{-H^+} CH_3CH_2-C\overset{CH_2}{\underset{CH_3}{\big\backslash}}$$

$$\xrightarrow{-H^+} CH_3CH=C\overset{CH_3}{\underset{CH_3}{\big\backslash}}$$

Sample Problem

Circle the β carbons and hydrogens in the following structures:

(a) $CH_3CHCH_2CH_3$ (b)

      |
     Br

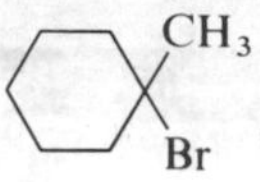

Solution: (a) $(CH_3)CH(CH_2)CH_3$ (b)

             |
          Br

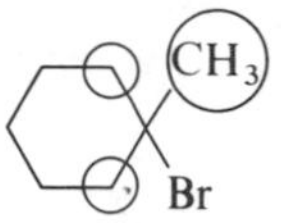

Sample Problem

In the preceding problem, tell how many different *types* of β hydrogen are in each structure.

Solution: (a) two types;   (b) two types (the ring CH_2 groups are equivalent to each other; the CH_3 is different).

Sample Problem

Write the structures of the alkenes that could result from E1 reaction of each of the preceding alkyl bromides.

Solution: (a) $CH_3CH{=}CHCH_3$, $CH_3CH_2CH{=}CH_2$

(b) 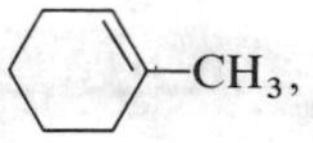 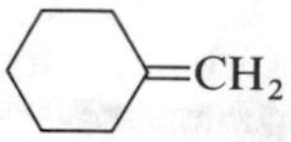 ⬡$-CH_3$,   ⬡$=CH_2$

B.   Which Alkene is Formed?

In 1875, the Russian chemist Alexander Saytseff formulated the following rule, now called the **Saytseff rule**: *In elimination reactions, the alkene with the greatest number of alkyl groups on the doubly-bonded carbon atoms predominates.* We will refer to this alkene as the *more highly substituted alkene*. The Saytseff rule predicts that 2-butene would predominate over 1-butene as a product in the E1 reaction of 2-bromobutane. This indeed is what occurs.

$$\underset{\text{2-bromobutane}}{CH_3CH_2\overset{\overset{\displaystyle Br}{|}}{C}HCH_3} \xrightarrow[\text{E1}]{OH^-} \underset{\substack{\text{2-butene}\\\text{(two R's on C=C)}\\80\%}}{CH_3CH{=}CHCH_3} + \underset{\substack{\text{1-butene}\\\text{(one R on C=C)}\\20\%}}{CH_3CH_2CH{=}CH_2}$$

2-Butene has two R groups (CH_3-) bonded to the sp^2 carbons, while 1-butene has only one R group (CH_3CH_2-) on the sp^2 carbons. In this case, 2-butene is the more highly substituted alkene.

It has been determined that *more highly substituted alkenes are more stable than less substituted alkenes* (this will be discussed further in Chapter 9). Therefore, an E1 elimination leads to the *more stable alkene*.

$$CH_2{=}CH_2 \qquad CH_3CH{=}CH_2 \qquad CH_3CH{=}CHCH_3 \qquad (CH_3)_2C{=}C(CH_3)_2$$

more adjacent R groups, increasing stability ⟶

To see why the more stable alkene (2-butene) is formed in preference to the less stable alkene (1-butene), let us consider the transition states leading to these two butenes. In either step-2 transition state (going from carbocation to alkene), the base is removing a proton and the double bond is being formed. We say that this transition state has some **double-bond character**, which we represent as a dotted line in the formula.

$$\textit{Step 1:} \qquad CH_3CH_2\overset{\overset{\displaystyle Br}{|}}{C}HCH_3 \xrightarrow{-Br^-} [CH_3CH_2\overset{+}{C}HCH_3]$$

Step 2:

$$[CH_3CH_2\overset{+}{C}HCH_3] \xrightarrow{OH^-}$$

$$\left[\begin{array}{c} HO\text{-}\text{-}\text{-}H \\ | \\ | \\ CH_3CH_2CH\!=\!=\!=\!CH_2 \end{array} \right] \longrightarrow CH_3CH_2CH\!=\!CH_2$$
transition state   1-butene

$$\left[\begin{array}{c} H\text{-}\text{-}\text{-}OH \\ | \\ | \\ CH_3CH\!=\!=\!=\!CHCH_3 \end{array} \right] \longrightarrow CH_3CH\!=\!CHCH_3$$
transition state   2-butene

Both transition states leading from the carbocation to the alkenes have some double-bond character. For this reason, the transition state leading to the more stable alkene is itself more stabilized and of lower energy. The reaction with the lower-energy transition state proceeds at a faster rate; therefore, the more stable alkene is the predominant product. *Although the energy of the transition state for Step 1 determines the rate of the reaction, the energy of the transition state for Step 2 determines the structure of the product.* (See Figure 5.9.)

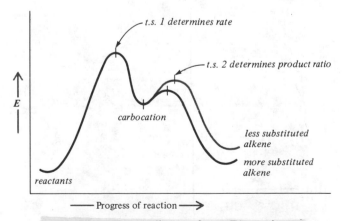

Figure 5.9. Energy diagram for an E1 reaction.

Sample Problem

Which is the more stable alkene, (a) $(CH_3)_3CCH=CHCH_3$, or (b) $CH_3CH=C(CH_3)_2$?

Solution: (b) with three R's is more stable than (a) with only two R's.

Sample Problem

Predict the major alkene product of E1 dehydrohalogenation of $CH_3CH_2C(CH_3)_2Cl$.

Solution: The two possible alkenes are $CH_3CH=C(CH_3)_2$ and $CH_3CH_2\underset{\underset{CH_3}{|}}{C}=CH_2$.

The first predominates (3 R's versus 2 R's).

STUDY PROBLEM

5.8 Predict the major alkene product of E1 dehydrohalogenation of 1-chloro-1-methyl-cyclohexane.

C. cis or trans?

Part of our question about which alkene would be formed in the dehydro-halogenation of 2-bromobutane has been answered: the most highly substituted alkene predominates in the product mixture. The most highly substituted alkene can often exist as geometric isomers. Is there a selectivity as to which geometric isomer is formed? Let us consider again the E1 reaction of 2-bromobutane.

$$CH_3CH_2\underset{\underset{Br}{|}}{C}HCH_3 \xrightarrow{E1} \underset{\substack{\text{2-butene}\\ \textit{cis or trans?}}}{CH_3CH=CHCH_3}$$

In E1 reactions, we observe that the *trans*-alkene is formed in preference to the *cis*-alkene. We could have predicted this result by inspecting the step-2 transition states leading to *cis*- and *trans*-2-butene and considering the steric repulsions of the methyl groups.

Second transition state leading to trans-2-butene:

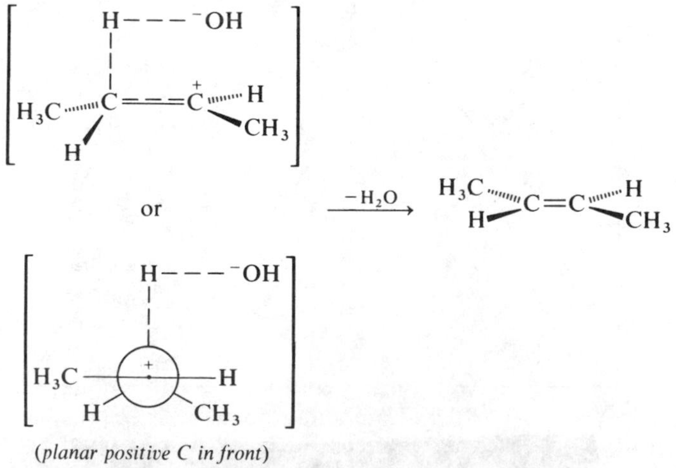

(planar positive C in front)

Second transition state leading to cis-2-butene:

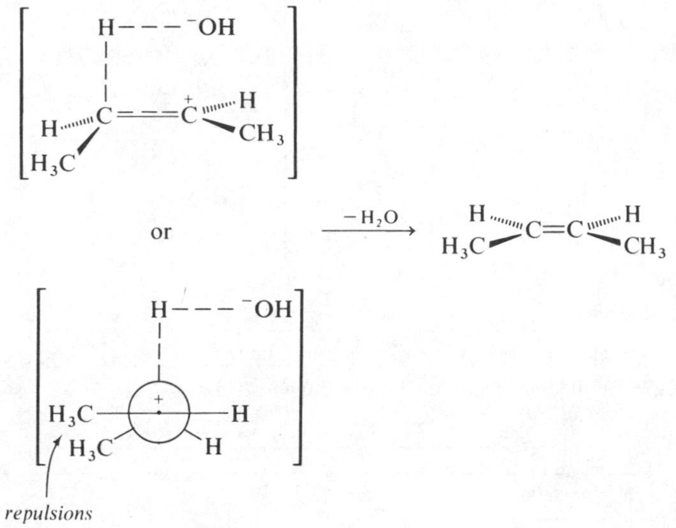
H---⁻OH
H C===C H
H₃C CH₃
or
−H₂O
H C=C H
H₃C CH₃
H---⁻OH
H₃C H
H₃C H
repulsions

The methyl groups are *eclipsed* in the *cis*-transition state, but *staggered* in the *trans*-transition state. Because eclipsing of groups leads to repulsions, the *trans*-transition state is the one of lower energy. Therefore, the rate leading to the *trans*-alkene is faster, and the *trans*-2-butene is formed in greater abundance.

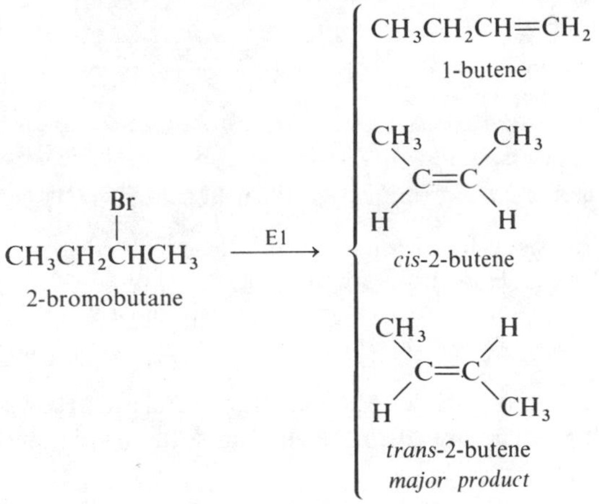
Br
CH₃CH₂CHCH₃
2-bromobutane
E1
CH₃CH₂CH=CH₂
1-butene
CH₃ CH₃
C=C
H H
cis-2-butene
CH₃ H
C=C
H CH₃
trans-2-butene
major product

D. *Rearrangements in E1 Reactions*

Like S_N1 reactions, E1 reactions proceed by way of carbocations. In an S_N1 reaction, a carbocation undergoes rearrangement when a more stable carbocation can be formed. The same is true in an E1 reaction; if a carbocation can undergo a 1,2-shift to yield a more stable carbocation, rearrangement occurs. For this reason, E1 reactions often lead to mixtures of alkenes.

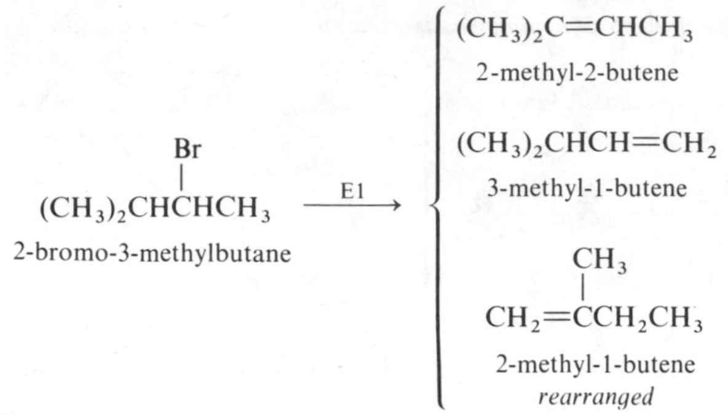

Alkyl Halides; Substitution and Elimination Reactions

$$(CH_3)_2C=CHCH_3$$
2-methyl-2-butene

$$(CH_3)_2CHCH=CH_2$$
3-methyl-1-butene

$$CH_2=\overset{\overset{\displaystyle CH_3}{|}}{C}CH_2CH_3$$
2-methyl-1-butene
rearranged

$$\overset{\overset{\displaystyle Br}{|}}{(CH_3)_2CHCHCH_3} \xrightarrow{\text{E1}}$$

2-bromo-3-methylbutane

STUDY PROBLEM

5.9   Show how each of the preceding alkenes could be formed. (*Hint*: There are two routes to the topmost alkene, one involving rearrangement.)

Section 5.10

The E2 Reaction

The last reaction we will discuss in this chapter is the **E2 reaction** (bimolecular elimination). This reaction, too, is a beta elimination. But, as you might have anticipated, it is a concerted reaction—that is, it occurs in one step, just as an S_N2 reaction does.

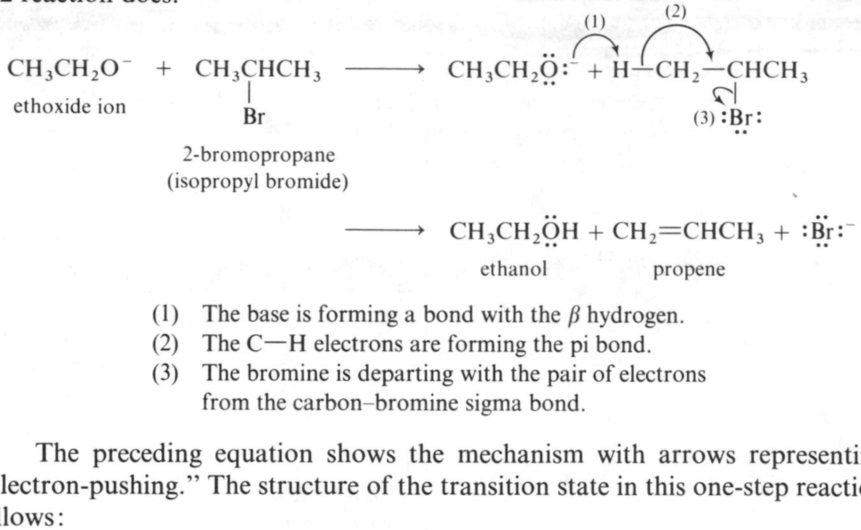

$$CH_3CH_2O^- + \underset{\underset{\displaystyle Br}{|}}{CH_3CHCH_3} \longrightarrow CH_3CH_2\overset{..}{\underset{..}{O}}:^- + H-CH_2-CHCH_3$$

ethoxide ion

2-bromopropane
(isopropyl bromide)

$$\longrightarrow CH_3CH_2\overset{..}{O}H + CH_2=CHCH_3 + :\overset{..}{\underset{..}{Br}}:^-$$

ethanol   propene

(1)   The base is forming a bond with the β hydrogen.
(2)   The C—H electrons are forming the pi bond.
(3)   The bromine is departing with the pair of electrons
      from the carbon–bromine sigma bond.

The preceding equation shows the mechanism with arrows representing "electron-pushing." The structure of the transition state in this one-step reaction follows:

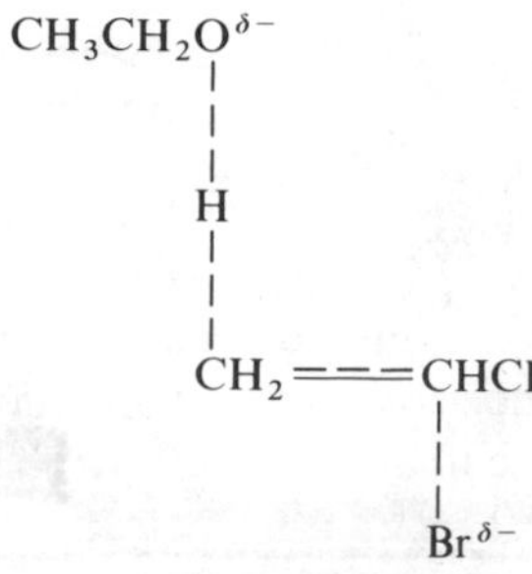

$$CH_3CH_2O^{\delta-}$$
$$|$$
$$|$$
$$H$$
$$|$$
$$|$$
$$CH_2===CHCH_3$$
$$|$$
$$|$$
$$Br^{\delta-}$$

E2 transition state

In an E2 reaction, as well as in an E1 reaction, tertiary alkyl halides undergo reaction fastest, and primary alkyl halides react slowest. (When treated with a base, primary alkyl halides usually undergo substitution so readily that little alkene is formed.)

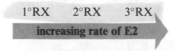

1°RX   2°RX   3°RX

increasing rate of E2

The transition state for the E2 reaction has double-bond character. Therefore, in an E2 reaction, as well as in an E1 reaction, the most stable alkene is usually formed preferentially. E2 reactions also usually follow the Saytseff rule: when mixtures of alkenes can be formed, the most highly substituted alkene predominates.

Here, the similarity to the E1 reaction ends. No rearrangements are observed in E2 reactions; for this reason, E2 reactions are preferred over E1 reactions by organic chemists. In the E2 reaction, replacement of β hydrogens by deuterium leads to a large difference in rate, an effect not observed in E1 reactions. Unlike the E1 reaction, the E2 reaction is stereospecific. In many cases, too, the least substituted alkene is formed instead of the most substituted one. We will discuss all these facets of the E2 reaction in the following sections.

A. Kinetic Isotope Effect

A difference in the rates of reaction between compounds containing different isotopes is called a **kinetic isotope effect**. Deuterium (^2_1H, or D) is an isotope of hydrogen containing one proton and one neutron. The C—D bond is stronger than the C—H bond by 1.2 kcal/mole.

We have postulated that the breaking of the C—H bond is an integral part of the transition state of the rate-determining step (the *only* step) of an E2 reaction. What happens when the H that is eliminated is replaced by D? The stronger C—D bond requires more energy to be broken. For this reason, the E_{act} is increased (Figure 5.10), and the rate for the elimination reaction is slower.

When rates of elimination of C—H versus C—D are compared, *all* beta hydrogens must be replaced by D, as in the following example of isopropyl bromide versus deuteriated isopropyl bromide. When these two compounds

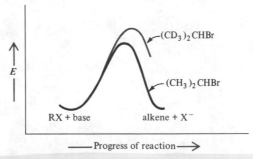

Figure 5.10. Energy diagrams for E2 reactions of compounds with C—H and C—D bonds.

are subjected to an E2 reaction with $CH_3CH_2O^-$ as the base, it has been observed that the deuteriated compound undergoes reaction at *one-seventh* the rate of ordinary isopropyl bromide, a fact that supports the E2 reaction mechanism.

$$CH_3CH_2O^- + CH_3\overset{\overset{\displaystyle Br}{|}}{C}HCH_3 \xrightarrow{fast} CH_3CH_2OH + CH_2{=}CHCH_3 + Br^-$$

$$CH_3CH_2O^- + CD_3\overset{\overset{\displaystyle Br}{|}}{C}HCD_3 \xrightarrow{slow} CH_3CH_2OD + CD_2{=}CHCD_3 + Br^-$$

Sample Problem

Why is a kinetic isotope effect not observed with $(CH_3)_3CBr$ and $(CD_3)_3CBr$ in E1 reactions?

Solution: The cleavage of a C—H bond is not involved in the transition state of the rate-determining step of an E1 reaction.

B.   Stereochemistry of an E2 Reaction

In the transition state of an E2 elimination, the attacking base and the leaving group are as far apart as possible, or *anti*. For this reason, bimolecular elimination is often referred to as ***anti*-elimination**.

anti-Elimination:

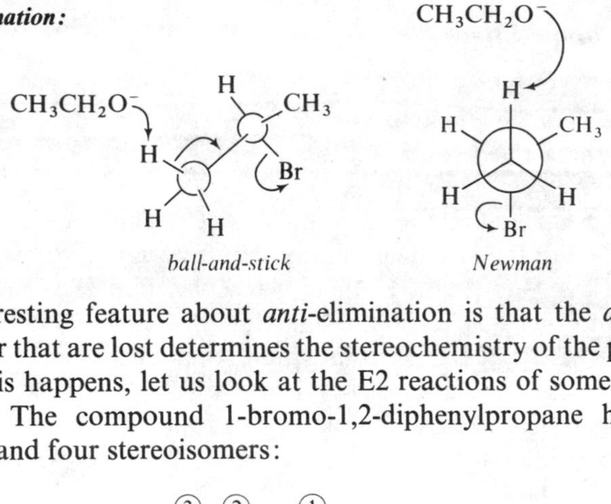

ball-and-stick   Newman

The interesting feature about *anti*-elimination is that the *anti*-positioning of the H and Br that are lost determines the stereochemistry of the product alkene. To see how this happens, let us look at the E2 reactions of some stereoisomeric alkyl halides. The compound 1-bromo-1,2-diphenylpropane has two chiral carbon atoms and four stereoisomers:

The four stereoisomers of $\overset{\text{③}}{C}H_3\overset{\text{②}}{C}H - \overset{\text{①}}{C}HBr$:

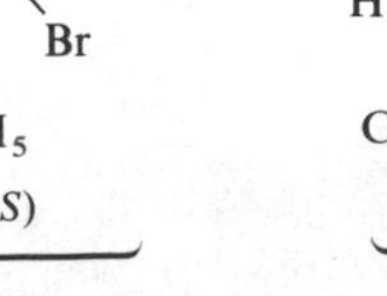

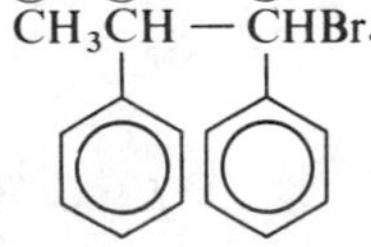

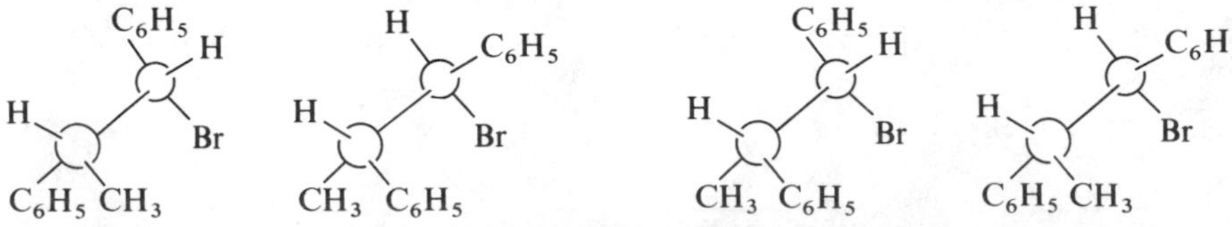

Because there is only one β hydrogen in the starting halide, any one of these stereoisomers yields $C_6H_5(CH_3)C{=}CHC_6H_5$. However, geometric isomerism is possible in this product.

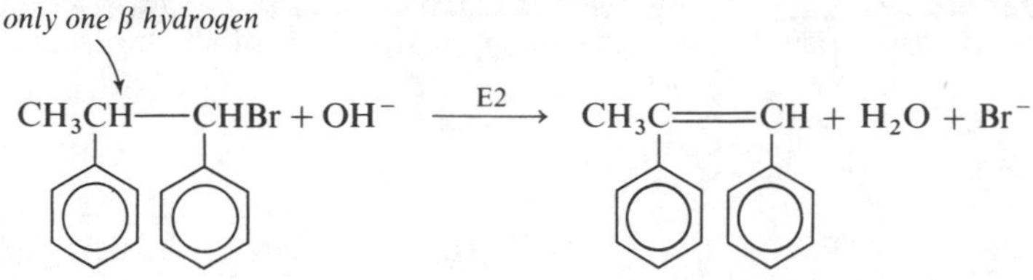

only one β hydrogen

$$CH_3CH{-}CHBr + OH^- \xrightarrow{\text{E2}} CH_3C{=}\!\!=\!\!CH + H_2O + Br^-$$

(E) or (Z)

When either (1*R*,2*R*)-1-bromo-1,2-diphenylpropane or its (1*S*,2*S*)-enantiomer undergoes E2 reaction, the (*Z*)-alkene is formed exclusively; no (*E*)-alkene is formed. When a reaction of one stereoisomer leads to only one product stereoisomer, the reaction is said to be **stereospecific**. Because the E2 reaction of the (1*R*,2*R*)-isomer or its enantiomer yields only the (*Z*)-alkene, the E2 reaction is stereospecific.

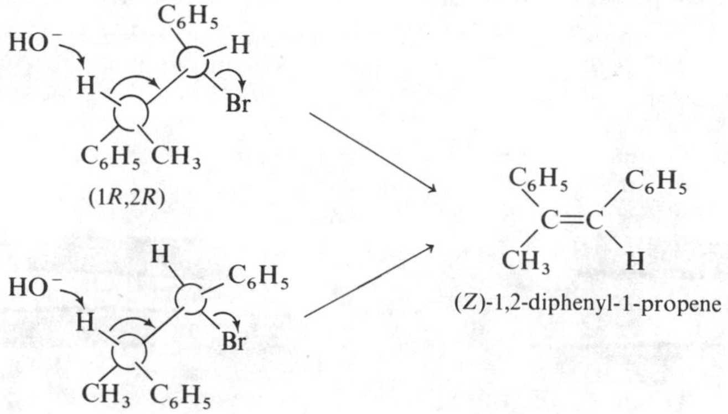

(1*R*,2*R*)

(1*S*,2*S*)

$$C_6H_5 \quad C_6H_5$$
$$C{=}C$$
$$CH_3 \qquad H$$

(Z)-1,2-diphenyl-1-propene

The reason for all (*Z*) and no (*E*) product is that there is only one conformation of either of these enantiomers in which the Br and the beta hydrogen are *anti*. In either the (1*R*,2*R*)- or the (1*S*,2*S*)-enantiomer, the *anti* alignment of H and Br puts the phenyl groups on the same side of the molecule, and the (*Z*)-alkene results. If the elimination could occur regardless of the conformation of the enantiomers, then some (*E*)-alkene would also be observed.

anti H and Br mean cis-phenyls

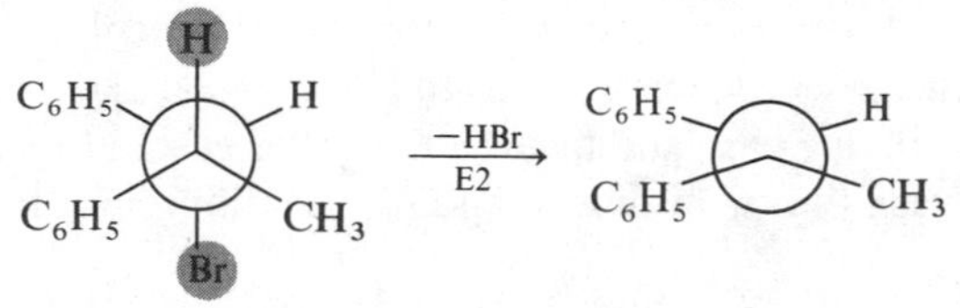

$$\xrightarrow[\text{E2}]{-\text{HBr}}$$

(1R,2R)   *(Z)-alkene*

STUDY PROBLEM

5.10 Write an equation using Newman projections for the *anti*-elimination of the (1*S*,2*S*)-enantiomer, as we have just done for the (1*R*,2*R*)-enantiomer.

Just the opposite situation prevails with the (1*R*,2*S*)- or (1*S*,2*R*)-enantiomers. Either of these isomers yields the (*E*)-alkene and not the (*Z*)-alkene. The reason, once again, is that there is only one conformation for each of these enantiomers in which the Br and the single beta hydrogen are in an *anti* relationship. In these conformations, the phenyl groups are on opposite sides of the molecule.

anti H and Br
mean
trans-phenyls

(1*R*,2*S*)   (1*S*,2*R*)

STUDY PROBLEMS

5.11   Draw ball-and-stick formulas for the conformers of (1*R*,2*S*)-1-bromo-1,2-diphenyl-propane and (1*S*,2*R*)-1-bromo-1,2-diphenylpropane that undergo E2 reaction.

5.12   1,2-Dibromo-1,2-diphenylethane contains two chiral carbon atoms and has a pair of enantiomers plus a *meso* diastereomer. Any of the stereoisomers of this compound undergoes E2 reaction to yield 1-bromo-1,2-diphenylethene. The *meso* form yields one geometric isomer of the alkene, while the racemic mixture of enantiomers yields the other geometric isomer. Predict the stereochemistry of the products of these two reactions.

C.   E2 Reactions in Cyclic Systems

Halocycloalkanes, such as chlorocyclohexane, can also undergo E2 reactions. In these cases, the conformations of the ring play an important role in the course of the reaction. In order to be *anti* on a cyclohexane ring, the leaving group (such as chlorine) and a β hydrogen must be 1,2-*trans* and *diaxial*. No other conformation places the H and Cl *anti* to each other. (Try it with models.)

Cl is axial and   *Cl is equatorial and*
anti to two β hydrogens   *not anti to any β hydrogens*

The E2 reactions of two isomeric menthyl chlorides follow. The difference between these two isomers is that the chlorine and the isopropyl group are *cis* to each other in one case and *trans* in the other case. Note (1) the difference in reactivity between the two isomers, and (2) the difference in products.

$\xrightarrow[\text{fast}]{\text{E2}}$

more stable
alkene predominates

25%   75%

less stable alkene predominates

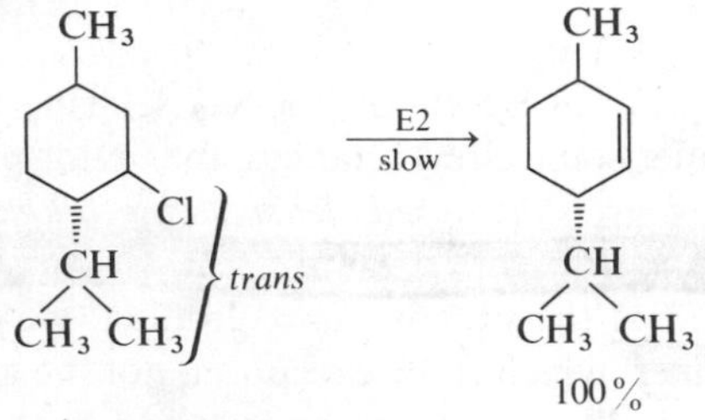

The *cis*-isomer yields two alkenes, with the more substituted alkene predominating in the product mixture (Saytseff rule). The *trans*-isomer yields only the less substituted alkene. The courses of these two reactions are dictated by the *trans*-diaxial requirement of the E2 reaction.

Let us consider the chair conformers of the two menthyl chlorides that have Cl in the required axial position.

cis
Cl has two axial β H's

trans
Cl has only one axial β H

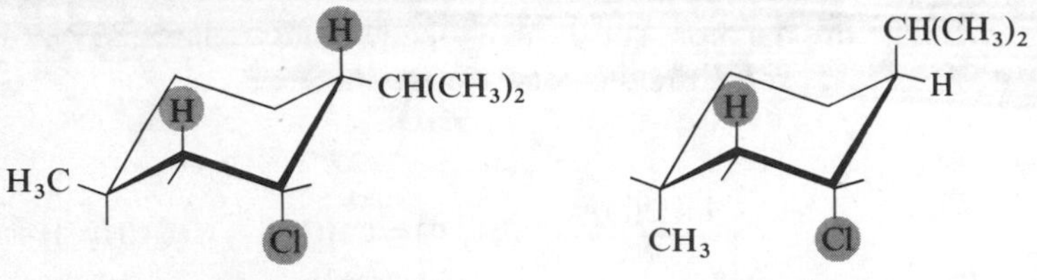

When the Cl of the *cis*-isomer is in an axial position, there are two axial β hydrogens. The molecule has a choice of direction of elimination, and a mixture of alkenes is formed. This is not the case with the *trans*-isomer. When the Cl is axial, there is only one axial β hydrogen. (The axial position on the other carbon is occupied by the isopropyl group.) Only one alkene can result, and this is the less stable one.

Sample Problem

In the preceding example, why does the *trans*-isomer undergo reaction at a slower rate than the *cis*-isomer?

Solution: There are two reasons. (1) The less stable alkene is formed from the *trans*-isomer; the energy of the transition state leading to it, and therefore the E_{act}, are higher. (2) Consider the chair conformers of the *cis*- and *trans*-isomers that have Cl in an axial position. The *cis*-isomer has its $-CH_3$ and $-CH(CH_3)_2$ groups both equatorial—a low-energy conformation that would predominate in the reaction mixture. However, the *trans*-isomer has its alkyl substituents both axial, a less favored conformation—the concentration of the reacting conformer is low because most of the *trans*-isomer molecules have the substituents equatorial:

all equatorial favored, but not set up for E2

trans

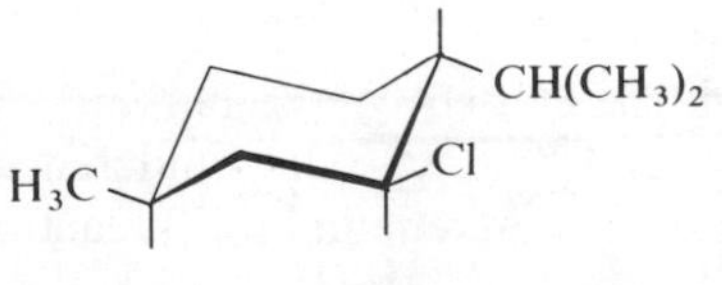

D. Hofmann Products

Most dehydrohalogenations (E1 or E2) follow the Saytseff rule and the most substituted alkene is formed. Under some circumstances, the major product of an E2 dehydrohalogenation is the *least substituted, least stable alkene.* We have just seen one such example. When the alkene with the least number of alkyl groups on the pi-bonded carbons is the predominant product, we say that the reaction yields the **Hofmann product** (which is the exception, not the general case).

When is the least substituted alkene likely to be formed? In the case of the menthyl chlorides, the least substituted alkene resulted from E2 reaction of one diastereomer because the arrangement of groups in that isomer could lead *only* to that product. However, menthyl chloride is unusual. A more common phenomenon leading to the least substituted alkene is *steric hindrance.*

Steric hindrance in the E2 transition state can raise the energy of the transition state and force the reaction to go to the less hindered, less substituted alkene. The steric hindrance may be caused by one of three factors. First of all, it may be caused by the size of the attacking base. In elimination by 2-bromobutane with the small ethoxide ion, the more substituted alkene predominates. With the bulky *t*-butoxide ion, the less substituted alkene predominates.

Bulk of base:

$$CH_3CH_2CHCH_3 \xrightarrow{\begin{array}{c} CH_3CH_2O^- \\ \text{small} \end{array}} CH_3CH=CHCH_3 + CH_3CH_2CH=CH_2$$

2-bromobutane

$$\xrightarrow[\text{2-butene}]{} \quad \text{2-butene} \quad \text{1-butene}$$
$$81\% \quad 19\%$$

$$\xrightarrow{\begin{array}{c} (CH_3)_3CO^- \\ \text{bulky} \end{array}} CH_3CH=CHCH_3 + CH_3CH_2CH=CH_2$$
$$\text{2-butene} \quad \text{1-butene}$$
$$47\% \quad 53\%$$

Reaction with t-butoxide ion:

$$(CH_3)_3CO^-$$

$$\text{repulsion} \left\{ \begin{array}{c} H \\ | \\ CH_3CHCHCH_3 \\ | \\ Br \end{array} \right. \longrightarrow CH_3CH=CHCH_3$$

2-butene
not favored

attack at carbon 3

$$^-OC(CH_3)_3$$

$$\left. \begin{array}{c} H \\ | \\ CH_3CH_2CHCH_2 \\ | \\ Br \end{array} \right\} \text{less repulsion} \longrightarrow CH_3CH_2CH=CH_2$$

1-butene
favored

attack at carbon 1

Second, steric hindrance might be caused by the bulkiness of groups surrounding the leaving group in the alkyl halide. The hindered 2-bromo-2,4,4-trimethylpentane yields the less substituted alkene in an E2 reaction, even with a small base like the ethoxide ion.

Bulk of RX:

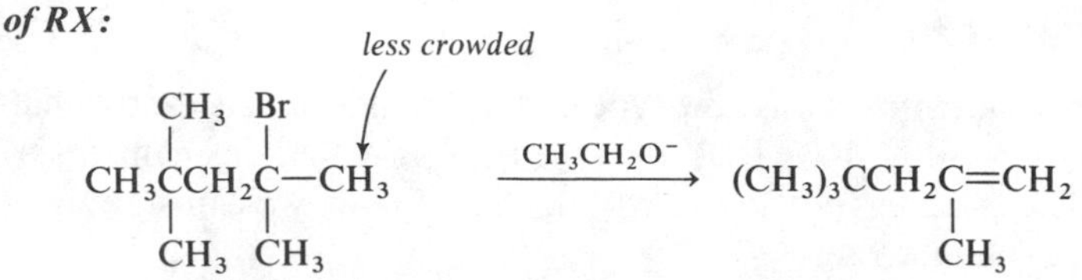

less crowded

$$CH_3CCH_2C-CH_3 \xrightarrow{CH_3CH_2O^-} (CH_3)_3CCH_2C=CH_2$$

2-bromo-2,4,4-trimethylpentane

2,4,4-trimethyl-1-pentene
86%

Third, if the leaving group is large and bulky, the Hofmann product is formed. (We will discuss R_3N as a leaving group in Chapter 15.)

Bulk of leaving group:

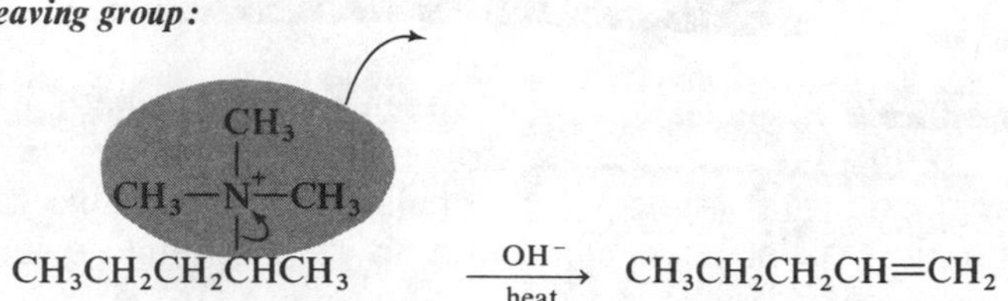

$$CH_3CH_2CH_2\overset{\overset{\displaystyle CH_3-\overset{+}{N}-CH_3}{|}}{C}HCH_3 \xrightarrow[heat]{OH^-} CH_3CH_2CH_2CH=CH_2$$

trimethyl(2-pentyl)ammonium ion

1-pentene
96%

STUDY PROBLEM

5.13 Predict the major alkene products of the following E2 reactions:

(a) $CH_3CH_2CH_2CHBrCH_3 + {}^-OC(CH_3)_3 \longrightarrow$

(b) 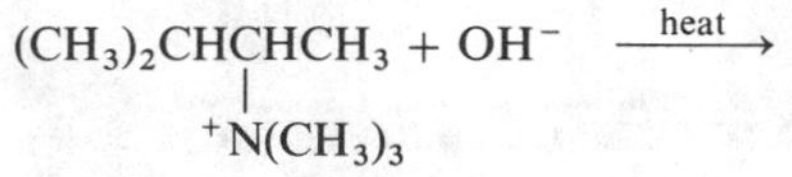 $(CH_3)_2CHCHCH_3 + OH^- \xrightarrow{heat}$
$\qquad\qquad \overset{|}{{}^+N(CH_3)_3}$

(c) $CH_3CH_2CHBrCH_3 + OH^- \longrightarrow$

Section 5.11

Pulling It All Together

At the start of this chapter, we mentioned that S_N1, S_N2, E1, and E2 are *competing reactions*. A single alkyl halide could be undergoing substitution, elimination, and rearrangements all in the same reaction flask. If this happens, a mixture of a large number of products results. However, a chemist can control the products of the reaction to a certain extent by using his knowledge of the factors that control these various pathways. By proper choice of the reaction conditions, he can modify the course of the reaction.

What, then, are the factors that affect the course of substitution and elimination reactions of alkyl halides? These factors are:

(1)   the structure of the alkyl halide;

(2)   the nature of the nucleophile;

(3)   the concentration of the nucleophile;

(4)   the temperature; and, finally,

(5)   the solvent.

Alkyl Halides; Substitution and Elimination Reactions

A.   The Alkyl Halide

We have mentioned that the type of alkyl halide affects the mechanism of the reaction. Now that we have looked at the four principal mechanisms by which an alkyl halide can undergo reaction with a nucleophile, we can summarize how the different alkyl halides act.

Primary alkyl halides   tend to undergo S_N2 reactions. They do not form carbocations and thus cannot undergo S_N1 or E1 reactions. They undergo E2 reactions slowly, if at all.

$$1°: \quad RX + Nu^- \xrightarrow{\;S_N2\;} RNu + X^-$$

Secondary alkyl halides   can undergo reaction by any path, but S_N2 and E2 are more common than E1 or S_N1. (Secondary carbocations are not formed easily.) The reactions of secondary alkyl halides are more subject to control by conditions in the reaction flask (concentration of nucleophile, solvent, etc.) than are reactions of other alkyl halides.

$$2°: \quad RX + Nu^- \xrightarrow{\;S_N2 + E2\;} RNu + \text{alkene}$$

Tertiary alkyl halides   undergo E1 and E2 reactions with a strong base, but undergo the S_N1 reaction with a very weak base. Because of the various pathways available to a tertiary alkyl halide, mixtures of alkenes and substitution products tend to be the rule.

$$3°: \quad RX + Nu^- \xrightarrow{\;S_N1, \; E1, \; E2\;} RNu + \text{alkenes}$$

Let us compare the products of a primary, a secondary, and a tertiary alkyl bromide under the same reaction conditions:

Reaction with Na^+ $^-OCH_2CH_3$ in CH_3CH_2OH at 25°:

$1°: \quad CH_3CH_2Br \longrightarrow CH_3CH_2OCH_2CH_3$
almost 100%

$2°: \quad (CH_3)_2CHBr \longrightarrow (CH_3)_2CHOCH_2CH_3 + CH_2{=}CHCH_3$
20%   80%

$3°: \quad (CH_3)_3CBr \longrightarrow (CH_3)_3COCH_2CH_3 + CH_2{=}C(CH_3)_2$
5%   95%

B.   The Nucleophile

The choice of nucleophile can change the course of a substitution or elimination reaction. The strength of a nucleophile, called the **nucleophilicity**, is determined by its action in S_N2 reactions. A stronger nucleophile is one that results in a faster reaction under the same conditions. Nucleophilicity is contrasted to **basicity**, which is determined in reactions with acids. Table 5.7 lists a number of nucleophiles in order of decreasing reactivity toward CH_3Br (an S_N2 reaction).

Table 5.7.   Reactivity of Nucleophiles
Toward Methyl Bromide

Nucleophile	Relative reactivity
CN^-	12,600
$HS^-(RS^-)$	12,600
I^-	10,200
RO^{-a}	—
HO^-	1,600
Br^-	775
R_3N^a	—
Cl^-	102
$CH_3CO_2^-$	52.5
ROH^a	—
H_2O	1.00

[a] Relative value not known, but listed in approximate order.

Several factors affect nucleophilicity, and no single factor can be used to explain every case. The first factor is *basicity*: a stronger base is generally a better nucleophile. The hydroxide ion (more basic) is a better nucleophile than the chloride ion (less basic).

A second factor that affects nucleophilicity is *polarizability*. The outer electrons of larger atoms are farther from the nucleus and less tightly held than those of smaller atoms. The outer electrons of larger atoms are therefore more easily distorted by attraction to a positive center and can attack a partially positive carbon atom more readily. Given two nucleophiles of approximately the same basicity, the nucleophile from a third-row element is larger, more polarizable, and more nucleophilic than the nucleophile from a second-row element. For example, the hydrogen sulfide ion (HS^-) is a better nucleophile than the hydroxide ion. Also, the iodide ion is usually a better nucleophile than the chloride ion.

A third factor that affects nucleophilicity is the *solvation of the nucleophile*. The choice of solvent can actually change the ranking of nucleophilicity within a group of nucleophiles. A solvent that can solvate (and thus stabilize) an anion reduces its nucleophilicity. By contrast, a solvent that cannot solvate an anion enhances its nucleophilicity. The chloride ion is a far better nucleophile in dimethylformamide (DMF), where it is not solvated, than in ethanol, where it is solvated.

$$Cl^- \quad \overset{\overset{\textstyle O}{\|}}{H}CN(CH_3)_2 \qquad CH_3CH_2OH---Cl^----HOCH_2CH_3$$

DMF   *solvation*
no solvation

A *strong nucleophile,* such as RS^-, favors S_N2 reactions (as opposed to carbocation reactions). Conversely, by slowing down the rate of the S_N2 reaction and allowing carbocation formation to occur, a weak nucleophile favors

S_N1 reaction. However, a *strong base* (such as OH^-, OR^-, or NH_2^-) favors elimination reactions.

> *strong nucleophile:* S_N2
> *weak nucleophile:* S_N1 and E1
> *strong base:* E1 and E2

C. Concentration of the Nucleophile

By controlling the concentration of nucleophile, a chemist has direct control over the rates of S_N2 and E2 reactions. Secondary alkyl halides are able to undergo S_N1, S_N2, E1, and E2 reactions. Increasing the concentration of nucleophile has no effect on the rates of S_N1 or E1 reactions, but increases S_N2 or E2 reaction rates proportionally. Therefore, a high concentration of nucleophile favors S_N2 or E2 reaction; a low concentration favors S_N1 or E1.

D. The Temperature

An increase in temperature increases the rates of all substitution and elimination reactions. However, an increase in temperature usually leads to an increase in elimination products.

E. The Solvent

The polarity of a solvent can affect the course of a reaction of an alkyl halide. We have already discussed the effect of solvent upon the nucleophilicity of an anion. The ability of a solvent to solvate ions is determined by its polarity, which is usually reported as the **dielectric constant**. Whereas a dipole moment is a measure of the polarity of a single molecule, the dielectric constant is a measure of the polarity of a liquid (many molecules with interactions between them). A highly polar solvent has a high dielectric constant. Table 5.8 lists some common organic solvents, their dielectric constants, and the relative rates of a typical S_N1 reaction in that solvent.

Table 5.8. Relative Rates of Typical S_N1 Reactions in Various Solvents

Solvent	Formula	Dielectric constant	Approximate relative rate
formic acid	HCO_2H	58	15,000
water	H_2O	78.5	4000
80% aqueous ethanol	$CH_3CH_2OH–H_2O$	67	185
acetic acid	CH_3CO_2H	6	100
ethanol	CH_3CH_2OH	24	95
acetone	$CH_3\overset{\displaystyle O}{\overset{\|}{C}}CH_3$	21	0.5

In general, a *very polar solvent*, especially one that forms hydrogen bonds (for example, H_2O or a carboxylic acid), has two effects:

(1)   encourages S_N1 reaction by helping stabilize the carbocation by solvation;

(2)   increases the amount of substitution products over elimination products.

A *less polar solvent*, such as acetone, $(CH_3)_2C{=}O$, favors S_N2 and E2 reactions because it does not encourage ionization.

for S_N1:	Nu^- in H_2O, HCO_2H, or CH_3CO_2H *(highly polar solvents)*
for S_N2 over E2:	KOH in H_2O
for E2 over S_N2:	KOH in CH_3CH_2OH

$$\text{for } S_N2 \text{ over } S_N1: \quad Nu^- \text{ in } CH_3\overset{\displaystyle O}{\overset{\displaystyle \|}{C}}CH_3 \text{ or } CH_3CH_2OH \quad \textit{(relatively nonpolar solvents)}$$

Some solvents can act as nucleophiles and give rise to **solvolysis reactions** (from *solvent* and *-lysis*, "breaking"). Water and ethanol are two solvents that can cause solvolysis of alkyl halides. These solvents are polar, but are weak nucleophiles; therefore, the S_N1 path is favored over the S_N2 path in their reactions with alkyl halides. (Because water and ethanol are weak bases, elimination reactions are not favored.)

$$(CH_3)_3C\ddot{B}r \begin{cases} \xrightarrow[25°]{CH_3CH_2OH} & (CH_3)_3COCH_2CH_3 + CH_2{=}C(CH_3)_2 \\ & \quad\quad 81\% \quad\quad\quad\quad\quad 19\% \\ \\ \xrightarrow[25°]{H_2O} & (CH_3)_3COH + CH_2{=}C(CH_3)_2 \\ & \quad 70\% \quad\quad\quad\quad 30\% \end{cases}$$

Sample Problem

Write out each step in the solvolysis reaction of *t*-butyl bromide with ethanol.

Solution:

(1)   formation of carbocation:

$$(CH_3)_3CBr \longrightarrow [(CH_3)_3C^+] + Br^-$$

(2)   attack of nucleophile:

$$[(CH_3)_3C^+] + \underset{\displaystyle H}{:\ddot{O}CH_2CH_3} \longrightarrow (CH_3)_3\overset{+}{C}\underset{\displaystyle H}{\ddot{O}CH_2CH_3}$$

(3)   loss of a proton:

$$(CH_3)_3\overset{+}{C}\underset{\displaystyle H}{\ddot{O}CH_2CH_3} \rightleftharpoons (CH_3)_3C\ddot{O}CH_2CH_3 + H^+$$

F.   The Right Conditions

Let us give a quick overview of how choice of reagents and conditions favor one type of reaction over another.

For S_N1:

(1)   A tertiary alkyl halide.

(2)   A weak nucleophile, such as H_2O or $CH_3CO_2^-$ (to decrease S_N2 and elimination).

(3)   A low concentration of nucleophile (to decrease S_N2 and E2).

(4)   A highly polar solvent, such as H_2O or RCO_2H (to encourage ionization).

(5)   Moderate temperature (to discourage elimination).

For S_N2:

(1)   A methyl, primary, or secondary alkyl halide.

(2)   A strong nucleophile, such as RO^- or CN^-.

(3)   A high concentration of nucleophile (to increase S_N2 rate).

(4)   A solvent of relatively low polarity, such as ROH (to discourage ionization).

(5)   Moderate temperature (to discourage elimination).

For E1:

(1)   A tertiary alkyl halide.

(2)   A low concentration of base (to decrease rates of S_N2 and E2).

(3)   High temperature.

For E2:

(1)   A secondary or tertiary alkyl halide.

(2)   A strong base.

(3)   A high concentration of base (to increase E2 rate).

(4)   A solvent of low polarity (to discourage ionization).

(5)   High temperature.

Table 5.9 summarizes the effects of different nucleophiles on different alkyl halides.

Sample Problem

1-Bromopropane is treated with the strong nucleophile $HC\equiv C^-$ in ether as the solvent. What organic product would you expect? By what mechanism?

Solution: A $1°$RX, a strong nucleophile, and a solvent of low polarity all favor S_N2. The product would be 1-pentyne.

$$CH_3CH_2CH_2Br + {}^-C\equiv CH \xrightarrow[S_N2]{-Br^-} CH_3CH_2CH_2C\equiv CH$$

Table 5.9.   *Reactions to Expect with Various Nucleophiles*

Alkyl halide	Reagent	Reaction type
CH_3X or 1° RX	OH^-, OR^-, CN^-, NH_3	S_N2
2° RX	*stronger base:*	
	OH^-, OR^-, CN^-, NH_3	S_N2 and E2
	weaker base: H_2O, ROH	S_N1 (some S_N2)
3° RX	*stronger base:*	
	OH^-, OR^-, CN^-, NH_3	E2
	weaker base: H_2O, ROH	S_N1

Section 5.12

Synthesis Problems

In this text, you will encounter many synthesis problems, problems in which you are asked to show by equations how you would prepare a compound. Alkyl halides are versatile starting materials for a variety of products. For the moment, let us ignore elimination reactions and consider only the substitution reactions of alkyl halides and discuss how they can be used in organic synthesis.

Methyl halides and almost all primary alkyl halides give good yields in S_N2 reactions. Under the proper reaction conditions, secondary alkyl halides, too, may give reasonable yields of S_N2 substitution products. (Chemists usually avoid S_N1 reactions of alkyl halides as synthesis reactions because of the possibilities of carbocation rearrangements.)

To answer a synthesis problem, use the following general approach:

(1) Ask yourself: ? + ? → product

(2) Use only reactions that give the product in reasonable yield. If one reaction gives 100% of the desired product, use that reaction. However, if no such reaction is available, use a reaction that gives 50 or 60% yield. Do not use reactions that give very low yields (under 25%).

(3) It is acceptable to use flow equations with reagents and reaction conditions above or below the arrows.

$$A \xrightarrow{\ xy\ } B \xrightarrow[100°]{\ yz\ } C$$

(4) Unless you are asked to do so, you need not balance equations nor indicate minor products.

(5) If the text shows a reaction of a simple compound, you may usually extrapolate the reaction to more complex, but similar, structures.

Example: $(CH_3)_2CHBr + CH_3S^- \longrightarrow (CH_3)_2CHSCH_3 + Br^-$

This reaction may be extrapolated to other secondary alkyl halides or to other alkylsulfide ions.

$$(CH_3CH_2)_2CHBr + CH_3S^- \longrightarrow (CH_3CH_2)_2CHSCH_3 + Br^-$$

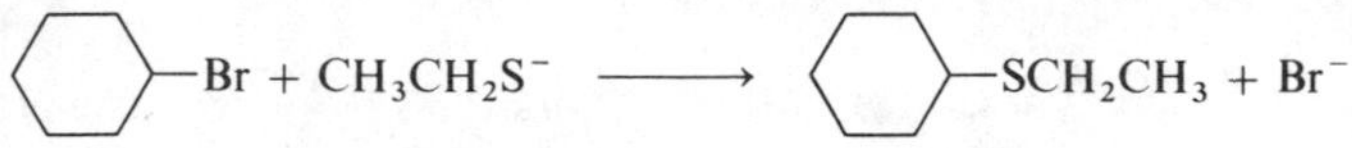

$-Br + CH_3CH_2S^- \longrightarrow$ $-SCH_2CH_3 + Br^-$

Sample Problem

How would you synthesize 2-cyclohexyl-1-ethanol from an alkyl halide?

Solution:

(1)   Write the structure: $-CH_2CH_2OH$

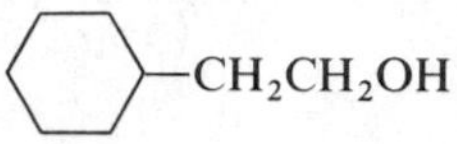

(2)   Decide on the nucleophile: OH^-

(3)   Choose the alkyl halide: $-CH_2CH_2Br$ (or Cl or I)

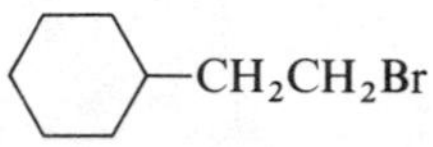

(4)   Write an equation with the reagent over the arrow.

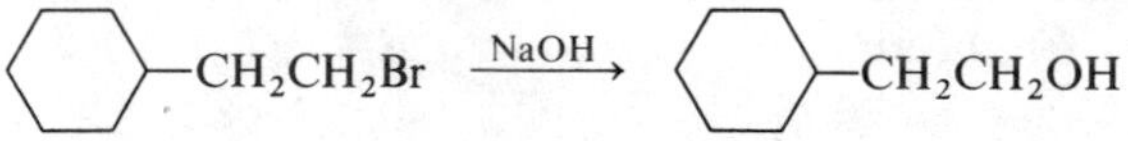

$-CH_2CH_2Br \xrightarrow{\text{NaOH}}$ $-CH_2CH_2OH$

Sample Problem

What alkyl chloride and nucleophile are needed to synthesize $CH_3(CH_2)_6CH_2CN$?

Solution: The nucleophile must be ^-CN. The alkyl chloride must be 1-chlorooctane. Your answer would be: $CH_3(CH_2)_6CH_2Cl + {}^-CN$.

We have used rather simple, straightforward structures as our examples. However, in a synthesis problem, *do not be intimidated by the complexity of the rest of the molecule.* Inspect the molecule for the important features and worry only about the small portion that undergoes reaction. When you have a larger vocabulary of organic reactions, you will want to inspect a complex structure for other functional groups that might also undergo reaction under the same conditions.

Sample Problem

How would you prepare the following compound from a compound that contains only C, H, and Cl?

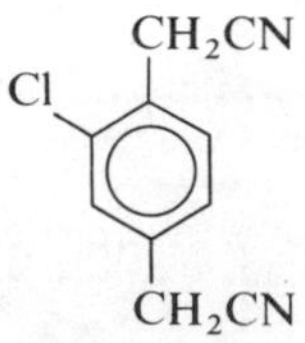

Solution:

(1)   Look at the functional groups and decide what nucleophile is needed.

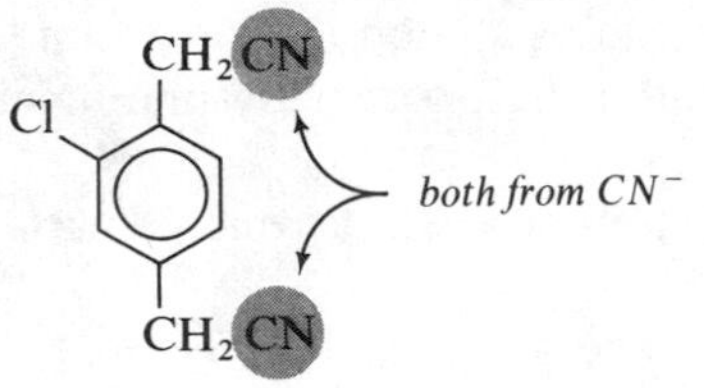

both from CN⁻

(2)   Decide what starting chloro compound is needed.

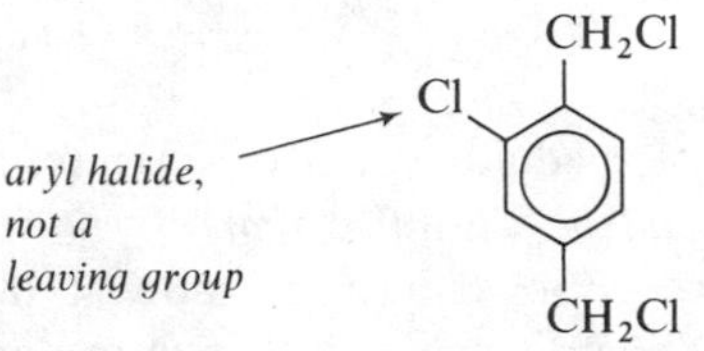

aryl halide, not a leaving group

(3)   Write the equation.

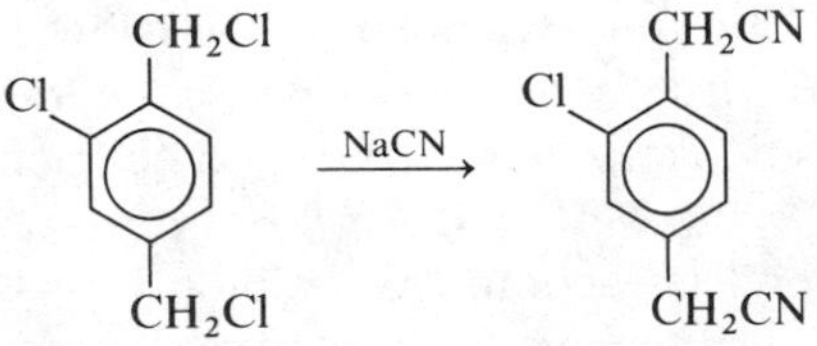

Sample Problem

Suggest two synthetic methods that could be used to prepare ⟨○⟩—CH_2OCH_3.

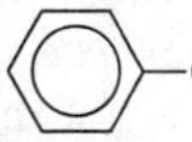

Solution:

(a) $C_6H_5CH_2$—OCH_3 from $C_6H_5CH_2Br$ and CH_3O^-

(b) $C_6H_5CH_2O$—CH_3 from $C_6H_5CH_2O^-$ and CH_3I

Sample Problem

What reagents are needed for the preparation of each of the following compounds from an alkyl halide?

(a) CH_3SH (b) 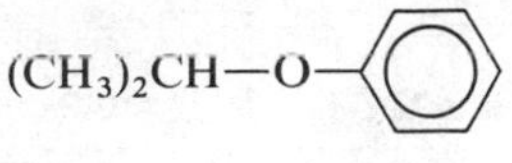 $(CH_3)_2CH$—O—⟨○⟩   (c) 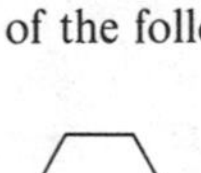 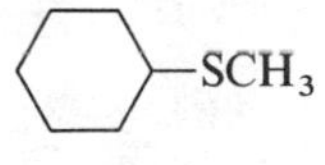   ⟨○⟩—SCH_3

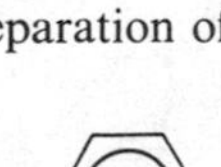

Solution: (a) CH_3I and HS^-;   (b) $(CH_3)_2CHBr$ and $C_6H_5O^-$ (Why could you *not* have

used $C_6H_5Br + (CH_3)_2CHO^-$?);   (c) 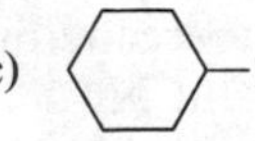   ⟨○⟩—$S^- + CH_3I$ or   ⟨○⟩—$I + CH_3S^-$

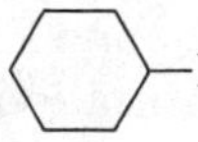

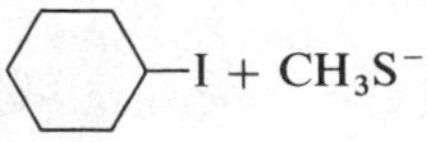

STUDY PROBLEM

5.14   Suggest a synthesis for each of the following compounds, starting with an alkyl halide. (*Hint*: The C=C and C≡C groups are not attacked by base.)

(a)   *cis*-CH_3CH=$CHCH_2CH_2SH$

(b) HC≡$CCH_2CH_2CH_2CH_2C$≡$CCH_2CH_2CH_2CH_2OCH_2CH_3$

SUMMARY   I M P O R T A N T !

An alkyl halide contains a good **leaving group** (X^-) and is readily attacked by **nucleophiles** (Nu^-). Reaction occurs by one or more of four possible paths: S_N1, S_N2, **E1, E2**.

An S_N1 or E1 reaction proceeds through a **carbocation intermediate**:

$$RX \xrightarrow{-X^-} [R^+] \quad \begin{array}{l} \xrightarrow[S_N1]{Nu^-} RNu \\ \\ \xrightarrow[E1]{-H^+} alkene \end{array}$$

A carbocation intermediate usually leads to a mixture of products: *a substitution product, an alkene*, and also *rearrangement products*. Rearrangement products occur if the carbocation can form a more stable carbocation by a 1,2-shift of H, Ar, or R. If RX is enantiomeric, racemization occurs in an S_N1 reaction.

The rate of an S_N1 or E1 reaction is **first order**: the rate depends only on the concentration of RX. The **rate-determining step** (slow step) is the formation of R^+. The stability of R^+ determines the **energy of the transition state** (E_{act}) in this step because the transition state has carbocation character. The *order of stability* of carbocations is $3° > 2° > 1° > CH_3^+$. For this reason, the likelihood of RX to undergo S_N1 or E1 reaction is $3° > 2° > 1° > CH_3X$. Allyl and benzyl halides undergo S_N1 reactions readily because of resonance-stabilization of the intermediate carbocation.

The energy of the E1 transition state in Step 2 ($R^+ \rightarrow$ alkene) determines the alkene product. The *more substituted alkene* has a faster rate of formation and is favored (**Saytseff rule**); if the alkene is capable of geometric isomerism, the *trans*-product is favored.

An S_N2 reaction is a **concerted reaction** that leads to *inversion of configuration*. Inversion can be observed if RX is enantiomeric. An E2 reaction is also a concerted reaction that results by *anti* elimination of H^+ and X^-.

$$Nu^- + R—X \xrightarrow{S_N2} NuR + X^-$$

$$\underset{\underset{\displaystyle X}{|}}{R_2C—CR_2} \xrightarrow{E2} NuH + R_2C{=}CR_2 + X^-$$

Both S_N2 and E2 reactions follow **second-order kinetics**: the rate is dependent on the concentrations of both RX and Nu^- because both are involved in the transition state. Because of steric hindrance, the order of reactivity of RX in S_N2 reactions is $CH_3X > 1° > 2° > 3°$.

Because the transition state has double-bond character, the order of reactivity of RX in E2 reactions is $3° > 2° > 1°$, the same order as in the E1 reaction. The *most substituted alkene* usually predominates. If stereochemistry or steric hindrance inhibits the formation of the most substituted alkene, then the *least substituted alkene* predominates (**Hofmann product**).

STUDY PROBLEMS

5.15 Which of the following compounds would be classed as an alkyl halide?

(a) 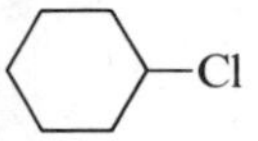 ⬡—Cl   (b) 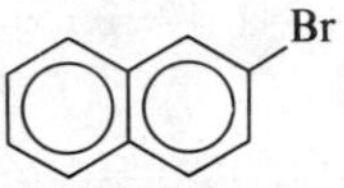 [naphthalene-Br structure]   (c) 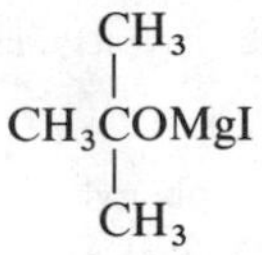 $CH_3\underset{\underset{CH_3}{|}}{\overset{\overset{CH_3}{|}}{C}}OMgI$

5.16 Name each of the following compounds by the IUPAC system:

(a) 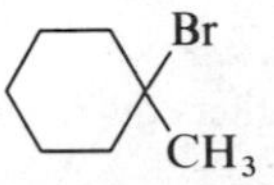 [cyclohexane with Br and CH₃]   (b) 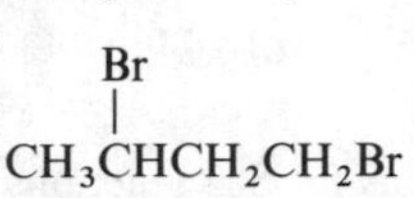 $CH_3\underset{\underset{Br}{|}}{C}HCH_2CH_2Br$ (c) [cyclopentane with OH and Cl]

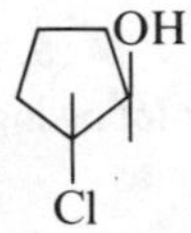

(d) $CCl_3CH{=}CH_2$

5.17 Give the structure for each of the following compounds: (a) isobutyl iodide; (b) 1-iodo-2-methylpropane; (c) *cis*-1,3-dichlorocyclohexane; (d) 2-bromo-3-methyl-1-butanol.

5.18 Classify the following alkyl halides as methyl, 1°, 2°, or 3°:

(a) $(CH_3)_3CCH_2Cl$ (b) 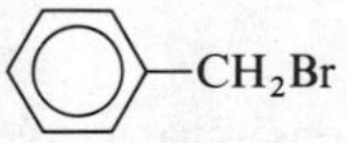 [phenyl]—CH_2Br (c) CH_3I

(d) $(CH_3CH_2)_3CCl$ (e) 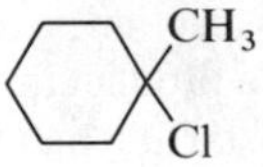 [cyclohexane with CH₃ and Cl]   (f) $CH_3CHClCH_3$

(g) $(CH_3)_2CHCH_2CH_2Br$ (h) 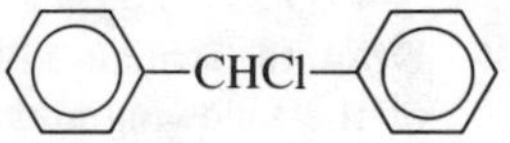 [phenyl]—CHCl—[phenyl]

5.19 Circle the carbon (or carbons) that would be attacked by a nucleophile in a substitution reaction of each of the following structures:

(a) CH_3CH_2Br (b) 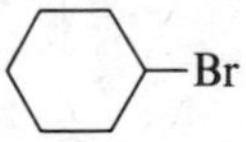 ⬡—Br   (c) 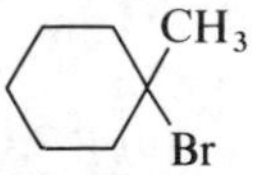 [cyclohexane with CH₃ and Br]   (d) 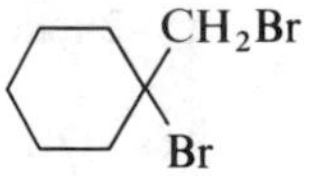 [cyclohexane with CH₂Br and Br]

5.20 Which of the following compounds contains a good leaving group?

(a) $(CH_3)_3Cl$ (b) 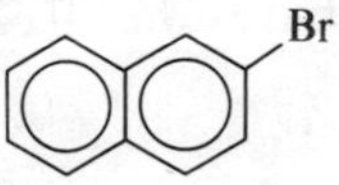 [naphthalene-Br structure]   (c) 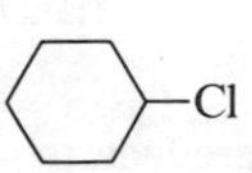 ⬡—Cl

5.21 Which compound in each of the following pairs would undergo reaction with ⁻OCH_3 more readily?

(a) CH_3Cl or CH_3I (b) 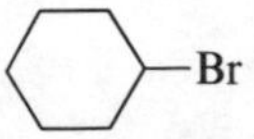 ⬡—Br or ⬡—I

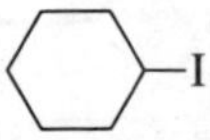

(c) 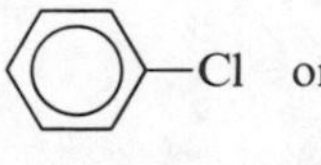 [phenyl]—Cl or ⬡—Cl

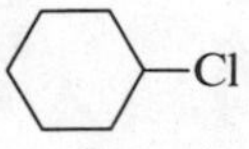

5.22 Suggest reagents for the preparation of each of the following compounds by an S_N2-type reaction of an alkyl halide with a nucleophile:

(a) diethyl ether ($CH_3CH_2OCH_2CH_3$)   (b) 2-butanol

(c) 1-hexyne (*Hint*: $CH\equiv CH + Na \longrightarrow CH\equiv C^- \ Na^+ + \frac{1}{2}H_2$)

(d) isopropyl phenyl ether, $(CH_3)_2CHOC_6H_5$ (e)

(f) $CH_3CH_2O\overset{\overset{\displaystyle O}{\|}}{C}CH_2CH(CH_3)_2$ (g) 1,6-heptadiyne

5.23 Complete the following equations for S_N2 reactions. (*Hint*: Ethers do not react under these conditions.)

(a) 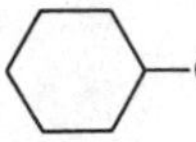 $-Cl + NaSCH_3 \longrightarrow$

(b) 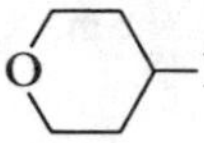 O $-Br + CH_3CH_2CH_2ONa \longrightarrow$

(c) $ICH_2CH_2CH_2I + NaOH \longrightarrow$

5.24 Which of the following descriptions is characteristic of an S_N2 mechanism? (a) second-order rate expression; (b) one-step reaction; (c) involves a carbocation intermediate; (d) inversion of configuration; (e) a product in which the hybridization of the reactive carbon is different from that of the starting material.

5.25 Draw the structure of the transition state for the S_N2 reaction of $^-OCH_3$ with each of the following alkyl bromides: (a) (*R*)-2-bromobutane; (b) (*S*)-2-bromobutane; (c) (*R*)-2-bromo-3-methylbutane; (d) (*S*)-2-bromo-3-methylbutane.

5.26 Predict the product of an S_N2 reaction of each of the following nucleophiles with (*S*)-2-iodohexane:

(a) OH^- (b) $^-SCH_2CH_3$

(c) $CH_3C\equiv C^-$ (d) (*R*)-$CH_3CH_2\overset{\overset{\displaystyle O^-}{|}}{C}HCH_2CH_2CH_2CH_3$

5.27 Predict the S_N2 product:

(a)  $+ OH^- \longrightarrow$

(b)  $+ OH^- \longrightarrow$

5.28 Label the indicated parts of the following energy diagram:

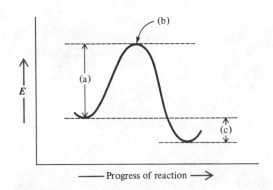

5.29 Reaction 1 and Reaction 2 are two different reactions of a single starting material. If Reaction 1 has a higher-energy transition state than Reaction 2, which of the following statements is true?

(a) Reaction 1 has the faster rate.
(b) The major product is the result of Reaction 1.
(c) The E_{act} is higher for Reaction 1.

5.30 What is the effect on the rate of S_N2 reaction of CH_3I and OH^- when:

(a) The concentration of CH_3I is tripled and that of OH^- is doubled?
(b) The concentration of OH^- is halved?
(c) The temperature is increased?
(d) The ratio of solvent to reactants is doubled?

5.31 Which compound in each of the following pairs would undergo more rapid S_N2 reaction?

(a) $(CH_3)_3CI$ or $(CH_3CH_2)_2CHI$ (b) $(CH_3)_2CHI$ or $(CH_3)_2CHCl$

(c) ⬡—Cl or ⬡—CH_2Cl (d) ⬡—Cl or ⬡$\langle$ CH_3 / Cl

5.32 Which of the following carbocations is most stable?

(a) $CH_3CH_2CH_2^+$ (b) $(CH_3CH_2)_2CH^+$ (c) $(CH_3CH_2)_3C^+$

5.33 Predict the order of reactivity of the following compounds with aqueous ethanol in an S_N1 reaction (least reactive first):

(a) $(CH_3)_2CHBr$ (b) $(CH_3)_3CBr$ (c) $(CH_3)_3CI$

5.34 True or false: Attack of a nucleophile on a carbocation:

(a) can take place from either of two sides because the carbocation is planar.
(b) leads to a racemic mixture of products.
(c) is the rate-determining step in an S_N1 reaction.
(d) does not have a transition state because the carbocation is so reactive.

5.35 Label the indicated parts of the following energy diagram for an S_N1 reaction:

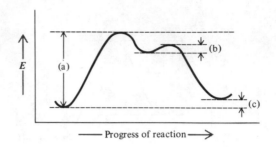

5.36 Heating the following alkyl halides with water results in S_N1 reactions leading to alcohols. Predict each of the products.

(a) *t*-butyl chloride   (b) (*R*)-2-iodooctane

(c) 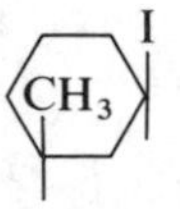 $\langle CH_3 \rangle$ I   (d) (2*R*,4*S*)-2-iodo-4-methylhexane

5.37 Each of the following carbocations is capable of undergoing rearrangement to a more stable carbocation. Suggest a structure for the rearranged carbocation.

(a) $(CH_3)_3C\overset{+}{C}HCH_2CH_3$ (b) $CH_2{=}CHCH_2\overset{+}{C}HCH_3$

(c) $(CH_3)_2CH\overset{+}{C}HCH_2CH(CH_3)_2$ (d) 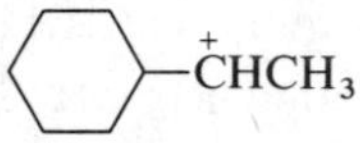 $\langle\text{cyclohexyl}\rangle{-}\overset{+}{C}HCH_3$

5.38 The following reactions proceed with rearrangement. Show the initial carbocation, the rearranged carbocation, and the major rearrangement product in each case.

(a) $(CH_3)_3CCHICH_3 + H_2O \longrightarrow$

(b) $(CH_3)_2CHCHICH_2CH_3 + CH_3CH_2OH \longrightarrow$

5.39 Reaction (a), which follows, is known to proceed readily. What is the organic product of reaction (b)?

(a) 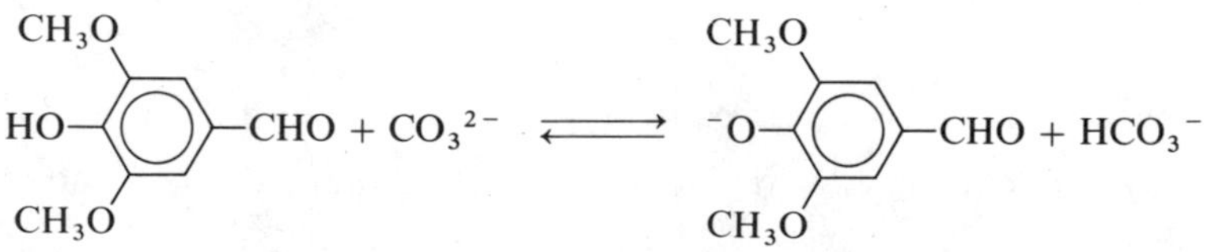 $HO{-}\overset{CH_3O}{\underset{CH_3O}{\langle\bigcirc\rangle}}{-}CHO + CO_3{}^{2-} \;\rightleftharpoons\; {}^-O{-}\overset{CH_3O}{\underset{CH_3O}{\langle\bigcirc\rangle}}{-}CHO + HCO_3{}^-$

(b) 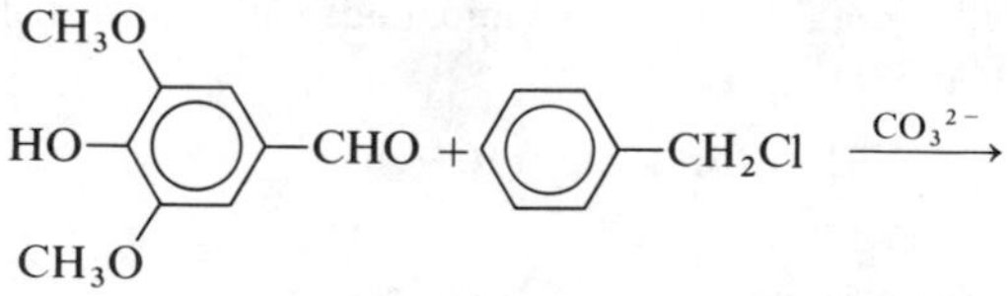 $HO{-}\overset{CH_3O}{\underset{CH_3O}{\langle\bigcirc\rangle}}{-}CHO + \langle\bigcirc\rangle{-}CH_2Cl \xrightarrow{\;CO_3{}^{2-}\;}$

5.40 Tell how to synthesize each of the following compounds from an organic halide:

(a) 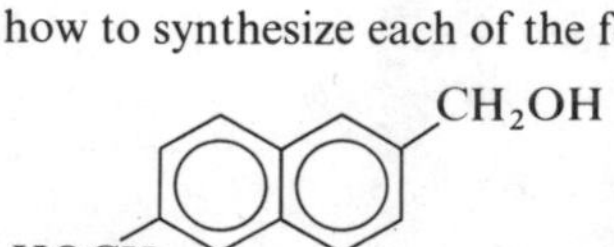 [structure: naphthalene with CH₂OH and HOCH₂ substituents]
CH_2OH ... $HOCH_2$

(b) $CH_2{=}CHCH_2SCH_3$

5.41 Give the important resonance structures of each of the following cations:

(a) $CH_2{=}CHCH{=}CH\overset{+}{C}H_2$

(b) 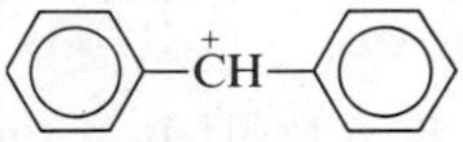 [benzene ring]$-\overset{+}{C}H-$[benzene ring]

(c) [cyclohexene ring]$\overset{+}{-}CH{=}CH_2$

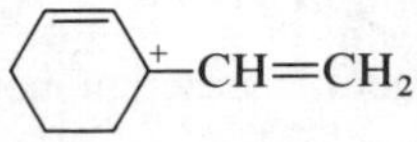

(d) 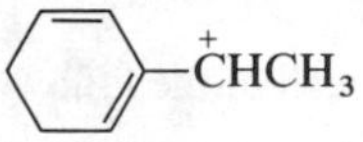 [benzene ring]$-\overset{+}{C}HCH_3$

5.42 Complete the following equations, showing structures of all likely substitution products:

(a) 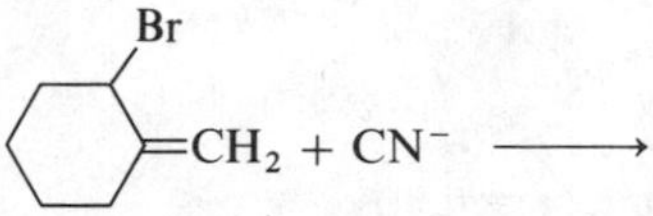 [cyclohexane ring with Br]$={=}CH_2 + CN^- \longrightarrow$

(b) 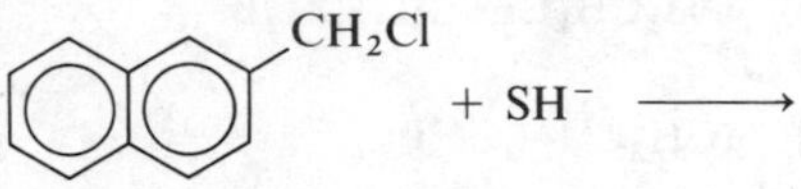 [naphthalene ring]$CH_2Cl + SH^- \longrightarrow$

(c) 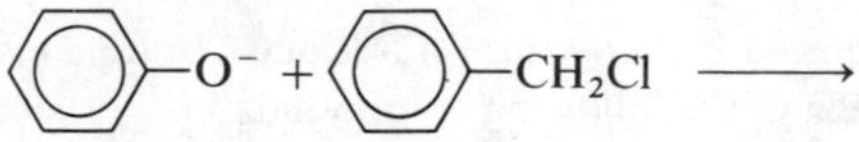 [benzene ring]$-O^- +$ [benzene ring]$-CH_2Cl \longrightarrow$

(d) $CH_3CH{=}CHCH{=}CHCH_2Cl + {}^-OCH_3 \longrightarrow$

(e) 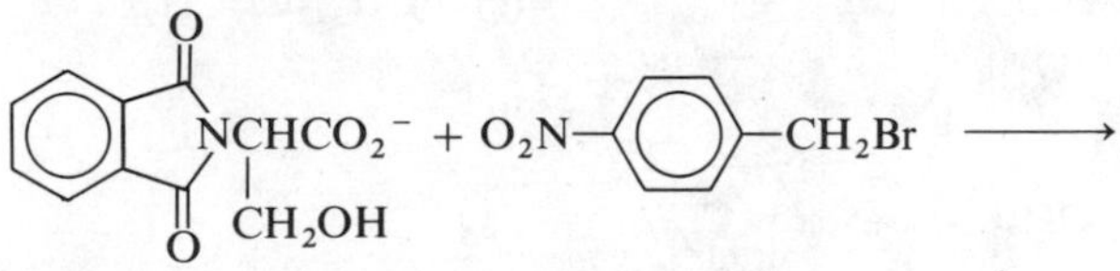 [phthalimide structure] $NCHCO_2{}^- + O_2N-$[benzene ring]$-CH_2Br \longrightarrow$
CH_2OH

5.43 (a) Write the equations for the steps of the E1 reaction of 2-iodohexane with a base going to 2-hexene.

(b) Which step determines the rate of reaction?

(c) What other alkene products could be formed?

(d) Which step determines the predominant products?

(e) Would you expect the 2-hexene to be *cis* or *trans*?

5.44 Which is the more stable alkene: (a) 1-butene or 2-butene? (b) 2,3-dimethyl-1-butene or 2,3-dimethyl-2-butene? (c) 2-methyl-2-pentene or 4-methyl-2-pentene? (d) 1-methyl-1-cyclohexene or 3-methyl-1-cyclohexene?

5.45 What would be the predominant product of E1 reaction of each of the following compounds?

(a) 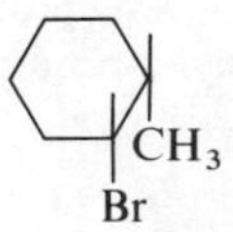 [cyclohexane with CH₃ and Br] (b) 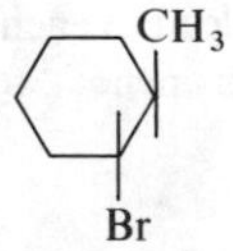 [cyclohexane with CH₃ and Br] (c) 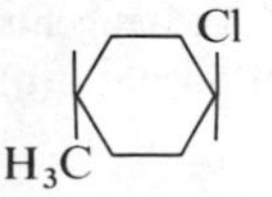 [cyclohexane with Cl and H₃C] (d) 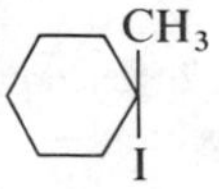 [cyclohexane with CH₃ and I]

5.46 What would be the predominant product of E2 reaction (NaOH as the base) of each of the compounds in Problem 5.45?

5.47 Each of the following alkyl halides can undergo rearrangement in an E1 reaction. For each, show the initial carbocation, the rearranged carbocation, and the anticipated major rearrangement product.

(a) $(CH_3)_2CHCHClCH(CH_3)_2$ (b) $(CH_3)_3CCHBrCH_2CH_2CH_3$

5.48 Which compound in each of the following pairs undergoes E2 reaction more rapidly?

(a) $(CH_3)_2CHCHBrCH_2CH_3$ or $(CH_3)_2CBrCH_2CH_2CH_3$

(b) $(CH_3)_2CHCHICH_3$ or $(CH_3)_2CHCH_2CH_2I$

(c) $CH_3CH_2CH_2Br$ or $CH_3CH=CHBr$

(d) CH_3CHICH_3 or $CH_3CHBrCH_3$

5.49 Circle any H atoms that could be lost in an E2 reaction:

(a) $CH_3CH_2CHBrCH_3$ (b) $CH_3CH_2CH(CH_3)CH_2Br$

(c) 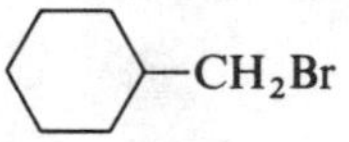 ⬡—CH_2Br (d) $(CH_3CH_2)_2CHI$

5.50 Which hydrogen(s) must be replaced by deuterium if a kinetic isotope effect is to be observed in an E2 reaction of each of the following compounds?

(a) $CH_3CH_2CH_2Br$ (b) 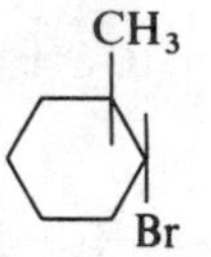 [structure with CH_3 and Br]   (c) $(CH_3)_2CHCH_2I$

(d) $(CH_3)_2CClCH_3$ (e) 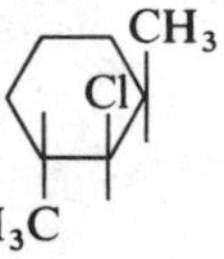 [structure with CH_3, Cl, H_3C]

5.51 For each of the following reactions, indicate whether the product is mainly the Saytseff product or the Hofmann product:

(a) $CH_3CHClCH_2CH_2CH_3 \longrightarrow CH_2=CHCH_2CH_2CH_3$

(b) $CH_3CHClCH_2CH_2CH_3 \longrightarrow CH_3CH=CHCH_2CH_3$

(c) 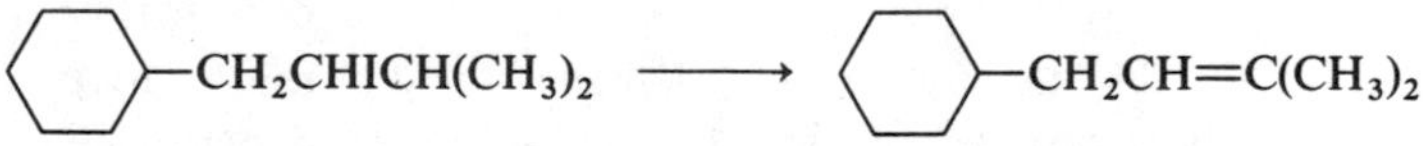 ⬡—$CH_2CHICH(CH_3)_2 \longrightarrow$ ⬡—$CH_2CH=C(CH_3)_2$

(d) 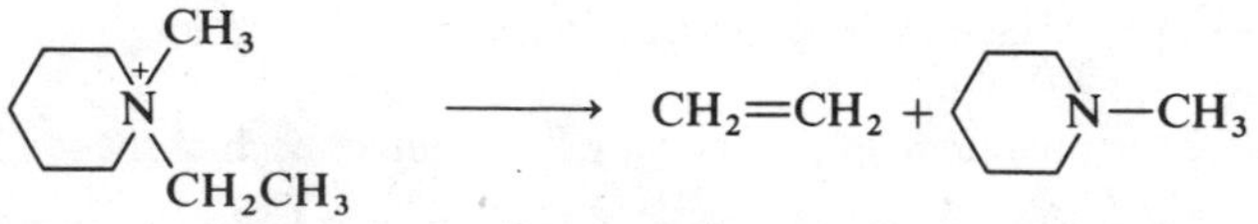 [structure with N$^+$, CH_3, CH_2CH_3] $\longrightarrow CH_2=CH_2$ + [⬡N—CH_3]

5.52 Suggest a combination of reagents that can lead to each of the following products by an E2 reaction: (a) propene; (b) methylpropene; (c) 4-methyl-2-pentene; (d) 1-pentene.

5.53 Predict the principal E1 and E2 products of the reaction of each of the following compounds with Na^+ $^-OCH_3$: (a) (S)-2-bromopentane; (b) 2,6-dichloroheptane; (c) (1S,2S)-1-bromo-1,2-diphenylbutane.

5.54 Predict the products of E2 reaction of the following alkyl halides with (1) Na^+ $^-OCH_3$ and (2) K^+ $^-OC(CH_3)_3$:

(a) 1-chloro-1-methylcyclohexane   (b) (*S*)-1-chloro-1-cyclohexylethane

5.55 In the reaction of 1-bromobutane with dilute sodium hydroxide solution, we would expect:

(a) the substitution product to predominate over the elimination product.

(b) 2-butene would not be an expected major product.

(c) second-order kinetics would be observed.

(d) if the concentration of OH^- were increased, the rate of reaction would increase.

5.56 Tell which reaction mechanism (S_N1, S_N2, E1, E2) is the most likely:

(a) $(CH_3)_2CHBr + KI \xrightarrow{\text{acetone}}$

(b) $(CH_3)_2CHBr + CH_3CO_2^- \ Na^+ \xrightarrow{H_2O}$

(c) $(CH_3)_2CHBr + KOH \xrightarrow[\text{heat}]{CH_3CH_2OH}$

(d) $(CH_3)_2CHBr + CH_3CH_2OH \xrightarrow{\text{heat}}$

5.57 What is the major organic product in each of the following reactions? Indicate the type of mechanism.

(a) $(CH_3)_3CI + CH_3OH \longrightarrow$

(b) 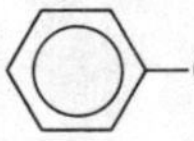 $-O^- + CH_3I \longrightarrow$

(c) $(CH_3)_2CClCH_2CH_3 + Na^+ \ ^-OCH_3 \longrightarrow$

(d) $CH_3CHBrCH_2CH_2CH_3 + KOH \xrightarrow[\text{heat}]{CH_3CH_2OH}$

(e) $(CH_3)_2CBrCH_2CH_3 + K^+ \ ^-OC(CH_3)_3 \longrightarrow$

5.58 For more substitution and less elimination, which of each of the following pairs would you choose:

(a) 1-bromobutane in *aqueous KOH* or in *ethanolic KOH*?

(b) *1-bromobutane* or *t-butyl bromide* in aqueous KOH?

(c) 2-bromobutane with aqueous KOH *warm* or *boiling*?

5.59 Which reaction would be more likely to give a rearrangement product: (a) isobutyl bromide with 10% aqueous KOH, or   (b) isobutyl bromide with 0.1% aqueous KOH?

5.60 What alkyl halides and reagents would you use to synthesize the following compounds?

(a) $CH_2{=}CHCH_2OH$ (b) $(CH_3)_2CHCH_2SH$

(c) *trans*-$C_6H_5CH{=}CHC_6H_5$ (d)

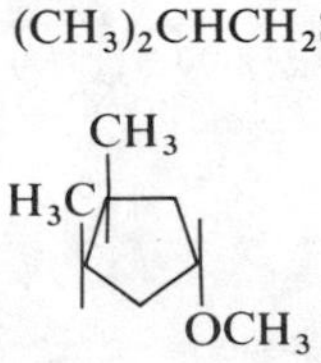

5.61 A compound with the formula C_4H_9Cl, upon treatment with a strong base, yields two isomeric alkenes. What is the structure of this alkyl halide?

5.62 List the following compounds in order of increasing reactivity in S_N1 reactions (least reactive first):

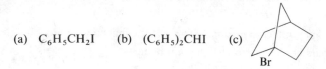

(a) $C_6H_5CH_2I$ (b) $(C_6H_5)_2CHI$ (c)

5.63 When (*R*)-2-iodooctane was treated with radioactive iodide ion, the rate of racemization was found to be exactly twice the rate of incorporation of radioactive iodine. Why?

5.64 Chloromethyl methyl ether ($ClCH_2OCH_3$) undergoes rapid S_N1 reaction. Explain.

5.65 Suggest syntheses for the following compounds from alkyl dibromides:

(a) 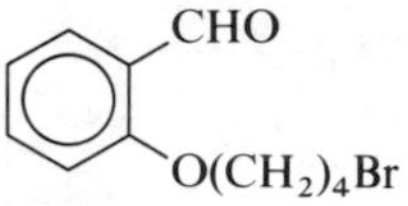 [benzene ring with CHO and $O(CH_2)_4Br$ substituents]

(b) 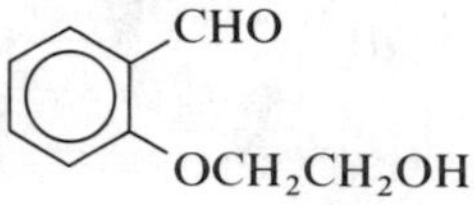 [benzene ring with CHO and OCH_2CH_2OH substituents]

5.66 Which of the two following structures would you expect to undergo an E2 reaction at the faster rate? What would be the expected product?

(a) 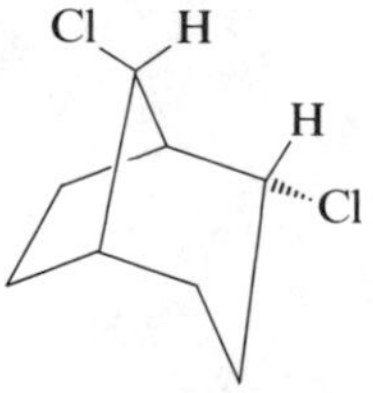 [bicyclic structure with Cl, H, H, Cl]

(b) 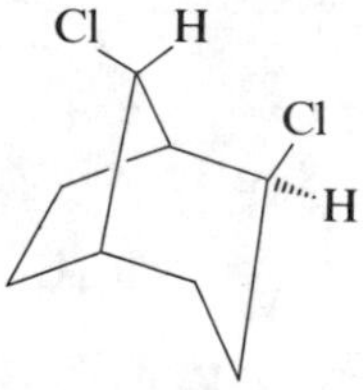 [bicyclic structure with Cl, H, Cl, H]

5.67 (2*R*,3*S*)-2-Bromo-3-deuteriobutane undergoes an E2 reaction when treated with $NaOCH_2CH_3$ in ethanol. The expected product(s) would be: (a) *trans*-2-butene; (b) *cis*-2-deuterio-2-butene; (c) 3-deuterio-1-butene; (d) *cis*-2-butene; (e) *trans*-2-deuterio-2-butene.

5.68 When heated in a solvent, (*S*)-4-bromo-*trans*-2-pentene undergoes racemization. Why?

5.69 Which of the following two syntheses for *t*-butyl ethyl ether would be preferred and why?

(a) $(CH_3)_3CO^- + CH_3CH_2Br$ (b) $(CH_3)_3CBr + CH_3CH_2O^-$

5.70 How would you distinguish (chemically) between each of the following pairs of compounds?

(a) 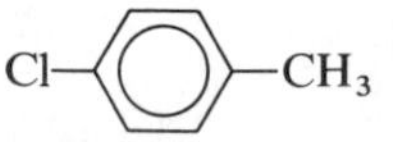 Cl—[benzene ring]—CH_3 and [benzene ring]—CH_2Cl

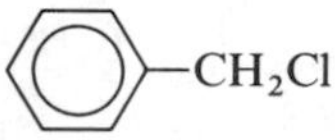

(b) 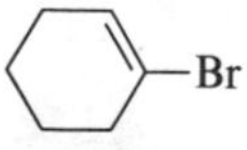 [cyclohexene ring]—Br and [cyclohexene ring]—Br

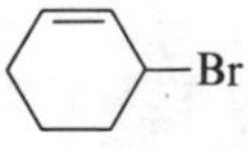

(c) (2*S*,3*R*)-2-chloro-3-methylpentane and its (2*S*,3*S*)-diastereomer

5.71 Suggest a mechanism for each of the following reactions:

(a) $(CH_3)_2CHCl + AgNO_3 + H_2O \longrightarrow (CH_3)_2CHOH + AgCl$

(b) 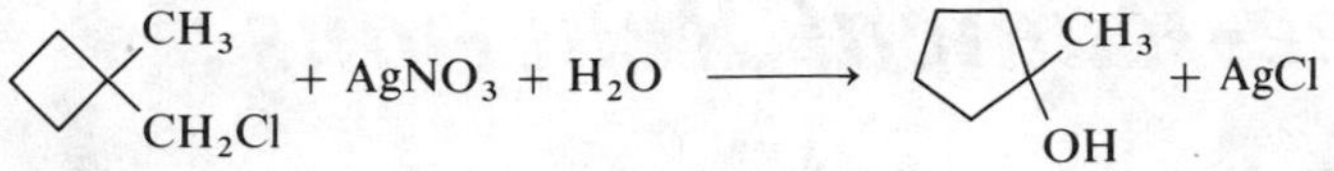 $+ AgNO_3 + H_2O \longrightarrow$ $+ AgCl$

(c) 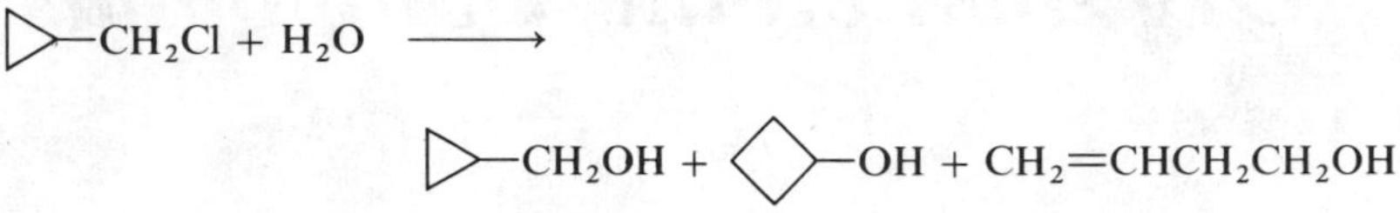 $-CH_2Cl + H_2O \longrightarrow$

$-CH_2OH +$ $-OH + CH_2{=}CHCH_2CH_2OH$

5.72 Suggest a synthesis for 1,4-dioxane from 1,2-dibromoethane and no other organic reagents. (*Hint*: $ROH \xrightarrow{\text{Na}} RO^- Na^+ + \frac{1}{2}H_2$.)

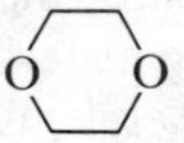

1,4-dioxane

Chapter 6

Free-Radical Reactions; Organometallic Compounds

Many alkyl halides are prepared industrially by the reaction of alkanes and halogens, two inexpensive starting materials. Direct halogenation reactions often proceed explosively and, as a general rule, give mixtures of products. For these reasons, direct halogenation is used only occasionally in the laboratory.

Direct halogenation reactions proceed by a **free-radical mechanism**, which is somewhat different from the mechanisms for nucleophilic substitutions and eliminations.

$$CH_4 + Cl_2 \xrightarrow{\text{ultraviolet light}} CH_3Cl + CH_2Cl_2 + HCl + \text{other products}$$
methane

$$CH_3CH_3 + Cl_2 \xrightarrow{\text{ultraviolet light}} CH_3CH_2Cl + ClCH_2CH_2Cl + HCl$$
ethane
$$+ \text{other products}$$

$-CH_3 + Cl_2 \xrightarrow{\text{ultraviolet light}}$ $-CH_2Cl + HCl$

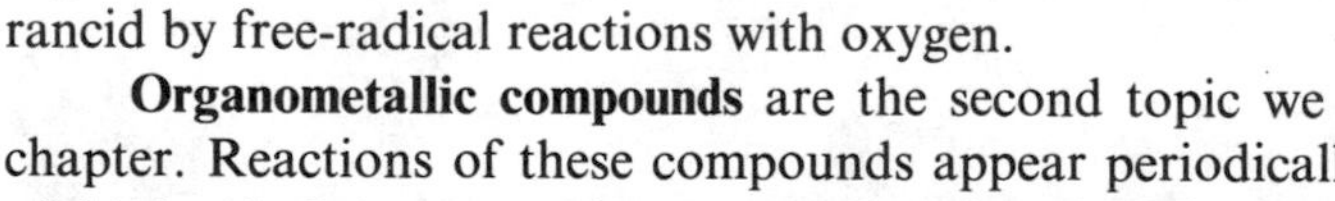

toluene

Free-radical reactions also have biological and practical importance. For example, organisms utilize atmospheric oxygen by a sequence of reactions that begins with a free-radical oxidation–reduction. Butter and other fats become rancid by free-radical reactions with oxygen.

Organometallic compounds are the second topic we will introduce in this chapter. Reactions of these compounds appear periodically throughout the rest of this book. It is appropriate to mention them here because most organometallic compounds are prepared from alkyl halides.

$$4\,CH_3CH_2Cl + 4\,Na/Pb \longrightarrow (CH_3CH_2)_4Pb + 3\,Pb + 4\,NaCl$$
sodium–lead alloy
tetraethyllead
an organometallic compound

$-Br + Mg \xrightarrow{\text{diethyl ether}}$ $-MgBr$

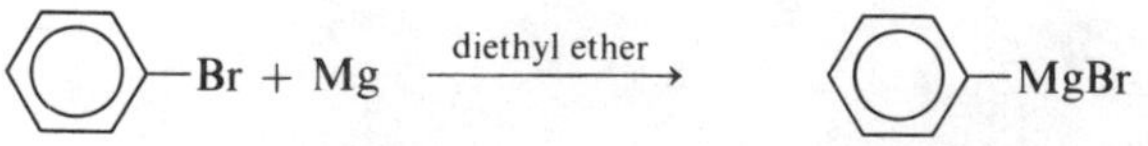

phenylmagnesium bromide
an organometallic compound

Section 6.1

What Is a Free Radical?

The term **free radical** refers to any atom or group of atoms that has an *odd number of electrons*. Because the number of electrons is odd, the electrons in a free radical cannot all be paired. Although a free radical usually has no positive or negative charge, such a species is highly reactive because of the unpaired electron and is usually found as a high-energy, nonisolable reaction intermediate.

We usually symbolize a free radical with a single dot representing the un-paired electron.

Lewis structures of typical free radicals:

$$:\ddot{C}l \cdot \qquad :\ddot{B}r \cdot \qquad H : \overset{\displaystyle H}{\underset{\displaystyle H}{\overset{\cdots}{C}}} \cdot$$

Usual symbolism for free radicals:

$$Cl \cdot \qquad Br \cdot \qquad H_3C \cdot \quad \text{or} \quad CH_3 \cdot \quad \text{or} \quad \cdot CH_3$$

STUDY PROBLEM

6.1 Give Lewis structures for the following free radicals:

   (a) $HO \cdot$ (b) $CH_3O \cdot$ (c) $CH_3CH_2 \cdot$

Section 6.2

A Typical Free-Radical Reaction: Chlorination of Methane

The chlorination of methane in the presence of ultraviolet light (symbolized hv; see page 316) is a classical example of a free-radical reaction. The result of the reaction of Cl_2 with CH_4 is the *substitution* of one or more chlorine atoms for hydrogen atoms on the carbon.

$$CH_4 \ + Cl_2 \ \xrightarrow{hv} \ CH_3Cl \ + \ CH_2Cl_2$$

methane   chloromethane   dichloromethane
                             (methyl chloride)   (methylene chloride)

$$+ \ CHCl_3 \ + \ CCl_4 \ + HCl$$

                      trichloromethane   tetrachloromethane
                       (chloroform)   (carbon tetrachloride)

Although methane is the simplest alkane, four organic products can be formed in its chlorination: CH_3Cl, CH_2Cl_2, $CHCl_3$, and CCl_4. Small amounts of higher alkanes, such as ethane, and their chlorinated products may also be formed. We will discuss first the reactions leading to CH_3Cl, then we will expand the discussion to the formation of other products.

The mechanism of a free-radical reaction is best thought of as a series of stepwise reactions, each step falling into one of the following categories: (1) **initiation** of the free-radical reaction; (2) **propagation** of the free-radical reaction; and (3) **termination** of the free-radical reaction.

A.   Initiation

As the term implies, the initiation step is the initial formation of free radicals. In the chlorination of methane, the initiation step is the homolytic cleavage of Cl_2 into two chlorine free radicals. The energy for this reaction step is provided by ultraviolet light.

Step 1 (initiation):

$$Cl\text{—}Cl + 58 \text{ kcal/mole} \longrightarrow 2 \text{ Cl·}$$

free radicals

B.   Propagation

After its formation, the chlorine free radical starts a series of reactions in which new free radicals are formed. Collectively, these reactions are called the **propagation steps** of the free-radical reaction. In effect, the initial formation of a few free radicals results in the propagation of new free radicals in a self-perpetuating reaction called a **chain reaction**.

As the first propagation step, the reactive chlorine free radical abstracts a hydrogen atom from methane to yield a methyl free radical and HCl.

$$Cl· + (H)CH_3 + 1 \text{ kcal/mole} \longrightarrow H:Cl + ·CH_3$$

The methyl free radical is also reactive. In the second propagation step, the methyl free radical abstracts a chlorine atom from Cl_2.

$$·CH_3 + Cl\text{:}Cl \longrightarrow CH_3Cl + Cl· + 25.5 \text{ kcal/mole}$$

methyl chloride

This step yields one of the products of the overall reaction, methyl chloride. This step also regenerates a new chlorine free radical that can abstract a new hydrogen from another methane molecule and start the propagation sequence over again.

The overall sequence so far is:

Initiation:
$$Cl_2 \xrightarrow{h\nu} 2 \text{ Cl·}$$

Propagation:

$$CH_4 + Cl· \longrightarrow ·CH_3 + HCl$$
$$·CH_3 + Cl_2 \longrightarrow CH_3Cl + Cl· \quad \begin{array}{l} \textit{can undergo} \\ \textit{reaction with } CH_4 \end{array}$$

Because a single Cl· causes reaction and a Cl· is also formed, the process could, in theory, continue indefinitely. However, as you might imagine, the reaction does not continue indefinitely. The *number of cycles* (that is, the number of passes through the propagation steps) is called the **chain length**. The chain length of a free-radical reaction depends partly upon the energies of the radicals involved in the propagation. (We will discuss this subject shortly.) For a free-radical chlorination, the chain length is about 1000.

C. Termination

The propagation cycle is broken by **termination reactions**. Any reaction that results in the destruction of free radicals or in the formation of stable, nonreactive free radicals can terminate the free-radical propagation cycle. The chlorination of methane is terminated principally by free radicals combining with other free radicals; this is a process of destruction of free radicals. In Section 6.11, we will mention termination by formation of stable, nonreactive free radicals.

Termination steps:
$$Cl \cdot + \cdot CH_3 \longrightarrow CH_3Cl$$
$$\cdot CH_3 + \cdot CH_3 \longrightarrow CH_3CH_3$$

STUDY PROBLEM

6.2   Write equations for the initiation, propagation, and termination reactions leading to the formation of chlorocyclohexane from cyclohexane and chlorine.

D. Why Free-Radical Reactions Yield Mixtures of Products

Free-radical reactions are often characterized by a multitude of products. The chlorination of methane can yield four organic products. The reason for the formation of these mixtures is that the high-energy chlorine free radical is not particularly selective about which hydrogen it abstracts during the propagation step.

While chlorine is undergoing reaction with methane, methyl chloride is being formed. In time, the chlorine free radicals are more likely to collide with methyl chloride molecules than with methane molecules, and a new propagation cycle is started. In this new cycle, chloromethyl free radicals ($\cdot CH_2Cl$) are formed. These undergo reaction with chlorine molecules to yield methylene chloride (CH_2Cl_2). As in the previous cycle leading to CH_3Cl, another chlorine free radical is regenerated in the process.

Propagation steps leading to methylene chloride:

$$Cl \cdot + CH_3Cl \longrightarrow HCl + \cdot CH_2Cl$$
$$\cdot CH_2Cl + Cl_2 \longrightarrow CH_2Cl_2 + Cl \cdot$$
$$\text{methylene chloride}$$

Sample Problem

Write the propagation steps leading to the formation of chloroform ($CHCl_3$) from methylene chloride.

Solution:
$$\cdot Cl + CH_2Cl_2 \longrightarrow HCl + \cdot CHCl_2$$
$$\cdot CHCl_2 + Cl_2 \longrightarrow Cl \cdot + CHCl_3$$

STUDY PROBLEM

6.3   Write the propagation steps leading to the formation of carbon tetrachloride (CCl_4) from chloroform.

The free-radical chlorination of methane yields four organic products. Higher alkanes can produce even larger numbers of products because there are more hydrogens available that can enter into propagation reactions.

STUDY PROBLEM

6.4   How many chloroalkanes could be produced in the chlorination of ethane?

Sample Problem

A chemist wishes to make chloroethane from chlorine and ethane. If he wants to avoid higher chlorination products, he would use: (a) an equimolar mixture of CH_3CH_3 and Cl_2;   (b) an excess of Cl_2; or   (c) an excess of CH_3CH_3.

Solution: (c) By using an excess of CH_3CH_3, the chemist increases the probability of collisions between $Cl\cdot$ and CH_3CH_3 and decreases the probability of collisions between $Cl\cdot$ and CH_3CH_2Cl.

STUDY PROBLEM

6.5   The same chemist is preparing carbon tetrachloride from methane and chlorine and is trapping the HCl given off in a dilute aqueous NaOH solution. For the complete chlorination of 1.0 mole of methane, how many moles of NaOH is the minimum needed (assuming that only HCl, and not Cl_2, is entering the trap)?

Section 6.3

Relative Reactivities of the Halogens

The halogens vary dramatically in their reactivity toward alkanes in free-radical reactions. Fluorine undergoes explosive reactions with hydrocarbons. Chlorine is next in terms of reactivity, followed by bromine. Iodine is nonreactive toward alkanes.

$$I_2 \quad Br_2 \quad Cl_2 \quad F_2$$

increasing reactivity as free-radical agents

The relative reactivity of the halogens toward alkanes is not due to the ease with which X_2 molecules are cleaved into free radicals. From the bond dissociation energies for the halogens, we can see that the relative ease of homolytic cleavage is almost the reverse of their reactivity in halogenation reactions.

	F_2	Cl_2	Br_2	I_2
bond dissociation energy (kcal/mole):	37	58	46	36

The order of reactivity is primarily a result of the ΔH of the propagation steps in free-radical halogenation. The propagation steps of fluorination are highly exothermic. More than enough energy is produced to rupture additional F—F bonds and cause an extremely rapid, explosive reaction.

$$F\cdot + CH_4 \longrightarrow HF + CH_3\cdot + 31 \text{ kcal/mole} \qquad \Delta H = -31 \text{ kcal/mole}$$
$$CH_3\cdot + F_2 \longrightarrow CH_3F + F\cdot + 71 \text{ kcal/mole} \qquad \Delta H = -71 \text{ kcal/mole}$$

$$CH_4 + F_2 \longrightarrow CH_3F + HF + 102 \text{ kcal/mole} \qquad \text{net } \Delta H = -102 \text{ kcal/mole}$$

Just the reverse situation is encountered with iodine: the propagation steps are *endothermic*—that is, the products are of higher energy than the reactants. Most important, the energy required by $I\cdot$ to abstract hydrogen from a C—H bond is *substantially* endothermic. The result is that the iodine free radical does not enter into a chain reaction; $I\cdot$ is an example of a *stable free radical*, a free radical that does not abstract hydrogens.

$$I\cdot + CH_4 + 33 \text{ kcal/mole} \longrightarrow HI + CH_3\cdot \qquad \Delta H = +33 \text{ kcal/mole}$$
$$CH_3\cdot + I_2 \longrightarrow CH_3I + I\cdot + 20 \text{ kcal/mole} \qquad \Delta H = -20 \text{ kcal/mole}$$

$$CH_4 + I_2 + 13 \text{ kcal/mole} \longrightarrow CH_3I + HI \qquad \text{net } \Delta H = +13 \text{ kcal/mole}$$

Chlorine and bromine are intermediate between fluorine and iodine in ΔH of the propagation steps and therefore are also intermediate in reactivity. Figure 6.1 shows energy diagrams for the reactions of Cl_2 and Br_2 with methane.

$$Cl\cdot + CH_4 + 1 \text{ kcal/mole} \longrightarrow HCl + CH_3\cdot \qquad \Delta H = +1 \text{ kcal/mole}$$
$$CH_3\cdot + Cl_2 \longrightarrow CH_3Cl + Cl\cdot + 25.5 \text{ kcal/mole} \qquad \Delta H = -25.5 \text{ kcal/mole}$$

$$CH_4 + Cl_2 \longrightarrow CH_3Cl + HCl + 24.5 \text{ kcal/mole} \qquad \text{net } \Delta H = -24.5 \text{ kcal/mole}$$

$$Br\cdot + CH_4 + 17 \text{ kcal/mole} \longrightarrow HBr + CH_3\cdot \qquad \Delta H = +17 \text{ kcal/mole}$$
$$CH_3\cdot + Br_2 \longrightarrow CH_3Br + Br\cdot + 24 \text{ kcal/mole} \qquad \Delta H = -24 \text{ kcal/mole}$$

$$CH_4 + Br_2 \longrightarrow CH_3Br + HBr + 7 \text{ kcal/mole} \qquad \text{net } \Delta H = -7 \text{ kcal/mole}$$

In summary, we find that only chlorine and bromine are useful as free-radical halogenating agents. Fluorine is too reactive toward alkanes, and iodine is not reactive enough.

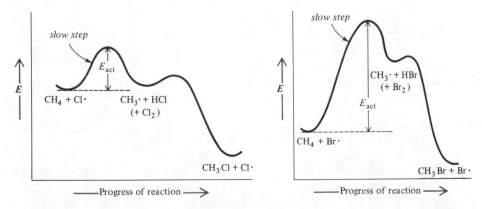

Figure 6.1. Energy diagrams for the free-radical chlorination and bromination of methane.

Section 6.4

Structure of an Alkyl Free Radical

An alkyl free radical is a species in which a carbon atom has three groups attached to it and a single, unpaired electron. We will look at the structure of the methyl free radical; other alkyl free radicals have similar bonding around the free-radical carbon.

Because there are only three attachments to the free-radical carbon, this carbon is in the sp^2-hybrid state. The three sp^2 orbitals are planar and the unpaired electron is in the p orbital. The structure is very similar to that of a carbocation except that the p orbital of a carbocation is empty.

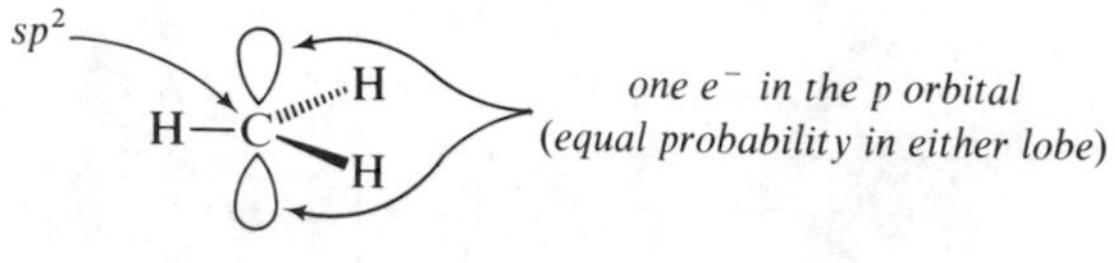

methyl free radical, $CH_3 \cdot$

STUDY PROBLEM

6.6 Draw the structure of the ethyl free radical. What is the hybridization of each of the two carbon atoms?

Sample Problem

Draw the structure of the allyl free radical. Would you expect it to be of higher or lower energy than the ethyl free radical? Why?

Solution:

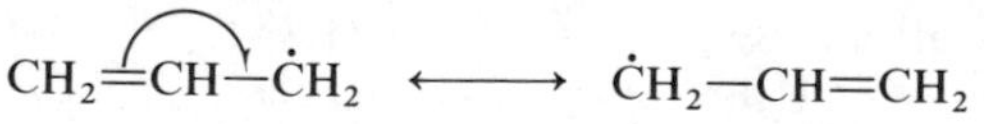

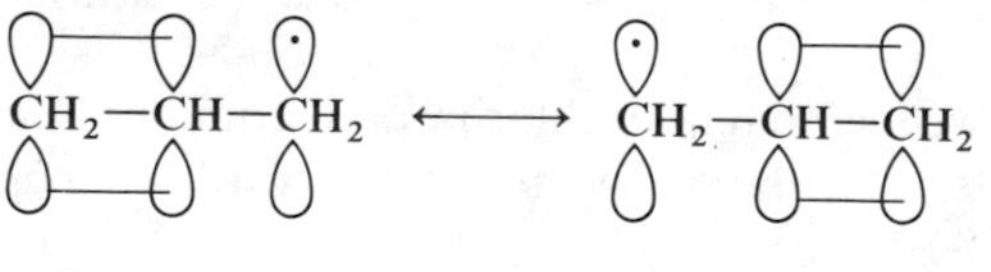

We would expect the allyl radical to be of lower energy because the unpaired electron is delocalized.

STUDY PROBLEM

6.7 Draw the structure of $\cdot$, showing the p orbitals and the resonance structures.

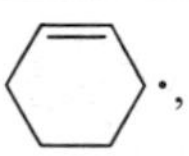

Section 6.5

Stereochemistry of Free-Radical Halogenation

An alkyl free radical has the same general structure as a carbocation. In either intermediate, the carbon atom is in the sp^2-hybrid state, and the p orbital (empty in the carbocation, but containing one electron in the free radical) is the site of reaction.

When a pure enantiomer of a chiral alkyl halide undergoes S_N1 reaction at the chiral center, racemization of that center is observed. As we discussed in Chapter 5, racemization arises from the nucleophile being able to attack either lobe of the empty p orbital of the carbocation. If a hydrogen is abstracted from the chiral carbon of a pure enantiomer in a free-radical reaction, racemization also occurs.

$$CH_3CH_2CHCH_2Cl \quad + Cl_2 \quad \xrightarrow{hv} \quad CH_3CH_2CCH_2Cl \quad + HCl$$

(S)-1-chloro-2-methylbutane   (R)(S)-1,2-dichloro-2-methylbutane
(*racemic*)

The preceding reaction can lead to a number of products; there are five carbon atoms in the molecule that can lose a hydrogen and gain a chlorine. We would also expect to find as products trichlorinated alkanes, tetrachlorinated alkanes, and so forth. But we are interested only in the one product that has been chlorinated at the chiral carbon. When we isolate this specific product, we find that it is a racemic mixture of the (R) and (S) isomers. Just as in an S_N1 reaction, this evidence leads us to believe that the free radical is flat (sp^2 hybrid) and that a chlorine atom can add to either lobe of the p orbital.

STUDY PROBLEM

6.8   Another dichloroalkane formed in the chlorination of (S)-1-chloro-2-methylbutane is $CH_3CHClCH(CH_3)CH_2Cl$. Is this dichloroalkane racemic or not?

Section 6.6

Hydrogen Abstraction: The Rate-Determining Step

Unlike the kinetics of substitution and elimination reactions, the kinetics of a free-radical reaction are quite complex. Simple rate expressions, such as first-order or second-order, are not encountered in free-radical chemistry. The reason for this complexity is that the steps in a free-radical reaction are enmeshed in a cyclical process of varying chain lengths. However, evidence does point to the **hydrogen-abstraction step** as the step governing the overall rate at which products are formed. For example, methane (CH_4) undergoes free-radical chlorination 12 times faster than perdeuteriomethane (CD_4), indicating that the C—H bond is broken in the rate-determining step of the reaction.

H (or D) abstraction is the rate-determining step:

$$CH_4 + Cl\cdot \xrightarrow{\text{faster}} CH_3\cdot + HCl$$

$$CD_4 + Cl\cdot \xrightarrow{\text{slower}} CD_3\cdot + DCl$$

Section 6.7

Which Hydrogen Is Abstracted?

The hydrogen atoms in organic compounds may be classified as **methyl** (CH_4), **primary** (attached to a 1° carbon), **secondary** (attached to a 2° carbon), **tertiary** (attached to a 3° carbon), **allylic** (on a carbon adjacent to a double bond), or **benzylic** (on a carbon adjacent to an aromatic ring).

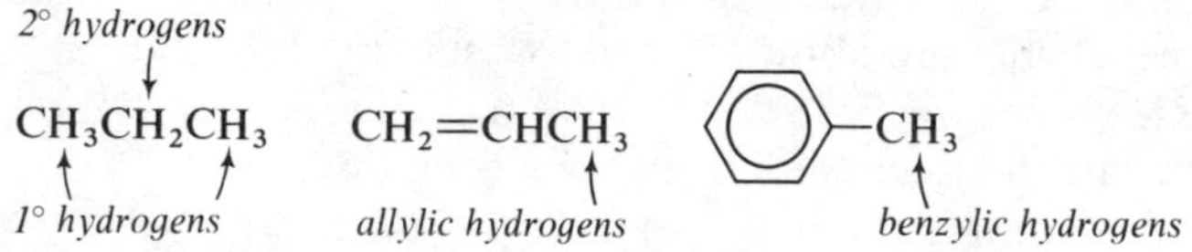

2° hydrogens

$CH_3CH_2CH_3$ $CH_2{=}CHCH_3$

1° hydrogens   *allylic hydrogens*   *benzylic hydrogens*

Sample Problem

Classify each circled H as 1°, 2°, 3°, allylic, or benzylic:

(a) $(CH_3)_3CC\textbf{H}_3$ (b) $(CH_3)_3C\textbf{H}$ (c)

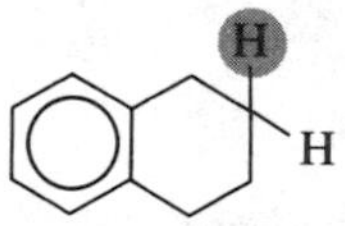

(d)

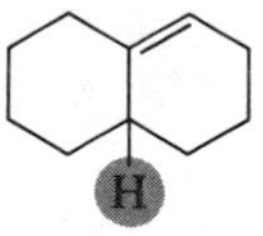

(e)

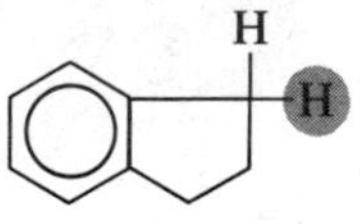

Solution: (a) 1°;   (b) 3°;   (c) 2°;   (d) allylic and 3°;   (e) benzylic and 2°

These different types of hydrogen are not abstracted at identical rates by free radicals. Instead, there is a degree of selectivity in hydrogen abstraction. The reaction of propane with a small amount of chlorine under free-radical conditions yields two monochlorinated products, 1-chloropropane and 2-chloropropane, with the 2-chloropropane predominating.

$$CH_3CH_2CH_3 + Cl_2 \xrightarrow{h\nu} \overset{\displaystyle Cl}{\underset{\displaystyle |}{CH_3CHCH_3}} + CH_3CH_2CH_2Cl$$

propane   2-chloropropane   1-chloropropane
                          (isopropyl chloride)   (*n*-propyl chloride)
                               55%   45%

There are a total of *six* primary hydrogens and *two* secondary hydrogens in propane; the ratio of primary to secondary hydrogens in propane is 6/2, or 3/1. If all the hydrogens underwent abstraction at equal rates, we would observe three times more 1-chloropropane than 2-chloropropane in the product mixture. This is *not* what is observed when the reaction is carried out; instead, the 2-chloropropane predominates. We conclude that secondary hydrogens are abstracted faster than primary hydrogens.

A similar selectivity is observed in the comparative reactivity of methane and ethane with chlorine. Let us consider the reaction of an equimolar mixture of methane and ethane with a small amount of chlorine.

$$CH_3CH_3 + CH_4 + Cl_2 \xrightarrow{hv} CH_3CH_2Cl + CH_3Cl + HCl$$
$$>99\% \qquad <1\%$$

Because ethane has six H's and methane has four H's, we would expect to obtain as products CH_3CH_2Cl and CH_3Cl in a ratio of 6/4 (or 1.5/1) if the rates of reaction were the same. However, the observed ratio of products is 1 part CH_3Cl to 400 parts CH_3CH_2Cl! It is apparent that CH_3CH_3 is far more reactive than CH_4 toward chlorination and that primary hydrogens are abstracted faster than methyl hydrogens.

Through these and similar experiments, the order of reactivity of hydrogens toward free-radical halogenation has been determined. (Any comparisons must be made under the same reaction conditions. Temperature, for example, plays an important role in the observed product ratios.) The relative rates for halogenation reactions of a few compounds are given in Table 6.1.

Table 6.1. **Average Relative Rates of Hydrogen Abstraction**

| | Reagent | |
Hydrocarbon	Br_2	Cl_2
CH_3—H	0.0007	0.004
CH_3CH_2—H	1	1
$(CH_3)_2CH$—H	220	4.3
$(CH_3)_3C$—H	19,400	6.0
$C_6H_5CH_2$—H	64,000	1.3
$(C_6H_5)_2CH$—H	6.2×10^5	2.6
$(C_6H_5)_3C$—H	1.14×10^6	9.5

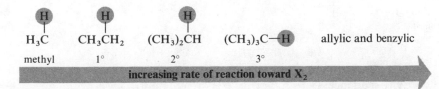

| H_3C | CH_3CH_2 | $(CH_3)_2CH$ | $(CH_3)_3C$—H | allylic and benzylic |
| methyl | 1° | 2° | 3° | |

increasing rate of reaction toward X_2

Some other examples of how the relative rates of hydrogen abstraction affect the product ratio follow:

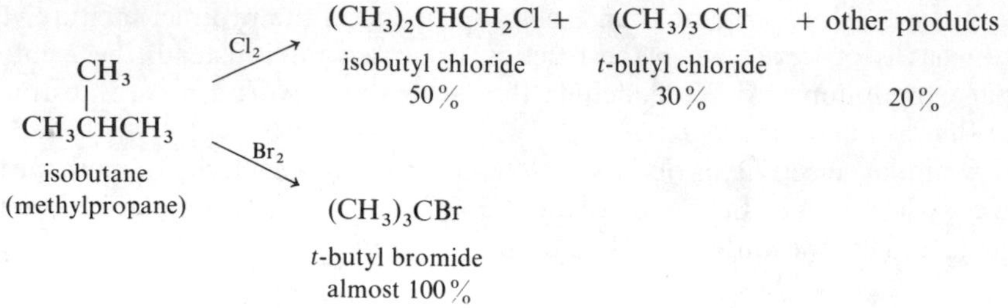

$$(CH_3)_2CHCH_2Cl + (CH_3)_3CCl + \text{other products}$$

isobutyl chloride   *t*-butyl chloride

50%   30%   20%

$$\begin{array}{c} CH_3 \\ | \\ CH_3CHCH_3 \end{array}$$

isobutane
(methylpropane)

$\xrightarrow{Cl_2}$

$\xrightarrow{Br_2}$

$$(CH_3)_3CBr$$

t-butyl bromide
almost 100%

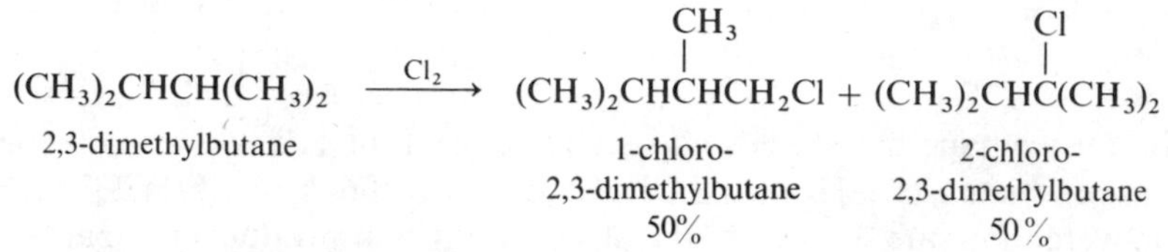

$$(CH_3)_2CHCH(CH_3)_2 \xrightarrow{Cl_2} \underset{CH_3}{(CH_3)_2CHCHCH_2Cl} + \underset{Cl}{(CH_3)_2CHC(CH_3)_2}$$

2,3-dimethylbutane   1-chloro-
2,3-dimethylbutane
50%

       2-chloro-
2,3-dimethylbutane
50%

STUDY PROBLEM

6.9 In the chlorination of isobutane, what would be the expected product ratio of isobutyl chloride to *t*-butyl chloride if all the hydrogens were abstracted at equal rates?

A. Relative Stabilities of Alkyl Free Radicals

To understand why some hydrogens are abstracted more easily than others, we must look at the transition states of the hydrogen-abstraction steps. The following equations show the hydrogen-abstraction steps in the chlorination of methane and isobutane. (The symbol $\delta\cdot$ is used to show that both the chlorine atoms and the carbon atoms have partial free-radical character in the transition states.)

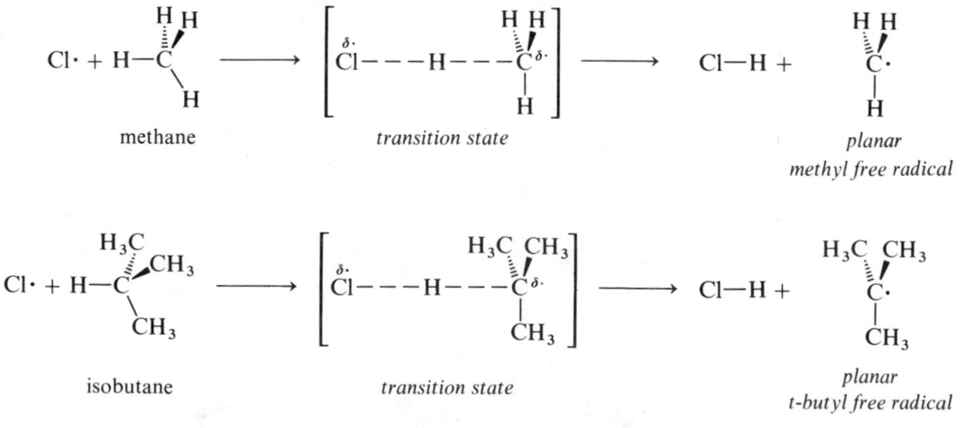

methane   *transition state*   *planar
methyl free radical*

isobutane   *transition state*   *planar
t-butyl free radical*

At the transition state, the C—H bond is breaking. Part of the reason for the reactivity sequence $3° > 2° > 1° > CH_4$ may be attributed to the increasing

C—H bond strength as we go from 3° to methyl. It is easier to break a 3° C—H bond than a 2° C—H bond.

	CH$_3$—H	CH$_3$CH$_2$—H	(CH$_3$)$_2$CH—H	(CH$_3$)$_3$C—H
bond dissociation energy (kcal/mole):	104	98	94.5	91

decreasing bond strength →

However, the C—H bond strength is probably not the only reason for the reactivity differences. The transition-state structure for hydrogen abstraction has some free-radical character; therefore, the energy of the transition state is largely determined by the stability of the alkyl free radical being formed. The order of free-radical stability, just like that of carbocation stability, increases as we proceed from methyl to tertiary. It is thought that the free-radical intermediates are stabilized by interaction with neighboring sigma bonds, possibly by hyperconjugation (see Section 5.7D).

·CH$_3$	·CH$_2$CH$_3$	(CH$_3$)$_2$ĊH	(CH$_3$)$_3$C·	allylic and benzylic
methyl	1°	2°	3°	

increasing stability →

As in the case of carbocation reactions, we find enhanced free-radical reactivity at allylic and benzylic positions. (Why?)

allylic

$$CH_2{=}CHCH_3 \xrightarrow[500°]{Cl_2} CH_2{=}CHCH_2Cl$$

propene   3-chloro-1-propene (allyl chloride) 90%

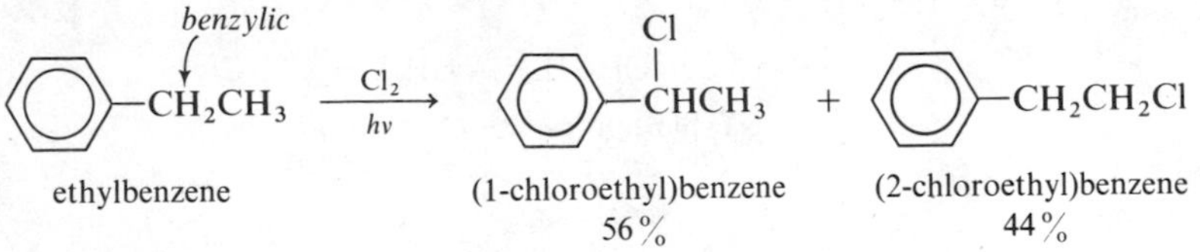

benzylic

ethylbenzene $\xrightarrow[hv]{Cl_2}$ (1-chloroethyl)benzene 56% + (2-chloroethyl)benzene 44%

STUDY PROBLEM

6.10 List the following free radicals in order of increasing stability (least stable first):

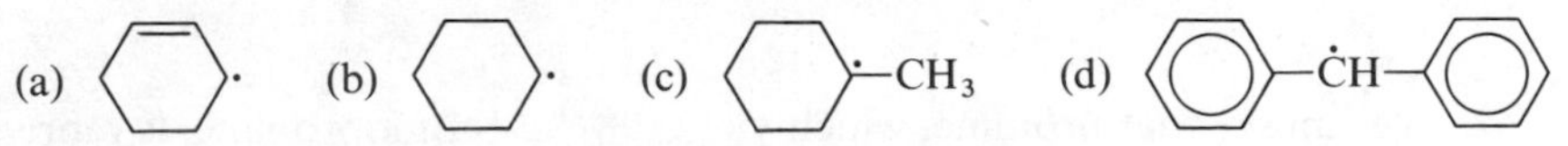

(a)   (b)   (c) —CH$_3$ (d) —ĊH—

B. Rearrangements of Free Radicals

Alkyl free radicals are, in many respects, similar to carbocations. Both are sp^2 hybrids; both undergo racemization if reaction occurs at a chiral center; and both show the same order of stability in terms of structure. If possible, carbocations undergo rearrangement to more-stable carbocations. Does the same hold true for free radicals? No, this is one of the differences between free radicals and carbocations. While free-radical rearrangements are not unknown, they are not common.

Rearrangement:

$$CH_3\underset{\underset{CH_3}{|}}{\overset{\overset{CH_3}{|}}{C}}-\overset{+}{C}HCH_3 \longrightarrow CH_3\underset{\underset{CH_3}{|}}{\overset{\overset{CH_3}{|}}{\overset{+}{C}}}-CHCH_3 \xrightarrow[-H^+]{H_2O} CH_3\underset{\underset{CH_3}{|}}{\overset{\overset{HO\ \ CH_3}{|\ \ \ \ \ |}}{C}}-CHCH_3$$

  a 2° carbocation   *a 3° carbocation*   *a 3° alcohol*

No rearrangement:

$$CH_3\underset{\underset{CH_3}{|}}{\overset{\overset{CH_3}{|}}{C}}-\overset{\cdot}{C}HCH_3 \xrightarrow[-Cl\cdot]{Cl_2} CH_3\underset{\underset{CH_3}{|}}{\overset{\overset{CH_3\ \ Cl}{|\ \ \ \ \ |}}{C}}-CHCH_3$$

      a 2° free radical   *a 2° alkyl halide*

Section 6.8

Selective Free-Radical Halogenations

A. Bromine versus Chlorine

Although free-radical halogenations often lead to mixtures of products, good yields of single products may be obtained in some cases. Compare the product ratios of the chlorination and the bromination of propane:

$$CH_3CH_2CH_3$$

$$\xrightarrow[hv]{Cl_2} \underset{\underset{55\%}{\text{2-chloropropane}}}{CH_3\overset{\overset{Cl}{|}}{C}HCH_3} + \underset{\underset{45\%}{\text{1-chloropropane}}}{CH_3CH_2CH_2Cl}$$

$$\xrightarrow[hv]{Br_2} \underset{\underset{98\%}{\text{2-bromopropane}}}{CH_3\overset{\overset{Br}{|}}{C}HCH_3} + \underset{\underset{2\%}{\text{1-bromopropane}}}{CH_3CH_2CH_2Br}$$

We can see that bromine, which yields 98% 2-bromopropane, is more selective about abstracting a secondary hydrogen than is chlorine. The selectivity of bromine arises from the fact that bromine is less reactive than chlorine in free-radical halogenations. To see why this is so, we will consider a pair of hypothetical energy diagrams (Figure 6.2).

Reaction 1 in Figure 6.2 is an *exothermic reaction with a low* E_{act}. Note that the structure of the transition state in Reaction 1 is *very close to that of the reactants*. Like Reaction 1, the hydrogen-abstraction step in the chlorination of propane is

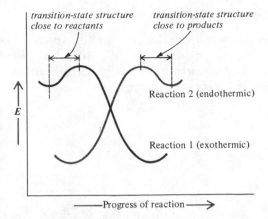

transition-state structure close to reactants

transition-state structure close to products

Reaction 2 (endothermic)

Reaction 1 (exothermic)

E

————Progress of reaction————→

Figure 6.2. Energy diagrams showing the relationship of transition-state structure to the exothermic or endothermic nature of a reaction.

exothermic and has a low E_{act}. Therefore, the transition state in this reaction step resembles the reactants more than it does the products:

$$
\begin{array}{ccc}
\underset{\substack{\text{propane}}}{\overset{\displaystyle CH_3}{\underset{\displaystyle CH_3}{H\cdots\!C-H}}}
& \xrightarrow{\ Cl\cdot\ } &
\left[\underset{\substack{\text{transition state}\\ \text{resembles reactants}}}{\overset{\displaystyle CH_3}{\underset{\displaystyle CH_3}{H\cdots\!C^{\delta\cdot}\!-H----\overset{\delta\cdot}{Cl}}}}\right]
& \longrightarrow &
\underset{\substack{\text{isopropyl}\\ \text{free radical}}}{\overset{\displaystyle H\quad CH_3}{\underset{\displaystyle CH_3}{C\cdot}}}
+ HCl
\end{array}
$$

Now let us look at Reaction 2 in Figure 6.2. This is an *endothermic reaction with a high E_{act}*. The structure of the transition state in Reaction 2 is *close to that of the products*. The hydrogen-abstraction step in free-radical bromination is more endothermic and has a higher E_{act} than chlorination. The structure of the transition state in bromination has a greater resemblance to the product alkyl free radical.

$$
\begin{array}{ccc}
\overset{\displaystyle CH_3}{\underset{\displaystyle CH_3}{H\cdots\!C-H}}
& \xrightarrow{\ Br\cdot\ } &
\left[\underset{\substack{\text{transition state}\\ \text{resembles products}}}{\overset{\displaystyle H\quad CH_3}{\underset{\displaystyle CH_3}{C^{\delta\cdot}----H--\overset{\delta\cdot}{Br}}}}\right]
& \longrightarrow &
\overset{\displaystyle H\quad CH_3}{\underset{\displaystyle CH_3}{C\cdot}}
+ HBr
\end{array}
$$

Because this transition state in bromination resembles the alkyl free radical, it is highly influenced by the stability of the alkyl free radical. The reaction proceeds through the lower-energy transition state to yield the lower-energy, more stable free radical: $CH_3\dot{C}HCH_3$ is highly favored over $CH_3CH_2\dot{C}H_2$. By contrast, the transition state in chlorination is less influenced by the stability of the alkyl free radical: $CH_3\dot{C}HCH_3$ is only slightly favored over $CH_3CH_2\dot{C}H_2$. Therefore, chlorine is more likely to yield product mixtures.

B. *Benzylic and Allylic Halogenations*

Toluene may be selectively halogenated at the benzylic position with either chlorine or bromine. If more than one alkyl position on a benzene side chain is open to attack, as in ethylbenzene, the more selective bromine is the reagent of choice for halogenation at the benzylic position.

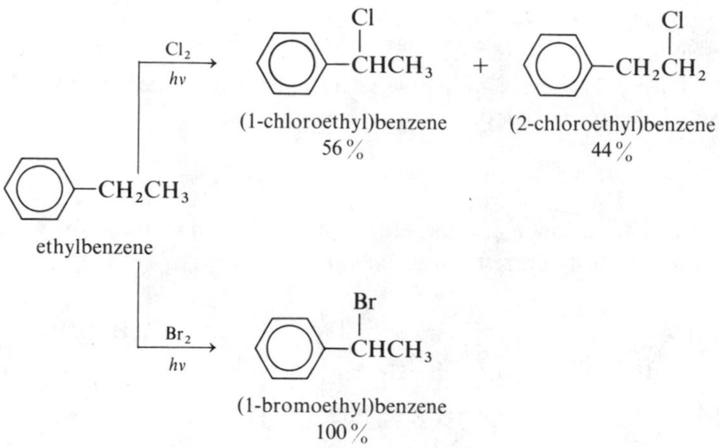

toluene   a benzyl halide 100%   where X = Cl or Br

(1-chloroethyl)benzene 56%   (2-chloroethyl)benzene 44%

ethylbenzene

(1-bromoethyl)benzene 100%

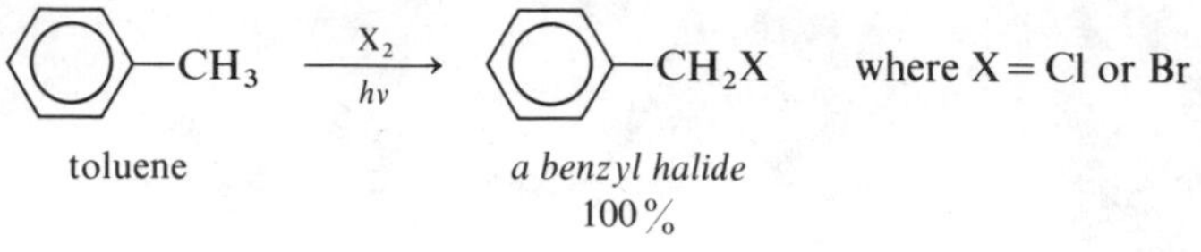

A convenient laboratory reagent for selective halogenation is **N-bromosuccinimide** (NBS), which introduces bromine at the allylic and benzylic positions. An NBS reaction is catalyzed by light or some source of free radicals.

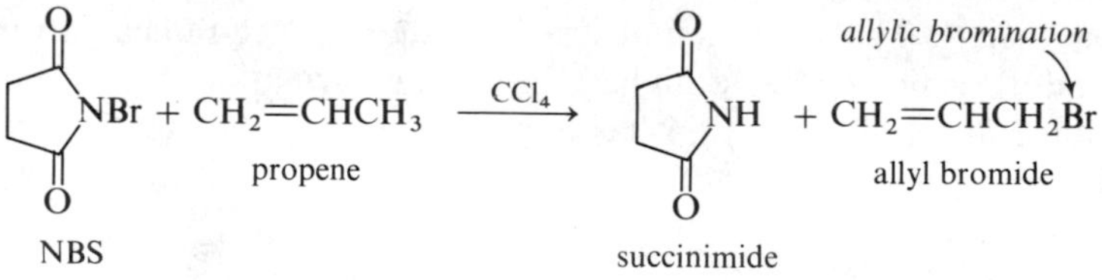

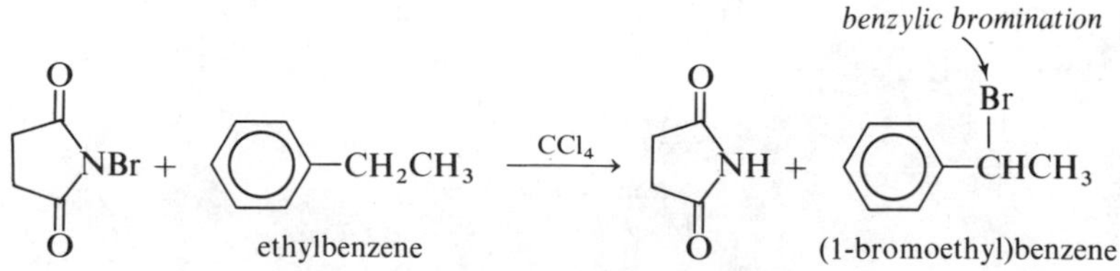

NBS   propene   succinimide   *allylic bromination*   allyl bromide

ethylbenzene   *benzylic bromination*   (1-bromoethyl)benzene

The selective action of NBS depends on its ability to provide a low, but constant, concentration of Br_2, which is the halogenating agent. The Br_2 is generated by the reaction of HBr (a product of the halogenation) and NBS. Therefore, as Br_2 is consumed, more is formed.

Br₂ consumed:

$$CH_2{=}CHCH_3 + Br_2 \longrightarrow CH_2{=}CHCH_2Br + HBr$$

Br₂ generated:

$$\text{(succinimide-NBr)} + HBr \longrightarrow \text{(succinimide-NH)} + Br_2$$

If the two carbon atoms in an allylic system are not equivalent, mixtures of products result; however, the products may not necessarily be formed in equal amounts. If groups are added to the allylic system, the energies of the resonance structures may not be equivalent; one resonance structure may be a greater contributor.

$$CH_3CH_2CH=CH_2 \xrightarrow{\text{NBS}} [CH_3\overset{\cdot}{C}HCH=CH_2 \longleftrightarrow CH_3CH=CH\overset{\cdot}{C}H_2]$$

1-butene   *resonance structures*

$$\begin{array}{ccc} & \underset{|}{Br} & \\ CH_3CHCH=CH_2 & & CH_3CH=CHCH_2Br \\ \text{3-bromo-1-butene} & & \text{1-bromo-2-butene} \end{array}$$

Sample Problem

In the NBS bromination of 1-butene, which of the two products would you expect to predominate? (*Hint*: Which free-radical resonance structure is of lower energy?)

Solution: The intermediate free radical has two resonance structures. Both are allylic free radicals, but one is 1° and one is 2°. A 2° free radical is more stable than a 1° free radical; therefore, the 2° structure is the major contributing resonance structure. The major product is 3-bromo-1-butene.

STUDY PROBLEM

6.11 Predict the major products of NBS halogenation of the following compounds: (a) *n*-butylbenzene; (b) cyclohexene; (c) 1-phenyl-1-propene.

Section 6.9

Other Free-Radical Reactions

As we have mentioned, free-radical reactions are not limited to the halogenation of hydrocarbons, but are encountered in many areas of organic chemistry. For example, free radicals add readily to double bonds (another complication in allylic halogenation). However, we will limit our present discussion to sigma-bond free-radical reactions and consider only a few of the many processes known to proceed by a free-radical mechanism.

A. Pyrolysis

In Section 3.4C, we defined **pyrolysis** as the *thermal decomposition of organic compounds in the absence of oxygen*. When organic molecules are heated to high temperatures, carbon–carbon sigma bonds rupture and the molecules are broken into free-radical fragments. (The temperature required depends on the bond dissociation energies.) This fragmentation step, called **thermally induced homolysis** (homolytic cleavage caused by heat), is the initiation step for a series of free-radical reactions. The following equations illustrate some possible pyrolysis reactions of pentane. (There are other possible positions of cleavage and subsequent reaction.)

Initiation:

$$CH_3CH_2CH_2-CH_2CH_3 \xrightarrow{\text{heat}} CH_3CH_2CH_2\cdot + CH_3CH_2\cdot$$

pentane

Once initiated, the free radicals can enter into typical propagation reactions yielding new free radicals. For example, a free radical can abstract a hydrogen atom from another pentane molecule.

$$CH_3CH_2\cdot + CH_3CH_2\overset{\frown}{C}HCH_2CH_3 \longrightarrow CH_3CH_3 + CH_3CH_2\dot{C}HCH_2CH_3$$

ethane

The free radicals can also undergo **β cleavage**, a reaction that, in our example, yields an alkene and a methyl free radical.

$$CH_3CH_2\dot{C}H-CH_2-CH_3 \longrightarrow CH_3CH_2CH{=}CH_2 + CH_3\cdot$$

1-butene

β *to free radical*

The termination steps in pyrolysis reactions may be either the joining together of two free radicals or the **disproportionation** of two radicals. Disproportionation is a general term used to describe a reaction in which two equivalent species react with each other so that *one is oxidized and one is reduced*. Disproportionation between two alkyl free radicals involves the transfer of the unpaired electron and a hydrogen atom from one free radical to the other. Two stable products, an alkane (the reduced product) and an alkene (the oxidized product) are formed.

Disproportionation:

$$CH_3\dot{C}H_2 + \dot{C}H_2-CH_2 \longrightarrow CH_3CH_3 + CH_2{=}CH_2$$

two ethyl radicals   ethane   ethylene

reduced   *oxidized*

Controlled pyrolysis has been used industrially for the cracking of high-molecular-weight compounds to lower-molecular-weight compounds, which are often more useful. Until about 1925, pyrolysis of wood provided the major source for methanol (wood alcohol). The thermal cracking of high-boiling petroleum fractions into lower-boiling gasoline fractions was once the only method available for obtaining more gasoline from petroleum. Both of these techniques have been replaced by more sophisticated chemical reactions. The cracking of petroleum is now accomplished with the help of catalysts (Section 3.5), while methanol is largely produced by the catalytic hydrogenation of carbon monoxide ($CO + 2H_2 \rightarrow CH_3OH$).

Pyrolysis is studied today primarily for gaining knowledge about the mechanism of combustion—for example, about the processes involved in the burning of wood or coal. The gaseous molecules that undergo combustion arise from free-radical pyrolysis of molecules on the surface of wood or coal. Fire retardants function not by directly reducing the flames, but by inhibiting the surface free-radical reactions.

B. Free Radicals in Biological Systems

Free-radical reactions are an integral part of the chemistry of living systems. Let us consider one example. Animals use food partly for energy. Carbohydrates, for example, are converted to glucose, which then can be converted to carbon dioxide, water, and energy.

$$\underset{\substack{\text{glucose} \\ \textit{from sugars and starches}}}{C_6H_{12}O_6} + 6O_2 \xrightarrow{\text{many steps}} 6CO_2 + 6H_2O + 686\,\text{kcal/mole}$$

The oxidation of glucose is not a direct oxidation like combustion. In an animal cell, a lengthy series of oxidation–reduction reactions is required for the conversion of glucose to CO_2 and H_2O. In the final steps of the oxidation, the electrons needed for the reduction of O_2 to H_2O are supplied by the iron(II) ion.

$$\tfrac{1}{2}O_2 + 2H^+ + 2Fe^{2+} \xrightarrow{\text{cell}} H_2O + 2Fe^{3+}$$

A key structure in this process is a **hydroquinone** (a dihydroxybenzene), a type of compound that is easily oxidized to a **quinone** (a dicarbonyl compound). Conversely, a quinone is easily reduced to a hydroquinone. The following equation shows the reversible oxidation–reduction reaction between the simplest members of these classes, hydroquinone and quinone.

The iron(II) ion in cells is regenerated from the iron(III) ion by reaction with a hydroquinone. The product quinone, which is found in all cells, is called **coenzyme Q**, or **ubiquinone** (for "ubiquitous quinone"). The ring of ubiquinone is substituted with two methoxyl groups (CH_3O—), a methyl group, and a long alkenyl hydrocarbon chain (R) that varies with the source (yeast, mammals, etc.).

The conversion of one Fe^{3+} ion to Fe^{2+} is a one-electron change. Chemists believe that the action of dihydroubiquinone depends upon the ability of a hydroquinone to lose a single electron at a time, the intermediate being a relatively stable **semiquinone** free radical.

STUDY PROBLEM

6.12   The semiquinone free radical is resonance-stabilized. Draw the resonance structures.

Let us now consider an example of undesirable free-radical reactions in living systems. Certain types of radiation (α, β, and γ radiation, and x-rays) are called **ionizing radiations** and are known to damage living cells by causing molecules to cleave into ions and free radicals. These cleavages can cause cellular damage by one of two routes: (1) direct destruction of cellular components, or (2) formation of radicals or ions that undergo abnormal reaction with other cellular components.

The nucleic acids are compounds that we will discuss in Chapter 16. These compounds carry the genetic code and, in this capacity, are responsible for cellular multiplication, reproduction of an organism, and the biosynthesis of proteins. When exposed to radiation, the nucleic acids are subject to **depolymerization**— that is, fragmentation of large molecules into smaller molecules. Mitotic (reproducing) cells are more vulnerable to radiation-caused damage than other cells. This fact is used to advantage in radiation treatment of cancer; cancer cells, which reproduce at an abnormally high rate, are more susceptible to radiation damage than are normal cells.

C.   Oxygen as a Free-Radical Reagent

Molecular oxygen is different from the compounds we have been studying because a stable molecule of O_2 has two unpaired electrons; oxygen is said to be a **diradical**. The structure of O_2 cannot be adequately explained by valence-bond

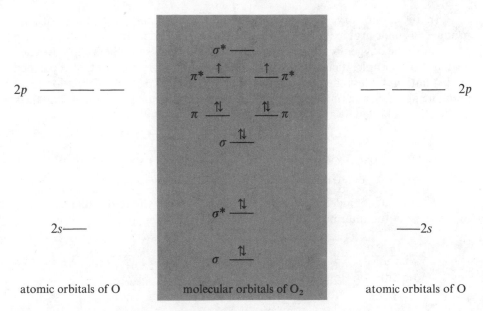

Figure 6.3. Orbital diagram for O_2. (The lower-energy σ and σ^* orbitals arise from the two $2s$ atomic orbitals of O. Two $2p$ atomic orbitals overlap to form a higher-energy σ orbital. Each oxygen atom in O_2 also has a pair of unshared electrons in a π orbital (from a $2p$ orbital) and one unshared electron in a π^* orbital.)

formulas because one pair of $2s$ electrons is in an antibonding orbital. An orbital diagram is shown in Figure 6.3. For our purposes, we will represent molecular oxygen as $\cdot O\!\!-\!\!O\cdot$ or simply O_2.

Oxygen is a stable diradical and therefore is a selective free-radical agent. A compound that contains double bonds, allylic or benzylic hydrogens, or tertiary hydrogens is susceptible to **air oxidation**, also called **auto-oxidation** or **autoxidation**. Compounds with only primary and secondary hydrogens are not as susceptible. (From our discussion of free-radical halogenation reactions, the relative reactivities of these hydrogens should not be surprising.)

Fats and vegetable oils often contain double bonds. Auto-oxidation of a fat yields a mixture of products that includes low-molecular-weight (and foul-smelling) carboxylic acids. For example, rancid butter contains the odorous butyric acid, $CH_3CH_2CH_2CO_2H$.

Linseed oil and other vegetable oils, which contain many double bonds, are used as drying oils in paint and varnish. These compounds are purposely allowed to undergo air oxidation because the molecules join together, or *polymerize*, into a tough film on the painted surface.

Auto-oxidation initially leads to **hydroperoxides**, compounds containing the $-OOH$ group, which are readily converted to mixtures of alcohols, ketones, and other products. Because mixtures are the usual result, auto-oxidation is rarely used as an organic synthetic technique.

$$R_3CH + \cdot O\!\!-\!\!O\cdot \longrightarrow \underset{\text{a hydroperoxide}}{R_3COOH} \longrightarrow \text{mixture of products}$$

In the laboratory, a chemist is most likely to encounter auto-oxidation products as undesirable impurities in ethers and aldehydes. In ethers, the carbon adjacent to the oxygen is the position of attack. Peroxides of ethers explode when heated. For example, diethyl ether is a common laboratory solvent that is purified by distillation. Unless the peroxides have been removed prior to distillation (by a reducing agent, for example), they will become concentrated in the distilling flask as the ether is boiled away. The result could easily be an explosion.

$$CH_3CH_2OCH_2CH_3 + O_2 \longrightarrow CH_3CH_2OCHCH_3$$
$$\overset{\displaystyle OOH}{\underset{\displaystyle |}{}}$$

diethyl ether   a hydroperoxide

The product of aldehyde auto-oxidation is a carboxylic acid, which is formed by reaction of the intermediate peroxy acid with the aldehyde.

$$\underset{\text{acetaldehyde}}{\overset{\displaystyle O}{\underset{\displaystyle ||}{CH_3CH}}} + O_2 \longrightarrow \overset{\displaystyle O}{\underset{\displaystyle ||}{CH_3COOH}}$$

acetaldehyde   (ethanal)   peroxyacetic acid

$$\overset{\displaystyle O}{\underset{\displaystyle ||}{CH_3COOH}} + \overset{\displaystyle O}{\underset{\displaystyle ||}{CH_3CH}} \longrightarrow 2\ \overset{\displaystyle O}{\underset{\displaystyle ||}{CH_3COH}}$$

acetic acid

STUDY PROBLEM

6.13 When exposed to air, diisopropyl ether forms peroxides at a more rapid rate than diethyl ether does. Suggest a reason for this behavior.

Section 6.10

Free-Radical Initiators

A **free-radical initiator** is anything that can initiate or accelerate a free-radical reaction. The action of ultraviolet light on free-radical halogenation is the action of an initiator. There are several types of compound that may be added to a reaction mixture to initiate free-radical reactions: these compounds are called **free-radical catalysts**.

Any compound that can easily decompose into free radicals can act as an initiator. **Peroxides** (ROOR) are one example. They form free radicals easily because the RO—OR bond dissociation energy is only 35 kcal/mole, lower than that for most bonds. Benzoyl peroxide and peroxybenzoic acid are two peroxides that are commonly used in conjunction with NBS brominations.

benzoyl peroxide

peroxybenzoic acid

Many compounds containing an **azo group** (—N=N—) also undergo thermal decomposition into free radicals and can be used as initiators. Azobisisobutyronitrile (AIBN) is an example. (Like *di, bis* means "two.")

$$\underset{\text{AIBN}}{(CH_3)_2\overset{\overset{\displaystyle CN}{|}}{C}-N=N-\overset{\overset{\displaystyle CN}{|}}{C}(CH_3)_2} \xrightarrow{\text{heat}} (CH_3)_2\overset{\overset{\displaystyle CN}{|}}{C}\cdot + N_2 + \cdot\overset{\overset{\displaystyle CN}{|}}{C}(CH_3)_2$$

The presence of trace amounts of transition-metal ions are effective catalysts for auto-oxidation. They function by transferring an electron to oxygen to yield an *anion-radical*, a reagent far more reactive than oxygen gas itself. A typical use of metal ions as free-radical catalysts is the addition of cobalt salts to house paints to increase the speed at which they dry.

$$Co^{2+} + \cdot O{-}O\cdot \longrightarrow Co^{3+} + \underset{\text{an anion radical}}{\cdot O{-}O{:}^-}$$

radical *anion*

Free-Radical Inhibitors

As the name implies, a **free-radical inhibitor** inhibits, or decreases the rate of, a free-radical reaction. An inhibitor is sometimes referred to as a **free-radical "trap."** The usual action of a free-radical inhibitor is to undergo reaction with reactive free radicals to form stable and nonreactive free radicals.

Iodine is a typical free-radical inhibitor. It undergoes reaction with an alkyl free radical to yield an iodine free radical that is stable and cannot abstract a new hydrogen.

$$\underset{\text{more reactive}}{\cdot CH_3} + I_2 \longrightarrow CH_3I + \underset{\text{less reactive}}{I\cdot}$$

In the chlorination of alkanes, oxygen acts as an inhibitor by forming a fairly stable radical with the alkyl radical. For this reason, free-radical chlorination reactions often have an induction period, a period of time when the reaction will not proceed. This induction period lasts until any oxygen in the system is tied up in the form of a radical.

$$\underset{\text{more reactive}}{\cdot CH_3} + \cdot O{-}O\cdot \longrightarrow \underset{\text{less reactive}}{CH_3{-}O{-}O\cdot}$$

An inhibitor used to control auto-oxidation is called an **antioxidant,** or, in the food industry, a **preservative.** *Phenols*, compounds with an —OH group attached to an aromatic ring carbon, are effective antioxidants. Recall that hydroquinone is a natural storehouse for unpaired electrons (Section 6.9B). The inhibitory powers of phenols are directly analogous. The free-radical products of these compounds are resonance-stabilized and thus nonreactive compared to most other free radicals.

phenol
*the simplest of
the phenols*

"*trapped*"

Resonance structures of the phenol free radical:

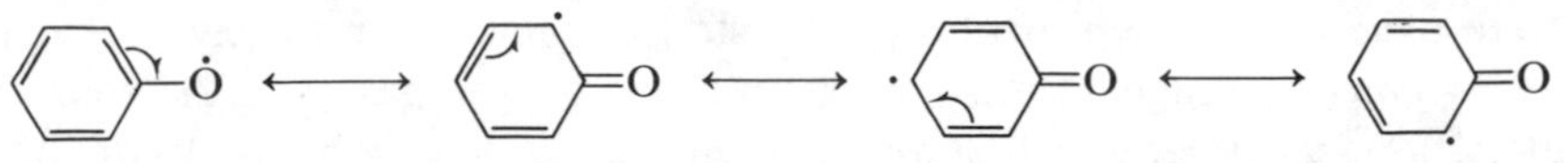

The food preservative BHT is a synthetic phenol. (BHA, another preservative, is closely related to BHT; instead of a methyl group on the ring, BHA has an —NH₂ group.) A naturally occurring preservative found in vegetable oils, especially wheat germ oil, is α-tocopherol, or vitamin E.

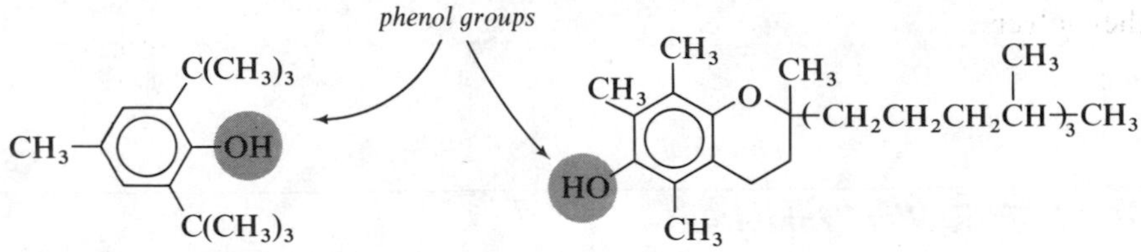

phenol groups

3,5-bis(*t*-butyl)-4-hydroxytoluene
"BHT"

vitamin E

Section 6.12

Organometallic Compounds

An **organometallic compound** is defined as a compound in which *carbon is bonded directly to a metallic atom* (such as mercury, zinc, lead, magnesium, or lithium) or to certain *metalloids* (such as boron, silicon, arsenic, or selenium).

$CH_3CH_2CH_2CH_2Li$ $(CH_3)_4Si$ CH_3ONa

n-butyllithium   tetramethylsilane (TMS)   sodium methoxide
organometallic   *organometallic*   *not considered organometallic*
          (no carbon–metal bond)

Organometallic compounds are named in one of two ways:

(1)   They are named as **alkylmetals** (one word):

$CH_3CH_2CH_2Li$ $(CH_3CH_2)_4Pb$

n-propyllithium   tetraethyllead

If the metal is bonded to an inorganic anion as well as to a carbon atom, the compound is named as a derivative of the inorganic salt.

CH_3MgBr —HgCl

methylmagnesium bromide   phenylmercuric chloride

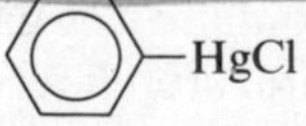

(2) Organometallic compounds of boron, silicon, and tin are named as derivatives of the hydrides of these elements: borane (BH_3), silane (SiH_4), and stannane (SnH_4).

$$(CH_3)_2SiH_2$$

dimethylsilane

$$\left(\bigcirc\!\!\!\!\bigcirc\right)_2\!\!-Si(CH_3)_2$$

dimethyldiphenylsilane

$$(CH_3)_3B$$

trimethylborane

Organomagnesium Halides: Grignard Reagents

One of the most powerful reagents in organic synthesis is the organomagnesium halide (RMgX). These compounds are called **Grignard reagents** after the French chemist Victor Grignard, who received the Nobel Prize in 1912 for work in this area of organometallic chemistry. A Grignard reagent is the product of a free-radical reaction between magnesium metal and an organohalogen compound in an ether solvent.

$$R\!-\!X + Mg \longrightarrow [R\cdot + \cdot MgX] \longrightarrow R\!-\!MgX$$

a Grignard reagent

The reaction is general and does not depend to any great extent upon the nature of the R group. Primary, secondary, and tertiary alkyl halides, as well as allyl and benzyl halides, all form Grignard reagents.

$$CH_3I \quad + Mg \longrightarrow \quad CH_3MgI$$

methyl iodide   methylmagnesium iodide

$$(CH_3)_3CBr \quad + Mg \longrightarrow \quad (CH_3)_3CMgBr$$

t-butyl bromide   *t*-butylmagnesium bromide

$$\bigcirc\!\!\!\!\bigcirc\!\!-CH_2Cl + Mg \longrightarrow \bigcirc\!\!\!\!\bigcirc\!\!-CH_2MgCl$$

benzyl chloride   benzylmagnesium chloride

Aryl and vinyl halides (X on the doubly bonded carbon) are generally quite inert toward nucleophilic substitution and elimination. These compounds are not as reactive as alkyl halides toward magnesium, but their Grignard reagents may still be prepared.

$$\bigcirc\!\!\!\!\bigcirc\!\!-Br + Mg \longrightarrow \bigcirc\!\!\!\!\bigcirc\!\!-MgBr$$

bromobenzene   phenylmagnesium bromide

an aryl Grignard reagent

$$CH_2\!\!=\!\!CHI \quad + Mg \longrightarrow \quad CH_2\!\!=\!\!CHMgI$$

vinyl iodide   vinylmagnesium iodide

(iodoethene)   *a vinyl Grignard reagent*

Organomagnesium halides are unstable unless they are solvated. The usual solvent for a Grignard reagent is diethyl ether ($CH_3CH_2OCH_2CH_3$), which is nonreactive toward Grignard reagents, but can donate unshared electrons to the empty d orbitals of Mg. The ethyl groups provide a hydrocarbon environment that acts as the solvent for the alkyl portion of the Grignard reagent.

$$CH_3CH_2 \quad CH_2CH_3$$
$$\ddot{O}$$
$$CH_3{-}Mg{-}I$$
$$\ddot{O}$$
$$CH_3CH_2 \quad CH_2CH_3$$

STUDY PROBLEM

6.14 Which of the following compounds would be a suitable solvent for a Grignard reagent?

(a) $CH_3CH_2CH_2CH_2CH_3$ (b) $CH_3OCH_2CH_2CH_3$

(c)   (d)   (e) $CH_3OCH_2CH_2Cl$

A.   Reactivity of Grignard Reagents

What is unique about a Grignard reagent? In most organic compounds, carbon carries either no partial charge or a partial positive charge. In a Grignard reagent, carbon is bonded to an electropositive element and consequently carries a *partial negative charge.*

$$\overset{\delta+}{C}H_3\overset{\delta-}{C}H_2{-}Br + Mg \xrightarrow{\text{ether}} CH_3\overset{\delta-}{C}H_2{-}\overset{\delta+}{Mg}{-}Br \qquad \textit{carbon is } \delta-$$

It is generally true that a carbon atom bonded to a metallic atom is the more electronegative of the two atoms and carries a partial negative charge. An ion with a negatively charged carbon atom is called a **carbanion**. A carbon bonded to a metallic atom therefore has **carbanion character**.

$$sp^3 \quad R$$
$$R\text{''''}C{:}^-$$
$$R$$
a carbanion

$$R_3\overset{\delta-}{C}{-}\overset{\delta+}{\text{Metal}}$$
has carbanion character

Carbanions are one of the strongest classes of base encountered in the laboratory. Because a Grignard reagent has a partially negative carbon, (1) it is an *extremely strong base*, and (2) the alkyl or aryl portion of the Grignard reagent can act as a *nucleophile*. We will discuss the action of a Grignard reagent as a nucleophile here and examine its basicity in Section 6.15.

The most important reactions of Grignard reagents are those with carbonyl compounds. In a carbonyl group (C=O), the electrons in the carbon–oxygen bonds (sigma and pi) are drawn toward the electronegative oxygen. The carbon of the carbonyl group, which has a partial positive charge, is attacked by the nucleophilic carbon of the Grignard reagent. The following equations show how Grignard reagents undergo reactions with ketones. (Note that these reactions are not free-radical reactions. When a Grignard reagent attacks a carbonyl group, the electrons move in pairs, not singly.)

Reactions of RMgX with ketones:

$$\textit{General:}\quad R-\underset{\delta+}{\overset{\overset{\displaystyle \overset{..}{\overset{..}{O}}:\,\delta-}{\|}}{C}}-R + R'-MgX \longrightarrow R-\underset{R'}{\overset{\overset{\displaystyle :\overset{..}{O}:^- \; ^+MgX}{|}}{C}}-R$$

$$\underset{\substack{\text{acetone}\\\text{(propanone)}}}{CH_3\overset{\overset{\displaystyle O}{\|}}{C}CH_3} + \overset{\delta-}{C}H_3-\overset{\delta+}{M}gI \longrightarrow CH_3\underset{CH_3}{\overset{\overset{\displaystyle O^- \; ^+MgI}{|}}{C}}CH_3$$

$$\underset{\text{cyclohexanone}}{\bigcirc\!\!=\!O} + CH_3CH_2-MgBr \longrightarrow \underset{CH_2CH_3}{\bigcirc\!\!\overset{O^- \; ^+MgBr}{}}$$

The product of the reaction of RMgX with a ketone is the magnesium salt of an alcohol. When treated with water, this magnesium salt yields the alcohol and a mixed inorganic magnesium salt. The hydrolyzed product of the reaction of a ketone with a Grignard reagent is a *tertiary alcohol*.

$$R-\underset{R'}{\overset{\overset{\displaystyle OMgX}{|}}{C}}-R + H_2O \xrightarrow{\;H^+\;} R-\underset{R'}{\overset{\overset{\displaystyle OH}{|}}{C}}-R + HOMgX$$

a 3° alcohol

The two steps of a Grignard reaction are usually combined into one equation:

$$\underset{\text{acetone}}{CH_3\overset{\overset{\displaystyle O}{\|}}{C}CH_3} \xrightarrow[\text{(2) } H_2O,\, H^+]{\text{(1) } CH_3MgI} \underset{CH_3}{\overset{\overset{\displaystyle OH}{|}}{C}H_3\overset{|}{C}CH_3}$$

t-butyl alcohol

Not only ketones, but almost all compounds containing carbonyl groups (aldehydes, esters, carbon dioxide, etc.) undergo reaction with Grignard reagents. For this reason, Grignard reactions are invaluable to the synthetic organic chemist for building up complicated carbon skeletons from simpler skeletons.

Some examples of reactions of Grignard reagents with aldehydes to yield *secondary alcohols* follow:

Reactions of RMgX with aldehydes:

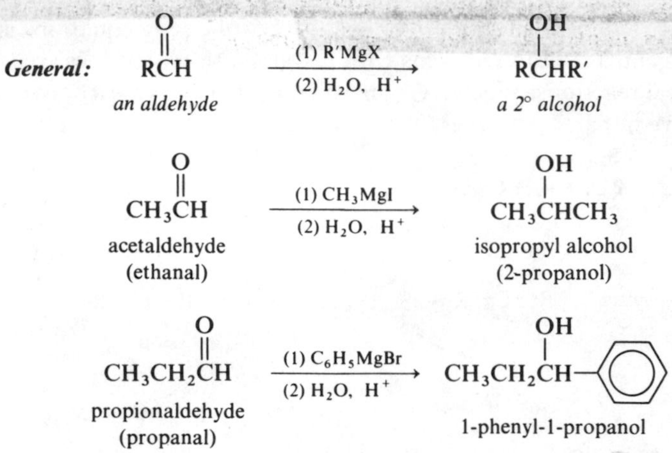

General:

$$\underset{\substack{\text{an aldehyde}}}{\overset{\overset{\displaystyle O}{\parallel}}{RCH}} \xrightarrow[\text{(2) } H_2O, \ H^+]{\text{(1) } R'MgX} \underset{\substack{\text{a } 2° \text{ alcohol}}}{\overset{\overset{\displaystyle OH}{|}}{RCHR'}}$$

$$\underset{\substack{\text{acetaldehyde}\\\text{(ethanal)}}}{\overset{\overset{\displaystyle O}{\parallel}}{CH_3CH}} \xrightarrow[\text{(2) } H_2O, \ H^+]{\text{(1) } CH_3MgI} \underset{\substack{\text{isopropyl alcohol}\\\text{(2-propanol)}}}{\overset{\overset{\displaystyle OH}{|}}{CH_3CHCH_3}}$$

$$\underset{\substack{\text{propionaldehyde}\\\text{(propanal)}}}{\overset{\overset{\displaystyle O}{\parallel}}{CH_3CH_2CH}} \xrightarrow[\text{(2) } H_2O, \ H^+]{\text{(1) } C_6H_5MgBr} \underset{\substack{\text{1-phenyl-1-propanol}}}{\overset{\overset{\displaystyle OH}{|}}{CH_3CH_2CH}} \!\!-\!\!\bigcirc$$

Sample Problem

A chemist (a) treats iodobenzene with magnesium metal and diethyl ether; (b) adds acetone (propanone); and finally, (c) adds a dilute solution of HCl. Write an equation to represent each reaction.

Solution: (a) $\quad C_6H_5I + Mg \longrightarrow C_6H_5MgI$

(b) $\quad \underset{\substack{}}{\overset{\overset{\displaystyle O}{\parallel}}{CH_3CCH_3}} + C_6H_5MgI \longrightarrow \underset{\substack{|\\C_6H_5}}{\overset{\overset{\displaystyle OMgI}{|}}{CH_3CCH_3}}$

(c) $\quad \underset{\substack{}}{\overset{\overset{\displaystyle OMgI}{|}}{(CH_3)_2CC_6H_5}} + H_2O \xrightarrow{\text{H}^+} \underset{\substack{}}{\overset{\overset{\displaystyle OH}{|}}{(CH_3)_2CC_6H_5}} + Mg(OH)I$

STUDY PROBLEM

6.15 Suggest a Grignard synthesis for 1-cyclohexyl-1-ethanol starting with bromocyclohexane and an aldehyde.

Section 6.14

Other Organometallics

Grignard reagents are but one type of a large number of useful organometallic compounds. **Lithium reagents,** another type of organometallic compound, are prepared by the reaction of lithium metal with an alkyl halide in a hydrocarbon solvent.

General: $\quad RX + 2 Li \longrightarrow \underset{\substack{\text{an alkyllithium}}}{R\!-\!Li} + LiX$

$$\underset{\substack{\textit{n}\text{-propyl bromide}}}{CH_3CH_2CH_2Br} + 2 Li \longrightarrow \underset{\substack{\textit{n}\text{-propyllithium}}}{CH_3CH_2CH_2Li} + LiBr$$

A lithium reagent is similar to a Grignard reagent in many ways and undergoes similar reactions. However, the C—Li bond has more ionic character than the C—Mg bond because lithium is more electropositive than magnesium. Lithium reagents are more reactive as nucleophiles than Grignard reagents because the carbon involved in a C—Li bond is more negative.

General:

$$\underset{\text{a ketone}}{R-\overset{\overset{\displaystyle O}{\|}}{C}-R} \xrightarrow[\text{(2) } H_2O,\ H^+]{\text{(1) } R'Li} \underset{\substack{| \\ R' \\ \text{a 3° alcohol}}}{R-\overset{\overset{\displaystyle OH}{|}}{C}-R}$$

$$\underset{\text{3-hexanone}}{CH_3CH_2CH_2\overset{\overset{\displaystyle O}{\|}}{C}CH_2CH_3} + CH_3CH_2\overset{\delta-}{C}H_2\overset{\delta+}{-}Li \longrightarrow$$

$$\underset{\substack{| \\ CH_2CH_2CH_3}}{CH_3CH_2CH_2\overset{\overset{\displaystyle O^-\ Li^+}{|}}{C}CH_2CH_3} \xrightarrow{H_2O,\ H^+} \underset{\substack{| \\ CH_2CH_2CH_3}}{CH_3CH_2CH_2\overset{\overset{\displaystyle OH}{|}}{C}CH_2CH_3}$$

4-ethyl-4-heptanol

Lithium dialkylcopper reagents, also called **cuprates**, are synthesized from an alkyllithium and a copper(I) halide, such as CuI.

$$2\ CH_3Li + CuI \longrightarrow \underset{\text{a cuprate}}{(CH_3)_2CuLi} + LiI$$

These reagents are especially useful in synthesizing *unsymmetrical alkanes* of the type R—R′, where R comes from the cuprate and R′ from an alkyl halide. Best yields are obtained when R′X is a primary alkyl halide, but the R group in R_2CuLi can be almost any alkyl or aryl group.

General:

$$\underset{\text{a cuprate}}{R_2CuLi} + R'X \longrightarrow \underset{\substack{\text{an unsymmetrical} \\ \text{alkane}}}{R-R'}$$

$$\underset{\text{isopropyl bromide}}{(CH_3)_2CHBr} \xrightarrow{Li} (CH_3)_2CHLi \xrightarrow{CuI} \underset{\text{a cuprate}}{[(CH_3)_2CH\!\!-\!\!]_2CuLi}$$

$$\xrightarrow{CH_3CH_2CH_2Br} \underset{\text{2-methylpentane}}{(CH_3)_2CH-CH_2CH_2CH_3}$$

bromocyclohexane   a cuprate

methylcyclohexane

STUDY PROBLEM

6.16 Suggest syntheses for (a) 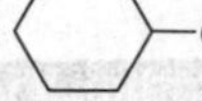 ⬡–CH$_2$CH$_2$CH$_3$, and (b) (CH$_3$)$_3$CCH$_2$CH$_2$CH$_3$, from compounds containing six or fewer carbon atoms.

Section 6.15

Reaction of Organometallics with Acidic Hydrogens

We have shown how some organometallic compounds can act as nucleophiles. Many organometallic reagents, such as Grignard reagents and lithium reagents, are also extremely strong bases. A hydrogen that can be abstracted from a compound by a Grignard reagent is said to be an *acidic hydrogen* in relation to the Grignard reagent. Grignard reagents and lithium reagents undergo rapid reaction with compounds that have acidic hydrogens, yielding hydrocarbons and metal salts.

$$\overset{\delta-}{R}\text{—MgX} + \text{H—}\overset{..}{\overset{..}{O}}\text{H} \longrightarrow \text{RH} + \text{XMg}\overset{..}{\overset{..}{O}}\text{H}$$

$$\overset{\delta-}{R}\text{—Li} + \text{H—}\overset{\frown}{O}\text{H} \longrightarrow \text{RH} + \text{LiOH}$$

Grignard reagents and lithium reagents are stronger bases than $^-$OH, $^-$OR, $^-$NH$_2$, or RC≡C$^-$. Therefore, the type of hydrogen that is acidic toward RMgX or RLi is any H bonded to *oxygen, nitrogen*, or an *sp-hybridized carbon*. (The reasons why RC≡CH can lose a proton will be discussed in Chapter 9.)

Some structures that contain hydrogens acidic toward RMgX or RLi:

HOH   H$_2$NH   ArOH
ROH   R$_2$NH   RCO$_2$H
RC≡CH

Sample Problem

What are the products of the reaction of methylmagnesium iodide with each of the seven structures shown that contain acidic hydrogens?

Solution:

CH$_3$MgI + H$_2$O ⟶ CH$_4$ + HOMgI

CH$_3$MgI + ROH ⟶ CH$_4$ + ROMgI

CH$_3$MgI + RC≡CH ⟶ CH$_4$ + RC≡CMgI

CH$_3$MgI + NH$_3$ ⟶ CH$_4$ + NH$_2$MgI

CH$_3$MgI + R$_2$NH ⟶ CH$_4$ + R$_2$NMgI

CH$_3$MgI + ArOH ⟶ CH$_4$ + ArOMgI

CH$_3$MgI + RCO$_2$H ⟶ CH$_4$ + RCO$_2$MgI

Sample Problem

A student maintains that a Grignard reagent undergoes reaction with water to yield an alcohol. What is wrong with this statement?

Solution: The carbon of the Grignard reagent is partially *negative* and undergoes reaction with a *positive group* (such as H$^+$), not with a negative group (such as $^-$OH).

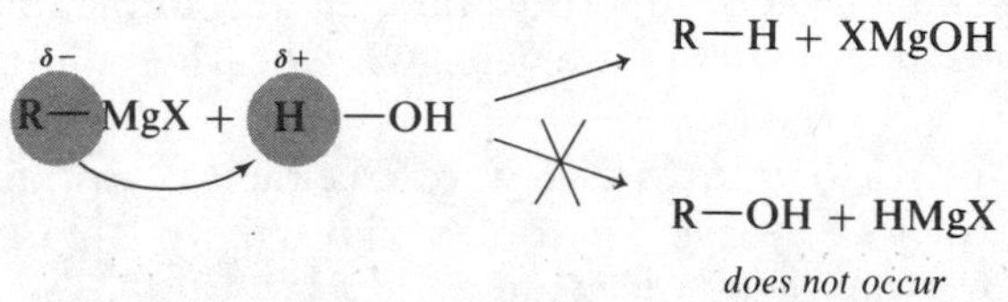

$$R-H + XMgOH$$

$$\overset{\delta-}{R}-MgX + \overset{\delta+}{H}-OH$$

$$R-OH + HMgX$$

does not occur

The principal ramifications of the reactivities of RMgX and RLi toward acidic hydrogens are that (1) water, alcohols, and other compounds with acidic hydrogens must be excluded from a Grignard or lithium reaction mixture (unless an alkane is the desired product), and (2) the presence of certain functional groups in an organohalogen preclude the formation of stable Grignard or lithium reagents.

STUDY PROBLEMS

6.17 A chemist attempts to prepare a Grignard reagent from 4-bromo-1-butanol. Why will this reaction fail?

6.18 Which of the following compounds could *not* be used to prepare a Grignard reagent?

(a) $\overset{\overset{\displaystyle NH_2}{|}}{CH_3CHCH_2CH_2Br}$

(b) 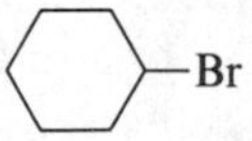 ⬡—Br

(c) 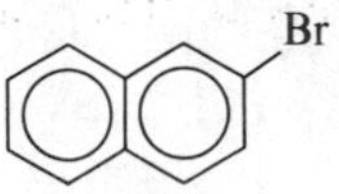 ⬡⬡—Br

(d) $BrCH_2\overset{\overset{\displaystyle O}{||}}{C}OH$

(e) $CH_3C\equiv CCH_2CH_2I$

6.19 Suggest reagents for the following conversion:

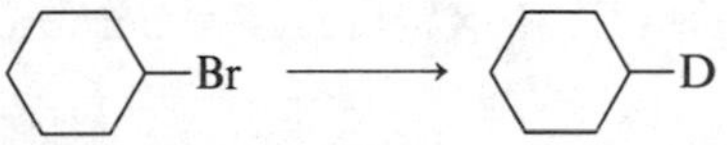

⬡—Br $\longrightarrow$ ⬡—D

SUMMARY

A **free radical** is an atom or group of atoms with an unpaired electron. Free-radical reactions are **chain reactions** that involve **initiation** (formation of free radicals); **propagation** (reactions in which new free radicals are formed); and **termination** (by coupling, disproportionation, or the formation of stable free radicals). Racemization occurs at a reacting chiral carbon during a free-radical reaction.

The order of reactivity of H's toward free-radical abstraction is $CH_4 <$ $1° < 2° < 3° <$ allyl or benzyl. The order of reactivity is partly the result of stabilities of the free-radical intermediates.

Cl_2 is more reactive and less selective than Br_2 in free-radical halogenations. *N*-**Bromosuccinimide** (NBS) is a selective brominating agent for *allylic* and *benzylic positions*.

$$CH_3CH_2CH_3 \xrightarrow[hv]{Cl_2} CH_3CHClCH_3 + CH_3CH_2CH_2Cl + HCl$$

$$CH_3CH_2CH_3 \xrightarrow[hv]{Br_2} CH_3CHBrCH_3 + HBr$$

$$CH_2{=}CHCH_3 \xrightarrow{NBS} CH_2{=}CHCH_2Br$$

$$\bigcirc{-}CH_2R \xrightarrow{NBS} \bigcirc{-}CHBrR$$

Other free-radical reactions besides halogenation include **pyrolysis**, a thermal free-radical decomposition of organic compounds; the **biological reduction** of O_2; and **auto-oxidation**, a free-radical oxidation by O_2 that results in decomposition of fats, oils, rubber, ethers, and aldehydes.

Free-radical initiators are substances that cause the formation of free radicals. Ultraviolet light and peroxides (which contain the easily broken $-O-O-$ bond) are examples. **Free-radical inhibitors**, such as I_2 or phenols, are substances that form nonreactive free radicals.

Organometallic compounds are compounds that contain a carbon–metal bond. A **Grignard reagent** (RMgX) is reactive because of the nucleophilic carbon bonded to Mg.

$$\underset{\delta+}{\overset{\displaystyle O}{-C-}} + \overset{\delta-}{R}{-}MgX \longrightarrow \underset{R}{\overset{\displaystyle OMgX}{-C-}} \xrightarrow{H_2O, H^+} \underset{R}{\overset{\displaystyle OH}{-C-}}$$

An **alkyllithium** (RLi) undergoes reactions similar to those of Grignard reagents. **Cuprates** (R_2CuLi) are used to prepare hydrocarbons.

Grignard reagents and lithium reagents both undergo reaction with compounds that contain acidic hydrogens to yield alkanes.

$$RMgX + H{-}OH \longrightarrow RH + HOMgX$$

$$RLi + H{-}OH \longrightarrow RH + LiOH$$

STUDY PROBLEMS

6.20 Give Lewis formulas for   (a) $CH_3CH_2O\cdot$ and   (b) $CH_2{=}CH{-}\dot{C}H_2$.

6.21 Label each of the following reactions as *initiation*, *propagation*, or *termination* steps:

(a) $(CH_3)_3C\cdot + CH_2{=}CH_2 \longrightarrow (CH_3)_3C{-}CH_2CH_2\cdot$

(b) $C_6H_5\overset{\overset{\textstyle O}{\|}}{C}OOH \longrightarrow C_6H_5\overset{\overset{\textstyle O}{\|}}{C}O\cdot + \cdot OH$

(c) $2\ CH_3CH_2CH_2\cdot \longrightarrow CH_3CH_2CH_3 + CH_3CH{=}CH_2$

(d) $2\ CH_3CH_2\cdot \longrightarrow CH_3CH_2CH_2CH_3$

(e) $Br\cdot + CH_2{=}CH_2 \longrightarrow \cdot CH_2CH_2Br$

6.22 Write equations for the steps in the free-radical dichlorination of cyclopentane to yield 1,2-dichlorocyclopentane.

6.23 If all H's were abstracted at equivalent rates, what would be the ratio of monochlorination products of an equimolar mixture of $CH_3CH_2CH_3$ and cyclohexane?

6.24 List the products that would be obtained from the free-radical monochlorination of each of the following compounds. (Do not forget to indicate stereoisomers.)   (a) (R)-1,2-dichloropropane;   (b) racemic 1,2-dichloropropane;   (c) (R)-2-chlorobutane.

6.25 Only one monochlorination product is obtained from an alkane with the molecular formula C_5H_{12}. What is the structure of the alkane?

6.26 Rank the following free radicals in order of increasing stability (least stable first):

(a) $CH_3CH_2\dot{C}(CH_3)_2$ (b) $CH_3\dot{C}HCH_3$ (c) $C_6H_5\dot{C}HCH_3$

(d) $CH_3CH{=}CHCH_2\dot{C}H_2$ (e) $C_6H_5\dot{C}HCH{=}CH_2$

6.27 Rank the following hydrocarbons in order of increasing ease of free-radical bromination:

(a) $CH_3CH_2CH(CH_3)_2$ (b) $CH_3CH_2CH_3$.   (c) $C_6H_5CH_2CH_3$

6.28 Draw all the important resonance structures for the following free radicals:

(a) 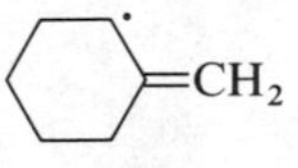 $={CH_2}$ (b) 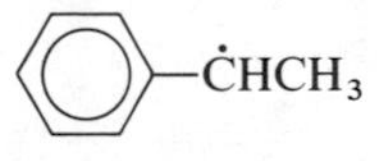 $-\dot{C}HCH_3$

6.29 Draw all the important resonance contributors for the following free radicals:

(a) 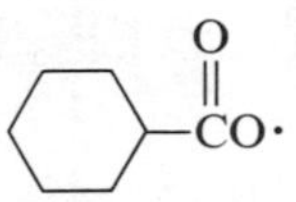 $-\overset{\overset{\textstyle O}{\|}}{C}O\cdot$ (b) $-O\cdot$ (c) $-\dot{N}CH_3$

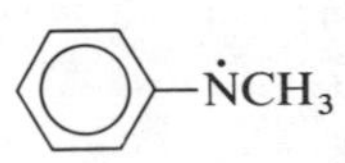

6.30 Rank the following compounds in terms of increasing selectivity in free-radical halogenation (least selective first):

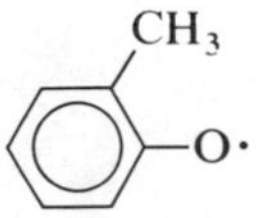

(a) Cl_2 (b) F_2 (c) 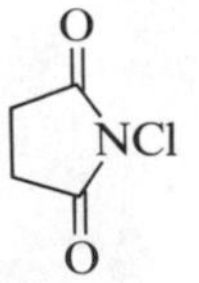 NCl (d) 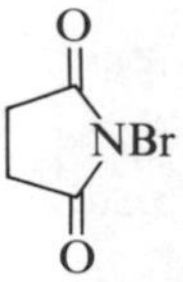 NBr

6.31 In each of the following structures, circle the position (or positions) that you would expect to be attacked by a low-energy free radical:

(a) 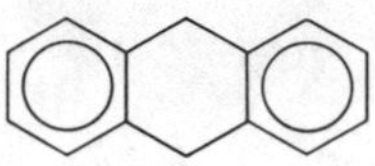 [structure of dihydroanthracene]

(b) 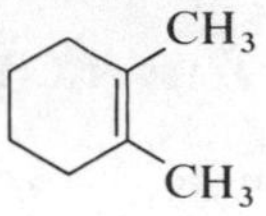 [cyclohexene with two CH₃ groups]

(c) 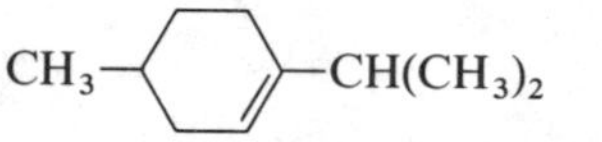 CH_3-[cyclohexene]$-CH(CH_3)_2$

(d) 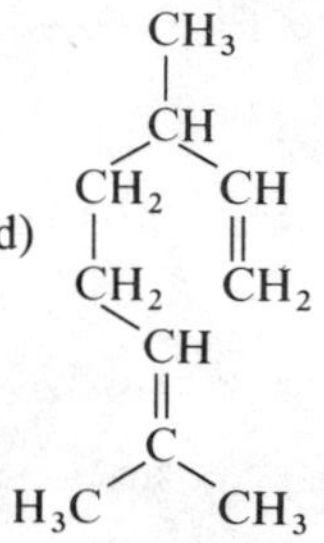 [branched structure with CH₃, CH, CH₂, CH, CH₂, CH₂, CH, C, H₃C, CH₃]

6.32 Complete the following equations, showing only the major organic products:

(a) 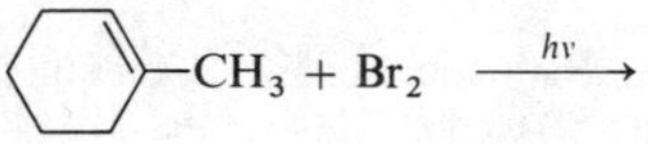 [cyclohexene]$-CH_3 + Br_2 \xrightarrow{hv}$

(b) 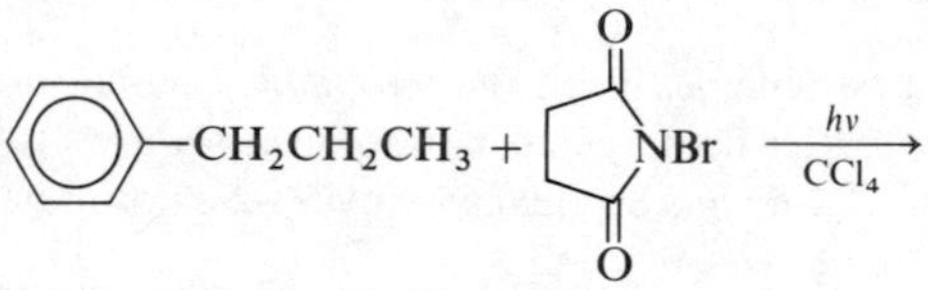 [benzene ring]$-CH_2CH_2CH_3 +$ [N-bromosuccinimide] $\xrightarrow[CCl_4]{hv}$

(c) 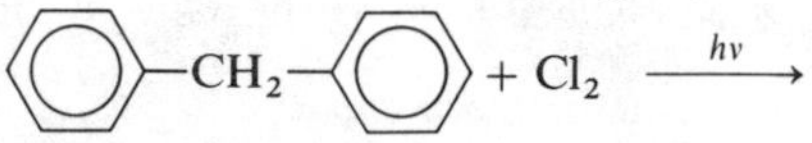 [benzene ring]$-CH_2-$[benzene ring]$+ Cl_2 \xrightarrow{hv}$

(d) 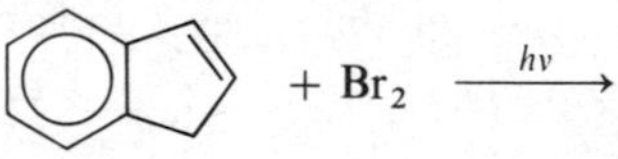 [indene structure] $+ Br_2 \xrightarrow{hv}$

6.33 Complete the following equations, showing the major organic products:

(a) 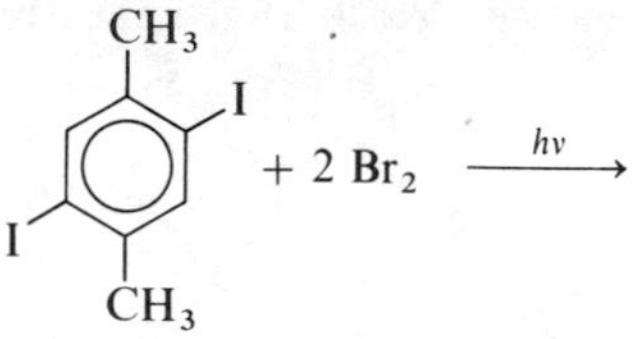 [benzene ring with CH₃, I, I, CH₃] $+ 2 Br_2 \xrightarrow{hv}$

(b) 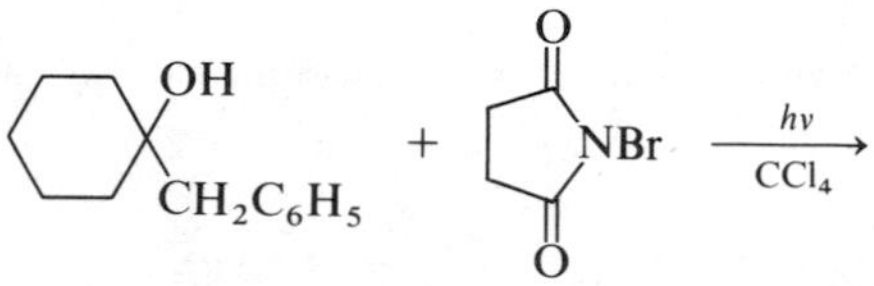 [cyclohexane with OH and CH₂C₆H₅] $+$ [N-bromosuccinimide] $\xrightarrow[CCl_4]{hv}$

(c) 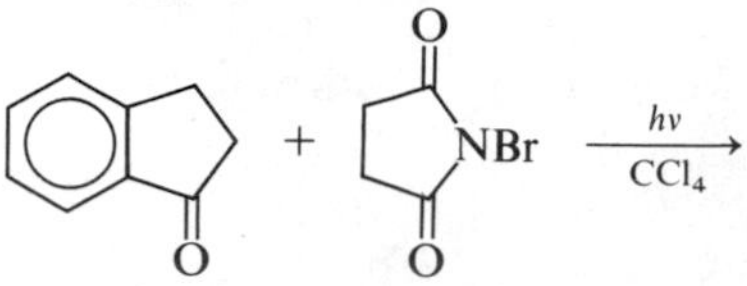 [indanone structure] $+$ [N-bromosuccinimide] $\xrightarrow[CCl_4]{hv}$

(d) 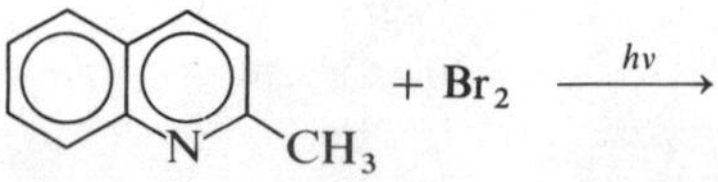 [quinoline with CH₃] $+ Br_2 \xrightarrow{hv}$

6.34 Suggest a mechanism that explains the following observation. (The * represents an isotopic label: ^{14}C.)

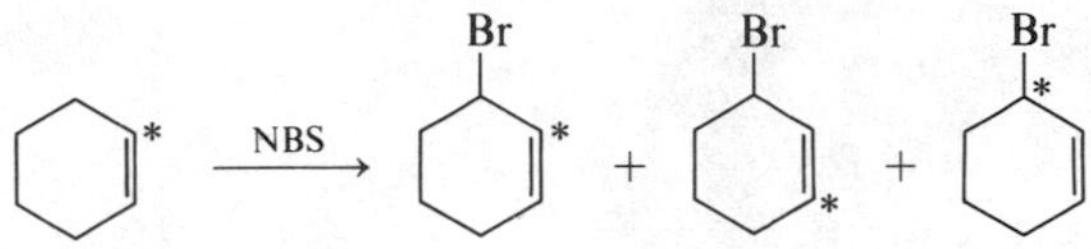

6.35 What would be the disproportionation products of (a) $CH_3CH_2CH_2CH_2 \cdot$ and (b) $CH_3\dot{C}HCH_3$?

6.36 What would be the coupling product for each of the examples in Problem 6.35?

6.37 Which of the following compounds would form a hydroperoxide (ROOH) readily upon exposure to air?

(a) 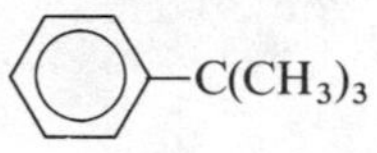 (b) 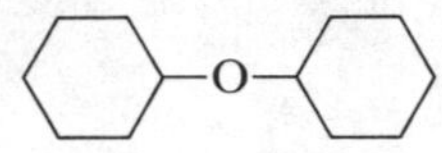 (c)

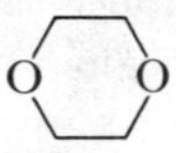

6.38 Label each of the following free radicals as *very reactive* or *not very reactive*:

(a) $C_6H_5O \cdot$ (b) $Cl \cdot$ (c) $I \cdot$

(d) $CH_3CH_2 \cdot$ (e) $F \cdot$ (f) $C_6H_5\dot{N}C_6H_5$

6.39 Which of the following compounds are organometallic compounds?

(a) CH_3HgOH (b) $(C_6H_5O)_2Mg$ (c) $(CH_3)_3SiO^- \ Na^+$

6.40 Name the following organometallic compounds:

(a) C_6H_5MgI (b) $CH_3CH_2CH_2MgCl$ (c) $CH_3(CH_2)_5CH_2Li$

6.41 Complete the following equations:

(a) 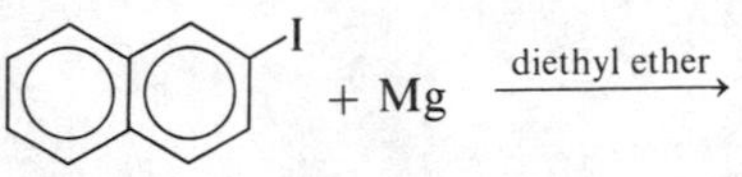 $+ \ Mg \xrightarrow{\text{diethyl ether}}$

(b) 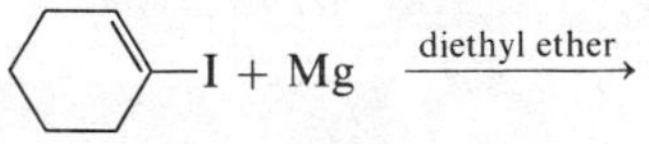 $-I + Mg \xrightarrow{\text{diethyl ether}}$

(c) 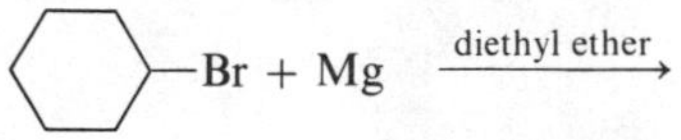 $-Br + Mg \xrightarrow{\text{diethyl ether}}$

(d) 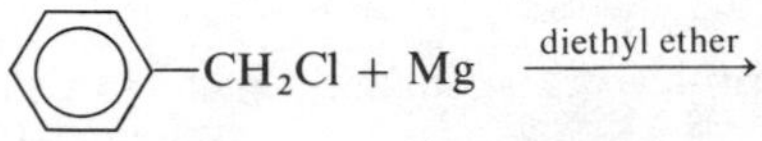 $-CH_2Cl + Mg \xrightarrow{\text{diethyl ether}}$

6.42 Which of the following compounds could be plausibly considered as a solvent for a Grignard reagent? (a) benzene; (b) ethanol; (c) dibutyl ether.

Free-Radical Reactions ; Organometallic Compounds

6.43 Predict the organic products:

(a) (cyclohexanone) $\xrightarrow[\text{(2) H}_2\text{O, H}^+]{\text{(1) CH}_3\text{MgI}}$

(b) $\text{CH}_3\text{CH}_2\overset{\displaystyle O}{\overset{\|}{\text{CH}}}$ $\xrightarrow[\text{(2) H}_2\text{O, H}^+]{\text{(1)} \text{—MgBr}}$

(c) $\text{C}_6\text{H}_5\overset{\displaystyle O}{\overset{\|}{\text{CH}}}$ $\xrightarrow[\text{(2) H}_2\text{O, H}^+]{\text{(1) CH}_3\text{CH}_2\text{MgBr}}$

(d) (cyclopentanone) $\xrightarrow[\text{(2) H}_2\text{O, H}^+]{\text{(1)} \text{—MgCl}}$

6.44 How could you prepare each of the following compounds, starting with 2-bromo-propane, magnesium, and other appropriate reagents? (a) 2,3-dimethyl-2-butanol; (b) 3-methyl-2-butanol.

6.45 Which of the following compounds contain acidic hydrogens that would be removed by CH_3MgI? Circle these hydrogens.

(a) $\text{C}_6\text{H}_5\text{C}\equiv\text{CCH}_3$

(b) $\text{HOCH}_2\text{CH}_2\text{OH}$

(c) $\text{H}_2\text{NCH}_2\text{CH}_2\text{CH}_2\overset{\displaystyle O}{\overset{\|}{\text{OC}}}\text{CH}_3$

(d) $\text{HO}_2\text{C}\overset{\displaystyle \text{CO}_2\text{H}}{\overset{|}{\text{—CH—}}}\text{CO}_2\text{H}$

6.46 Complete the following equations, showing all principal products:

(a) (cyclohexyl)$-\text{Br} + \text{Li} \longrightarrow$

(b) $\text{CH}_3\text{CH}_2\text{Br} + \text{NaOH} \xrightarrow{\text{H}_2\text{O}}$

(c) $\text{Li}-$(benzene ring)$-\text{CH}_2\text{CH}_2\text{CO}_2^- + \text{H}_3\text{O}^+ \longrightarrow$

(d) (cyclopentyl)$-\text{Li} +$ (piperidine ring)$\text{NH} \longrightarrow$

(e) (benzene ring)$-\text{MgBr} +$ (benzene ring)$-\overset{\displaystyle O}{\overset{\|}{\text{CH}}}$ (with OH) $\longrightarrow$

6.47 Starting with any alkyl halide of four carbons or less, suggest a method for the preparation of each of the following alkanes:

(a) $\text{CH}_3\text{CH}_2\text{CH}_2\text{CH}_2\text{CH}_3$

(b) $\text{CH}_3(\text{CH}_2)_6\text{CH}_3$

(c) $(\text{CH}_3)_2\text{CHCH}_2\text{CH}_2\text{CH}_2\text{CH}_3$

6.48 The free-radical bromination of $C_6H_5CH_2D$ with Br_2 shows a kinetic isotope effect. Suggest a reason for the fact that, if HBr is removed from the reaction mixture as soon as it is formed, the isotope effect is even greater.

6.49 Explain why Compound (a) decomposes to free radicals about 75 times faster than (b).

(a) 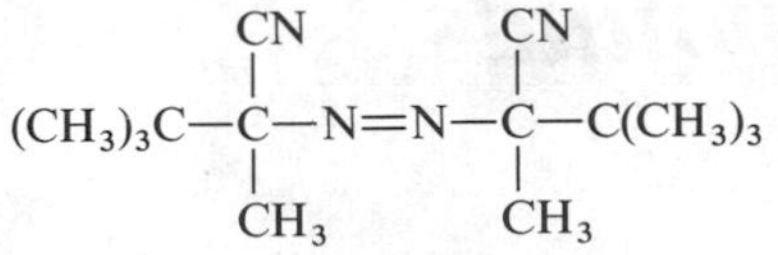 $(CH_3)_3C-\underset{\underset{CH_3}{|}}{\overset{\overset{CN}{|}}{C}}-N{=}N-\underset{\underset{CH_3}{|}}{\overset{\overset{CN}{|}}{C}}-C(CH_3)_3$

(b) 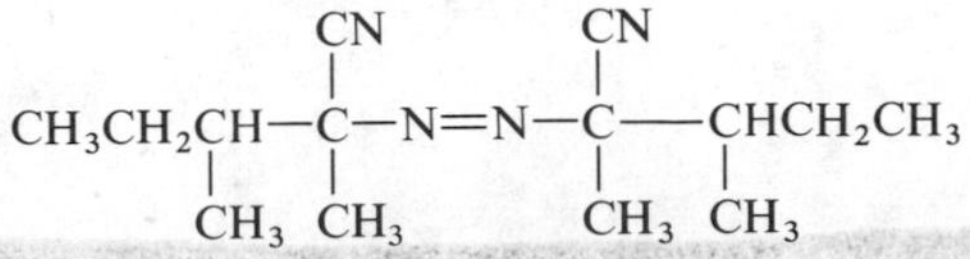 $CH_3CH_2CH-\underset{\underset{CH_3\ CH_3}{|\ \ \ |}}{\overset{\overset{CN}{|}}{C}}-N{=}N-\underset{\underset{CH_3\ CH_3}{|\ \ \ |}}{\overset{\overset{CN}{|}}{C}}-CHCH_2CH_3$

6.50 A chemist treated $CH_3CH{=}CHCH_2Cl$ with magnesium in anhydrous ether and then added acetone (propanone). After hydrolysis, instead of a single alkenyl alcohol as a product, the chemist obtained *two* alcohols. What are the structures of the two alcohols?

6.51 Starting with an organohalogen compound and D_2O, show how you would prepare the following isotopically labeled compounds:

(a) $(C_6H_5)_2CHD$ (b) 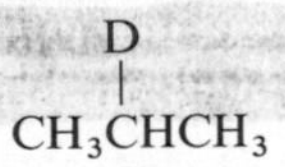 $CH_3\overset{\overset{D}{|}}{C}HCH_3$ (c) $CH_2{=}CHCH_2D$

6.52 Show how you could prepare the starting organohalogen compounds in Problem 6.51 from hydrocarbons.

6.53 Reaction of ethylsodium with (R)-2-chlorooctane yields (R)-3-methylnonane.

(a) Has the chiral center been inverted?

(b) Draw a transition-state structure that would explain the observed stereochemistry.

6.54 Upon free-radical bromination, *n*-pentane yields almost exclusively two monobromo compounds, A and B. Upon treatment with $NaOCH_3$ under E2 conditions, A and B yield predominantly the same product, C. What are the structures of A, B, and C?

Chapter 7

Alcohols, Ethers, and Related Compounds

Alcohols (ROH) and ethers (ROR) are so much a part of our everyday lives that even laymen are familiar with the terms. Diethyl ether (ether) is used as an anesthetic. Ethanol (ethyl alcohol, grain alcohol, or just "alcohol") is used in beverages. 2-Propanol (isopropyl alcohol, or rubbing alcohol) is used as a bacteriocidal agent. Methanol (methyl alcohol, or wood alcohol) is used as an automobile gas-line antifreeze. In the laboratory and in industry, all these compounds are used as solvents and reagents.

In this chapter we will discuss alcohols, ethers, and epoxides (which are a special type of ether). We will also mention briefly phenols and some sulfur analogs of alcohols and ethers.

CH_3CH_2OH	⬡—OH	$CH_3CH_2OCH_2CH_3$	$CH_3\overset{O}{\overset{\diagup\diagdown}{CH-CH_2}}$
ethanol	phenol	diethyl ether	propylene oxide
an alcohol	*a phenol*	*an ether*	*an epoxide*

Section 7.1

Bonding in Alcohols and Ethers

The bonding in alcohols and ethers was mentioned in Chapter 2. Both types of compound have bonding similar to that in water. In all three cases, the oxygen is in the sp^3-hybrid state. Two of the sp^3 orbitals of the oxygen atom are bonded to other atoms, and the remaining two orbitals are filled with two electrons each (see Figure 2.20, page 61).

$$\overset{\cdot\cdot}{\underset{H \quad\quad H}{\overset{\diagup\diagdown}{O}}} \qquad \overset{\cdot\cdot}{\underset{R \quad\quad H}{\overset{\diagup\diagdown}{O}}} \qquad \overset{\cdot\cdot}{\underset{R \quad\quad R}{\overset{\diagup\diagdown}{O}}}$$

$$\text{water} \qquad \text{an alcohol} \qquad \text{an ether}$$

Alcohols and ethers are composed of polar molecules. In either type of compound, the oxygen carries a partial negative charge. However, an alcohol molecule is more polar than an ether molecule. The reason for this is that hydrogen is more electropositive than carbon, and therefore an O—H bond is more polar than an O—R bond. The dipole moments of the following compounds show decreasing polarity in the series H_2O, ROH, and ROR.

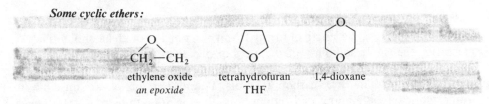

	$\underset{H}{\overset{\delta+}{\diagup}} \overset{\overset{\delta-}{O}}{\underset{H}{\diagdown}} \overset{\delta+}{}$	$\underset{H_3C}{\overset{(\delta+)}{\diagup}} \overset{\overset{\delta-}{O}}{\underset{H}{\diagdown}} \overset{\delta+}{}$	$\underset{H_3C}{\overset{(\delta+)}{\diagup}} \overset{\overset{\delta-}{O}}{\underset{CH_3}{\diagdown}} \overset{(\delta+)}{}$
μ:	1.8 D	1.7 D	1.3 D

Ethers can be either open-chain or cyclic. When the ring size (including the oxygen) is five or greater, the chemistry of the ether may be extrapolated from that of open-chain counterparts. (There are some differences in rates of reaction because the oxygen in a cyclic ether is less sterically hindered—its alkyl substituents are tied back in a ring.) Epoxides contain three-membered ether rings. We will find that epoxides are more reactive than other ethers because of ring strain.

Some cyclic ethers:

$$\underset{\substack{\text{ethylene oxide} \\ \textit{an epoxide}}}{\overset{O}{\underset{CH_2-CH_2}{\triangle}}} \qquad \underset{\substack{\text{tetrahydrofuran} \\ \text{THF}}}{\langle O \rangle} \qquad \underset{\text{1,4-dioxane}}{\langle O \rangle}$$

Section 7.2

Physical Properties of Alcohols and Ethers

A. Boiling Points

Because alcohols can form hydrogen bonds with other alcohol molecules, they have higher boiling points than alkyl halides or ethers of comparable molecular weights. Table 7.1 compares the boiling points of some alcohols and alkyl halides with the same number of carbons.

Table 7.1. *Comparison of the Boiling Points of Some Alcohols and Alkyl Chlorides*

Alcohol	Bp, °C	Alkyl chloride	Bp, °C
CH_3OH	64.5	CH_3Cl	−24
CH_3CH_2OH	78.3	CH_3CH_2Cl	13
$CH_3CH_2CH_2OH$	97.2	$CH_3CH_2CH_2Cl$	46
$HOCH_2CH_2OH$	197	$ClCH_2CH_2Cl$	83.5
$\underset{}{\overset{OH}{\underset{|}{HOCH_2CHCH_2OH}}}$	290	$ClCH_2CHClCH_2Cl$	157

B. Solubility in Water

The alcohols of low molecular weight are miscible with water, while the corresponding alkyl halides are water-insoluble. This water solubility is directly attributable to hydrogen bonding between alcohols and water.

Alcohols, Ethers, and Related Compounds

Table 7.2. Physical Properties of Some Alcohols

IUPAC name	Trivial name	Formula	Bp, °C	Density, g/cc at 20°C	Solubility in H_2O
methanol	methyl alcohol	CH_3OH	64.5	0.79	∞
ethanol	ethyl alcohol	CH_3CH_2OH	78.3	0.79	∞
1-propanol	propyl alcohol	$CH_3CH_2CH_2OH$	97.2	0.80	∞
2-propanol	isopropyl alcohol	$(CH_3)_2CHOH$	82.3	0.79	∞
1-butanol	butyl alcohol	$CH_3(CH_2)_3OH$	117	0.81	8.3 g/100 cc

The hydrocarbon portion of an alcohol is **hydrophobic**—that is, it repels water molecules. As the length of the hydrocarbon portion of an alcohol molecule increases, the water solubility of the alcohol decreases. When the hydrocarbon chain is long enough, it overcomes the **hydrophilic** (water-loving) properties of the hydroxyl group. The three-carbon alcohols, 1- and 2-propanol, are miscible in water, while only 8.3 grams of 1-butanol dissolves in 100 grams of water. (These solubilities are summarized in Table 7.2.)

Branching increases water solubility. Although 1-butanol is only slightly soluble, *t*-butyl alcohol, $(CH_3)_3COH$, is miscible with water. The reason for this is that the *t*-butyl group is more compact and less hydrophobic than the *n*-butyl group. An increase in the number of —OH groups also increases hydrophilicity and solubility. Sucrose (table sugar, page 820) has twelve carbons, but it also has eight hydroxyl groups and is readily soluble in water.

Ethers cannot form hydrogen bonds with themselves because they have no hydrogen attached to the oxygen. However, ethers can form hydrogen bonds with water, alcohols, or phenols. Because of hydrogen bonding with H_2O, the solubilities of the four-carbon compounds diethyl ether and 1-butanol (Tables 7.2 and 7.3) are about the same.

Table 7.3. Physical Properties of Some Ethers and Epoxides

Name	Formula	Bp, °C	Density, g/cc at 20°C	Solubility in H_2O
dimethyl ether	CH_3OCH_3	−24	gas	∞
diethyl ether	$CH_3CH_2OCH_2CH_3$	34.6	0.71	8 g/100 cc
tetrahydrofuran	(structure)	66	0.89	∞
ethylene oxide (oxirane)	CH_2CH_2 (epoxide)	13.5	0.88 (at 10°)	∞
propylene oxide (methyloxirane)	CH_3CHCH_2 (epoxide)	34.3	0.86	∞

C. Solvent Properties

Water is an excellent solvent for ionic compounds. The O—H bond is polar and provides the dipole necessary to solvate both cations and anions. Alcohols also can dissolve ionic compounds, but to a lesser extent. (Ethers cannot dissolve ionic compounds.) Table 7.4 lists the solubility of sodium chloride in water and in a few alcohols. Note that the solubility of NaCl decreases as the hydrocarbon chain of the alcohol increases in length.

Table 7.4. Solubility of Sodium Chloride in Water and in Some Alcohols

Solvent	Dielectric constant	Solubility of NaCl, g/100 cc at 25°C
H_2O	78	36.2
CH_3OH	32	1.4
CH_3CH_2OH	24	0.06
$CH_3CH_2CH_2OH$	20	0.01

Section 7.3

Nomenclature of Alcohols and Ethers

A. IUPAC Names of Alcohols

The IUPAC names of alcohols are taken from the names of the parent alkanes, but with the ending **-ol**. A prefix number, chosen to be as low as possible, is used if necessary.

	CH_3OH	$CH_3CH_2CH_2OH$	$\overset{\displaystyle OH}{\underset{\displaystyle |}{CH_3CHCH_3}}$
IUPAC:	methanol	1-propanol	2-propanol

More than one hydroxyl group is designated by *di-*, *tri-*, etc., just before the -ol ending.

$$\overset{\displaystyle OH}{\underset{\displaystyle |}{CH_3CHCH_2CH_2OH}}$$

1,3-butanediol
a diol

STUDY PROBLEMS

7.1 Name the following compounds:

(a) $(CH_3)_2CH\overset{\displaystyle OH}{\underset{\displaystyle |}{C}}HCH(CH_3)_2$ (b)

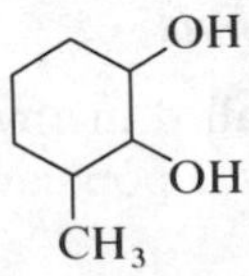

7.2 Write the structures for   (a) 3-ethyl-3-methyl-2-pentanol, and   (b) 2,2-dimethyl-1,4-hexanediol.

A hydroxyl group is often found in a molecule that contains other functional groups. In the IUPAC system, the numbering and the suffix in the name of a multifunctional compound is determined by nomenclature priority (Section 3.3N).

$$-R, -X, \text{etc.} \qquad \overset{/}{\underset{/}{\text{C}}}=\overset{\backslash}{\underset{\backslash}{\text{C}}} \qquad -OH \qquad \overset{O}{\underset{\|}{-\text{C}-}} \qquad \overset{O}{\underset{\|}{-\text{CH}}} \qquad -CO_2H$$

increasing nomenclature priority →

Carboxylic acids, aldehydes, and ketones have higher nomenclature priority than the hydroxyl group; one of these groups receives the lowest nomenclature number and is also given the suffix position in the name. The lower-priority OH group is then named by the prefix **hydroxy-**, as may be seen in the following examples:

$$\overset{\text{HO}}{\underset{|}{\text{CH}_3}}\overset{\text{O}}{\underset{\|}{\text{CHCOH}}} \qquad\qquad HOCH_2CH_2\overset{O}{\underset{\|}{CH}} \qquad\qquad HOCH_2CH_2\overset{O}{\underset{\|}{CCH}}_3$$

2-hydroxypropanoic acid   3-hydroxypropanal   4-hydroxy-2-butanone
(lactic acid)

In a compound that contains an —OH group and also a double bond or a group usually named as a prefix, the hydroxyl group has the higher nomenclature priority. In these cases, the OH receives the lowest prefix number and is given the *-ol* ending. Note in the examples how a double-bond suffix is inserted into the name of an unsaturated alcohol.

$$CH_2=CHCH_2CH_2OH$$

3-buten-1-ol   4-methyl-2-cyclohexen-1-ol   3,3-dichloro-1-cyclohexanol

STUDY PROBLEM

7.3   Name the following compounds by the IUPAC system:

(a) [cyclopentene]—OH   (b) HO—[cyclohexane]=O   (c) $BrCH_2CH_2OH$

B.   *Trivial Names of Alcohols*

Just as CH_3I may be called methyl iodide, CH_3OH may be called methyl alcohol. This type of name is a popular way of naming alcohols with common alkyl groups.

$$(CH_3)_3COH \qquad\qquad (CH_3)_2CHOH$$

t-butyl alcohol   isopropyl alcohol

A diol (especially a 1,2-diol) is often referred to as a **glycol**. The trivial name for a 1,2-glycol is that of the corresponding **alkene** followed by the word **glycol**. Epoxides and 1,2-dihalides are often named similarly. The naming of a saturated compound as a derivative of an alkene is unfortunate; however, the practice arose quite innocently in the early years of organic chemistry because all these compounds can be prepared from alkenes.

$$CH_2{=}CH_2 \qquad \overset{\displaystyle OH \quad OH}{\underset{\displaystyle CH_2{-}CH_2}{\big| \quad \big|}} \qquad \overset{\displaystyle Br \quad Br}{\underset{\displaystyle CH_2{-}CH_2}{\big| \quad \big|}} \qquad \overset{\displaystyle O}{CH_2{-}CH_2}$$

trivial:	ethylene	ethylene glycol	ethylene dibromide
IUPAC:	ethene	1,2-ethanediol	1,2-dibromoethane

ethylene oxide
oxirane

C. *Classification of Alcohols*

Alcohols, like alkyl halides, may be classed as **methyl**, **primary**, **secondary**, **tertiary**, **allyl**, or **benzyl**.

$$CH_3OH \qquad CH_3CH_2OH \qquad (CH_3)_2CHOH \qquad (CH_3)_3COH$$

methyl   1°   2°   3°

$$CH_2{=}CHCH_2OH \qquad \text{⬡}{-}CH_2OH$$

allyl   benzyl

STUDY PROBLEM

7.4 Name each of the preceding alcohols by IUPAC names and by trivial names.

D. *Ethers*

Simple open-chain ethers are named almost exclusively by their trivial names, as **alkyl ethers**.

$$CH_3CH_2OCH_2CH_3 \qquad (CH_3)_2CHOCH(CH_3)_2 \qquad CH_3OCH_2CH_3$$

diethyl ether
(or ethyl ether, or
simply "ether")

diisopropyl ether

methyl ethyl ether

An **alkoxy-** prefix is used when there is more than one alkoxyl (RO—) group or when there is a functional group of higher priority. (Note that a hydroxyl group has priority over an alkoxyl group.)

$$CH_3CH_2OCH_2CH_2CH_2\overset{\displaystyle OH}{\underset{\displaystyle |}{C}}HCH_3$$

1,2-dimethoxycyclohexane

1-isopropoxy-2-
methoxycyclohexane

5-ethoxy-2-pentanol

E.   Epoxides

In the IUPAC system, epoxides are called **oxiranes**. In the numbering of these rings, the oxygen is always considered position 1.

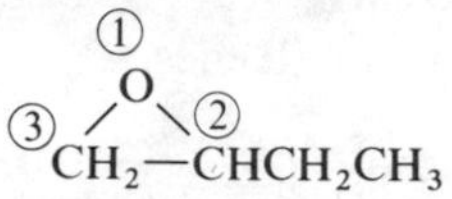

$$\overset{\textcircled{1}}{\underset{\textcircled{3}}{CH_2}}\overset{O}{\diagup\diagdown}\overset{\textcircled{2}}{CHCH_2CH_3}$$

2-ethyloxirane

Sample Problem

Name the following compounds:

(a) $(CH_3)_3COCH_3$ (b) 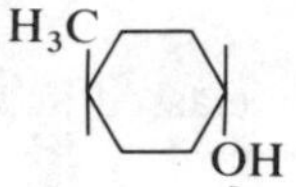   (c) 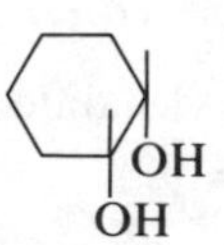   (d)

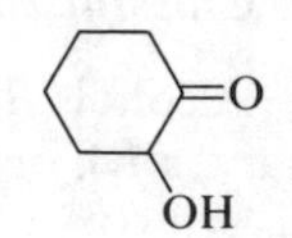

Solution: (a) *t*-butyl methyl ether; (b) *trans*-4-methylcyclohexanol; (c) *cis*-cyclohexene glycol, or *cis*-1,2-cyclohexanediol; (d) 2-hydroxycyclohexanone.

STUDY PROBLEM

7.5   Give structures for (a) ethyl phenyl ether; (b) 2-butanol; (c) *sec*-butyl alcohol; and (d) 2,2-dimethyloxirane.

Section 7.4

Preparation of Alcohols

We have already discussed two reactions that yield alcohols as products: (1) RX + OH⁻ (Chapter 5), and (2) Grignard reactions (Section 6.13A). In this section, we will present a survey of these reactions and a few others that are commonly used to synthesize alcohols.

A.   Nucleophilic Substitution Reactions

The reaction of an alkyl halide with hydroxide ions is a nucleophilic substitution reaction. When primary alkyl halides are heated with aqueous sodium hydroxide, reaction occurs by an S_N2 path. Primary alcohols may be prepared in good yields by this technique. Because secondary and tertiary alkyl halides are likely to give elimination products, they are not generally as useful for preparing alcohols.

$$CH_3CH_2CH_2Br + OH^- \xrightarrow{\text{heat}} CH_3CH_2CH_2OH + Br^-$$

1-bromopropane   1-propanol
a 1° alkyl halide   *a 1° alcohol*

B. Grignard Reactions

Grignard reactions provide an excellent route to alcohols with complex carbon skeletons. A Grignard reaction:

(1) with formaldehyde yields a *primary alcohol*;

(2) with any other aldehyde yields a *secondary alcohol*; and

(3) with a ketone yields a *tertiary alcohol*.

For 1° alcohols:

$$\underset{\substack{\text{formaldehyde}\\ \text{(methanal)}}}{\overset{\overset{\textstyle O}{\|}}{HCH}} \xrightarrow[\text{(2)} \quad H_2O,\ H^+]{\text{(1) }(CH_3)_2CHMgBr} \underset{\substack{\text{isobutyl alcohol}\\ \text{(2-methyl-1-propanol)}}}{(CH_3)_2CHCH_2OH}$$

For 2° alcohols:

$$\underset{\substack{\text{propionaldehyde}\\ \text{(propanal)}}}{\overset{\overset{\textstyle O}{\|}}{CH_3CH_2CH}} \xrightarrow[\text{(2) }H_2O,\ H^+]{\text{(1) }C_6H_5MgBr} \underset{\text{1-phenyl-1-propanol}}{CH_3CH_2\overset{\overset{\textstyle OH}{|}}{CH}-\bigcirc}$$

For 3° alcohols:

$$\underset{\text{2-butanone}}{\overset{\overset{\textstyle O}{\|}}{CH_3CH_2CCH_3}} \xrightarrow[\text{(2) }H_2O,\ H^+]{\text{(1) }CH_3MgI} \underset{\text{2-methyl-2-butanol}}{CH_3CH_2\overset{\overset{\textstyle OH}{|}}{C}(CH_3)_2}$$

The reactions of Grignard reagents with aldehydes and ketones may be generalized as follows:

R″ may be alkyl or aryl

$$\underset{\substack{R \text{ and } R' \text{ may be}\\ \text{alkyl, aryl, or H}}}{R-\overset{\overset{\textstyle O}{\|}}{C}-R'} \xrightarrow[\text{(2) }H_2O,\ H^+]{\text{(1) }R''MgX} R-\overset{\overset{\textstyle OH}{|}}{\underset{\underset{\textstyle R''}{|}}{C}}-R'$$

Other Grignard reactions also lead to alcohols. The reaction of a Grignard reagent with an *ester* leads to a *tertiary alcohol*. This reaction will be discussed in Section 13.5C. The reaction of a Grignard reagent with *ethylene oxide* yields a *primary alcohol*. This reaction will be discussed later in this chapter (Section 7.12).

3° alcohols from esters:

from RMgX

$$\underset{\text{ethyl acetate}}{\overset{\overset{\textstyle O}{\|}}{CH_3COCH_2CH_3}} \xrightarrow[\text{(2) }H_2O,\ H^+]{\text{(1) 2 }CH_3CH_2MgBr} \underset{\text{3-methyl-3-pentanol}}{CH_3\overset{\overset{\textstyle OH}{|}}{\underset{\underset{\textstyle CH_2CH_3}{|}}{C}}-CH_2CH_3}$$

Alcohols, Ethers, and Related Compounds

1° alcohols from ethylene oxide:

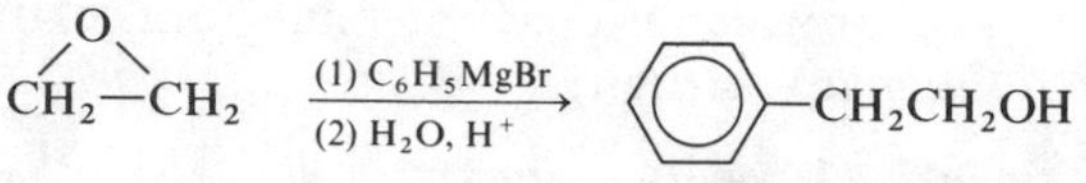

$$CH_2-CH_2 \xrightarrow[\text{(2) } H_2O,\ H^+]{\text{(1) } C_6H_5MgBr} \text{(ring)}-CH_2CH_2OH$$

2-phenyl-1-ethanol

STUDY PROBLEM

7.6   Write equations to show how the following conversions could be made:

(a) 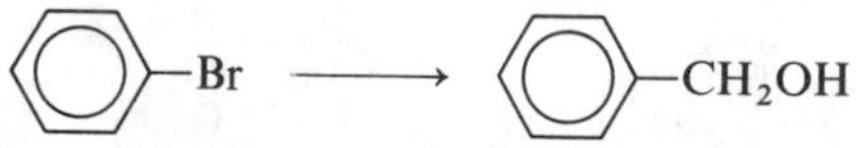   (ring)—Br $\longrightarrow$ (ring)—CH_2OH

(b) $CH_3CH_2CH_2CH_2Cl \longrightarrow CH_3CH_2CH_2CH_2OH$

(c) 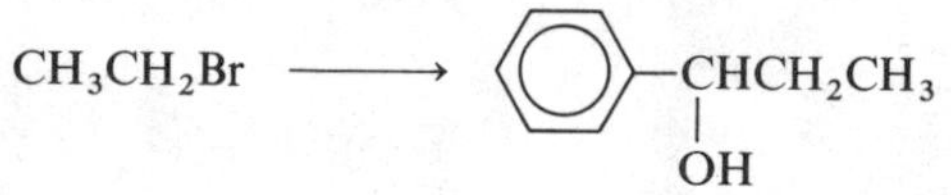 $CH_3CH_2Br \longrightarrow$ (ring)—$\underset{\underset{OH}{|}}{C}HCH_2CH_3$

C.   Reduction of Carbonyl Compounds

Alcohols may be prepared from carbonyl compounds by **reduction reactions** in which hydrogen atoms are added to the carbonyl group. For example, *reduction of a ketone* by catalytic hydrogenation or with a metal hydride yields a *secondary alcohol*. Yields are often 90–100%. These reactions will be discussed in more detail in Section 11.14.

$$\underset{\text{acetone}}{CH_3\overset{\overset{O}{\|}}{C}CH_3} \xrightarrow{NaBH_4} \underset{\substack{\text{isopropyl alcohol} \\ \text{(2-propanol)}}}{CH_3\overset{\overset{OH}{|}}{C}HCH_3}$$

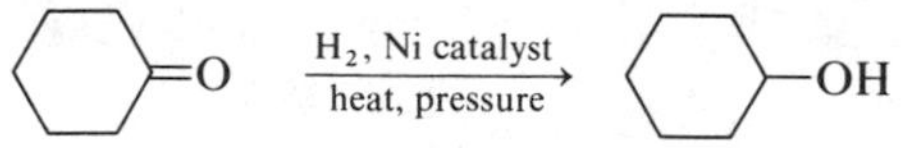

$$\underset{\text{cyclohexanone}}{\text{(ring)}=O} \xrightarrow[\text{heat, pressure}]{H_2,\ \text{Ni catalyst}} \underset{\text{cyclohexanol}}{\text{(ring)}-OH}$$

STUDY PROBLEM

7.7   Write general equations using R and [H] for the reduction of aldehydes and ketones. State if each reduction yields a 1°, 2°, or 3° alcohol.

D.   Hydration of Alkenes

When an alkene is treated with water plus a trace of strong acid to act as a catalyst, the elements of water (H^+ and OH^-) add to the double bond in a **hydration reaction**. The product is an alcohol. Many alcohols, such as laboratory ethanol, are made commercially by the hydration of alkenes. Limitations and variations of hydration reactions, as well as the mechanism, will be discussed in Chapter 9.

$$CH_2{=}CH_2 + H_2O \xrightarrow{\text{H}^+} CH_3CH_2OH$$

ethylene   ethanol

$$CH_3CH{=}CHCH_3 + H_2O \xrightarrow{\text{H}^+} \overset{\displaystyle OH}{\overset{|}{CH_3CHCH_2CH_3}}$$

2-butene   2-butanol

$$\bigcirc\hspace{-1em} + H_2O \xrightarrow{\text{H}^+} \bigcirc\hspace{-1em}-OH$$

cyclohexene   cyclohexanol

E.   *Ethanol by Fermentation*

The ethanol used in beverages is obtained by the enzyme-catalyzed **fermentation of carbohydrates** (sugars and starches). One type of enzyme converts carbohydrates to ethanol; another type leads to vinegar (acetic acid).

$$C_6H_{12}O_6 \xrightarrow{\text{enzymes}} CH_3CH_2OH$$

a sugar   ethanol

The source of the carbohydrates used for fermentation depends on availability and on the purposes of the alcohol. In the U.S., carbohydrates are obtained primarily from corn and from the molasses residue of sugar refining. However, potatoes, rice, rye, or fruit (grapes, blackberries, etc.) may also be used.

Fermentation of any of these fruits, vegetables, or grains ceases when alcoholic content reaches 14 to 16 percent. If a higher concentration of alcohol is desired, the mixture is distilled. The distillate, which is 95% ethanol, may then be used to fortify the fermentation mixture or may be diluted with water to the desired strength.

Because alcoholic beverages are taxed in almost all countries of the world, most ethanol sold for laboratory or industrial purposes (and not taxed as a liquor) is **denatured**—that is, small amounts of toxic impurities are added so that the ethanol cannot be diverted from the laboratory or factory into illegal beverages.

Section 7.5

Preparation of Ethers

A.   *Diethyl Ether*

Under the proper conditions, the reaction of sulfuric acid with ethanol produces diethyl ether by way of the intermediate ethyl hydrogen sulfate. (This reaction was first reported in the 1500's! Until 1800, it was thought that diethyl ether contained sulfur in its structure when, in fact, sulfur was an impurity arising from the sulfuric acid.) The reaction of alcohols and H_2SO_4 will be discussed in more detail in Sections 7.10 and 7.16B.

$$CH_3CH_2OH \xrightarrow{\text{H}_2\text{SO}_4} CH_3CH_2OSO_3H \xrightarrow{\text{CH}_3\text{CH}_2\text{OH}} CH_3CH_2OCH_2CH_3$$

ethanol   ethyl hydrogen sulfate   diethyl ether

Alcohols, Ethers, and Related Compounds

Diethyl ether is undoubtedly the most popular laboratory solvent. Of historical interest is its introduction in the 1800's, along with chloroform and nitrous oxide (N_2O, laughing gas), as a general anesthetic. Diethyl ether and nitrous oxide are still used as anesthetics. (Chloroform, however, has a narrow margin of safety and leads to liver damage, as do many of the chlorinated hydrocarbons.) Diethyl ether is volatile, its vapors are explosive, and it has a tendency to cause nausea. Despite these drawbacks, it is physiologically a relatively safe anesthetic. Other ethers that are used as anesthetics are methyl propyl ether ($CH_3OCH_2CH_2CH_3$) and ethyl vinyl ether ($CH_3CH_2OCH=CH_2$).

B.   Williamson Ether Synthesis

The **Williamson ether synthesis** is the most versatile laboratory procedure for synthesizing ethers. The Williamson synthesis is the S_N2 reaction of an alkyl halide with an alkoxide, a reaction we discussed in detail in Chapter 5.

$$RO^- + R'X \xrightarrow{S_N2} ROR' + X^-$$

$R' = CH_3$ or $1°$

$R = CH_3, 1°, 2°, 3°,$ or Ar

Best yields are obtained when the alkyl halide is methyl or primary. (Secondary and tertiary alkyl halides lead to alkenes, while aryl and vinyl halides do not undergo S_N2 reactions.) The alkoxide that may be used in a Williamson synthesis has fewer limitations. It may be methyl, primary, secondary, tertiary, allyl, or aryl. Usually either the sodium or the potassium alkoxide is used; their preparation will be discussed in Section 7.14.

Synthesis of dialkyl ethers:

$$CH_3O^- + CH_3CH_2CH_2-Cl \xrightarrow{S_N2} CH_3OCH_2CH_2CH_3 + Cl^-$$
methoxide ion   1-chloropropane   methyl propyl ether

$$CH_3CH_2CH_2O^- + CH_3I \xrightarrow{S_N2} CH_3OCH_2CH_2CH_3 + I^-$$
propoxide ion   methyl iodide   methyl propyl ether

$$(CH_3)_3CO^- + CH_3I \xrightarrow{S_N2} (CH_3)_3COCH_3 + I^-$$
t-butoxide ion   t-butyl methyl ether

but not $CH_3O^- + (CH_3)_3CI$ (Why not?)

Synthesis of an alkyl aryl ether:

$$\langle\bigcirc\rangle-O^- + CH_3CH_2Br \xrightarrow{S_N2} CH_3CH_2O-\langle\bigcirc\rangle + Br^-$$
phenoxide ion   ethyl bromide   ethyl phenyl ether

but not $CH_3CH_2O^- + \langle\bigcirc\rangle-Br$ (Why not?)

STUDY PROBLEM

7.8 Show by equations the best method for preparing each of the following ethers by a Williamson synthesis:

(a) 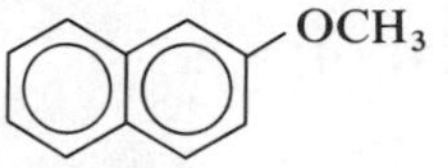 [naphthalene ring structure]—OCH$_3$

(b) $(CH_3)_2CHOCH_2CH_3$

Reactivity of Alcohols and Ethers

An alcohol can lose its hydroxyl proton to a base in an acid–base reaction. The product is an alkoxide. This reaction will be discussed in Section 7.14.

O—H bond broken:

$$CH_3O\text{—}H + Na^+ \; \ddot{N}H_2^- \longrightarrow CH_3O^- \; Na^+ + NH_3$$

methanol   sodamide   sodium methoxide

a strong base

Alcohols and ethers can undergo substitution reactions in which the C—O bond is broken.

C—O bond broken:

$$CH_3CH_2\text{—}OH + HBr \longrightarrow CH_3CH_2\text{—}Br + H_2O$$

an alcohol   *an alkyl halide*

$$CH_3CH_2\text{—}OCH_2CH_3 + HI \xrightarrow{\text{heat}} CH_3CH_2I + CH_3CH_2OH$$

an ether   *an alkyl halide*

Alcohols (but not ethers) also undergo elimination reactions to yield alkenes.

$$CH_2\text{—}CH_2\text{—}OH \xrightarrow[\text{heat}]{H_2SO_4} CH_2\text{=}CH_2 + H_2O$$

an alcohol   *an alkene*

These substitution and elimination reactions are similar to the substitution and elimination reactions of alkyl halides. Unlike alkyl halides, however, alcohols and ethers do not undergo substitution or elimination reactions in neutral or alkaline solution; therefore, treatment of an alcohol with a nucleophile such as CN^- or HS^- in neutral or alkaline solution does not result in substitution products or alkenes. Why not? The answer is that, in general, a leaving group must be a *weaker base* than the attacking nucleophile. A chloride ion is a very weak base and a good leaving group. But $^-$OH and $^-$OR are *strong bases* and therefore very poor leaving groups.

good leaving group

$$CH_3CH_2\!-\!Br + \ ^-OH \longrightarrow CH_3CH_2OH + Br^-$$

poor leaving group

$$CH_3CH_2\!-\!OH + Br^- \longrightarrow \text{no reaction}$$

Substitution and elimination reactions of alcohols do proceed in acidic solution. We will first consider what happens initially to alcohols and ethers in acidic solution and then consider the further reactions of these compounds.

Section 7.7

Alcohols and Ethers in Acidic Solution

In acidic solution, alcohols and ethers are protonated. This reaction is an acid–base equilibrium with the alcohol or ether acting as a base. It is the same type of reaction that occurs between water and a hydrogen ion.

$$\underset{\text{hydronium ion}}{H\!-\!\overset{\overset{\displaystyle H}{|}}{\underset{\cdot\cdot}{O}}\!: + HCl \rightleftharpoons H\!-\!\overset{\overset{\displaystyle H}{|}}{\underset{\cdot\cdot}{\overset{+}{O}}}\!-\!H + Cl^-}$$

$$\underset{\text{an alcohol}}{R\!-\!\overset{\overset{\displaystyle H}{|}}{\underset{\cdot\cdot}{O}}\!: + HCl} \rightleftharpoons \underset{\text{an oxonium ion}}{R\!-\!\overset{\overset{\displaystyle H}{|}}{\underset{\cdot\cdot}{\overset{+}{O}}}\!-\!H + Cl^-}$$

$$\underset{\text{an ether}}{R\!-\!\overset{\overset{\displaystyle R}{|}}{\underset{\cdot\cdot}{O}}\!: + HCl} \rightleftharpoons \underset{\text{an oxonium ion}}{R\!-\!\overset{\overset{\displaystyle R}{|}}{\underset{\cdot\cdot}{\overset{+}{O}}}\!-\!H + Cl^-}$$

In each case, an empty $1s$ orbital of H^+ overlaps with one of the filled orbitals of the oxygen, and an O—H sigma bond is formed (see Figure 7.1). The product of the reaction with water is the protonated water molecule, or the **hydronium ion**. A protonated alcohol or ether molecule is called an **oxonium ion**.

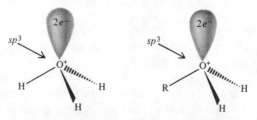

Figure 7.1. Bonding in the hydronium ion (H_3O^+) and in an oxonium ion ($ROH_2{}^+$).

Protonation reactions are rapid and reversible. Because any hydrogen attached to the oxygen may be lost in the reverse reaction, the OH protons of alcohols undergo rapid exchange with other acidic protons. For example, if methanol is treated with DCl, the solution soon contains CH_3OD.

$$CH_3OH \;\underset{}{\overset{D^+}{\rightleftharpoons}}\; CH_3\overset{+}{O}H \;\underset{}{\overset{-H^+}{\rightleftharpoons}}\; CH_3OD$$
$$\underset{D}{|}$$

Substitution Reactions of Alcohols

In acidic solution, the —OH group of an alcohol is protonated. Although —OH is a poor leaving group, this new group, $—OH_2{}^+$, is a good leaving group because it leaves as water, a very weak base.

good leaving group

$$R—\overset{..}{\underset{..}{O}}H \;\overset{H^+}{\rightleftharpoons}\; R—\overset{+}{\underset{\underset{H}{|}}{O}}H \;\overset{Nu^-}{\longrightarrow}\; R—Nu + H_2\overset{..}{\underset{..}{O}}{:}$$

The most useful reagents in substitution reactions of alcohols are the hydrogen halides. The product of the reaction of an alcohol with HX is an alkyl halide.

$$CH_3CH_2CH_2OH + HBr \longrightarrow CH_3CH_2CH_2Br + H_2O$$

n-propyl alcohol   *n*-propyl bromide
(1-propanol)   (1-bromopropane)

$$(CH_3)_2CHOH + HI \longrightarrow (CH_3)_2CHI + H_2O$$

isopropyl alcohol   isopropyl iodide
(2-propanol)   (2-iodopropane)

$$(CH_3)_3COH + HCl \longrightarrow (CH_3)_3CCl + H_2O$$

t-butyl alcohol   *t*-butyl chloride

A. Reactivity of the Hydrogen Halides

In alcohol substitution reactions, the reactivity of the hydrogen halides is as follows:

	HF	HCl	HBr	HI
pK_a:	3.2	−7	−9	−9.5

increasing acid strength; increasing reactivity toward ROH ⟶

Although HI, HBr, and HCl are all considered strong acids (almost completely ionized in water), HI is the strongest acid of the group. HF is a weak acid. (Some reasons for this order of acid strength will be discussed in Chapter 12.) The order of reactivity of these acids toward alcohols simply parallels the relative acid strengths.

$$ROH + HI \longrightarrow RI + H_2O$$

increasing rate of reaction

$$ROH + HBr \longrightarrow RBr + H_2O$$

$$ROH + HCl \longrightarrow RCl + H_2O$$

B. *Reactivity of Alcohols*

The order of reactivity of alcohols toward the hydrogen halides follows:

methyl $1°$ $2°$ $3°$ benzyl   allyl

increasing reactivity of ROH toward HX

All alcohols undergo reaction with HBr and HI readily to yield alkyl bromides and iodides. Tertiary alcohols, benzyl alcohols, and allyl alcohols also undergo reaction readily with HCl. However, primary and secondary alcohols are less reactive and require the help of anhydrous $ZnCl_2$ or a similar catalyst before they can undergo reaction with the less reactive HCl.

increasing reactivity toward HX

$3°$: $(CH_3)_3COH + HCl \xrightarrow{25°} (CH_3)_3CCl + H_2O$

$2°$: $(CH_3)_2CHOH + HCl \xrightarrow{ZnCl_2} (CH_3)_2CHCl + H_2O$

$1°$: $CH_3CH_2OH + HCl \xrightarrow{ZnCl_2} CH_3CH_2Cl + H_2O$

The function of the zinc chloride is similar to that of H^+. Anhydrous zinc chloride is a powerful Lewis acid with empty orbitals that can accept electrons from the oxygen. The formation of a complex of $ZnCl_2$ with the alcohol oxygen weakens the C—O bond and thus enhances the leaving ability of the oxygen group.

$$CH_3CH_2\ddot{O} : + ZnCl_2 \longrightarrow CH_3CH_2\overset{+}{\ddot{O}}{-}\bar{Z}nCl_2$$
$$\qquad\qquad | \qquad\qquad\qquad\qquad\qquad |$$
$$\qquad\qquad H \qquad\qquad\qquad\qquad\qquad H$$

the complex

$$Cl^- + CH_2{-}\overset{+}{O}{-}\bar{Z}nCl_2 \longrightarrow Cl{-}CH_2 + HOZnCl + Cl^-$$
$$\qquad\quad | \quad\; | \qquad\qquad\qquad\qquad |$$
$$\qquad\quad CH_3 \; H \qquad\qquad\qquad\quad CH_3$$

displacement by Cl⁻   *the product*

C. $S_N 1$ *or* $S_N 2$?

It has been observed that secondary alcohols and tertiary alcohols sometimes undergo rearrangement when treated with HX. Most primary alcohols do not. The conclusion is that secondary and tertiary alcohols undergo reaction with hydrogen halides by the S_N1 path (through a carbocation), while primary alcohols undergo reaction by an S_N2 path (backside displacement).

Methyl and primary alcohols, S_N2:

$$CH_3CH_2OH \xrightleftharpoons{H^+} CH_3CH_2-\overset{+}{O}H_2 \xrightarrow{X^-}$$

protonated

$$\left[\overset{\delta-}{X} ---CH_2--- \overset{\delta+}{\underset{\underset{CH_3}{|}}{O}}H_2 \right] \longrightarrow \underset{\underset{CH_3}{|}}{X-CH_2} + H_2O$$

S_N2 *transition state*

Other alcohols, S_N1:

$$(CH_3)_2CHOH \xrightleftharpoons{H^+} (CH_3)_2CH-\overset{+}{O}H_2 \xrightleftharpoons{-H_2O} [(CH_3)_2\overset{+}{CH}] \xrightarrow{X^-} (CH_3)_2CHX$$

protonated   *carbocation intermediate*

Because of the possibility of rearrangements with secondary alcohols, the reaction of ROH + HX is most useful with primary and tertiary alcohols.

Sample Problem

The only alkyl halide formed in the reaction of 3-methyl-2-butanol with HBr is a product of rearrangement. Give the structure of the product and show how it is formed.

Solution:

$$\underset{\underset{H}{|} \quad \underset{OH}{|}}{CH_3\overset{\overset{CH_3}{|}}{C}-CHCH_3} \xrightarrow[-H_2O]{H^+} \left[CH_3\overset{\overset{CH_3}{|}}{C}-\overset{+}{C}HCH_3 \right] \longrightarrow$$

a 2° carbocation

$$\left[CH_3\overset{\overset{CH_3}{|}}{\underset{+}{C}}-CH_2CH_3 \right] \xrightarrow{Br^-} CH_3\overset{\overset{CH_3}{|}}{\underset{\underset{Br}{|}}{C}}-CH_2CH_3$$

a 3° carbocation   2-bromo-2-methylbutane

Section 7.9

Other Reagents Used to Convert Alcohols to Alkyl Halides

Other halogenating reagents, such as PX_3, $SOCl_2$, and PX_5, can be used to convert alcohols to alkyl halides without rearrangement. We will discuss only two of these reagents, phosphorus trichloride and thionyl chloride.

Both these reagents undergo reaction with alcohols to form inorganic esters, a topic that will be discussed in Section 7.16. What is germane to the present discussion is that the resulting inorganic ester groups, like $-OH_2^+$, are *good leaving groups.* The following reactions are excellent for the preparation of alkyl chlorides from alcohols.

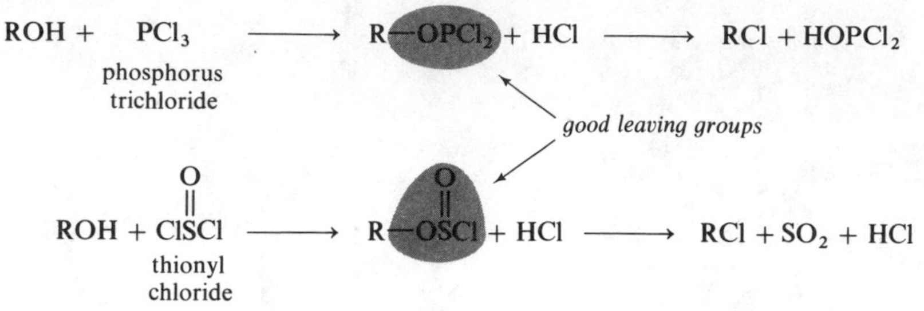

$$ROH + PCl_3 \longrightarrow R\text{—}OPCl_2 + HCl \longrightarrow RCl + HOPCl_2$$

phosphorus
trichloride

good leaving groups

$$ROH + ClSCl \longrightarrow R\text{—}OSCl + HCl \longrightarrow RCl + SO_2 + HCl$$

thionyl
chloride

Phosphorus trichloride first undergoes reaction with an alcohol to yield a phosphite ester and HCl. This initial reaction step does not involve cleavage of the C—O bond. No racemization of a pure enantiomeric alcohol is observed, as would happen if the reaction went through a carbocation. Of course, if the starting alcohol is either achiral or racemic, so is the product.

Step 1:

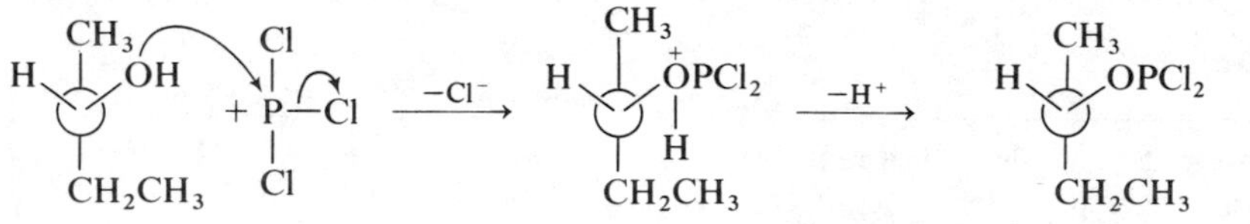

(S)-2-butanol

an (S)-chlorophosphite

The second step in the reaction is the S_N2 attack by Cl^-. As in any S_N2 reaction, inversion of configuration is observed if the starting material is a single enantiomer.

Step 2:

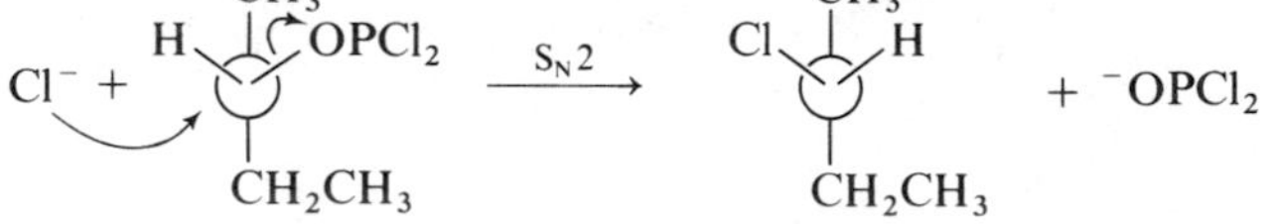

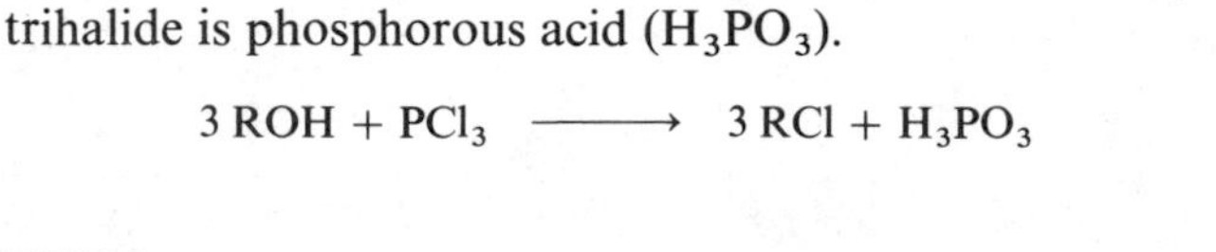

(R)-2-chlorobutane
(*inverted*)

Each of the three P—Cl bonds can undergo reaction; the end product of the phosphorus trihalide is phosphorous acid (H_3PO_3).

$$3\,ROH + PCl_3 \longrightarrow 3\,RCl + H_3PO_3$$

STUDY PROBLEM

7.9   Would you expect deuterium and chlorine to be *cis* or *trans* in the product of the following reaction?

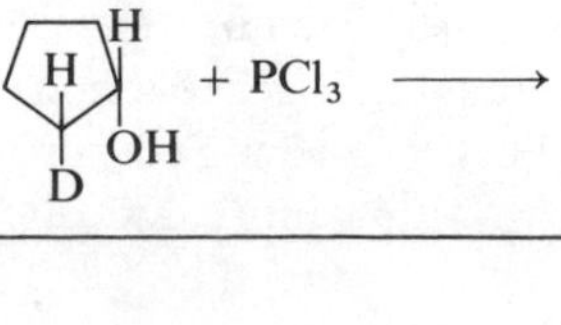

The first step in the reaction sequence of an alcohol with **thionyl chloride** is analogous to that of the reaction with phosphorus trichloride—the formation of an inorganic ester. Again, the C—O bond is not broken in this first step. If the starting alcohol is a pure enantiomer, the chlorosulfite has the same configuration as the alcohol.

Step 1:

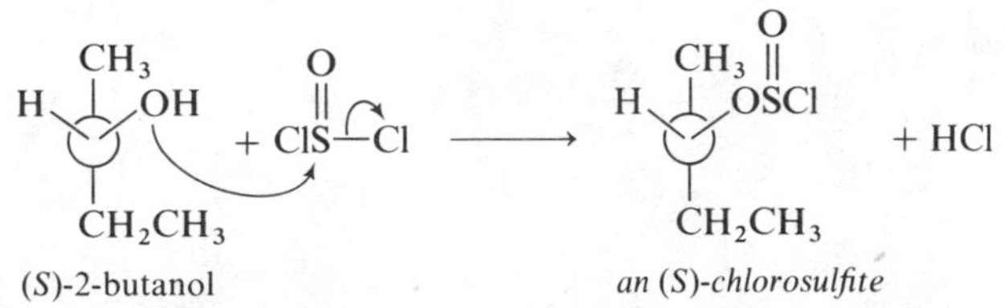

(S)-2-butanol   *an (S)-chlorosulfite*

The pathway for Step 2 depends on the solvent. Generally, amines or ethers are used as solvents. If an amine is used, Cl^- attacks by an S_N2 path. The configuration of the product alkyl halide is inverted compared to the configuration of the starting alcohol.

Step 2 in an amine solvent, an $S_N 2$ reaction:

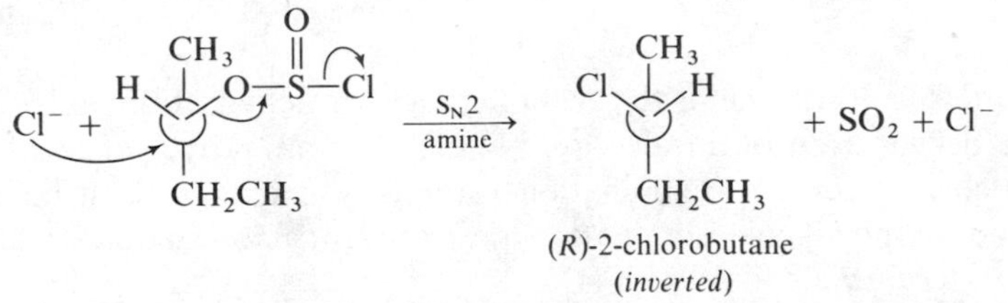

(R)-2-chlorobutane
(*inverted*)

On the other hand, if diethyl ether is the solvent, inversion is not observed. The product from the reaction of (S)-2-butanol is (S)-2-chlorobutane. We say that the reaction with $SOCl_2$ in ether proceeds with **retention of configuration**. How does a product retain the same configuration as the reactant? The reason in this case is that an **ion-pair** is formed and never completely dissociates. The Cl^- then forms a bond on the same side of the molecule. This type of reaction is called an **$S_N i$ reaction**, where "i" stands for *internal return*.

Step 2 in an ether solvent, an $S_N i$ reaction:

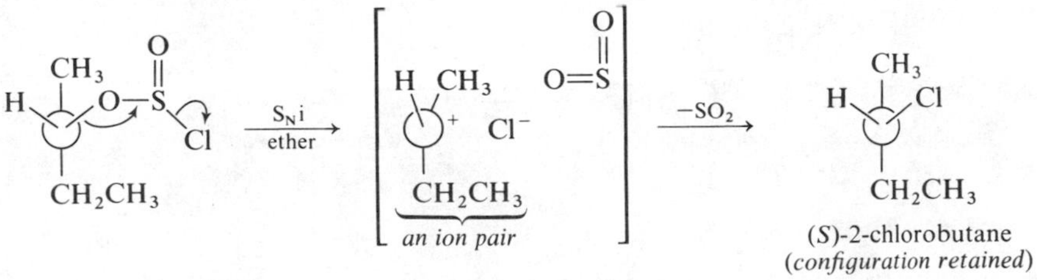

an ion pair   (S)-2-chlorobutane
(*configuration retained*)

STUDY PROBLEM

7.10 List three reagents that could be used to prepare 2-chlorooctane from (R)-2-octanol. Tell whether each would lead to *racemization, inversion, or retention of configuration.*

Section 7.10

Elimination Reactions of Alcohols

Alcohols, like alkyl halides, undergo elimination reactions to yield alkenes. Because the elements of water are lost in the elimination, this reaction is called a **dehydration reaction**.

$$(CH_3)_3COH \xrightarrow[60°]{\text{conc. } H_2SO_4} (CH_3)_2C{=}CH_2 + H_2O$$

t-butyl alcohol   methylpropene
a 3° alcohol

$$(CH_3)_2CHOH \xrightarrow[100°]{\text{conc. } H_2SO_4} CH_3CH{=}CH_2 + H_2O$$

2-propanol   propene
a 2° alcohol

$$CH_3CH_2OH \xrightarrow[180°]{\text{conc. } H_2SO_4} CH_2{=}CH_2 + H_2O$$

ethanol   ethylene
a 1° alcohol

Although sulfuric acid is the acid of choice for dehydration, any strong acid can cause dehydration of an alcohol. Note the comparative ease with which a tertiary alcohol undergoes elimination—simply warming it with concentrated H_2SO_4 leads to the alkene. Elimination is a prevalent side reaction in substitution reactions of tertiary alcohols with HX.

1° ROH   2° ROH   3° ROH

increasing ease of dehydration

For secondary and tertiary alcohols, dehydration follows an E1 path. The hydroxyl group is protonated, a carbocation is formed, and then a proton is eliminated to yield the alkene.

Step 1 (slow):

$$CH_3{-}\overset{\overset{\displaystyle {}^+OH_2}{|}}{CH}{-}CH_3 \underset{}{\overset{-H_2O}{\rightleftharpoons}} [CH_3{-}\overset{+}{CH}{-}CH_3]$$

protonated   *a carbocation*

Step 2 (fast):

$$\left[CH_3{-}\overset{+}{CH}{-}\overset{\overset{\displaystyle H}{\frown}}{CH_2} \right] \xrightarrow{-H^+} CH_3CH{=}CH_2$$

If there is a possibility of more than one alkene forming, the alcohol yields the *more substituted, more stable alkene* (Saytseff rule). The more stable alkene is formed because the transition state of Step 2 has double-bond character, just as in dehydrohalogenation E1 reactions (Section 5.9B).

$$\underset{\substack{| \\ \text{2-butanol}}}{CH_3CH_2\overset{\displaystyle OH}{\overset{|}{C}}HCH_3} \xrightarrow{H_2SO_4} \underset{\substack{\text{2-butene} \\ \textit{major product}}}{CH_3CH{=}CHCH_3} \quad \text{and very little} \quad \underset{\text{1-butene}}{CH_3CH_2CH{=}CH_2}$$

STUDY PROBLEM

7.11 Would you expect to find *cis-* or *trans-*2-butene as the predominant product in the preceding reaction? (*Hint*: see Section 5.9C.)

In any elimination reaction in which the double bond can be in *conjugation with a benzene ring*, the conjugated product is formed in preference to the non-conjugated product. The conjugated alkene is of lower energy, as is the transition state leading to its formation. In fact, it is often difficult to isolate alcohols in which the hydroxyl group is one or two carbons away from a benzene ring; dehydration is usually spontaneous.

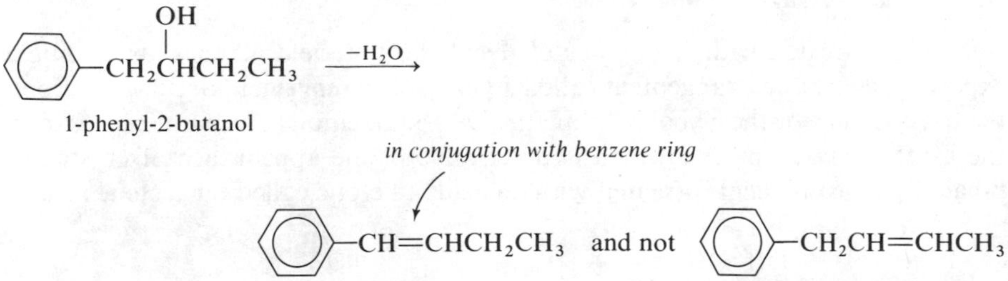

in conjugation with benzene ring

Since dehydration reactions of secondary and tertiary alcohols involve intermediate carbocations, rearrangements may occur. Also, dehydration reactions of primary alcohols are very slow. For these reasons, dehydration of an alcohol is not usually the best method for preparing an alkene. It is generally preferable to convert the alcohol to the alkyl halide and subject the alkyl halide to E2 elimination.

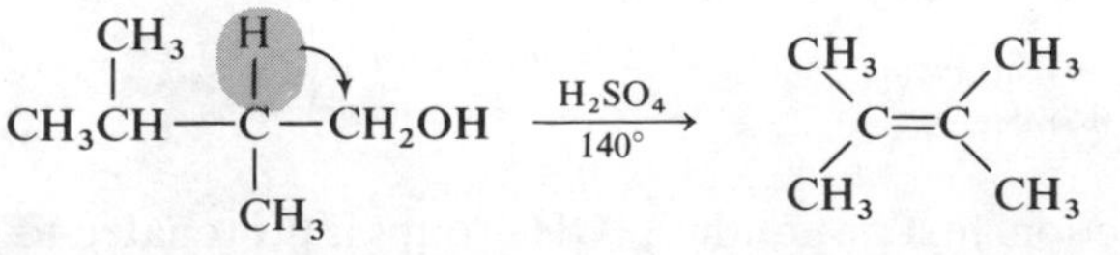

Rearrangements:

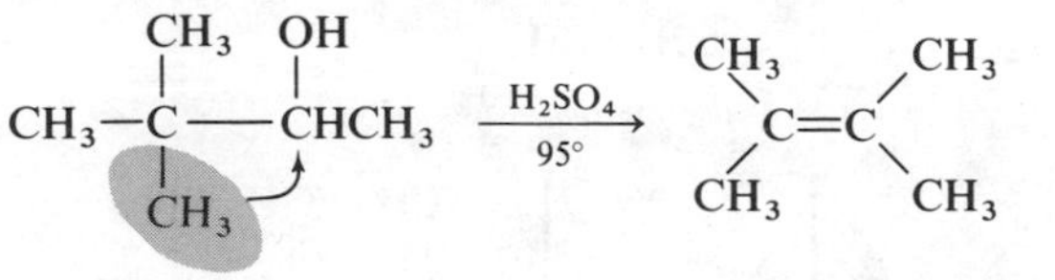

Sample Problem

Predict the major products of dehydration of (a) 2-pentanol and (b) neopentyl alcohol (2,2-dimethyl-1-propanol). (*Hint*: Neopentyl alcohol undergoes rearrangement when treated with H_2SO_4.)

Solution:

(a)
$$\underset{\substack{|\\OH}}{CH_3CH_2CH_2CHCH_3} \xrightarrow{-H_2O} \underset{\substack{trans\text{-2-pentene}\\more\ stable\ alkene}}{CH_3CH_2CH=CHCH_3}$$

(b)
$$\underset{\substack{|\\CH_3}}{(CH_3)_2C-CH_2-\overset{+}{O}H_2} \xrightarrow{-H_2O} \left[\underset{\substack{|\\CH_3}}{(CH_3)_2\overset{+}{C}-CH_2}\right] \xrightarrow{-H^+} \underset{\substack{2\text{-methyl-2-butene}\\more\ stable\ alkene}}{(CH_3)_2C=CHCH_3}$$

$$\text{rearranged}$$

A.   Pinacol Rearrangement

When treated with strong acids, glycols do not yield alkenes, as we might expect. Instead, a rearrangement called a **pinacol rearrangement** occurs. **Pinacol** is the trivial name for the glycol 2,3-dimethyl-2,3-butanediol. (The name comes from the Greek *pinox*, "plate," which is descriptive of the appearance of crystalline pinacol.) When pinacol is treated with an acid, a ketone called **pinacolone** results.

$$\underset{\substack{2,3\text{-dimethyl-2,3-butanediol}\\(pinacol)}}{\underset{\substack{|\quad\ \ |\\OH\ \ OH}}{(CH_3)_2C-C(CH_3)_2}} \xrightarrow{H^+} \underset{\substack{3,3\text{-dimethyl-2-butanone}\\(pinacolone)}}{\underset{\substack{\|\\O}}{(CH_3)_3CCCH_3}} + H_2O$$

This reaction is another example of a carbocation rearrangement.

$$\underset{\text{pinacol}}{\underset{\substack{|\quad\ \ |\\CH_3\ \ CH_3}}{\underset{\substack{|\quad\ \ |\\OH\ \ OH}}{CH_3C-CCH_3}}} \underset{H^+}{\rightleftharpoons} \underset{\text{protonated}}{\underset{\substack{|\quad\ \ |\\CH_3\ \ CH_3}}{\underset{\substack{|\quad\ \ |\\{}^+OH_2\ \ OH}}{CH_3C-CCH_3}}} \xrightarrow{-H_2O}$$

$$\underset{\substack{carbocation\ rearranging\\(less\ stable)}}{\left[\underset{\substack{|\quad\ \ |\\CH_3\ \ CH_3}}{\overset{\substack{:\ddot{O}H}}{CH_3\overset{+}{C}-CCH_3}}\right]} \longrightarrow \underset{\substack{a\ protonated\ ketone\\(more\ stable)}}{\left[\underset{\substack{|\\CH_3}}{\underset{\substack{\|\\CH_3\ \ {}^+OH}}{CH_3C-CCH_3}}\right]} \underset{-H^+}{\rightleftharpoons} \underset{\text{pinacolone}}{\underset{\substack{\|\\O}}{(CH_3)_3CCCH_3}}$$

In this reaction, first one of the —OH groups is protonated to yield —$OH_2{}^+$, which leaves as water. The resulting carbocation undergoes a 1,2-shift of a methyl group to yield a resonance-stabilized cation (the protonated ketone) that loses a proton to yield a ketone.

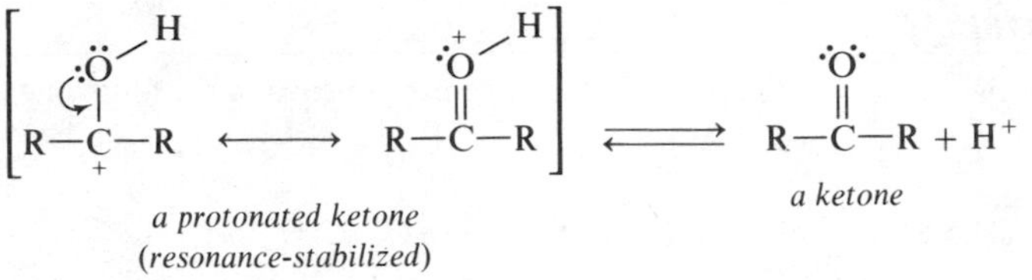

a protonated ketone
(resonance-stabilized)

a ketone

The term "pinacol rearrangement" is used to describe similar rearrangements of any 1,2-glycols, not just pinacol itself. The pinacol rearrangements of compounds containing a variety of groups have been studied to show which groups are most apt to migrate, or shift, in a rearrangement. We will consider one example. The first step in the pinacol rearrangement of 1-phenyl-1,2-propanediol is carbocation formation:

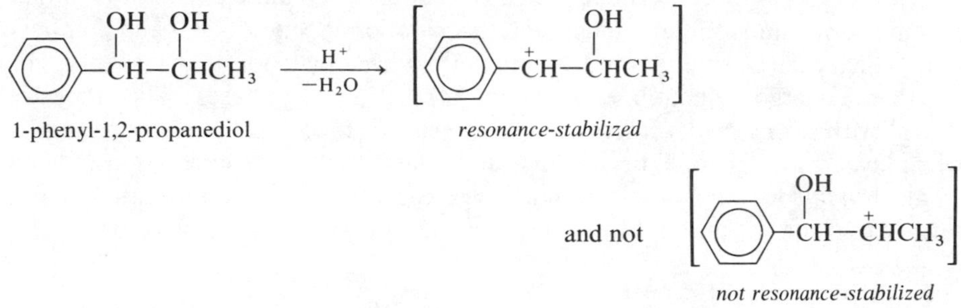

1-phenyl-1,2-propanediol

resonance-stabilized

and not

not resonance-stabilized

Which migrates, the H or the CH_3? We can tell by identifying the product:

If H migrates:

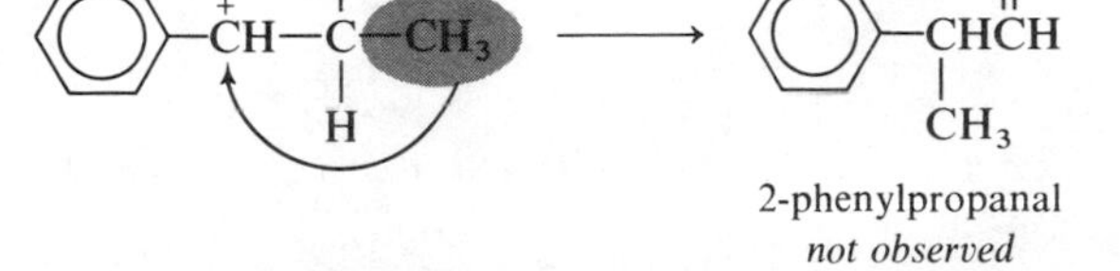

1-phenyl-2-propanone
observed product

If CH_3 migrates:

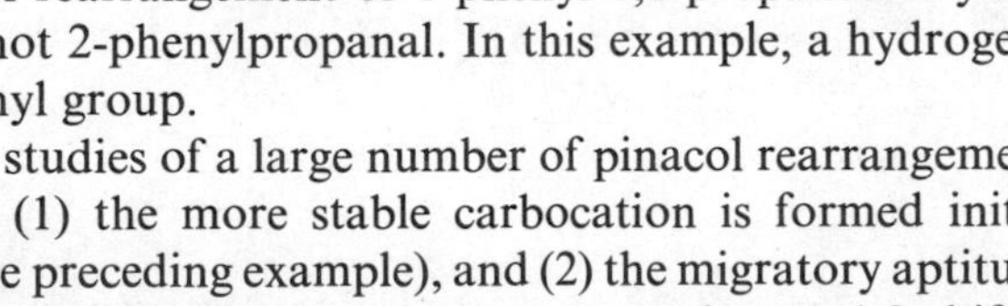

2-phenylpropanal
not observed

The pinacol rearrangement of 1-phenyl-1,2-propanediol yields 1-phenyl-2-propanone and not 2-phenylpropanal. In this example, a hydrogen has migrated instead of a methyl group.

From such studies of a large number of pinacol rearrangements, it has been determined that (1) the more stable carbocation is formed initially (a benzyl carbocation in the preceding example), and (2) the migratory aptitude is Ar > R— that is, when either an alkyl or an aryl group can undergo a 1,2-shift, the aryl group shifts rather than the alkyl group. It has also been found that hydrogen atoms are unpredictable in their migratory aptitudes. With some glycols, a hydrogen atom

Alcohols, Ethers, and Related Compounds

migrates in preference to an Ar or R group; with other glycols, an Ar or R group migrates in preference to H.

STUDY PROBLEM

7.12 Predict the product of the pinacol rearrangement of each of the following glycols:

$$\text{(a)} \quad (C_6H_5)_2\overset{\displaystyle OH}{\underset{\displaystyle |}{C}}CH_2OH \qquad \text{(b)} \quad C_6H_5-\overset{\displaystyle OH}{\underset{\displaystyle |}{\underset{\displaystyle CH_3}{C}}}-\overset{\displaystyle OH}{\underset{\displaystyle |}{\underset{\displaystyle CH_3}{C}}}-C_6H_5$$

Section 7.11

Substitution Reactions of Ethers

Ethers are quite nonreactive and behave more like alkanes than like functional organic compounds. Ethers undergo auto-oxidation (Section 6.9C) and combustion (which occurs readily), but they are not oxidized by laboratory reagents; nor do ethers undergo reduction, elimination, or reactions with bases. When they are heated with strong acids, ethers do undergo substitution reactions. For example, when heated with HI or HBr, an ether undergoes a substitution reaction to yield an alcohol and an alkyl halide. (Under these conditions, the alcohol can undergo further reaction with the HI or HBr to yield additional alkyl iodide or bromide.)

$$CH_3CH_2OCH_2CH_3 + HI \xrightarrow{\text{heat}} CH_3CH_2I + HOCH_2CH_3$$

diethyl ether ⟶ ethyl iodide ⟶ ethanol

$$\overset{\text{HI}}{\longrightarrow} CH_3CH_2I$$

Ether cleavage with HI or HBr proceeds by almost the same path as the reaction of an alcohol with HX: protonation of the oxygen, followed by S_N1 or S_N2 reaction. (Protonation is necessary because RO^- is a poor leaving group, while ROH, like H_2O, is easily displaced.)

$$CH_3CH_2-O-CH_2CH_3 \underset{}{\overset{H^+}{\rightleftharpoons}} CH_3CH_2-\overset{\displaystyle H}{\overset{\displaystyle |}{\underset{+}{O}}}-CH_2CH_3 \xrightarrow{I^-}$$

protonated

$$\left[\overset{\delta-}{I}---\overset{\displaystyle CH_3}{\underset{\displaystyle |}{CH_2}}---\overset{\displaystyle H}{\underset{\delta+}{\underset{\displaystyle |}{O}}}-CH_2CH_3 \right] \longrightarrow CH_3CH_2I + HOCH_2CH_3$$

S_N2 *transition state*

An alkyl phenyl ether, such as anisole, yields the alkyl iodide and phenol (not iodobenzene) because the bond from the sp^2 carbon is stronger than the bond from the sp^3 carbon (Section 2.4F).

not cleaved

methyl phenyl ether (anisole) ⟶ phenol ⟶ methyl iodide

Give the steps for the cleavage of diisopropyl ether by HI (an S_N1 reaction).

Solution:

$$(CH_3)_2CH-O-CH(CH_3)_2 \xrightarrow{H^+} (CH_3)_2CH-\overset{\overset{\displaystyle H}{\displaystyle |_+}}{O}-CH(CH_3)_2 \underset{}{\overset{-HOCH(CH_3)_2}{\rightleftarrows}}$$

protonated

$$[(CH_3)_2\overset{+}{C}H] \xrightarrow{I^-} (CH_3)_2CHI$$

a carbocation

STUDY PROBLEM

7.13. The **Zeisel procedure** for estimating the number of methoxyl (CH_3O-) or ethoxyl (CH_3CH_2O-) groups in an alkyl aryl ether consists of ether cleavage with excess HI, followed by distillation of the volatile methyl or ethyl iodide from the reaction mixture. The amount of volatile iodide is determined by reaction with aqueous silver nitrate. Write the equations for the reactions that would occur in the determination of the methoxyl groups in 1,2,3-trimethoxybenzene:

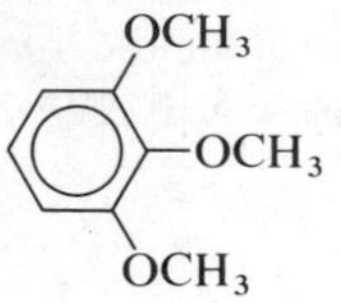

Substitution Reactions of Epoxides

Before we discuss the reactions of epoxides, let us consider a few aspects of the structure of an epoxide. An epoxide ring, like a cyclopropane ring, cannot have normal sp^3 bond angles of 109°; instead, the angles are 60°, a geometric requirement of the three-membered ring. The orbitals forming the ring bonds are incapable of maximum overlap; therefore, epoxide rings are strained. The polarity of the C—O bonds along with this ring strain contributes to the high reactivity of epoxides compared to the reactivity of other ethers.

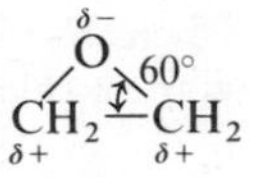

polar and strained

Because an epoxide is cyclic, a substituted epoxide may be capable of geometric isomerism.

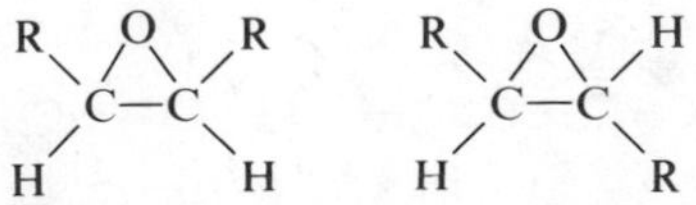

cis   *trans*

Epoxide rings may be part of fused-ring systems; in these cases, the epoxide must be *cis* on the other ring. (The required bond angles for the three-membered ring make the *trans*-configuration impossible.)

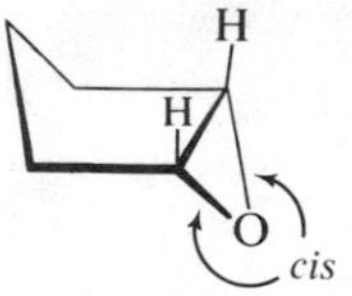

cyclopentene oxide
a fused-ring system

STUDY PROBLEM

7.14   Which of the following epoxides can exist as a pair of geometric isomers?

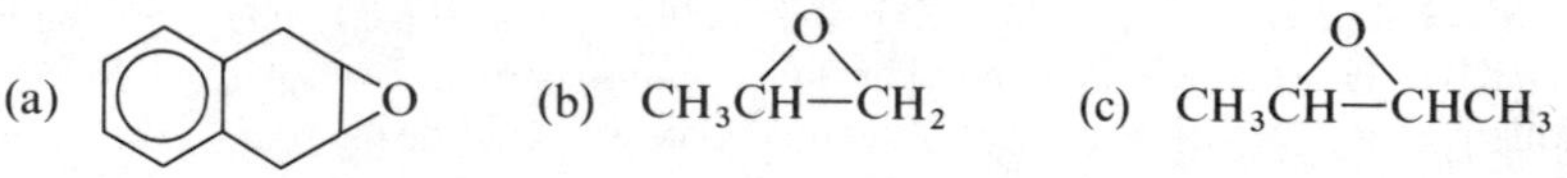

(a)   (b) $CH_3CH—CH_2$ (c) $CH_3CH—CHCH_3$

Opening of the strained three-membered ring results in a lower-energy, more stable product. The characteristic reaction of epoxides is ring opening, which can occur under either alkaline or acidic reaction conditions. These reactions of epoxides are referred to as **base-catalyzed** or **acid-catalyzed cleavage reactions**.

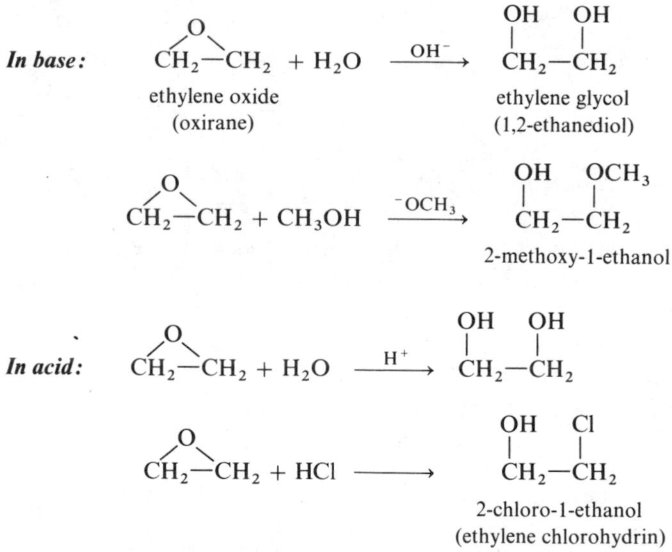

In base: $CH_2—CH_2 + H_2O$ $\xrightarrow{OH^-}$ $CH_2—CH_2$ (OH OH)

ethylene oxide
(oxirane)

ethylene glycol
(1,2-ethanediol)

$CH_2—CH_2 + CH_3OH$ $\xrightarrow{^-OCH_3}$ $CH_2—CH_2$ (OH OCH$_3$)

2-methoxy-1-ethanol

In acid: $CH_2—CH_2 + H_2O$ $\xrightarrow{H^+}$ $CH_2—CH_2$ (OH OH)

$CH_2—CH_2 + HCl$ $\longrightarrow$ $CH_2—CH_2$ (OH Cl)

2-chloro-1-ethanol
(ethylene chlorohydrin)

There is good stereochemical evidence that both base- and acid-catalyzed cleavages proceed through S_N2 mechanisms—that is, backside attack on one of the epoxide carbon atoms.

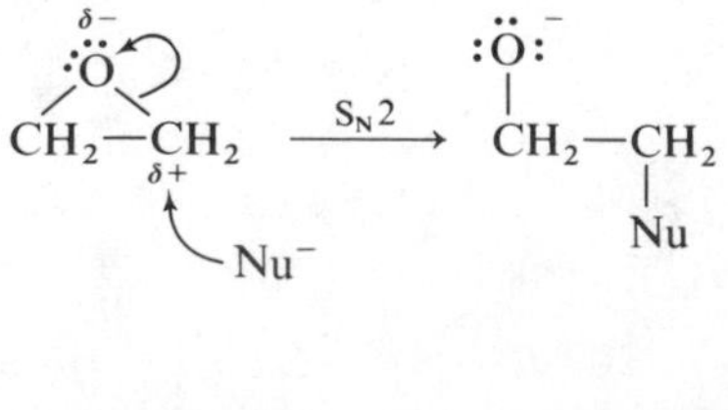

$CH_2—CH_2$ $\xrightarrow{S_N2}$ $CH_2—CH_2$
Nu^- Nu

A. Base-Catalyzed Cleavage

Epoxides undergo S_N2 attack by nucleophiles such as the hydroxide ion or alkoxides. The steps in the reactions of ethylene oxide with hydroxide ion (NaOH or KOH in water) and methoxide ion ($NaOCH_3$ in methanol) follow:

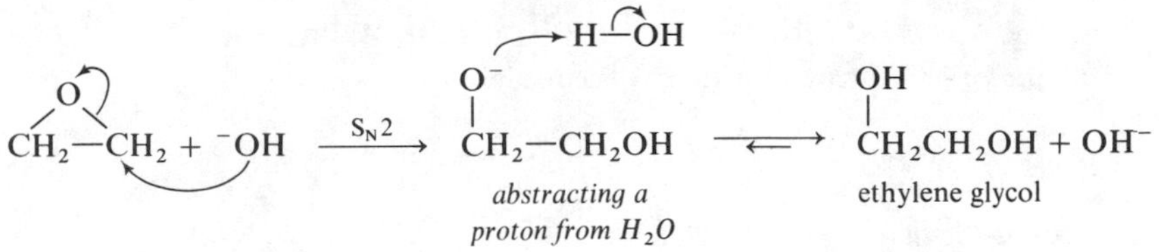

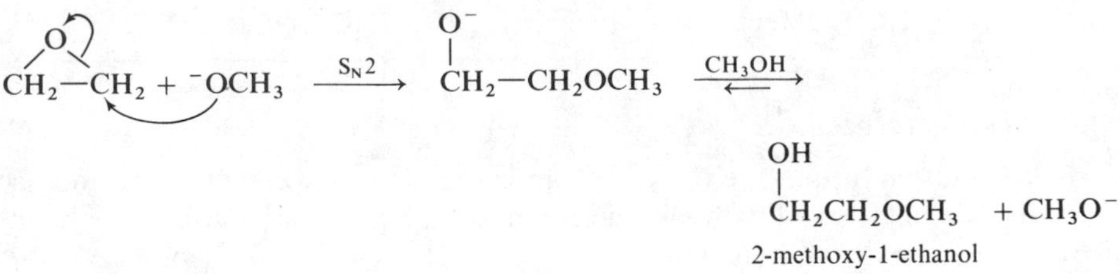

$$CH_2-CH_2 + {}^-OH \xrightarrow{S_N2} \underset{\text{abstracting a}}{\underset{\text{proton from } H_2O}{CH_2-CH_2OH}} \rightleftharpoons \underset{\text{ethylene glycol}}{CH_2CH_2OH} + OH^-$$

$$CH_2-CH_2 + {}^-OCH_3 \xrightarrow{S_N2} CH_2-CH_2OCH_3 \xrightarrow{CH_3OH}$$

$$\underset{\text{2-methoxy-1-ethanol}}{CH_2CH_2OCH_3} + CH_3O^-$$

In base-catalyzed cleavage, the nucleophile attacks the *less hindered carbon*, just as we would expect from an S_N2 attack ($1° > 2° > 3°$).

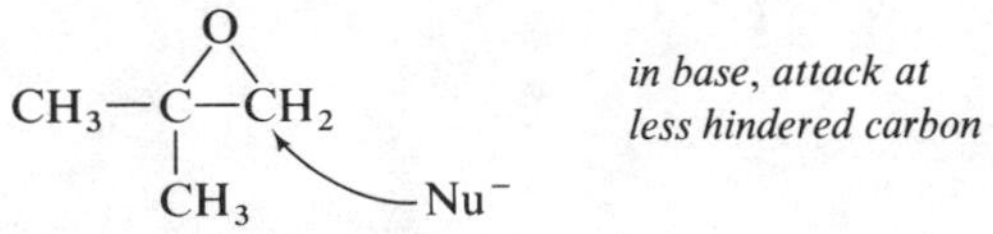

in base, attack at less hindered carbon

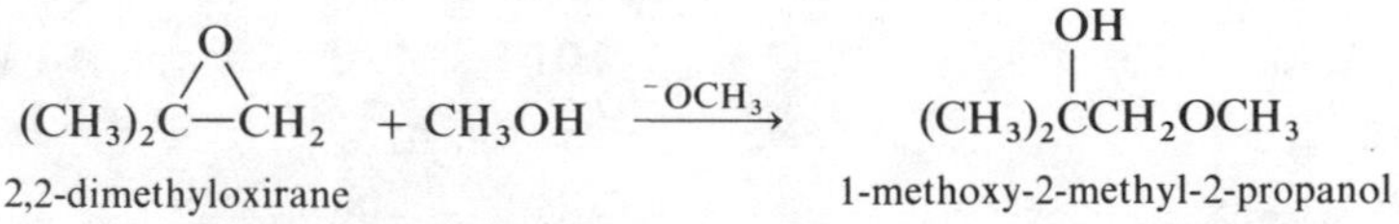

$$\underset{\text{2,2-dimethyloxirane}}{(CH_3)_2C-CH_2} + CH_3OH \xrightarrow{{}^-OCH_3} \underset{\text{1-methoxy-2-methyl-2-propanol}}{(CH_3)_2CCH_2OCH_3}$$

A Grignard reagent contains a partially negative carbon atom and attacks an epoxide ring in the same manner as other nucleophiles. The product is the magnesium salt of an alcohol; the alcohol may be obtained by hydrolysis. The reaction of a Grignard reagent with ethylene oxide is a method by which the hydrocarbon chain of the Grignard reagent may be *extended by two carbons*.

From methylmagnesium iodide to 1-propanol:

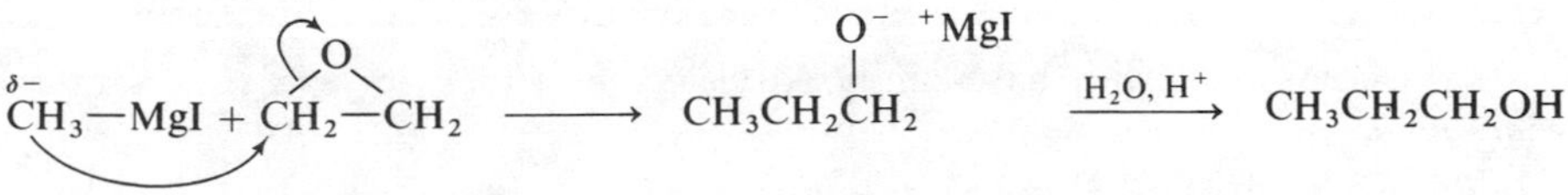

$$\overset{\delta-}{CH_3}-MgI + CH_2-CH_2 \longrightarrow \underset{}{CH_3CH_2CH_2}\overset{O^- \, ^+MgI}{} \xrightarrow{H_2O, \, H^+} CH_3CH_2CH_2OH$$

From cyclohexylmagnesium bromide to 2-cyclohexyl-1-ethanol:

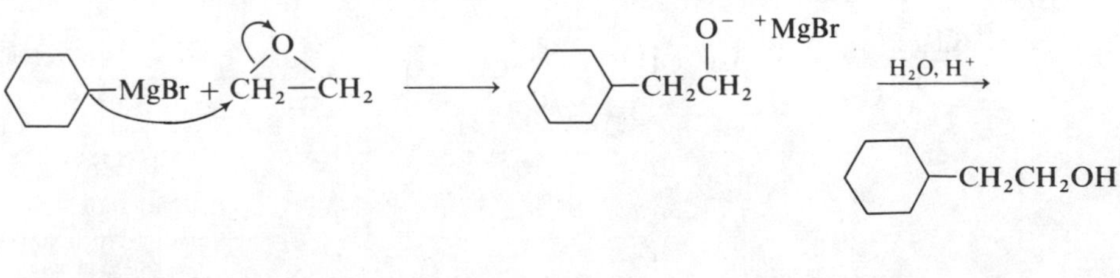

Sample Problem

Suggest a synthesis for 2-phenyl-1-ethanol starting with bromobenzene.

Solution:

(1) Convert bromobenzene to a Grignard reagent.

$$C_6H_5Br + Mg \xrightarrow{\text{ether}} C_6H_5MgBr$$

(2) Treat the Grignard reagent with ethylene oxide.

$$C_6H_5MgBr + CH_2-CH_2 \quad (\text{epoxide O}) \longrightarrow C_6H_5CH_2CH_2OMgBr$$

(3) Hydrolyze the magnesium alkoxide.

$$C_6H_5CH_2CH_2OMgBr + H_2O \xrightarrow{\text{H}^+} C_6H_5CH_2CH_2OH + HOMgBr$$

B. Acid-Catalyzed Cleavage

In acidic solution, the oxygen of an epoxide is protonated. A protonated epoxide can be attacked by weak nucleophiles such as water, alcohols, or halide ions.

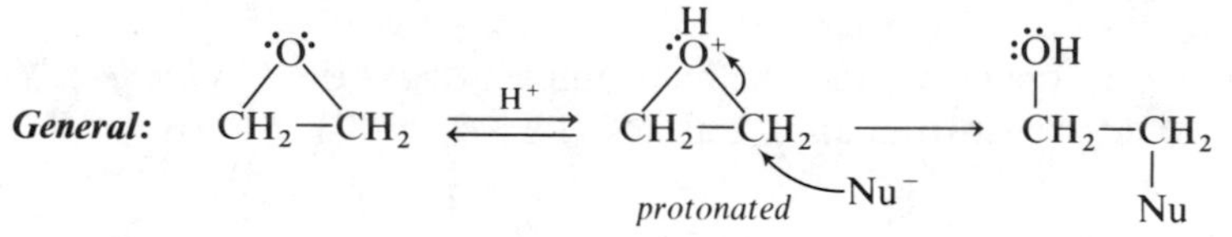

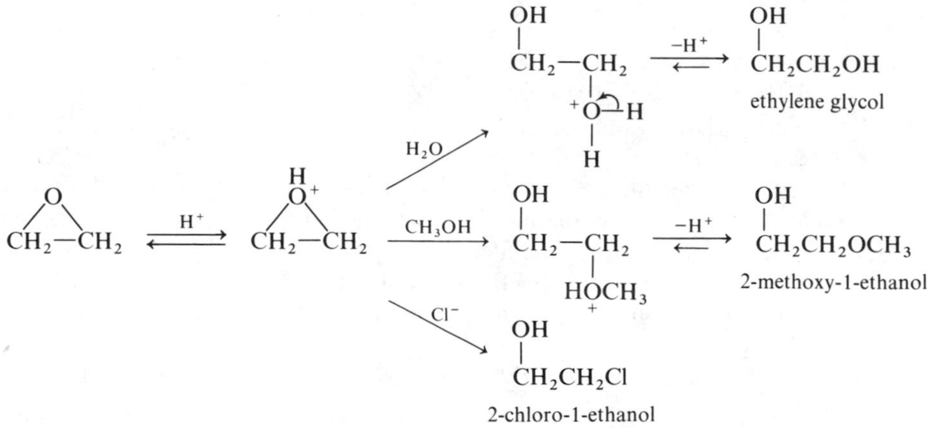

General:

$$CH_2-CH_2 \text{ (O)} \rightleftharpoons CH_2-CH_2 \text{ (O}^+\text{H)} \xrightarrow{\quad} CH_2-CH_2 \text{ (ÖH / Nu)}$$
protonated $-Nu^-$

$$CH_2-CH_2 \text{ (O)} \xrightarrow{H^+} CH_2-CH_2 \text{ (O}^+\text{)}$$
2,2-dimethyloxirane section reactions

ethylene glycol

2-methoxy-1-ethanol

2-chloro-1-ethanol

As contrasted with base-catalyzed cleavage, attack in acid occurs at the *more hindered carbon*.

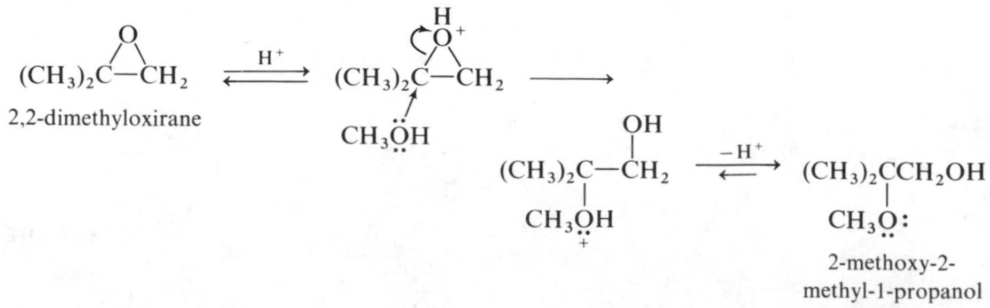

$$(CH_3)_2C-CH_2 \text{ (O)} \xrightarrow{H^+} (CH_3)_2C-CH_2 \text{ (O}^+\text{H)} \longrightarrow$$
2,2-dimethyloxirane

$$CH_3\ddot{O}H$$

$$(CH_3)_2C-CH_2 \text{ (OH / CH}_3\overset{+}{O}H\text{)} \xrightarrow{-H^+} (CH_3)_2CCH_2OH \text{ (CH}_3\ddot{O}:\text{)}$$

2-methoxy-2-methyl-1-propanol

We must conclude that the protonated epoxide has a fair amount of carbocation character. If this is the case, there is a partial positive charge on the carbon with the greater number of alkyl groups (carbocation stability: 3° > 2° > 1°). The subsequent nucleophilic attack is favored at the more positive carbon even though this carbon is more hindered.

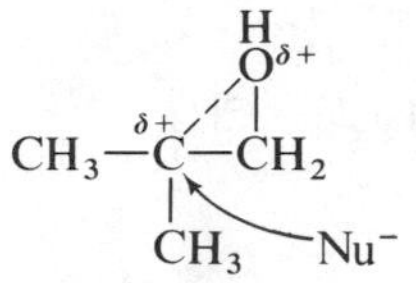
H
O δ+
δ+
CH3—C—CH2
CH3
Nu⁻

In acid, attack occurs at the more hindered carbon because it has a greater + charge.

How do we know that a true carbocation is not formed? When the product of an epoxide-cleavage reaction is capable of geometric isomerism, only the *trans*-product is observed. If the reaction went through a true carbocation intermediate, we would observe both *cis*- and *trans*-products.

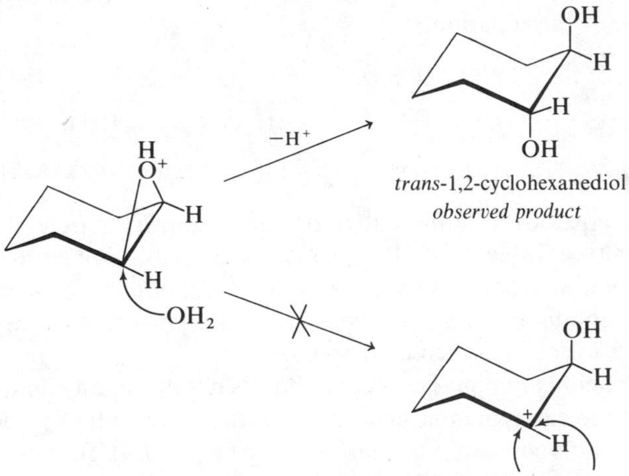
OH
H
H
OH
−H⁺
H
O⁺
H
H
OH2
trans-1,2-cyclohexanediol
observed product
OH
H
+
H

attack from either side would give both cis and trans, which does not occur

Sample Problem

Predict the products:

(a) 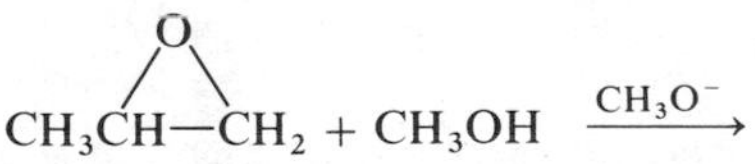
O
CH3CH—CH2 + CH3OH
CH3O⁻

(b) 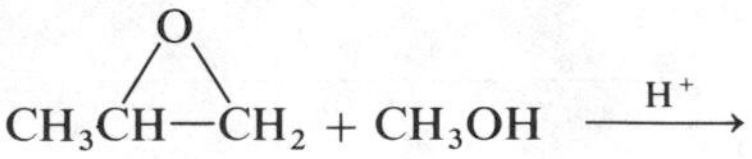
O
CH3CH—CH2 + CH3OH
H⁺

Solution:

(a) In base, attack occurs at the less hindered carbon: 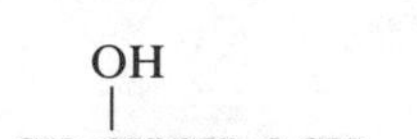
OH
CH3CHCH2OCH3.

(b) In acid, attack occurs at the more hindered carbon: 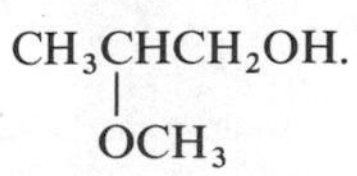
CH3CHCH2OH.
OCH3

STUDY PROBLEMS

7.15   What are the products of the reactions of cyclopentene oxide with   (a) methanol and a trace of H_2SO_4, and   (b) sodium methoxide in methanol?

7.16   What are the products from the reactions of the following epoxide with the reagents in Problem 7.15?

$$CH_3CH_2CH_2\overset{\displaystyle O}{\overset{\displaystyle \diagup\!\diagdown}{CH-CH_2}}$$

Section 7.13

Alcohols as Acids

As we have mentioned, an alcohol can lose its hydroxyl proton to form RO^-. This reaction is analogous to the loss of H^+ from water to form OH^-. Like water, alcohols are very weak acids; the equilibrium for the ionization reaction lies on the nonionized side of the equation.

Water: $\qquad HO{-}H + H_2O \quad \underset{\longleftarrow}{\overset{\longrightarrow}{}} \quad HO^- + H_3O^+$

Methanol: $\qquad CH_3O{-}H + CH_3OH \quad \underset{\longleftarrow}{\overset{\longrightarrow}{}} \quad CH_3O^- + CH_3\overset{+}{O}H_2$

Methanol in H_2O: $CH_3O{-}H + H_2O \quad \underset{\longleftarrow}{\overset{\longrightarrow}{}} \quad CH_3O^- + H_3O^+$

In dilute aqueous solution, alcohols have approximately the same pK_a values as water (see Table 7.5). However, in their pure liquid state (no water), alcohols are much weaker acids than water. The pK_a of pure methanol is around 17, and other alcohols are even weaker acids. For comparison, the pK_a value for pure water is 15.7 (not 14, which is the pK_w).

The lower acidity of nonaqueous alcohols is not due to any unique structural inability of RO^- to carry an ionic charge, but rather is a result of the low dielectric constants of alcohols compared to that of water (Table 7.4). Because they are less polar, alcohols are less able to support ions in solution than are water molecules.

Table 7.5.   **pK_a Values for Water and Some Alcohols in Dilute Aqueous Solution**

Compound	pK_a
H_2O	15.7
CH_3OH	15.5
CH_3CH_2OH	15.9
$(CH_3)_3COH$	~ 18

Section 7.14

Alkoxides

An **alkoxide** is the salt of an alcohol. (The name is analogous to *hydroxide*.)

$CH_3O^-\ Na^+ \qquad CH_3CH_2O^-\ K^+ \qquad (CH_3)_2CHO^-\ Na^+$

sodium methoxide   potassium ethoxide   sodium isopropoxide

To prepare an alkoxide from an alcohol, a base stronger than the alkoxide itself is required. Sodamide ($NaNH_2$) and Grignard reagents are strong enough bases to abstract a hydrogen ion from an alcohol.

$$ROH + NaNH_2 \longrightarrow RO^- \ Na^+ + NH_3$$

$$ROH + R'MgX \longrightarrow RO^- \ ^+MgX + R'H$$

The most convenient method for the preparation of alkoxides is the treatment of an alcohol with an alkali metal such as sodium or potassium. The reaction is not an acid–base reaction, but an oxidation–reduction reaction. The alkali metal is oxidized to a cation, and the hydrogen of the —OH group is reduced to hydrogen gas.

$$CH_3OH + Na \longrightarrow CH_3O^- \ Na^+ + \tfrac{1}{2}H_2\uparrow$$

$$CH_3CH_2OH + Na \longrightarrow CH_3CH_2O^- \ Na^+ + \tfrac{1}{2}H_2\uparrow$$

$$(CH_3)_3COH + K \longrightarrow (CH_3)_3CO^- \ K^+ + \tfrac{1}{2}H_2\uparrow$$

Methanol and ethanol undergo fairly vigorous reaction with sodium metal. As the size of the R group is increased, the vigor of the reaction decreases. Sodium and water react explosively; sodium and ethanol undergo reaction at a very controllable rate; and sodium and 1-butanol undergo a very sluggish reaction. With alcohols of four or more carbons, the more reactive potassium metal is generally used to prepare the alkoxide.

$$H_2O \quad CH_3OH \quad CH_3CH_2OH \quad CH_3CH_2CH_2OH$$
decreasing reactivity toward Na or K

Alkoxides are good nucleophiles. The use of these reagents for reaction with alkyl halides to yield ethers was discussed earlier in this chapter (Section 7.5). Larger alkoxides, such as potassium *t*-butoxide, are sufficiently hindered that substitution reactions are slow; however, they cause elimination reactions of alkyl halides readily. The high degree of hindrance of these alkoxides favors Hofmann elimination products (Section 5.10D).

Section 7.15

Esterification Reactions

Alcohols undergo reaction with carboxylic acids and carboxylic acid derivatives to yield *esters of carboxylic acids*. These reactions, called **esterification reactions**, and the product esters will be covered in detail in Chapters 12 and 13.

$$CH_3COOH + HOCH_2CH_3 \xrightleftharpoons{H^+, heat} CH_3COOCH_2CH_3 + H_2O$$

acetic acid   ethanol   ethyl acetate
a carboxylic acid   *an ester*

$$C_6H_5COOH + HOCH_2CH_2CH_3 \xrightleftharpoons{H^+, heat} C_6H_5COOCH_2CH_2CH_3 + H_2O$$

benzoic acid   1-propanol   propyl benzoate
a carboxylic·acid   *an ester*

STUDY PROBLEM

7.17　Predict the esterification product of each of the following reactions:

(a)　$CH_3CH_2CH_2CO_2H + CH_3OH \xrightleftharpoons{H^+, \text{ heat}}$

(b) 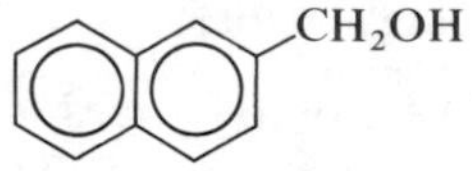　[naphthalene ring]$CH_2OH + CH_3CO_2H \xrightleftharpoons{H^+, \text{ heat}}$

Section 7.16

Inorganic Esters of Alcohols

Inorganic esters of alcohols are compounds prepared by the reaction of alcohols and either mineral acids (such as HNO_3 or H_2SO_4) or acid halides of mineral acids (such as $SOCl_2$).

$$
\begin{array}{l}
CH_2O\textcircled{H} \\
| \\
CHO\textcircled{H} \quad + \quad 3\,\textcircled{HO}NO_2 \\
| \\
CH_2O\textcircled{H}
\end{array}
\quad\longrightarrow\quad
\begin{array}{l}
CH_2ONO_2 \\
| \\
CHONO_2 \quad + 3\,H_2O \\
| \\
CH_2ONO_2
\end{array}
$$

glycerol　　　　nitric acid　　　　　　　　nitroglycerin
　　　　　　　　　　　　　　　　　　　　　an inorganic ester

$$
2\,CH_3O\textcircled{H} + \underset{\underset{O}{\|}}{\overset{\overset{O}{\|}}{\textcircled{HO}S\textcircled{OH}}} \longrightarrow \underset{\underset{O}{\|}}{\overset{\overset{O}{\|}}{CH_3OSOCH_3}} + 2\,H_2O
$$

methanol

　　　　　　　sulfuric acid　　　　　　dimethyl sulfate
　　　　　　　　　　　　　　　　　　　an inorganic ester

$$
CH_3CH_2O\textcircled{H} + \boxed{Cl}\overset{\overset{O}{\|}}{-}S-Cl \longrightarrow CH_3CH_2OSCl + HCl
$$

ethanol　　　　thionyl chloride　　　　ethyl chlorosulfite
　　　　　　　　　　　　　　　　　　　an inorganic ester

　　　In the preceding equations, the H and OH groups that are lost as water are circled. We usually think of a mineral acid as losing H^+, but in these reactions it loses OH^- (or Cl^- if the acid chloride is used).

A.　Nitrates

　　　To see how an inorganic ester of an alcohol is formed, let us consider the formation of an alkyl nitrate ($RONO_2$). (Do not confuse the alkyl nitrates with nitroalkanes, RNO_2, in which carbon is attached to the N.) A nitrate esterification proceeds by (1) an ionization reaction of HNO_3 to yield a nitronium ion ($^+NO_2$), followed by (2) attack on $^+NO_2$ by the alcohol oxygen. This second reaction is a typical Lewis acid–base reaction. Loss of a proton from the intermediate adduct yields the nitrate ester.

(1) Formation of NO_2^+ :

$$2 \text{ HO}-NO_2 \quad \rightleftharpoons \quad H_2\overset{+}{O}-NO_2 + NO_3^-$$

$$H_2\overset{+}{O}-NO_2 \quad \rightleftharpoons \quad H_2O + \overset{+}{N}O_2$$

(2) Formation of ester:

$$CH_3\ddot{\underset{H}{O}}: + \overset{+}{N}O_2 \quad \rightleftharpoons \quad CH_3\underset{H}{\overset{+}{O}}-NO_2 \quad \xrightarrow{-H^+} \quad CH_3ONO_2$$

methanol $\qquad\qquad$ *protonated* $\qquad\qquad$ methyl nitrate
$\qquad\qquad\qquad\qquad$ *nitrate*

STUDY PROBLEM

7.18 Give the steps in the formation of ethyl nitrite (CH_3CH_2ONO) from nitrous acid (HONO) and ethanol.

Nitric acid is a strong oxidizing agent, and oxidation of the alcohol (sometimes explosively) can accompany the formation of nitrate esters. The nitrate esters themselves (for example, nitroglycerin and PETN) are explosives. When detonated, these compounds undergo fast, intramolecular, oxidation–reduction reactions to yield large volumes of gases (N_2, CO_2, H_2O, O_2). Organic nitrates (such as nitroglycerin) and nitrites are also used as *vasodilators* (substances that dilate blood vessels) in the treatment of certain types of heart disease.

$$\begin{array}{c} CH_2ONO_2 \\ | \\ O_2NOCH_2CCH_2ONO_2 \\ | \\ CH_2ONO_2 \end{array}$$

pentaerythritol nitrate (PETN)
an explosive

B. Sulfates

The reaction of concentrated sulfuric acid with alcohols can lead to mono-alkyl or dialkyl sulfate esters. The monoesters are named as **alkyl hydrogen sulfates**, **alkylsulfuric acids**, or **alkyl bisulfates**; the three terms are synonymous. The names of the diesters are straightforward; the alkyl groups are named and the word **sulfate** is added. Alkyl hydrogen sulfates are strong acids, but dialkyl sulfates are not acidic.

$$\begin{array}{ccc} O & O & O \\ \| & \| & \| \\ CH_3OSOH & CH_3OSOCH_3 & CH_3OSOCH_2CH_3 \\ \| & \| & \| \\ O & O & O \end{array}$$

methyl hydrogen $\qquad$ dimethyl sulfate $\qquad$ methyl ethyl sulfate
sulfate

STUDY PROBLEM

7.19 Ethyl hydrogen sulfate is mixed with an equimolar amount of NaOH. What is the organic product?

Earlier in this chapter, we mentioned that the action of sulfuric acid on alcohols results in alkenes, and we also mentioned that diethyl ether is prepared by the reaction of ethanol and sulfuric acid. What actually happens when an alcohol is treated with concentrated sulfuric acid?

When an alcohol is mixed with H_2SO_4, a series of reversible reactions occurs. (The scheme that follows is simplified; alkenes can also go to sulfates, sulfates can go to ethers, etc.) Which reaction product predominates depends on the structure of the alcohol, the relative concentrations of reactants, and the temperature of the reaction mixture. In general, *primary alcohols* give sulfate esters at low temperatures, ethers at moderate temperatures, and alkenes at high temperatures. (In all cases, mixtures would be expected.) *Tertiary alcohols* and, to a large extent, *secondary alcohols* yield alkene products.

$$ROSO_2OH + ROSO_2OR + H_2O$$

$$\nearrow\!\!\!\!\swarrow \; 0°$$

$$1°: \quad ROH + H_2SO_4 \; \underset{\longleftarrow}{\overset{140°}{\longrightarrow}} \; ROR + H_2O$$

$$\searrow\!\!\!\!\nwarrow \; 170°$$

$$\text{alkenes} + H_2O$$

$$2° \text{ and } 3°: \quad ROH + H_2SO_4 \; \rightleftharpoons \; \text{alkenes} + H_2O$$

Dimethyl sulfate and diethyl sulfate are volatile and therefore can easily be isolated from a reaction mixture by distillation. The other alkyl sulfates are not so volatile; the high temperatures needed for distillation are sufficient to crack the sulfates and yield alkenes.

A more general method for preparing sulfates is by using one of the chlorides of sulfuric acid:

$$
\begin{array}{ccc}
\text{O} & \text{O} & \text{O} \\
\| & \| & \| \\
\text{HOSOH} & \text{HOSCl} & \text{ClSCl} \\
\| & \| & \| \\
\text{O} & \text{O} & \text{O} \\
\text{sulfuric acid} & \text{chlorosulfonic acid} & \text{sulfuryl chloride}
\end{array}
$$

$$
\begin{array}{c}
\quad\quad\quad\quad \text{O} \quad\quad\quad\quad\quad\quad\quad\quad \text{O} \\
\quad\quad\quad\quad \| \quad\quad\quad\quad\quad\quad\quad\quad \| \\
2\,CH_3OH + Cl{-}S{-}Cl \; \longrightarrow \; CH_3O{-}S{-}OCH_3 + 2\,HCl \\
\quad\quad\quad\quad \| \quad\quad\quad\quad\quad\quad\quad\quad \| \\
\quad\quad\quad\quad \text{O} \quad\quad\quad\quad\quad\quad\quad\quad \text{O} \\
\quad\quad\quad\quad\quad\quad\quad\quad\quad \text{dimethyl sulfate}
\end{array}
$$

An alkyl sulfate group is a good leaving group. Dimethyl sulfate, which is commercially available, is often used as an alkylating agent. The following examples show its use in preparing a methyl ester and a methyl ether.

$$\underset{\substack{\text{acetate ion}}}{CH_3\overset{\displaystyle O}{\overset{\|}{C}}O^- + CH_3\underset{\substack{\text{dimethyl sulfate}}}{-OSO_2OCH_3}} \longrightarrow \underset{\substack{\text{methyl acetate}\\ \textit{an ester}}}{CH_3\overset{\displaystyle O}{\overset{\|}{C}}OCH_3} + {}^-OSO_2OCH_3$$

$$\underset{\substack{\text{ethoxide ion}}}{CH_3CH_2O^- + CH_3-OSO_2OCH_3} \longrightarrow \underset{\substack{\text{methyl ethyl ether}\\ \textit{an ether}}}{CH_3CH_2OCH_3} + {}^-OSO_2OCH_3$$

C. Sulfonates

A **sulfonate** is an inorganic ester with the general formula RSO_2OR. (Do not confuse the sulfonate structure with the sulfate structure. A sulfonate has an alkyl or aryl group attached *directly to the sulfur atom.*)

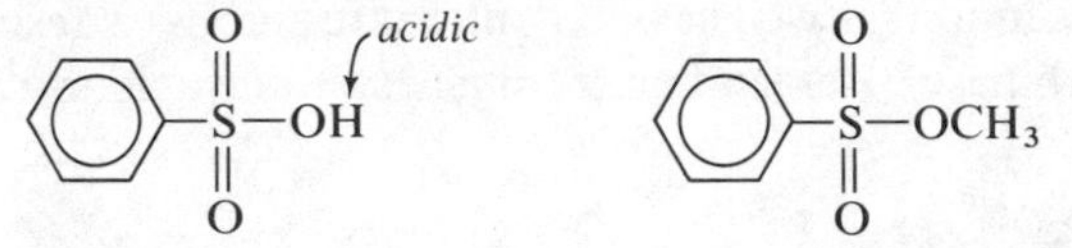

benzenesulfonic acid   methyl benzenesulfonate
a strong acid   *a sulfonate*

Sulfonates are the most widely used of the various sulfur derivatives of alcohols. They are often solids, a fact that simplifies their laboratory purification. In addition, a sulfonate group ($RSO_2O—$) is an excellent leaving group and can be displaced by a variety of nucleophiles. Conversion of an alcohol to a sulfonate, followed by nucleophilic displacement, provides an excellent synthetic avenue to a variety of products.

We will concentrate our attention on only one class of sulfonates—the *p*-toluenesulfonates (4-methylbenzenesulfonates), usually called **tosylates** and abbreviated ROTs.

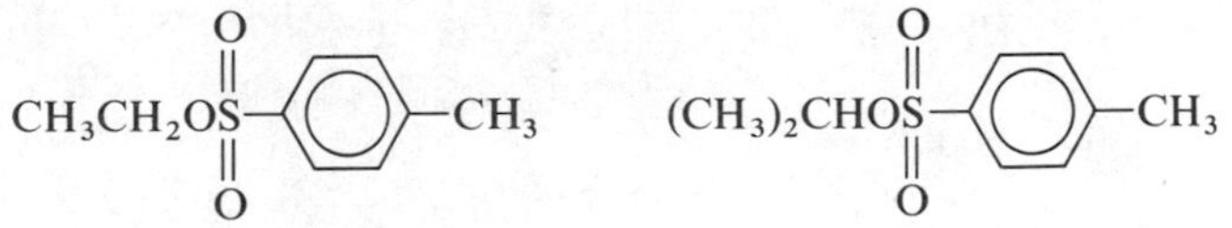

ethyl tosylate   isopropyl tosylate
CH_3CH_2OTs $(CH_3)_2CHOTs$

The tosylates are prepared by the reaction of an alcohol with *p*-toluene-sulfonyl chloride (tosyl chloride).

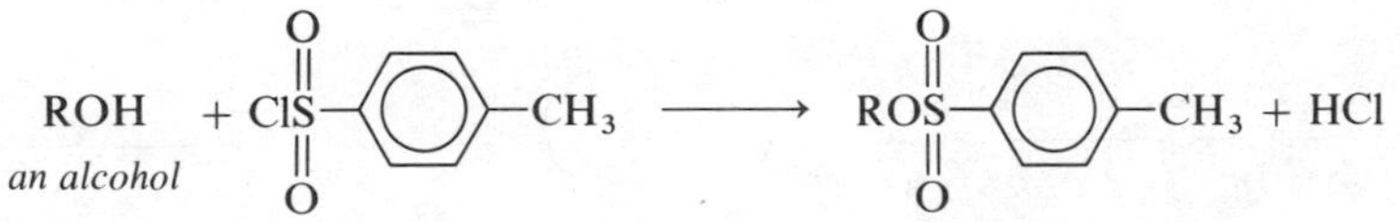

$\underset{\textit{an alcohol}}{ROH}$ + tosyl chloride $\longrightarrow$ an alkyl tosylate + HCl

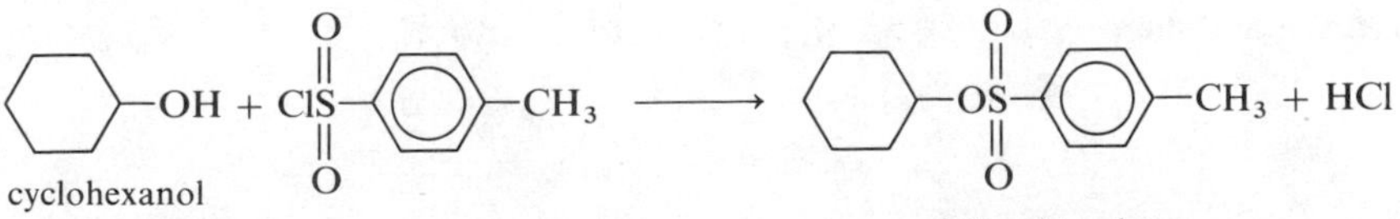

cyclohexanol   cyclohexyl tosylate

In the formation of the tosylate, the carbon–oxygen bond of the alcohol is not broken. If a tosylate is prepared using a single enantiomer of a chiral alcohol, the tosylate retains the configuration of the starting alcohol.

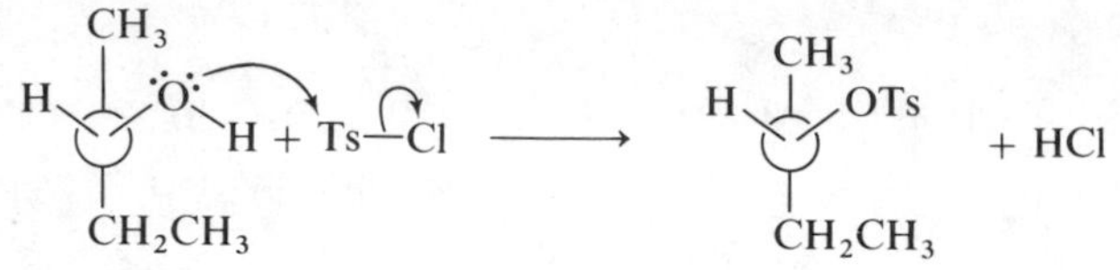

(S)-2-butanol   (S)-2-butyl tosylate

STUDY PROBLEM

7.20   How would you prepare   (a) dipropyl sulfate;   (b) propyl tosylate; and   (c) (R)-2-hexyl tosylate?

The tosylate anion (as well as other sulfonate anions) is resonance-stabilized, and is a very weak base. (Remember, *p*-toluenesulfonic acid is a strong acid.)

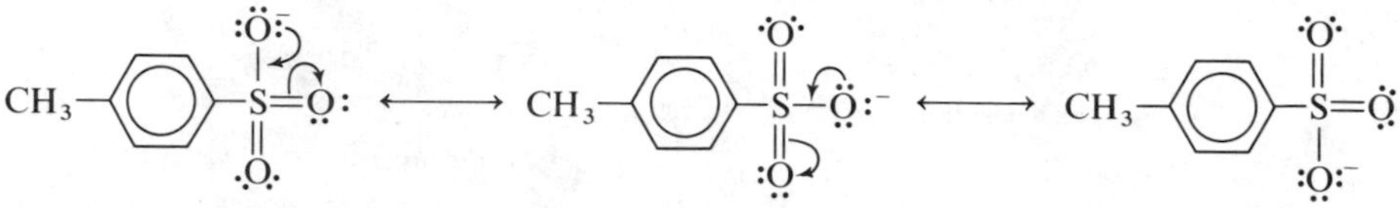

For this reason, the tosylate group is a far better leaving group than an —OH group. The tosylate group may be displaced in S_N2 reactions by such weak nucleophiles as halide ions or alcohols. (No acidic catalyst is necessary.)

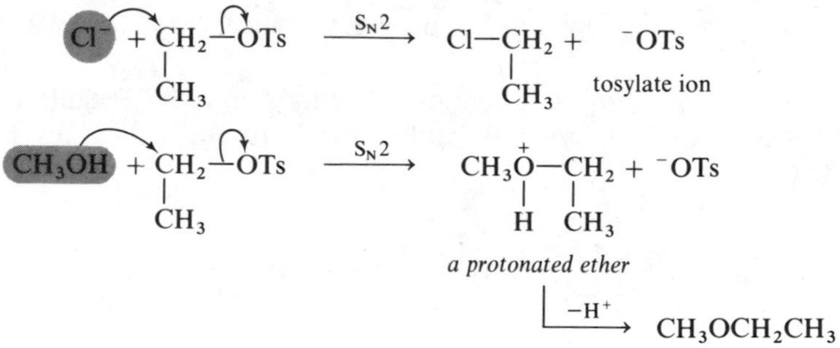

STUDY PROBLEMS

7.21   Give resonance structures for the methylsulfonate ion.

7.22   Predict the S_N2 product of the reaction of water with (R)-2-octyl tosylate.

Section 7.17

Oxidation of Alcohols

In inorganic chemistry, **oxidation** is defined as the *loss of electrons* by an atom, while **reduction** is the *gain of electrons* by an atom.

Oxidation: *Reduction:*

$$Na^0 \xrightarrow{-e^-} Na^+ \qquad\qquad Fe^{3+} \xrightarrow{+e^-} Fe^{2+}$$

$$Mg^0 \xrightarrow{-2e^-} Mg^{2+} \qquad\qquad Cu^{2+} \xrightarrow{+2e^-} Cu^0$$

In organic reactions, it is not always easy to determine whether a carbon atom gains or loses electrons. However, oxidation and reduction of organic compounds are common reactions. Good rules of thumb to determine if an organic compound has been oxidized or reduced follow.

If a molecule gains oxygen or loses hydrogen, it is oxidized:

$$CH_3CH_2OH \xrightarrow{\text{[O]}} CH_3CO_2H$$

$$\underset{CH_3\overset{\displaystyle OH}{\overset{|}{C}}HCH_3}{} \xrightarrow{\text{[O]}} \underset{CH_3\overset{\displaystyle O}{\overset{\|}{C}}CH_3}{}$$

If a molecule loses oxygen or gains hydrogen, it is reduced:

$$CH_3CO_2H \xrightarrow{\text{[H]}} CH_3CH_2OH$$

$$\underset{CH_3\overset{\displaystyle O}{\overset{\|}{C}}CH_3}{} \xrightarrow{\text{[H]}} \underset{CH_3\overset{\displaystyle OH}{\overset{|}{C}}HCH_3}{}$$

We may list a series of compounds according to the increasing oxidation state of carbon:

$$
\begin{array}{cccccc}
 & CH_2{=}CH_2 & CH{\equiv}CH & \overset{\displaystyle O}{\overset{\|}{CH_3COH}} & \\
CH_3CH_3 & CH_3CH_2OH & CH_3CHO & & CO_2 \\
 & CH_3CH_2Cl & CH_3CHCl_2 & \text{and its derivatives} &
\end{array}
$$

increasing oxidation state of C →

Note that $CH_2{=}CH_2$ and CH_3CH_2OH are at the same oxidation level. This is not surprising because the difference between the two molecules is only a molecule of water. No oxidation–reduction reaction takes place in the interconversion of ethylene and ethanol.

$$CH_2{=}CH_2 \underset{-H_2O}{\overset{H_2O}{\rightleftarrows}} CH_3CH_2OH$$

STUDY PROBLEM

7.23 List the following carboxylic acids in order of increasing oxidation state:

(a) $\quad HOCH_2\overset{\displaystyle O}{\overset{\|}{C}}OH$ (b) $CH_3\overset{\displaystyle O}{\overset{\|}{C}}OH$ (c) $HO\overset{\displaystyle O}{\overset{\|}{C}}{-}\overset{\displaystyle O}{\overset{\|}{C}}OH$

    hydroxyacetic acid   acetic acid   oxalic acid

Alcohols may be oxidized to ketones, aldehydes, or carboxylic acids. These oxidations are widely used in the laboratory and in industry, and they also occur in biological systems.

$$RCH_2OH \xrightarrow{\;[O]\;} \underset{\text{an aldehyde}}{RCH\!\!=\!\!O}$$

$$\underset{\text{a } 1° \text{ alcohol}}{RCH_2OH} \xrightarrow{\;[O]\;} \underset{\text{a carboxylic acid}}{RCO_2H}$$

$$\underset{\text{a } 2° \text{ alcohol}}{\overset{\displaystyle OH}{\underset{|}{RCHR}}} \xrightarrow{\;[O]\;} \underset{\text{a ketone}}{\overset{\displaystyle O}{\overset{||}{RCR}}}$$

Theoretically, alcohols can also be reduced to hydrocarbons; however, such reactions are not common. Instead, indirect methods of reduction are used; for example, dehydration of an alcohol leads to an alkene, which is readily reduced with H_2 to the alkane (Section 9.13).

$$\underset{\text{cyclohexanol}}{\bigcirc\!\!-\!OH} \xrightarrow[\text{heat}]{H_2SO_4} \underset{\text{cyclohexene}}{\bigcirc} \xrightarrow[\text{Ni catalyst}]{H_2} \underset{\text{cyclohexane}}{\bigcirc}$$

A. Combustion of Ethanol

Alcohols, like other organic compounds, can undergo combustion.

$$\underset{\text{ethanol}}{CH_3CH_2OH} + 3\,O_2 \longrightarrow 2\,CO_2 + 3\,H_2O + \text{energy}$$

The burning of ethanol has an interesting history. In the days of pirates and sailing ships, the alcoholic content of rum or whiskey was determined by pouring it on a small pile of gunpowder and igniting the vapor. If the flames died down and the gunpowder did not burn, the conclusion was that the rum had been watered down. If the gunpowder did burn, this was proof that the rum had not been diluted. The term "proof" derives from this custom of testing alcoholic beverages. Proof is twice the percent of alcohol; 100-proof spirits are 50 percent ethanol.

B. Biological Oxidation of Ethanol

In a mammalian system, ingested ethanol is oxidized primarily in the liver with the aid of an enzyme called *alcohol dehydrogenase*. The product of this dehydrogenation is acetaldehyde, CH_3CHO. (The biological oxidation of methanol leads to formaldehyde, $HCHO$, which is toxic.) The acetaldehyde from ethanol is further oxidized enzymatically to the acetate ion, $CH_3CO_2{}^-$, which undergoes esterification with the thiol **coenzyme A** (often abbreviated HSCoA). The product of the esterification is **acetylcoenzyme A**. (The complete structure of acetylcoenzyme A is shown on page 636.) The acetyl group ($CH_3CO\!-$) in acetylcoenzyme A can be converted to CO_2, H_2O, and energy, or it can be converted to other compounds, such as fat.

$$CH_3CH_2OH \xrightarrow{\text{alcohol dehydrogenase}} CH_3\overset{\overset{\displaystyle O}{\|}}{C}H \xrightarrow{[O]} CH_3\overset{\overset{\displaystyle O}{\|}}{C}O^- \xrightarrow{HSCoA}$$

$$CH_3\overset{\overset{\displaystyle O}{\|}}{C}-SCoA$$

acetylcoenzyme A

$\longrightarrow CO_2 + H_2O$

$\longrightarrow$ fat, etc.

C. Laboratory Oxidation of Alcohols

In general, laboratory oxidizing agents oxidize primary alcohols to carboxylic acids and secondary alcohols to ketones.

$$RCH_2OH \xrightarrow{[O]} R\overset{\overset{\displaystyle O}{\|}}{C}OH$$

a 1° alcohol   *a carboxylic acid*

$$\overset{\overset{\displaystyle OH}{|}}{R}CHR \xrightarrow{[O]} R\overset{\overset{\displaystyle O}{\|}}{C}R$$

a 2° alcohol   *a ketone*

Some typical oxidizing agents used for these oxidations are:

(1) alkaline potassium permanganate: $KMnO_4 + {}^-OH$;

(2) hot, concentrated HNO_3;

(3) chromic acid: H_2CrO_4 (prepared *in situ* from CrO_3 or Na_2CrO_4 with H_2SO_4).

Primary alcohols are oxidized first to aldehydes. Aldehydes are more easily oxidized than alcohols; therefore, the oxidation usually continues until the carboxylic acid (or, in alkaline solution, its anion) is formed.

$$CH_3CH_2CH_2OH + H_2CrO_4 \xrightarrow{H^+} \left[CH_3CH_2\overset{\overset{\displaystyle O}{\|}}{C}H\right] \longrightarrow CH_3CH_2CO_2H + Cr^{3+}$$

1-propanol   propanoic acid

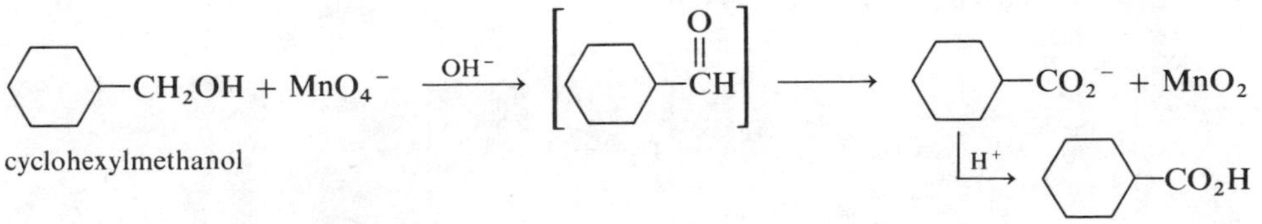

cyclohexylmethanol

cyclohexane-carboxylic acid

If the intermediate aldehyde has a low boiling point, it can be distilled from the reaction mixture before it is oxidized to the carboxylic acid. Yields of aldehydes by this method are usually low; therefore, this technique is of limited synthetic value. A better reagent for oxidizing a primary alcohol to an aldehyde is a chromic oxide–pyridine complex, a reagent that does not oxidize an aldehyde to a carboxylic acid.

$$CH_3CH_2CH_2OH + CrO_3 \cdot 2 \bigcirc N \xrightarrow[25°]{CH_2Cl_2} CH_3CH_2\overset{\overset{\displaystyle O}{\|}}{C}H$$

1-propanol   propanal

Secondary alcohols are oxidized to ketones in excellent yields by standard oxidizing agents.

$$CH_3(CH_2)_5\overset{\overset{\displaystyle OH}{|}}{C}HCH_3 \xrightarrow[H^+]{H_2CrO_4} CH_3(CH_2)_5\overset{\overset{\displaystyle O}{\|}}{C}CH_3$$

2-octanol   2-octanone
                                            96 %

$$\bigcirc\!\!-OH \xrightarrow[OH^-]{KMnO_4} \bigcirc\!\!=O$$

cyclohexanol   cyclohexanone
                               95 %

Tertiary alcohols are not oxidized under alkaline conditions. If the oxidation is attempted in acidic solution, the tertiary alcohol undergoes dehydration and then the alkene is oxidized. Alkene oxidation will be discussed in Chapter 9.

$$R_3COH \begin{array}{c} \xrightarrow[OH^-]{[O]} \text{no reaction} \\[4pt] \xrightarrow{H^+} \end{array}$$

a 3° alcohol   *alkenes* $\xrightarrow{[O]}$ *alkene oxidation products*

The mechanisms of many oxidation reactions are not completely understood. Because of the possible variations of reduced forms of Mn(VII) from MnO_4^-, or Cr(VI) from CrO_4^{2-}, the mechanisms have the potential for being quite complicated. In some reactions, the oxidizing agent probably forms an inorganic ester with the alcohol and, by appropriate shifts of electrons and protons, the oxidized product results.

A simplified mechanism:

$$R_2CHOH + HCrO_4^- \xrightarrow{-H_2O} \left[\begin{array}{c} \overset{\displaystyle H}{\underset{|}{}} \quad \overset{\displaystyle O}{\|} \\ R_2C\!-\!O\!-\!CrO^- \\ \| \\ O \end{array}\right] \longrightarrow R_2C\!=\!O + \overset{\overset{\displaystyle HO}{|}}{\underset{\underset{\displaystyle O}{\|}}{Cr}}O^-$$

Cr(VI)   *an inorganic ester*   Cr(IV)

STUDY PROBLEM

7.24 Predict the organic products of $KMnO_4$ oxidation of: (a) cyclopentanol, and (b) benzyl alcohol. (*Hint:* The benzene ring is not affected by $KMnO_4$.)

D.   Oxidation of Glycols

The **periodic acid oxidation** is a test for 1,2-glycols and for 1,2-hydroxy carbonyl compounds. A compound containing such a grouping is oxidized and cleaved by periodic acid (HIO_4).

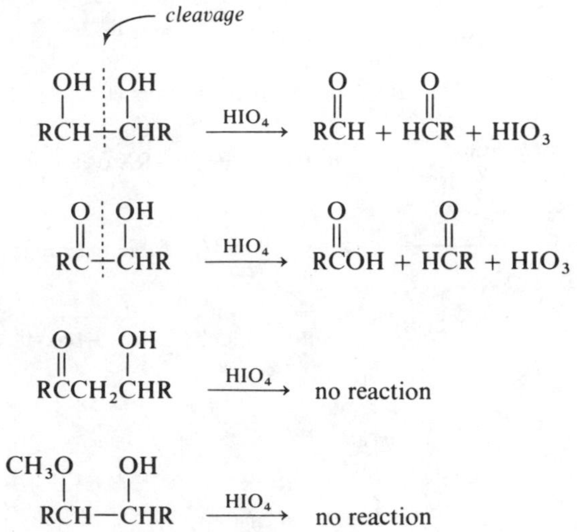

```
                  cleavage

   OH : OH                    O     O
   |   | |                    ||    ||
   RCH--CHR    ──HIO₄→    RCH + HCR + HIO₃
```

```
   O : OH                     O      O
   || | |                     ||     ||
   RC--CHR     ──HIO₄→    RCOH + HCR + HIO₃
```

```
   O    OH
   ||   |
   RCCH₂CHR    ──HIO₄→    no reaction
```

```
   CH₃O   OH
   |      |
   RCH─── CHR   ──HIO₄→    no reaction
```

Note that a hydroxyl group is oxidized to an aldehyde, while a carbonyl group is oxidized to a carboxylic acid. The products of the periodic acid oxidation of the 2-hydroxypropanal are ethanal (acetaldehyde) and formic acid.

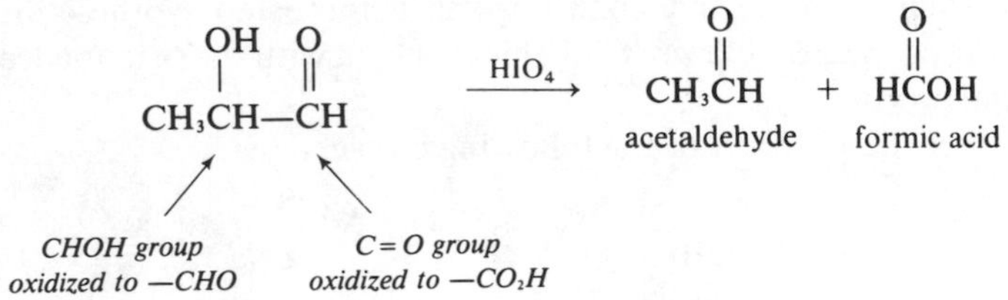

```
   OH  O                        O            O
   |   ||          ──HIO₄→      ||           ||
   CH₃CH─CH                   CH₃CH    +    HCOH
                             acetaldehyde   formic acid
    ↗      ↖
CHOH group      C=O group
oxidized to —CHO   oxidized to —CO₂H
```

The periodic acid reaction goes through a cyclic intermediate, a fact that explains why isolated hydroxyl groups are not oxidized.

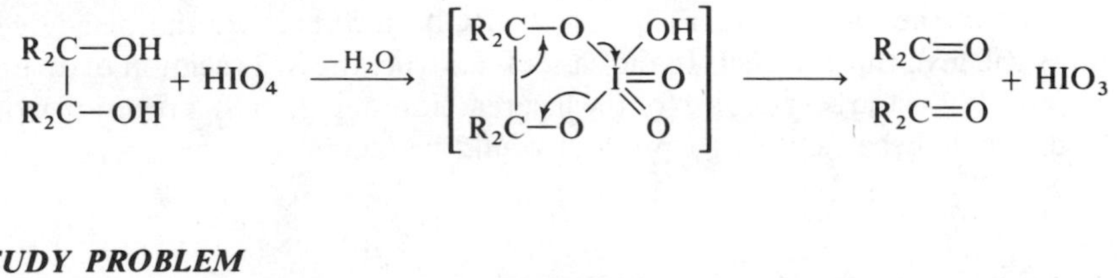

```
R₂C—OH                    ⎡ R₂C—O    OH ⎤          R₂C=O
|        + HIO₄  ─−H₂O→   ⎢      I=O    ⎥  ──→            + HIO₃
R₂C—OH                    ⎣ R₂C—O    O  ⎦          R₂C=O
```

STUDY PROBLEM

7.25   Predict the products of the periodic acid oxidation of the following compound:

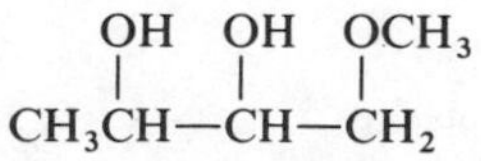

```
        OH  OH  OCH₃
        |   |   |
     CH₃CH—CH—CH₂
```

Section 7.18

Use of Alcohols in Synthesis

Alcohols are versatile starting materials for the preparation of alkyl halides, alkenes, carbonyl compounds, and ethers.

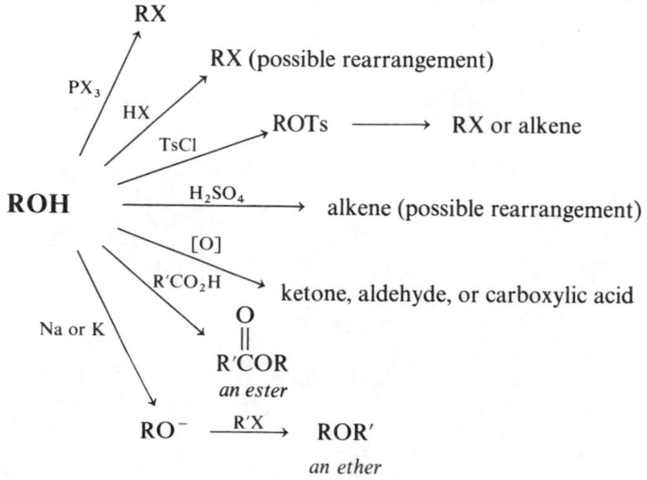

A. *Multistep Synthetic Sequences*

In Chapter 5, we considered the solving of one-step synthesis problems. We have now presented enough organic reactions that we may consider synthesis problems requiring more than one step. In a multistep synthesis, it is best to approach the problem *backwards*—that is, to begin with the reaction leading to the desired final product.

Consider the problem of the following conversion:

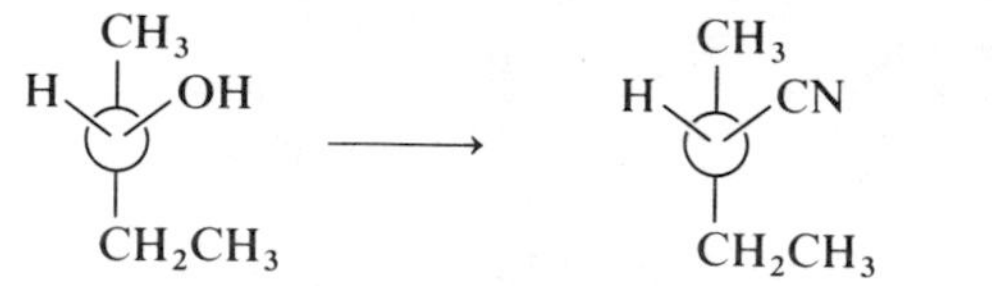

(*S*)-2-butanol (*S*)-2-methylbutanenitrile

Rather than listing the reactions that the starting alcohol can undergo, we should look at the final product (the nitrile, RCN, in this case) and decide what reactants will give this product. In the case of a nitrile, the S_N2 reaction of an alkyl halide and CN^- is the best choice for the last reaction step. (An S_N1 reaction would not be desirable because the S_N1 product would be racemic.)

Last step first:

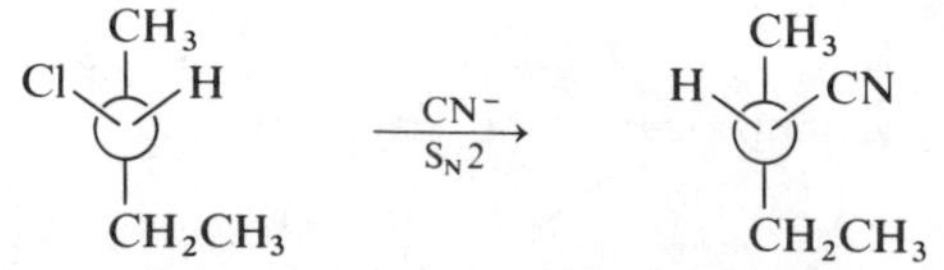

(*R*)-2-chlorobutane (*S*)-2-methylbutanenitrile *inverted*

Now we can consider the next-to-last step. In the present example, we want a route to (*R*)-2-chlorobutane. We can prepare this compound from (*S*)-2-butanol and a halogenating agent that gives *inversion*. We would not choose HCl, which would give racemization, but rather PCl_3 (or $SOCl_2$ with an amine solvent).

First step:

$$\underset{\substack{(S)\text{-2-butanol}}}{\overset{\substack{CH_3 \\ \\ H \diagup \diagdown OH \\ \\ \\ CH_2CH_3}}{}} \xrightarrow{PCl_3} \underset{\substack{(R)\text{-2-chlorobutane} \\ \textit{inverted}}}{\overset{\substack{CH_3 \\ \\ Cl \diagup \diagdown H \\ \\ \\ CH_2CH_3}}{}}$$

Now we can propose an entire synthesis:

$$\overset{\substack{CH_3 \\ \\ H \diagup \diagdown OH \\ \\ \\ CH_2CH_3}}{} \xrightarrow{PCl_3} \overset{\substack{CH_3 \\ \\ Cl \diagup \diagdown H \\ \\ \\ CH_2CH_3}}{} \xrightarrow[S_N 2]{NaCN} \overset{\substack{CH_3 \\ \\ H \diagup \diagdown CN \\ \\ \\ CH_2CH_3}}{}$$

Sample Problem

Suggest a synthesis for 3-methyl-3-hexanol from alcohols of four carbons or less.

Solution:

(1) Write the structure:

$$\underset{\underset{CH_3}{|}}{\overset{\overset{OH}{|}}{CH_3CH_2CH_2CCH_2CH_3}}$$

(2) Decide on the reactants. This is a 3° alcohol, so it may be prepared by a Grignard reaction.

$$\overset{\overset{O}{\|}}{CH_3CCH_2CH_3} \xrightarrow[\text{(2) } H_2O,\ H^+]{\text{(1) } CH_3CH_2CH_2MgBr} \text{product}$$

(3) The organic reactants in the preceding step may be obtained from alcohols.

$$\underset{}{\overset{\overset{OH}{|}}{CH_3CHCH_2CH_3}} \xrightarrow{KMnO_4} \overset{\overset{O}{\|}}{CH_3CCH_2CH_3}$$

$$CH_3CH_2CH_2OH \xrightarrow{HBr} CH_3CH_2CH_2Br \xrightarrow{Mg} CH_3CH_2CH_2MgBr$$

(4) Write the entire synthetic sequence.

$$CH_3CH_2CH_2OH \xrightarrow{HBr} CH_3CH_2CH_2Br \xrightarrow{Mg} CH_3CH_2CH_2MgBr$$

$$\underset{}{\overset{\overset{OH}{|}}{CH_3CHCH_2CH_3}} \xrightarrow{KMnO_4} \overset{\overset{O}{\|}}{CH_3CCH_2CH_3} \xrightarrow[\text{(2) } H_2O,\ H^+]{\text{(1) } CH_3CH_2CH_2MgBr} \text{product}$$

STUDY PROBLEMS

7.26   Suggest a method for preparing ethyl acetate ($CH_3CO_2CH_2CH_3$) from ethanol and *no other organic reagent*.

7.27   Suggest a method of converting cyclopentanol to 1-cyclopentyl-1-ethanol. (Other organic reagents may be used.)

Section 7.19

Phenols

A **phenol** is a compound in which a hydroxyl group is attached to an sp^2 carbon of an aromatic ring. We will discuss primarily the reactions of phenol itself; the chemistry of other phenols is similar.

Some phenols:

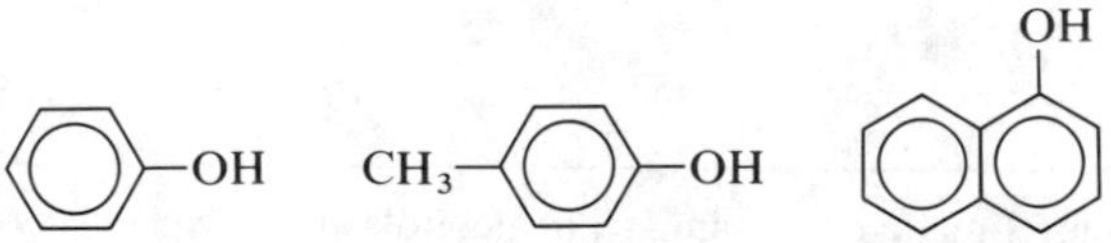

phenol

p-cresol
(4-methylphenol)

α-naphthol
(1-naphthol)

Because a bond from an sp^2 carbon is stronger than a bond from an sp^3 carbon (Section 2.4F), the C—O bond of a phenol is not easily broken. Phenols do not undergo S_N1 or S_N2 reactions or elimination reactions as alcohols do.

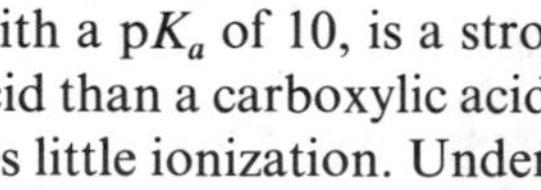

strong bond

A.   Phenol as an Acid

Although the C—O bond of a phenol is not easily broken, the O—H bond is readily broken. Phenol, with a pK_a of 10, is a stronger acid than an alcohol or water, but is still a weaker acid than a carboxylic acid. When treated with aqueous NaOH, an alcohol undergoes little ionization. Under the same conditions, phenol forms a **phenoxide**.

$$CH_3CH_2OH \quad + \; NaOH \; \longleftrightarrow \quad CH_3CH_2O^- \; Na^+ + H_2O$$

ethanol, $pK_a = 15.9$
favored

sodium ethoxide

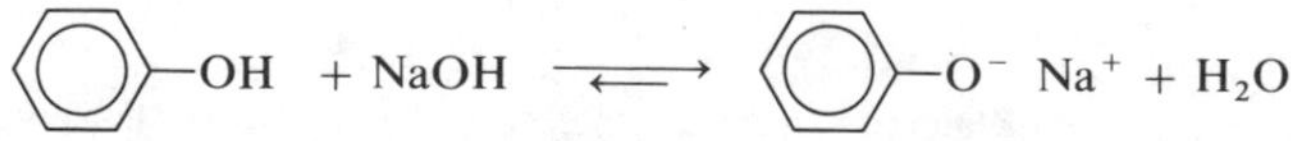

$$\text{—OH} + NaOH \; \longrightarrow \quad \text{—O}^- \; Na^+ + H_2O$$

phenol, $pK_a = 10$

sodium phenoxide
favored

The degree of ionization of a weak acid is determined by the relative stabilities of the nonionized compound and the anion:

$$HA \rightleftharpoons H^+ + A^-$$

If A^- is stabilized relative to HA, acidity is increased

The reason for the acidity of phenols is that the product anion is *resonance-stabilized*, with the negative charge delocalized by the aromatic ring.

Resonance structures for the phenoxide ion:

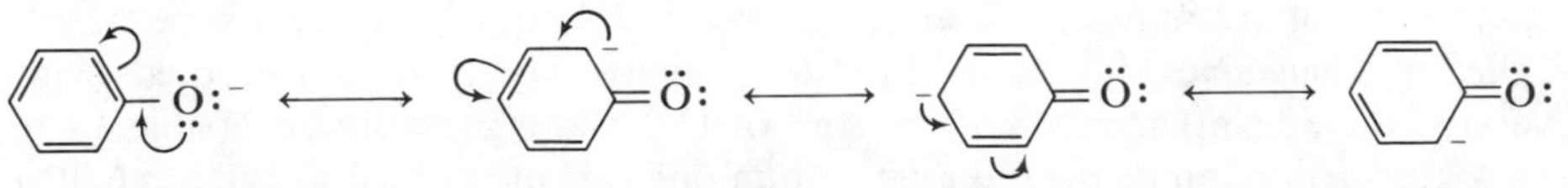

The negative charge in an alkoxide ion (RO^-) cannot be delocalized. Therefore, an alkoxide ion is of higher energy relative to the alcohol, and alcohols are not as strong acids as phenols.

Because of its acidity, phenol was originally called *carbolic acid.* In the 1800's, the British surgeon Joseph Lister urged that phenol be used as a hospital antiseptic. Prior to that time, no antiseptics were used because it was thought that odors, not microorganisms, were the cause of infection. As an antiseptic, phenol itself has been replaced by less irritating compounds. Interestingly, many modern antiseptics still contain phenolic groups.

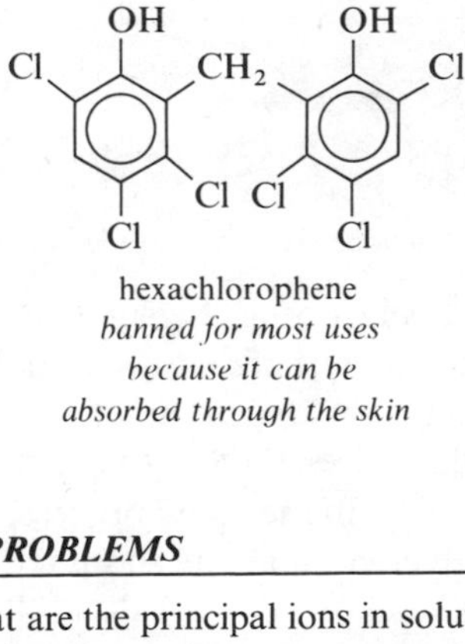

hexachlorophene
banned for most uses because it can be absorbed through the skin

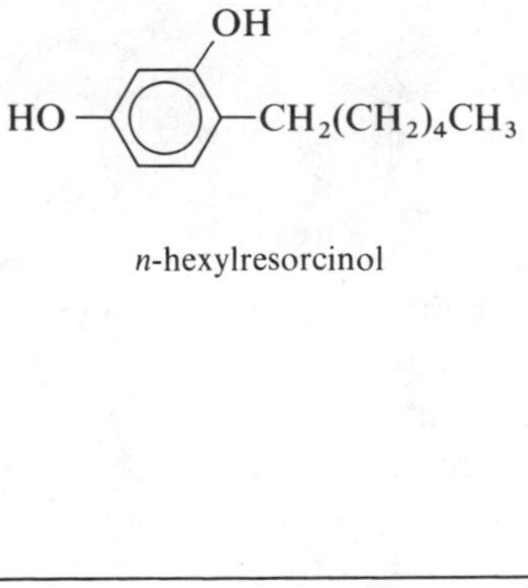

n-hexylresorcinol

STUDY PROBLEMS

7.28   What are the principal ions in solution when the following reagents are mixed?

(a)   sodium ethoxide and phenol   (b) sodium phenoxide and ethanol

7.29   The boiling point of toluene ($C_6H_5CH_3$) is 111°, while that of phenol is 182°. Explain.

B.   Ester Formation

Esterification of phenol does not involve cleavage of the strong C—O bond of the phenol. Therefore, esters of phenols may be synthesized by the same reactions that lead to alkyl esters. Although we show the reaction of phenol with a carboxylic acid, usually the more reactive derivatives of carboxylic acids are used to esterify phenols (see Section 13.5B).

$$\underset{\text{acetic acid}}{CH_3\overset{\displaystyle O}{\overset{\|}{C}}OH} + \underset{\text{phenol}}{HO-\bigcirc} \;\overset{H^+}{\rightleftharpoons}\; \underset{\substack{\text{phenyl acetate}\\ \textit{an ester}}}{CH_3\overset{\displaystyle O}{\overset{\|}{C}}O-\bigcirc} + H_2O$$

C.   Oxidation of Phenols

Phenol itself resists oxidation because formation of a carbonyl group would lead to loss of aromatic stabilization. However, 1,2- and 1,4-dihydroxybenzenes, called **hydroquinones**, can be oxidized to **quinones**. The oxidation proceeds with very mild oxidizing agents, such as Ag^+ or Fe^{3+}, and is readily reversible. (The biological reduction of the quinone ubiquinone was mentioned in Section 6.9B.) Although simple hydroquinones are colorless, quinones are colored. The quinone ring system is found in many dyes (Section 20.6).

$$\underset{\text{hydroquinone}}{\text{OH}\;\text{OH}} \quad \overset{[O]}{\underset{[H]}{\rightleftharpoons}} \quad \underset{\substack{\text{1,4-benzoquinone}\\ \text{(quinone)}}}{\text{O}\;\text{O}} \quad + 2\,H^+ + 2\,e^-$$

$$\underset{\text{catechol}}{\text{OH, OH}} \quad \overset{[O]}{\underset{[H]}{\rightleftharpoons}} \quad \underset{\text{1,2-benzoquinone}}{\text{O, O}} \quad + 2\,H^+ + 2\,e^-$$

The ability of hydroquinone to reduce silver ions to silver metal is the chemical basis of photography. Silver ions in a silver halide crystal that has been exposed to light are more easily reduced than the silver ions of an unexposed crystal. Hydroquinone in the developer fluid reduces these light-activated silver ions at a faster rate than the nonexposed silver ions. In the fixing process, unreacted silver halide is converted to a water-soluble silver complex by sodium thiosulfate, $Na_2S_2O_3$ (called *hypo*), and washed from the film. The result is the familiar photographic negative.

Section 7.20

Thiols and Sulfides

Sulfur is just below oxygen in the periodic table. Many organic compounds containing oxygen have sulfur analogs. The sulfur analog of an alcohol is called an **alkanethiol**, or simply **thiol**, or by its older name **mercaptan**. The —SH group is called a **thiol group** or a **sulfhydryl group**.

$$CH_3SH \qquad \overset{\displaystyle SH}{\underset{\displaystyle |}{CH_3CH_2CHCH_3}}$$

methanethiol   2-butanethiol

The most characteristic property of a thiol is its odor! The human nose is very sensitive to these compounds and can detect their presence at levels of about 0.02 parts thiol to one billion parts air. The odor of a skunk's spray is due primarily to a few simple thiols. Thiols also contribute to the odor of onions and natural gas (to which small amounts of thiol are added so that we *can* smell it).

We may deduce some of the properties of thiols as compared to alcohols by comparing hydrogen sulfide and water. For example, H_2S ($pK_a = 7.04$) is a stronger acid than water ($pK_a = 15.7$). Thiols ($pK_a = \sim 8$) are also substantially stronger acids than alcohols ($pK_a = \sim 16$).

$$CH_3CH_2SH + OH^- \; \rightleftharpoons \; CH_3CH_2S^- + H_2O$$

Sulfur is less electronegative than oxygen, and its outer electrons are more diffuse; therefore, sulfur atoms form weaker hydrogen bonds than oxygen atoms. For this reason, H_2S (bp $-61°$) is more volatile than water (bp $100°$), and thiols are more volatile than their analogous alcohols.

The sulfur analog of an ether is called a **sulfide** and is named in a manner analogous to ethers.

$$CH_3-S-CH_3 \qquad CH_3-S-\!\!\bigcirc$$

dimethyl sulfide

methyl phenyl sulfide

Treatment of an alkyl halide with the hydrogen sulfide ion (HS^-) leads to thiols. Good yields are obtained only if an excess of inorganic hydrogen sulfide is used, because the resulting thiol (which is acidic) can ionize to form the RS^- ion, also a good nucleophile. The subsequent reaction of RS^- with the alkyl halide yields the sulfide.

$$CH_3I + SH^- \longrightarrow \underset{\text{methanethiol}}{CH_3SH} + I^-$$

$$CH_3SH \; \underset{}{\overset{-H^+}{\rightleftharpoons}} \; CH_3S^- \; \xrightarrow[-I^-]{CH_3I} \; \underset{\text{dimethyl sulfide}}{CH_3SCH_3}$$

When a thiol is treated with a mild oxidizing agent (such as I_2), it undergoes coupling (a reaction in which two molecules become joined) to form a **disulfide**, a compound containing the S—S linkage. This reaction can be reversed by treatment of the disulfide with a reducing agent (such as lithium metal in liquid NH_3).

$$2 \, \underset{\text{ethanethiol}}{CH_3CH_2SH} \; \underset{[H]}{\overset{[O]}{\rightleftharpoons}} \; \underset{\text{diethyl disulfide}}{CH_3CH_2S-SCH_2CH_3}$$

This disulfide link is an important structural feature of some proteins (Section 18.1B). The disulfide bond helps hold protein chains together in the proper shapes. The locations of the disulfide bonds determine, for example, whether hair (a protein) is curly or straight.

A sulfide can be oxidized to a **sulfoxide** or a **sulfone**, depending upon the reaction conditions. For example, 30% hydrogen peroxide in the presence of an acid oxidizes a sulfide to a sulfoxide at 25° or to a sulfone at 100°.

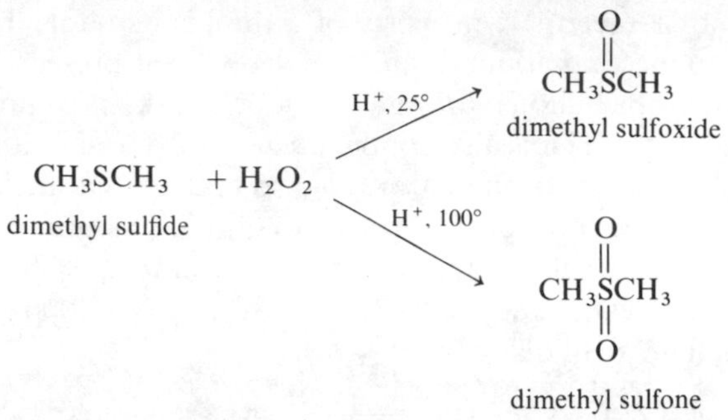

$$CH_3SCH_3 \ + H_2O_2$$
dimethyl sulfide

$\xrightarrow{H^+, 25°}$

$$\overset{\displaystyle O}{\overset{\displaystyle \|}{CH_3SCH_3}}$$
dimethyl sulfoxide

$\xrightarrow{H^+, 100°}$

$$\overset{\displaystyle O}{\overset{\displaystyle \|}{\underset{\displaystyle \|}{\underset{\displaystyle O}{CH_3SCH_3}}}}$$
dimethyl sulfone

Dimethyl sulfoxide (DMSO) is prepared industrially by the air oxidation of dimethyl sulfide; it is also a by-product of the paper industry. DMSO is a unique and versatile solvent. It has a high dielectric constant (49 D), but does not form hydrogen bonds in the pure state. (Why not?) It is a powerful solvent for both inorganic ions and organic compounds. Reactants often have enhanced reactivities in DMSO, compared to alcohol solvents. DMSO readily penetrates the skin and has been used to promote the dermal absorption of drugs; however, DMSO can also cause the absorption of dirt and poisons. A common complaint of people working with DMSO is that, when it is spilled on their hands, they can taste it!

STUDY PROBLEMS

7.30   Dimethylsulfoxide is miscible in water. Why?

7.31   Why is dimethylsulfoxide a weak acid?

SUMMARY

Alcohols and ethers each contain an sp^3 oxygen with two filled orbitals. These compounds are *polar*. Alcohols can undergo *hydrogen bonding* with themselves, and either type of compound can undergo hydrogen bonding with water or any other compound with a partially positive hydrogen.

Alcohols may be prepared in the laboratory by the S_N2 reaction of a primary alkyl halide with OH^-; by the reaction of a Grignard reagent with a carbonyl compound or with an epoxide; or by the hydration of alkenes. Ethers may be prepared by the reaction of a primary alkyl halide with an alkoxide or phenoxide.

Alcohols undergo *substitution reactions* with HX (1° alcohols, S_N2; 2° and 3° alcohols, S_N1). Alcohols undergo *elimination reactions* with H_2SO_4 or other strong acids. In either case, the order of reactivity of alcohols is 3° > 2° > 1°. Ethers undergo substitution reactions when heated with HBr or HI.

Substitution: $ROH + HX \longrightarrow RX + H_2O$

$$
\begin{array}{c}
\quad\quad\quad\quad OH \\
\quad\quad\quad\quad | \\
\textit{Elimination:}\quad R_2CH-CR_2 \xrightarrow[\text{heat}]{H_2SO_4} R_2C{=}CR_2 + H_2O
\end{array}
$$

Substitution: $ROR + HI \xrightarrow{\text{heat}} RI + ROH \xrightarrow{\text{HI}} RI$

Alkyl halides may be prepared from alcohols without rearrangement with $SOCl_2$ or PCl_3.

$$ROH \xrightarrow{SOCl_2 \text{ or } PCl_3} RCl$$

Epoxides are more reactive than other ethers and undergo S_N2 ring opening with nucleophiles in alkaline solution or acidic solution.

$$
\begin{array}{c}
\quad\quad O \\
\quad\quad / \backslash \\
R_2C-CR_2 + H_2O \xrightarrow{H^+ \text{ or } OH^-}
\end{array}
\quad
\begin{array}{c}
OH \\
| \\
R_2C-CR_2 \\
| \\
OH
\end{array}
$$

An **alkoxide** (RO^-) can be prepared from an alcohol and a strong base or an alkali metal ($RMgX$, NH_2^-, Na, K). A **phenoxide** (ArO^-) can be formed by the reaction of a phenol and OH^-.

$$ROH + Na \longrightarrow RO^-\ Na^+ + \tfrac{1}{2}H_2$$

$$ArOH + NaOH \rightleftharpoons ArO^-\ Na^+ + H_2O$$

Alkoxides and phenoxides are good nucleophiles.

$$RO^- + RX \longrightarrow ROR + X^-$$

$$ArO^- + RX \longrightarrow ArOR + X^-$$

Alcohols, Ethers, and Related Compounds

An alcohol may undergo reaction with an acid or an acid derivative to yield an **ester of a carboxylic acid** (RCO_2R) or an **inorganic ester**, such as $RONO_2$ or $ROSO_2OH$. Most inorganic ester groups are good leaving groups.

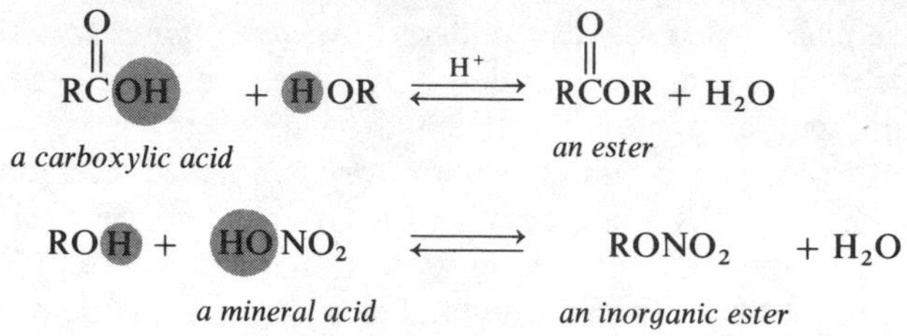

$$\underset{a\ carboxylic\ acid}{\overset{O}{\overset{\|}{RC}OH}} + H OR \underset{}{\overset{H^+}{\rightleftharpoons}} \underset{an\ ester}{\overset{O}{\overset{\|}{RCOR}}} + H_2O$$

$$\underset{a\ mineral\ acid}{ROH + HONO_2} \rightleftharpoons \underset{an\ inorganic\ ester}{RONO_2} + H_2O$$

Primary alcohols are oxidized to carboxylic acids (or aldehydes), while secondary alcohols are oxidized to ketones.

$$1°:\quad RCH_2OH \xrightarrow{[O]} RCO_2H \quad a\ carboxylic\ acid$$

$$2°:\quad R_2CHOH \xrightarrow{[O]} R_2C{=}O \quad a\ ketone$$

Thiols may be used to prepare **sulfides** or **disulfides**. **Sulfides** may be oxidized to **sulfoxides** or **sulfones**.

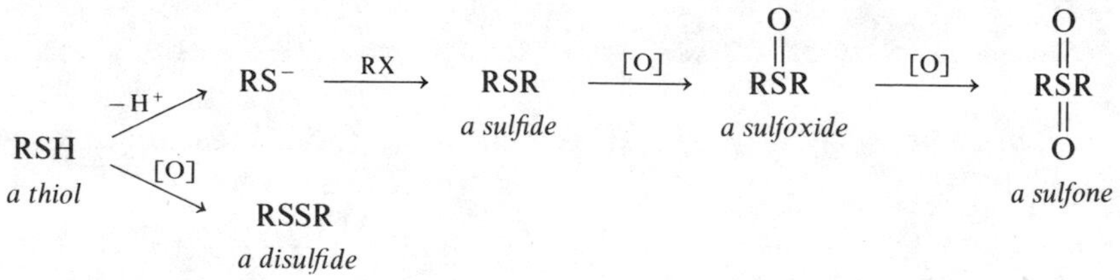

$$\underset{a\ thiol}{RSH} \overset{-H^+}{\underset{[O]}{\diagdown}} \begin{array}{l} RS^- \xrightarrow{RX} \underset{a\ sulfide}{RSR} \xrightarrow{[O]} \underset{a\ sulfoxide}{\overset{O}{\overset{\|}{RSR}}} \xrightarrow{[O]} \underset{a\ sulfone}{\overset{O}{\underset{\|}{\overset{\|}{\underset{O}{RSR}}}}} \\ RSSR \\ a\ disulfide \end{array}$$

STUDY PROBLEMS

7.32 Classify each of the following compounds as an alcohol, an ether, or a phenol:

(a)

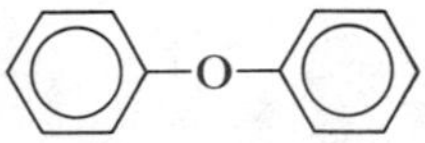

(b)

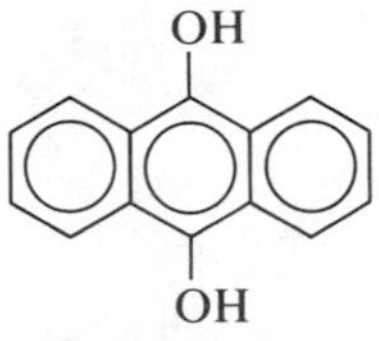

(c)

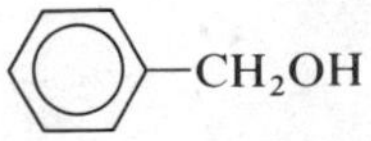

(d)

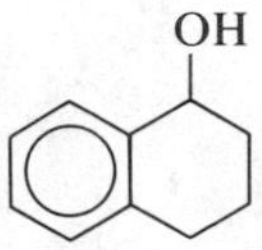

7.33 Name all the oxygen-containing functional groups in the following compounds:

(a)   the antihistamine *Benadryl*, $(CH_3)_2NCH_2CH_2OCH(C_6H_5)_2$

(b)   the drug morphine (p. 766)

(c)   tetrahydrocannabinol (the principal active ingredient in marijuana):

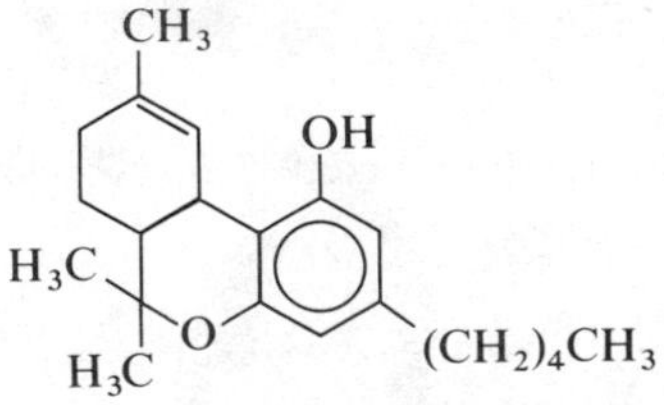

7.34 Which compound in each group would be most water-soluble?

(a)   *n*-butyl alcohol, isobutyl alcohol, *t*-butyl alcohol

(b)   diethyl ether, tetrahydrofuran

(c)   1-bromooctane, 1-octene, 1-octanol

(d)   pentane, 1-pentanol, 3-pentanol, 1,5-pentanediol

7.35 Give an acceptable name for each of the following alcohols, and classify each as 1°, 2°, 3°, allyl, or benzyl:

(a) $(CH_3)_2CHOH$

(b) $(CH_3)_2CHCH_2CH_2OH$

(c) $CH_3CH_2\overset{\underset{|}{OH}}{C}HCH_3$

(d) $CH_3\overset{\underset{|}{OH}}{C}HCH_2CH_2\overset{\underset{|}{OH}}{C}HCH_2CH_3$

(e) $C_6H_5\overset{\underset{|}{CH_3}}{C}HCH_2\overset{\underset{|}{OH}}{C}HCH_3$

(f)

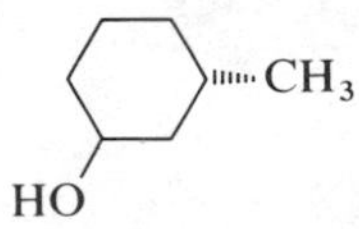

(g)

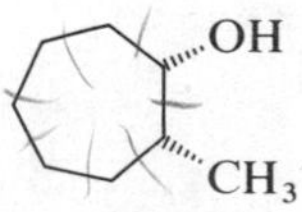

(h)

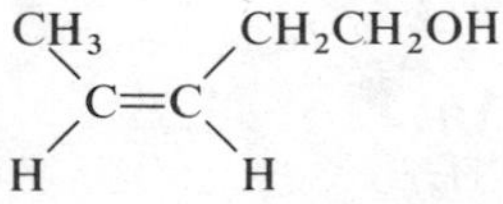

7.36 Provide suitable names for the following structures:

(a) $CH_3OCH_2CH_2OCH_3$

(b) $(CH_3)_2CHOCH_2CH_2CH_3$

(c)

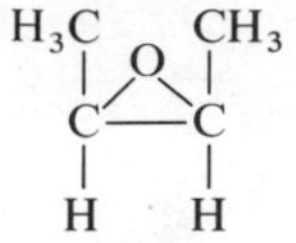

(d)

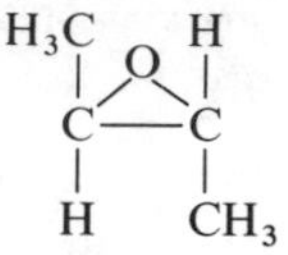

7.37 Complete the following equations, giving the major organic products:

(a) $(CH_3)_2CHCH_2CH_2Cl + OH^- \xrightarrow{\text{heat}}$

(b) $(CH_3)_3CI + OH^- \xrightarrow{\text{heat}}$

(c)

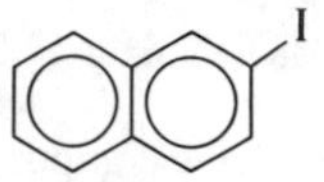

$\xrightarrow[\substack{(2)\ HCHO \\ (3)\ H_2O,\ H^+}]{(1)\ Mg}$

(d)

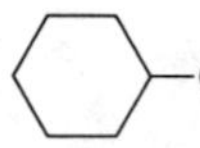

—CHO $\xrightarrow[(2)\ H_2O,\ H^+]{(1)\ (CH_3)_2CHMgBr}$

(e)

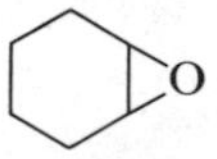

$\xrightarrow[(2)\ H_2O,\ H^+]{(1)\ CH_3MgI}$

7.38 Suggest reaction sequences for the conversion of cycloheptanone to   (a) cycloheptanol, and   (b) 1-propyl-1-cycloheptanol.

7.39 There are two ways to prepare $C_6H_5CH_2OCH_2CH_3$ by a Williamson synthesis. Give the equations.

7.40 Write an equation for the preparation of $C_6H_5OCH_2CH_2CH_3$.

7.41 Write the equation for the reaction that occurs when each of the following alcohols is treated with HI. (Show the mechanisms.)

(a) isopropyl alcohol   (b) cyclohexanol   (c) 1-butanol

7.42 Complete the following equations:

(a) $(CH_3)_2CHCH_2CH_2OH + HBr \longrightarrow$

(b)

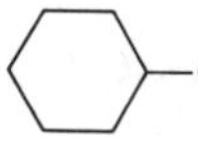

—OH + HCl $\xrightarrow{ZnCl_2}$

(c)

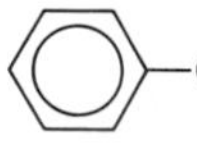

—CH_2CH_2OH + HI \longrightarrow

(d)

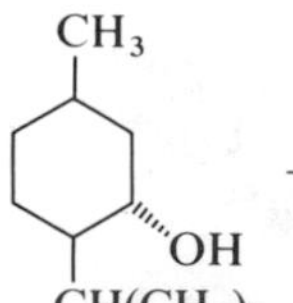

$+ HBr \longrightarrow$

7.43 Complete the following equations for substitution reactions. Which one has the fastest rate of reaction? Which has the slowest rate?

(a) 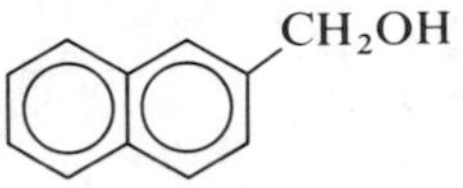
$$\text{(naphthalene ring)} \quad \text{CH}_2\text{OH} \quad + \text{ HBr} \longrightarrow$$

(b) $CH_3CH_2CH_2OH + HBr \longrightarrow$

(c) 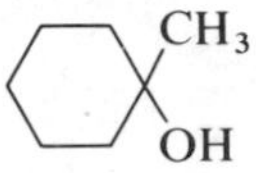
$$\text{(cyclohexane ring with)} \quad \overset{\text{CH}_3}{\underset{\text{OH}}{\big|}} \quad + \text{ HBr} \longrightarrow$$

7.44 Show, by equations, the mechanisms for the reactions in Problems 7.43(b) and (c).

7.45 Sketch energy diagrams for the reactions in Problems 7.43(b) and (c). (Use the *protonated* alcohol as the organic reactant.)

7.46 Give the structure of the expected rearranged alkyl halide from each of the following reactions:

(a)   3,3-dimethyl-2-butanol + HCl + $ZnCl_2$ $\longrightarrow$
(b)   2,2-diphenyl-1-ethanol + HI $\longrightarrow$

7.47 In Problem 7.46, what alkenes would you expect as by-products in each case?

7.48 What reagents could be used to distinguish between the following pairs of compounds:

(a)   *n*-butyl alcohol and *t*-butyl alcohol   (b) diethyl ether and pentane

7.49 What would be the product when (S)-2-hexanol is treated with: (a) PCl_3;   (b) $SOCl_2$ in ether; and   (c) HCl + $ZnCl_2$?

7.50 Predict the major organic products of dehydration reactions of the following alcohols. Include the stereochemistry of the product if applicable.   (a) 2-hexanol;   (b) 1-phenyl-2-propanol;   (c) 1-butanol;   (d) 2-butanol;   (e) 4-methyl-1,4-pentanediol (elimination of 1.0 mole H_2O only).

7.51 Upon dehydration, 2,2-dimethyl-1-cyclohexanol yields two alkenes, both the result of rearrangements. One contains a five-membered ring. What are these alkenes?

7.52 Predict the major products:

(a) 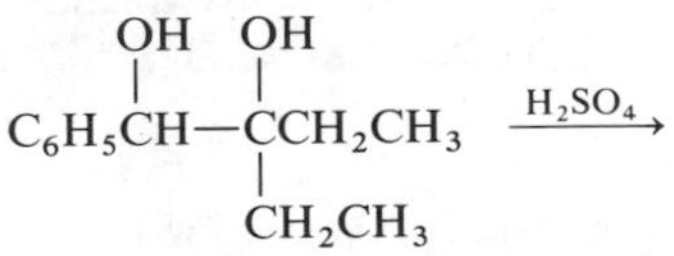
$$\overset{\text{OH}\quad\text{OH}}{\underset{\underset{\text{CH}_2\text{CH}_3}{|}}{C_6H_5\text{CH}-\text{CCH}_2\text{CH}_3}} \quad \xrightarrow{\text{H}_2\text{SO}_4}$$

(b) 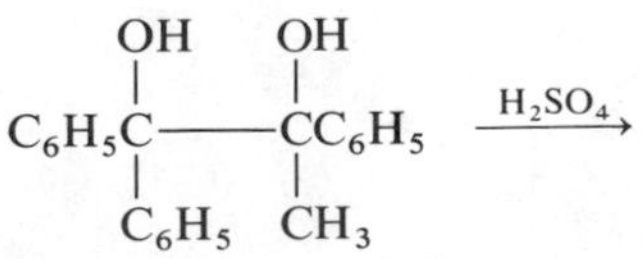
$$\overset{\text{OH}\qquad\text{OH}}{\underset{\underset{\text{C}_6\text{H}_5\quad\text{CH}_3}{|\qquad\quad|}}{C_6H_5\text{C}-\!-\!-\!-\text{CC}_6\text{H}_5}} \quad \xrightarrow{\text{H}_2\text{SO}_4}$$

7.53 Predict the principal organic products:

(a) 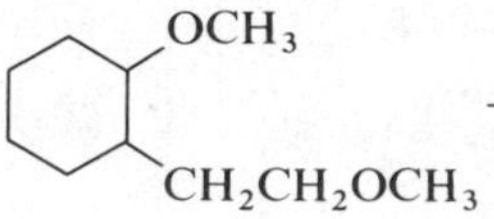 [cyclohexane ring with OCH$_3$ and CH$_2$CH$_2$OCH$_3$ substituents] + excess HI $\xrightarrow{\text{heat}}$

(b) 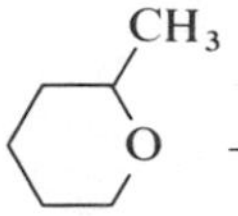 [pyran ring with CH$_3$ and O] + one equivalent HI $\xrightarrow{\text{heat}}$

(c) 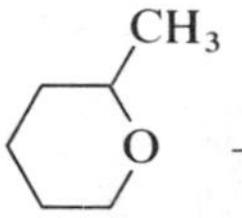 [pyran ring with CH$_3$ and O] + excess HI $\xrightarrow{\text{heat}}$

7.54 Predict the major organic products when propylene oxide (methyloxirane) is treated with the following reagents: (a) NH$_3$; (b) 1-pentanol and HCl; (c) CH$_2$=CHCH$_2$MgBr, then dilute HCl; (d) phenyllithium, then dilute HCl; (e) a solution of phenol and NaOH.

7.55 What would be the product of the following reaction?

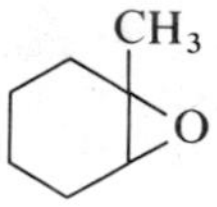

[cyclohexane ring with CH$_3$ and O] + HBr $\longrightarrow$

7.56 Complete the following equations for acid–base reactions:

(a)   CH$_3$CH$_2$OH + H$^+$ $\rightleftharpoons$ (b) 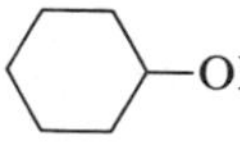 [benzene ring]—OH + OH$^-$ $\rightleftharpoons$

(c) 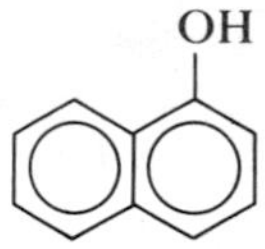 [naphthalene ring with OH] + OH$^-$ $\rightleftharpoons$ (d) (CH$_3$)$_3$CO$^-$ + H$_2$O $\rightleftharpoons$

7.57 What will be the products of reaction (if any) of the following compounds with sodium ethoxide? (a) isopropyl bromide; (b) diisopropyl ether; (c) water; (d) acetic acid; (e) phenol.

7.58 If 1-butanol is added to each of the following reagents, what would be the expected major products? (a) methylmagnesium iodide; (b) phenyllithium; (c) sodium phenoxide; (d) sodium acetate; (e) HBr; (f) potassium metal.

7.59 Which of the following compounds are resonance-stabilized? Write the important resonance structures.

(a) 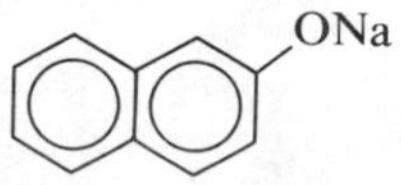 [naphthalene ring with ONa]   (b) CH$_2$=CHCH$_2$OK   (c) (CH$_3$)$_3$COK

7.60 Suggest a series of reactions for each of the following conversions: (a) 2-propanol and propylene oxide to 1-isopropoxy-2-propanol; (b) ethanol and 2-propanol to ethyl isopropyl ether.

7.61 What reagent would you use to convert 4-chloro-1-butanol to tetrahydrofuran (page 259)?

7.62 Give the major organic product of the reaction (if any) of (*R*)-2-heptanol with each of the following reagents: (a) $KMnO_4 + OH^-$; (b) HI; (c) Li metal; (d) hot, conc. H_2SO_4; (e) CH_3MgI; (f) aqueous NaCl; (g) aqueous NaOH; (h) $SOCl_2$ in ether.

7.63 Write equations for the following reactions: (a) (*S*)-2-pentanol and tosyl chloride; (b) (*R*)-2-butanol and H_2SO_4 at 180°; (c) (*R*)-2-butanol and $ClSO_3H$; (d) $C_6H_5CO_2H$ and diethyl sulfate; (e) (*R*)-2-butyl tosylate and ethanol under S_N1 conditions.

7.64 Suggest a method for the preparation of each of the following compounds from an alcohol or a phenol:

(a) $CH_2(CH_2ONO_2)_2$

(b)

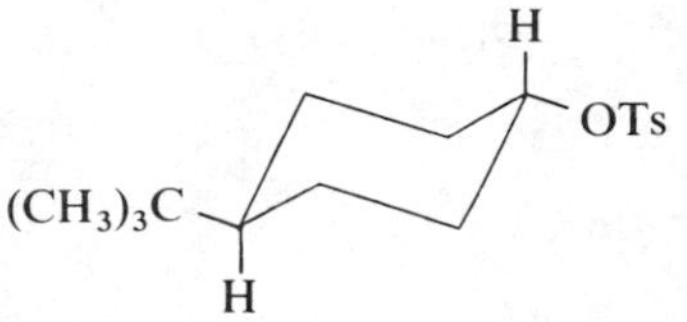

(c)

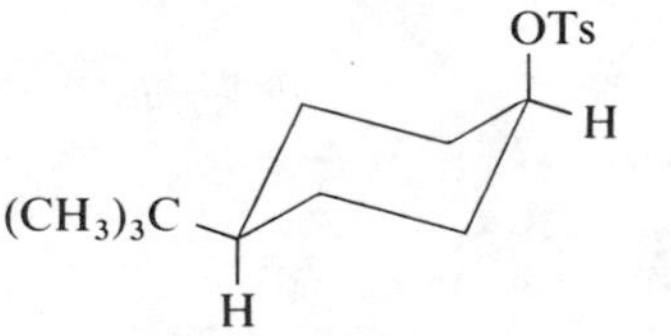

(d)

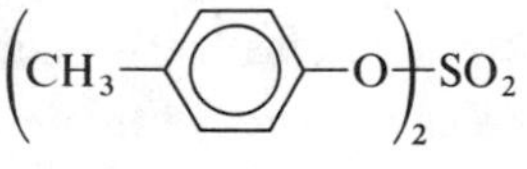

7.65 If α-D-glucose (following) is treated with excess dimethyl sulfate in alkaline solution, what is the product?

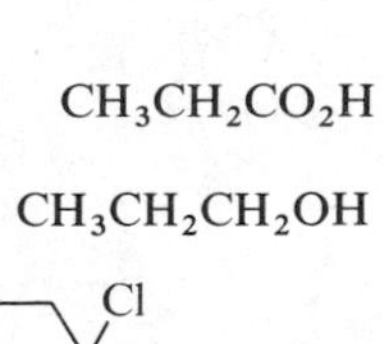

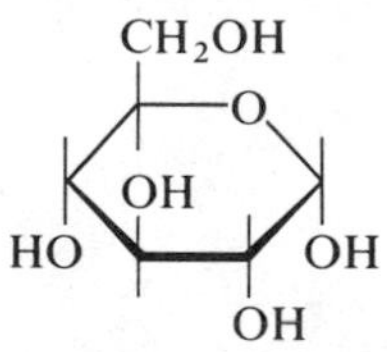

7.66 In which one of each of the following pairs of compounds is carbon in the higher oxidation state?

(a) $CH_3CH_2C{\equiv}CH$ or $CH_3CH_2CO_2H$

(b) CH_3CH_2CHO or $CH_3CH_2CH_2OH$

(c)

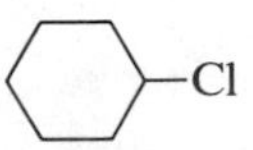

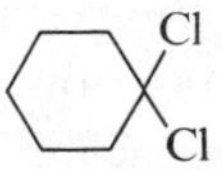

7.67 Suggest an alcohol and an oxidizing agent for preparing: (a) 3-methylcyclohexanone; (b) 2-butanone; (c) butanal ($CH_3CH_2CH_2CHO$); (d) butanoic acid.

7.68 What was the starting material?

(a) ? $\xrightarrow{\text{HIO}_4}$ $CH_3\overset{O}{\overset{\|}{C}}OH + H\overset{O}{\overset{\|}{C}}CH_2CH_3$

(b) ? $\xrightarrow{\text{HIO}_4}$ $CH_3\overset{O}{\overset{\|}{C}}CH_2CH_2CH_2\overset{O}{\overset{\|}{C}}H$

(c) ? $\xrightarrow{\text{HIO}_4}$ $H\overset{O}{\overset{\|}{C}}H + CH_3\overset{O}{\overset{\|}{C}}CH_3$

7.69 Complete the following equations, giving only the major organic products:

(a) $CH_3CH_2SCH_2CH_3 + H_2O_2 \xrightarrow[\text{heat}]{H^+}$

(b)  $S + H_2O_2 \xrightarrow[\text{room temperature}]{H^+}$

(c) $CH_3CH_2OH + CH_3\overset{O}{\overset{\|}{C}}Cl \longrightarrow$

(d) $CH_3CH_2SH + C_6H_5\overset{O}{\overset{\|}{C}}Cl \longrightarrow$

(e) 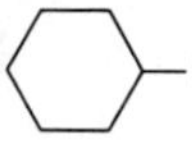 —SH + NaOH $\longrightarrow$

7.70 How would you make the following conversions?
(a) bromobenzene to benzoic acid ($C_6H_5CO_2H$)
(b) benzyl bromide to stilbene (*trans*-1,2-diphenylethene)
(c) (*R*)-2-butanol to (*S*)-2-butanol

7.71 Suggest a synthesis for each of the following compounds from an alcohol of four carbons or less and any other reagents needed:

(a) $CH_3CH_2\overset{\overset{\displaystyle CH_3}{|}}{C}HCH_2OCH_3$ (b) $(CH_3)_3COCH_2CH_3$ (c) $(CH_3)_2CHC\overset{O}{\overset{\|}{C}}CH_3$

(d)  $\overset{\overset{\displaystyle CH_2}{\diagup\diagdown}}{CH_2}{\!-\!}CHCH_2CHClCH_2CH_3$ (e) $(CH_3)_2C{=}CHCH_3$

(f) $(CH_3)_2CHCH_2CH_2CH_2OH$ (g) $(CH_3)_2CHCH_2\overset{\overset{\displaystyle }{|}}{C}HCH_3$
$\qquad\qquad\qquad\qquad\qquad\qquad\qquad\qquad\qquad\quad CN$

(h) $(CH_3)_2CHOCH_2CH_2Cl$ (i) $CH_3CH_2CH_2\overset{\overset{\displaystyle }{|}}{C}HCH(CH_3)_2$
$\qquad\qquad\qquad\qquad\qquad\qquad\qquad\qquad\qquad\quad ONO_2$

7.72 Allyl disulfide ($CH_2{=}CHCH_2SSCH_2CH{=}CH_2$) is a contributor to the odor of garlic. How would you prepare this compound from allyl alcohol?

7.73 Vinyl alcohol ($CH_2{=}CHOH$) is unstable and spontaneously forms acetaldehyde ($CH_3CH{=}O$). Suggest a mechanism for this reaction.

7.74 When *trans*-2-chloro-1-cyclohexanol is treated with base, cyclohexene oxide is the product; however, when *cis*-2-chloro-1-cyclohexanol is treated with base, the product is cyclohexanone.

(a) Why does the *cis*-isomer not yield the oxide?

(b) Write a mechanism for each reaction.

7.75 Which would you expect to be the stronger acid, cyclohexanol or 2-chloro-1-cyclo-hexanol? Explain your answer.

7.76 A chemist had at his disposal a mixture of HCl + $ZnCl_2$, called the **Lucas reagent**, and methylmagnesium iodide. He found that a compound of unknown structure underwent rapid reaction with the Grignard reagent and slow reaction with the Lucas reagent. Which compound was it?

(a) $(CH_3CH_2)_3COH$ (b) ⬡—OCH_3 (c) $(CH_3)_3CCl$

(d) ⬡—CH_2CH_2OH (e) ⬡

7.77 Each of the following hydroxy compounds can undergo intramolecular hydrogen bonding (that is, hydrogen bonding between two groups in the same molecule). Rewrite each structure, showing the intramolecular hydrogen bond.

(a) [benzene ring with NO₂ and OH groups]

(b) $\overset{OH}{\underset{|}{CH_3CHCH_2}}\overset{O}{\underset{||}{CCH_3}}$

(c) [cyclohexane ring with OH and O groups]

7.78 Why cannot the following compound undergo intramolecular hydrogen bonding? Use structures to show an intermolecular hydrogen bond between its molecules.

HO—◯—NO_2

7.79 Propose a reaction sequence for each of the following conversions. Use any inorganic or organic reagents you wish.

(a) $C_6H_5CH_3$ to $C_6H_5CH_2\overset{OH}{\underset{|}{CHCH_3}}$

(b) [cyclohexane ring with epoxide O] to *cis*- [cyclohexane ring with two Cl]

(c) [cyclohexane ring with epoxide O] to *trans*- [cyclohexane ring with two Cl]

(d) CH_2——CH_2 (epoxide O) to $C_6H_5OCH_2CH_2OC_6H_5$

(e) $(CH_3CH_2)_2C$——$C(CH_2CH_3)_2$ (epoxide O) to $(CH_3CH_2)_3C\overset{O}{\underset{||}{C}}CH_2CH_3$

7.80 When treated with $SOCl_2$, Compound A yields Compound B. Reaction of B with magnesium, followed by reaction with acetaldehyde (CH_3CHO) and then aqueous acid, results in 5-methyl-2-heptanol. What are the structures of Compounds A and B?

Chapter 8

Spectroscopy I:
Infrared and Nuclear Magnetic Resonance

Spectroscopy is the study of the interactions between radiant energy and matter. The colors that we see and the fact that we can see at all are consequences of energy absorption by organic and inorganic compounds. The capture of the sun's energy by plants in the process of photosynthesis is another aspect of the interaction of organic compounds with radiant energy. Of primary interest to the organic chemist is the fact that the wavelengths at which an organic compound absorbs radiant energy are *dependent upon the structure of the compound*. Therefore, spectroscopic techniques may be used to determine the structures of unknown compounds and to study the bonding characteristics of known compounds.

In this chapter, our emphasis will be on **infrared spectroscopy** and **nuclear magnetic resonance spectroscopy**, both of which are used extensively in organic chemistry. In Chapter 20, we will broaden our discussion to include some other types of spectroscopy.

Section 8.1

Electromagnetic Radiation

Electromagnetic radiation is energy that is transmitted through space in the form of waves. Each type of electromagnetic radiation (radio waves, ultraviolet, infrared, visible, and so forth) is characterized by its **wavelength** (λ), the distance from the crest of one wave to the crest of the next wave (see Figure 8.1).

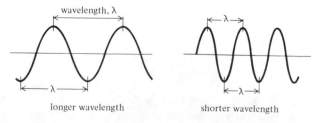

Figure 8.1. Wavelength of electromagnetic radiation.

The entire spectrum of electromagnetic radiation is represented in Figure 8.2. The wavelengths that lead to vision range from 400 nm to 750 nm (1 nm = 10^{-9} m or 10^{-7} cm); however, the visible region is a very small part of the entire electromagnetic spectrum. Wavelengths slightly shorter than those of the visible region fall into the ultraviolet region, while slightly longer wavelengths fall into the infrared region. Radio waves, with wavelengths measured in meters, are far removed from the visible region of the spectrum.

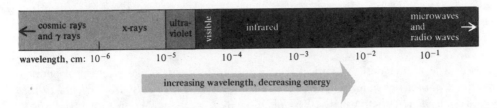

Figure 8.2. The electromagnetic spectrum.

In addition to being characterized by its wavelength, radiation may be characterized by its **frequency** (v), which is defined as the number of complete cycles per second (cps), also called *Hertz* (Hz). (See Figure 8.3.) Radiation of a higher frequency contains more waves per second; therefore, the wavelength must be shorter. By their definitions, wavelength and frequency are *inversely proportional*. This relationship may be expressed mathematically:

$$v = \frac{c}{\lambda}$$

where v = frequency in Hz,
         $c = 3 \times 10^{10}$ cm/sec (the speed of light),   and
         λ = wavelength in cm.

In infrared spectroscopy, frequency is expressed as **wavenumbers**: the number of cycles per centimeter. Wavenumbers have units of *reciprocal centimeters* (1/cm, or cm^{-1}) and may be calculated from the wavelength by the following formula:

$$\text{wavenumber in } cm^{-1} = \frac{1}{\lambda \text{ in cm}}$$

A few common symbols and units used in spectroscopy are listed in Table 8.1.

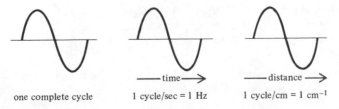

one complete cycle   1 cycle/sec = 1 Hz   1 cycle/cm = 1 cm^{-1}

Figure 8.3. Frequency of electromagnetic radiation.

Table 8.1.   Symbols Commonly Encountered in Spectroscopy

Symbol	Definition
v	frequency in Hz (cycles per second)
λ	wavelength
μm	micrometer, same as micron (μ), 10^{-6} m
nm	nanometer, same as millimicron (mμ), 10^{-9} m
Å	Angstrom, 10^{-10} m or 10^{-1} nm
cm^{-1}	wavenumber: frequency in reciprocal cm, or $1/\lambda$

Electromagnetic radiation is transmitted in particle-like packets of energy called **photons** or **quanta**. The energy of a photon is *inversely proportional to the wavelength*. (Mathematically, $E = hc/\lambda$, where $h =$ Planck's constant.) Radiation of shorter wavelength has a higher energy; therefore, a photon of ultraviolet light has more energy than a photon of visible light and has substantially more energy than a photon of radio waves.

Conversely, the energy of a photon of radiation is *directly proportional to the frequency* (more waves per unit time mean higher energy). The relationship is expressed in the equation $E = hv$. (The symbol hv is often used in chemical equations to represent electromagnetic radiation.)

ultraviolet   visible   infrared   radio

increasing λ (or decreasing v) means decreased energy

Molecules absorb only specific wavelengths of electromagnetic radiation. Absorption of ultraviolet light (high-energy radiation) results in the promotion of an electron to a higher-energy orbital. Infrared radiation does not contain enough energy to promote an electron; absorption of infrared radiation results in increased amplitudes of vibration of bonded atoms. When a sample absorbs photons of radiation, the number of photons being transmitted through the sample decreases. This absorption is observed as a decrease in **intensity**, or quantity, of radiation. It is this change in intensity that is used as a measurement in spectroscopy.

STUDY PROBLEMS

8.1   Which has the higher energy?

(a)   Infrared radiation of 1500 cm^{-1} or of 1600 cm^{-1}
(b)   Ultraviolet radiation of 200 nm or of 300 nm
(c)   Radio waves of 60,000 Hz or of 60,004 Hz

8.2   Infrared spectra are sometimes labeled in cm^{-1} and sometimes in μm (10^{-6} m) or μ (also 10^{-6} m). Make the following conversions:

(a)   6.000 μm to cm^{-1} (b)   800 cm^{-1} to μm (c)   1.5 μ to μm

Section 8.2

Features of a Spectrum

A **spectrum** of a compound is a graph of either *wavelength* or *frequency*, continuously changing over a small portion of the electromagnetic spectrum, versus either *percent transmission* ($\%T$) or *absorbance* (A). The percent transmission is the percent of the intensity of the original radiation that passes through a sample.

$$\% \, T = \frac{\text{intensity}}{\text{original intensity}} \times 100$$

If a sample does not absorb any radiation at a particular wavelength, the percent transmission is 100 at that wavelength. Absorption of radiation at a particular wavelength results in a decrease in the percent transmission and appears in the spectrum as a dip, called a *peak*, or *absorption band*.

Absorbance is a measure of the absorption of radiation by a sample:

$$A = \log\left(\frac{\text{original intensity}}{\text{intensity}}\right)$$

In this case, an increase in absorption appears as an increase (not a decrease) of the signal. The general appearance of spectra using $\%T$ and A is shown in Figure 8.4.

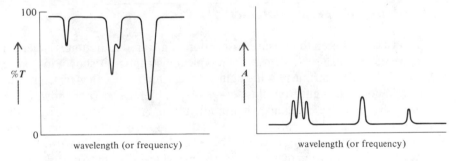

Figure 8.4. Spectra are graphs of percent transmission ($\%T$) or absorbance (A) by a sample versus wavelength or frequency.

Section 8.3

Absorption of Infrared Radiation

Nuclei of atoms bonded by covalent bonds undergo vibrations, or oscillations, in a manner similar to two balls attached by a spring. When molecules absorb infrared radiation, the absorbed energy causes an increase in the amplitude of the vibrations of the bonded atoms. The molecule is then in an **excited vibrational state**. (The absorbed energy is subsequently dissipated as heat when the molecule returns to the ground state.) The exact wavelength of absorption by a given type of bond depends upon the type of vibration of that bond. Therefore, different types of bonds (C—H, C—C, O—H and so forth) absorb infrared radiation at different wavelengths.

A bond within a molecule may undergo different types of oscillation; therefore, a particular bond may absorb energy at more than one wavelength. For example, an O—H bond absorbs energy at about 3330 cm^{-1} (3.0 μm); energy of this wavelength causes increased **stretching vibrations** of the O—H bond. An O—H bond also absorbs at about 1250 cm^{-1} (8.0 μm); energy of this wavelength causes increased **bending vibrations**. These different types of vibration are called different **modes of vibration**.

O   O

CH$_3$ H   CH$_3$ H

stretching   *bending*

The relative amounts of energy absorbed also vary from bond to bond. This is partly due to changes in bond moment when energy is absorbed. Nonpolar bonds (such as C—H or C—C bonds) give rise to weak absorption, while polar bonds (such as C=O) exhibit much stronger absorption.

Section 8.4

The Infrared Spectrophotometer

The instrument used to measure absorption of infrared radiation is called an **infrared spectrophotometer**. A diagram of a typical instrument is shown in Figure 8.5. At one end of the instrument is the light source, which emits all wavelengths of infrared radiation. The light from this source is split by mirrors (not shown) into two beams, the reference beam and the sample beam. After passing through the reference cell (which contains solvent, if used in the sample, or nothing if the sample is pure) and the sample cell, the two beams are combined in the chopper (another mirror system) into one beam that alternates from reference beam to sample beam. This alternating beam is diffracted by a grating that separates the beam into its different wavelengths. The detector measures the difference in intensities of the two segments of the beam at each wavelength and passes this information on to the recorder, which produces the spectrum.

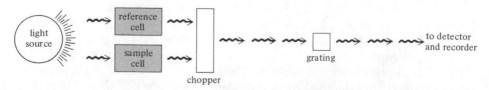

Figure 8.5. The infrared spectrophotometer.

Section 8.5

The Infrared Spectrum

Figure 8.6 shows the infrared spectrum of 1-propanol. The horizontal scale shows the wavelength from 2.5 μm to 15 μm. The legend on the top of the spectrum gives the corresponding wavenumbers, from 4000 cm^{-1} to 670 cm^{-1}. The vertical scale is percent transmission. (The break in the middle of the spectrum at 5 μm arises from a change of gratings in the wavelength selector. Note that the horizontal scale changes at this break.) The wavelength of the *minimum point* of an absorption band is used to identify each band. This point is more reproducible than the range of a wide band, which may vary with concentration or with the sensitivity of the instrument.

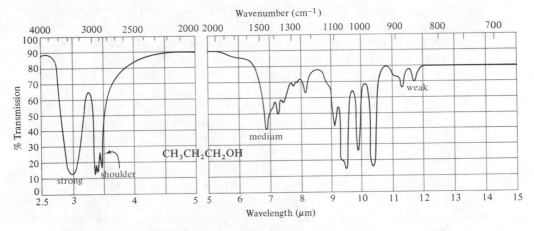

Figure 8.6.   Infrared spectrum of 1-propanol.

The infrared bands in a spectrum may be classified by intensity: *strong* (*s*), *medium* (*m*), and *weak* (*w*). A weaker band overlapping a stronger band is called a *shoulder* (*sh*). These terms are relative, and the assignment of any given band as *s*, *m*, *w*, or *sh* is qualitative at best. In Figure 8.6, a few bands are labeled according to this classification method.

The number of identical groups in a molecule alters the relative strengths of the absorption bands in a spectrum. For example, a single —OH group in a molecule produces a relatively strong absorption, while a single C—H absorption is relatively weak. However, if a compound has many C—H bonds, the collective effect of the C—H absorption gives a peak that is medium or even strong.

Section 8.6

Interpretation of an Infrared Spectrum

Chemists have studied thousands of infrared spectra and have determined the likely wavelengths of absorption for each of the functional groups. **Correlation charts** provide summaries of this information.

Infrared and Nmr Spectroscopy

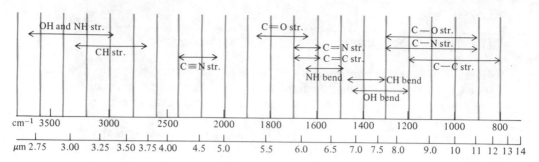

Figure 8.7. Correlation chart for group assignments in infrared spectra.

Figure 8.7 is a typical correlation chart for the stretching and bending frequencies of various groups. From the chart we see that O—H and N—H stretching bands are found between 2970–3700 cm^{-1} (2.7–3.3 μm). (Figure 8.6, the infrared spectrum of 1-propanol, shows absorption at this position.) If the infrared spectrum of a compound of unknown structure shows absorption in this region, then we suspect that the compound contains either an OH or an NH group in its structure. If this region does not contain an absorption band, we conclude that the structure probably does not have an OH group or an NH group.

The region from 1500–4000 cm^{-1} (2.5 μm to about 6.5 μm), to the left in the infrared spectrum, is especially useful for identification of the various functional groups. This region shows absorption arising from stretching modes. The region to the right of 1500 cm^{-1} is usually quite complex because both stretching and bending modes give rise to absorption here. In this region, correlation of an individual band with a specific functional group usually cannot be made with accuracy; however, each organic compound has its own unique absorption here. This part of the spectrum is therefore called the **fingerprint region**. Although the left-hand portion of a spectrum may appear the same for similar compounds, the fingerprint region must also match for two spectra to represent the same compound.

Figure 8.8 shows the infrared spectra of two alkanes of the formula C_6H_{14}: *n*-hexane and 3-methylpentane. Note that the two spectra are practically identical from 1250–4000 cm^{-1} (2.5 μm to about 8 μm), but that the fingerprint regions are quite different.

In the following sections, we will discuss the characteristic infrared absorption of compounds containing aliphatic C—C and C—H bonds and a few functional groups. Our intent is to develop familiarity with the features of typical infrared spectra. As we discuss the various functional groups in future chapters, we will also include discussions of their infrared spectral characteristics.

A.   Carbon–Carbon

Bonds between sp^3 carbon atoms (C—C single bonds) usually give weak absorption in the infrared spectrum. Bonds between sp^2 carbons (C=C), as in alkenes or benzene, give absorption (variable in strength) around 1600–1700 cm^{-1} (5.8–6.2 μm). Bonds between sp carbons (C≡C) give very characteristic absorption at 2100–2300 cm^{-1} (4.2–4.7 μm). These absorption patterns will be discussed in more detail in Chapters 9 and 10; however, it is usually the case that nmr

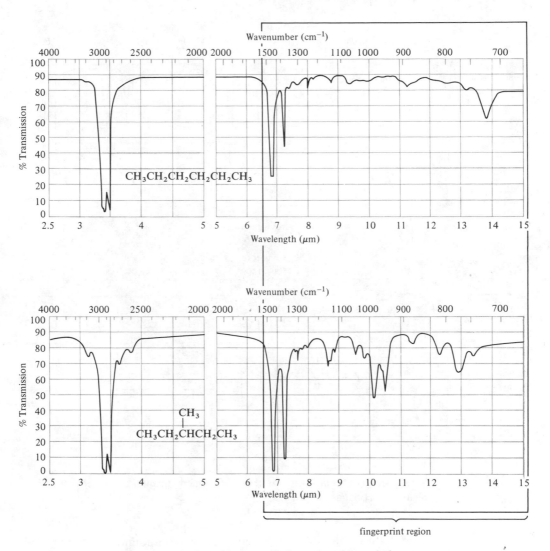

Figure 8.8. Infrared spectra of *n*-hexane and 3-methylpentane.

spectra are more useful than infrared spectra in determining whether a carbon atom is sp^3 or sp^2 hybridized.

B. Carbon–Hydrogen

Almost all organic compounds contain C—H bonds. Absorption arising from C—H stretching is seen at about 2700–3300 cm⁻¹ (3.1–3.75 μm). The C—H stretching peaks are often useful in determining the hybridization of the carbon atom.

sp^3 *C* — *H* (*alkanes or alkyl groups*):   2800–3000 cm⁻¹ (3.3–3.6 μm)
sp^2 *C* — *H* (=*CH*—):   3000–3100 cm⁻¹ (3.2–3.3 μm)
sp C — *H* (≡*CH*):   ~3300 cm⁻¹ (3.0 μm)

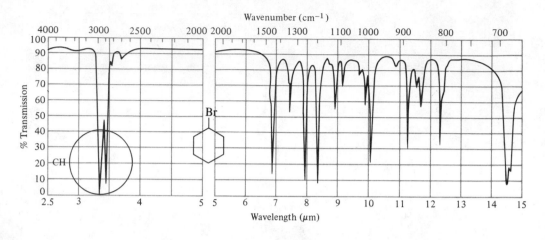

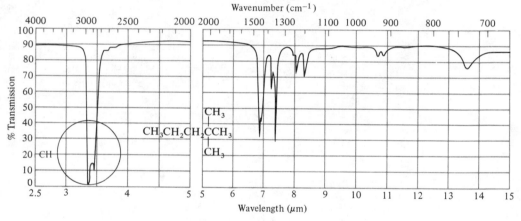

Figure 8.9. Infrared spectra of bromocyclohexane and 2,2-dimethylpentane, showing typical aliphatic C—H bands (circled).

Figure 8.9 shows the infrared spectra of two compounds containing sp^3 C—H bonds. Spectra showing the C—H absorption by alkenes, alkynes, and benzene compounds will be presented in Chapters 9 and 10.

C. Alkyl Halides

The stretching absorption of the C—X bond of an alkyl halide falls in the fingerprint region of the infrared spectrum, from 500–1430 cm^{-1} (7–20 μm). Without additional information, the presence or absence of a band in this region cannot be used for verifying the presence of a halogen in an organic compound.

D. Alcohols and Amines

Alcohols and amines each exhibit two infrared stretching bands, one arising from O—H (or N—H) stretching and the other from the C—O (or C—N) stretching. The C—O and C—N bands are found at 900–1300 cm^{-1} (8–11 μm)

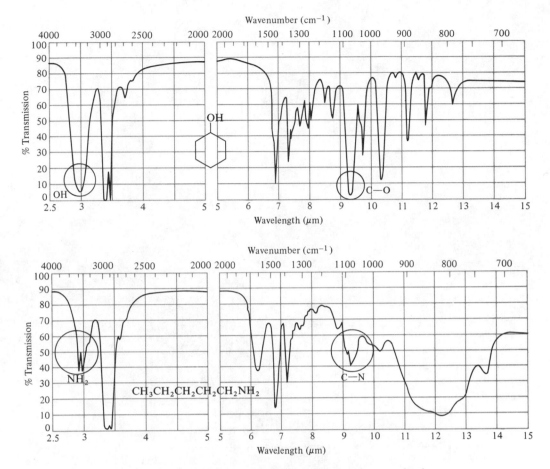

Figure 8.10. Infrared spectra of cyclohexanol and *n*-pentylamine.

in the fingerprint region; these bands are not always easy to identify. However, the O—H and N—H stretching bands are very characteristic. Both are found at 3000–3700 cm^{-1} (2.7–3.3 μm), just to the left of C—H absorption in a spectrum.

Figure 8.10 shows infrared spectra of an alcohol and an amine. The O—H and N—H absorption bands are circled. Because oxygen is more electronegative than nitrogen, O—H stretching results in a greater change in bond moment than does N—H stretching. As you can see, the O—H band is stronger than the N—H band.

If there are two hydrogens on an amine nitrogen (—NH$_2$), the N—H absorption appears as a double peak. If there is only one H on the N, then one peak is observed. Of course, if there is no N—H (as in the case of a tertiary amine, R$_3$N), then there is no absorption in this region (see Figure 8.11, page 324).

Hydrogen bonding changes the position and appearance of an infrared absorption band. The spectra in Figures 8.10 and 8.11 are those of pure liquids, in which hydrogen bonding is extensive. Note that the O—H absorption in Figure 8.10 appears as a wide band at about 3330 cm^{-1} (3.0 μm). When hydrogen bonding is less extensive, a sharper, less intense O—H peak is observed at about

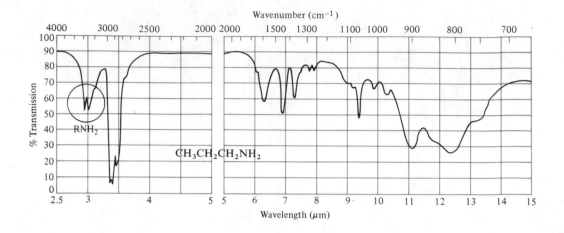

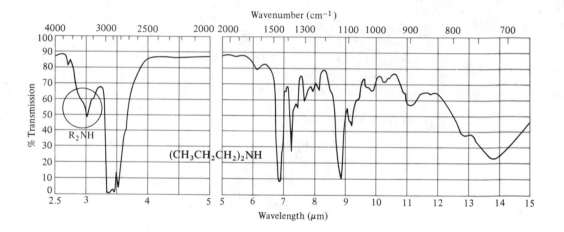

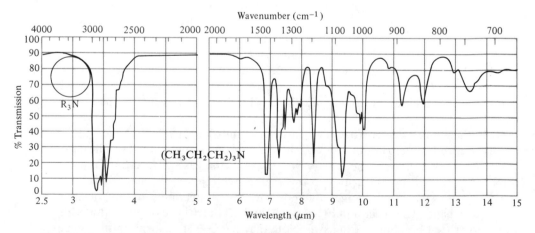

Figure 8.11. Infrared spectra of *n*-propylamine (top), dipropylamine (center), and tripropyl-amine (bottom).

3600 cm^{-1} (2.75 μm). Figure 8.12 shows two partial spectra of an alcohol. One spectrum is of a pure liquid (hydrogen bonded); the other spectrum is of the alcohol in the vapor phase (not hydrogen bonded). The differences in OH absorption are apparent in this figure.

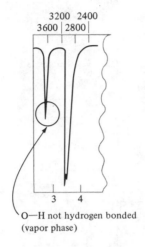

O—H not hydrogen bonded
(vapor phase)

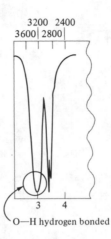

O—H hydrogen bonded

Figure 8.12. Partial infrared spectra of an alcohol showing hydrogen-bonded and non-hydrogen-bonded O—H absorption.

STUDY PROBLEM

8.3   Figure 8.13 (page 326) gives the infrared spectra of two compounds, I and II, both of which appear in the following list. Which is I and which is II?

(a) $CH_3(CH_2)_6CH_3$ (b) $CH_3(CH_2)_6CH_2OH$
(c) $CH_3(CH_2)_5N(CH_3)_2$ (d) $CH_3(CH_2)_6CH_2NH_2$
(e) $CH_3(CH_2)_6CH_2I$

E.   Ethers

Ethers have a C—O stretching band that falls in the fingerprint region at 1050–1260 cm^{-1} (7.9–9.5 μm). Because oxygen is electronegative, the stretching causes a large change in bond moment; therefore, the C—O absorption is usually strong (see Figure 8.14). If there is good reason to suspect that an unknown compound is an ether, the C—O band may often be identified. However, the presence of a strong band in this region does not necessarily mean that the compound is an ether; corroborating evidence is needed.

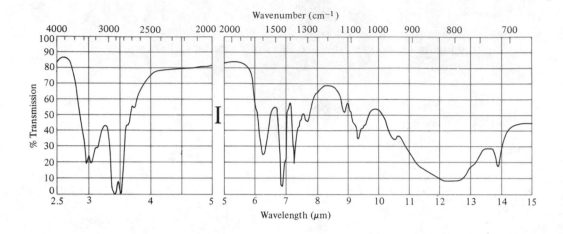

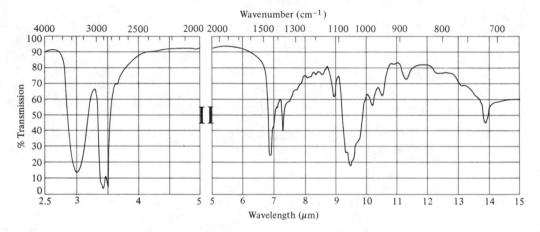

Figure 8.13. Infrared spectra for Problem 8.3.

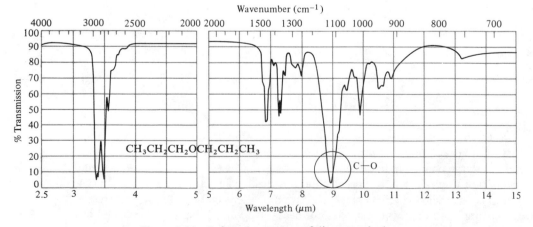

$CH_3CH_2CH_2OCH_2CH_2CH_3$

C—O

Figure 8.14. Infrared spectrum of di-*n*-propyl ether.

STUDY PROBLEM

8.4   A compound yielded only ethyl iodide as a product when heated with HI. The infrared spectrum of the original compound is shown in Figure 8.15. What is its structure?

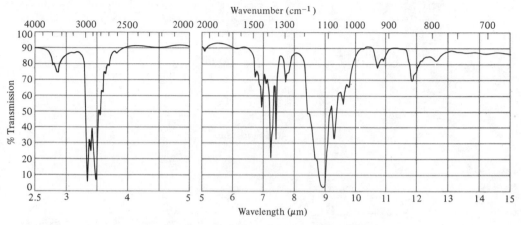

Figure 8.15.   Infrared spectrum of unknown compound for Problem 8.4.

F.   *Carbonyl Compounds*

One of the most distinctive bands in an infrared spectrum is the one arising from the carbonyl stretching mode. This is a strong peak observed somewhere between 1640 and 1820 cm^{-1} (5.5–6.1 μm).

The carbonyl group is part of a number of functional groups. The exact position of the carbonyl absorption, the positions of other absorption bands in the infrared spectrum, and other spectral techniques (particularly nmr) may be used to identify the functional group. The positions of C=O absorption for aldehydes, ketones, carboxylic acids, and esters are listed in Table 8.2.

Table 8.2.   *Stretching Vibrations for Some Carbonyl Compounds[a]*

	Position of absorption	
Type of compound	cm^{-1}	μm
aldehyde, $\text{R}\overset{\overset{\textstyle O}{\|}}{\text{C}}\text{H}$	1720–1740	5.75–5.80
ketone, $\text{R}\overset{\overset{\textstyle O}{\|}}{\text{C}}\text{R}$	1705–1720	5.80–5.87
carboxylic acid, $\text{R}\overset{\overset{\textstyle O}{\|}}{\text{C}}\text{OH}$	1700–1725	5.80–5.88
ester, $\text{R}\overset{\overset{\textstyle O}{\|}}{\text{C}}\text{OR}$	1735–1750	5.71–5.76

[a] In each case, R is saturated and aliphatic.

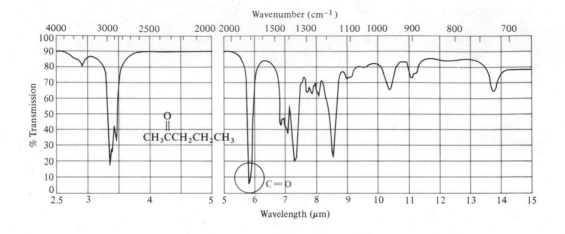

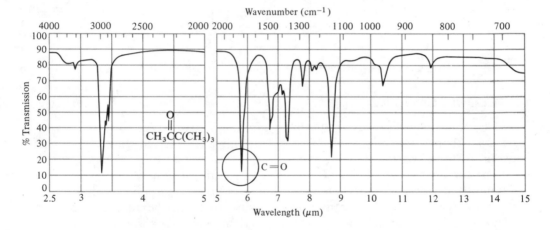

Figure 8.16.   Infrared spectra of two ketones: 2-pentanone (top) and 3,3-dimethyl-2-butanone (bottom).

Ketones give the simplest spectra of the carbonyl compounds. If a compound is an aliphatic ketone, all strong stretching infrared absorption arises from either C=O or C—H. Other functionality may increase the complexity of the spectrum, of course. The infrared spectra of two ketones are shown in Figure 8.16.

Aldehydes give infrared spectra very similar to those of ketones. The important difference between an aldehyde and a ketone is that an aldehyde has an H bonded to the carbonyl carbon. This particular C—H bond shows two characteristic stretching bands (just to the right of the aliphatic C—H band) at 2820–2900 cm^{-1} (3.45–3.55 μm) and 2700–2780 cm^{-1} (3.60–3.70 μm). Both these C—H peaks are sharp, but weak, and the peak at 2900 cm^{-1} (3.45 μm) may be obscured by overlapping C—H absorption (see Figure 8.17). The aldehyde C—H also has a very characteristic nmr absorption (see Section 8.8). If the infrared spectrum of a compound suggests that the structure is an aldehyde, the nmr spectrum should be checked.

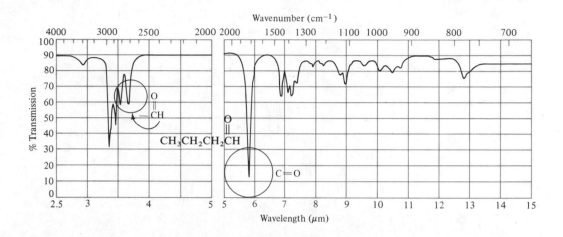

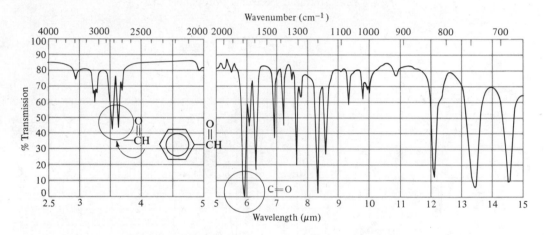

Figure 8.17. Infrared spectra of two aldehydes: butanal (top) and benzaldehyde (bottom).

Carboxylic acids exhibit typical C=O absorption and also show a very distinctive O—H band, which begins at about 3330 cm^{-1} (3.0 μm) and slopes into the aliphatic C—H absorption band (Figure 8.18, page 330). The reason that a carboxyl —OH gives a different-looking spectrum from that of an alcohol —OH is that carboxylic acids form hydrogen-bonded *dimers*:

$$R—C\overset{\textstyle O\cdots H—O}{\underset{\textstyle O—H\cdots O}{\Big\langle}}C—R$$

Esters exhibit both a typical carbonyl band and a C—O band. The C—O band, like that in ethers, is observed in the fingerprint region, 1110–1300 cm^{-1} (7.7–9.0 μm) and is sometimes difficult to assign. However, this C—O band is strong and, in some cases, may be used to distinguish between esters and ketones. See Figure 8.19 for the infrared spectra of some typical esters.

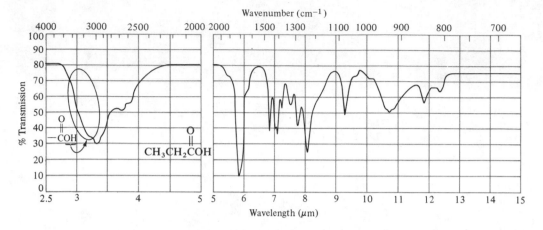

Figure 8.18. Infrared spectrum of propanoic acid.

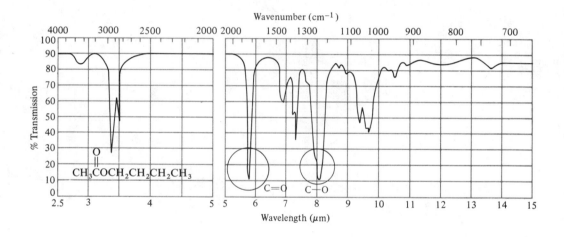

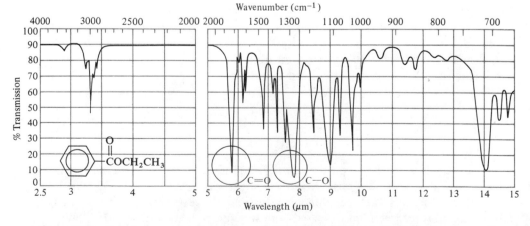

Figure 8.19. Infrared spectra of two esters: *n*-butyl acetate (top) and ethyl benzoate (bottom).

STUDY PROBLEM

8.5 One of the two spectra in Figure 8.20 is that of a ketone; the other is of an ester. Which is which?

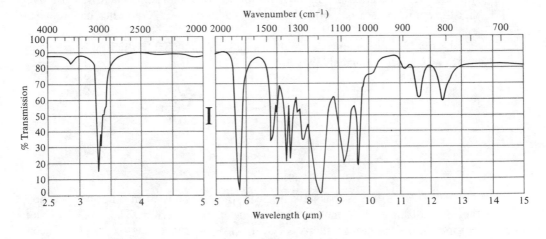

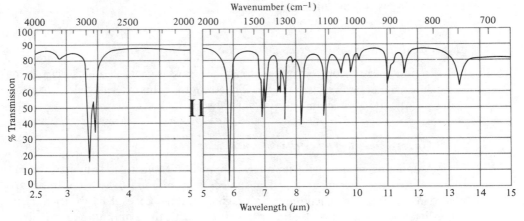

Figure 8.20. Infrared spectra of unknown compounds for Problem 8.5.

Section 8.7

Nuclear Magnetic Resonance Spectroscopy

The infrared spectrum of a compound gives a picture of the different functional groups in an organic molecule, but gives only meager clues about the hydrocarbon portion of the molecule. **Nuclear magnetic resonance (nmr) spectroscopy** fills this gap by providing a picture of the hydrogen atoms in the molecule.

Nmr spectroscopy is based upon the absorption of radio waves by certain nuclei in organic molecules when they are in a strong magnetic field. Before proceeding with a discussion of nmr spectra and their use in organic chemistry, let us first consider the physical principles that give rise to the nmr phenomenon.

A.   *Nuclear Spin and Magnetic Moment*

The nuclei of atoms of all elements can be classified as either *having spin* or *not having spin*. To the organic chemist, the important isotopes that have nuclear spin are ^1_1H, $^{13}_6C$, and $^{19}_9F$. Equally important to the organic chemist is the fact that the common isotopes of carbon ($^{12}_6C$) and oxygen ($^{16}_8O$) do not have nuclear spin.

A nucleus with spin gives rise to a small magnetic field, which is described by a **nuclear magnetic moment**, a vector.

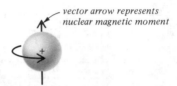

While all isotopes that have nuclear spin can be used in nmr spectroscopy, they do not all absorb energy at the same radiofrequency. The most common isotope studied by nmr methods is ^1_1H, the proton; consequently, we will concentrate our discussion on this one isotope.

B.   *The Effect of an External Magnetic Field on Protons*

In nmr spectroscopy, an **external magnetic field** is generated by a permanent horseshoe magnet or an electromagnet. The strength of this external field is symbolized by H_0, and its direction is represented by an arrow.

Symbol representing the external magnetic field: $\uparrow H_0$

A spinning proton with its nuclear magnetic moment is similar, in many respects, to a tiny bar magnet. When molecules containing hydrogen atoms are placed in an external magnetic field, the magnetic moment of each hydrogen nucleus aligns itself in one of two different orientations with the external magnetic field. (Keep in mind that it is only the magnetic moments of *hydrogen nuclei*, not molecules, that become aligned.) The two orientations that the nuclear magnetic moment may assume are **parallel** and **antiparallel** to the external field. In the parallel state, the magnetic moment of the proton points in the *same direction* as that of the external field. In the antiparallel state, the magnetic moment of the proton *opposes* the external field.

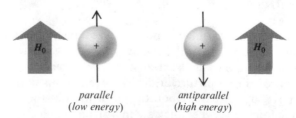

The parallel state of a proton is more stable (lower energy) than the antiparallel state. When exposed to the proper frequency of radio waves, the magnetic moment of a proton parallel to the magnetic field absorbs energy and turns around, or *flips*, to the higher-energy antiparallel state. The amount of energy required to flip the magnetic moment of a proton from parallel to antiparallel depends upon the strength of H_0. If H_0 is stronger, the nucleus is more resistant to being flipped and higher-energy, higher-frequency radiation is required. (The relationship between frequency and H_0 is given by the equation $v = \gamma H_0/2\pi$. For the proton, $\gamma = 26,750$.)

When the particular combination of external magnetic field strength and radiofrequency causes a proton to flip from parallel to antiparallel, the proton is said to be in **resonance** (a different type of resonance from that of "resonance" structures of benzene). The term **nuclear magnetic resonance** means "nuclei in resonance in a magnetic field."

It would seem that all protons should come into resonance at the same combination of H_0 and radiofrequency; however, this is not the case. The strength of the magnetic field around a particular proton is affected by the rest of the molecule and varies with the structure of the molecule. It is the variation in the energy needed to bring a proton into resonance that is useful in structure determination.

C. The Nmr Spectrometer

A schematic diagram of an nmr spectrometer is shown in Figure 8.21. The sample is placed between the poles of a magnet and is irradiated with radio waves. When the protons flip from the parallel to antiparallel state, the absorption of energy is detected by a power indicator.

In one type of nmr spectrometer, the radiofrequency is held constant at 60 MHz (60 megaHertz, or 60×10^6 Hz), H_0 is varied over a small range, and the frequency of energy absorption is recorded at the various values for H_0. Figure 8.22 shows an nmr spectrum of methanol on which we have indicated the direction of the field sweep from weak H_0 to strong H_0. The protons that flip more easily

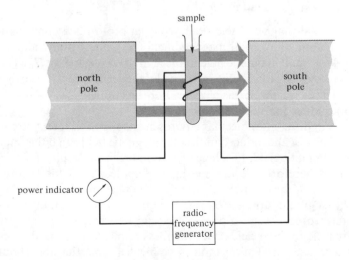

Figure 8.21. Schematic diagram of an nmr spectrometer.

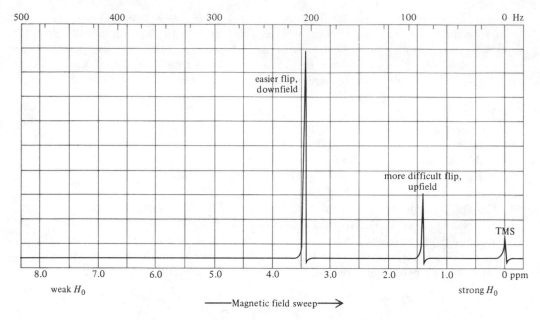

Figure 8.22.   Nmr spectrum of methanol, showing the relation between H_0 and proton flips (radiofrequency held constant, $CDCl_3$ solvent).

absorb energy at a lower H_0; they give rise to an absorption peak **downfield** (farther to the left). The protons that flip with greater difficulty absorb energy at a higher H_0 and give a peak that is **upfield** (to the right).

D.   Effect of the Molecular Field

The external magnetic field observed by a proton is a combination of two fields: (1) the applied external magnetic field (H_0), and (2) an **induced molecular magnetic field**, a small magnetic field induced in the molecule by H_0. The magnetic field observed by a proton is also modified by the spin states of nearby protons, a topic we will discuss later in this chapter. For the moment, we want to explore the effects of the induced molecular magnetic field.

Protons in different molecular environments flip at different strengths of the applied field because the induced molecular magnetic field can either aid or oppose the external magnetic field. (Technically, all induced molecular fields oppose the external field; therefore, we are speaking of molecular fields relative to other molecular fields.) If the two fields (H_0 and the induced molecular field) oppose one another, then a greater applied H_0 is needed to bring a proton into resonance. In this case, the proton is said to be **shielded**, and we observe its absorption *upfield* in a spectrum. If the two fields add, then less applied H_0 is needed to bring the proton into resonance. This proton is **deshielded**, and the absorption appears *downfield* (see Figure 8.23).

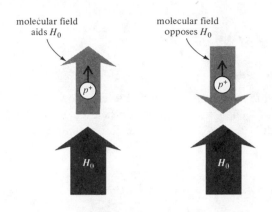

molecular field aids H_0

molecular field opposes H_0

Figure 8.23. The field observed by the hydrogen nucleus (p^+) is the applied field plus or minus the induced molecular field.

E. Chemical Shift

Shielding and deshielding are relative terms. In order to obtain quantitative measurements, we need a reference point. The compound that has been chosen for this reference point is tetramethylsilane (TMS), $(CH_3)_4Si$, the protons of which absorb to the far right in the nmr spectrum. The absorption for most other protons is observed downfield from that of TMS. In practice, a small amount of TMS is added directly to the sample, and the peak for TMS is observed on the spectrum along with any absorption peaks from the sample compound. The difference between the position of absorption of TMS and that of a particular proton is called the **chemical shift**.

Chemical shifts are reported in **δ values**, which are expressed as *parts per million (ppm) of the applied radiofrequency*. At 60 MHz, 1.0 ppm is 60 Hz; therefore, a δ value of 1.0 ppm is 60 Hz downfield from the position of absorption of TMS, which is set at 0 ppm. As may be seen in Figure 8.24, the two types of proton in CH_3OH have δ values of 1.4 ppm and 3.45 ppm.

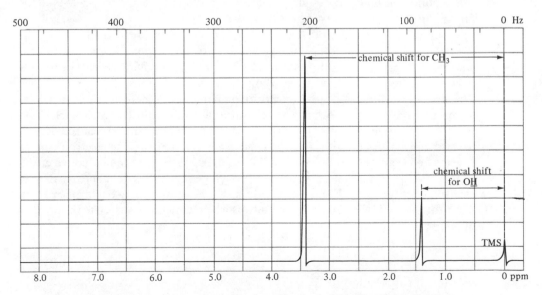

Figure 8.24. Nmr spectrum of methanol, showing the chemical shifts.

Section 8.8

Types of Induced Molecular Magnetic Field

A. Fields Induced by Sigma Electrons

Any hydrogen atom in an organic compound is bonded to carbon, oxygen, or some other atom by a sigma bond. The external magnetic field causes these sigma-bond electrons to circulate; the result is a small molecular magnetic field that *opposes* H_0 (Figure 8.25).

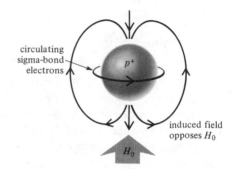

Figure 8.25. The induced field from circulating sigma-bond electrons opposes H_0.

Because the induced field opposes the external field, the sigma-bonded proton is shielded. It takes a slightly higher external field strength to overcome the effect of the induced field in order to bring the proton into resonance; therefore, the proton absorbs upfield compared to a hypothetical naked proton. The strength of the induced field depends upon the electron density near the hydrogen atom in the sigma bond. The higher the electron density, the greater is the induced field (and the farther upfield is the observed absorption).

The electron density of a carbon–hydrogen covalent bond is affected by the electronegativity of the other atoms bonded to the carbon. Let us consider a specific example. The C—F bond in CH_3F is polar: the fluorine atom carries a partial negative charge and the carbon atom carries a partial positive charge. Because the carbon has a partial positive charge, the electrons in each C—H sigma bond are drawn toward the carbon and away from the hydrogen atom. Recall from our discussion of carbocation stability that the shift in electron density toward a positive center is called the **inductive effect**. This shift in electron density toward an electronegative element (F) is another example of the inductive effect. In this case, the result of the electron-withdrawing effect of F is that there is a greater electron density around F and a lesser electron density around each hydrogen atom. The protons of CH_3F are deshielded and absorb downfield compared to the protons of CH_4.

$$H \rightarrow \overset{\displaystyle \overset{H}{\downarrow}}{\underset{\displaystyle \overset{\uparrow}{H}}{C}} \rightarrow F$$

F causes a decrease in
e^- *density around H*

The following series of methane and the methyl halides shows increased deshielding of the hydrogen nuclei with increasing electronegativity of the atom attached to $-CH_3$.

$$H_3C-H \qquad H_3C-I \qquad H_3C-Br \qquad H_3C-Cl \qquad H_3C-F$$

increased deshielding of H

Sample Problem

Which of the circled protons is the most shielded? The most deshielded? What are the relative positions of nmr absorption?

(a) CH_3CH_2Cl (b) CH_3CH_3 (c) CH_3CH_2I

Solution: Chlorine is more electronegative than iodine, which in turn is more electronegative than hydrogen. Therefore, (a) is the most deshielded and absorbs downfield; (b) is the most shielded and absorbs upfield, closer to TMS; and (c) is intermediate.

In a single molecule, a proton that is attached to the same carbon as an electronegative atom is more deshielded than protons on other carbons. Figure 8.33 (page 343) shows the spectrum of ethyl chloride. The peaks at 1.5 ppm arise from the CH_3 protons, while the deshielded CH_2Cl protons absorb farther downfield, at 3.55 ppm. (The complexity of these peaks will be discussed later in this chapter.)

The inductive effect of an electronegative atom falls off rapidly when it is passed through a number of sigma bonds. In nmr spectra, the inductive effect of an electronegative atom is negligible three carbons away from the electronegative center.

effect of X is | *effect of X is important*
of little importance | *in decreasing*
in decreasing | *e⁻ density around*
e⁻ density | *this proton*
around this proton

$$\begin{array}{ccccc} & H & H & H & \\ & | & | & | & \\ H- & C- & C- & C- & X \\ & | & | & | & \\ & H & H & H & \end{array}$$

Most elements encountered in organic compounds are more electronegative than carbon. Their inductive effect is one of electron-withdrawal, and protons affected by them are deshielded. However, silicon is *less* electronegative than carbon. The silicon–carbon bond is polarized such that carbon carries a partial negative charge. The electrons in the C—H bond of an Si—CH_3 group are repelled from the negative carbon and pushed toward the hydrogen atoms. In this case, the inductive effect is *electron-releasing*. The protons of an $SiCH_3$ group are highly shielded because of the increased electron density around them. This is the reason that the protons of TMS absorb upfield and that TMS provides a good reference peak in an nmr spectrum.

greater e⁻ density on H; highly shielded

$$CH_3$$
$$\uparrow$$
$$H_3C \leftarrow Si \rightarrow CH_3$$
$$\downarrow$$
$$CH_3$$

B. Fields Induced by Pi Electrons

We will now consider molecular magnetic fields induced by the action of H_0 on *pi electrons*. The magnetic fields induced by pi electrons are directional (that is, unsymmetrical). A measurement that varies depending on the direction in which the measurement is taken is said to be **anisotropic**. Because the effects of molecular fields induced by pi electrons are direction-dependent, they are called **anisotropic effects**. (These effects are contrasted to inductive effects, which are symmetrical around the proton.) Anisotropic effects occur in addition to the ever-present molecular fields induced by sigma-bond electrons.

In benzene, the pi electrons are delocalized around the ring. Under the influence of an external magnetic field, these pi electrons *circulate around the ring*. This circulation, called **ring current**, induces a molecular magnetic field with the geometry shown in Figure 8.26. (All the benzene rings, of course, do not line up as we have represented the ring in Figure 8.26; Figure 8.26 shows the net effect of the vector forces.)

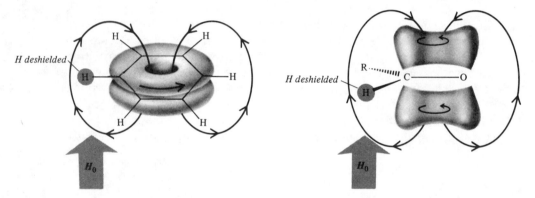

Figure 8.26.   Circulating pi electrons in benzene or aldehydes induce a magnetic field that deshields the adjacent protons.

The result of this induced field is that H_0 is augmented (relatively speaking) in the vicinity of the benzene protons. Less applied field is required to bring aryl protons into resonance than is necessary for alkyl protons. Therefore, aryl protons are deshielded and absorb farther downfield than alkyl protons.

An analogous situation is observed in the case of a vinyl hydrogen or an aldehyde hydrogen. In either case, the pi electrons are set in motion and induce a field that adds to the applied field in the vicinity of the =CH proton (see Figure 8.26). A proton attached to an sp^2 carbon of C=O or C=C absorbs downfield from an alkyl proton.

Figure 8.27 shows the nmr spectrum of a compound with aryl protons, vinyl protons, and a CH_3 group. In this spectrum, it is evident that the vinyl protons absorb downfield from CH_3 protons and that aryl protons absorb even farther downfield.

Figure 8.28 shows the spectrum of an aldehyde. The aldehyde proton is shifted downfield both by anisotropic effects and by electron-withdrawal by the carbonyl oxygen. The combination of effects results in absorption that is far

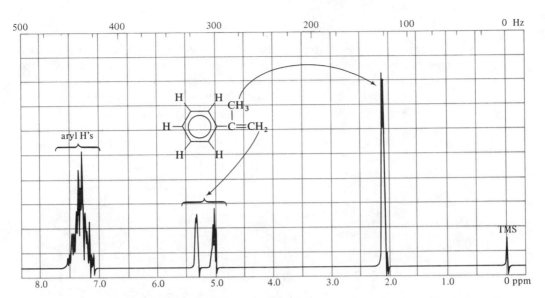

Figure 8.27. Nmr spectrum of 2-phenylpropene, showing absorption by aryl, vinyl, and methyl protons.

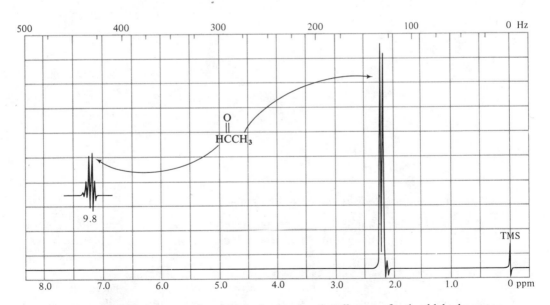

Figure 8.28. Nmr spectrum of acetaldehyde, showing the offset scan for the aldehyde proton.

downfield (9–10 ppm), outside the normal scan for an nmr spectrometer. Instrument design allows scanning at field strengths that are lower than normal; the scan of this region (8–20 ppm), traced above the standard nmr scan, is called an **offset scan**.

C. Summary of Induced-Field Effects

The presence of an electronegative atom causes a decrease in electron density around a proton by the **inductive effect**. Such a proton is deshielded and absorbs downfield. In aromatic compounds, alkenes, and aldehydes, a proton attached to the sp^2 carbon is deshielded by **anisotropic effects** and absorbs even farther downfield. The absorption positions are summarized in Figure 8.29 and Table 8.3.

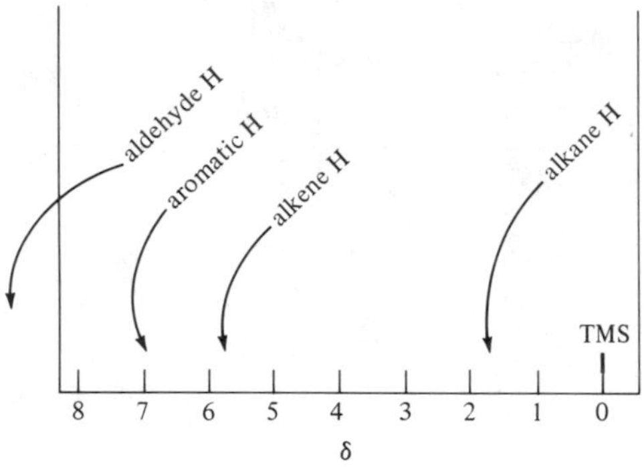

Table 8.3. Typical Chemical Shifts in Nmr Spectra

Group	δ value (ppm)
proton on sp^3 carbon:	
$RC\underline{H}_3$	0.8–1.2
$RC\underline{H}_2R$	1.1–1.5
$ArC\underline{H}_3$	2.2–2.5
$C\underline{H}_3NR_2$	2.2–2.6
$R_2C\underline{H}OR$	3.2–4.3
$R_2C\underline{H}Cl$	3.5–3.7
proton on sp^2 carbon:	
$R_2C{=}C\underline{H}R$	5.0–5.7
$Ar\underline{H}$	6.0–7.5
$RC\underline{H}O$	9.4–10.4
proton on N or O:	
$R_2N\underline{H}$	2–4
$RO\underline{H}$	1–6
$ArO\underline{H}$	6–8
$RCO_2\underline{H}$	10–12

Figure 8.29. Relative positions of proton absorption in the nmr spectrum.

Section 8.9

Counting the Protons

A. Equivalent and Nonequivalent Protons

Protons that are in the same magnetic environment in a molecule have the same chemical shift in an nmr spectrum. Such protons are said to be **equivalent protons**. Protons that are in different magnetic environments have different chemical shifts and are said to be **nonequivalent protons**.

Equivalent protons in nmr spectroscopy are the same as structurally equivalent protons. In ethyl chloride, the three methyl protons are equivalent. Replacing any one of these protons in a chemical reaction leads to the same product, not to isomers. In the following example, note that replacement of any of the methyl protons by Br leads to the same compound, 1-bromo-2-chloroethane.

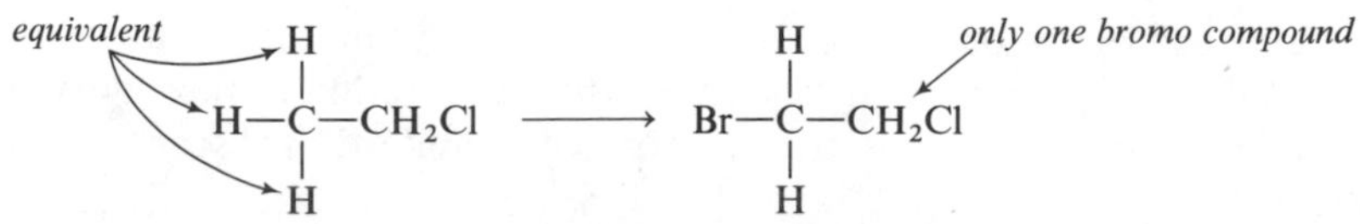

The two protons of the CH_2Cl group are also equivalent to each other. However, the three protons of the CH_3 group are not equivalent to the two CH_2Cl protons.

three equivalent protons
(but nonequivalent to CH_2) —↘

two equivalent protons
↙— *(but nonequivalent to CH_3)*

$$CH_3CH_2Cl$$

The three CH_3 protons have the same chemical shift and absorb at the same position in the nmr spectrum. The two CH_2 protons are deshielded compared to the methyl protons and have a greater chemical shift. A low-resolution spectrum of ethyl chloride would look like the stylized spectrum shown in Figure 8.30.

ClCH$_2$CH$_3$

TMS

8 7 6 5 4 3 2 1 0

Figure 8.30. Stylized low-resolution nmr spectrum of CH_3CH_2Cl.

In vinyl chloride (chloroethene), the proton *cis* to the Cl atom is in a different environment from that of the *trans*-proton. Both of these protons are in different environments from that of the proton on the C—Cl carbon. In vinyl chloride, all three protons are nonequivalent.

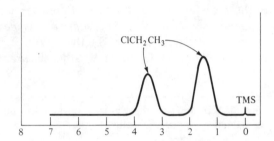

cis to Cl

trans to Cl

vinyl chloride
three nonequivalent protons

Sample Problem

Which protons in *p*-chlorotoluene (1-chloro-4-methylbenzene) are chemically equivalent, and which are nonequivalent?

Solution:

H$_3$C—⬡—Cl
H$_b$ H$_a$ (top)
H$_b$ H$_a$ (bottom)

$\left\{\begin{array}{l} \text{the three methyl protons are equivalent;} \\ \text{the two } H_a\text{'s are equivalent;} \\ \text{the two } H_b\text{'s are equivalent;} \\ \text{the methyl protons, } H_a, \text{ and } H_b \text{ are nonequivalent} \end{array}\right.$

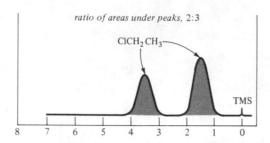

Figure 8.31. Stylized low-resolution nmr spectrum of CH_3CH_2Cl, showing areas under the peaks.

B.   Areas under the Peaks

If we measure the areas under the peaks in an nmr spectrum, we find that *the areas are in the same ratio as the number of hydrogen atoms that give rise to each signal.* In the case of ethyl chloride (Figure 8.31), the ratio is 2:3. (Note that the *height* of the peak is not the important feature, but rather the *area* under the peak.)

Sample Problem

How many types of equivalent protons are there in each of the following structures? What would be the relative areas under the nmr absorption bands?

(a) $(CH_3)_2CHCl$ (b) $CH_3CH_2OCH_2CH_3$ (c)   Cl—⟨benzene ring⟩—OCH_3

Solution: (a) two, 6:1;   (b) two, 3:2;   (c) three, 3:2:2 (3 for CH_3, 2 for aryl protons adjacent to the oxygen, 2 for aryl protons adjacent to Cl).

Most nmr spectrometers are equipped with **integrators**, which give a signal that shows the relative areas under the peaks in a spectrum. The integration appears as a series of steps superimposed upon the nmr spectrum; the height of the step over each absorption peak is proportional to the area under that peak. From the relative heights of the steps on the integration curve, the relative areas under the peaks may be determined. In Figure 8.32, the heights of the steps of the integration curve were measured with a ruler and found to be 33 mm, 100 mm, and 50 mm. For determining the relative numbers of equivalent protons, these values are converted to ratios of small whole numbers, 2:6:3. We can compare these values with the numbers of protons in the known structure of 1-bromo-2,4,6-trimethylbenzene and, indeed, the values agree.

In this text, we will not show the integration lines in the spectra, but will indicate relative areas as numbers directly above the proton absorption peaks, as shown in Figure 8.33.

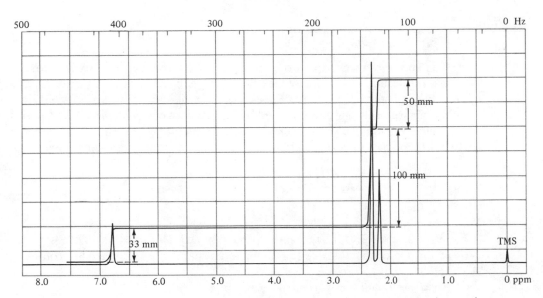

Figure 8.32.   The nmr spectrum of 1-bromo-2,4,6-trimethylbenzene, showing integration.

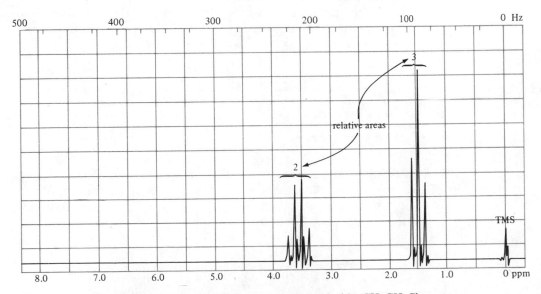

Figure 8.33.   Nmr spectrum of ethyl chloride, CH_3CH_2Cl.

Section 8.10

Spin–Spin Coupling

The spectrum of ethyl chloride in Figures 8.30 and 8.31 is a stylized low-resolution spectrum. If we increase the resolution (that is, the sensitivity), the peaks are resolved, or split, into groups of peaks (see Figure 8.33). This type of splitting is called **spin–spin splitting** and is caused by the presence of *vicinal protons (protons on an adjacent carbon) that are nonequivalent to the proton in question*. Protons that split the signals of each other are said to have undergone **spin–spin coupling**.

*these protons split
the signal for ——
the CH₂ protons*   *these protons split
                                    — the signal for
                                    the CH₃ protons*

$$CH_3CH_2Cl$$

Why do protons undergo spin–spin coupling? The splitting of the signal arises from the two spin states (parallel and antiparallel) of the vicinal protons.

Signal for H_a split by two spin states of H_b:

        parallel   *antiparallel*

The spin of a proton generates a magnetic moment. If the spin of the vicinal proton is parallel, its magnetic moment *adds* to the applied magnetic field; consequently, the first proton sees a slightly stronger field and comes into resonance at a slightly lower applied field strength. If the vicinal proton is in the antiparallel state, its magnetic moment *decreases* the magnetic field around the first proton. In this case, it takes slightly more applied H_0 for that proton to come into resonance.

We can predict the number of spin–spin splitting peaks in the nmr absorption of a particular proton (or a group of equivalent protons) by counting *the number (n) of vicinal protons nonequivalent to the proton in question and adding 1*. This is called the **n + 1 rule**.

| These three equivalent protons see *two* vicinal, nonequivalent protons. Their nmr band is split into 2 + 1, or 3, peaks. | These two equivalent protons see *three* vicinal, nonequivalent protons. Their nmr band is split into 3 + 1, or 4, peaks. |

$$CH_3CH_2Cl$$

Protons that have the same chemical shift do not split the signals of each other. (This is true whether the same chemical shift arises from equivalency of the protons or is simply coincidental.) Only vicinal protons that have different chemical shifts cause splitting. Some examples follow:

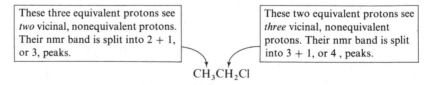

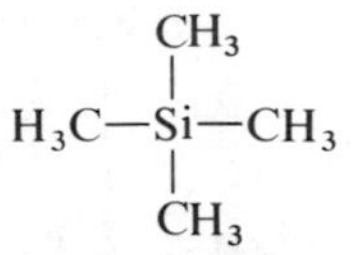

$$CH_3$$
$$H_3C-\underset{\underset{CH_3}{|}}{\overset{\overset{|}{CH_3}}{Si}}-CH_3$$

twelve equivalent H's:
no splitting

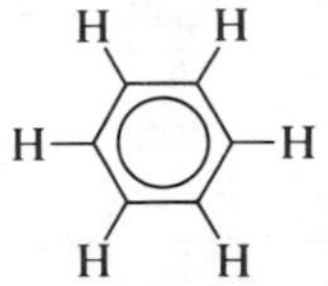

six equivalent H's:
no splitting

In summary, the **chemical shift** for a particular proton is determined by the molecular magnetic field surrounding it. The **area** under an absorption band is determined by the number of equivalent protons giving rise to the particular signal. **Spin–spin splitting** of a signal is dependent on the number of vicinal protons nonequivalent to the proton giving the signal.

Sample Problem

Predict the spin–spin splitting patterns for the protons in 2-chloropropane.

Solution:

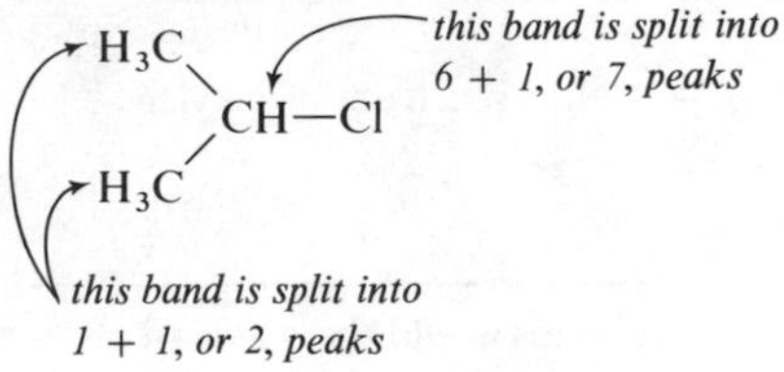

H_3C
CH—Cl
H_3C

this band is split into
6 + 1, or 7, peaks

this band is split into
1 + 1, or 2, peaks

STUDY PROBLEM

8.6 By the $n + 1$ rule, predict the number of nmr peaks for each of the indicated protons:

(a) 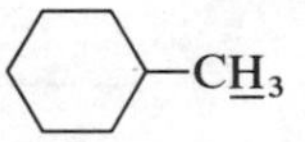 ⬡—C$\underline{H}_3$ (b) $CH_3C\underline{H}_2CH_3$ (c) $(CH_3)_3C\underline{H}$ (d) $(C\underline{H}_3)_3CH$

Section 8.11

Splitting Patterns

A.   The Singlet

A proton with no vicinal protons nonequivalent to it gives a single peak, called a **singlet**, in the nmr spectrum. Figure 8.34, the nmr spectrum of *p*-xylene (1,4-dimethylbenzene), shows two singlets—one for the protons on the ring carbons and the other for the —CH_3 protons. In the structure of *p*-xylene, note that these protons have no vicinal, nonequivalent protons. (Also note that these two nmr signals are in an area ratio of $3:2$.)

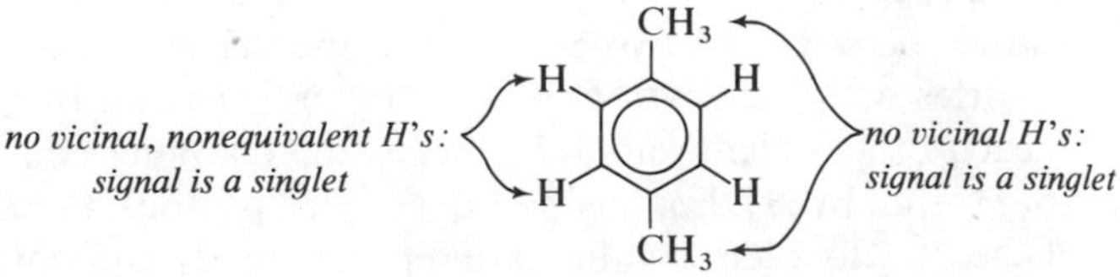

no vicinal, nonequivalent H's:
signal is a singlet

CH_3

CH_3

no vicinal H's:
signal is a singlet

p-xylene

Infrared and Nmr Spectroscopy

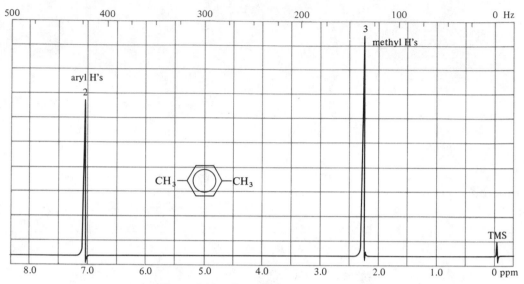

Figure 8.34.   Nmr spectrum of *p*-xylene.

STUDY PROBLEMS

8.7   Which of the following compounds would show at least one singlet in the nmr spectrum?

(a) CH_3CH_3 (b) $(CH_3)_2CHCH(CH_3)_2$ (c) $(CH_3)_3CCl$
(d) Cl_3CCHCl_2 (e) $ClSi(CH_3)_3$

8.8   How many peaks would you expect to observe in the nmr spectra of   (a) cyclohexane, and   (b) benzene?

B.   The Doublet

A proton with one vicinal, nonequivalent proton gives a signal that is split into a double peak, or **doublet**. In the following example, a pair of doublets is produced, one for each proton.

H_a *gives a doublet* ⟶   ⟵ H_b *also gives a doublet*

$$\begin{array}{cc} H_a & H_b \\ | & | \\ -C & -C- \\ | & | \end{array}$$

In the nmr spectrum of the preceding hypothetical structure, the δ value for each proton is the value at the *center* of the doublet (see Figure 8.35). The relative areas under the entire doublets in this case are 1:1, reflecting the fact that each doublet arises from the absorption by one proton. (The two peaks *within* any doublet also have an area ratio that is ideally 1:1, but may be slightly different, as may be seen in Figure 8.36.)

The separation between the two peaks of a doublet is called the **coupling constant J**, and varies with the environment of the protons and their geometric relationship to each other. The symbol J_{ab} means the coupling constant for H_a split by H_b or for H_b split by H_a. For any pair of coupled protons, the J value is the same in each of the two doublets. J values are reported in Hz and not in δ values.

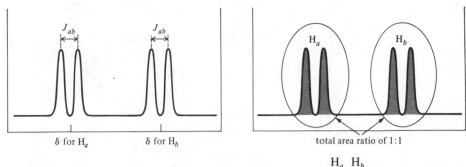

Figure 8.35. Spin–spin splitting pattern for $-\overset{\displaystyle H_a}{\underset{\displaystyle |}{\overset{\displaystyle |}{C}}}-\overset{\displaystyle H_b}{\underset{\displaystyle |}{\overset{\displaystyle |}{C}}}-$.

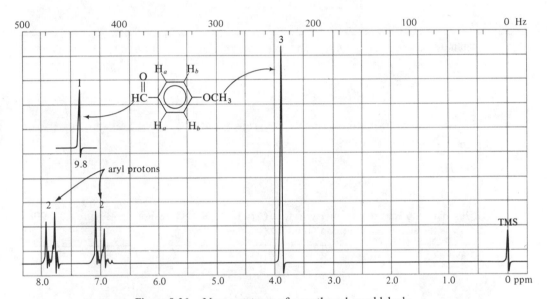

Figure 8.36. Nmr spectrum of *p*-methoxybenzaldehyde.

For a pair of vicinal, nonequivalent protons attached to freely rotating carbons, the *J* value is about 7 Hz.

Figure 8.36, the nmr spectrum of *p*-methoxybenzaldehyde, shows a pair of doublets in the aromatic region. The two protons labeled H_a are equivalent, as are the two H_b protons. H_a and H_b are nonequivalent to each other and vicinal; their signals are split into a pair of doublets. Note that the peaks within the doublets are not perfectly symmetrical; the inside peaks of a doublet are taller. This phenomenon is called **leaning**.

STUDY PROBLEM

8.9 Each of the following indicated protons or groups of protons gives rise to a doublet in the nmr spectrum. Tell how many peaks arise from the signal for the *other, single proton*. (Use the *n* + 1 rule.)

(a) $-\underset{|}{\underline{C}H}-\underset{|}{C}H-$ (b) $-\underset{|}{\underline{C}H_2}-\underset{|}{C}H-$ (c) $\underline{C}H_3-\underset{|}{C}H-$

Sample Problem

Which of the following alkyl chlorides would show a doublet (as well as other signals) in its nmr spectrum?

(a) CH_3CHCl_2 (b) $CH_3CH_2CH_2Cl$ (c) $CH_3CHClCH_3$

Solution: Underlined protons would appear as doublets: (a) $C\underline{H}_3CHCl_2$; (b) no doublet; (c) $C\underline{H}_3CHClC\underline{H}_3$ as one doublet and not as a pair of doublets. (Why?)

Sample Problem

Give the total relative areas under all of the absorption bands for the compounds in the preceding problem.

Solution: (a) 3:1   (b) 3:2:2   (c) 6:1

Sample Problem

Tell how many singlets and how many doublets would appear in the nmr spectrum of each of the following substituted benzenes:

(a) CH_3—⬡—OCH_3 (b) Cl—⬡—NH_2

Solution: (a) two singlets ($C\underline{H}_3$ and $OC\underline{H}_3$) and two doublets for the aryl protons; (b) one singlet ($N\underline{H}_2$) and two doublets.

STUDY PROBLEM

8.10 The nmr spectrum of an aryl ketone ($Ar\overset{\displaystyle O}{\overset{\|}{C}}R$), C_8H_7ClO, is shown in Figure 8.37. What is the structure of this compound?

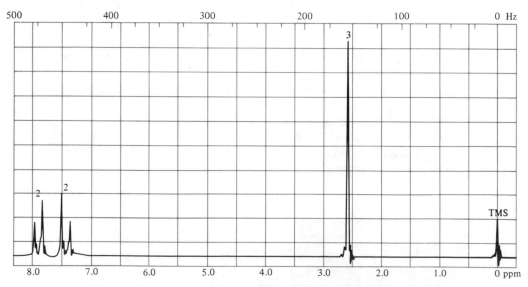

Figure 8.37. Nmr spectrum for unknown aryl ketone in Problem 8.10.

C. The Triplet

If a proton (H_a) sees two vicinal protons equivalent to each other, but not equivalent to itself, the nmr signal of H_a is a **triplet** ($2 + 1 = 3$). If the two protons labeled H_b are equivalent, they give a single signal that is split into a doublet by H_a.

H_a sees two vicinal H's,
signal is a triplet

H_b sees one vicinal H,
signal is a doublet

$$\begin{array}{cc} H_a & H_b \\ | & | \\ -\!\!\overset{|}{C}\!-\!\overset{|}{C}\!-\!H_b \\ | & | \end{array}$$

The nmr absorption pattern for all three protons in the preceding partial structure consists of a doublet and a triplet. The peaks in the triplet each are separated by the *same J value as that for the doublet*. The total width of the triplet (from side peak to side peak) is therefore $2J$ (see Figure 8.38). The areas under the entire triplet and the entire doublet in our example are in the ratio of 1 for H_a to 2 for H_b. (The relative areas *within* the triplet, however, are in a ratio of 1:2:1. The reasons for this will be discussed in Section 8.12.)

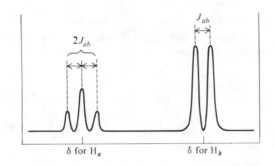

Figure 8.38. Spin–spin splitting pattern for $\begin{array}{cc} H_a & H_b \\ | & | \\ -\!\overset{|}{C}\!-\!\overset{|}{C}\!-\!H_b \\ | & | \end{array}$.

The nmr spectrum of 1,1,2-trichloroethane, which has a doublet and a triplet, is found in Figure 8.39 (page 350).

$$\begin{array}{c} Cl \\ | \\ Cl-\!\!\overset{|}{C}\!-\!C\underline{H}_2-\!Cl \\ | \\ \underline{H} \end{array}$$

$\left\{ \begin{array}{l} \textit{more shielded: upfield} \\ \textit{sees one H: doublet} \\ \textit{relative total area: 2} \end{array} \right.$

$\left\{ \begin{array}{l} \textit{less shielded: downfield} \\ \textit{sees two H's: triplet} \\ \textit{relative total area: 1} \end{array} \right.$

STUDY PROBLEM

8.11   Suggest a reason for the fact that the proton in the Cl_2CH group in 1,1,2-trichloroethane is more deshielded than the protons in the CH_2Cl group.

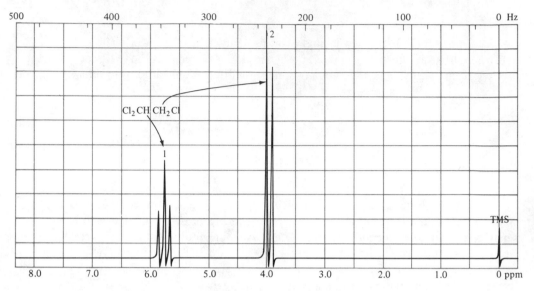

Figure 8.39.   Nmr spectrum of 1,1,2-trichloroethane.

Sample Problem

Which of the following compounds shows a triplet (among other signals) in the nmr? How many triplets will each compound show?

$$\begin{array}{cc} Cl & OCH_3 \\ | & | \\ \end{array}$$

(a) CH_2CH_2 (b) $CH_3CH_2-\langle\bigcirc\rangle$ (c) $Cl_2CHCH_2CHCl_2$

Solution: (a) two triplets, one for each CH_2;   (b) one triplet for CH_3;   (c) two triplets, H_a split by two H_b's and H_b split by two H_a's.

$$\begin{array}{ccc} H_a & H_b & H_a \\ | & | & | \\ Cl_2C & -C & -CCl_2 \\ & | & \\ & H_b & \end{array}$$

STUDY PROBLEM

8.12   Figure 8.40 shows the nmr spectrum of 2-phenylethyl acetate. Assign each signal to the proper protons.

D.   The Quartet

Consider a compound with a methyl group and one nonequivalent proton on the adjacent carbon.

$$\text{quartet for } H_a \quad \begin{array}{cc} H_a & H_b \\ | & | \\ -C & -C-H_b \\ | & | \\ H_b & \end{array} \quad \text{doublet for } CH_3 \ (H_b)$$

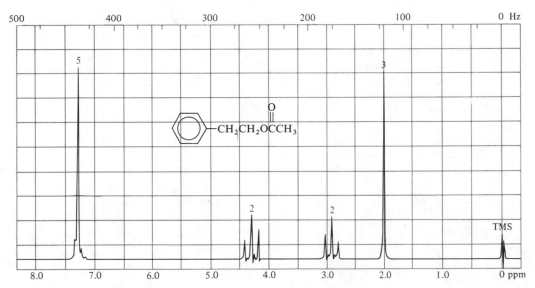

Figure 8.40. Nmr spectrum of 2-phenylethyl acetate.

The three equivalent methyl protons (H_b) see one vicinal proton and appear in the spectrum as a doublet, the total relative area of which is 3 (for three protons).

The signal arising from H_a is observed as a **quartet** (3 + 1) because it sees three vicinal protons. The *J* values between each pair of peaks in the quartet is the same as the *J* value between the peaks in the doublet. In our example, the total area under the quartet for H_a is 1. (The area ratio *within* a quartet is 1 : 3 : 3 : 1; see Figure 8.41.)

The ethyl group (CH_3CH_2-), which is very common in organic compounds, exhibits a characteristic nmr pattern, a triplet and a quartet.

C$\underline{H}_3$ sees two vicinal H's and is split into a triplet

$$CH_3CH_2-$$

C$\underline{H}_2$ sees three vicinal H's and is split into a quartet

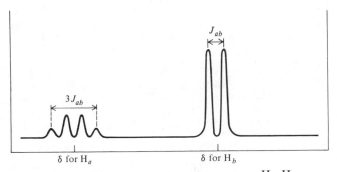

Figure 8.41. Spin–spin splitting pattern for $-\underset{|}{\overset{H_a}{C}}-\underset{\underset{H_b}{|}}{\overset{\overset{H_b}{|}}{C}}-H_b$.

The chemical shifts of an ethyl group are also characteristic. The CH_2 is often bonded to an electronegative atom, such as oxygen, which deshields the CH_2 protons. The quartet is thus observed downfield, while the triplet for the more shielded CH_3 group is observed upfield. The nmr spectrum of ethyl chloride (Figure 8.33, page 343) shows typical ethyl absorption. Figure 8.42 contains other examples of nmr spectra that show ethyl patterns, an upfield triplet and a downfield quartet.

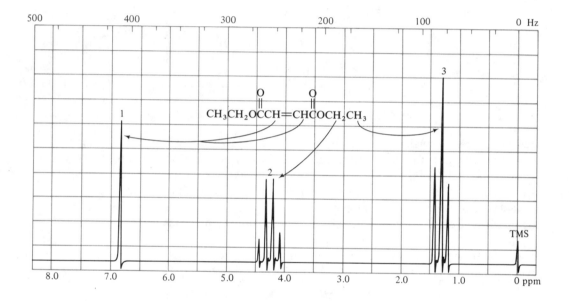

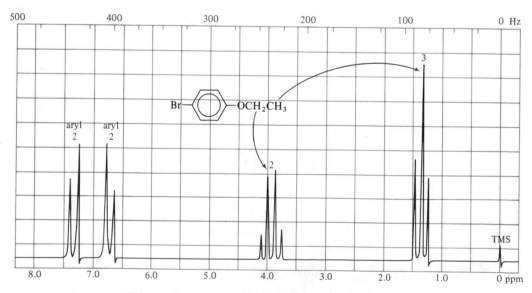

Figure 8.42. Nmr spectra showing typical ethyl patterns.

STUDY PROBLEM

8.13 Match each nmr spectrum in Figure 8.43 with a compound in the following list:

(a) $CH_3CO_2CH_2CH_3$ (b) CH_3CH_2—⟨benzene ring⟩—I (c) $CH_3CO_2CH(CH_3)_2$

(d) $CH_3CH_2CH_2NO_2$ (e) CH_3CH_2I (f) $(CH_3)_2CHNO_2$

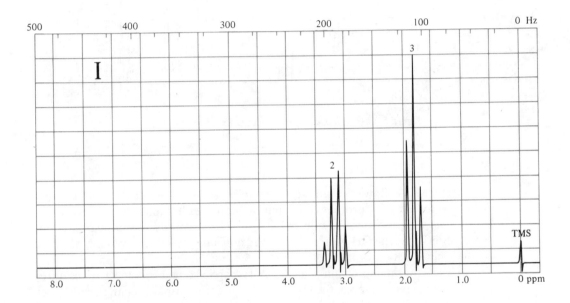

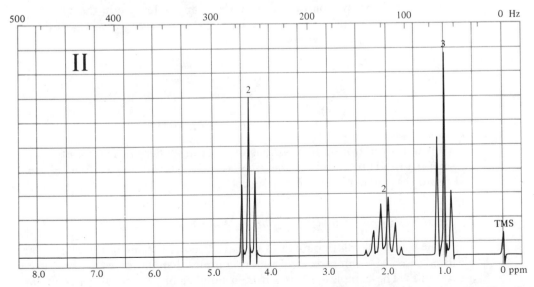

Figure 8.43. Nmr spectra for Problem 8.13.   (*continued*)

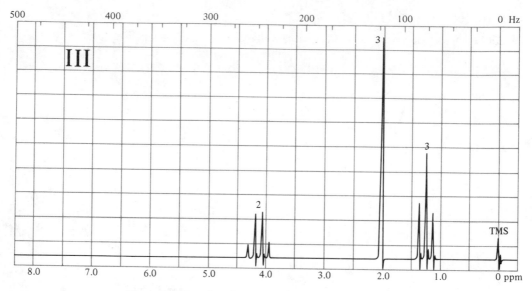

Figure 8.43 (continued). Nmr spectra for Problem 8.13.

E.   Chemical Exchange

Figure 8.44 shows the nmr spectrum of ethanol. Although we would expect the signal for the CH_2 protons to be split by both the CH_3 and the OH protons, it is not. The CH_2 protons are split only by the CH_3 protons, and a quartet is observed. Similarly, the OH proton is observed as a singlet; it is not split into a triplet by the vicinal CH_2 protons.

Unless the nmr spectrum of an alcohol is carried out at very low temperatures or with a very pure sample, the OH proton undergoes rapid exchange with other OH protons. This exchange, called **chemical exchange**, is so fast that the OH proton and a vicinal proton cannot distinguish any difference in the spin states of each other, and therefore the signals are not split. In using the $n + 1$ rule, we can usually ignore the OH protons.

$$CH_3CH_2OH$$

singlet
(not split)

triplet
(split by CH_2)

quartet
(split by CH_3 only)

Protons on nitrogen, like protons on oxygen, undergo chemical exchange. In general, the NH protons in amines (RNH_2 or R_2NH) are singlets, and adjacent CH protons are not split by their presence.

F.   Other Factors that Affect Splitting Patterns

The spin–spin splitting patterns we have been discussing in this chapter are idealized cases. Most nmr spectra are more complex than those we have been using as examples. The complexity arises from a number of factors, of which we will

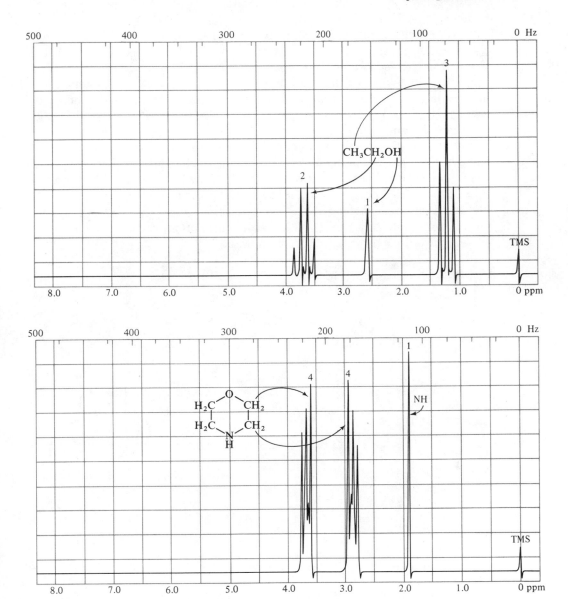

Figure 8.44. Nmr spectra of an alcohol and an amine, showing the OH and NH protons as singlets.

mention only two. One factor that adds complexity to an nmr spectrum is the *nonequivalence of vicinal protons*:

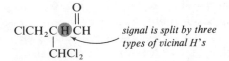

signal is split by three types of vicinal H's

Another factor that adds complexity is the *magnitude of the chemical shift.* The $n + 1$ splitting patterns are truly apparent in an nmr spectrum only if the signals for coupled protons are separated from one another by a fairly large chemical shift. When the chemical shifts are close, the inside peaks of a multiplet increase in size, while the outside peaks decrease in size. This is the phenomenon of **leaning**, mentioned previously. When chemical shifts become very close, the peaks can coalesce into a singlet.

Figure 8.45 is the nmr spectrum of a typical alkane, *n*-octane. The chemical shifts of the CH_2 groups are all about the same (1.27 ppm); the CH_2 signal is a single, rather broad peak. The two methyl groups, which are equivalent to each other, are shielded compared to the methylene protons and absorb at a slightly higher field strength (0.83 ppm). According to spin–spin splitting rules, the methyl absorption should be a triplet. With a little imagination, you can see the triplet leaning toward the methylene absorption peak.

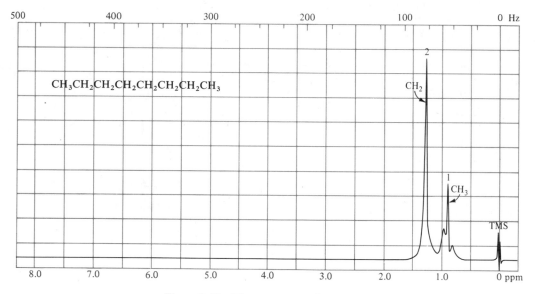

Figure 8.45.   Nmr spectrum of *n*-octane.

Section 8.12

Spin–Spin Splitting Diagrams

A **spin–spin splitting diagram**, also called a **tree diagram**, is a convenient technique for the analysis of splitting patterns. Let us consider H_a in the simple partial structure $>CH_a—CH_b<$. The splitting of the signal for H_a into a doublet by H_b may be symbolized by the following tree diagram:

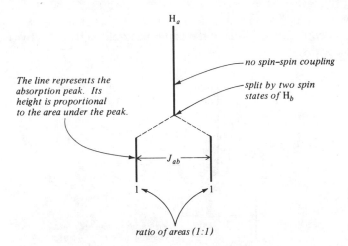

The line represents the absorption peak. Its height is proportional to the area under the peak.

no spin–spin coupling

split by two spin states of H_b

J_{ab}

1   1

ratio of areas (1:1)

The splitting of the signal for H_b by the spin states for H_a may be represented by a similar tree diagram. These two diagrams may then be superimposed on an nmr spectrum (see Figure 8.46).

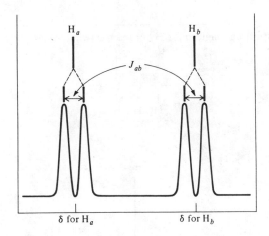

H_a H_b

J_{ab}

δ for H_a δ for H_b

Figure 8.46. Spin–spin splitting pattern of two nonequivalent, vicinal H's.

The tree diagram describing a triplet is a direct extension of that for a doublet. Consider the absorption pattern for H_a in the following grouping:

$$\begin{matrix} H_a & H_b \\ | & | \\ -C-C-H_b \\ | & | \end{matrix}$$

In this case, H_a sees two vicinal protons and is split into a triplet. The coupling constant is J_{ab}. The triplet comes about because the peak for H_a is split twice, once for each H_b. Using a tree diagram, we can see the result of each of the two splits. H_a is first split into a pair of doublets, then the resulting two peaks are split again.

We observe a triplet because the center two peaks absorb at the same position in the nmr. Consequently, the area of the center peak of the triplet is twice that of the two outside peaks.

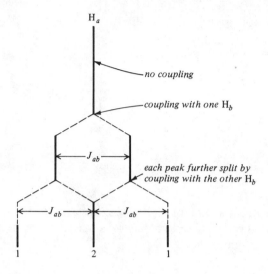

Sample Problem

Draw a spin–spin splitting diagram for H_m of the following system, where $J_{am} = 10$ Hz and $J_{mx} = 5$ Hz:

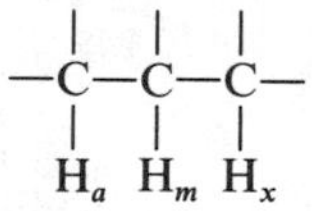

$$-\overset{|}{\underset{H_a}{C}}-\overset{|}{\underset{H_m}{C}}-\overset{|}{\underset{H_x}{C}}-$$

Solution:

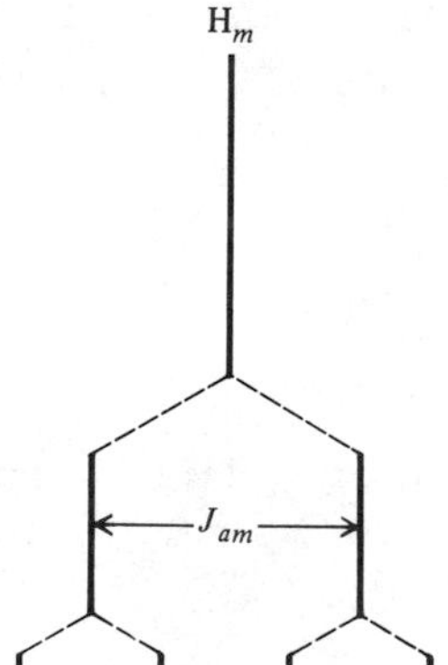

Note that the absorption pattern is not a triplet, as would be predicted by the $n + 1$ rule. Instead, four distinct lines of equal heights are observed because the coupling constants J_{am} and J_{mx} are not equal.

Draw a splitting diagram for the absorption of H_a in the partial structure

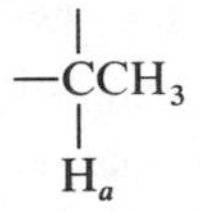

$$-\overset{|}{\underset{|}{C}}CH_3$$
$$H_a$$

Solution:

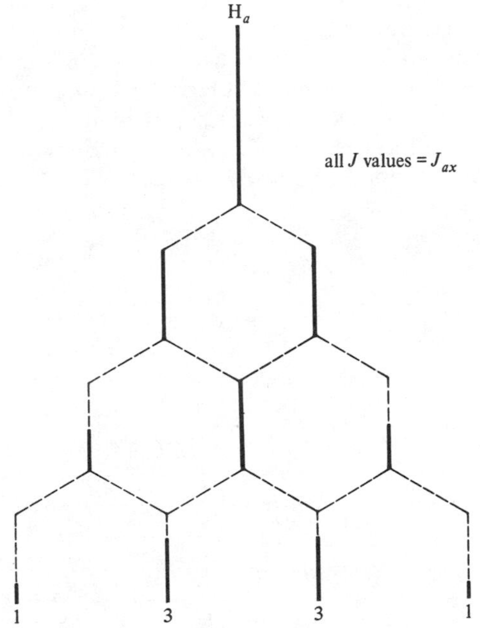

H_a

all J values $= J_{ax}$

```
1        3        3        1
```

The original signal is split three times. The $1:3:3:1$ ratio of the areas arises from the fact that all the protons have the same coupling constant and consequently have superimposed absorption positions.

Section 8.13

Using Infrared and Nmr Spectra for the Identification of Organic Structures

From an infrared spectrum, we can deduce the identities of functional groups. From an nmr spectrum, we can often deduce the structure of the hydrocarbon portion of a molecule. Sometimes it is possible to deduce the complete structure of a compound from just the infrared and nmr spectra. More commonly, additional information is needed (such as chemical reactivity, elemental analysis, or other spectra). In this text, we provide additional information generally in the form of a molecular formula. From the molecular formula, we can calculate the number of rings or double bonds. (*Example*: C_6H_{12} is C_nH_{2n}; the structure contains either one double bond or a ring.) We can determine fragments of the structure from the spectra. Then, we try to match the fragments with the molecular formula.

Sample Problem

A compound has a molecular formula of C_3H_6O. Its infrared and nmr spectra are given in Figure 8.47. What is the structure of this compound?

Solution: From the molecular formula, we know that the compound has one oxygen; therefore, the compound must be an alcohol, an ether, an aldehyde, or a ketone. Because the molecular formula is of the type $C_nH_{2n}O$, we know that the structure contains either one double bond (C=C or C=O) or one ring. To distinguish between the possible functional groups, we use the infrared spectrum. We see strong absorption in the C=O region of 1750 cm^{-1} (5.8 μm). We conclude that the oxygen is not in a hydroxyl group or ether group, but rather is in a carbonyl group (aldehyde or ketone). This means, then, that no ring is present.

In the nmr spectrum, we see no downfield, offset absorption; we conclude that the compound is a ketone, rather than an aldehyde. The rest of the nmr spectrum shows only a singlet; therefore all six hydrogens are equivalent and have no vicinal, nonequivalent hydrogens. The compound must be acetone (propanone): $(CH_3)_2C=O$.

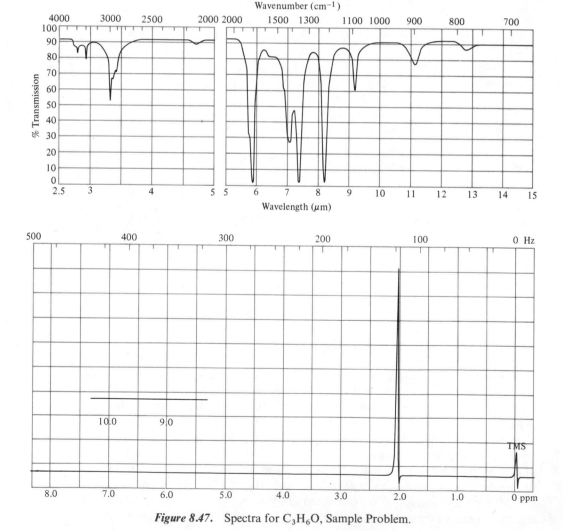

Figure 8.47.   Spectra for C_3H_6O, Sample Problem.

STUDY PROBLEMS

8.14 A compound has a formula C_3H_8O. Its infrared and nmr spectra are given in Figure 8.48. What is the structure of this compound?

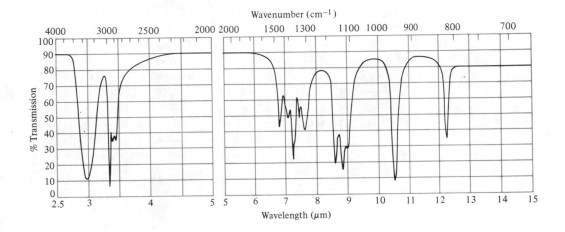

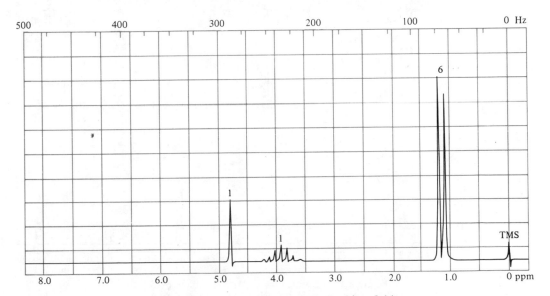

Figure 8.48. Spectra for C_3H_8O, Problem 8.14.

8.15   Figure 8.49 shows the infrared and nmr spectra for a compound with the molecular formula C_7H_8O. What is the structure of this compound?

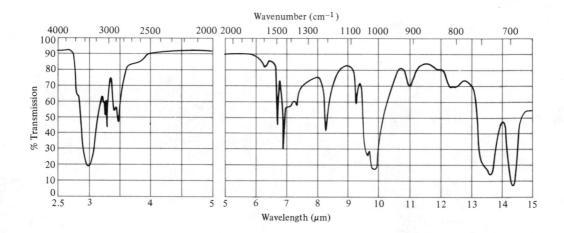

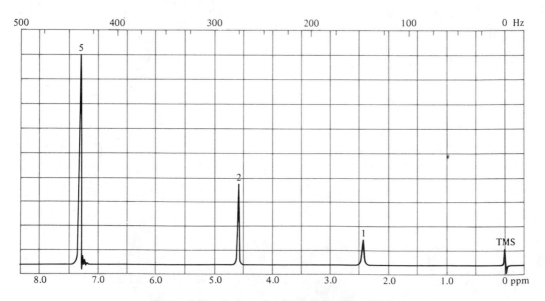

Figure 8.49.   Spectra for C_7H_8O, Problem 8.15.

8.16 Figure 8.50 shows nmr and infrared spectra for a compound with the molecular formula $C_4H_7BrO_2$. What is the structure of the compound?

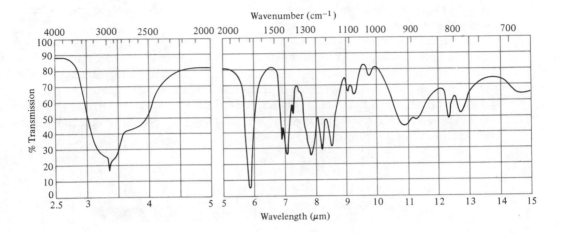

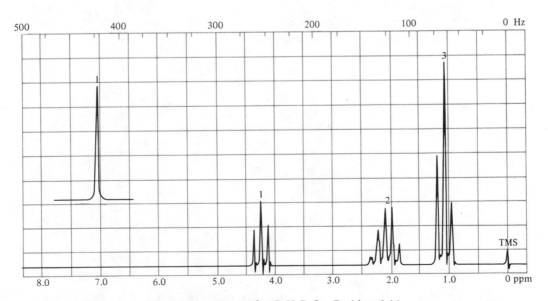

Figure 8.50. Spectra for $C_4H_7BrO_2$, Problem 8.16.

SUMMARY

Organic compounds can absorb **electromagnetic radiation** of various wavelengths. Absorption in the **infrared region** results in **vibrational excitations** of bonds. Different types of bonds require differing amounts of energy for vibrational excitations. In an infrared spectrum, the region of 1500–4000 cm^{-1} (2.5–6.5 μm) is useful for determination of functional groups, while the region beyond is the **fingerprint region**.

Nuclear magnetic resonance is the result of protons in a magnetic field (H_0) absorbing electromagnetic radiation in the radiofrequency region and flipping from the *parallel* to the *antiparallel spin state*. An **induced molecular magnetic field** can *shield* protons (oppose H_0) or *deshield* protons (augment H_0) and cause a *chemical shift* (δ) of the absorption band. The induced field is a result of **anisotropic effects** and **inductive effects**. A shielded proton absorbs *upfield*, close to the reference TMS, while a deshielded proton absorbs *downfield*.

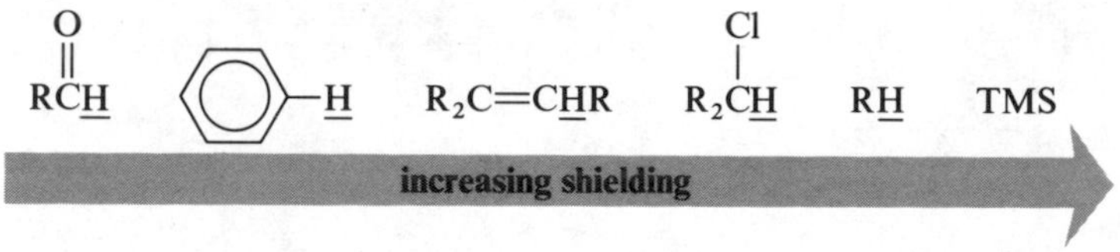

Spin–spin splitting of an absorption band results from the spin states of vicinal nonequivalent protons. The signal of a particular proton (or group of equivalent protons) is split into $n + 1$ peaks, where n is the number of vicinal protons equivalent to each other, but nonequivalent to the proton in question.

The distance (in Hz) between any two peaks in a split band is the **coupling constant J**. For protons that are *coupled* (splitting the signals of each other), the *J* values are the same.

The *area* under an entire absorption band is proportional to the relative number of protons giving rise to that signal.

STUDY PROBLEMS

8.17 Make the following conversions: (a) 3000 cm^{-1} to μm; (b) 1760 cm^{-1} to μm; (c) 5.60 μm to cm^{-1}; (d) 8.20 μm to cm^{-1}; (e) 30 Hz to MHz.

8.18 Which contains more energy:

(a) electromagnetic radiation of wavelength 10 μm or that of 8 nm?
(b) electromagnetic radiation of 3000 cm^{-1} or that of 1500 cm^{-1}?
(c) radio waves or infrared radiation?
(d) electromagnetic radiation with a frequency of 60 Hz or that with a frequency of 30 Hz?

8.19 As you view a typical infrared spectrum, do you observe the higher-energy absorption to the right or to the left?

8.20 In otherwise similar compounds, which one of each of the following pairs of partial structures would give stronger infrared absorption, and why?

(a) C=O or C=C   (b) C=C—Cl or C=C—H
(c) O—H or N—H

8.21 Tell how you could distinguish each of the following pairs of compounds by their infrared spectra:

(a) $CH_3CH_2CH_2N(CH_3)_2$ and $CH_3CH_2CH_2NH_2$
(b) $CH_3CH_2CH_2CO_2H$ and $CH_3CH_2CO_2CH_3$

$$\overset{\displaystyle O}{\overset{\displaystyle \|}{}}$$

(c) $CH_3CH_2\overset{\displaystyle O}{\overset{\displaystyle \|}{C}}CH_3$ and $CH_3CH_2CO_2CH_3$

8.22 A chemist is oxidizing cyclohexanol to cyclohexanone. How can infrared spectroscopy tell him when his reaction is completed?

8.23 A compound with the molecular formula $C_5H_{10}O$ contains no double bonds and undergoes reaction when heated with HI to yield $C_5H_{10}I_2$. The infrared spectrum of the original compound shows absorption at about 2850 cm^{-1} (3.5 μm) and 1110 cm^{-1} (9 μm), but none near 3330 cm^{-1} (3 μm) nor 1720 cm^{-1} (5.8 μm). What are the possible structures of the compound and the diiodide?

8.24 When an induced molecular magnetic field *opposes* H_0, a proton affected by this field: (a) is *shielded* or *deshielded*? (b) absorbs *upfield* or *downfield*? (c) is to the *right* or *left* in a typical nmr spectrum?

8.25 When an induced molecular magnetic field *augments* H_0, a proton affected by this field: (a) is *shielded* or *deshielded*? (b) absorbs *upfield* or *downfield*? (c) is to the *right* or *left* in a typical nmr spectrum?

8.26 At 60 MHz, how many Hz downfield from TMS is a chemical shift of 7.5 ppm?

8.27 Indicate which underlined proton in each of the following groups of compounds will absorb farther upfield:

(a) $CH_3CH_2\underline{CH}_2Cl$, $CH_3CHClC\underline{H}_3$, $CH_2ClCH_2C\underline{H}_3$

(b) $CH_3C\underline{H}_2Cl$, $CH_3C\underline{H}Cl_2$ (c) 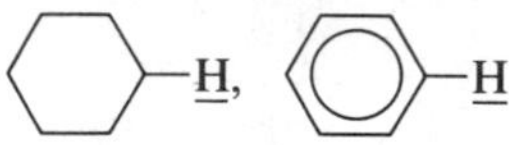 [cyclohexane]—$\underline{H}$, [benzene]—$\underline{H}$

(d) 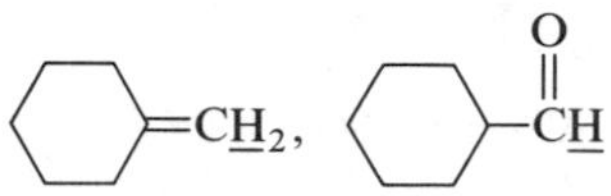 [cyclohexane]$=CH_2$, [cyclohexane ring with $-C\underline{H}$ and $C=O$] (e) $CH_3\overset{\overset{\displaystyle O}{\|}}{C}C\underline{H}_3$, $CH_3\overset{\overset{\displaystyle O}{\|}}{C}NHC\underline{H}_3$

8.28 How many different groups of equivalent protons are present in each of the following structures? If more than one, indicate each group.

(a) $CH_3CH_2CH_2CH_3$ (b) $CH_3CH_2OCH_2CH_3$
(c) $CH_3CH=CH_2$ (d) *trans*-$CHCl=CHCl$
(e) *cis*-$CHCl=CHCl$ (f) $CH_3CH_2CO_2CH_2CH_3$
(g) (*R*)-2-chlorobutane   (h) (*S*)-2-chlorobutane
(i) $(CH_3)_2CHN(CH_3)CH(CH_3)_2$ (j) $BrCH_2CH_2CH(CH_3)_2$

(k) 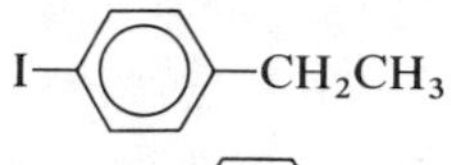 I—[benzene]—CH_2CH_3 (l) 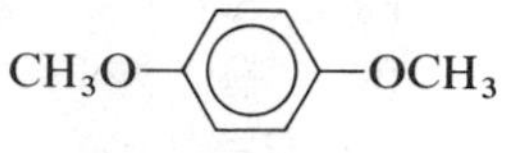 CH_3O—[benzene]—OCH_3

(m) 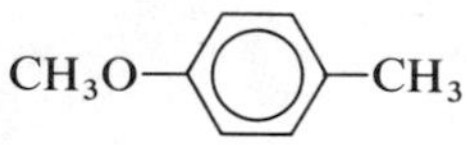 CH_3O—[benzene]—CH_3

8.29 In Problem 8.28, tell how many principal signals would probably be observed in the nmr spectrum of each compound.

8.30 Why would tetraethylsilane, $(CH_3CH_2)_4Si$, not be as good an internal standard as TMS in nmr spectra?

8.31 What would be the total relative areas under the principal nmr absorption bands for the protons in each of the following compounds?

(a) $(CH_3)_2NCH_2CH_3$ (b) $CH_3CH_2CHClCH_2CH_3$

(c) $(CH_3)_3COCH_3$ (d) 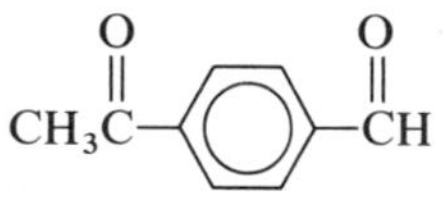 $CH_3\overset{\overset{\displaystyle O}{\|}}{C}$—[benzene]—$\overset{\overset{\displaystyle O}{\|}}{C}H$

8.32 An nmr spectrum shows two principal signals with an area ratio of 3:1. Based on this information only, which of the following structures are possibilities?

(a) $CH_2=CHCH_3$ (b) $CH_2=CHCO_2CH_3$
(c) $CH_3CH_2CH_2CH_2CH_2CH_3$ (d) $CH_3CH_2CH_3$
(e) $CH_2=C(CH_3)_2$ (f) $CH_3CO_2CH_3$

8.33 What is the predicted multiplicity (number of peaks arising from spin–spin coupling) for each set of equivalent protons in the following structures?

(a) $CCl_3CH_2CH_2Br$ (b) $(CH_3)_2CHCO_2CH_3$

(c) $(CH_3)_3COCH_3$ (d) 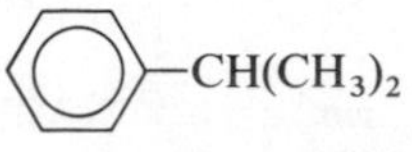 [benzene]—$CH(CH_3)_2$

8.34 For each of the following compounds, predict the *multiplicity* and *total relative area* under the signal of each set of equivalent protons:

(a) $CH_3CH_2CO_2CH_3$ (b) $CH_3OCH_2CH_2OCH_3$ (c) $CH_3\overset{\displaystyle O}{\overset{\|}{C}}CH_2CH_3$

(d) 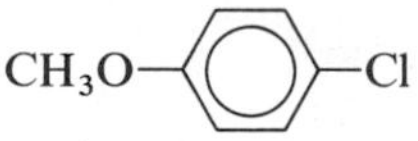 CH_3O—⟨○⟩—Cl (e) Cl_2CHCH_2Br

8.35 For Cl_2CHCH_3: (a) Which proton(s) absorb downfield in the nmr spectrum?
                        (b) Which proton(s) absorb upfield?

8.36 Sketch the expected nmr spectrum for 1,1-dichloroethane. Be sure to include (*qualitatively*) anticipated chemical shifts, splitting patterns, and appropriate areas.

8.37 Sketch the expected nmr spectrum for each of the following compounds:

(a) $CH_3CH_2\overset{\displaystyle O}{\overset{\|}{C}}CH_2CH_3$ (b) $CH_3CHClCHClCH_3$

8.38 A chemist has two isomeric chloropropanes, A and B. The nmr spectrum of A shows a doublet and a septet (seven peaks), while that of B shows two triplets and a sextet (six peaks). Identify the structures of A and B.

8.39 How would you distinguish between each of the following pairs of compounds by nmr spectroscopy?

(a) $CH_3CH_2CH_2CH_2CH=CH_2$ and $(CH_3)_2C=C(CH_3)_2$

(b) CH_3CH_2CHO and $CH_3\overset{\displaystyle O}{\overset{\|}{C}}CH_3$

(c) $CH_3\overset{\displaystyle O}{\overset{\|}{C}}CH_3$ and $CH_3\overset{\displaystyle O}{\overset{\|}{C}}OCH_3$

(d) 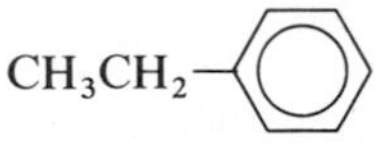 CH_3CH_2—⟨○⟩ and CH_3—⟨○⟩—CH_3

8.40 Under the influence of H_0, [18]annulene has an induced ring current not too different from that of benzene. Predict the shielding and deshielding of the protons of this ring system.

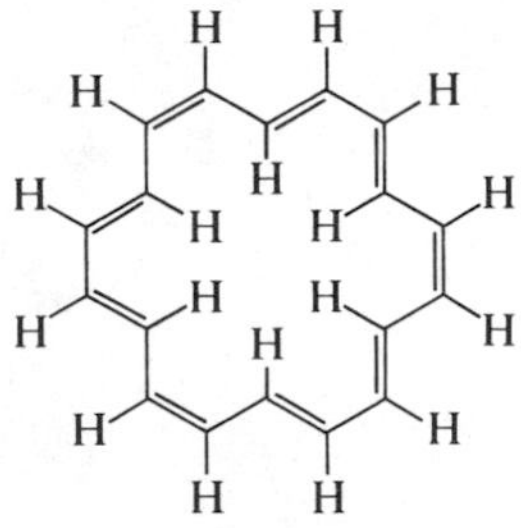

[18]annulene

8.41 The methyl protons of 15,16-dimethylpyrene do not have the same chemical shift as those of $C_6H_5C\underline{H}_3$. Instead, their absorption is *upfield* from TMS ($\delta = -4.2$ ppm). Why?

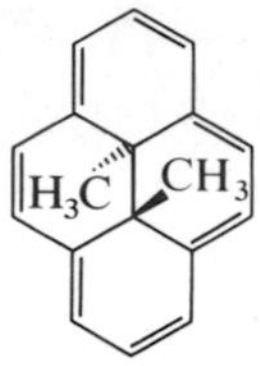

15,16-dimethylpyrene

8.42 Predict   (a) the number of principal peaks in the nmr spectrum of the local anesthetic *xylocaine* (following);   (b) the splitting patterns of these peaks; and   (c) the characteristic absorption peaks in the infrared spectrum.

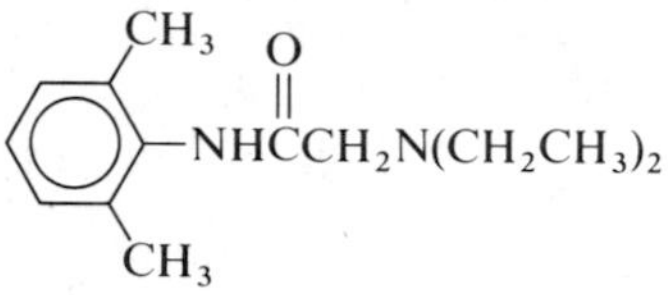

xylocaine

8.43 How would you use either infrared or nmr spectroscopy to distinguish between:

(a)   1-propanol and propylene oxide?

(b)   diisopropyl ether and di-*n*-propyl ether?

(c)   ethanol and 1,2-ethanediol?

(d)  NCH_3 and NH?

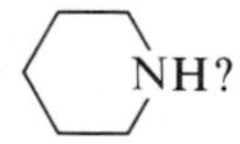

(e)   ethanol and ethyl chloride?

(f)   acetic acid and acetone?

8.44 Make a tree diagram for each of the indicated protons:

(a) $ClCH_2C\underline{H}_2CH_2Cl$ (b) $Cl_2CHC\underline{H}_3$ (c) $CH_3C\underline{H}_2OCH_3$

8.45 Figures 8.51 through 8.57 each gives a molecular formula, an infrared spectrum, and an nmr spectrum for an unknown compound. What is the structure of each compound?

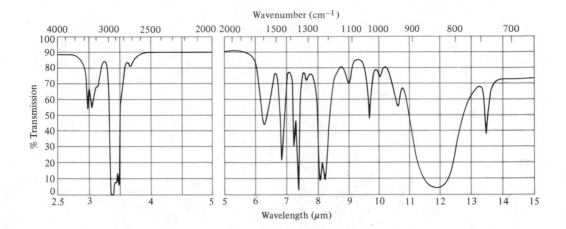

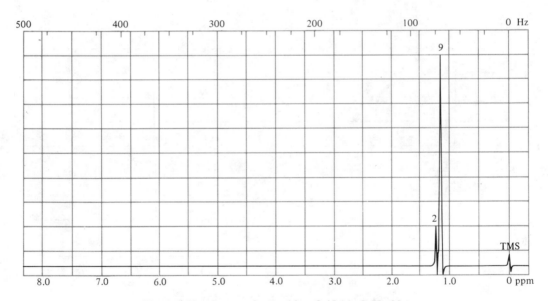

Figure 8.51. Spectra for Problem 8.45 (a), $C_4H_{11}N$.

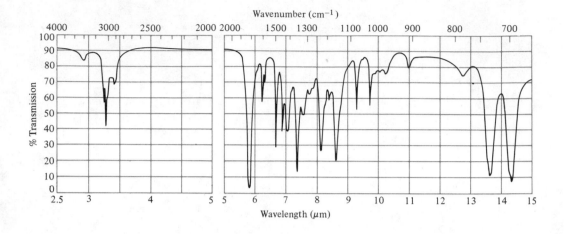

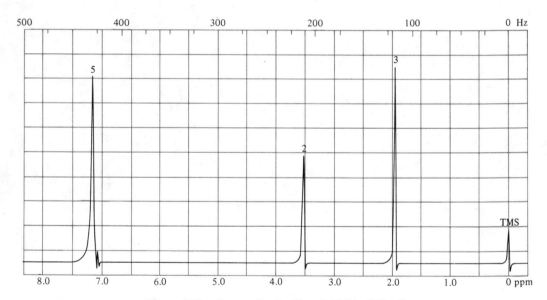

Figure 8.52.   Spectra for Problem 8.45 (b), $C_9H_{10}O$.

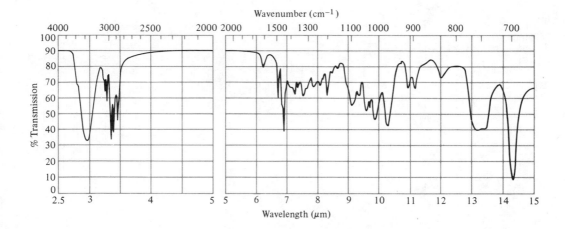

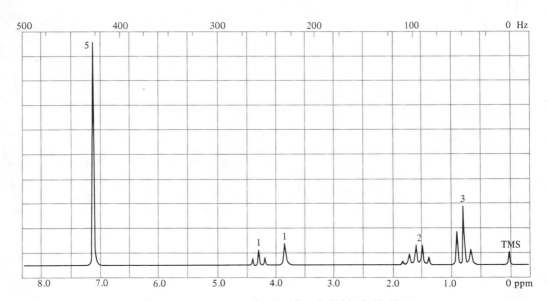

Figure 8.53. Spectra for Problem 8.45 (c), $C_9H_{12}O$.

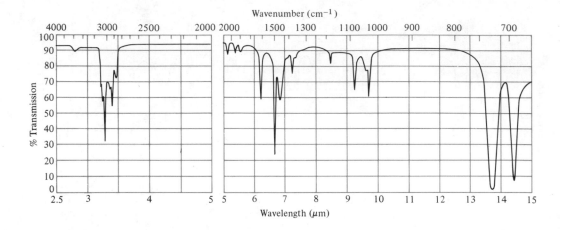

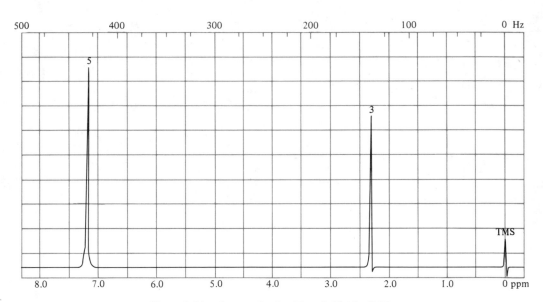

Figure 8.54. Spectra for Problem 8.45 (d), C_7H_8.

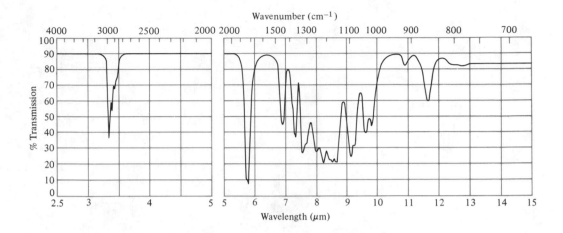

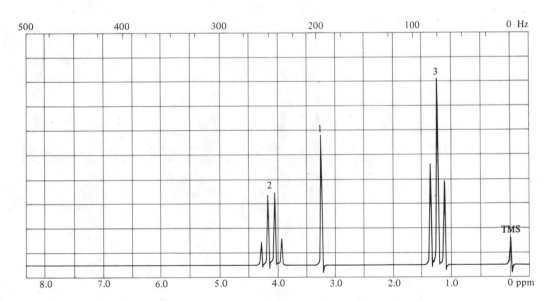

Figure 8.55. Spectra for Problem 8.45 (e), $C_7H_{12}O_4$.

Infrared and Nmr Spectroscopy

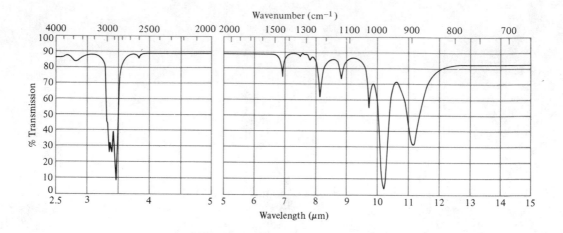

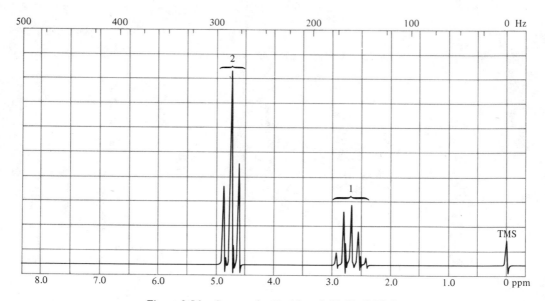

Figure 8.56. Spectra for Problem 8.45 (f), C_3H_6O.

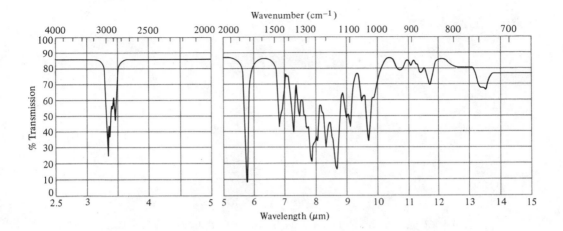

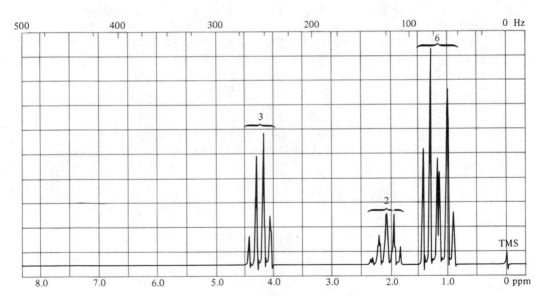

Figure 8.57. Spectra for Problem 8.45 (g), $C_6H_{11}BrO_2$.

Chapter 9

Alkenes and Alkynes

An **alkene** is a hydrocarbon with one double bond. Alkenes are sometimes called **olefins**, from *olefiant gas* ("oil-forming gas"), an old name for ethylene (CH_2=CH_2). An **alkyne** is a hydrocarbon with one triple bond; acetylene (CH≡CH) is the simplest alkyne.

A carbon–carbon double bond is a common functional group in natural products. Most frequently, the double bond is found in conjunction with other functional groups. However, alkenes with no other functionality are not at all rare and are often found as plant products and in petroleum. Two interesting examples of naturally occurring compounds containing carbon–carbon double bonds follow.

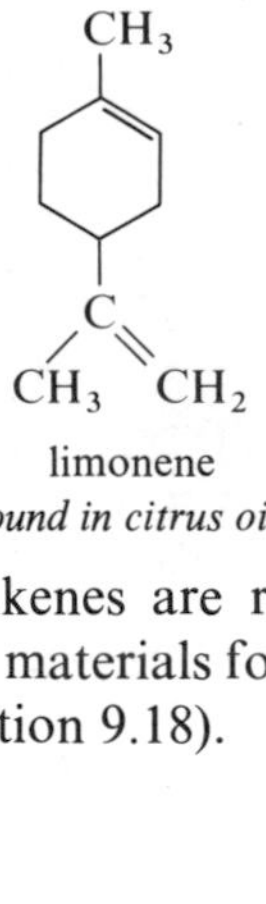

$$(CH_3)_2C=CHCH_2CH_2\overset{\overset{\displaystyle CH_3}{|}}{C}=CHCH_2CH_2\overset{\overset{\displaystyle CH_2}{||}}{C}CH=CH_2$$

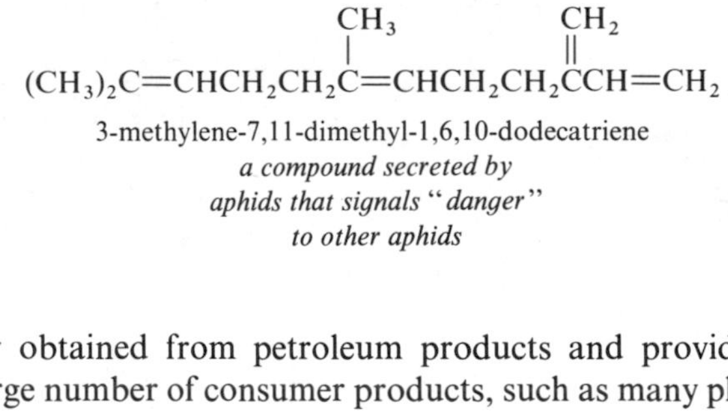

3-methylene-7,11-dimethyl-1,6,10-dodecatriene
*a compound secreted by
aphids that signals "danger"
to other aphids*

limonene
found in citrus oils

Alkenes are readily obtained from petroleum products and provide the starting materials for a large number of consumer products, such as many plastics (see Section 9.18).

Section 9.1

Bonding in Alkenes and Alkynes

The bonding in ethylene and acetylene was discussed in detail in Chapter 2. Recall that the two carbon atoms in ethylene are in the sp^2-hybrid state. The three sp^2 bonds from each carbon atom lie in the same plane with bond angles of approximately 120°. The pi bond joining the two sp^2 carbons lies above and below the plane of the sigma bonds (see Figure 2.14, page 50).

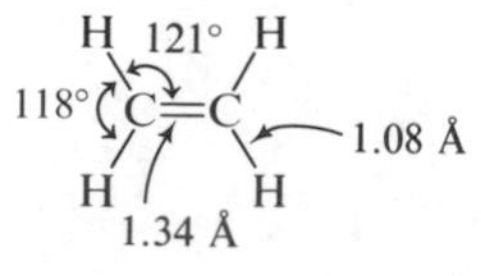

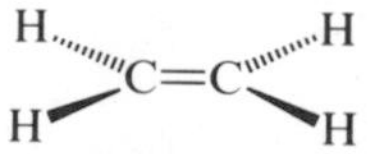

side view

All the atoms in the ethylene molecule lie in the same plane; however, in a molecule that also has sp^3 carbons, only those atoms bonded to the double-bond carbons lie in the same plane.

these atoms lie in a plane

The electronic structure of the triple bond of an alkyne is very similar to that of the double bond in an alkene. Acetylene has two sp carbons with linear sigma bonds and *two* pi bonds joining the sp carbons. (Figure 2.18, page 55.)

$$180°$$
$$H-C\equiv C-H$$

acetylene

A triple-bond carbon is in the sp-hybrid state. The sp orbital is one-half s, while an sp^2 orbital is one-third s and an sp^3 orbital is only one-fourth s. Because an sp orbital has more s character, the electrons in this orbital are closer to the carbon nucleus than electrons in an sp^2 or sp^3 orbital. (See Section 2.4F.) In an alkyne, the sp carbon is therefore *more electronegative* than most other carbon atoms. Thus, an alkynyl C—H bond is *more polar* than an alkane C—H bond or an alkene C—H bond.

$$\overset{\delta+}{R}-\overset{\delta-}{C}\equiv\overset{\delta-}{C}-\overset{\delta+}{H}$$

sp carbons electron-withdrawing

One of the most important results of the polarity of the alkynyl carbon–hydrogen bond is that RC≡CH can lose a hydrogen ion to a strong base. The resulting anion (RC≡C⁻) is called an **acetylide ion**. With a pK_a of 26, alkynes are not strong acids. They are weaker acids than water (p$K_a \sim 15$), but stronger acids than ammonia (p$K_a \sim 35$). Alkynes undergo reaction with a strong base like sodamide (NaNH₂) or a Grignard reagent or with sodium metal. Alkanes and alkenes do not react under these conditions.

$$\underset{\text{propyne}}{CH_3C\equiv CH} + NH_2^- \xrightarrow{\text{liq. NH}_3} \underset{\text{an acetylide ion}}{CH_3C\equiv C^-} + NH_3$$

$$CH_3C\equiv CH + CH_3MgI \longrightarrow CH_3C\equiv CMgI + CH_4$$

$$CH_3C\equiv CH + Na \longrightarrow CH_3C\equiv C^- + Na^+ + \tfrac{1}{2}H_2$$

Section 9.2

Nomenclature of Alkenes and Alkynes

In the IUPAC system, the continuous-chain alkenes are named after their alkane parents, but with the **-ane** ending changed to **-ene**. For example, CH_3CH_3 is ethane and $CH_2=CH_2$ is ethene (trivial name, ethylene).

$$CH_2=CH_2 \qquad CH_3CH=CH_2$$

IUPAC: ethene   propene

cyclohexene

A hydrocarbon with two double bonds is called a **diene**, while one with three double bonds is called a **triene**. The following examples illustrate diene and triene nomenclature:

$$
\begin{array}{ccc}
 & CH_3 & \\
 & | & \\
CH_2=CHCH=CH_2 & CH_2=CCH=CH_2 & CH_2=CHCH=CHCH=CH_2 \\
\text{1,3-butadiene} & \text{2-methyl-1,3-butadiene} & \text{1,3,5-hexatriene} \\
\textit{a diene} & \textit{a diene} & \textit{a triene}
\end{array}
$$

In the names of most alkenes, we need a prefix number to show the position of the double bond. Unless there is functionality of higher nomenclature priority, the chain is numbered from the end that gives the lowest number to the double bond. The prefix number specifies the carbon atom in the chain where the double bond begins.

$$
\begin{array}{ccc}
 & CH_3 & \\
 & | & \\
CH_3CH=CHCH_2CH_3 & CH_3C=CHCH_2CH_3 & CH_2=CHCH_2CH_2OH \\
\text{2-pentene} & \text{2-methyl-2-pentene} & \text{3-buten-1-ol}
\end{array}
$$

Sample Problem

Give the IUPAC name for $CH_3CH_2CH_2\underset{\underset{CH_2}{\|}}{C}CH_2CH_2CH_3$.

Solution: While indeed the molecule does have a seven-carbon chain, the longest continuous chain that *contains the double bond* has only five carbons. Consequently, the structure is named as a pentene. The IUPAC name is 2-propyl-1-pentene.

Some alkenes and alkenyl groups have trivial names that are in common use. A few of these are summarized in Table 9.1.

A pi bond prevents free rotation of groups around a double bond; consequently, alkenes may exhibit geometric isomerism. This topic and the nomenclature of geometric isomers was covered in Section 4.1. (Because alkynes can have only one group attached to each *sp* carbon atom, they do not exhibit geometric isomerism.)

$$
\begin{array}{cc}
\underset{H}{CH_3}\!\diagdown \atop \diagup \; C=C \; \underset{H}{\diagup} \atop \diagdown CH_3 & \underset{H}{CH_3}\!\diagdown \atop \diagup \; C=C \; \underset{CH_3}{\diagup} \atop \diagdown H
\end{array}
$$

cis-2-butene   *trans*-2-butene
or (Z)-2-butene   or (E)-2-butene

Table 9.1. Trivial Names of Some Alkenes and Alkenyl Groups

Structure	Name	Example
alkenes:		
$CH_2=CH_2$	ethylene	—
$CH_3CH=CH_2$	propylene	—
$\underset{\displaystyle CH_3}{CH_3\overset{\textstyle \mid}{C}=CH_2}$	isobutylene	—
$\underset{\displaystyle CH_3}{CH_2=\overset{\textstyle \mid}{C}CH=CH_2}$	isoprene	—
$CH_2=C=CH_2$	allene	—

alkenyl groups:

$CH_2=$	methylene	

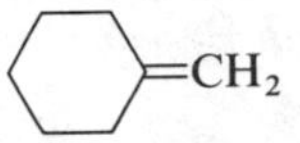

methylenecyclohexane

$CH_2=CH-$	vinyl	$CH_2=CHCl$

vinyl chloride

$CH_2=CHCH_2-$	allyl	$CH_2=CHCH_2Br$

allyl bromide

The IUPAC nomenclature of alkynes is directly analogous to that of the alkenes. The suffix for an alkyne is **-yne,** and a position number is used to signify the position of the triple bond in the parent hydrocarbon chain. Unless there is functionality of higher nomenclature priority in the molecule, the chain is numbered to give the triple bond the lowest number.

$$CH_3CH_2C\equiv CH \qquad CH_3CH_2C\equiv CCH_2CH_2CH_3 \qquad CH\equiv CCH_2OH$$

1-butyne   3-heptyne   2-propyn-1-ol

In an older, trivial system of nomenclature for the simple alkynes, acetylene ($CH\equiv CH$) is considered the parent. Groups attached to the *sp* carbons are named as substituents on acetylene. In this text we will use the IUPAC nomenclature system for the alkynes except for acetylene itself.

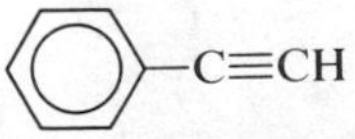

$$\text{—}C\equiv CH \qquad\qquad CH_3C\equiv CCH_2CH_3$$

IUPAC: phenylethyne   2-pentyne
trivial: phenylacetylene   ethylmethylacetylene

STUDY PROBLEMS

9.1   Give the structures of (a) (*E*)-1-chloro-3,4-dimethyl-3-hexene; (b) *cis*-1,3-penta-diene; (c) cyclohexylethyne; and (d) diphenylethyne.

9.2   Name the following compounds:

(a) 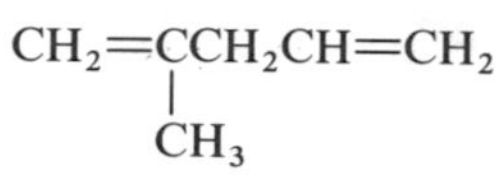 $CH_2{=}CCH_2CH{=}CH_2$ (b) 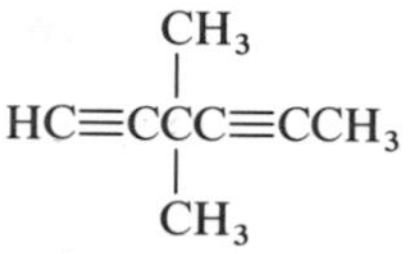 $HC{\equiv}CCC{\equiv}CCH_3$
            | |
          CH_3 with CH_3 above and CH_3 below the central carbon

Section 9.3

Physical Properties of Alkenes and Alkynes

The physical properties of alkenes (but not the chemical properties) are practically identical to those of their alkane parents. Table 9.2 lists the boiling points of a few alkenes and alkynes. The boiling points of an homologous series of alkenes increase about 30° per CH_2 group. This is the same increase observed for an homologous series of alkanes. As with alkanes, branching in an alkene lowers the boiling point slightly.

Although alkenes are considered to be nonpolar, they are slightly more soluble in water than the corresponding alkanes because the pi electrons, which are somewhat exposed, are attracted to the partially positive hydrogen of water.

Table 9.2.   *Physical Properties of Some Alkenes and Alkynes*

Name	Structure	Bp, °C
alkenes:		
ethene (ethylene)	$CH_2{=}CH_2$	−102
propene (propylene)	$CH_3CH{=}CH_2$	−48
methylpropene (isobutylene)	$(CH_3)_2C{=}CH_2$	−7
1-butene	$CH_3CH_2CH{=}CH_2$	−6
1-pentene	$CH_3CH_2CH_2CH{=}CH_2$	30
alkynes:		
ethyne (acetylene)	$CH{\equiv}CH$	−75
propyne	$CH_3C{\equiv}CH$	−23
1-butyne	$CH_3CH_2C{\equiv}CH$	8.1
2-butyne	$CH_3C{\equiv}CCH_3$	27

Section 9.4

Spectra of Alkenes and Alkynes

A. Infrared Spectra

Alkenes Stretching of the $C＝C$ double bond gives rise to absorption at
1620–1680 cm^{-1} (5.95–6.17 μm) in the infrared spectrum. Because the double
bond is nonpolar, the stretching results in only a small change in bond moment;
consequently, the absorption is weak, ten to 100 times less intense than that of a
carbonyl group. The absorption due to the stretching of the alkenyl, or vinyl,
carbon–hydrogen bond ($＝C—H$) at about 3135 cm^{-1} (3.2 μm) is also weak.
Alkenyl carbon–hydrogen bonds exhibit bending absorption in the fingerprint
region of the infrared spectrum (see Table 9.3, page 383). Figure 9.1 shows the
spectra of heptane and 1-heptene; the differences between an alkane and an alkene
are evident in these spectra.

The phenyl group shows $C—C$ and $C—H$ absorption at about the same
frequencies as the alkenyl $C＝C$ and $C—H$ absorption; however, the nmr spectra
of aromatic compounds are quite distinctive (see Sections 8.8B and 10.3B.)
Therefore, a combination of infrared and nmr spectra should be used to distinguish
between alkenes and aromatic compounds.

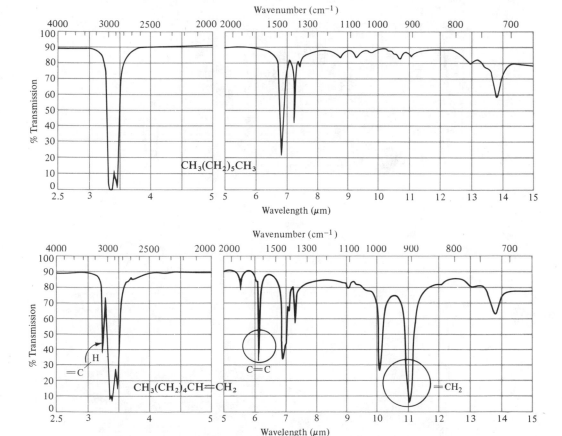

Figure 9.1. Infrared spectra of heptane and 1-heptene.

STUDY PROBLEM

9.3   Which of the infrared spectra in Figure 9.2 is that of an alkene?

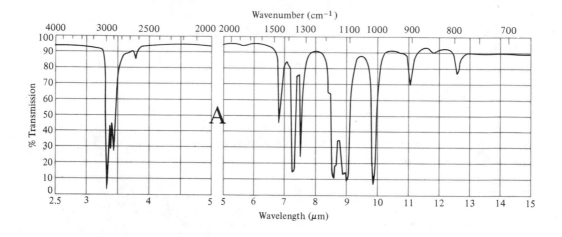

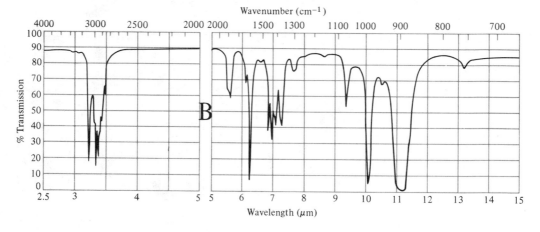

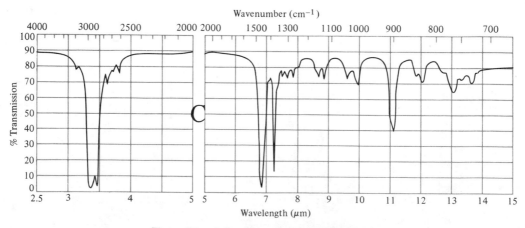

Figure 9.2.   Infrared spectra for Problem 9.3.

Table 9.3. *Infrared Absorption Characteristic of Alkenes and Alkynes*

	Position of absorption	
Type of vibration	cm^{-1}	μm
alkenes:		
=C—H stretching	3135	3.2
=C—H bending	798	12.5
=CH_2 bending	887	11.3
C=C stretching	1620–1680	5.95–6.17
alkynes:		
≡C—H stretching	3333	3.0
C≡C stretching	2083–2272	4.4–4.8

Alkynes The C≡C stretching frequency of alkynes is at 2083–2272 cm^{-1} (4.4–4.8 μm). This absorption is quite weak and can easily be lost in the background noise of the spectrum. However, with the exception of C≡N and Si—H, no other groups show absorption in this region. The ≡C—H stretching frequency is found at 3333 cm^{-1} (3.0 μm) as a sharp peak (see Figure 9.3).

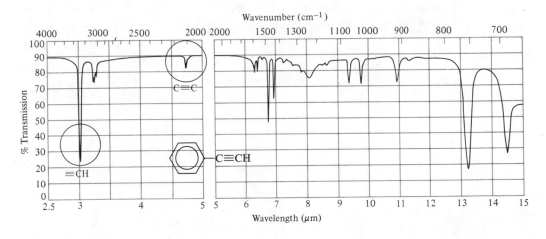

Figure 9.3. Infrared spectrum of phenylethyne.

B. Nmr Spectra

Alkenes The chemical shift for a vinyl proton is about 5.0 ppm; the exact position of the absorption depends on the location of the double bond in the hydrocarbon chain. In general, protons on terminal alkenyl carbons absorb near 4.7 ppm, while the protons on nonterminal carbons absorb slightly farther downfield, at about 5.3 ppm.

$$CH_3CH_2\underline{CH}{=}\underline{CH}_2$$

5.3 ppm   4.7 ppm

The splitting patterns for vinyl protons are more complex than those for alkyl protons. The complexity arises from the lack of rotation around the double bond. Let us look at a general example:

$$\begin{array}{c} H_x \quad\quad H_a \\ \diagdown\;\;\;\diagup \\ C{=}C \\ \diagup\;\;\;\diagdown \\ R \quad\quad H_b \end{array}$$

In this example, all three vinyl protons (H_a, H_b, and H_x) are nonequivalent and thus have different chemical shifts and give rise to three separate signals. In addition, the coupling constants between any two of the protons (J_{ax}, J_{bx}, and J_{ab}) are different. Each of the three signals is therefore split into four peaks. (For example, the signal for H_x is split into two by H_b and again into two by H_a.) A total of twelve peaks is observed for these three protons in the nmr spectrum.

This pattern of twelve peaks can be seen in the nmr spectrum of *p*-chloro-styrene in Figure 9.4. Figure 9.5 shows tree diagrams for the splitting patterns of the double-bond protons in *p*-chlorostyrene. With the aid of the tree diagram, we can see that none of the absorption peaks are superimposed because of the differences in J values.

In the spectrum of *p*-chlorostyrene (Figure 9.4), note that the chemical shift for H_a is 5.3 ppm, while the chemical shift for H_b, which is *cis* (and closer) to the

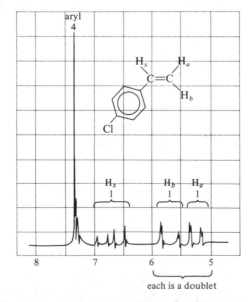

Figure 9.4.   Partial nmr spectrum of *p*-chlorostyrene.

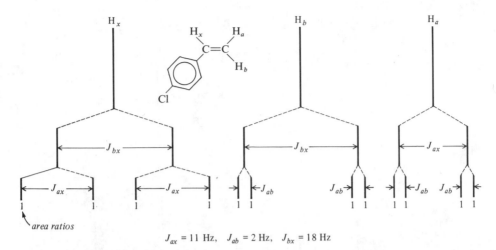

$J_{ax} = 11$ Hz, $J_{ab} = 2$ Hz, $J_{bx} = 18$ Hz

Figure 9.5.   Tree diagrams for the splitting patterns of the three double-bond protons in *p*-chlorostyrene.

benzene ring, is 5.7 ppm. The signal for H_b is downfield because H_b is somewhat deshielded by the induced field of the benzene ring. The signal for H_x is even farther downfield because H_x is more deshielded by the induced field of the ring.

Although any terminal vinyl group of the type $RCH=CH_2$ should give a spectrum with twelve vinyl-proton peaks, the twelve peaks are not always evident. For example, in the spectrum of *p*-chlorostyrene, the four peaks for H_a almost look like two peaks because J_{ab} is small. Figures 9.6 and 9.7 contain additional examples of spectra of compounds that have terminal vinyl groups. These spectra also show almost-superimposed vinyl proton signals.

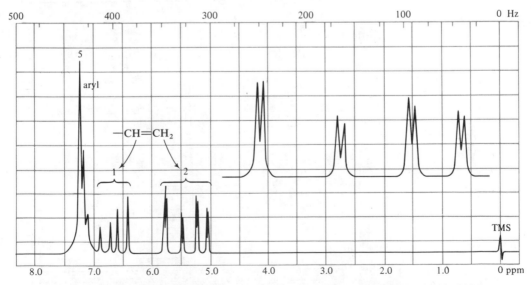

Figure 9.6.   Nmr spectrum of styrene, $C_6H_5CH=CH_2$. (The superimposed line is a higher-resolution, expanded spectrum of the eight peaks between 5.0 and 6.0 ppm.)

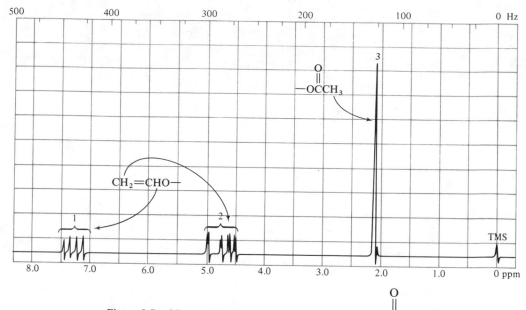

Figure 9.7. Nmr spectrum of vinyl acetate, $CH_2{=}CHOCCH_3$.

STUDY PROBLEMS

9.4   Figure 9.8 is the nmr spectrum of methyl vinyl sulfone, $CH_2{=}CHSO_2CH_3$. The spectrum contains eight peaks (not 12) in the alkene region. Construct a tree diagram that would explain the "missing" peaks.

9.5   In the nmr spectrum for *p*-chlorostyrene, the absorption for the aryl protons is observed as a *singlet*. In styrene ($C_6H_5CH{=}CH_2$), the absorption for the aryl protons is observed as a *multiplet*. Suggest a reason for these observations.

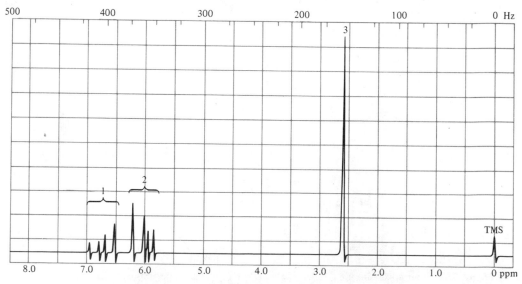

Figure 9.8.   Nmr spectrum of $CH_2{=}CHSO_2CH_3$ for Problem 9.4.

Alkynes An alkyne of the type RC≡CR has no acetylenic protons; therefore, a disubstituted alkyne has no characteristic nmr absorption. (The rest of the molecule may give rise to absorption, however.) A monosubstituted alkyne, RC≡CH, shows absorption for the alkynyl proton at about 3 ppm. This absorption is not nearly as far downfield as that for a vinyl or aryl proton because the alkynyl proton is *shielded* by the induced field of the triple bond. Figure 9.9 shows how the circulation of the pi electrons results in this field. Note the difference between this anisotropic effect and the effect for a vinyl proton, =CHR (Section 8.8B). In the case of an alkyne, the induced field opposes, rather than augments, H_0.

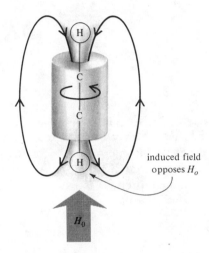

Figure 9.9. An alkynyl proton is shielded by the induced magnetic field of the triple bond.

Preparation of Alkenes and Alkynes

Alkenes may be prepared by E1 or E2 reactions of alkyl halides (Sections 5.9–5.10) or of alcohols (Section 7.10).

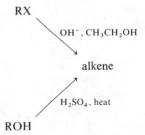

Primary alcohols undergo elimination reactions slowly. In hot, concentrated H_2SO_4, the product alkene may also undergo isomerization and other reactions; therefore, primary alcohols are not usually useful in alkene preparation. *Primary alkyl halides* also undergo elimination reactions slowly by an E2 path. However, if a bulky base such as the *t*-butoxide ion is used, an alkene may be obtained in good yield (along with some S_N2 product).

1° RX (E2 and S_N2):

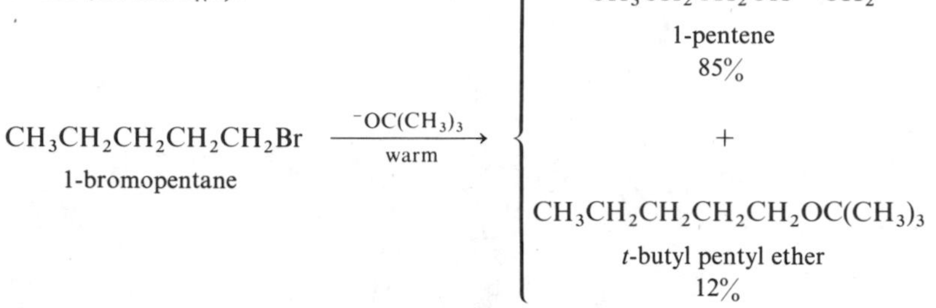

$$CH_3CH_2CH_2CH_2CH_2Br \xrightarrow[\text{warm}]{^-OC(CH_3)_3}$$

1-bromopentane

$$\begin{cases} CH_3CH_2CH_2CH=CH_2 \\ \text{1-pentene} \\ 85\% \\ \\ + \\ \\ CH_3CH_2CH_2CH_2CH_2OC(CH_3)_3 \\ \text{\textit{t}-butyl pentyl ether} \\ 12\% \end{cases}$$

Secondary alcohols undergo elimination by an E1 path, and rearrangement of the intermediate carbocation may occur. Except in simple cases, secondary alcohols are therefore not useful intermediates for the preparation of alkenes. *Secondary alkyl halides* can undergo E2 reactions. Although product mixtures may be expected, the predominant product is usually the more highly substituted *trans*-alkene.

2° RX (E2):

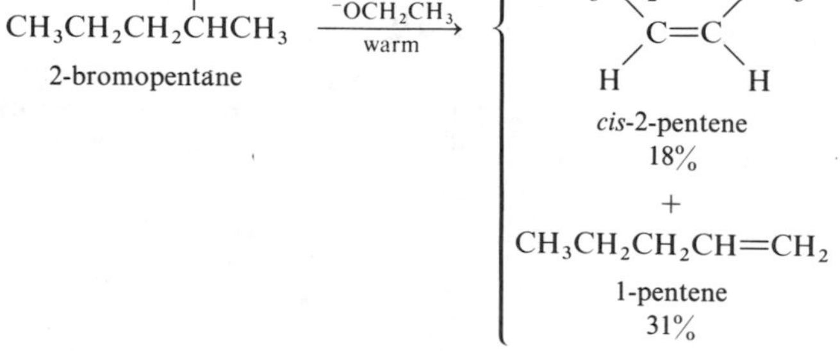

$$\begin{array}{c} Br \\ | \\ CH_3CH_2CH_2CHCH_3 \end{array} \xrightarrow[\text{warm}]{^-OCH_2CH_3}$$

2-bromopentane

$$\begin{cases} \underset{H}{\overset{CH_3CH_2}{\diagdown}}C=C\underset{CH_3}{\overset{H}{\diagup}} \\ \textit{trans}\text{-2-pentene} \\ 51\% \\ + \\ \underset{H}{\overset{CH_3CH_2}{\diagdown}}C=C\underset{H}{\overset{CH_3}{\diagup}} \\ \textit{cis}\text{-2-pentene} \\ 18\% \\ + \\ CH_3CH_2CH_2CH=CH_2 \\ \text{1-pentene} \\ 31\% \end{cases}$$

Tertiary alkyl halides and alcohols undergo elimination readily through carbocations (E1). Excellent yields can be obtained in cases where there is no chance for rearrangement of the carbocation.

STUDY PROBLEM

9.6 Each of the following reactions yields one alkene in a yield of over 80 percent. Give the structure of each alkene product.

(a) 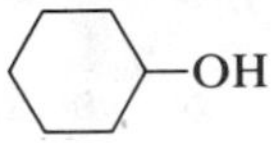 ⬡—OH $\xrightarrow[\text{heat}]{\text{conc. H}_2\text{SO}_4}$

(b) $(CH_3)_3CBr \xrightarrow{\text{Na}^+ \ ^-\text{OCH}_2\text{CH}_3}$

(c) $CH_3CH_2\overset{\overset{\text{OH}}{|}}{C}(CH_3)_2 \xrightarrow[\text{heat}]{50\% \ \text{H}_2\text{SO}_4}$

(d) $(CH_3)_3COH \xrightarrow[\text{warm}]{\text{H}_2\text{SO}_4}$

Alkynes may also be prepared by elimination reactions. In the following examples, note that a stronger base than OH^- is needed for dehydrohalogenation of the vinyl halide. The reason for this is that the sp^2 bonds of a vinyl halide are stronger than the sp^3 bonds of an alkyl halide. (Why?)

$$CH_3\overset{\overset{\text{Br}}{|}}{C}H\overset{\overset{}{}}{C}HCH_3 \xrightarrow[-HBr]{OH^-} CH_3CH=\overset{\overset{}{}}{C}CH_3 \xrightarrow[-HBr]{NH_2^-} CH_3C\equiv CCH_3$$

with Br below second carbon (first) and Br below (middle).

2,3-dibromobutane · · · 2-bromo-2-butene (a vinyl halide) · · · 2-butyne

In Section 9.1, we mentioned that treatment of an alkyne with a strong base yields an acetylide. An acetylide ion may be used as a nucleophile in S_N2 reactions with primary alkyl halides. (Secondary and tertiary alkyl halides are more likely to give elimination products.) This reaction provides a synthetic route for obtaining large alkynes from smaller ones.

Preparation of acetylide:

$$CH_3C\equiv CH + NaNH_2 \xrightarrow[-30°]{\text{liq. NH}_3} CH_3C\equiv C^- \ Na^+ + NH_3$$

propyne

Reaction with an alkyl halide:

$$CH_3C\equiv C^- + CH_3CH_2CH_2-Cl \xrightarrow{S_N2} CH_3CH_2CH_2C\equiv CCH_3 + Cl^-$$

1-chloropropane · · · 2-hexyne

STUDY PROBLEM

9.7 Suggest synthetic routes, starting with propyne, to: (a) 2-pentyne, and (b) 4-phenyl-2-pentyne.

As we also mentioned in Section 9.1, alkynyl Grignard reagents may be prepared by the reaction of a Grignard reagent and a 1-alkyne. In this reaction, the Grignard reagent acts as a base while the alkyne acts as an acid.

Preparation of RC≡CMgX:

$$CH_3C≡C\overset{\delta+}{\underset{}{\textbf{H}}} \overset{\delta-}{} + CH_3MgI \longrightarrow CH_3C≡CMgI + CH_4$$

propyne

As with other Grignard reagents, the nucleophilic carbon of an alkynyl Grignard reagent attacks partially positive centers, such as the carbon of a carbonyl group. The advantage of this type of Grignard synthesis is that more-complex alkynes may be prepared this way than by S_N2 reactions.

Reaction with a ketone:

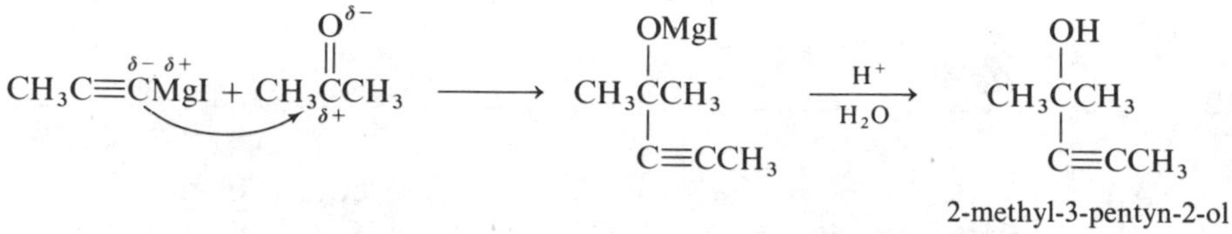

$$CH_3C≡CMgI + CH_3\overset{O^{\delta-}}{\underset{}{\overset{||}{C}}}CH_3 \longrightarrow CH_3\overset{OMgI}{\underset{C≡CCH_3}{\overset{|}{\underset{|}{C}}}}CH_3 \xrightarrow[H_2O]{H^+} CH_3\overset{OH}{\underset{C≡CCH_3}{\overset{|}{\underset{|}{C}}}}CH_3$$

2-methyl-3-pentyn-2-ol

STUDY PROBLEM

9.8 Show how you would synthesize 1-pentyn-3-ol from acetylene, propanal (CH_3CH_2CHO), and ethylmagnesium bromide.

Section 9.6

Addition Reactions

Three typical reactions of alkenes are the reactions with hydrogen, with chlorine, and with a hydrogen halide:

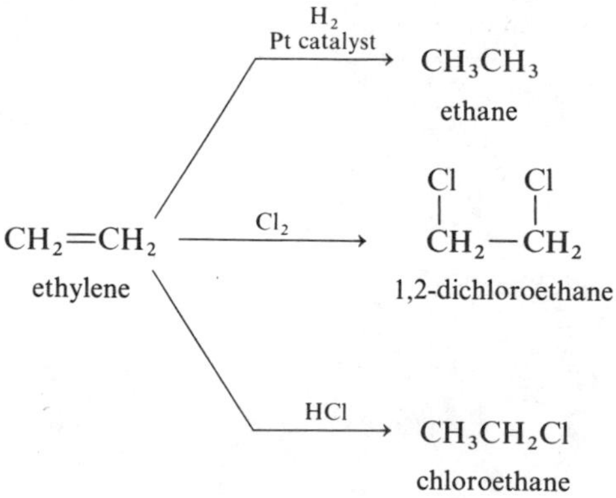

$$CH_2=CH_2 \begin{cases} \xrightarrow[\text{Pt catalyst}]{H_2} CH_3CH_3 \text{ (ethane)} \\ \xrightarrow{Cl_2} \overset{Cl}{\underset{}{\overset{|}{C}H_2}}-\overset{Cl}{\underset{}{\overset{|}{C}H_2}} \text{ (1,2-dichloroethane)} \\ \xrightarrow{HCl} CH_3CH_2Cl \text{ (chloroethane)} \end{cases}$$

ethylene

Each of these reactions is an **addition reaction**. In each case, a reagent has added to the alkene without the loss of any other atoms. We will find that the principal characteristic of unsaturated compounds is the *addition of reagents to pi bonds*.

In an addition reaction of an alkene, the pi bond is broken and its pair of electrons is used in the formation of two new sigma bonds. In each case, the sp^2 carbon atoms are rehybridized to sp^3. Compounds containing pi bonds are usually of higher energy than comparable compounds containing only sigma bonds; consequently, an addition reaction is usually exothermic.

Section 9.7

Addition of Hydrogen Halides to Alkenes and Alkynes

Hydrogen halides add to the pi bonds of alkenes to yield alkyl halides. Alkynes react in an analogous manner and yield either vinyl halides or alkyl dihalides. We will not stress alkynes in our discussions, however, because alkenes are more important both in the laboratory and in nature.

$$CH_2{=}CH_2 + HX \longrightarrow CH_3CH_2X$$

ethylene   *an ethyl halide*

$$CH{\equiv}CH + HX \longrightarrow CH_2{=}CHX$$

acetylene   *a vinyl halide*

$$CH{\equiv}CH + 2\,HX \longrightarrow CH_3CHX_2$$

                               an ethyl dihalide

The addition of hydrogen halides to alkenes to prepare alkyl halides is often used as a synthetic reaction. Usually, the gaseous HX is bubbled through a solution of the alkene. (Concentrated aqueous solutions of hydrogen halides give mixtures of products because water can also add to double bonds.) The relative reactivity of HX in this reaction is HI > HBr > HCl > HF. The strongest acid (HI) is the most reactive toward alkenes, while the weakest acid (HF) is the least reactive.

The mechanism of the addition of HX to an alkene is a direct result of the pi-electron distribution around the sp^2 carbon atoms. The carbon–carbon pi bond is nonpolar. Therefore, nucleophiles are not attracted to either carbon of a double bond, but rather are repelled by the exposed electrons of the pi bond. On the other hand, an electrophile, such as H^+, is electron-deficient and is attracted by the pi-bond electrons. An alkenyl (or alkynyl) carbon is therefore subject to **electrophilic attack**, attack by a positively charged species such as H^+.

two electrons in the pi bond   *an alkene*   *a carbocation*

A hydrogen halide contains a highly polar H—X bond and can easily lose H^+ to the pi bond of an alkene. The result of the attack of H^+ is an intermediate carbocation which quickly undergoes reaction with a negative halide ion to yield an alkyl halide. Because the initial attack is by an electrophile, the addition of HX to an alkene is called an **electrophilic addition reaction**.

Step 1 (slow):

$$H-Cl$$

$$CH_3CH=CHCH_3 \longrightarrow \left[CH_3\overset{+}{C}HCHCH_3 \overset{H}{|} \right] + Cl^-$$

2-butene   *intermediate carbocation*

Step 2 (fast):

$$\left[CH_3\overset{+}{C}HCH_2CH_3 \right] + Cl^- \longrightarrow CH_3\overset{Cl}{\underset{|}{C}}HCH_2CH_3$$

2-chlorobutane

A.   Markovnikov's Rule

If an alkene is *unsymmetrical* (that is, the groups attached to the two sp^2 carbons differ), there is the possibility of two different products from the addition of HX:

$$CH_3CH=CHCH_3 \xrightarrow{HCl} CH_3\overset{H}{\underset{|}{C}}H-\overset{Cl}{\underset{|}{C}}HCH_3$$

2-butene   2-chlorobutane
symmetrical   *only one possible product*

$$CH_3CH=CH_2 \xrightarrow{HCl}$$

$$CH_3CH_2-CH_2Cl$$
1-chloropropane

$$CH_3\overset{Cl}{\underset{|}{C}}H-CH_3$$
2-chloropropane

propene   *two possible products*
unsymmetrical

In an electrophilic addition that can lead to two products, one product predominates over the other. In 1869, the Russian chemist Vladimir Markovnikov formulated the following rule: *In additions of HX to unsymmetrical alkenes, the H^+ of HX goes to the double-bonded carbon that already has the greatest number of hydrogens.* By Markovnikov's rule, we would predict that the reaction of HCl with propene yields 2-chloropropane (and not the 1-chloro isomer). Examples of reactions that obey Markovnikov's rule follow:

H goes here

$$CH_3CH=CH_2 \xrightarrow{HCl} CH_3\overset{Cl}{\underset{|}{C}}H-CH_3$$

propene   2-chloropropane

H goes here

$$(CH_3)_2C=CHCH_3 \xrightarrow{HBr} (CH_3)_2\overset{Br}{\underset{|}{C}}-CH_2CH_3$$

2-methyl-2-butene   2-bromo-2-methylbutane

H goes here

1-methyl-1-cyclohexene   1-iodo-1-methylcyclohexane

B.   The Reason for Markovnikov's Rule

Markovnikov formulated his rule because of experimental observations. Why is this empirical rule followed? To answer this question, let us return to the mechanism of HX addition. *Step 1* is the formation of a carbocation. For propene, two possible carbocations could be formed:

A primary carbocation:

$$H^+$$
$$CH_3CH{=}CH_2 \longrightarrow \left[\begin{array}{c} H^{\delta+} \\ CH_3CH{\cdots}\overset{\delta+}{CH_2} \end{array}\right] \longrightarrow CH_3CH_2\overset{+}{C}H_2$$

transition state   1°, *less stable*

A secondary carbocation:

$$H^+$$
$$CH_3CH{=}CH_2 \longrightarrow \left[\begin{array}{c} H^{\delta+} \\ \overset{\delta+}{CH_3CH}{\cdots}CH_2 \end{array}\right] \longrightarrow CH_3\overset{+}{C}HCH_3$$

transition state   2°, *more stable*

The order of stability of carbocations is 3° > 2° > 1°. For propene, the two positions of H⁺ addition lead to (1) a high-energy, unstable, primary carbocation, or (2) a lower-energy, more-stable, secondary carbocation. The transition states leading to these intermediates have carbocation character. Therefore, the secondary carbocation has a lower-energy transition state and a faster rate of formation (see Figure 9.10).

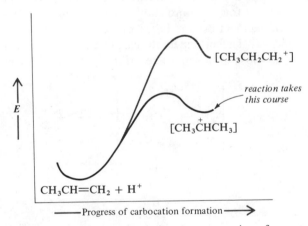

Figure 9.10.   Energy diagram for the protonation of propene.

Addition of a reagent to an unsymmetrical alkene proceeds by way of the more stable carbocation. This is the reason that Markovnikov's rule is followed.

$$CH_3CH{=}CH_2 \xrightarrow{H^+} [CH_3\overset{+}{C}HCH_3] \xrightarrow{Cl^-} CH_3\overset{\text{Cl}}{\underset{|}{C}}HCH_3$$

$$(CH_3)_2C{=}CHCH_3 \xrightarrow{H^+} [(CH_3)_2\overset{+}{C}CH_2CH_3] \xrightarrow{Br^-} (CH_3)_2\overset{\text{Br}}{\underset{|}{C}}CH_2CH_3$$

Sample Problem

Predict the relative rates of reaction of the following alkenes toward HBr (lowest rate first):

(a) $CH_3CH_2CH{=}CH_2$ (b) $CH_2{=}CH_2$ (c) $(CH_3)_2C{=}CHCH_3$

Solution: The alkene that can form the most stable carbocation has the lowest E_{act} and the fastest rate. Therefore,

$$CH_2{=}CH_2 \qquad CH_3CH_2CH{=}CH_2 \qquad (CH_3)_2C{=}CHCH_3$$

increasing rate of reaction

STUDY PROBLEMS

9.9   For the alkenes in (a) and (c) in the preceding sample problem, give the structures of the carbocation intermediate and the major product of the reaction with HBr.

9.10   When propene is treated with HCl in ethanol, one of the products is ethyl isopropyl ether. Suggest a mechanism for its formation.

C.   Rearrangements

In Section 5.7E, we discussed carbocation rearrangements in S_N1 reactions. When a carbocation can form a more stable carbocation by a 1,2-shift of —H, —R, or —Ar, rearrangement occurs. Is rearrangement observed in HX addition reactions? Yes, indeed. The intermediate carbocations in these HX additions are no different from those in S_N1 or E1 reactions.

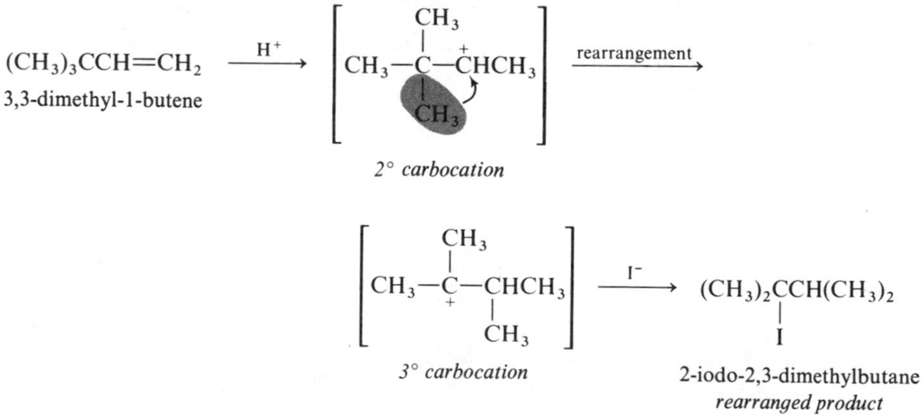

$(CH_3)_3CCH{=}CH_2$

3,3-dimethyl-1-butene

2° carbocation

3° carbocation

$(CH_3)_2CCH(CH_3)_2$

2-iodo-2,3-dimethylbutane

rearranged product

STUDY PROBLEM

9.11   Predict the rearrangement product of each of the following reactions:

(a)   3-methyl-1-butene + HCl $\longrightarrow$

(b)   4,4-dimethyl-2-pentene + HBr $\longrightarrow$

D.   Anti-Markovnikov Addition of HBr

The addition of HBr to alkenes sometimes proceeds by Markovnikov's rule, but sometimes it does not. (This effect is not observed with HCl or HI.)

$$
CH_3CH{=}CH_2 \xrightarrow{\text{HBr}} \underset{\text{2-bromopropane}}{CH_3\overset{\overset{\displaystyle Br}{|}}{C}HCH_3} \qquad \text{but sometimes} \quad \underset{\substack{\text{1-bromopropane}\\ \textit{anti-Markovnikov product}}}{CH_3CH_2CH_2Br}
$$

$$
\underset{\text{propene}}{}
$$

It has been observed that the primary alkyl bromide is obtained only when peroxides are present in the reaction mixture. Peroxides (ROOR) are easily cleaved into free radicals. When peroxides are present, then, HBr addition proceeds through a *free-radical* mechanism instead of an ionic one.

Formation of Br·: $ROOR \longrightarrow 2\,RO\cdot$

$$RO\cdot + HBr \longrightarrow ROH + Br\cdot$$

Addition of Br· to alkene:

$$
Br\cdot + CH_3CH{=}CH_2 \longrightarrow \underset{\substack{Br\\ 2°,\ \textit{more stable}}}{CH_3\overset{\displaystyle\cdot}{C}HCH_2} \quad \text{and not} \quad \underset{\substack{Br\\ 1°,\ \textit{less stable}}}{CH_3CH\overset{\displaystyle\cdot}{C}H_2}
$$

Formation of product:

$$
CH_3\overset{\displaystyle\cdot}{C}HCH_2Br + HBr \longrightarrow CH_3CH_2CH_2Br + Br\cdot
$$

When Br· attacks the alkene, the more stable free radical is formed. (The stability of free radicals, like that of carbocations, is in the order 3° > 2° > 1°.) The result of the free-radical addition is 1-bromopropane in our example.

STUDY PROBLEM

9.12 Predict the products:

(a) $(CH_3)_2C{=}CH_2 + HBr \xrightarrow{\text{ROOR}}$

(b) $(CH_3)_2C{=}CH_2 + HBr \xrightarrow{\text{no peroxides}}$

Section 9.8

Addition of H₂SO₄ and H₂O to Alkenes and Alkynes

Sulfuric acid undergoes addition to an alkene just as a hydrogen halide does. The product is an alkyl sulfate, which may be used to prepare alcohols and ethers (see Section 7.16).

$$
\underset{\text{propene}}{CH_3CH{=}CH_2} + H{-}OSO_3H \longrightarrow \underset{\text{2-propyl hydrogen sulfate}}{CH_3\overset{\overset{\displaystyle OSO_3H}{|}}{C}H{-}CH_3}
$$

If a trace of strong acid, such as sulfuric acid, is present as a catalyst, water also adds to a double bond to yield an alcohol. This reaction is called the **hydration of an alkene**.

$$CH_3CH{=}CH_2 + H_2O \xrightarrow{\text{H}^+} CH_3\overset{\displaystyle OH}{\overset{|}{CH}}{-}CH_3$$

propene   2-propanol
                                                     60%

Both reactions occur in two steps, just as does the addition of a hydrogen halide. The first step is the protonation of the alkene to yield a carbocation. The second step is the addition of a nucleophile to the carbocation. Because initially a carbocation is formed, both reactions follow Markovnikov's rule. Rearrangements are to be expected if the carbocation can undergo a 1,2-shift to a more stable carbocation.

Addition of H$_2$O:

Step 1: $R_2C{=}CHR + H^+ \longrightarrow [R_2\overset{+}{C}{-}CH_2R]$

               an alkene

Step 2:

$$[R_2\overset{+}{C}{-}CH_2R] + H_2O \longrightarrow R_2C{-}CH_2R \overset{\longrightarrow}{\longleftarrow} R_2C{-}CH_2R + H^+$$

$$\overset{\displaystyle{}^+OH_2}{\overset{|}{\phantom{R_2C{-}CH_2R}}} \qquad \overset{\displaystyle OH}{\overset{|}{\phantom{R_2C{-}CH_2R}}}$$

                   a protonated alcohol   *an alcohol*

STUDY PROBLEMS

9.13 Show the mechanism for the addition of H_2SO_4 to 1-butene to yield a butyl hydrogen sulfate.

9.14 Predict the major products:

(a) $CH_3CH_2CH{=}CH_2 + H_2O \xrightarrow{\text{H}^+}$

(b) $(CH_3)_3CCH{=}CH_2 + H_2O \xrightarrow{\text{H}^+}$

(c) $(CH_3)_2CHCH{=}CH_2 + H_2SO_4 \longrightarrow$

Alkynes also undergo hydration, but the initial product is a vinyl alcohol, or **enol**. An enol is in equilibrium with an aldehyde or ketone (see Section 11.17). The equilibrium favors the carbonyl compound; therefore, hydration of an alkyne actually results in an aldehyde or ketone. (The hydration of alkynes proceeds more smoothly when a mercuric salt is added to catalyze the reaction.)

$$HC{\equiv}CH + H_2O \xrightarrow[\text{Hg}^{2+}]{\text{H}^+} \left[H_2C{=}CH \right] \rightleftharpoons CH_3CH$$

acetylene   *an enol*   acetaldehyde
                                 (*unstable*)   (ethanal)

$$CH_3C{\equiv}CH + H_2O \xrightarrow[\text{Hg}^{2+}]{\text{H}^+} \left[CH_3C{=}CH_2 \right] \rightleftharpoons CH_3CCH_3$$

propyne   acetone
                                                    (propanone)

Section 9.9

Hydration with Mercuric Acetate

Mercuric acetate, $Hg(O_2CCH_3)_2$, adds to alkenes in a reaction called **oxymercuration**. Unlike the addition reactions we have discussed so far, oxymercuration proceeds *without rearrangement*. The product of oxymercuration is usually reduced with sodium borohydride ($NaBH_4$) in a subsequent reaction called **demercuration** to yield an alcohol, the same alcohol that would be formed if water had been added across the double bond. Oxymercuration–demercuration reactions usually give better yields of alcohols than the addition of water with H_2SO_4 because the latter conditions can also lead to polymerization of the alkene (Section 9.18).

Oxymercuration:

$$CH_3CH_2CH_2CH{=}CH_2 \xrightarrow[\;H_2O\;]{Hg\left(O_2CCH_3\right)_2} \underset{\overset{\displaystyle |}{HgO_2CCH_3}}{CH_3CH_2CH_2\overset{\overset{\displaystyle OH}{\displaystyle |}}{C}HCH_2}$$

1-pentene

Demercuration:

$$\underset{}{CH_3CH_2CH_2\overset{\overset{\displaystyle OH}{\displaystyle |}}{C}HCH_2}{-}HgO_2CCH_3 \xrightarrow{NaBH_4} CH_3CH_2CH_2\overset{\overset{\displaystyle OH}{\displaystyle |}}{C}HCH_3 + Hg$$

2-pentanol
90% overall

Like the addition of other reagents to alkenes, oxymercuration is a two-step process. The addition proceeds by electrophilic attack of $^+HgO_2CCH_3$ followed by nucleophilic attack of H_2O. Because rearrangements do not occur, the intermediate formed by electrophilic attack cannot be a true carbocation. On the other hand, since Markovnikov's rule is followed, the intermediate must have some carbocation character. Chemists believe that the intermediate is a **bridged ion**, or **cyclic ion**, as is shown in the following path.

Dissociation of mercuric acetate:

$$Hg(O_2CCH_3)_2 \rightleftharpoons {}^+HgO_2CCH_3 + {}^-O_2CCH_3$$

Electrophilic attack:

$$R_2C{=}CHR \xrightarrow{\quad} \left[R_2\overset{+}{C}{-}CHR \atop \qquad\;\; HgO_2CCH_3 \right]$$

$^+HgO_2CCH_3$

a bridged intermediate

Attack of H_2O and proton loss:

$$\left[R_2\overset{+}{C}{-}CHR \atop \quad\; HgO_2CCH_3 \right] \xrightarrow{H_2O} \left[R_2C{-}\overset{\overset{\displaystyle ^+OH_2}{\displaystyle |}}{C}HR \atop HgO_2CCH_3 \right] \xrightarrow{-H^+} R_2C{-}\overset{\overset{\displaystyle OH}{\displaystyle |}}{C}HR \atop HgO_2CCH_3$$

The formation of a bridged intermediate is not very different from the formation of a carbocation. The reaction of this intermediate is also very similar to that of a carbocation. The difference between this bridged intermediate and a true carbocation is that Hg is partially bonded to *each* double-bond carbon and rearrangements cannot occur. The more positive carbon in the bridged intermediate (the carbon attacked by H_2O) may be predicted by knowledge of carbocation stabilities ($3° > 2° > 1°$). We can compare the reaction of this type of bridged ion with the one formed in acid-catalyzed substitution of an epoxide (Section 7.12B).

more positive carbon;
H_2O attacks here

$$\overset{+}{R_2C}-CHR \qquad \text{similar to} \qquad \overset{+}{R_2C}-CHR$$
$$\underset{HgO_2CCH_3}{|} \qquad\qquad\qquad\qquad \underset{HgO_2CCH_3}{|}$$

The reducing agent in the demercuration reaction, sodium borohydride, is an important reducing agent to organic chemists. It forms stable solutions in aqueous base, but decomposes and releases H_2 in acidic solution. We will encounter this reagent again as a reducing agent for aldehydes and ketones (Section 11.14).

$$Na^+ \quad H-\overset{\overset{\textstyle H}{|}}{\underset{\underset{\textstyle H}{|}}{B}}{=}H$$

sodium borohydride

STUDY PROBLEM

9.15 (a) Write the steps in the oxymercuration–demercuration of 3,3-dimethyl-1-butene.
   (b) Compare the product of this reaction sequence to the product from the reaction of 3,3-dimethyl-1-butene with dilute, aqueous HCl.

Section 9.10

Addition of Borane to Alkenes

Diborane (B_2H_6) is a toxic gas. In ether solution, diborane dissociates into borane (BH_3) solvated by an ether molecule ($R_2O - - -BH_3$). Borane undergoes rapid and quantitative reaction with alkenes to form **organoboranes** (R_3B). The overall reaction is the result of three separate reaction steps. In each step, one alkyl group is added to borane, until all three hydrogen atoms have been replaced by alkyl groups.

Step 1: $CH_2{=}CH_2 + B-H \longrightarrow CH_3{-}CH_2$ (with H and BH_2)

Step 2: $CH_2{=}CH_2 + CH_3CH_2BH_2 \longrightarrow (CH_3CH_2)_2BH$

Step 3: $CH_2{=}CH_2 + (CH_3CH_2)_2BH \longrightarrow (CH_3CH_2)_3B$

an organoborane

Borane is different from the other addition reagents we have mentioned because H is the *electronegative* portion of the molecule instead of the electropositive portion, as it is in HCl or H_2O. When borane adds to a double bond, the hydrogen (as a hydride ion, H^-) becomes bonded to the *more substituted carbon*. The result is what appears to be anti-Markovnikov addition.

$$CH_3CH{=}CH_2 \longrightarrow CH_3CH{-}CH_2$$

H on more substituted carbon

Organoboranes are easily oxidized to alcohols by hydrogen peroxide. The final result of borane addition, followed by H_2O_2 oxidation, appears as if water had been added to the double bond in an anti-Markovnikov manner. Overall yields are usually 95–100%.

$$(CH_3CH_2CH_2)_3B + 3\ H_2O_2 \longrightarrow 3\ CH_3CH_2CH_2OH + B(OH)_3$$

tripropylborane   1-propanol   boric acid

STUDY PROBLEM

9.16 Write an equation or equations for the preparation of each of the following compounds from methylenecyclohexane, ⬡=CH_2:

(a) ⬡ with CH_3 and OH

(b) ⬡—CH_2OH

(c) ⬡—CH_2Br

Section 9.11

Addition of Halogens to Alkenes and Alkynes

Like acids, chlorine and bromine add to carbon–carbon double bonds and triple bonds. A common laboratory test for the presence of a double or triple bond in a compound of unknown structure is the treatment of the compound with a dilute solution of bromine in CCl_4. The test reagent has the reddish-brown color of Br_2; disappearance of this color is a positive test. The decolorization of a Br_2/CCl_4 solution by an unknown is suggestive, but not definitive proof, that a double or triple bond is present. A few other types of compound, such as ketones and phenols, also decolorize Br_2/CCl_4 solution.

$$CH_3CH{=}CHCH_3 + Br_2 \longrightarrow CH_3CH{-}CHCH_3$$

2-butene   *red*   2,3-dibromobutane
colorless

$$CH_3C{\equiv}CCH_3 + 2\ Br_2 \longrightarrow CH_3C{-}CCH_3$$

2-butyne   *red*

2,2,3,3-tetrabromobutane
colorless

Table 9.4. Relative Reactivities of Some Alkenes Toward Br$_2$ in Methanol

Compound	Relative rate
$CH_2=CH_2$	1
$CH_3CH_2CH=CH_2$	10^3
cis-$CH_3CH_2CH=CHCH_3$	10^5
$(CH_3)_2C=C(CH_3)_2$	10^7

Neither F_2 nor I_2 are useful reagents in alkene addition reactions. Fluorine undergoes violent reaction with organic compounds, while iodine is not reactive enough. The C—I bond is weak, and compounds with vicinal iodine atoms lose I_2 in the reverse reaction:

$$R_2CI—CIR_2 \rightleftarrows R_2C=CR_2 + I_2$$

Therefore, we can say this addition reaction is general only for *chlorine* and *bromine*.

A more substituted alkene is more reactive toward X_2 than a less substituted alkene (see Table 9.4). This is the same order of reactivity as that toward HX.

$$CH_2=CH_2 \quad RCH=CH_2 \quad R_2C=CH_2 \quad R_2C=CHR \quad R_2C=CR_2$$

increasing reactivity toward X$_2$ or HX addition

A. Electrophilic Attack of X_2

The reaction of X_2 with alkenes is similar to that of HX. But what is the source of the electrophile in X_2? When X_2 approaches the pi-bond electrons, polarity is induced in the X_2 molecule by repulsion between the pi electrons and the electrons in the X_2 molecule.

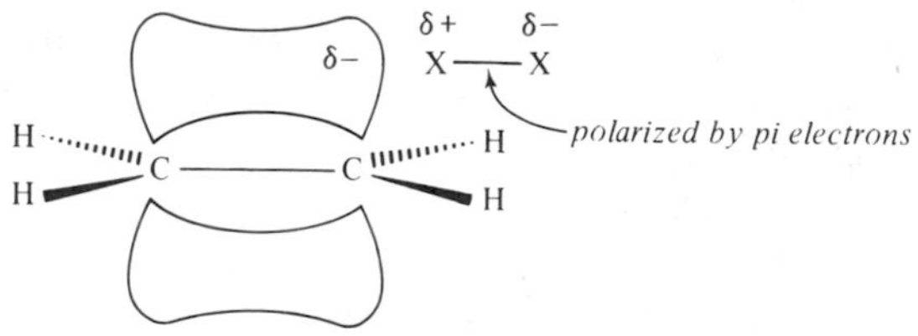

As the X—X bond becomes more polarized, it becomes progressively weaker until it finally breaks. The result is a halide ion and a positively charged organohalogen ion, called a **halonium ion**. There is evidence that the halonium ion is not a simple carbocation, but is bridged, similar to the intermediate in oxymercuration. In the case of addition of X_2 to ethylene or some other symmetrical alkene, the bridged halonium ion is symmetrical, with X equally bonded to each carbon.

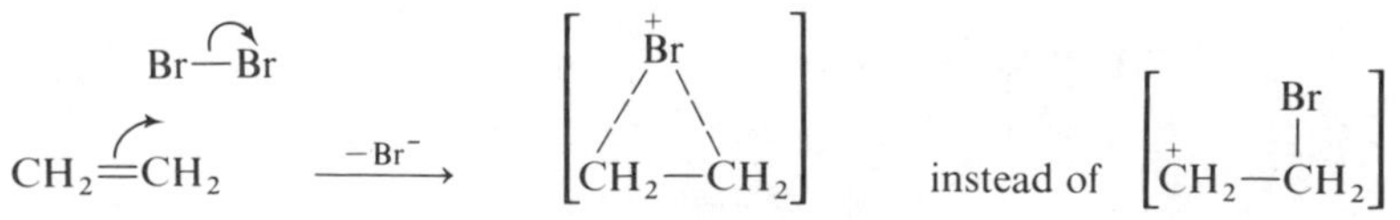

a bridged bromonium ion

If the alkene is unsymmetrical, most of the positive charge is carried on the more substituted carbon. Carbocation stability is followed.

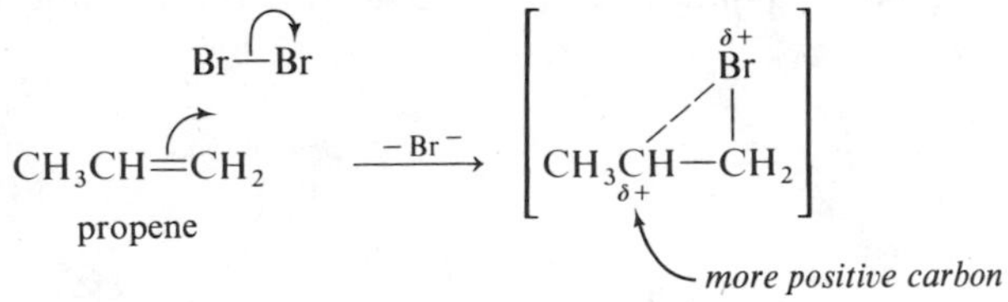

B. *anti-Attack of* X⁻

The bridged intermediate ion is positively charged and of high energy. Like a carbocation, it exists only momentarily in solution; reaction is completed by attack of a nucleophile (in this case, Br^-). A negative Br^- cannot attack a carbon of the bridged intermediate from the top (as we have shown the structure); that path is blocked by the Br bridge. Therefore, Br^- attacks from the opposite side of the intermediate. The result is *anti-addition* of Br_2 to the double bond.

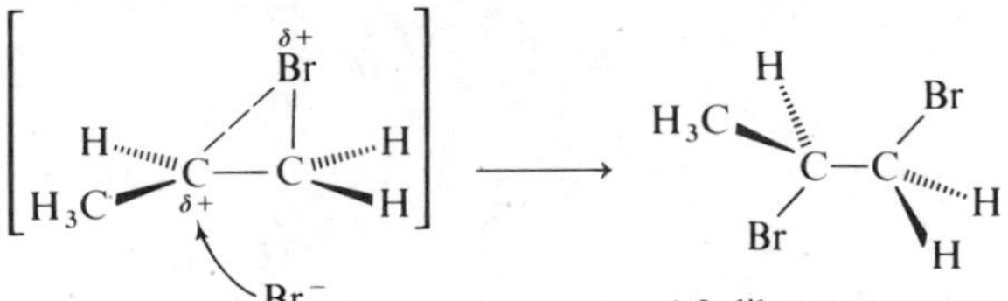

General mechanism:

Step 1 (slow):
$$R_2C{=}CHR + X_2 \longrightarrow \left[R_2\overset{\delta+}{C}{-}CHR \right] + X^-$$

Step 2 (fast):
$$\left[R_2\overset{\delta+}{C}{-}CHR \right] + X^- \longrightarrow R_2C{-}CHR$$

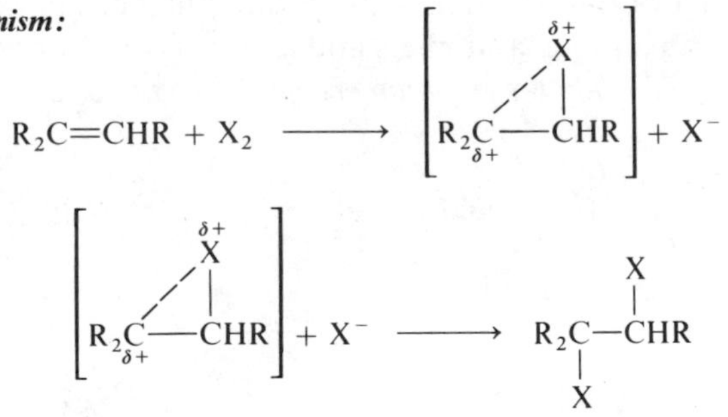

STUDY PROBLEM

9.17 Predict the products of Br_2 addition to:

    (a) $CH_3CH{=}CHCH_3$ (b) $(CH_3)_2C{=}CH_2$ (c) $(CH_3)_2C{=}CHCH_3$

C. *Evidence for anti-Addition*

Two pieces of evidence point to a bridged ion as the intermediate in halogenation addition and to *anti*-addition as the mechanism. Both pieces of evidence are based upon the fact that only one stereoisomeric product is observed in reactions where two or more products would be expected from a simple carbocation intermediate.

The first piece of evidence is that *trans*-dihalides (and not *cis*-dihalides) are formed when the product of halogen addition is capable of geometric isomerism. If the intermediate were a simple carbocation, both the *cis*- and *trans*-isomers would be formed.

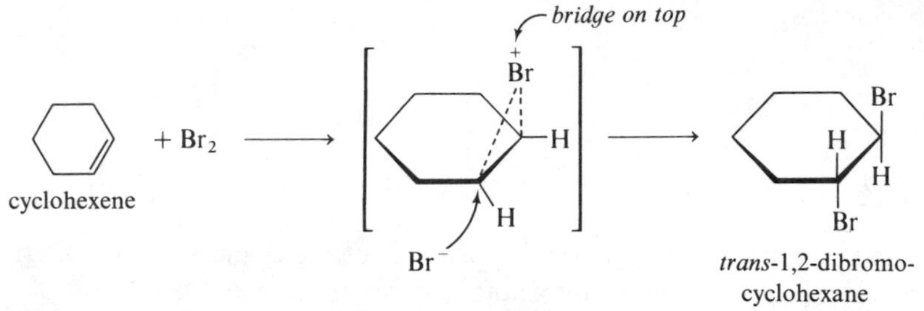
bridge on top
+ Br_2
cyclohexene
Br
H
H
Br^-
Br
H
H
Br
trans-1,2-dibromo-cyclohexane

Additional evidence for *anti*-addition is encountered in the reactions of geometric isomers of open-chain alkenes. When either *cis*- or *trans*-2-butene is treated with Br_2, two chiral centers are generated.

$$CH_3CH{=}CHCH_3 \longrightarrow CH_3\overset{*}{C}H(Br)-\overset{*}{C}H(Br)CH_3$$

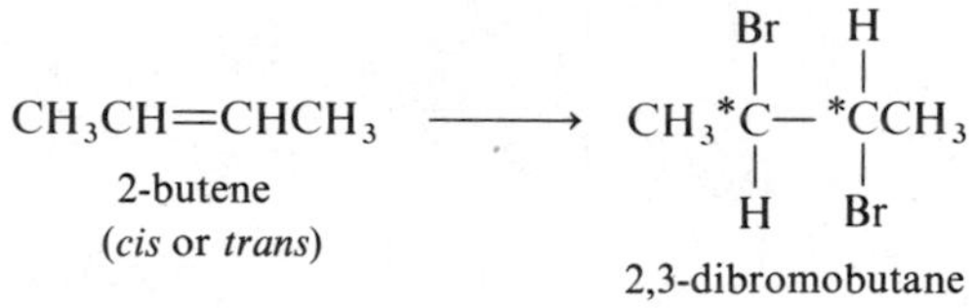

2-butene (*cis* or *trans*) → 2,3-dibromobutane

The product of this addition, 2,3-dibromobutane, can exist in three stereoisomeric forms: a pair of enantiomers and a *meso* form. The addition of bromine to *cis*-2-butene yields *only the enantiomeric pair*. No *meso* form is produced in this reaction.

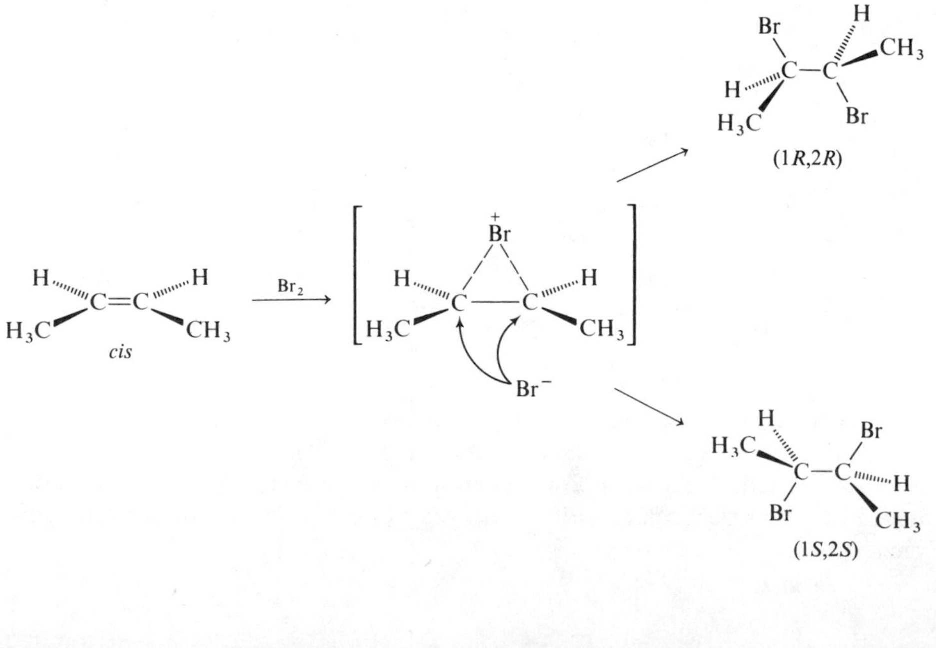
cis
Br_2
Br^-
(1*R*,2*R*)
(1*S*,2*S*)

On the other hand, the *trans*-isomer yields only the *meso* form and not the enantiomeric pair.

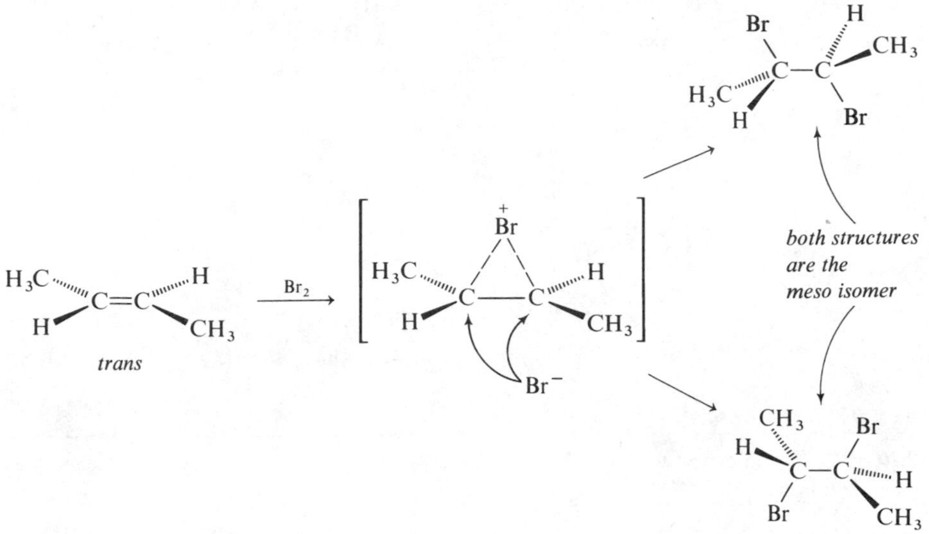

both structures are the meso isomer

The conclusion is that the intermediate is not an open carbocation. If it were, then rotation around the carbon 2–carbon 3 sigma bond would allow all three stereoisomers to be formed regardless of the geometry of the starting alkene.

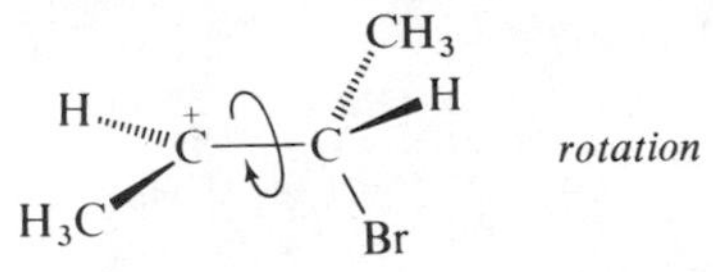

rotation

STUDY PROBLEMS

9.18 Predict the product of the addition reaction of Br_2 with 1-methyl-1-cyclohexene. (Show the geometry of the intermediate and of the product.)

9.19 What would be the stereochemistry of the reaction of bromine with (a) (*E*)-1,2-dideuterioethene, and (b) (*Z*)-1,2-dideuterioethene?

D. Mixed Addition

Bromination reactions of alkenes proceed by way of a bromonium-ion intermediate, followed by attack by a bromide ion to yield the dibromide. Is the second step limited to attack only by bromide ion? Can other nucleophiles compete with bromide ion in the second step to yield other products? Consider the case of a bromination reaction carried out with Br_2 in a solution containing Cl^- (from, say, NaCl). In this reaction, two nucleophiles (Br^- and Cl^-) are present. In such a case, *mixed dihalide products* are observed—along with the dibromo-alkane, we find some bromochloroalkane.

Step 1: $CH_2{=}CH_2 + Br_2 \longrightarrow$ $\left[\begin{array}{c} \overset{+}{Br} \\ \diagup \diagdown \\ CH_2{-}CH_2 \end{array} \right] + Br^-$

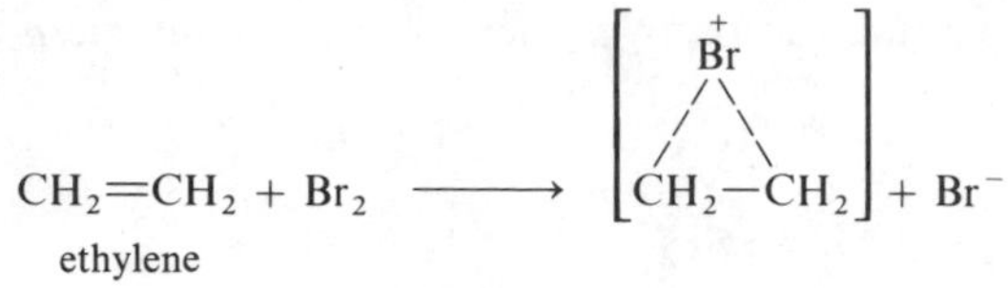

ethylene

Step 2: $\left[\begin{array}{c} \overset{+}{Br} \\ \diagup \diagdown \\ CH_2{-}CH_2 \end{array} \right]$

$\xrightarrow{Br^-}$ $\begin{array}{c} Br \\ | \\ CH_2{-}CH_2Br \end{array}$

1,2-dibromoethane

$\xrightarrow{Cl^-}$ $\begin{array}{c} Br \\ | \\ CH_2{-}CH_2Cl \end{array}$

1-bromo-2-chloroethane

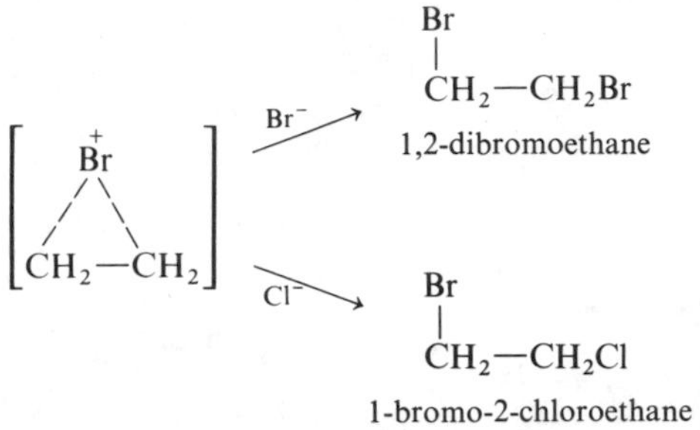

STUDY PROBLEM

9.20 Would you expect to find 1,2-dichloroethane as a product in the preceding example? Explain.

Sample Problem

When propene is treated with $Br_2 + Cl^-$, only one bromochloropropane is isolated as a product. What is its structure? Show, by equations, its formation.

Solution:

Step 1:

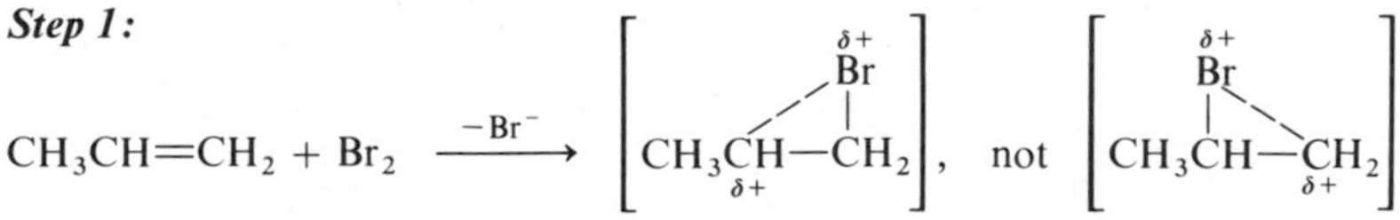

$CH_3CH{=}CH_2 + Br_2 \xrightarrow{-Br^-}$ $\left[\begin{array}{c} \overset{\delta+}{Br} \\ \diagup | \\ CH_3\underset{\delta+}{CH}{-}CH_2 \end{array} \right]$, not $\left[\begin{array}{c} \overset{\delta+}{Br} \\ | \diagdown \\ CH_3CH{-}\underset{\delta+}{CH_2} \end{array} \right]$

Step 2:

$\left[\begin{array}{c} \overset{\delta+}{Br} \\ \diagup | \\ CH_3\underset{\delta+}{CH}{-}CH_2 \end{array} \right] + Cl^- \longrightarrow$ $\begin{array}{c} Br \\ | \\ CH_3CHCH_2 \\ | \\ Cl \end{array}$, not $\begin{array}{c} Br \\ | \\ CH_3CHCH_2Cl \end{array}$

1-bromo-2-
chloropropane

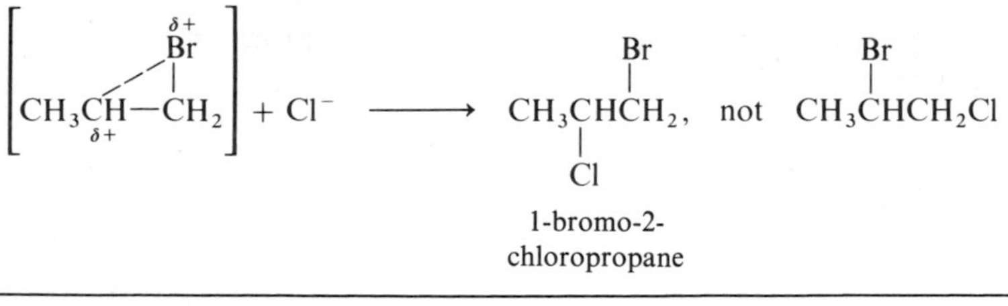

E. Addition of Halogens and Water

When an alkene is treated with a mixture of Cl_2 or Br_2 in water, a **halohydrin** (a compound with X and OH on adjacent carbon atoms) is formed.

General: $R_2C{=}CH_2 \xrightarrow{X_2, H_2O}$ $\begin{array}{c} X \\ | \\ R_2C{-}CH_2 \\ | \\ OH \end{array}$

an alkene

a halohydrin

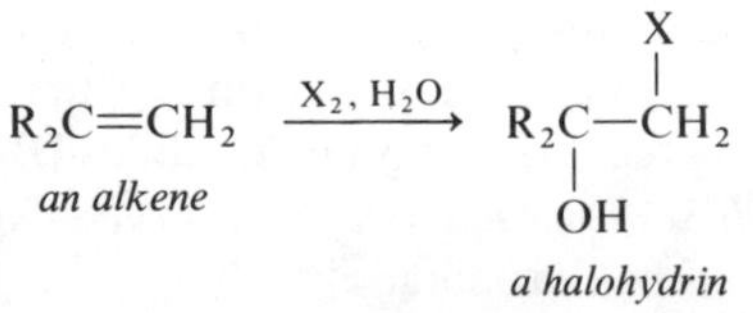

The path is similar to that for mixed halogen addition:

Step 1: $CH_3CH{=}CH_2 + Cl_2 \longrightarrow$ $\left[CH_3\overset{\overset{\overset{\delta+}{Cl}}{|}}{\underset{\delta+}{CH}}{-}CH_2 \right] + Cl^-$

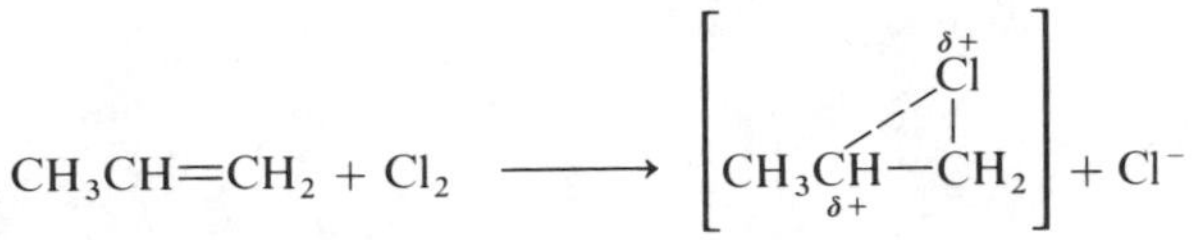

Step 2:

$\left[CH_3\overset{\overset{\overset{\delta+}{Cl}}{|}}{\underset{\delta+}{CH}}{-}CH_2 \right] + H_2O \longrightarrow CH_3\overset{\overset{Cl}{|}}{CH}\underset{\underset{{}^+OH_2}{|}}{CH_2} \underset{\longleftarrow}{\overset{-H^+}{\longrightarrow}} CH_3\overset{\overset{Cl}{|}}{CH}\underset{\underset{OH}{|}}{CH_2}$

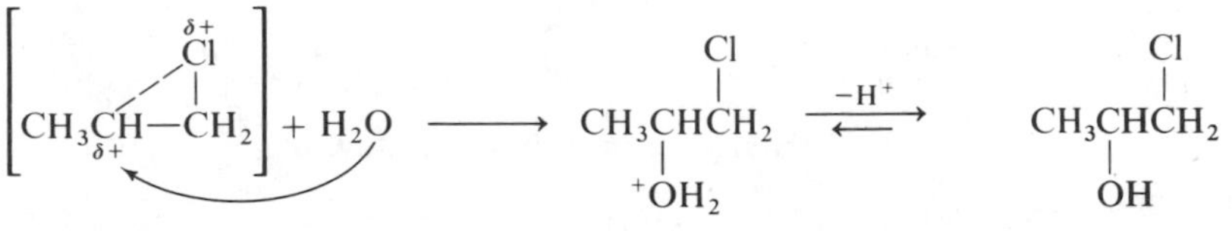

1-chloro-2-propanol
(propylene chlorohydrin)

STUDY PROBLEM

9.21 What would be the product of the reaction of cyclopentene with aqueous Cl_2? Give equations for the steps in this reaction (complete with stereochemistry).

Section 9.12

Addition of Carbenes to Alkenes

If a student were asked whether a compound with the structure CH_2 exists, the reply might be, "No, because the carbon only has two bonds." However, such a species does have a fleeting existence. It is called *methylene* and belongs to a class of highly reactive intermediates called **carbenes** (R_2C:).

The existence of :CH_2 was established spectroscopically in 1959. It has been shown that there are two different methylenes, each with a carbon containing six bonding electrons rather than the usual eight. **Singlet methylene*** (:CH_2) has an sp^2-hybridized carbon and a pair of unshared electrons. **Triplet methylene** ($H\dot{C}H$) contains an sp-hybridized carbon and two unpaired electrons. The orbital pictures of these two structures are presented in Figure 9.11 (page 406).

Singlet methylene is formed by the **photolysis** (cleavage by light) of diazomethane (CH_2N_2) or ketene ($CH_2{=}C{=}O$), both of which are unusual and reactive compounds themselves.

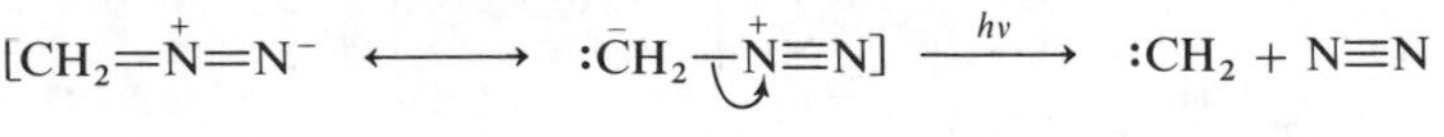

$[CH_2{=}\overset{+}{N}{=}N^- \longleftrightarrow :\bar{C}H_2{-}\overset{+}{N}{\equiv}N] \overset{h\nu}{\longrightarrow} :CH_2 + N{\equiv}N$

resonance structures for diazomethane

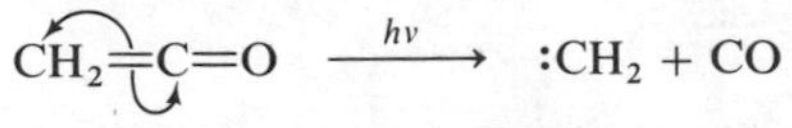

$CH_2{=}C{=}O \overset{h\nu}{\longrightarrow} :CH_2 + CO$

ketene

---

* The electron spin number of an electron may be denoted as $+1/2$ or $-1/2$ depending on the direction of spin. We define $S =$ the sum of the spin numbers. If all electrons are paired, $S = 0$. $[(+1/2) + (-1/2) = 0.]$ If two electrons are unpaired, $S = +1$ or -1. $[(+1/2) + (+1/2) = 1.]$ The *multiplicity of electronic states* (the number of electronic orientations) is given as $2S + 1$. For :CH_2 with only paired electrons, the multiplicity $= 2(0) + 1 = +1$. (*Singlet* denotes $+1$.) For $H\dot{C}H$, the multiplicity $= 2(1) + 1 = 3$. (*Triplet* denotes 3.)

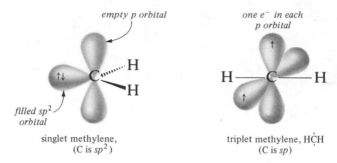

empty p orbital

one e⁻ in each p orbital

filled sp² orbital

singlet methylene,
(C is sp^2)

triplet methylene, HĊH
(C is *sp*)

Figure 9.11. Orbital pictures of the two methylenes.

Triplet methylene cannot be prepared directly. However, if singlet methylene is dissolved in an inert gas, it undergoes a slow transformation to triplet methylene, which is the more stable of the two methylenes.

Both methylenes are electron-deficient and electrophilic. Their most important reaction is addition to alkenes to yield substituted cyclopropanes. Singlet methylene gives a stereospecific **syn-addition** (*syn* means "same side"). This type of addition suggests a concerted, or one-step, reaction.

a cis-dialkylcyclopropane
(*meso*)

a trans-dialkylcyclopropane
(*racemic*)

Triplet methylene, on the other hand, gives nonstereospecific addition. Its addition follows a free-radical path, in which rotation can occur in the diradical intermediate. The result is a mixture of stereoisomeric products.

mixture of
cis and trans

rotation

A major side reaction in the formation of cyclopropane rings with singlet methylene is an **insertion reaction**, in which $:CH_2$ inserts itself into a C—H bond. Because of the high reactivity of $:CH_2$, insertion reactions are unselective and give mixtures.

$$CH_3CHCH_2 + :CH_2 \longrightarrow CH_3CH_2CH_2CH_3 + CH_3CHCH_3$$

H H

CH₃

Another carbene, dichlorocarbene ($Cl_2C:$), is formed by the reaction of strong base and chloroform. This reaction is related to elimination reactions of alkyl halides in that the base removes the elements of HCl from the molecule. The elimination reaction of $CHCl_3$ is an α **elimination** instead of a β elimination. (A molecule that has a β hydrogen will lose the β hydrogen in preference; however, $CHCl_3$ has no β hydrogen.)

Step 1:

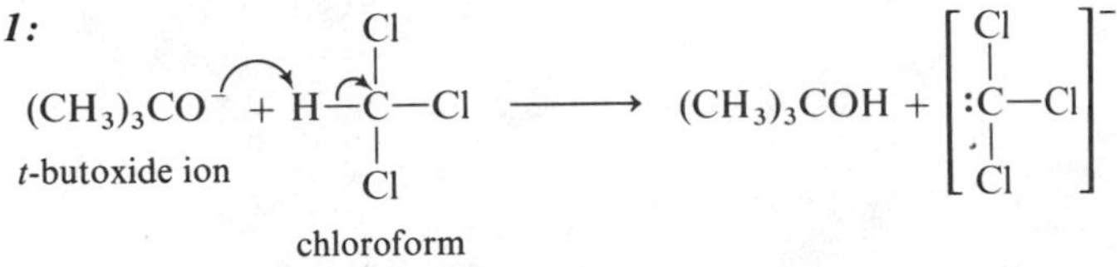

$(CH_3)_3CO^-$ + $H-C-Cl$ (with Cl substituents, chloroform) ⟶ $(CH_3)_3COH$ + $[:C-Cl]^-$ (with Cl substituents)

t-butoxide ion

chloroform

Step 2:

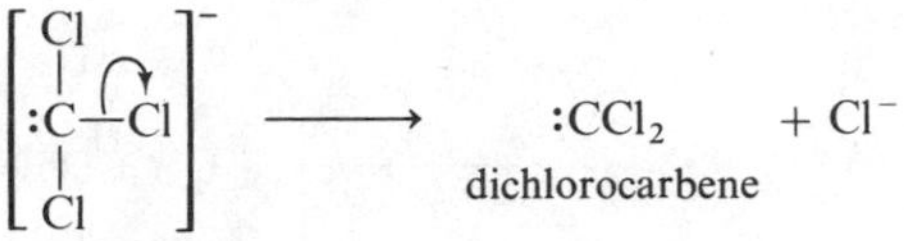

$[:C-Cl]^-$ (with Cl substituents) ⟶ $:CCl_2$ + Cl^-

dichlorocarbene

Dichlorocarbene adds to double bonds to yield *gem*-dihalocyclopropanes. (*Gem* means "on the same carbon.")

(cyclohexene) + $:CCl_2$ ⟶ (bicyclic product with Cl, Cl)

STUDY PROBLEMS

9.22 Predict the structures and stereochemistry of the products of the following addition reactions:

(a) *cis*-3-hexene + singlet methylene ⟶

(b) *cis*-3-hexene + triplet methylene ⟶

(c) *trans*-3-hexene + singlet methylene ⟶

(d) *trans*-3-hexene + triplet methylene ⟶

9.23 Give equations for the carbene reactions that would yield the following products:

(a) 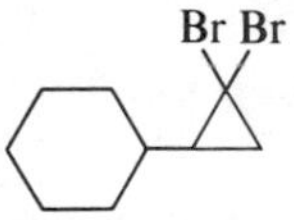 (structure with Br Br) (b) 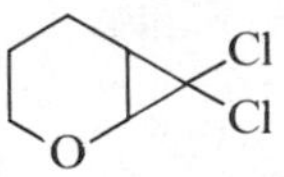 (structure with O, Cl, Cl)

Catalytic Hydrogenation

The catalytic addition of hydrogen gas to an alkene or alkyne is a reduction of the pi-bonded compound. The reaction is general for alkenes, alkynes, and other compounds with pi bonds.

Alkenes and alkynes:

$$CH_3CH{=}CH_2 + H_2 \xrightarrow{\text{Pt}} CH_3CH_2CH_3$$
propene   propane

$$CH_3C{\equiv}CH + 2\ H_2 \xrightarrow{\text{Pt}} CH_3CH_2CH_3$$
propyne   propane

1,4-cyclohexadiene $\quad + 2\ H_2 \xrightarrow{\text{Pt}}$ cyclohexane

Other pi systems:

$$\underset{\text{acetone}}{CH_3\overset{\displaystyle O}{\overset{\|}{C}}CH_3} + H_2 \xrightarrow[\text{heat, pressure}]{\text{Pt}} \underset{\text{isopropyl alcohol}}{CH_3\overset{\displaystyle OH}{\overset{|}{C}}HCH_3}$$

$$CH_3C{\equiv}N + 2\ H_2 \xrightarrow{\text{Pt}} CH_3CH_2NH_2$$
acetonitrile   ethylamine
(ethanenitrile)

benzene $\quad + 3\ H_2 \xrightarrow[\text{heat, pressure}]{\text{Pt}}$ cyclohexane

A.   Action of the Catalyst

Hydrogenation reactions are exothermic, but they do not proceed spontaneously because the energies of activation are extremely high. Heating cannot supply the energy needed to get the molecules to the transition state; however, reaction proceeds smoothly when a catalyst is added.

A finely divided metal or a metal adsorbed onto an inert carrier (such as elemental carbon or barium carbonate) is often used as a hydrogenation catalyst. Platinum, palladium, and nickel on carbon are typical catalysts.

A **poisoned catalyst** (one that is partly deactivated) is used for hydrogenation of an alkyne to an alkene instead of to an alkane. Palladium that has been treated with quinoline (page 761) is a typical poisoned catalyst.

$$CH_3C{\equiv}CH + H_2 \xrightarrow{\text{deactivated Pd}} CH_3CH{=}CH_2$$
propyne   propene

How does a hydrogenation catalyst ease the course of a hydrogenation reaction? Chemists believe that the hydrogen molecules are adsorbed onto the metallic surface, then the H_2 sigma bonds are broken, and metal–H bonds are formed. The alkene is also adsorbed onto the metallic surface with its pi bond interacting with the empty orbitals of the metal. The alkene molecule moves around on the surface until it collides with a metal-bonded hydrogen atom, undergoes reaction, and then leaves as the hydrogenated product (see Figure 9.12).

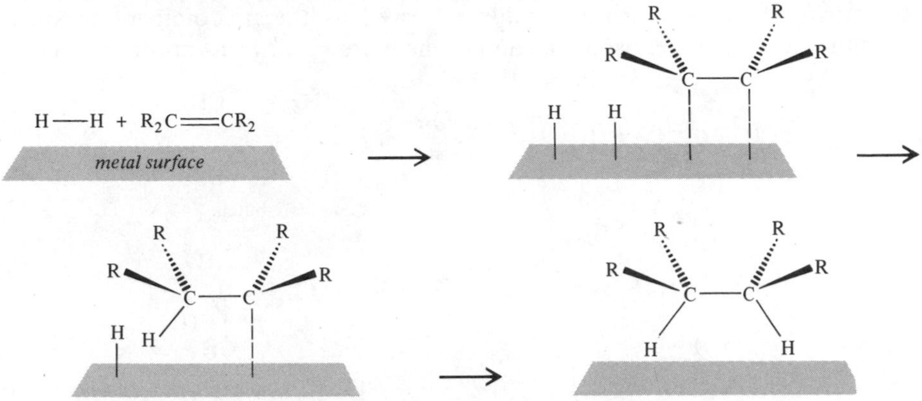

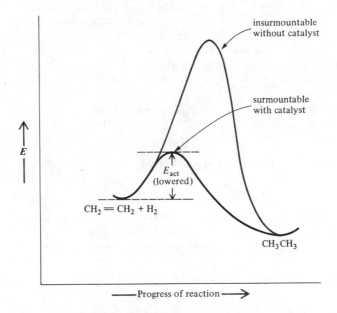

Figure 9.12. Hydrogenation of an alkene.

The overall effect of the catalyst is to provide a surface on which the reaction can occur and to weaken the bonds of both H_2 and the alkene. The result is a *lowering of the energy of activation for the reaction.* Figure 9.13 shows energy diagrams for a hydrogenation reaction. Note that *the catalyst does not affect the energies of reactants or products*: ΔH for the reaction is not changed by catalytic action; only the E_{act} is changed.

Figure 9.13. Energy diagrams for a hydrogenation reaction.

B. Stereochemistry of Hydrogenation

Evidence shows that the two hydrogen atoms add to the same side of, or *syn* to, the double bond. The *syn*-addition arises from the fact that the reaction occurs on a surface; access by H_2 to only one side of the pi bond is more favorable than access to both sides. If the hydrogenation products are capable of geometric isomerism, the *cis*-product is usually observed as the predominant product. (In some cases, however, isomerization to the more stable *trans*-product occurs.)

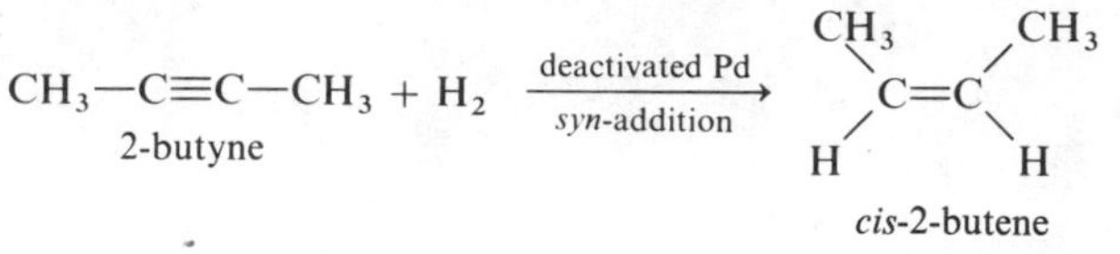

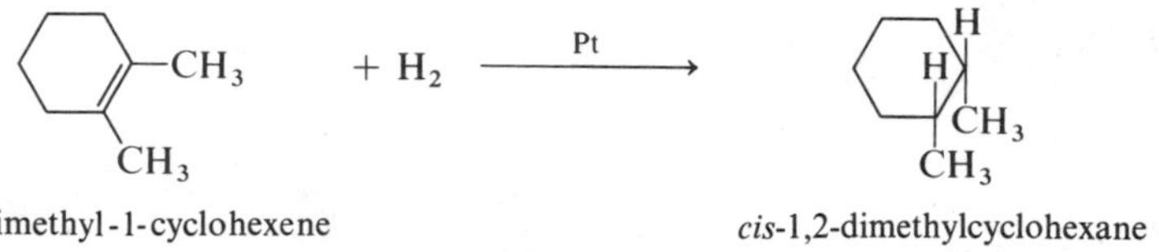

$$CH_3-C\equiv C-CH_3 + H_2 \xrightarrow[\text{syn-addition}]{\text{deactivated Pd}}$$

2-butyne

cis-2-butene

1,2-dimethyl-1-cyclohexene   cis-1,2-dimethylcyclohexane

C.   How Heats of Hydrogenation Show Alkene Stability

The **heat of hydrogenation** of an alkene is the energy difference between the starting alkene and the product alkane. It is calculated from the amount of heat released in a hydrogenation reaction. Table 9.5 lists the heats of hydrogenation of a few alkenes.

Table 9.5.   Heats of Hydrogenation for Some Alkenes

Name	*Structure*	$-\Delta H$, *kcal/mole*
ethene (ethylene)	$CH_2=CH_2$	32.8
propene (propylene)	$CH_3CH=CH_2$	30.1
1-butene	$CH_3CH_2CH=CH_2$	30.3
cis-2-butene	*cis*-$CH_3CH=CHCH_3$	28.6
trans-2-butene	*trans*-$CH_3CH=CHCH_3$	27.6
2-methyl-2-butene	$CH_3\overset{\overset{\displaystyle CH_3}{\|}}{C}=CHCH_3$	26.9
3-methyl-1-butene	$CH_3\overset{\overset{\displaystyle CH_3}{\|}}{C}HCH=CH_2$	30.3
1,3-butadiene	$CH_2=CHCH=CH_2$	57.1
1,4-pentadiene	$CH_2=CHCH_2CH=CH_2$	60.8

Let us consider the three alkenes that can be reduced to butane:

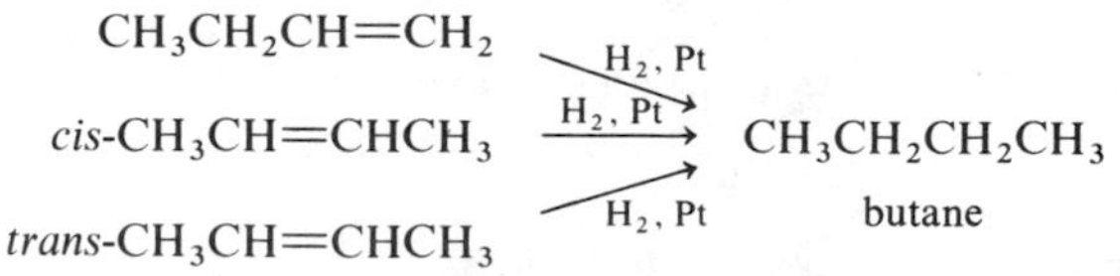

$$CH_3CH_2CH=CH_2$$

$$\text{cis-}CH_3CH=CHCH_3 \xrightarrow{H_2, Pt} CH_3CH_2CH_2CH_3$$

$$\text{trans-}CH_3CH=CHCH_3 \qquad \text{butane}$$

The product butane has the same energy regardless of the starting alkene. Any differences in ΔH for the three reactions reflect *differences in the energies of the starting alkenes*. The greater the value of the ΔH of hydrogenation, the higher is the energy of the starting alkene (see Figure 9.14).

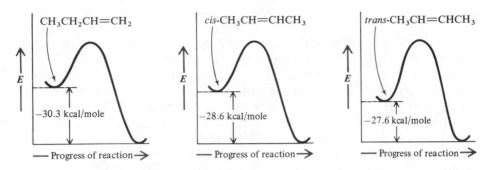

Figure 9.14. Comparison of ΔH values for the butenes.

From the differences in ΔH, we can see that 1-butene contains 1.7 kcal/mole more energy than *cis*-2-butene. *cis*-2-Butene, in turn, contains 1.0 kcal/mole more energy than *trans*-2-butene. The relative heats of hydrogenation of these compounds show that *trans*-2-butene is the most stable of the three butenes and that 1-butene is the least stable.

From just such ΔH comparisons, the relative stabilities of a large number of alkenes have been determined. The following statements summarize what we have learned about alkene stabilities:

(1)   Alkenes with more alkyl groups on the pi-bond carbons are more stable (probably because of the inductive effect of alkyl groups, which release electron density toward the sp^2 carbons).

$CH_2{=}CH_2$ $RCH{=}CH_2$ $RCH{=}CHR$ $R_2C{=}CH_2$ $R_2C{=}CHR$ $R_2C{=}CR_2$

increasing stability $\longrightarrow$

(2)   Conjugated dienes are more stable than dienes with isolated double bonds (because of delocalization of the pi-electron density).

(3)   *trans*-Alkenes are more stable than *cis*-alkenes (because there are fewer steric repulsions in *trans*-isomers).

repulsion

less stable   *more stable*

STUDY PROBLEM

9.24   Which of each of the following pairs of alkenes would you expect to show the greater difference in energy between the *cis*- and *trans*-isomers? Why?

(a) $(CH_3)_3CCH{=}CHCH_2CH_3$ and $CH_3CH{=}CHCH_3$
(b) $ClCH{=}CHCl$ and $CH_3CH{=}CHCl$

D. Hydrogenation of Fats and Oils

The molecules of animal fats and vegetable oils contain long hydrocarbon chains. In vegetable oils, these chains are **polyunsaturated** (have several double bonds). Solid fats, on the other hand, usually contain few, if any, double bonds.

A vegetable oil may be converted to a substance of more solid consistency by partial hydrogenation of the double bonds. The process of converting liquid oils to solid fats by this technique is called **hardening**. Although the polyunsaturates may be more healthful, the hydrogenated products are generally more palatable. Partially hydrogenated peanut oil is used to make peanut butter, and partially hydrogenated corn oil or safflower oil is used in margarine.

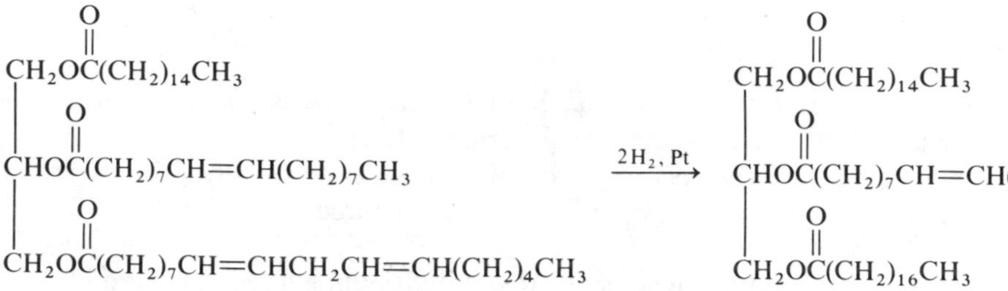

$$\begin{array}{c}
\text{O} \\
\parallel \\
CH_2OC(CH_2)_{14}CH_3 \\
\quad\ \text{O} \\
\quad\ \parallel \\
CHOC(CH_2)_7CH=CH(CH_2)_7CH_3 \\
\quad\ \text{O} \\
\quad\ \parallel \\
CH_2OC(CH_2)_7CH=CHCH_2CH=CH(CH_2)_4CH_3 \\
\textit{a typical vegetable oil}
\end{array}
\xrightarrow{2\,H_2,\ Pt}
\begin{array}{c}
\text{O} \\
\parallel \\
CH_2OC(CH_2)_{14}CH_3 \\
\quad\ \text{O} \\
\quad\ \parallel \\
CHOC(CH_2)_7CH=CH(CH_2)_7CH_3 \\
\quad\ \text{O} \\
\quad\ \parallel \\
CH_2OC(CH_2)_{16}CH_3 \\
\textit{a typical fat}
\end{array}$$

Notice that the carbonyl groups in the vegetable oil do not undergo hydrogenation. Carbonyl groups do contain a pi bond and can be hydrogenated; however, they are generally more difficult to hydrogenate than carbon–carbon double bonds. Control of reaction conditions therefore allows selective hydrogenation of a carbon–carbon double bond in the presence of a carbonyl group.

Sample Problem

Dehydrogenation, the reverse reaction of hydrogenation, is carried out by heating a compound in the presence of the same type of catalyst as used for hydrogenation.

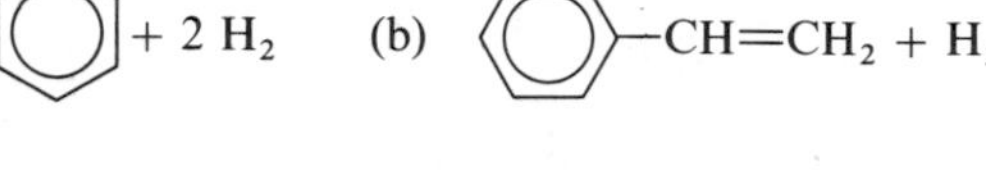

Predict the dehydrogenation products of the following reactions:

(a) 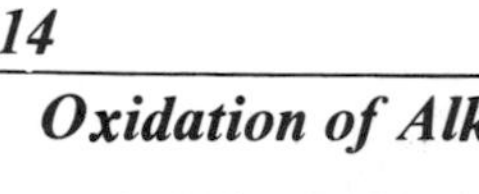   (b)

Solution: (a) 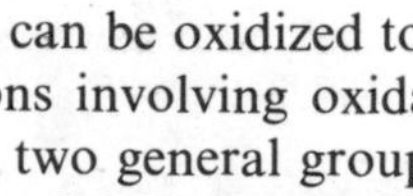 + 2 H₂   (b)

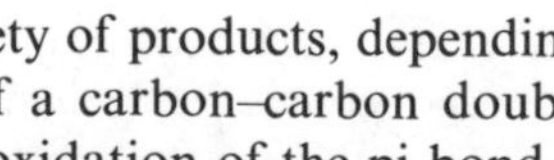

Section 9.14

Oxidation of Alkenes

Alkenes can be oxidized to a variety of products, depending on the reagent used. Reactions involving oxidation of a carbon–carbon double bond may be classified into two general groups: (1) oxidation of the pi bond *without cleavage of the sigma bond*, and (2) oxidation of the pi bond *with cleavage of the sigma bond*. The products of oxidation without cleavage are either glycols or epoxides.

Without cleavage:

$$\overset{\pi}{\underset{\sigma}{\diagdown}}C{=}C\diagup \quad \xrightarrow{[O]} \quad \diagup\underset{}{C}{-}\underset{}{C}\diagdown \quad \text{or} \quad \overset{OH \quad OH}{\underset{}{-C-C-}}$$

an epoxide   *a glycol*

When both the sigma bond and the pi bond of an alkene are cleaved in an oxidation, the products are ketones, aldehydes, or carboxylic acids.

With cleavage:

$$\diagdown C{=}C\diagup \quad \xrightarrow{[O]} \quad \overset{O}{\underset{}{-\overset{\|}{C}-}} \quad \text{or} \quad \overset{O}{\underset{}{-\overset{\|}{C}H}} \quad \text{or} \quad \overset{O}{\underset{}{-\overset{\|}{C}OH}}$$

ketones   *aldehydes*   *carboxylic acids*

A variety of reagents are used to oxidize alkenes. Some of the more common ones are listed in Table 9.6.

Table 9.6.   *Common Reagents for Oxidation of Alkenes*

Reagent	Product
Oxidation without cleavage:	
$KMnO_4$ with OH^- (cold)	glycols
OsO_4 followed by Na_2SO_3	glycols
$C_6H_5CO_3H$	epoxides
Oxidation with cleavage:	
$KMnO_4$ (hot)	carboxylic acids and ketones
O_3 followed by H_2O_2 with H^+	carboxylic acids and ketones
O_3 followed by Zn with H^+	aldehydes and ketones

A. Glycol Formation

The most popular reagent used to convert an alkene to a glycol is a cold, alkaline, aqueous solution of potassium permanganate (even though this reagent usually gives low yields). Osmium tetroxide (OsO_4) gives better yields of glycols, but the use of this reagent is limited because it is both expensive and toxic. Both the permanganate and the OsO_4 oxidations proceed by way of cyclic inorganic esters, which give the *cis*-diols if the product is capable of geometric isomerism.

$$CH_2{=}CH_2 \xrightarrow[25°]{MnO_4^-} \underset{\underset{O \diagdown \underset{\underset{O}{\|} }{Mn} \diagup O^-}{O \quad\quad O}}{CH_2{-}CH_2} \xrightarrow{OH^-} \underset{OH \quad OH}{CH_2{-}CH_2} + MnO_2$$

ethylene   ethylene glycol
(1,2-ethanediol)

cyclohexene   *cis*-1,2-cyclohexanediol

General: R_2C=CR_2 $\xrightarrow[\textit{syn}\text{-addition}]{\text{cold MnO}_4^-\text{ or OsO}_4}$ R_2C——CR_2
                                                                    | |
                                                                   OH   OH

an alkene

a glycol, or 1,2-diol

The reaction with cold permanganate solution constitutes the **Baeyer test** for unsaturation in compounds of unknown structure. The test solution ($KMnO_4$) is purple. As the reaction proceeds, the purple color disappears and a brown precipitate of MnO_2 is observed. The Baeyer test for double bonds, while widely used, has a serious limitation: any easily oxidized group (aldehyde, alkene, alkyne) gives a positive test result.

STUDY PROBLEM

9.25 The following compounds are treated with OsO_4, followed by Na_2SO_3. What products would you expect? (Indicate any geometric isomerism.)

(a) CH_3CH=$C(CH_3)_2$ (b) 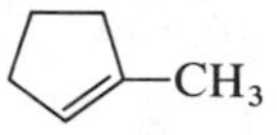 ⬠—CH_3

B. Epoxide Formation

Treatment of an alkene with peroxybenzoic acid in an inert solvent yields an *epoxide*.

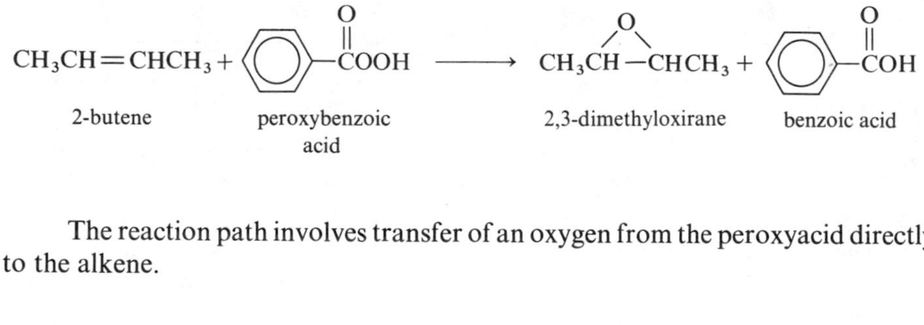

CH_3CH=$CHCH_3$ + ⬡—$\overset{\overset{\textstyle O}{\|}}{C}OOH$ $\longrightarrow$ $CH_3\overset{\textstyle O}{\overset{\diagdown\diagup}{CH}}$—$CHCH_3$ + ⬡—$\overset{\overset{\textstyle O}{\|}}{C}OH$

2-butene   peroxybenzoic   2,3-dimethyloxirane   benzoic acid
                        acid

The reaction path involves transfer of an oxygen from the peroxyacid directly to the alkene.

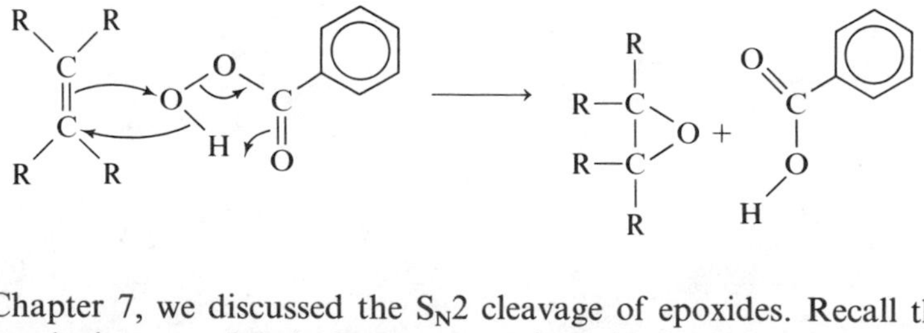

In Chapter 7, we discussed the S_N2 cleavage of epoxides. Recall that this reaction results in *trans*-glycols. By contrast, the oxidation of alkenes with OsO_4 or cold $KMnO_4$ yields *cis*-glycols. Starting with an alkene, either a *cis*-glycol or a *trans*-glycol may be prepared, depending on the choice of reagents.

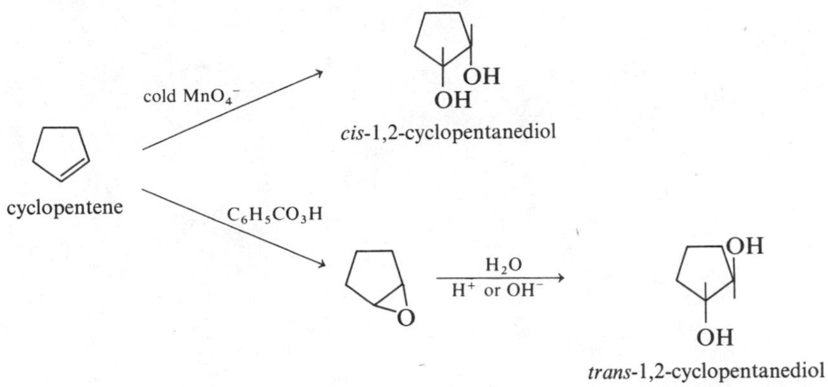

cyclopentene

cold MnO$_4^-$

cis-1,2-cyclopentanediol

C$_6$H$_5$CO$_3$H

$\xrightarrow[\text{H}^+ \text{ or OH}^-]{\text{H}_2\text{O}}$

trans-1,2-cyclopentanediol

C. Oxidation with Cleavage

The products of oxidation with cleavage depend both upon the oxidizing conditions and upon the structure of the alkene. Let us consider first the structure of the alkene.

The structural feature of the alkene that determines the products of oxidative cleavage is the *presence or absence of a hydrogen on the alkene carbon*. If an alkene carbon contains *no hydrogen* (that is, the alkene carbon is disubstituted), then oxidative cleavage results in a *ketone*.

a ketone

disubstituted
(*no hydrogens*)

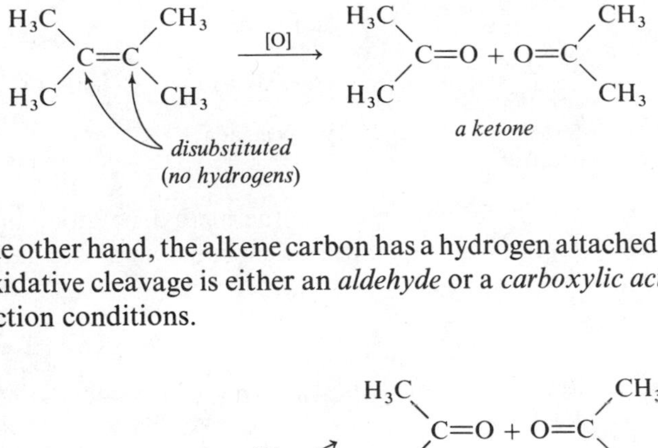

If, on the other hand, the alkene carbon has a hydrogen attached to it, then the product of oxidative cleavage is either an *aldehyde* or a *carboxylic acid*, depending upon the reaction conditions.

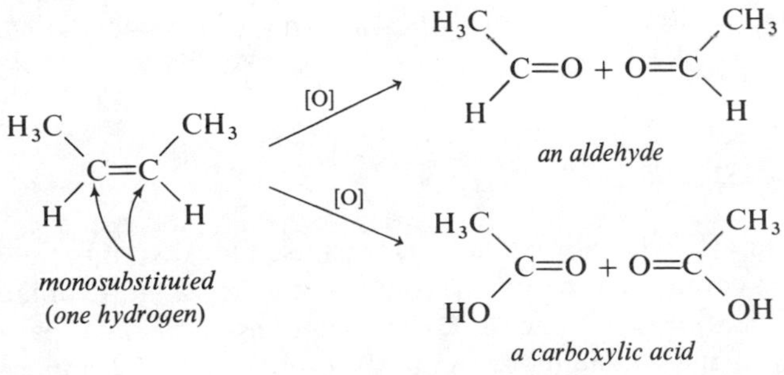

an aldehyde

a carboxylic acid

monosubstituted
(*one hydrogen*)

If one side of the double bond is disubstituted while the other side is mono-substituted, then oxidative cleavage results in a ketone from the disubstituted side, and an aldehyde or carboxylic acid from the monosubstituted side.

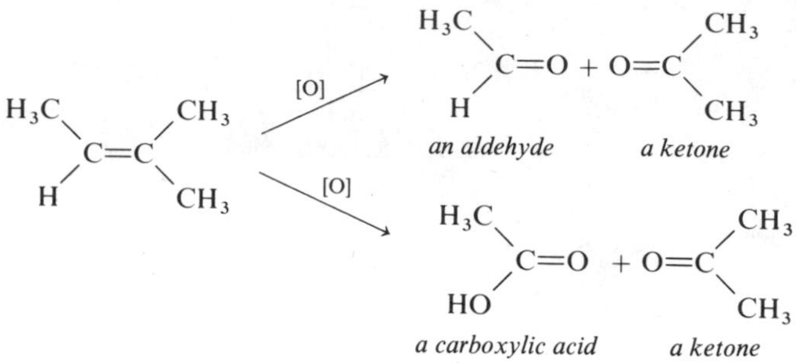

D. Cleavage with $KMnO_4$

A hot solution of $KMnO_4$ is a vigorous oxidizing agent that leads to only ketones and carboxylic acids. (Aldehydes cannot be isolated from hot $KMnO_4$ solutions; they are oxidized promptly to carboxylic acids.)

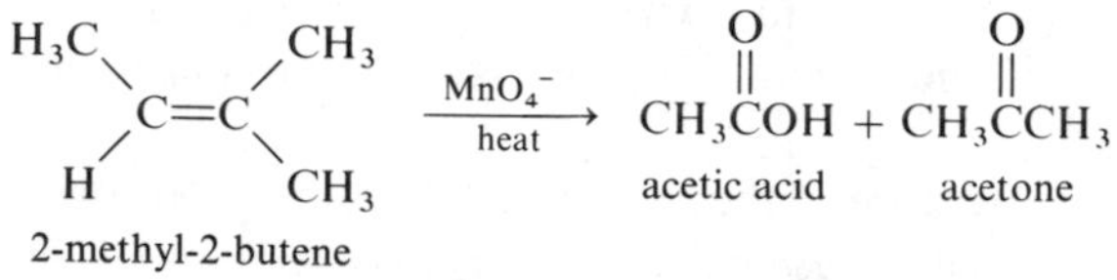

Under these vigorous oxidizing conditions, the carbon of a terminal double bond is oxidized to CO_2.

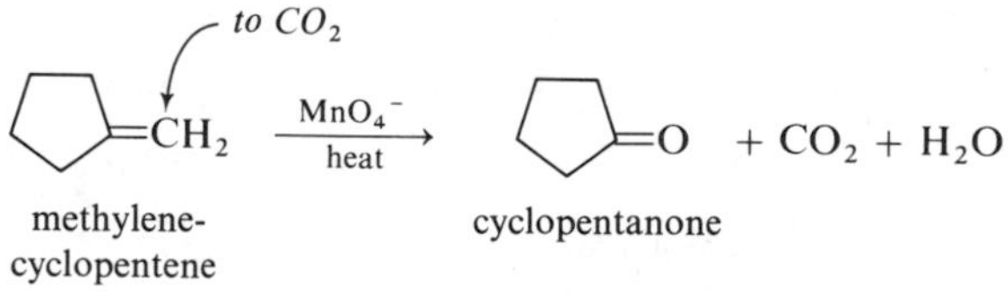

The reason for CO_2 formation is that the methylene group is first oxidized to formic acid, which is further oxidized to carbonic acid. The latter undergoes spontaneous decomposition to CO_2 and H_2O.

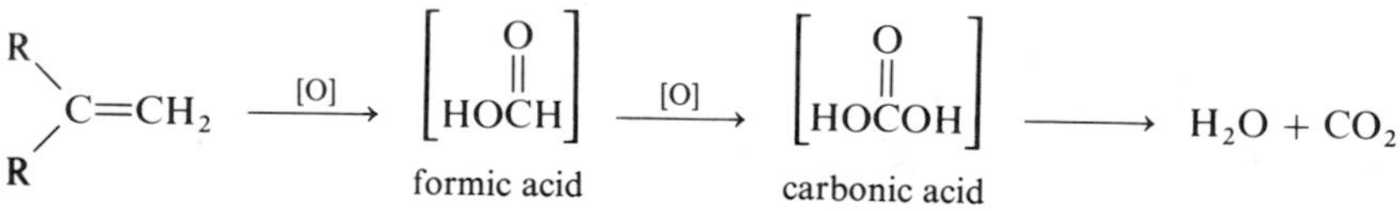

E. Ozonolysis

Ozonolysis (cleavage by ozone) has been used for determining the structures of unsaturated compounds because it results in the degradation of large molecules into smaller, identifiable fragments. Ozonolysis consists of two separate reactions: (1) oxidation of the alkene by ozone to an **ozonide**, and (2) either oxidation or reduction of the ozonide to the final products.

The initial oxidation is usually carried out by bubbling ozone through a solution of the alkene in an inert solvent such as CCl_4. Ozone attacks the pi bond to yield an unstable intermediate called a 1,2,3-trioxolane. This intermediate then goes through a series of transformations in which the carbon–carbon sigma bond is cleaved. The product is an ozonide (a 1,2,4-trioxolane), which is rarely isolated, but is carried on to the second step.

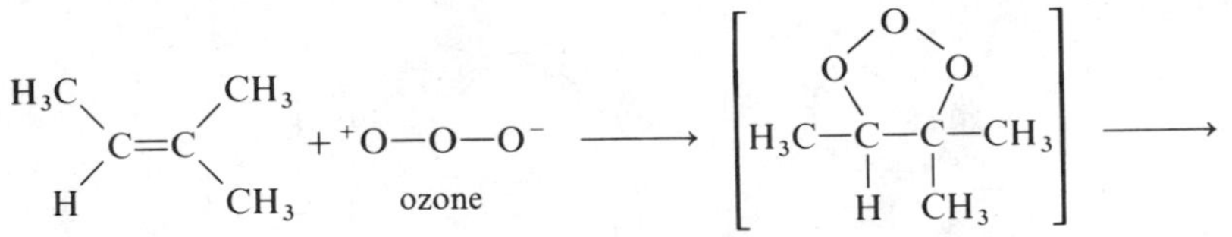

2-methyl-2-butene   ozone   *a 1,2,3-trioxolane*

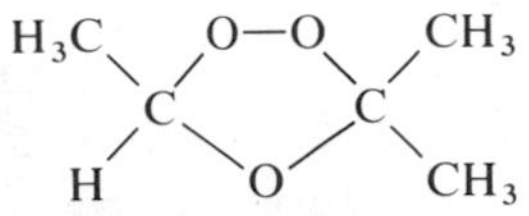

an ozonide
(a 1,2,4-trioxolane)

The second step is either the oxidation or the reduction of the ozonide. If the ozonide is subjected to a *reductive work-up*, a monosubstituted carbon of the original alkene yields an aldehyde. If an *oxidative work-up* is used, then a monosubstituted carbon yields a carboxylic acid. In either case, a disubstituted carbon of the alkene yields a ketone.

Reductive work-up to aldehydes and ketones:

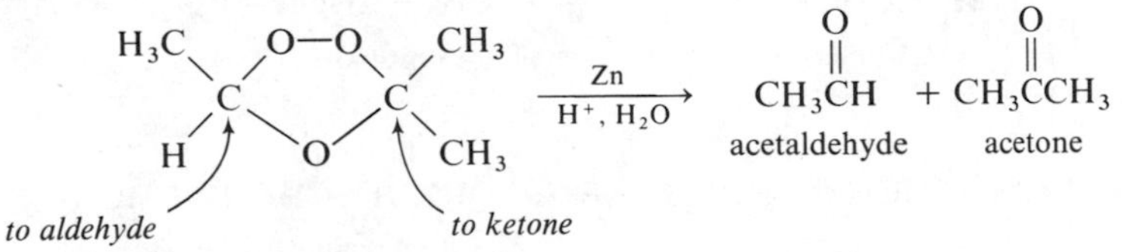

acetaldehyde   acetone

Oxidative work-up to carboxylic acids and ketones:

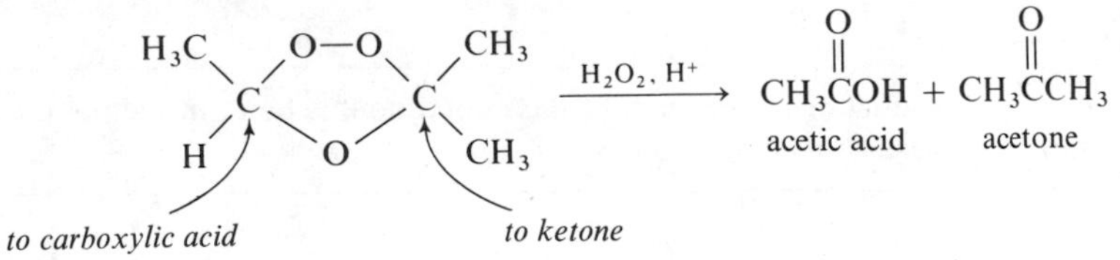

acetic acid   acetone

Sample Problem

Predict the products of reductive ozonolysis of γ-terpinene, a compound found in coriander oil:

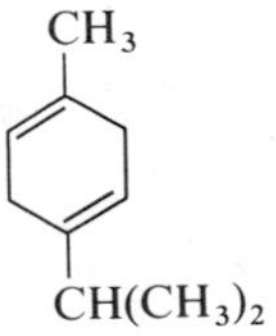

Solution:

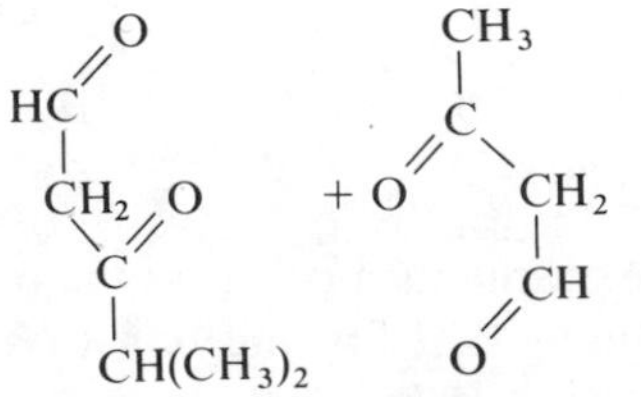

STUDY PROBLEM

9.26 What would be the products of both reductive and oxidative ozonolyses of each of the following alkenes or dienes?

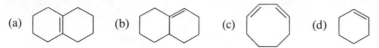

(a)　　　　(b)　　　　(c)　　　　(d)

Section 9.15

1,4-Addition to Conjugated Dienes

Many of the reactions of conjugated dienes are identical to those of isolated double bonds. Acidic reagents and the halogens can add across one or both of the pi bonds. In conjugated-diene systems, these simple addition reactions are called **1,2-additions**, a term that refers to addition to the first and second carbons of a four-carbon, conjugated-diene system, and not necessarily to nomenclature numbers.

1,2-Addition reactions:

$$CH_2{=}CHCH{=}CH_2 \xrightarrow{\text{HBr}} \overset{\overset{\displaystyle H}{|}}{CH_2}{-}\overset{\overset{\displaystyle Br}{|}}{CH}CH{=}CH_2$$

1,3-butadiene　　　　　3-bromo-1-butene

$$CH_3CH{=}CHCH{=}CHCH_3 \xrightarrow{\text{Cl}_2} CH_3\overset{\overset{\displaystyle Cl}{|}}{CH}{-}\overset{\overset{\displaystyle Cl}{|}}{CH}CH{=}CHCH_3$$

2,4-hexadiene　　　　　4,5-dichloro-2-hexene

STUDY PROBLEM

9.27 Predict the product of 1,2-addition to the second double bond in each of the two preceding examples.

Along with 1,2-addition, conjugated dienes can also undergo **1,4-addition**. In these reactions, one equivalent of the reagent adds to the two end carbons (carbons 1 and 4) of the diene system; the remaining double bond ends up in the center of the original diene system.

1,4-Addition reactions:

$$CH_2{=}CHCH{=}CH_2 \xrightarrow{\text{HBr}} \overset{\overset{\displaystyle H}{|}}{CH_2}{-}CH{=}CH{-}\overset{\overset{\displaystyle Br}{|}}{CH_2}$$

1,3-butadiene　　　　　1-bromo-2-butene

$$CH_3CH{=}CHCH{=}CHCH_3 \xrightarrow{\text{Cl}_2} CH_3\overset{\overset{\displaystyle Cl}{|}}{CH}{-}CH{=}CH{-}\overset{\overset{\displaystyle Cl}{|}}{CH}CH_3$$

2,4-hexadiene　　　　　2,5-dichloro-3-hexene

Let us look at the mechanism of each type of addition. The mechanism for 1,2-addition is the same as that for addition to an isolated double bond. (The reaction of 1,3-butadiene goes through the more stable secondary carbocation and not through the less stable $^+CH_2CH_2CH=CH_2$.)

1,2-Addition:

$$CH_2=CHCH=CH_2 \xrightarrow{\ H^+\ } \left[\begin{array}{c} H \\ | \\ CH_2-\overset{+}{C}HCH=CH_2 \end{array}\right] \xrightarrow{\ Br^-\ } \begin{array}{cc} H & Br \\ | & | \\ CH_2-CHCH=CH_2 \end{array}$$

$$\qquad\qquad\qquad\qquad\quad a\ 2°\ carbocation \qquad\qquad\qquad\quad \text{3-bromo-1-butene}$$

The mechanism for 1,4-addition is a direct extension of that for 1,2-addition. The carbocation in the preceding example is an *allylic cation* (Section 5.8A) and is resonance-stabilized. Because of the resonance-stabilization of the allylic cation, there is a partial positive charge on carbon 4 of the diene system as well as on carbon 2. Attack at carbon 4 leads to the 1,4-addition product.

1,4-Addition:

$$CH_2=CHCH=CH_2 \xrightarrow{\ H^+\ } \left[\begin{array}{ccc} H \\ | \\ CH_2-\overset{+}{C}H\!\frown\!CH=CH_2 & \longleftrightarrow & \begin{array}{c} H \\ | \\ CH_2-CH=CH-\overset{+}{C}H_2 \end{array} \end{array}\right]$$

$$\xrightarrow{\ Br^-\ } \begin{array}{cc} H & Br \\ | & | \\ CH_2-CH=CH-CH_2 \end{array}$$

$$\qquad\qquad\qquad\qquad\qquad\qquad\qquad\quad \text{1-bromo-2-butene}$$

If just one equivalent of reagent is added to 1,3-butadiene, a mixture of two products results: 3-bromo-1-butene from 1,2-addition, and 1-bromo-2-butene from 1,4-addition.

Sample Problem

(a) Give the structures of *all possible* carbocation intermediates in the addition of one equivalent of HI to 2,4-hexadiene.

(b) Which carbocation would you expect to be formed at the faster rate?

Solution:

(a) $\quad CH_3CH=CH-CH=CHCH_3 \xrightarrow{\ H^+\ } [CH_3CH_2-\overset{+}{C}H-CH=CHCH_3]$

$$\qquad\qquad\qquad\qquad\qquad\qquad or\quad [CH_3\overset{+}{C}H-CH_2-CH=CHCH_3]$$

(Addition of H^+ to the other double bond gives identical intermediates.)

(b) The first carbocation shown would be formed at the faster rate because it is a resonance-stabilized, allylic carbocation.

STUDY PROBLEMS

9.28 (a) Give the *resonance structures* for the principal intermediate in the preceding sample problem.

  (b) Give the structures of the principal products.

9.29 Predict the products of addition of one equivalent of bromine to the following dienes:

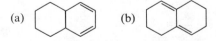

9.30 Predict the products of addition of *two* equivalents of bromine to each of the dienes in Problem 9.29.

In the reaction of 1,3-butadiene with one equivalent of HBr, the ratio of 1,2-addition to 1,4-addition varies with the temperature at which the reaction is carried out. At $-80°$, the 1,2-addition product predominates. At $40°$, the 1,4-addition product predominates.

$$CH_2=CHCH=CH_2 + HBr$$
1,3-butadiene

$-80°$

$$\underset{\substack{\text{Br}}}{CH_3CHCH=CH_2} + CH_3CH=CHCH_2Br$$
1,2-product   *1,4-product*
80%   20%

$40°$

$$\underset{\substack{\text{Br}}}{CH_3CHCH=CH_2} + CH_3CH=CHCH_2Br$$
20%   80%

It has also been observed that warming 3-bromo-1-butene (the 1,2-addition product) to $40°$ with a trace of acid results in an equilibrium mixture that is predominantly 1-bromo-2-butene (the 1,4-addition product).

$$\underset{\substack{\text{Br}\\20\%}}{CH_3CHCH=CH_2} \xrightleftharpoons{H^+, 40°} \underset{80\%}{CH_3CH=CHCH_2Br}$$

How can we explain these observations? At low temperature, the reaction yields predominantly the 1,2-addition product because the 1,2-addition has the lower E_{act} and the faster rate. The relative rates of the reactions control the product ratios. We say that the reaction is under **kinetic control** at low temperatures. Figure 9.15 shows the energy diagram for the competing reactions.

At higher temperatures, a greater percentage of molecules can reach the higher-energy transition state, and the two products are in equilibrium. The more stable 1,4-product (which is the more substituted alkene) predominates. At the higher temperatures, the relative stabilities of the products control the product ratios, and the reaction is under **equilibrium control**. Figure 9.16 shows the energy diagram for the equilibrium.

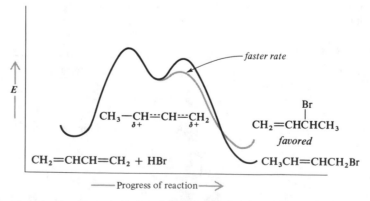

Figure 9.15.   At low temperatures, 1,2-addition has the faster rate, and the 1,2-addition product predominates.

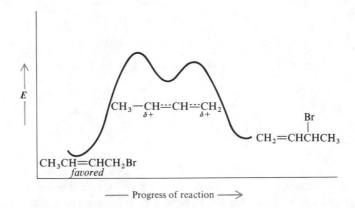

Figure 9.16. At high temperatures, the 1,2- and 1,4-addition products are in equilibrium.

STUDY PROBLEMS

9.31 Which *geometric isomer* of 1-bromo-2-butene would predominate at 40°?

9.32 1,3-Butadiene is treated with one equivalent of Br_2 at $-15°$. Two structural isomers are obtained: 46% A and 54% B. When the reaction is carried out at 60°, the product mixture contains 90% A. What are the structures of A and B?

Section 9.16

Electrocyclic Reactions

Related to 1,4-addition is the intramolecular reaction of a conjugated diene or polyene to form a cyclic compound. These reactions are called **electrocyclic reactions** and are induced either *thermally* or *photochemically* (by the action of ultraviolet light).

$$
\begin{array}{ccc}
\begin{array}{c}
\quad\nearrow CH_2 \\
CH \\
| \\
CH \\
\quad\searrow CH_2
\end{array}
&
\xrightleftharpoons{\text{heat or } h\nu}
&
\begin{array}{c}
CH-CH_2 \\
\| \quad | \\
CH-CH_2 \\
\text{cyclobutene}
\end{array}
\\
\text{1,3-butadiene} & &
\end{array}
$$

$$
\begin{array}{ccc}
\begin{array}{c}
\quad CH{=}CH_2 \\
\diagup \\
CH \\
\| \\
CH \\
\diagdown \\
\quad CH{=}CH_2
\end{array}
&
\xrightleftharpoons{\text{heat or } h\nu}
&
\begin{array}{c}
\quad CH \\
\quad\diagup\diagdown \\
CH \quad CH_2 \\
| \qquad | \\
CH \quad CH_2 \\
\quad\diagdown\diagup \\
\quad CH
\end{array}
\\
\text{1,3,5-hexatriene} & & \text{1,3-cyclohexadiene}
\end{array}
$$

Before we discuss electrocyclic reactions, let us first consider a few definitions. Both in this section and later, we will find that line formulas are handy for representing open-chain, as well as cyclic, compounds.

|| or =   means $CH_2=CH_2$

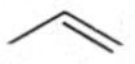

⟋⟍ or ⟍⟋   means $CH_3CH=CH_2$

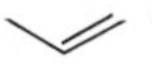

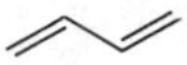

⟋⟍⟋ or //⟍   means $CH_2=CHCH=CH_2$

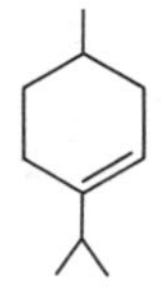

means

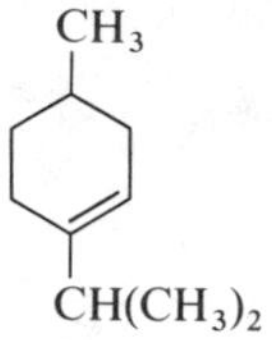

$$\begin{array}{c} CH_3 \\ \bigcirc \\ CH(CH_3)_2 \end{array}$$

Another convention is the use of the terms s-*cis* and s-*trans* to describe the conformations of conjugated dienes. (The letter "s" is used because it is the geometry around the central *single bond* that determines the conformation.) The following compounds illustrate the use of the terms. For open-chain compounds, these formulas do not represent true isomers, but conformers, because sigma-bond rotation (requiring about 5 kcal/mole for 1,3-butadiene) is all that is needed for conversion from one to the other.

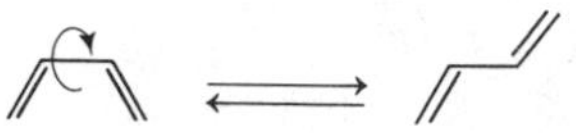

⟋⟍ ⇌ ⟋⟍//

s-*cis*   s-*trans*

H_3C—⟋⟍—CH_3

s-*cis*
even though the
stereochemistry at
each double bond is
(E), or trans

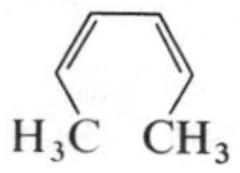

H_3C CH_3

s-*cis*
and (Z), or
cis, at each
double bond

When the diene function is part of a cyclic system, the s-*cis* and s-*trans* structures represent different compounds; interconversion cannot occur without bonds being broken.

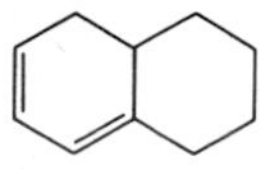

s-*cis* 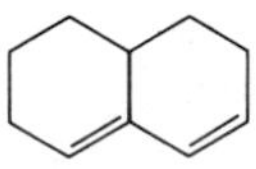   s-*trans*

STUDY PROBLEM

9.33 Classify each of the following dienes or trienes as s-*cis* or s-*trans*. Indicate which is interconvertible with the other forms.

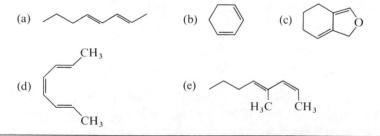

(a)   (b)   (c)

(d)   (e)

CH_3 H_3C CH_3

CH_3

A. The Cyclization

For cyclization to occur, dienes must be in the s-*cis* conformation. In the conversion of 1,3-butadiene to cyclobutene, two of the four pi electrons are then used for ring closure, while two form the double bond in the product. The cyclization is similar to 1,4-addition in this respect.

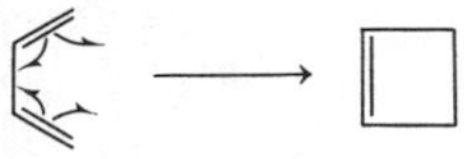

An intriguing feature about electrocyclic reactions is that the stereochemistry of the product is dependent on whether the reaction is thermally induced or photoinduced.

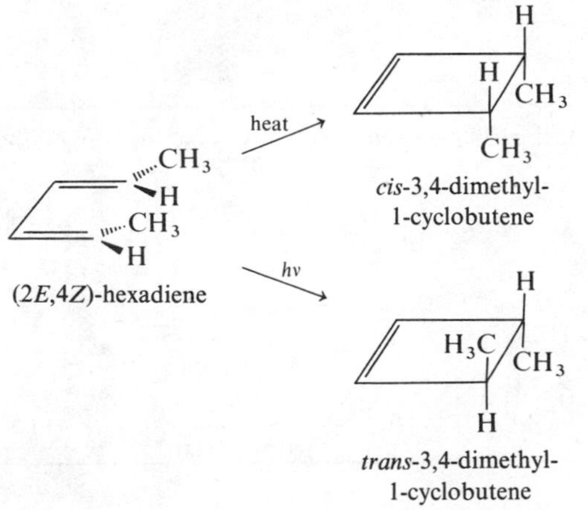

In the preceding equations, the product in each case is a 3,4-dimethyl-1-cyclobutene; however, the stereochemistry of the product depends upon the experimental conditions. When the reaction is carried out thermally, *cis*-3,4-dimethyl-1-cyclobutene is the product. When the cyclization is induced by ultraviolet light, the corresponding *trans*-isomer is the product. The stereochemical course of these electrocyclic reactions may be predicted by the **Woodward–Hoffmann rules** (Table 9.7). Presently, we will give a brief discussion of the basis of these rules and how to use them.

Table 9.7. *Woodward–Hoffmann Rules for Electrocyclic Reactions*

Number of pi electrons	*Reaction*	*Motion*
$4n$	thermal	conrotatory
$4n$	photochemical	disrotatory
$4n + 2$	thermal	disrotatory
$4n + 2$	photochemical	conrotatory

B. Number of Pi Electrons

Table 9.7 contains a few more new terms that need definition before we can continue with the discussion of the cyclization reaction. The *total number of pi electrons in a conjugated polyene* must fit one of two formulas: $4n$ or $4n + 2$, where n is an integer (1, 2, 3, . . .). In the following examples, note that 1,3-butadiene, which has four pi electrons, fits the formula $4n$ where $n = 1$. 1,3,5-Hexatriene fits the formula $4n + 2$, where $n = 1$. 1,3,5,7-Octatetraene, which has a total of eight pi electrons, fits the formula $4n$, where $n = 2$.

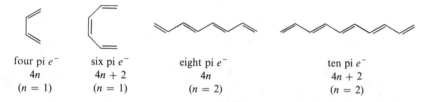

four pi e^-	six pi e^-	eight pi e^-	ten pi e^-
$4n$	$4n + 2$	$4n$	$4n + 2$
$(n = 1)$	$(n = 1)$	$(n = 2)$	$(n = 2)$

STUDY PROBLEM

9.34 Classify each of the following conjugated polyenes as being either $4n$ or $4n + 2$:

(a) [structure with CH₃ groups] (b) [structure with CH₃ groups] (c) [bicyclic structure]

(d) [bicyclic structure] (e) [cyclic structure]

C. Conrotatory and Disrotatory Motion

The two lobes of each *p* orbital that will form the new sigma bond in cyclization are either *in phase* or *out of phase* with each other (see Section 2.4D). We depict the two phases as shaded and unshaded in the following representations of 1,3-butadiene.

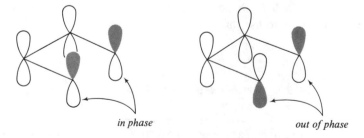

in phase   *out of phase*

To form a new sigma bond, the existing C—C sigma bonds must rotate so that the *p* orbitals undergo end-to-end (not side-to-side) overlap. For this to occur, the existing pi bonds must be broken. The energy for the pi-bond breakage and the bond rotation is supplied by the heat or ultraviolet light. To form a sigma bond, the pair of overlapping lobes of the two *p* orbitals must be *in phase* after rotation.

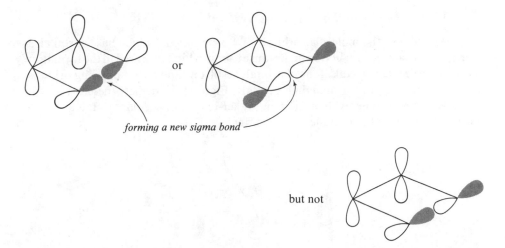

forming a new sigma bond

or

but not

There are two different ways in which the existing C—C sigma bonds can rotate in order to position the p orbitals for overlap. (1) The two C—C sigma bonds can rotate in the *same direction* (either both clockwise or both counterclockwise). This type of rotation is referred to as **conrotatory motion**. (2) The two C—C sigma bonds can rotate in *different* directions, one clockwise and one counterclockwise. This type of rotation is **disrotatory motion**.

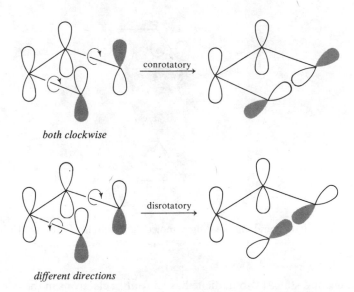

both clockwise

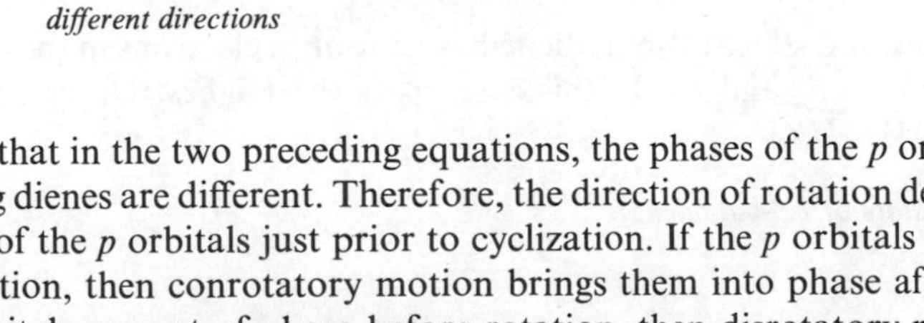

conrotatory

different directions

disrotatory

Note that in the two preceding equations, the phases of the p orbitals in the two starting dienes are different. Therefore, the direction of rotation depends upon the phases of the p orbitals just prior to cyclization. If the p orbitals are in phase before rotation, then conrotatory motion brings them into phase after rotation. If the p orbitals are out of phase before rotation, then disrotatory motion is required. To determine which diene system is present just prior to reaction, we must consider the phases of the p orbitals in the ground and excited states of the diene.

D.   The Molecular Orbitals of a 4n System

We will use the molecular orbitals of 1,3-butadiene, which has four pi electrons, as an example of a 4n system. Because four p orbitals are used in the formation of the pi molecular orbitals, four pi orbitals result; π_1 and π_2 are bonding orbitals, while π_3^* and π_4^* are antibonding orbitals. Figure 9.17 depicts these orbitals in terms of increasing energy. Note that the higher-energy molecular orbitals are those with a greater number of nodes between nuclei.

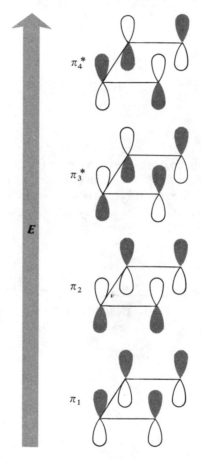

Figure 9.17.   The bonding and antibonding π molecular orbitals of $CH_2=CHCH=CH_2$. π_1 and π_2 are bonding orbitals; π_3^* and π_4^* are antibonding orbitals.

In the ground state, 1,3-butadiene has its four pi electrons in the two orbitals of lowest energy: π_1 and π_2. In this case, π_2 is the **Highest Occupied Molecular Orbital**: the **HOMO**.

Ground state of 1,3-butadiene:

When 1,3-butadiene absorbs a photon of the proper wavelength, an electron is promoted from the HOMO to the **Lowest Unoccupied Molecular Orbital**: the **LUMO** (which then becomes the new HOMO).

Excited state of 1,3-butadiene:

$$\pi_4^* \ \underline{\quad\quad}$$

$$\pi_3^* \ \underline{\downarrow\quad} \longleftarrow e^- \ promoted \ to \ LUMO;$$
$$\pi_3^* \ is \ now \ the \ HOMO$$

$$\pi_2 \ \underline{\uparrow\quad}$$

$$\pi_1 \ \underline{\updownarrow\quad}$$

E

E. Thermally Induced Cyclization of a 4n System

When 1,3-butadiene is heated, no electrons are promoted; the compound is still in its ground state. The electrons that are used for sigma-bond formation are the electrons in the HOMO (π_2, in this case). In Figure 9.17, it can be seen that the p orbitals in this HOMO are out of phase with each other. For the new sigma bond to form, rotation must be *conrotatory*. Only in this way are the in-phase lobes allowed to overlap. (Disrotatory motion would not place the in-phase lobes together.)

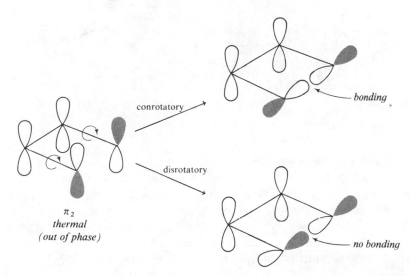

With conrotatory motion, two in-phase lobes come together and can overlap. This motion, which leads to cyclization, is said to be **symmetry-allowed**. Disrotatory motion, which cannot lead to bonding, is said to be **symmetry-forbidden**.

F. Photo-Induced Cyclization of a 4n System

In photo-induced cyclization, the phases of the p orbitals of the HOMO (now π_3^*) are the reverse of that in thermal cyclization (see Figure 9.17); therefore, the symmetry-allowed rotation is disrotatory instead of conrotatory.

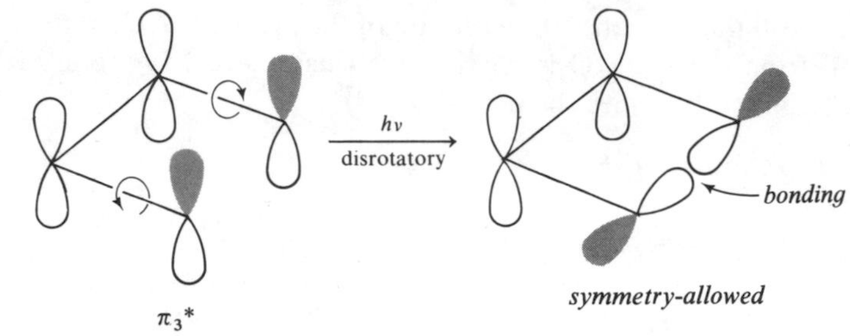

$\pi_3{}^*$
photo
(in phase)

symmetry-allowed

bonding

$\xrightarrow[\text{disrotatory}]{hv}$

STUDY PROBLEM

9.35   Draw structures showing conrotatory motion in the preceding example. Are the potential bonding *p* orbitals in a symmetry-allowed or symmetry-forbidden orientation?

G. The Stereochemical Consequences of Conrotatory and Disrotatory Motion

Let us return to (2E,4Z)-hexadiene to see why the *cis*-dimethylcyclobutene results from thermal cyclization and the *trans*-isomer results from photocyclization.

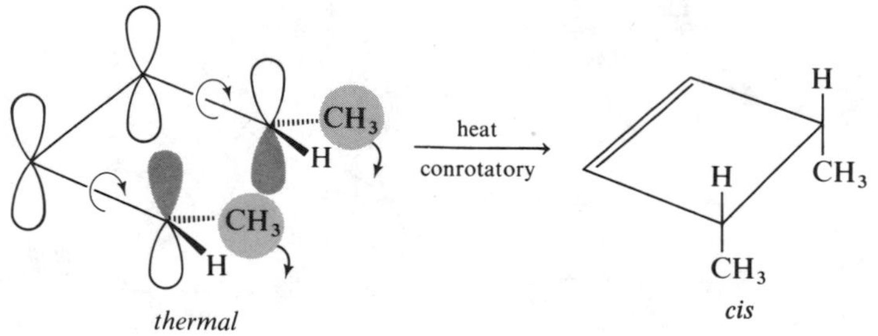

thermal
(out of phase)

cis

$\xrightarrow[\text{conrotatory}]{\text{heat}}$

In the case of thermal cyclization, the *p* orbitals in question are out of phase; conrotatory motion is required for sigma-bond formation. Both methyl groups rotate in the same direction; as a result they end up on the same side of the ring, or *cis*, in the product.

Just the reverse occurs in photochemical cyclization. In the disrotatory motion, one of the methyl groups rotates up and the other rotates down. The result is that the two methyl groups are *trans* in the product.

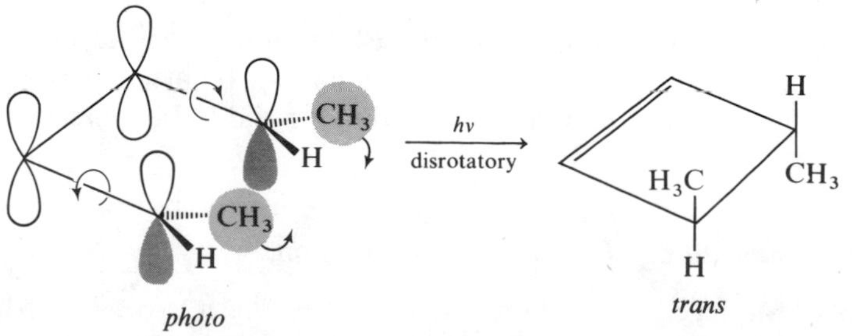

photo
(in phase)

trans

$\xrightarrow[\text{disrotatory}]{hv}$

Sample Problem

Will the photochemical electrocyclic reaction of (2E, 4E)-hexadiene yield *cis-* or *trans-*3,4-dimethyl-1-cyclobutene?

Solution: 2,4-Hexadiene is a 4n polyene; therefore, the photochemical electrocyclic reaction takes place by disrotatory motion. (Draw the *p*-orbital picture to see why this is so.)

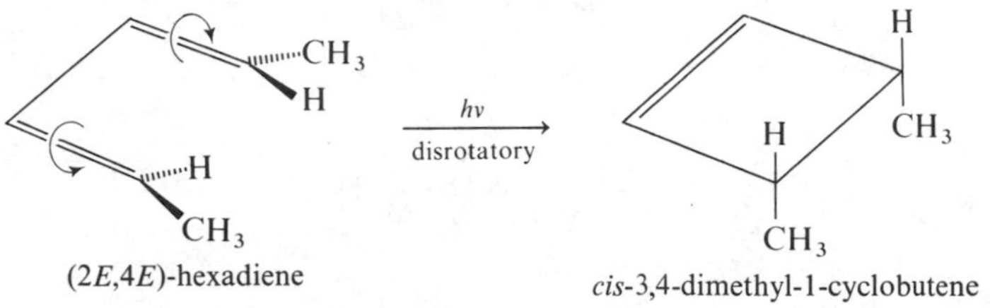

(2E,4E)-hexadiene $\xrightarrow[\text{disrotatory}]{hv}$ *cis*-3,4-dimethyl-1-cyclobutene

Sample Problem

Electrocyclic reactions are *reversible*. What is the structure and expected stereochemistry of the ring-opened product when *trans*-3,4-dimethyl-1-cyclobutene is heated?

Solution:

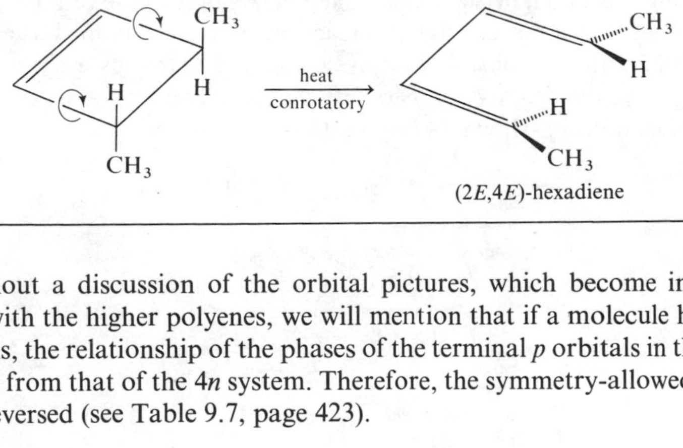

$\xrightarrow[\text{conrotatory}]{\text{heat}}$ (2E,4E)-hexadiene

Without a discussion of the orbital pictures, which become increasingly complex with the higher polyenes, we will mention that if a molecule has $4n + 2$ pi electrons, the relationship of the phases of the terminal *p* orbitals in the HOMO is reversed from that of the $4n$ system. Therefore, the symmetry-allowed rotations are also reversed (see Table 9.7, page 423).

4n + 2 Cyclizations:

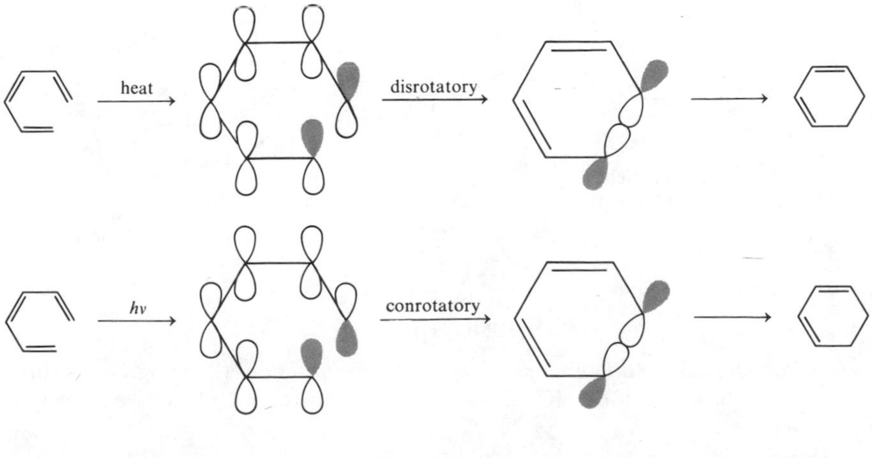

STUDY PROBLEM

9.36   Each of the following electrocyclic reactions follows the Woodward–Hoffmann rules. Predict the stereochemistry of the products.

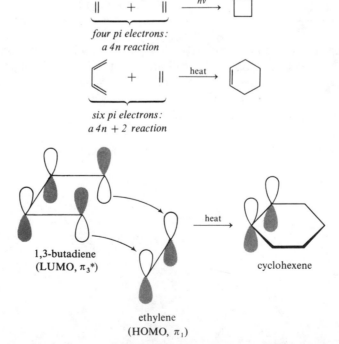

(a)

(b)

Section 9.17

Cycloaddition: The Diels–Alder Reaction

Dienes and polyenes can undergo *intermolecular* cyclization as well as intramolecular cyclization. An intermolecular reaction of two unsaturated compounds to form a ring is called a **cycloaddition reaction**. As in the case of the electrocyclic reactions we have just discussed, these reactions may be classified as either $4n$ or $4n + 2$ pi-electron reactions. The $4n$ cycloaddition reactions are *photo-induced*, while $4n + 2$ cycloadditions are *thermally induced*. The p-orbital picture for the $4n + 2$ cycloaddition is shown in Figure 9.18.

four pi electrons:
a 4n reaction

six pi electrons:
a 4n + 2 reaction

1,3-butadiene
(LUMO, $\pi_3{}^*$)

cyclohexene

ethylene
(HOMO, π_1)

Figure 9.18.   Orbital picture of a $4n + 2$ cycloaddition reaction. (Bonding occurs through interaction of the HOMO of one reactant and the LUMO of the other.)

The most important cycloaddition reaction is the **Diels–Alder reaction**—a thermally induced $4n + 2$ cycloaddition. The reaction is named after the German chemists Otto Diels and Kurt Alder, who jointly received the 1950 Nobel prize for their work in this area.

A Diels–Alder reaction:

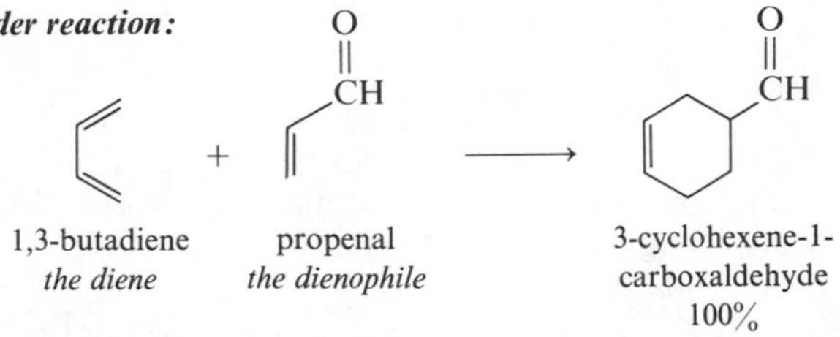

1,3-butadiene	propenal	3-cyclohexene-1-
the diene	*the dienophile*	carboxaldehyde
		100%

In a Diels–Alder reaction, the diene is called (not surprisingly) the **diene**, while the other alkene is called the **dienophile** ("diene-lover"). As in any cyclization, the diene must have the s-*cis*, not the s-*trans*, conformation. In some structures (such as 1,3-butadiene) the s-*cis* and s-*trans* conformers are readily interconvertible. In other diene systems (such as in ring systems), the s-*trans* isomer does not undergo reaction.

Some s-cis dienes that can be used in a Diels–Alder reaction:

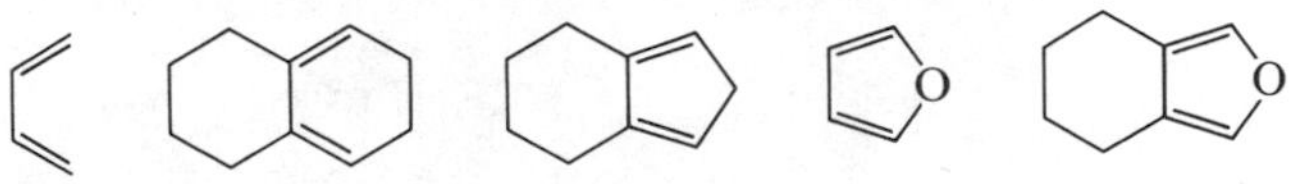

Some s-trans dienes that cannot be used:

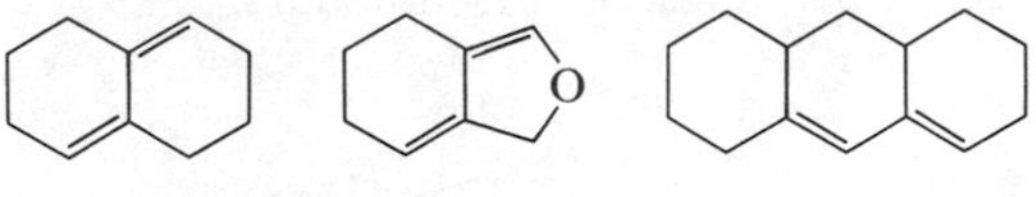

In a Diels–Alder cyclization, the dienophile usually contains other unsaturation to enhance its reactivity. (These pi electrons are not involved in the cyclization reaction; therefore, the reaction is still classified as a $4n + 2$ reaction.) The presence of another unsaturated group gives rise to two modes of addition, called *endo* (inside) and *exo* (outside) addition, as the following examples show. The *endo* addition is usually favored, probably because of favorable interactions of the pi orbitals of the developing double bond and the pi orbitals in the unsaturated group.

Endo (favored):

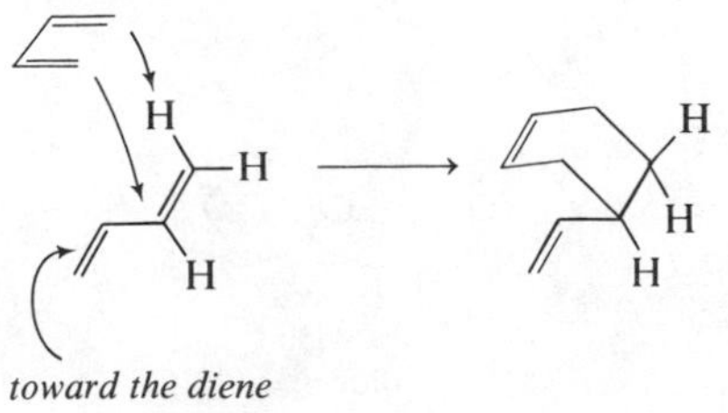

toward the diene

Exo:

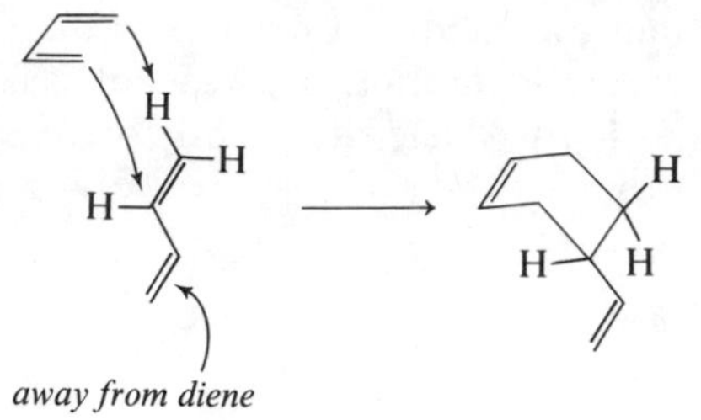

away from diene

A few examples of the types of dienes and dienophiles used in Diels–Alder reactions follow. You can see from these examples the versatility of this reaction in the synthesis of cyclic compounds.

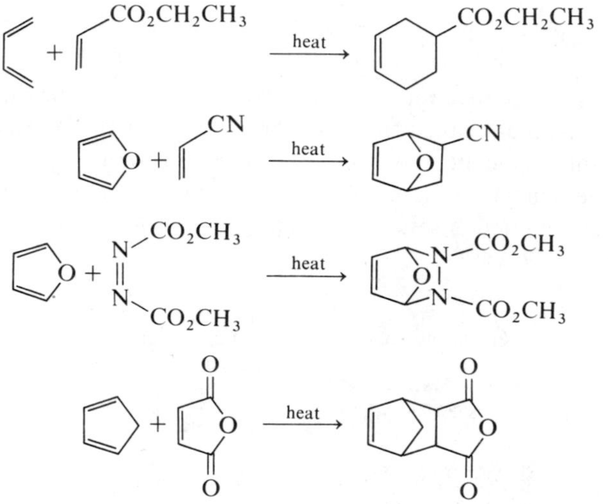

Industrially, a number of insecticides are prepared by Diels–Alder reactions.

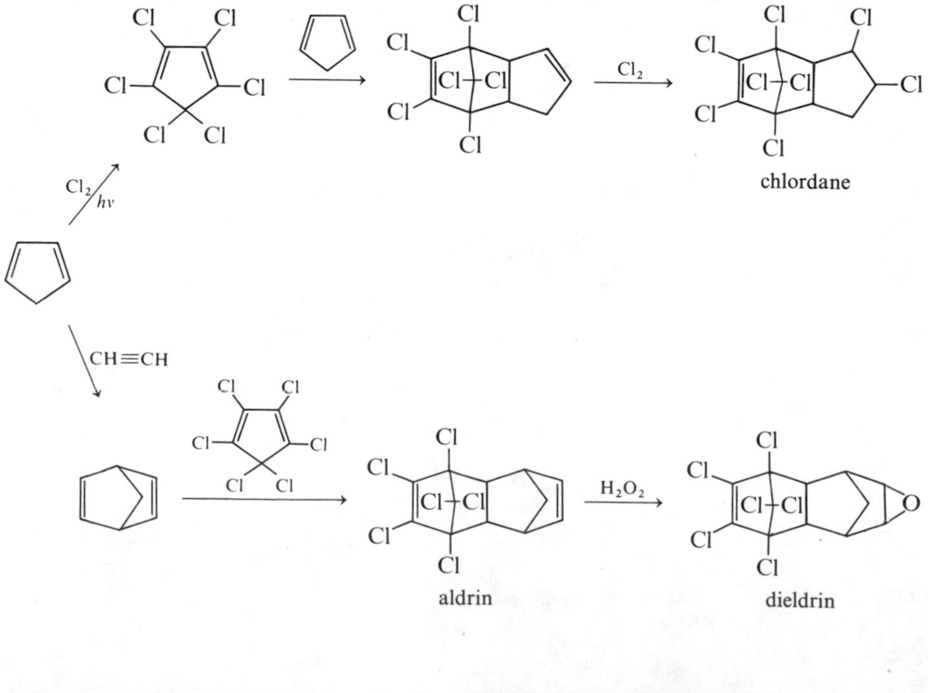

chlordane

aldrin   dieldrin

STUDY PROBLEMS

9.37 Predict the Diels–Alder products:

(a) + $\longrightarrow$ (b) + $\longrightarrow$

9.38 Suggest a synthesis for the following compound. (*Hint*: An alkyne may be used as a dienophile.)

Section 9.18

Polymers

Polymers are giant molecules, or **macromolecules**. Natural polymers include proteins (such as silk, muscle fibers, and enzymes), polysaccharides (starch and cellulose), rubber, and nucleic acids. Man-made polymers are almost as diverse as nature's polymers. We wear polyester clothes, sit on vinyl chairs, and write on Formica table tops. Our rugs may be made of polyester, polyacrylic, or polypropylene. Sky divers use nylon parachutes. We paint walls with latex paint and wood floors with polyurethane. Automobiles may have synthetic rubber tires and vinyl upholstery. Dishes may be melamine. Other common polymeric products include food wrap, Teflon coating for frying pans, hairbrushes, toothbrushes, epoxy glue, electrical insulators, plastic jugs, heart valves, airplane windshields— the list could continue! The technology of macromolecules has become a giant in the world of industry.

Polymers fall into three general classifications: *elastomers*, those polymers with elastic properties, like rubber; *fibers*, the threadlike polymers, such as cotton, silk, or nylon; and *plastics*, which can be thin sheets (kitchen wrap), hard and moldable solids (piping, children's toys), or coatings (car finishes, varnishes). The multiplicity of properties depends on the variety of structures that are possible in polymers.

Many useful polymers come from alkenes, and we will discuss some of these here. Other types of polymers will be covered in appropriate sections elsewhere in this text.

A polymer (Greek, "many parts") is made up of thousands of repeating units of small parts, the **monomers** (Greek, "one part"). In a polymerization reaction, the first products are **dimers** ("two parts"), then **trimers**, **tetramers**, and finally, after a series of reaction steps, the polymer molecules. The polymers that we will discuss here are called **addition polymers** because they are formed by the addition of monomers to each other without the loss of atoms or groups.

A synthetic polymer is usually named from the name of its monomer prefixed with **poly-**. For example, ethylene forms the simple polymer *polyethylene*, which is used for things like cleaners' bags and plastic piping.

repeating monomeric units

$$CH_2{=}CH_2 \xrightarrow[\text{or catalyst}]{O_2, \text{ heat, pressure}} -CH_2CH_2-CH_2CH_2-CH_2CH_2-$$

ethylene   polyethylene

the monomer   *the polymer*

The equations for polymerization are conveniently represented in the following format, where x is used to mean "a large number."

$$x\ CH_2{=}CH_2 \xrightarrow{\text{catalyst}} \ {+}CH_2CH_2{+}_x$$

Frequently, the end groups of macromolecules are unknown—they may arise from impurities in the reaction mixture. In some cases, the end groups can be controlled. The properties of a polymer are governed almost entirely by the bulk of the polymer molecule rather than by the end groups. To emphasize the basic structure of the polymer, it is customary not to include the end groups in the formula unless they are specifically known.

A. Free-Radical Polymers

A common mode of polymerization of alkenes is by a free-radical path. The polymerization is started by an initiator such as O_2 or a peroxide. The resulting polymer is formed by a chain-propagation process. Let us use the polymerization of propylene as our example.

Overall reaction:

$$x\ CH_2{=}\overset{\overset{\displaystyle CH_3}{|}}{CH} \xrightarrow{\text{catalyst}} \left({+}CH_2\overset{\overset{\displaystyle CH_3}{|}}{CH}{+}\right)_x$$

propylene   polypropylene

used for rugs and upholstery

Initiation: ROOR $\longrightarrow$ 2 RO·

Propagation: RO· ⌒ $CH_2{=}\overset{\overset{\displaystyle CH_3}{|}}{CH} \longrightarrow$ RO$-$CH$_2$$\overset{\overset{\displaystyle CH_3}{|}}{\dot{C}H}$

$$RO CH_2\overset{\overset{\displaystyle CH_3}{|}}{\dot{C}H} \ ⌒ \ CH_2{=}\overset{\overset{\displaystyle CH_3}{|}}{CH} \longrightarrow ROCH_2\overset{\overset{\displaystyle CH_3}{|}}{CH}{-}CH_2\overset{\overset{\displaystyle CH_3}{|}}{\dot{C}H} \quad \text{etc.}$$

Theoretically, the chain growth could go on indefinitely, which of course does not happen. The termination steps for polymerization are typical free-radical termination steps. Two radicals may meet and join, or two radicals might undergo disproportionation. (The squiggles in the following formulas are used to indicate that a much larger molecule than shown is involved in the reaction.)

Joining:

$$\text{\textasciitilde}CH_2\overset{\overset{\displaystyle CH_3}{|}}{\dot{C}H} + \overset{\overset{\displaystyle CH_3}{|}}{\dot{C}H}CH_2\text{\textasciitilde} \longrightarrow \text{\textasciitilde}CH_2\overset{\overset{\displaystyle CH_3}{|}}{CH}{-}\overset{\overset{\displaystyle CH_3}{|}}{CH}CH_2\text{\textasciitilde}$$

terminated

Disproportionation:

$$\text{+CH}_2\dot{\text{C}}\text{H} + \dot{\text{C}}\text{HCH}_2\text{-}\!\!\dagger \longrightarrow \text{+CH}=\text{CH} + \text{CH}_2\text{CH}_2\text{-}\!\!\dagger$$
$$\quad\quad |\qquad\quad |\qquad\qquad\qquad\qquad |\qquad\quad |$$
$$\quad\ \ \text{CH}_3\quad \text{CH}_3\qquad\qquad\qquad\quad \text{CH}_3\quad \text{CH}_3$$

terminated

There are two ways propylene could join together to form polypropylene:
(1) **head-to-tail**, or (2) **head-to-head and tail-to-tail**.

tail ⟶ ⟵ *head*

$$\text{CH}_2=\text{CH}$$
$$\qquad\quad |$$
$$\qquad\ \ \text{CH}_3$$

head to tail ⟵   *head-to-head*   *tail-to-tail*

$$\text{+CH}_2\text{CH}-\text{CH}_2\text{CH}-\text{CH}_2\text{CH}-\!\!\dagger \qquad\qquad \text{+CH}_2\text{CH}-\text{CHCH}_2-\text{CH}_2\text{CH}-\!\!\dagger$$
$$\qquad\ |\qquad\qquad |\qquad\qquad |\qquad\qquad\qquad\qquad\quad |\qquad\ |\qquad\qquad\ |$$
$$\qquad \text{CH}_3\qquad \text{CH}_3\qquad \text{CH}_3 \qquad\qquad\qquad\quad\ \text{CH}_3\ \text{CH}_3\qquad \text{CH}_3$$

Polypropylene is an example of a *head-to-tail polymer*. Let us discuss the reason for this orientation of the monomers. A more stable free-radical intermediate means a lower-energy transition state and a faster rate of reaction. Of the two possible modes of free-radical attack, one leads to a less stable *primary* free radical, while the other leads to the more stable *secondary* free radical. The repetitive formation of secondary free radicals leads to a head-to-tail joining of propylene monomers.

$$\text{R}\cdot + \text{CH}_2=\text{CH} \longrightarrow \text{RCH}_2-\dot{\text{C}}\text{H} \quad \text{and not} \quad \text{RCH}-\dot{\text{C}}\text{H}_2$$
$$\qquad\qquad\quad\ |\qquad\qquad\qquad\quad\ |\qquad\qquad\qquad\qquad\ |$$
$$\qquad\qquad\ \text{CH}_3\qquad\qquad\quad\ \text{CH}_3\qquad\qquad\qquad\ \text{CH}_3$$

$$\qquad\qquad\qquad\qquad\qquad\qquad\ 2°,\ more\ stable \qquad\qquad\quad 1°,\ less\ stable$$

$$\xrightarrow{\text{CH}_2=\text{CHCH}_3} \text{RCH}_2\text{CH}-\text{CH}_2\dot{\text{C}}\text{H} \quad \text{etc.}$$
$$\qquad\qquad\qquad\qquad\qquad\quad |\qquad\qquad\ |$$
$$\qquad\qquad\qquad\qquad\quad\ \text{CH}_3\qquad \text{CH}_3$$

A large number of polymers may be synthesized from alkenes in analogous reactions to those of ethylene and propylene.

$$\qquad\qquad\qquad \text{Cl} \qquad\qquad\qquad\qquad\qquad\ \text{Cl}$$
$$\qquad\qquad\qquad\ |\qquad\qquad\qquad\qquad\qquad\quad |$$
$$x\ \text{CH}_2=\text{CH} \xrightarrow{\text{catalyst}} \big(\text{CH}_2-\text{CH}\big)_x$$

vinyl chloride   polyvinyl chloride (PVC)
                             *used for flooring and
for phonograph records*

$$\qquad\qquad\qquad \text{CH}_3 \qquad\qquad\qquad\qquad\qquad \text{CH}_3$$
$$\qquad\qquad\qquad\ |\qquad\qquad\qquad\qquad\qquad\quad |$$
$$x\ \text{CH}_2=\text{C} \xrightarrow{\text{catalyst}} \big(\text{CH}_2-\text{C}\!\!-\!\!\big)$$
$$\qquad\qquad\qquad\ |\qquad\qquad\qquad\qquad\qquad\quad |$$
$$\qquad\qquad\quad \text{CO}_2\text{CH}_3 \qquad\qquad\qquad\quad \text{CO}_2\text{CH}_3 \big)_x$$

methyl methacrylate   polymethyl methacrylate
                              Plexiglas and Lucite

$$x \ CH_2{=}CH \xrightarrow{\text{catalyst}} {+}CH_2{-}CH{+}_x$$

styrene

polystyrene

used in toothbrush handles and in the manufacture of styrofoam

A chemist is not limited to using a single monomer in the production of a polymer. To achieve desired properties, he might use a mixture of two, three, or even more monomers. A mixture of two different monomers results in a **copolymer**, such as Saran (used in kitchen wrap).

$$x \ CH_2{=}CHCl + \ x \ CH_2{=}CCl_2 \xrightarrow{\text{catalyst}} {+}CH_2CHCl{-}CH_2CCl_2{+}_x$$

vinyl chloride
(chloroethene)

vinylidene chloride
(1,1-dichloroethene)

Saran
a copolymer
(not necessarily alternating)

STUDY PROBLEMS

9.39 The monomer for *Teflon* is $CF_2{=}CF_2$. What is the structure of Teflon?

9.40 *Orlon* has the formula $\left({+}CH_2\underset{\underset{CN}{|}}{CH}{+}\right)_x$. What is the structure of its monomer?

Until 1955, most addition polymers were made by free-radical paths. In that year, however, Karl Ziegler and Giulio Natta introduced a new technique for polymerization. These two chemists received the 1963 Nobel prize for their discovery, a type of catalyst that permits control of the stereochemistry of a polymer during its formation. (A commonly used Ziegler–Natta catalyst is $(CH_3CH_2)_3Al$ complexed with $TiCl_4$.) Ziegler–Natta catalysts function by undergoing reaction with the monomeric alkene; then new monomers are *inserted* between the catalyst and the growing polymer.

$$\boxed{\text{catalyst}}{-}CH_2CH_3 + CH_2{=}CH_2 \longrightarrow \boxed{\text{catalyst}}{-}CH_2CH_2{-}CH_2CH_3 \quad \text{etc.}$$

B. 1,4-Addition Polymers

Conjugated dienes can be polymerized by **1,4-addition**. The product still contains unsaturation; therefore, the polymer could contain all *cis*-units, all *trans*-units, or a mixture of *cis*- and *trans*-units. The following equation shows the free-radical, 1,4-polymerization of isoprene (2-methyl-1,3-butadiene).

$$RO\cdot + CH_2{=}\underset{\underset{CH_3}{|}}{C}{-}CH{=}CH_2 \xrightarrow{\text{1,4-addition}} ROCH_2{-}\underset{\underset{CH_3}{|}}{C}{=}CH{-}\dot{C}H_2 \quad \text{etc.} \longrightarrow$$

catalyst

isoprene

$$\left(\begin{array}{c} CH_3 \quad\quad H \\ C{=}C \\ {+}CH_2 \quad\quad CH_2{+}_x \end{array}\right) \quad \text{or} \quad \left(\begin{array}{c} CH_3 \quad\quad CH_2{+} \\ C{=}C \\ {+}CH_2 \quad\quad H \end{array}\right)_x$$

all-*cis*-polyisoprene
(natural rubber)

all-*trans*-polyisoprene
(gutta percha)

Natural rubber is polyisoprene with *cis* double bonds. The *trans*-polymer, called **gutta percha**, is a hard polymer used as a golf-ball covering and in temporary dental fillings. The reason for the difference in properties of these two polymers will be discussed in Section 9.18D. Neither one of these polymers is synthesized in nature from isoprene itself, as was once believed. Instead, their precursor is mevalonic acid (Section 19.6).

STUDY PROBLEM
───

9.41 *Neoprene*, developed in 1932, was the first synthetic rubber. It is used in washers, tubing, and the like. Neoprene is the all-*trans*, head-to-tail polymer of 2-chloro-1,3-butadiene. What is the structure of this polymer?

───

C. *Ionic Addition Polymers*

Besides free-radical addition, polymers may be formed through **cationic addition**, a reaction that proceeds through a carbocation intermediate. An acid such as H_2SO_4 or $AlCl_3$ may be used to form the initial carbocation. (This procedure is not used for the synthesis of polyethylene because of the difficulty in forming a primary carbocation.)

Sample Problem
───

Suggest a termination step in the carbocation polymerization of isobutylene.

Solution: Tertiary carbocations often undergo elimination in the presence of H_2SO_4 or other strong acid:

$$RCH_2\overset{CH_3}{\underset{CH_3}{\overset{|}{\underset{|}{C^+}}}} \longrightarrow RCH{=}C(CH_3)_2 + H^+$$

terminated

───

D. *Stereochemistry of Polymers*

Polymers, like any other organic molecules, may have functional groups and chiral centers. They can undergo hydrogen bonding and dipole–dipole interactions. The chemical composition of a polymer chain is referred to as its **primary structure**. How the chain is arranged in relation to itself and to other chains is called the **secondary structure**. This secondary structure may be as important to the properties of a polymer as its chemical composition.

A polymer may be a tangled mass of continuous chains or branched chains. The result is a soft amorphous solid such as soft rubber. On the other hand, a polymer may be composed of continuous chains held together by hydrogen bonds or by other dipole–dipole attractions. This type of polymer structure lends itself to fibers or hard, moldable plastics. A more-ordered polymer is said to have a higher degree of **crystallinity** than the amorphous, or noncrystalline, polymer.

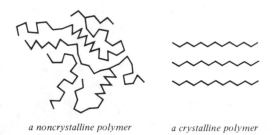

a noncrystalline polymer   *a crystalline polymer*

The differences in properties between crystalline and noncrystalline polymers are beautifully demonstrated by gutta percha and natural rubber. Gutta percha is a highly crystalline polymer, while natural rubber has a molecular shape that does not lend itself to an ordered, crystalline arrangement.

gutta percha (all *trans*)   natural rubber (all *cis*)

Let us reconsider the polymerization of propylene. There are three types of product that could result from the head-to-tail polymerization of propylene. (1) The methyl groups at the newly formed chiral carbons could be protruding from

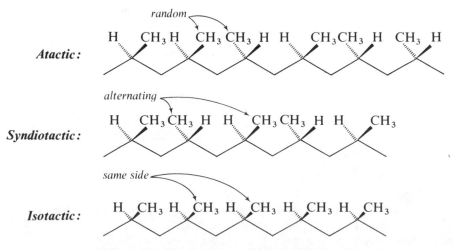

Figure 9.19.   The three types of polypropylene polymer.

the chain in a random fashion; this is an **atactic polymer** (a soft, amorphous product). (2) The methyl groups could alternate from one side of the chain to the other; this is a **syndiotactic polymer**. (3) The methyl groups could all be on the same side; then the polymer is said to be **isotactic** (see Figure 9.19). Because of their orderly arrangements, the chains of the latter two polymers can lie closer together and the polymers are more crystalline.

SUMMARY

The reactivities of alkenes and alkynes arise from the weakness and exposure of the pi bond, as well as from the exposure of the trigonal or linear carbon. Unlike other hydrocarbons, an alkyne with a $-C\equiv CH$ group is *acidic*.

Alkenes are susceptible to **electrophilic attack**. If the alkene and reagent are unsymmetrical, reaction goes through the most stable carbocation. (**Markovnikov's rule**: H^+ adds to the carbon that already has the most H's.) As reagents, hydrogen halides, H_2SO_4, $H_2O + H^+$, or BH_3 may be used. Reactions with halogens, halogens plus water, and $Hg(O_2CCH_3)_2$ proceed through bridged ions.

Alkenes:

$$R_2C{=}CHR \xrightarrow{\ H^+\ } [R_2\overset{+}{C}CH_2R] \xrightarrow{\ X^-\ } R_2\overset{\overset{X}{|}}{C}CH_2R$$

an alkyl halide

$$R_2C{=}CHR \xrightarrow{\ X_2\ } \left[R_2\overset{\delta+}{C}\overset{\overset{\delta+}{X}}{-\!\!-\!\!-}CHR \right] \xrightarrow{\ X^-\ } R_2\overset{\overset{X}{|}}{C}\underset{\underset{X}{|}}{C}HR$$

a 1,2-dihaloalkane

$$R_2C{=}CHR \xrightarrow{\ BH_3\ } (R_2CH\overset{\overset{R}{|}}{C}H\!\!\!-\!\!\!)_3B \xrightarrow{\ H_2O_2,\ OH^-\ } R_2CH\overset{\overset{R}{|}}{C}HOH$$

an alcohol

Alkynes:

$$RC{\equiv}CH \xrightarrow{\ HX\ } R\overset{\overset{X}{|}}{C}{=}CH_2 \xrightarrow{\ HX\ } RCX_2CH_3$$

a 1,1-dihaloalkane

$$RC{\equiv}CH \xrightarrow[Hg^{2+}]{H_2O,\ H^+} \left[R\overset{\overset{OH}{|}}{C}{=}CH_2 \right] \longrightarrow R\overset{\overset{O}{\|}}{C}CH_3$$

a ketone

If peroxides are present, HBr adds anti-Markovnikov to the double bond.

$$R_2C{=}CHR \xrightarrow[ROOR]{HBr} R_2CH\overset{\overset{Br}{|}}{C}HR \quad \text{(via a free radical)}$$

Methylene (a **carbene**) adds to double bonds to yield cyclopropanes.

$$R_2C{=}CR_2 + {:}CH_2 \longrightarrow R_2C\underset{CH_2}{\overset{}{-}}CR_2 \quad \text{(\textit{syn}-addition, stereospecific)}$$

singlet

$$R_2C{=}CR_2 + \overset{\cdot}{\underset{\cdot}{C}}H_2 \longrightarrow R_2C\underset{CH_2}{\overset{}{-}}CR_2 \quad \text{(nonstereospecific)}$$

triplet

Hydrogen undergoes *syn*-addition to alkenes and alkynes.

$$R_2C{=}CR_2 \xrightarrow[\text{Pt}]{H_2} R_2CHCHR_2$$

$$RC{\equiv}CR \xrightarrow[\text{deactivated Pd}]{H_2} cis\text{-}RCH{=}CHR \xrightarrow[\text{Pt}]{H_2} RCH_2CH_2R$$

Hydrogenation reactions may be used to determine relative *stabilities of alkenes*. The most highly substituted alkenes are the most stable. *trans*-Alkenes are more stable than *cis*-alkenes. Conjugated dienes are more stable than non-conjugated dienes.

Oxidation of alkenes can lead to glycols, epoxides, ketones, aldehydes, or carboxylic acids.

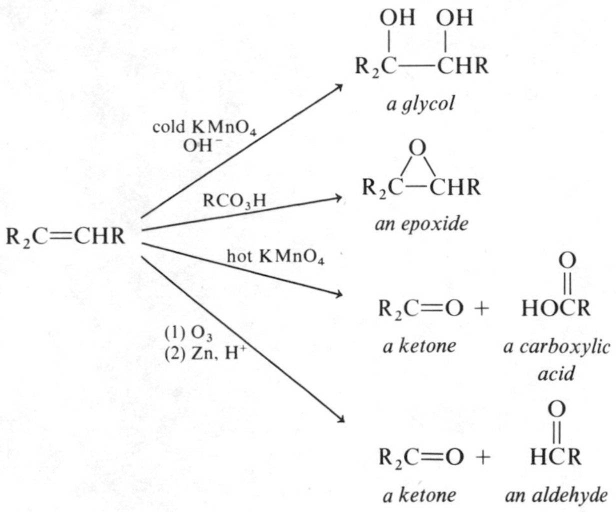

Conjugated dienes can undergo **1,2-addition** or **1,4-addition**.

$$CH_2{=}CHCH{=}CH_2 \xrightarrow[1,2]{X_2} XCH_2CHXCH{=}CH_2$$

$$CH_2{=}CHCH{=}CH_2 \xrightarrow[1,4]{X_2} XCH_2CH{=}CHCH_2X$$

Conjugated dienes can also undergo **electrocyclic reactions** or **cycloaddition reactions**. The stereochemistry of the products of electrocyclic additions may be determined by the **Woodward–Hoffmann rules** (page 423).

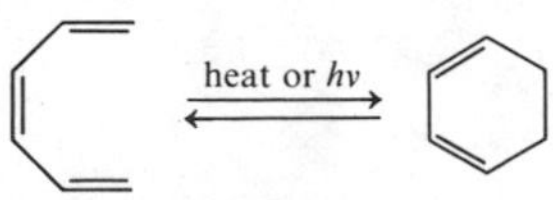

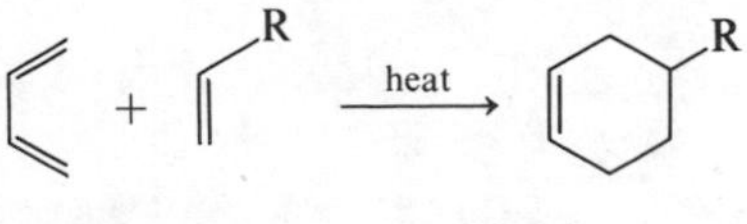

(Diels–Alder reaction)

   Addition polymers are formed by free-radical or ionic addition reactions of alkenes or by 1,4-addition of conjugated dienes.

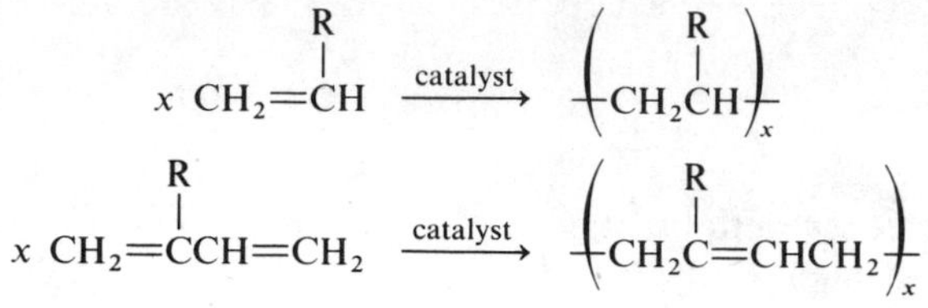

$$x \ CH_2{=}\underset{\underset{R}{|}}{CH} \xrightarrow{\text{catalyst}} \left(CH_2\underset{\underset{R}{|}}{CH} \right)_x$$

$$x \ CH_2{=}\underset{\underset{R}{|}}{C}CH{=}CH_2 \xrightarrow{\text{catalyst}} \left(CH_2\underset{\underset{R}{|}}{C}{=}CHCH_2 \right)_x$$

STUDY PROBLEMS

9.42 Write the IUPAC name for each of the following compounds:

(a) $CH_3CH{=}CHCH_3$

(b) $(CH_3)_2C{=}CHCH_3$

(c) 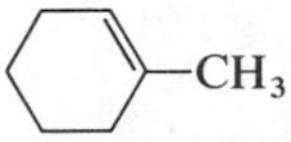 —CH_3

(d) $(CH_3)_2CHC{\equiv}CH$

(e) $CH_3CH{=}CHCHCH_2OH$
     |
     CH_3

(f) $CH_2{=}CHCH{=}CH_2$

(g) $CH_3CH{=}C(CH_2CH_2CH_3)_2$

(h)

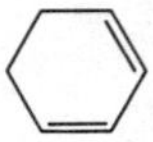

9.43 Write the IUPAC name for each of the following compounds:

(a) $BrCH_2CH{=}CH_2$

(b) $(CH_3)_2C{=}CHCH_2OH$

(c) $CH_2{=}CHCO_2H$

(d)

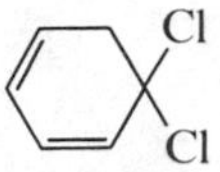

9.44 Give the structure for each of the following compounds:

(a) 2-methyl-1-butene

(b) 2-pentyne

(c) 1,3-hexadiene

(d) *cis*-2-hexene

(e) *trans*-1,2-diphenylethene

(f) *cis*-1,2-dibromoethene

9.45 Tell whether each of the following alkenes is (*E*), (*Z*), or neither:

(a)

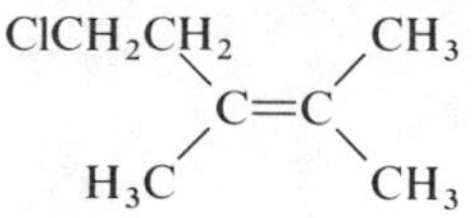

(b)

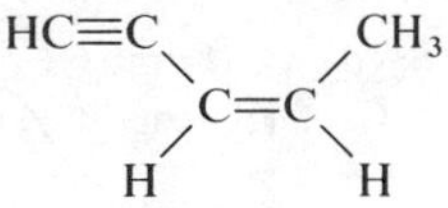

(c)

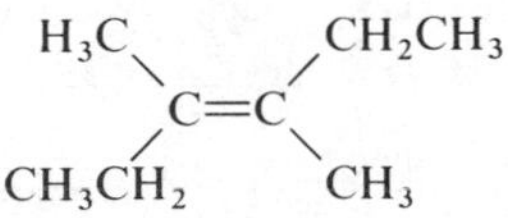

(d)

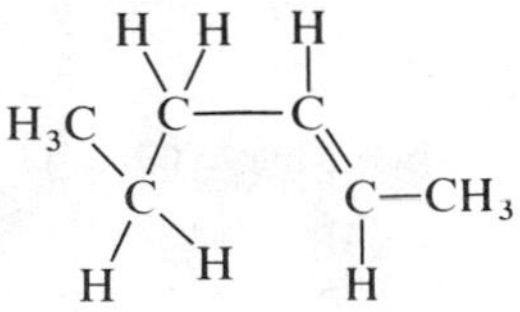

(e)

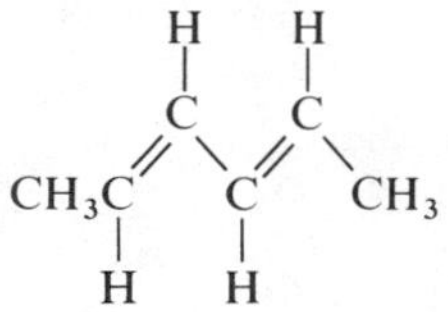

(f)

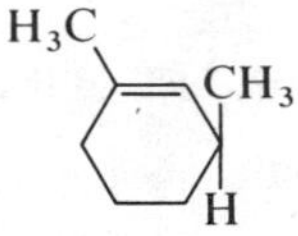

(g)

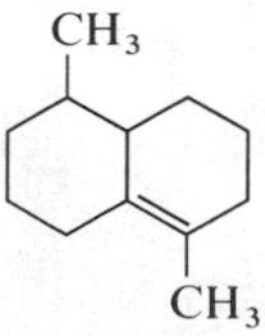

(h)

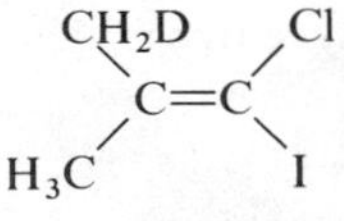

9.46 Tell which would be the reaction of choice in each of the following pairs of syntheses. (Each reaction is carried out in ethanol.)

(a)
(1) $CH_3CH_2CH_2CH_2Br$ $\xrightarrow{OH^-}$
(2) $CH_3CH_2CHBrCH_3$ $\xrightarrow{OH^-}$
$CH_3CH_2CH=CH_2$

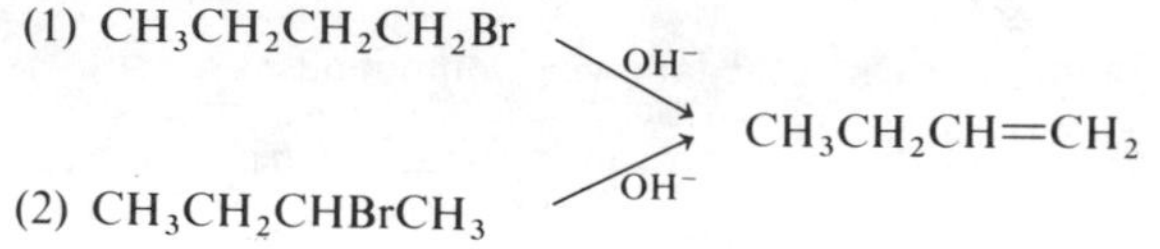

(b)
(1)
(2)
$\xrightarrow{OH^-}$
$\xrightarrow{OH^-}$

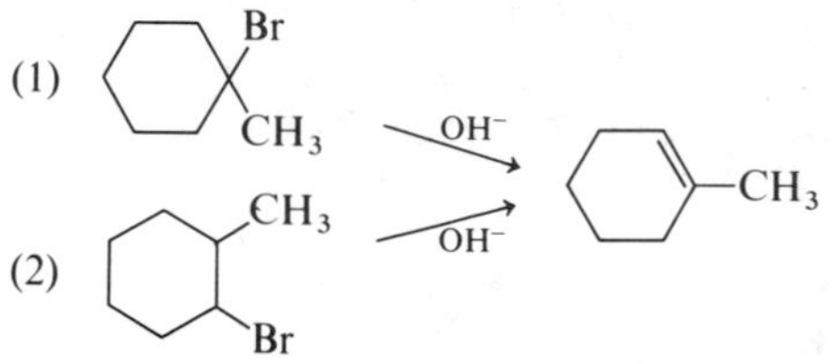

9.47 Starting with propyne, how would you prepare the following compounds?

(a) propene   (b) 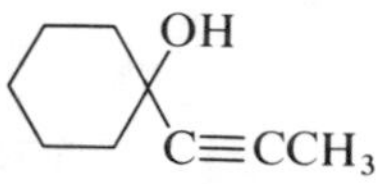   (c) 2-butyne

9.48 What would be the product if 1-pentyne were treated with each of the following reagents? (*Hint*: Alkynes also follow Markovnikov's rule.)   (a) 1 equivalent Cl_2; (b) 2 equivalents Cl_2;   (c) 2 equivalents HCl;   (d) phenylmagnesium bromide; (e) $NaNH_2$ and methyl iodide.

9.49 One equivalent of HI is added to each of the following alkenes. Give the structure of the likely products in each case.   (a) 1-pentene;   (b) 1,3-pentadiene;   (c) 2-methyl-1,3-butadiene;   (d) 2,2-dimethyl-3-heptene.

9.50 Which one of each pair would be more reactive toward addition of HCl?

(a) $ClCH=CHCl$ or $CH_2=CHCl$
(b) $CH_3CH_2CH=CHCH_3$ or $CH_3CH=C(CH_3)_2$

9.51 Arrange the following compounds in order of increasing reactivity toward H_2SO_4 (least reactive first):

(a) propene   (b) 2-methylpropene   (c) 2-butene

9.52 In Problem 9.51, give the structures of the intermediate and the major product in each case.

9.53 Predict the major organic products of the following reactions:

(a) 3-methyl-2-pentene with aqueous H_2SO_4
(b) 2-methylpropene with H_2SO_4 in ethanol
(c) 2,2-dimethyl-3-hexene with aqueous H_2SO_4
(d) 1-butene with $0.1M$ aqueous HI
(e) methylenecyclohexane (page 379) with the strong acid trifluoroacetic acid (CF_3CO_2H).

9.54 Give the steps in the mechanism of the reaction in Problem 9.53(c).

9.55 Predict the major organic products:

(a) $(CH_3)_3CCH=CHCH_3$ $\xrightarrow[\text{(2) NaBH}_4]{\text{(1) Hg(O}_2\text{CCH}_3)_2, \text{ H}_2\text{O}}$

(b) $(CH_3)_2CHCH=CH_2$ $\xrightarrow[\text{(2) NaBH}_4]{\text{(1) Hg(O}_2\text{CCH}_3)_2, \text{ CH}_3\text{CH}_2\text{OH}}$

(c) 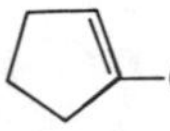 $-CH_3$ $\xrightarrow[\text{(2) H}_2\text{O}_2, \text{ OH}^-]{\text{(1) BH}_3}$

(d) $(CH_3)_2CHCH=CH_2$ $\xrightarrow[\text{(2) H}_2\text{O}_2, \text{ OH}^-]{\text{(1) BH}_3}$

9.56 Complete the following equations:

(a) 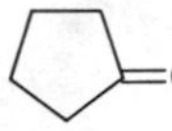 $=CHCH_3 + HBr$ $\xrightarrow{\text{no peroxides}}$

(b) 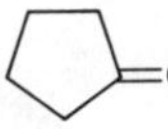 $=CHCH_3 + HBr$ $\xrightarrow{\text{ROOR}}$

9.57 Suggest a reason why HCl does *not* undergo free-radical addition to an alkene.

9.58 Predict the likely organic products of the following reactions: (a) *cis*-2-pentene with Cl_2; (b) 1-methyl-1-cyclohexene with Br_2; (c) 1-methyl-1-cyclohexene with aqueous Br_2; (d) myrcene, which is found in the oil of bayberry, with one equivalent of Cl_2.

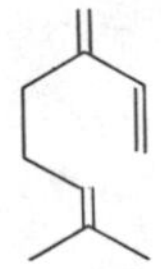

myrcene

9.59 (a) What products would probably be observed when 1-butene is treated with bromine water that contains sodium chloride?

(b) Write mechanisms that explain the formation of each product.

9.60 Suggest reagents for the conversion of cyclopentene to (a) cyclopentane, and (b) *trans*-2-bromo-1-cyclopentanol.

9.61 When 2-methyl-1,3-butadiene is treated with one equivalent of Br_2, four possible dibromoalkenes could result. However, only two dibromoalkenes are actually formed in this reaction. (a) Which two are formed? (b) Why are the other ones not formed?

9.62 The following reaction proceeds by a carbene-type mechanism. What is the product?

$(CH_3)_3\overset{+}{N}-\overset{-}{C}H_2 +$ 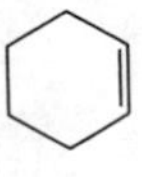 $\xrightarrow{\text{heat}}$

9.63 Predict the major organic products (showing stereochemistry):

(a) 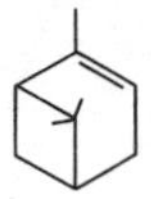 $+ H_2$ $\xrightarrow{Pt}$

(b) 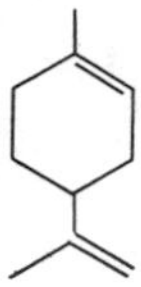 $+$ excess H_2 $\xrightarrow{Pt}$

limonene

(c) 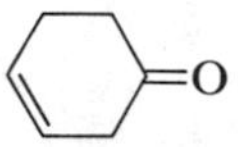 $=O + H_2$ $\xrightarrow{Pt}$

(d) 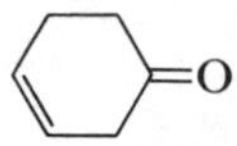 $=O + H_2$ $\xrightarrow[\text{heat, pressure}]{Pt}$

(e) $CH_3CH_2C{\equiv}CCH(CH_3)_2 + H_2$ $\xrightarrow{\text{deactivated Pd}}$

9.64 Of each of the following pairs of compounds, tell which one would be the more stable.

(a) 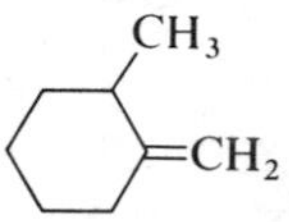 or

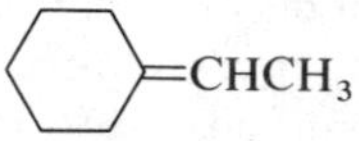

(b) *cis*- or *trans*-$CH_3CH_2CH{=}CHCH_3$

(c) (*E*)- or (*Z*)-$CH_3\overset{\overset{\displaystyle O}{\|}}{C}OCH{=}CH\overset{\overset{\displaystyle O}{\|}}{C}OCH_3$

(d) $CH_2{=}CHCH_2\overset{\overset{\displaystyle O}{\|}}{C}OCH_3$ or $CH_2{=}CH\overset{\overset{\displaystyle O}{\|}}{C}OCH_2CH_3$

9.65 Predict the products:

(a) 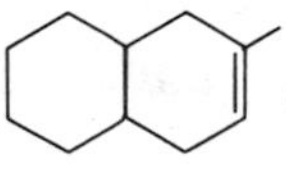 $+ C_6H_5CO_3H$ $\longrightarrow$

(b) 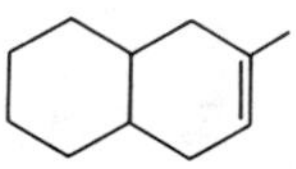 $\xrightarrow[\text{(2) Na}_2SO_3]{\text{(1) OsO}_4}$

(c) 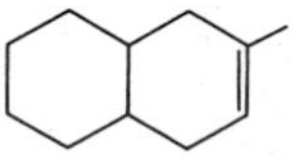 $+$ hot $KMnO_4$ solution $\longrightarrow$

(d) 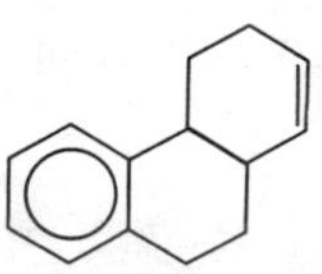 $\xrightarrow[\text{(2) Na}_2SO_3]{\text{(1) OsO}_4}$

(e) + cold KMnO₄ solution $\xrightarrow{\text{OH}^-}$

(f) $\xrightarrow[\text{(2) H}_2\text{O. OH}^-]{\text{(1) C}_6\text{H}_5\text{CO}_3\text{H}}$

9.66 Predict the ozonolysis products when each of the following alkenes is subjected to:
(1) reaction with O_3, and   (2) reaction with H_2O_2 and H^+:

(a)   (b)   (c)   (d)

α-pinene
found in turpentine

9.67 Predict the organic product of the reaction of *trans*-2-butene with each of the following
reagents. (Show the stereochemistry where appropriate.)   (a) HI;   (b) aqueous Cl_2;
(c) Br_2 in CCl_4;   (d) OsO_4, followed by treatment with Na_2SO_3;   (e) $C_6H_5CO_3H$
followed by H_2O + HCl;   (f) H_2SO_4;   (g) singlet $:CH_2$;   (h) O_3, followed by Zn
and aqueous HCl.

9.68 Give the structure of the product when 1-methyl-1-cyclopentene is treated with each
of the following reagents: (a) H_2 (Pt catalyst);   (b) Cl_2 in H_2O;   (c) Cl_2 in CCl_4;
(d) cold alkaline $KMnO_4$;   (e) hot $KMnO_4$ solution;   (f) dilute solution of Br_2 in
CH_3OH;   (g) BH_3 followed by H_2O_2–NaOH solution;   (h) HCl;   (i) HBr with
H_2O_2;   (j) dilute aqueous H_2SO_4;   (k) mercuric acetate in water followed by $NaBH_4$;
(l) CH_3CO_3H.

9.69 Each of a series of unknown alkenes is treated with (1) O_3, and (2) Zn, H^+, H_2O.
The following products are obtained. Give the structure (or structures, if there is more
than one possibility) of each unknown alkene.

(a) $\overset{O}{\overset{\|}{H C}}CH_2CH_2CH_2\overset{O}{\overset{\|}{C H}}$ only

(b) $CH_3CH_2\overset{O}{\overset{\|}{C H}}$ + $CH_3\overset{O}{\overset{\|}{C}}CH_3$

(c) $CH_3\overset{O}{\overset{\|}{C H}}$ only

(d) $H\overset{O}{\overset{\|}{C}}H$ + =O

(e) $CH_3\overset{O}{\overset{\|}{C}}{-}\overset{O}{\overset{\|}{C H}}$ + 2 $CH_3\overset{O}{\overset{\|}{C}}CH_3$

(f) $CH_3\overset{O}{\overset{\|}{C H}}$ + $H\overset{O}{\overset{\|}{C}}H$ + $H\overset{O}{\overset{\|}{C}}CH_2\overset{O}{\overset{\|}{C H}}$

9.70 A chemist has obtained the following information about an alkene of unknown structure. What is the structure of the alkene?

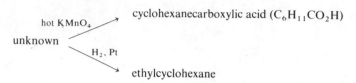

9.71 When subjected to catalytic hydrogenation, a hydrocarbon takes up 1.0 equivalent of H_2. When oxidized with a hot solution of $KMnO_4$, only one compound is obtained, $HO_2CCHCH_2CHCO_2H$. What is the structure of the hydrocarbon?

$$\underset{CH_3}{|} \qquad \underset{CH_3}{|}$$

9.72 What organic products would you expect from the following reactions?

(a) limonene (Problem 9.63) + 2 equivalents Cl_2 ⟶

(b) myrcene (Problem 9.58) + 1 equivalent HCl ⟶

9.73 Each of the following dienes is shown in the s-*trans* form. Which of these compounds are interconvertible with their s-*cis* forms? Show the s-*cis* conformations in these cases.

(a) 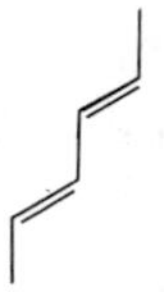   (b) 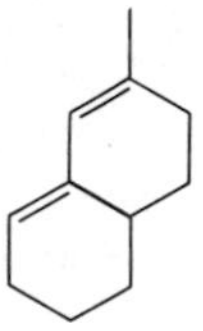   (c)

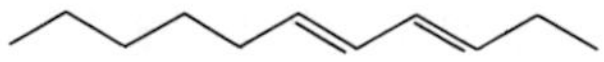

(d) 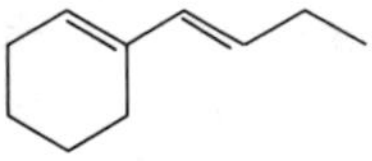   (e)

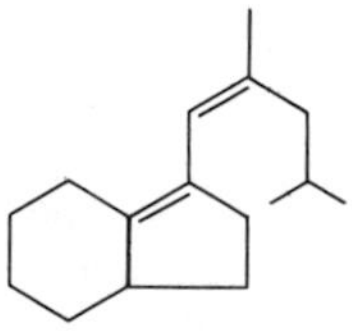

9.74 Tell whether each of the following compounds or pairs of compounds has $4n$ or $(4n + 2)$ pi electrons that could be involved in electrocyclic or cycloaddition reactions:

(a) 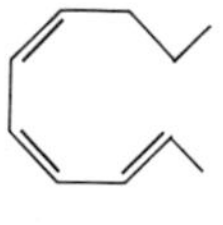   (b) 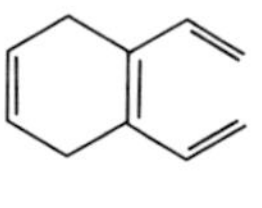   (c) 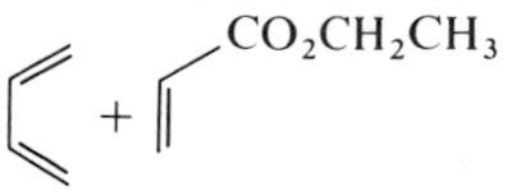   + $CO_2CH_2CH_3$

(d) 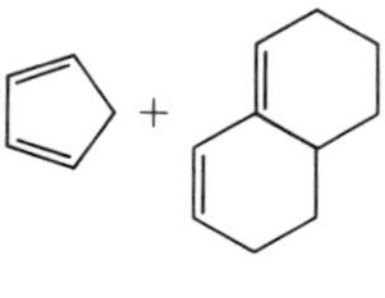   +   (e) 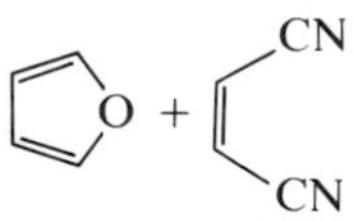   + CN CN

9.75 Tell whether each of the following dienes or trienes would undergo conrotatory or disrotatory motion in a cyclization reaction:

(a) 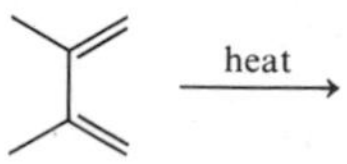 $\xrightarrow{\text{heat}}$

(b) 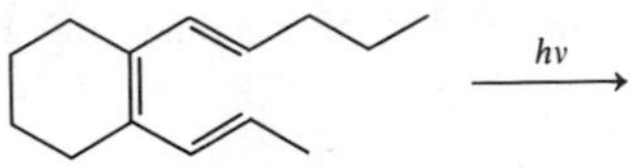 $\xrightarrow{hv}$

(c) 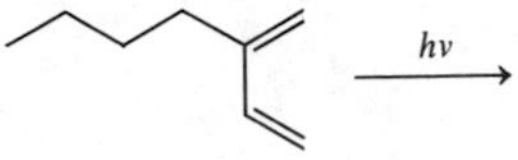 $\xrightarrow{hv}$

(d) 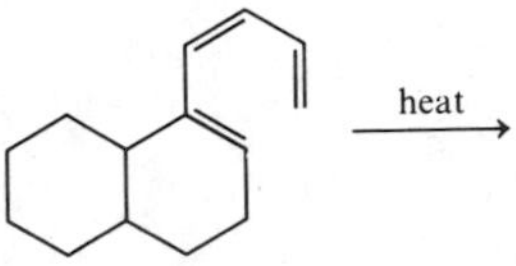 $\xrightarrow{heat}$

9.76 Predict the product and its stereochemistry:

(a) 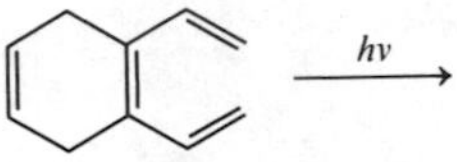 $\xrightarrow{hv}$

(b) 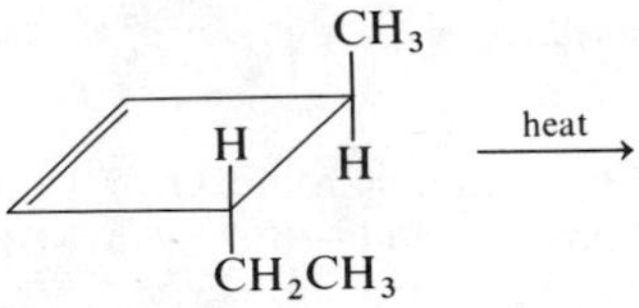 $\xrightarrow{heat}$

(c) 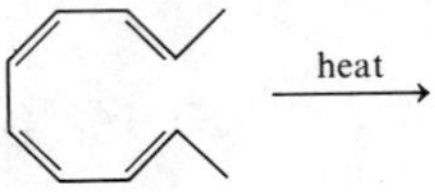 $\xrightarrow{heat}$

(d) 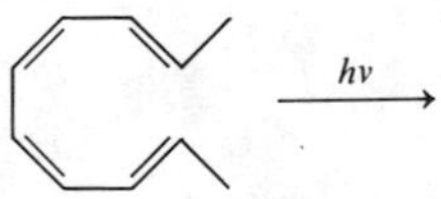 $\xrightarrow{hv}$

9.77 Predict the products of the following Diels–Alder reactions:

(a) 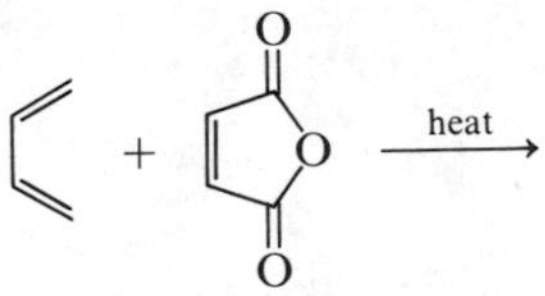 $+$ $\xrightarrow{heat}$

(b) 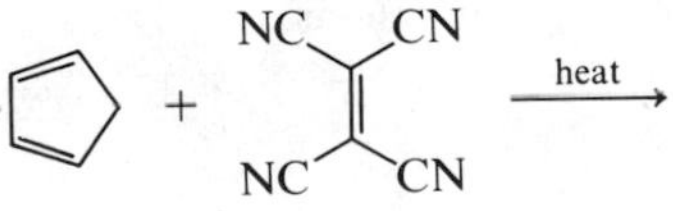 $+$ $\xrightarrow{heat}$

(c) 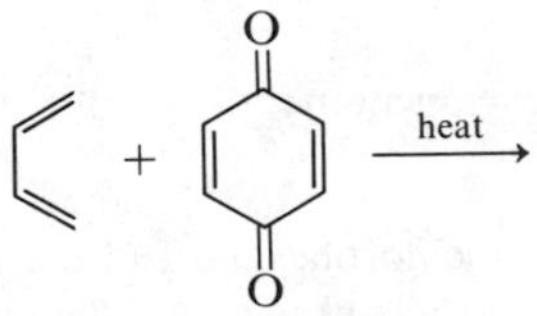 $+$ $\xrightarrow{heat}$

(d) 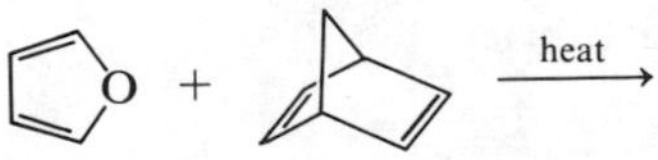 $+$ $\xrightarrow{heat}$

(e) 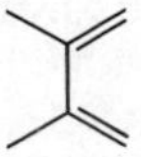 $+$ $CH_3CH_2O_2CC{\equiv}CCO_2CH_2CH_3$ $\xrightarrow{heat}$

9.78 Suggest a Diels–Alder reaction that would lead to each of the following cyclic compounds:

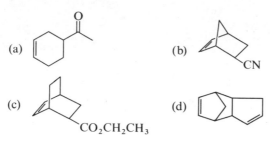

(a)

(b)

(c)

(d)

9.79 Styrene may be copolymerized with maleic anhydride. Give an equation for this reaction.

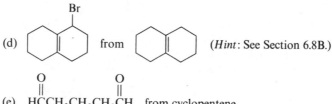

maleic anhydride

9.80 Dimers, as well as polymers, may be made by a cationic route. Give the mechanisms for the acid-catalyzed dimerizations of (a) propene, and (b) 2-methyl-1-butene.

9.81 Suggest synthetic paths for the following conversions:

  (a) propene from propane
  (b) 1,2-dibromopropane from 1-bromopropane
  (c) 2-bromopropane from 1-propanol

  (d) [structure with Br] from [bicyclic structure] (*Hint*: See Section 6.8B.)

  (e) $HCCH_2CH_2CH_2CH$ (with two O) from cyclopentene
  (f) cyclopentanol from cyclopentene

9.82 Suggest synthetic paths for each of the following conversions:

  (a) 1,2-dideuteriopropane from propane
  (b) acetic acid from 1-bromopropane
  (c) 1-propanol from 2-bromopropane
  (d) *trans*-1,2-cyclohexanediol from cyclohexane
  (e) *trans*-2-chloro-1-cyclopentanol from chlorocyclopentane

9.83 Reaction of 3-hexene with $Cl_2 + H_2O$ yields 3,4-dichlorohexane and the 3,4-chlorohydrin. However, the chlorohydrin obtained from *cis*-3-hexene is different from the chlorohydrin obtained from *trans*-3-hexene. Explain.

9.84 The toxic components of poison ivy and poison oak are a group of 1,2-hydroquinones called *urushiols*. One of these urushiols (A), $C_{21}H_{29}O_2$, is treated with dilute NaOH, followed by methyl iodide, and yields a dimethylated compound (B), $C_{23}H_{33}O_2$. When

B is treated with ozone, followed by treatment with Zn dust and water, the products are:

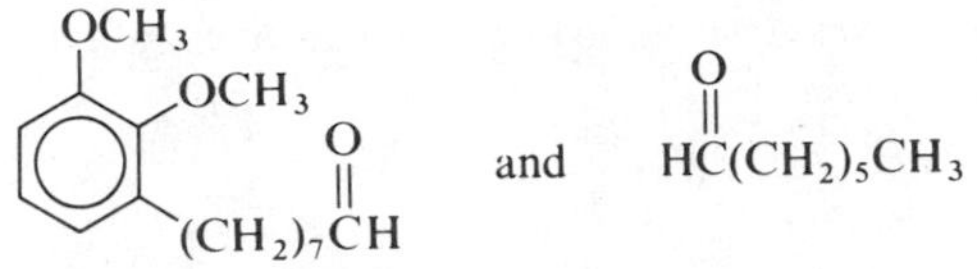

and $HC(CH_2)_5CH_3$

What are the structures of A and B?

9.85 Suggest a mechanism for each of the following reactions:

(a) $(CH_3)_2C\!=\!CH(CH_2)_2CH\!=\!C(CH_3)_2$ $\xrightarrow{\text{H}^+}$

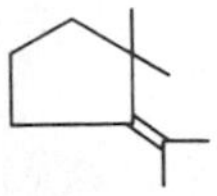

(b) $(CH_3)_2C\!=\!CH(CH_2)_2\overset{\overset{\displaystyle CH_3}{|}}{C}\!=\!CHCH_3$ $\xrightarrow{\text{H}^+}$

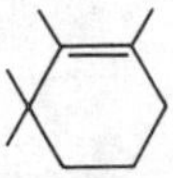

9.86 A chemist treated (R)-3-butene-1,2-diol with OsO_4, obtaining two tetraols. What were they? (Specify the stereochemistry.)

9.87 How would you prepare the following compounds from nondeuteriated hydrocarbons?

(a) 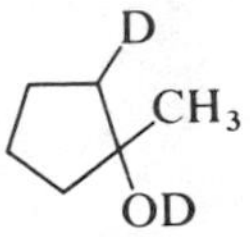   (b) 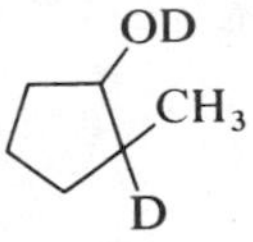   (c)

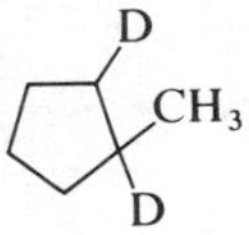

(d) 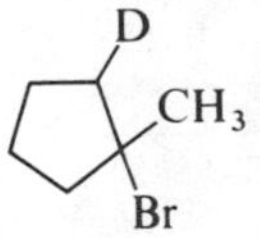   (e)

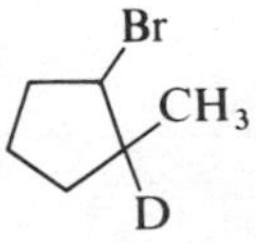

9.88 The sex attractant of the housefly is a hydrocarbon with the formula $C_{23}H_{46}$. Catalytic hydrogenation of this compound yields $C_{23}H_{48}$, while oxidation with a hot solution of $KMnO_4$ yields $CH_3(CH_2)_{12}CO_2H$ and $CH_3(CH_2)_7CO_2H$. Addition of bromine to the hydrocarbon yields one pair of enantiomeric dibromides ($C_{23}H_{46}Br_2$). What is the structure of the housefly sex attractant?

9.89 A chemist wants to devise a catalytic hydrogenation experiment that will determine if *endocyclic double bonds* are more or less stable than *exocyclic double bonds*. (An *endocyclic* double bond is one that joins two ring carbons, while an *exocyclic* double bond is one that goes from a ring carbon to a non-ring carbon.) Of the following pairs of compounds, which pair would give the best hydrogenation data for comparison purposes? Why?

(a) 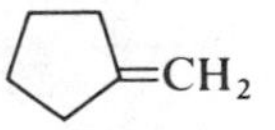 $=\!CH_2$ and $-\!CH_3$

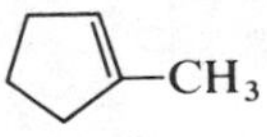

   exocyclic   *endocyclic*

(b) 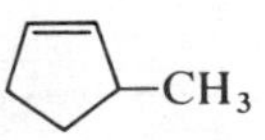 $-\!CH_3$ and $-\!CH_3$

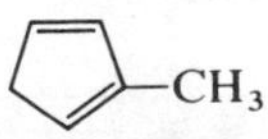

(c)  $=\!CHCH_3$ and $-\!CH_2CH_3$

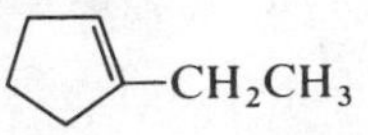

9.90 Because of its geometry, *trans*-cyclooctene exists as a pair of enantiomers.

    (a)   Give the structure of the enantiomer of the structure shown.

    (b)   Would *cis*-cyclooctene also exist as a pair of enantiomers? Explain.

trans-cyclooctene
one enantiomer

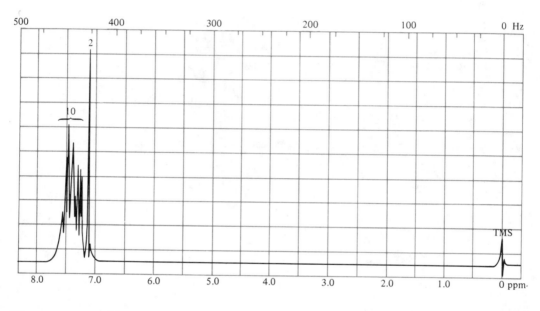

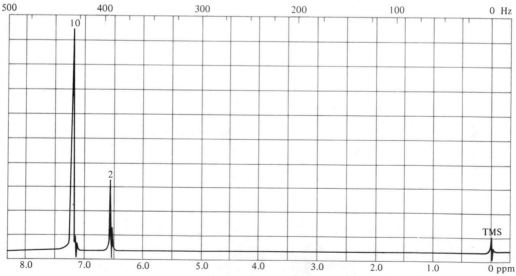

Figure 9.20.   Nmr spectra for unknown hydrocarbons ($C_{14}H_{12}$) in Problem 9.92.

9.91 Cyclopentene is treated with cold $KMnO_4$ solution to yield a diol. When cyclopentene is treated with (1) peroxybenzoic acid, and (2) H_2O, H^+, another diol is formed.

(a) Which diol is a racemic mixture?
(b) Which diol is a *meso* compound?
(c) If bromine were added to the double bond of cyclopentene, what stereoisomer(s) would you expect?

9.92 The two nmr spectra in Figure 9.20 were obtained from samples of two hydrocarbons, each with the formula $C_{14}H_{12}$. Both samples yielded only benzoic acid upon treatment with hot $KMnO_4$ solution. What are the structures of these two hydrocarbons?

9.93 An alkyl halide ($C_6H_{13}Br$), when treated with a base, gave only two alkenes, A and B. Hydrogenation of either alkene yielded 2-methylpentane. The infrared spectrum of each alkene is shown in Figure 9.21. What is the structure of the alkyl halide and of each alkene? Which alkene was formed in greater abundance?

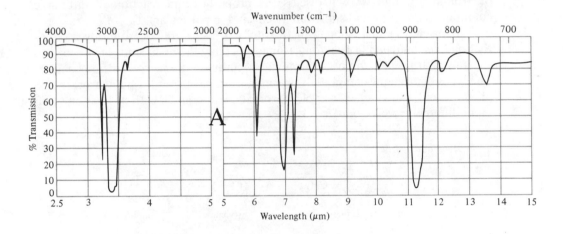

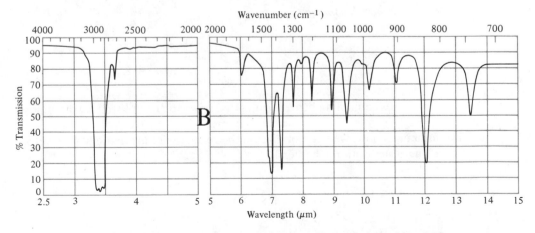

Figure 9.21. Infrared spectra for unknown alkenes in Problem 9.93.

Chapter 10

Aromaticity, Benzene, and Substituted Benzenes

Benzene is the simplest of the aromatic compounds and one that we have already encountered many times. In this chapter, we will formalize the definition of aromaticity, and we will discuss the properties and reactions of aromatic compounds (benzene and substituted benzenes in particular).

Benzene was first isolated in 1825 by Michael Faraday from oily residues that had accumulated in London gas mains. Today the main sources of benzene, substituted benzenes, and other aromatic compounds are petroleum and coal tar. The types of aromatic compounds obtained from these sources are hydrocarbons, phenols, and aromatic heterocycles (aromatic compounds with at least one ring atom different from carbon).

Aromatic hydrocarbons:

benzene 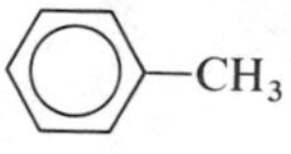   toluene 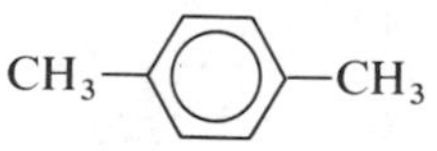   *p*-xylene 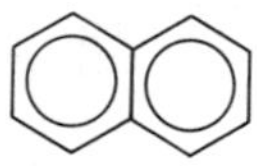   naphthalene

Aromatic nitrogen heterocycles:

pyridine    quinoline

Compounds containing benzene rings and aromatic heterocyclic compounds are exceedingly common in biological systems. Although we mention some of these compounds now, we will not discuss the reactions of aromatic heterocycles or fused-ring systems until Chapter 16.

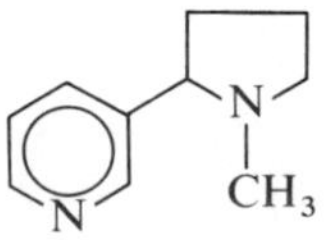

nicotine
in tobacco

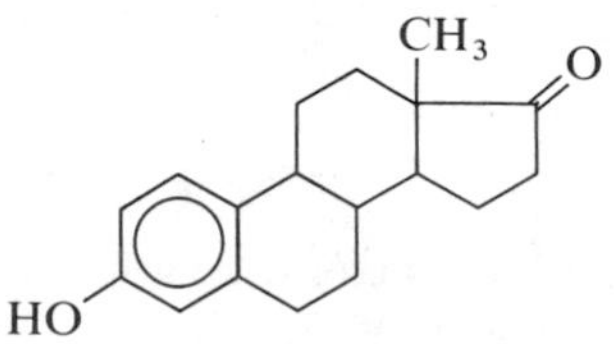

estrone
*an estrogen, or
female hormone*

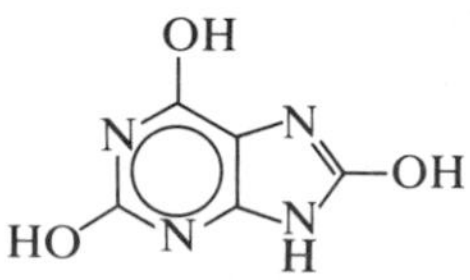

uric acid
associated with gout

Section 10.1

Nomenclature of Substituted Benzenes

The naming of monosubstituted benzenes was mentioned in Section 3.3M. Many common benzene compounds have their own names, names that are not necessarily systematic. Some of these more-commonly used names are listed in Table 10.1.

Disubstituted benzenes are named with the prefixes *ortho*, *meta*, and *para* rather than with position numbers. The prefix *ortho* signifies that two substituents are 1,2 to each other on a benzene ring; *meta* signifies a 1,3-relationship; and *para* means a 1,4-relationship. The use of *ortho*, *meta*, and *para* in lieu of position numbers is reserved exclusively for disubstituted benzenes—the system is never used with cyclohexanes or other ring systems.

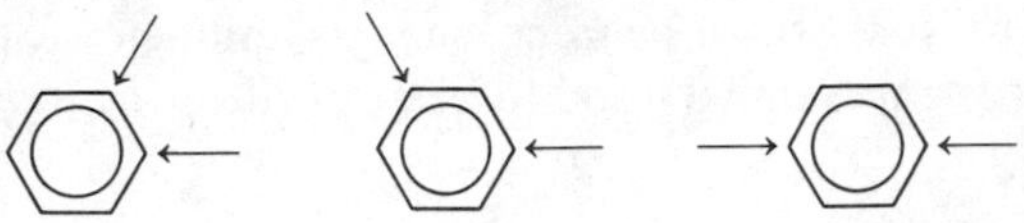

ortho-, or o-   meta-, or m-   para, or p-

The use of these prefixes in the naming of some disubstituted benzenes follows:

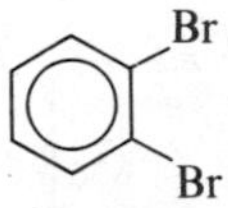

o-dibromobenzene 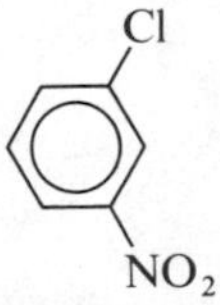   m-chloronitrobenzene 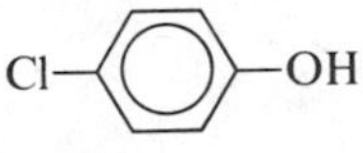   p-chlorophenol

Table 10.1. Structures and Names of Some Common Benzene Compounds

Structure	Name	Structure	Name
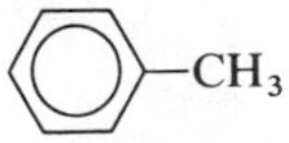 C_6H_5—CH$_3$	toluene	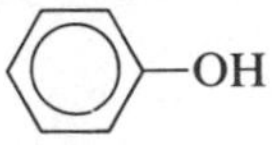 C_6H_5—OH	phenol
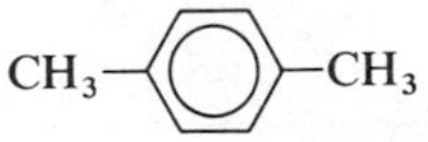 CH$_3$—C_6H_4—CH$_3$	p-xylene	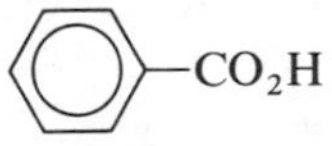 C_6H_5—CO$_2$H	benzoic acid
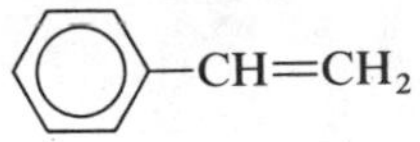 C_6H_5—CH=CH$_2$	styrene	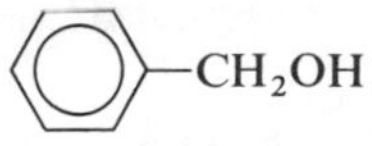 C_6H_5—CH$_2$OH	benzyl alcohol
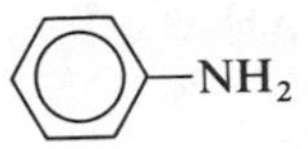 C_6H_5—NH$_2$	aniline	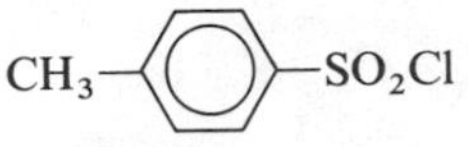 CH$_3$—C_6H_4—SO$_2$Cl	p-toluenesulfonyl chloride (tosyl chloride)
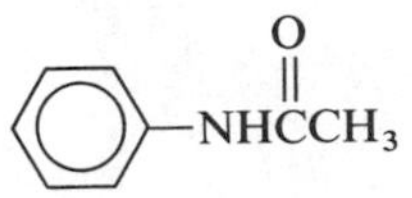 C_6H_5—NHCCH$_3$ (O)	acetanilide	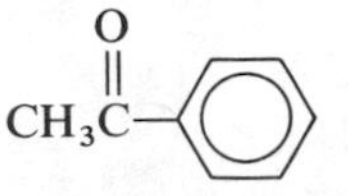 CH$_3$C(O)—C_6H_5	acetophenone
		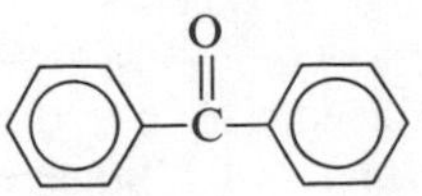 C_6H_5—C(O)—C_6H_5	benzophenone

Aromaticity, Benzene, and Substituted Benzenes

In reactions of benzene compounds, we will speak of *ortho*-substitution (or *meta*- or *para*-substitution). Note that a monosubstituted benzene has two *ortho* and two *meta* positions, but only one *para* position.

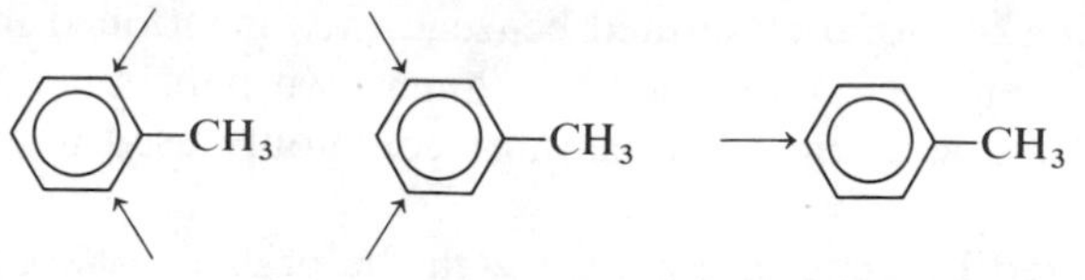

ortho   meta   para

If there are three or more substituents on a benzene ring, the *o-*, *m-*, *p*-system is no longer applicable. In this case, numbers must be used. As in numbering any compound, we number the benzene ring in such a way as to keep the prefix numbers as low as possible and give preference to the group of highest nomenclature priority. If a substituted benzene, such as aniline or toluene, is used as the parent, that substituent is understood to be at position 1 on the ring.

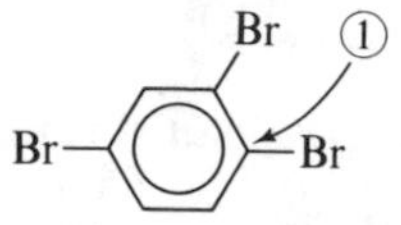

1,2,4-tribromobenzene 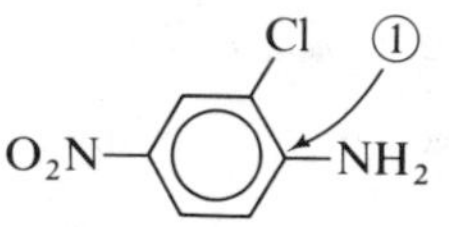   2-chloro-4-nitroaniline 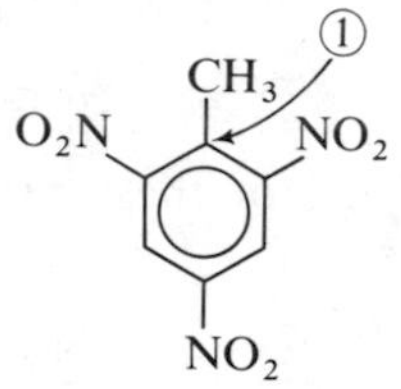   2,4,6-trinitrotoluene (TNT)

Benzene as a substituent is called a **phenyl group**. How a *toluene* substituent is named depends on the point of attachment.

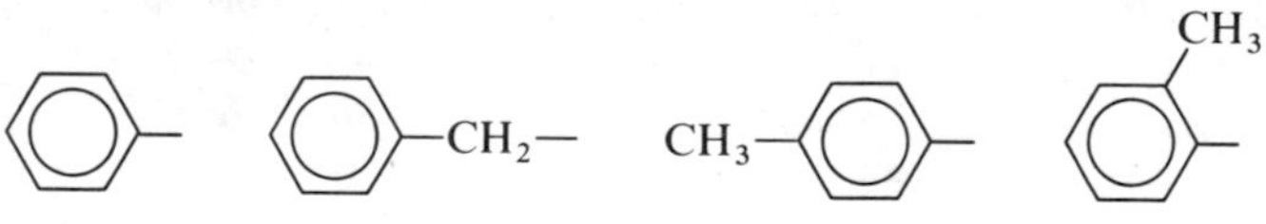

phenyl   benzyl   *p*-tolyl   *o*-tolyl

Sample Problem

Name the following substituted benzenes:

(a) 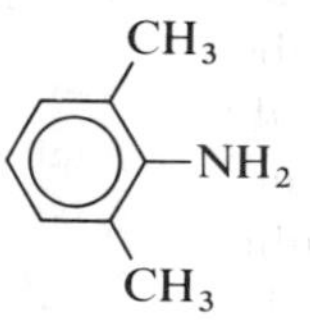   (b) 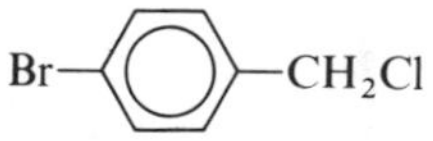   (c) 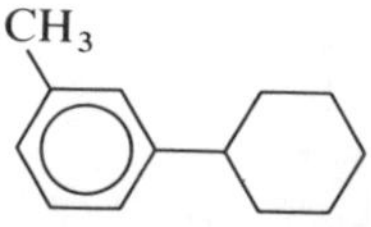   (d)

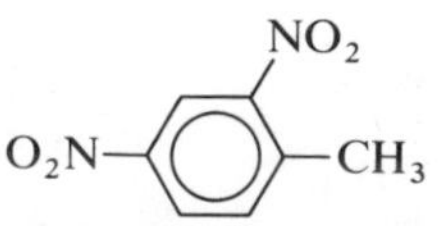

Solution: (a) 2,6-dimethylaniline; (b) *p*-bromobenzyl chloride; (c) *m*-tolylcyclohexane (or *m*-cyclohexyltoluene); (d) 2,4-dinitrotoluene.

STUDY PROBLEM

10.1 Write structures for: (a) ethylbenzene; (b) 2,4,6-tribromoaniline; (c) *p*-ethylphenol; (d) 2-phenyl-1-ethanol; and (e) benzyl bromide.

Section 10.2

Physical Properties of Aromatic Hydrocarbons

Like aliphatic and alicyclic hydrocarbons, benzene and other aromatic hydrocarbons are nonpolar. They are insoluble in water, but are soluble in organic solvents such as ether, carbon tetrachloride, or hexane. Benzene itself is a widely used solvent. It has the useful property of forming an azeotrope with water. (The azeotrope, a mixture that distills with a constant composition, consists of 91% benzene–9% H_2O and boils at 69.4°C.) Compounds dissolved in benzene are easily dried by distillation of the azeotrope.

Although the boiling points and melting points of aromatic hydrocarbons (listed in Table 10.2) are typical of those of nonpolar organic compounds, note

Table 10.2. Melting Points and Boiling Points of Some Aromatic Hydrocarbons

Name	Structure	Mp, °C	Bp, °C
benzene		5.5	80
toluene	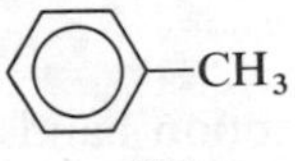 —CH₃	−95	111
o-xylene	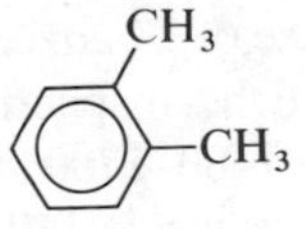 CH₃ / —CH₃	−25	144
m-xylene	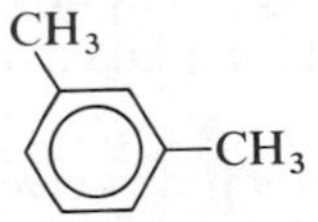 CH₃ / —CH₃	−48	139
p-xylene	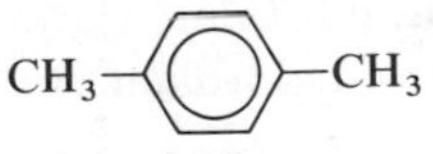 CH₃——CH₃	13	138
naphthalene	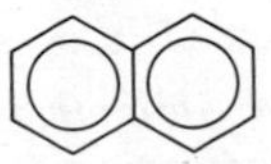	80	218
anthracene	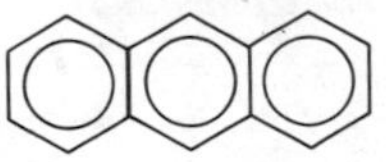	217	354
phenanthrene	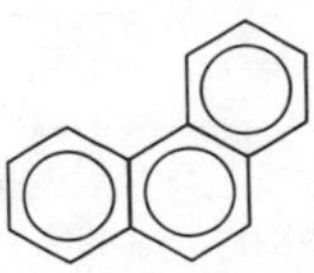	101	340

that *p*-xylene has a higher melting point than *o*- or *m*-xylene. A higher melting point is typical of *p*-substituted benzenes; a *p*-isomer is more symmetrical and can form a more orderly and stronger crystal lattice in the solid state than the less symmetrical *o*- or *m*-isomers.

It is interesting to note that many of the compounds found in coal tar (and cigarette tar) that contain four or more fused benzene rings are carcinogenic (cancer-causing).

Two carcinogenic hydrocarbons:

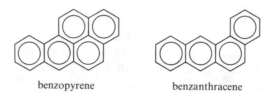

benzopyrene   benzanthracene

Section 10.3

Spectra of Substituted Benzenes

Both infrared and nmr spectra provide data that are useful in the structure determination of substituted benzenes. The nmr spectrum provides the most clean-cut answer to absence or presence of aromatic protons (and thus an aromatic ring). The infrared spectrum generally provides more useful data on the position of substitution.

A.   Infrared Spectra

The pertinent infrared absorption bands of substituted benzenes are summarized in Table 10.3. The presence of a benzene ring in a compound of unknown structure can often be determined by inspection of two regions of the infrared spectrum, around 3030 cm^{-1} and 1400–1700 cm^{-1}. The aromatic absorption for C—H stretching, which is generally weak, falls near 3030 cm^{-1} (3.3 μm), just to the left of aliphatic C—H absorption. (Alkenyl C—H absorption appears in this same general region.)

Absorption for aryl C—C vibrations gives a series of four peaks, generally between 1430 and 1670 cm^{-1} (6 and 7 μm); however, all four peaks are not always apparent. In the spectrum of chlorobenzene, the first peak is visible, but

Table 10.3. Infrared Absorption Characteristics of Benzene Compounds

Type of vibration	Position of absorption	
	cm^{-1}	μm
aryl C—H	3030	3.3
aryl C—C (four peaks)	1430–1670	6.0–7.0

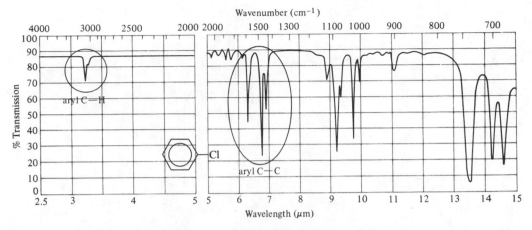

Figure 10.1. Infrared spectrum of chlorobenzene.

the second peak is a barely visible shoulder (Figure 10.1). In this spectrum, the third and fourth peaks are quite evident; however, in some spectra, the fourth peak at 1450 cm^{-1} (6.90 μm) is obscured by aliphatic CH_2 bending absorption.

The positions of substitution on a benzene ring may sometimes be determined by examination of the infrared spectrum. Differently substituted benzene rings give characteristic absorption at about 670–900 cm^{-1} (11–15 μm). The patterns observed are summarized in Table 10.4. Figure 10.2 (page 460) shows infrared spectra of the three isomeric chlorotoluenes. By comparison of these spectra with Table 10.4, you can see how the absorption in the fingerprint region may be used. Also compare these spectra with that of chlorobenzene in Figure 10.1.

STUDY PROBLEM

10.2 Which of the two infrared spectra (A or B) in Figure 10.3 (page 461) is that of a substituted benzene? Is the substituted benzene monosubstituted or disubstituted?

Table 10.4. **The C—H Bending Absorption of Substituted Benzenes**

Substitution	Appearance	Position of absorption	
		cm^{-1}	μm
monosubstituted	two peaks	730–770	12.9–13.7
		690–710	14.0–14.4
o-disubstituted	one peak	735–770	12.9–13.6
m-disubstituted	three peaks	860–900	11.1–11.6
		750–810	12.3-13.3
		680–725	13.7-14.7
p-disubstituted	one peak	800–860	11.6-12.5

Aromaticity, Benzene, and Substituted Benzenes

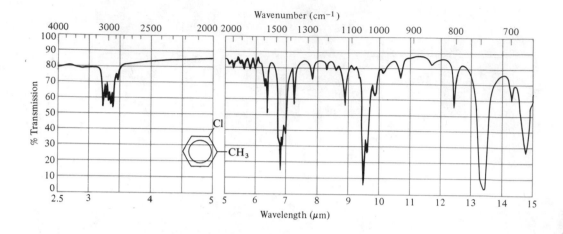

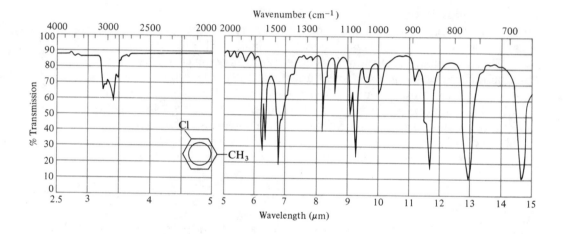

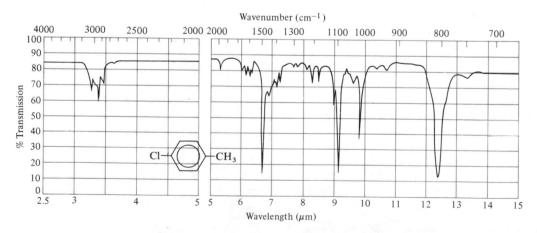

Figure 10.2. Infrared spectra for *o*-, *m*-, and *p*-chlorotoluene.

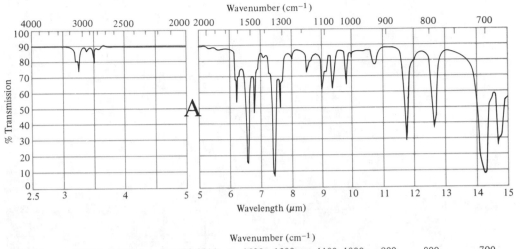

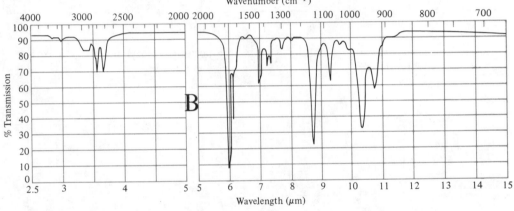

Figure 10.3. Infrared spectra for Problem 10.2.

B. Nmr Spectra

The nmr spectra of aromatic compounds are distinctive. Protons on an aromatic ring absorb downfield, between 6.5 ppm and 8 ppm. This downfield absorption arises from the ring current, which gives rise to a molecular magnetic field that deshields protons attached to the ring. The chemical shift for the protons on benzene itself is 7.27 ppm. Electronegative substituents on the ring shift the absorption of adjacent protons farther *downfield*, while electron-donating groups shift absorption *upfield* from that of unsubstituted benzene. Simple splitting patterns of aryl protons are sometimes observed (Figure 10.4); in many cases, however, the splitting patterns are complex and cannot be interpreted without the aid of a computer (Figure 10.5).

Benzylic protons are not as affected by the aromatic ring current as are ring protons; their absorption is observed farther upfield, in the region of 2.3 ppm. (See the nmr spectrum of toluene in Figure 10.4.)

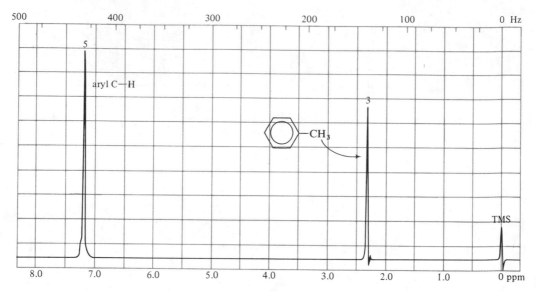

Figure 10.4. Nmr spectrum of toluene, showing the positions of aryl and benzyl C—H absorption.

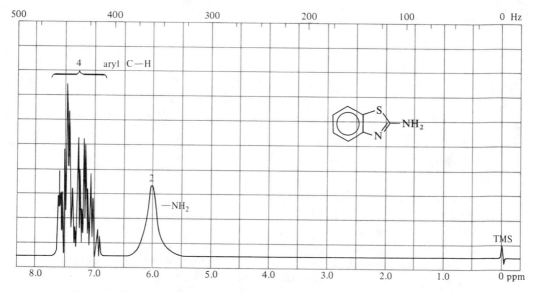

Figure 10.5. Nmr spectrum of 2-aminobenzothiazole, showing extensive splitting in the aromatic region.

STUDY PROBLEM

10.3 Figure 10.6 shows two nmr spectra (without the relative areas under the peaks). One spectrum is that of *p*-chloroaniline, while the other is that of *p*-iodoanisole (p-IC$_6$H$_4$OCH$_3$). On the basis of the chemical shifts (compared to the chemical shift of benzene protons), assign structures to the two spectra.

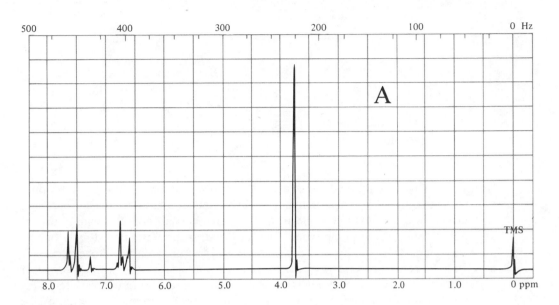

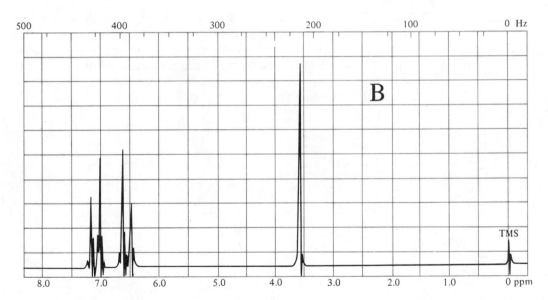

Figure 10.6. Nmr spectra of *p*-chloroaniline and *p*-iodoanisole for Problem 10.3.

Section 10.4

Stability of the Benzene Ring

The heat of hydrogenation of cyclohexene is 28.6 kcal/mole. If benzene contained three alternating single and double bonds without any pi-electron delocalization, we would expect its heat of hydrogenation to be 3 × 28.6, or 85.8, kcal/mole. However, benzene liberates only 49.8 kcal/mole of energy when it is hydrogenated. (See Figure 10.7, page 465.)

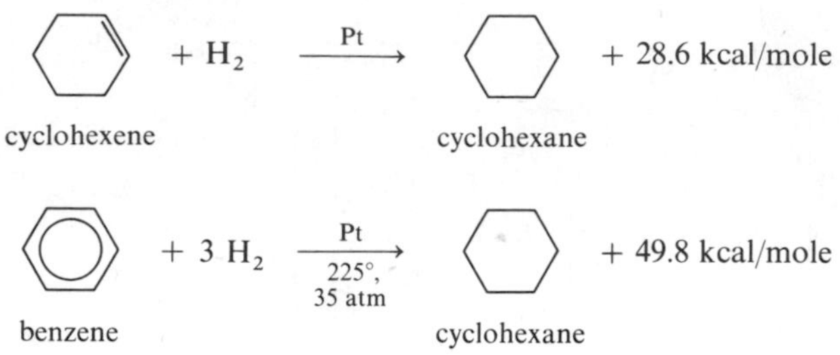

Aromaticity, Benzene, and Substituted Benzenes

$$\text{cyclohexene} + H_2 \xrightarrow{\text{Pt}} \text{cyclohexane} + 28.6 \text{ kcal/mole}$$

$$\text{benzene} + 3 H_2 \xrightarrow[\substack{225°, \\ 35 \text{ atm}}]{\text{Pt}} \text{cyclohexane} + 49.8 \text{ kcal/mole}$$

The hydrogenation of benzene liberates 36 kcal/mole less energy than would be liberated by the hydrogenation of the hypothetical cyclohexatriene. Therefore, benzene, with delocalized pi electrons, contains 36 kcal/mole less energy than it would contain if the pi electrons were localized in three isolated double bonds. This difference in energy between benzene and the imaginary cyclohexatriene is called the **resonance energy** of benzene. The resonance energy is the energy lost (stability gained) by the complete delocalization of electrons in the pi system. It is a measure of the added stability of the aromatic system compared to that of the localized system.

What does the resonance energy of benzene mean in terms of chemical reactivity? It means that more energy is required for a reaction in which the aromatic character of the ring is lost. Hydrogenation is one example of such a reaction (see Figure 10.7). Whereas an alkene can be hydrogenated at room temperature under atmospheric pressure, benzene required high temperature and high pressure. Also, benzene does not undergo most reactions that are typical of alkenes.

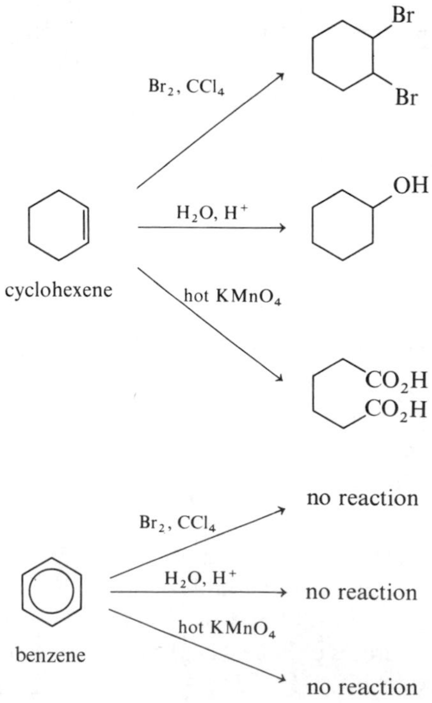

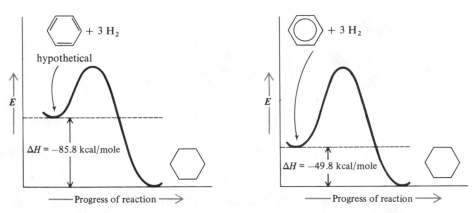

Figure 10.7. Energy diagrams for the hydrogenation of cyclohexatriene (hypothetical) and benzene.

Section 10.5

The Bonding in Benzene

Although benzene was discovered in 1825 and its molecular formula (C_6H_6) was soon determined, it was not until 1865 that Kekulé proposed a hexagonal structure. In 1872, this structure was modified to the familiar resonance structures that are still commonly used to represent the structure of benzene.

benzene in 1865   benzene in 1872

The Kekulé structures do not truly explain the stability of benzene, nor the inability of benzene to undergo reactions typical of alkenes. Until the application of quantum mechanics to the structure of benzene (in the 1930's), benzene remained an enigma to chemists.

Benzene has six sp^2 carbons in a ring. The ring is planar, and each carbon atom has a p orbital perpendicular to this plane. Figure 2.23 (page 66) shows a representation of the p orbitals of benzene and how they overlap in the lowest-energy bonding molecular orbital.

Overlap of six atomic p orbitals leads to the formation of six π molecular orbitals. When we look at all six possible π molecular orbitals of benzene (Figure 10.8), we see that our representation of the aromatic pi cloud as a double donut represents only one of the six molecular orbitals, π_1. In the π_1 orbital, all six p orbitals of benzene are in phase and overlap equally; this orbital is of lowest energy because it has no nodes between carbon nuclei.

The π_2 orbital and the π_3 orbital each has one node. These two bonding orbitals are degenerate (equal in energy) and of higher energy than the π_1 molecular orbital. Benzene, with six p electrons, has the π_1, π_2, and π_3 orbitals each filled with a pair of electrons. These are the bonding orbitals of benzene.

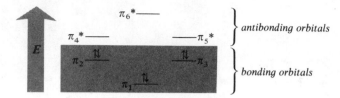

Along with the three bonding orbitals in benzene, there are three antibonding orbitals. Two of these antibonding orbitals ($\pi_4{}^*$ and $\pi_5{}^*$) have two nodes each, and the highest-energy orbital ($\pi_6{}^*$) has three nodes. Recall that a node is a region of very low electron density. A molecular orbital with a node between nuclei is of higher energy than a molecular orbital without a node between nuclei. Note that as we progress from π_1 to $\pi_6{}^*$, the number of nodes increases; this is the reason that the energy associated with these orbitals increases.

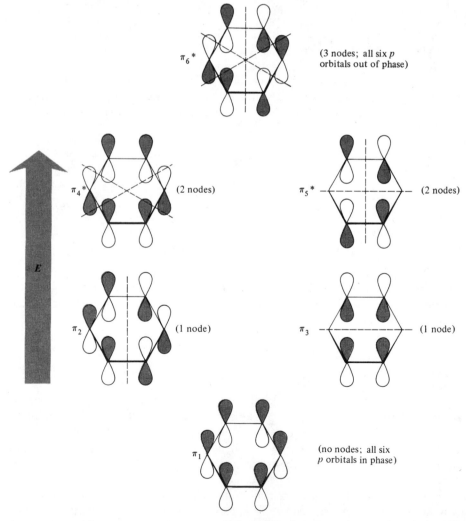

Figure 10.8.   The π orbitals in benzene. (Nodes are represented by dashed lines; the "missing orbitals" in π_3 and $\pi_5{}^*$ are a result of a node at the location of those orbitals.)

Section 10.6

What Is an Aromatic Compound?

Benzene is one member of a large class of aromatic compounds, compounds that are *substantially stabilized by pi-electron delocalization.* The resonance energy of an aromatic compound is a measure of its gain in stability. (The structural features that give rise to aromaticity will be discussed shortly.)

 is 36 kcal/mole more stable than the imaginary

 is 61 kcal/mole more stable than the imaginary

 is 22 kcal/mole more stable than the imaginary

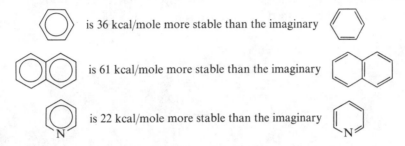

The most convenient way to determine if a compound is aromatic is by the position of absorption in the nmr spectrum by protons attached to ring atoms. Protons attached to the outside of an aromatic ring are highly deshielded and absorb far downfield from most other protons, usually beyond 7 ppm.

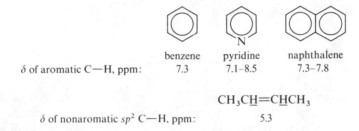

	benzene	pyridine	naphthalene
δ of aromatic C—H, ppm:	7.3	7.1–8.5	7.3–7.8

$CH_3C\underline{H}{=}C\underline{H}CH_3$

δ of nonaromatic sp^2 C—H, ppm: 5.3

STUDY PROBLEM

10.4 The nmr spectrum of cyclooctatetraene shows only a singlet at 5.7 ppm. On the basis of this piece of data, would you say that cyclooctatetraene is aromatic or not?

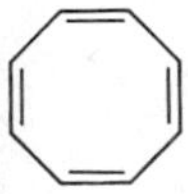

cyclooctatetraene

Section 10.7

Requirements for Aromaticity

What structural features are necessary for a molecule to be aromatic? The first two criteria are that the molecule must be *cyclic* and *planar*. Third, each atom of the ring or rings must have a *p orbital perpendicular to the plane of the ring.* If a system does not fit these criteria, there cannot be complete delocalization of the *p* electrons. Whether or not these three criteria are met may often be deduced from inspection of the formula of an organic compound. The valence-bond formula of an aromatic compound usually shows a ring with alternating single and double bonds. There are cases, however, of cyclic organic compounds with alternating single and double bonds that are *not* aromatic. Cyclooctatetraene is such a compound. Cyclooctatetraene undergoes addition reactions with the hydrogen halides and with the halogens. These reactions are typical of alkenes, but are not typical of benzene and other aromatic compounds. Cyclooctatetraene is not planar, but has been shown to be shaped like a tub.

cyclooctatetraene
a cyclic conjugated tetraene: not aromatic

Why is cyclooctatetraene not aromatic? To answer this question, we must proceed to a fourth criterion for aromaticity, a criterion usually called **the Hückel rule**.

A.   The Hückel Rule

In 1931, the German chemist Erich Hückel proposed that, to be aromatic, a monocyclic (one ring), planar compound must have **$4n + 2$ pi electrons**, where *n* is an integer. According to the Hückel rule, a ring with 2, 6, 10, or 14 pi electrons may be aromatic, but a ring with 8 or 12 pi electrons may not. Cyclooctatetraene (with 8 pi electrons) does not fit the Hückel rule for aromaticity.

B.   Why 4n + 2?

Why can a monocyclic compound with six or ten pi electrons be aromatic, but not a compound with eight pi electrons? The answer is found in the number of pi electrons versus the number of pi orbitals available. To be aromatic, a molecule must have *all pi electrons paired*. This system provides the maximum and complete overlap required for aromatic stabilization. If some pi orbitals are *not* filled (that is, there are unpaired pi electrons), overlap is not maximized, and the compound is not aromatic. Benzene has six pi electrons and three bonding pi orbitals. The three bonding pi orbitals are filled to capacity, all pi electrons are paired, and benzene is aromatic.

Let us look at the π molecular orbitals for cyclooctatetraene. This compound has eight *p* orbitals on the ring. Overlap of eight *p* orbitals would result in eight π molecular orbitals.

$$\pi_8^* \underline{\quad\quad} \left.\right\} \text{antibonding}$$

$$\pi_6^* \underline{\quad\quad} \quad\quad \underline{\quad\quad} \pi_7^*$$

$$\pi_4 \underline{\uparrow} \quad\quad \underline{\uparrow} \pi_5 \quad\} \text{nonbonding (not filled)}$$

$$\pi_2 \underline{\uparrow\downarrow} \quad\quad \underline{\uparrow\downarrow} \pi_3$$

$$\pi_1 \underline{\uparrow\downarrow} \quad\quad \left.\right\} \text{bonding}$$

E

If cyclooctatetraene were planar, the π_1, π_2, and π_3 orbitals would be filled with six of the pi electrons. The remaining two electrons would be found, one each, in the degenerate π_4 and π_5 orbitals. The pi electrons of cyclooctatetraene would not all be paired, and overlap would not be maximal.

C. The Ions of Cyclopentadiene

Cyclopentadiene is a conjugated diene and is not aromatic. The principal reason that cyclopentadiene is not aromatic is that one of the carbon atoms is sp^3, not sp^2. This sp^3 carbon has no p orbital available for bonding; however, removal of a hydrogen ion from cyclopentadiene changes the hybridization of that carbon so that it is sp^2 and has a p orbital containing a pair of electrons.

cyclopentadiene   cyclopentadienyl anion

The cyclopentadiene cation also has all its carbon atoms in the sp^2 state. (The orbital pictures for the ions of cyclopentadiene are shown in Figure 10.9.)

cyclopentadienyl cation

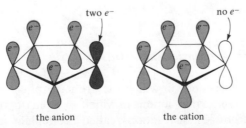

the anion   the cation

Figure 10.9. Orbital pictures of the anion and the cation of cyclopentadiene. (Each carbon is sp^2-hybridized and is also attached to one H.)

Would either or both of these ions be aromatic? Either ion would have five molecular π orbitals (from five p orbitals, one per carbon). The cyclopentadienyl anion, with six pi electrons ($4n + 2$), has three pi orbitals filled and all pi electrons paired. *The anion is aromatic.* The cation, however, would have only four p electrons ($4n$) in the three orbitals. The pi electrons would *not* all be paired, and there would *not* be maximum overlap. *The cation is not aromatic.*

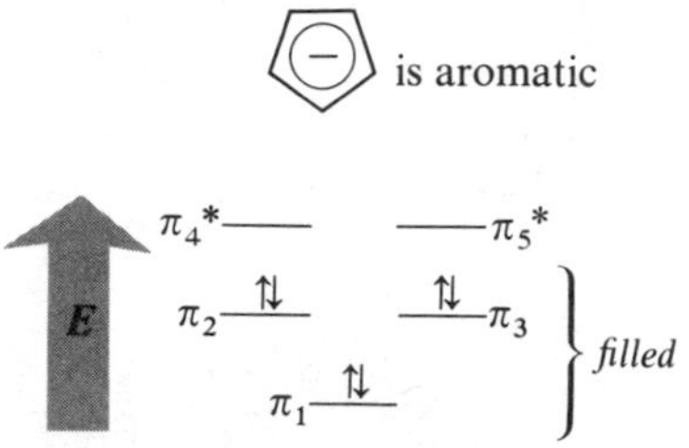

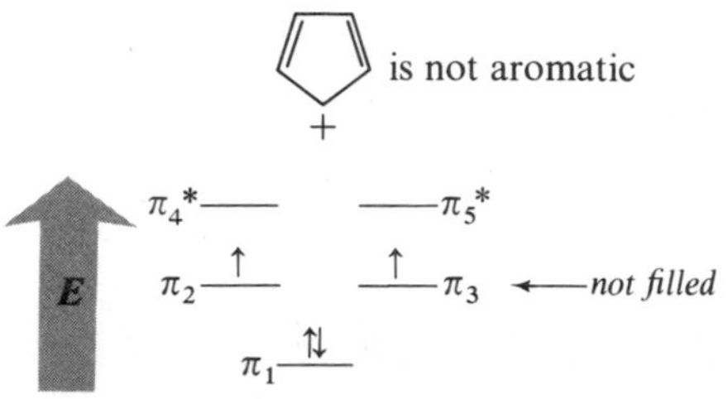

Cyclopentadiene is a weak acid because its anion is aromatic and thus is resonance-stabilized. Although cyclopentadiene is not nearly as strong an acid as a carboxylic acid, it is a proton donor in the presence of a strong base. (The pK_a of cyclopentadiene is 16, similar to that of an alcohol. By contrast, the pK_a of cyclopentane is about 50.)

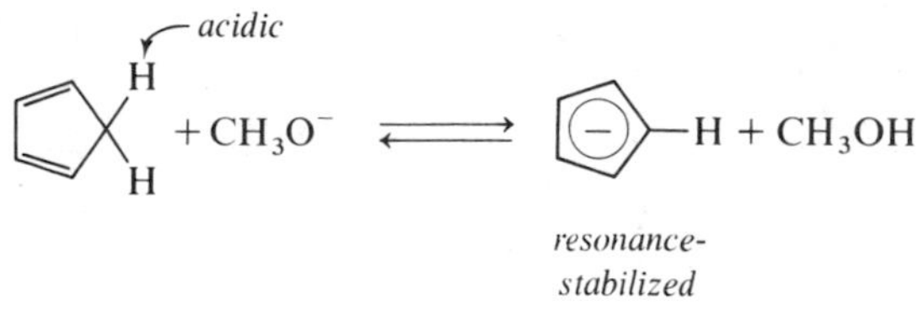

STUDY PROBLEM

10.5 Which of the following compounds or ions could be aromatic?

(a)   (b)   (c)

Section 10.8

Electrophilic Aromatic Substitution

Benzene resists reactions in which the aromatic pi cloud is lost. However, benzene undergoes a series of reactions in which an atom or group replaces one of the ring hydrogen atoms. These reactions, called **electrophilic aromatic substitution reactions**, are the result of attack of an electrophile on the ring and subsequent loss of a proton.

Chlorination:

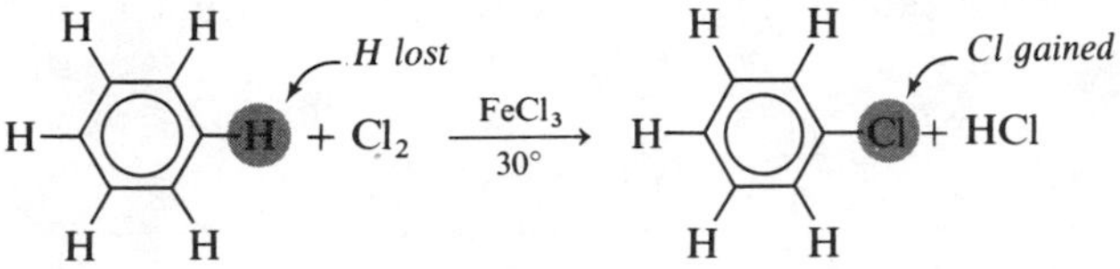

chlorobenzene
90%

Nitration:

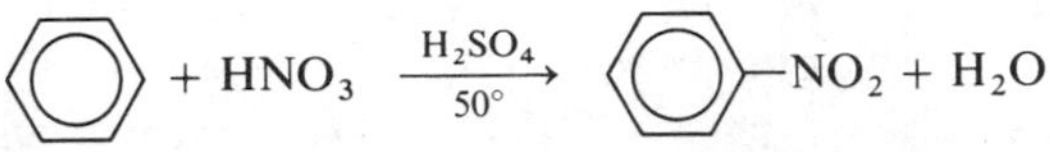

$$+ HNO_3 \xrightarrow[50°]{H_2SO_4} -NO_2 + H_2O$$

nitrobenzene
85%

Alkylation:

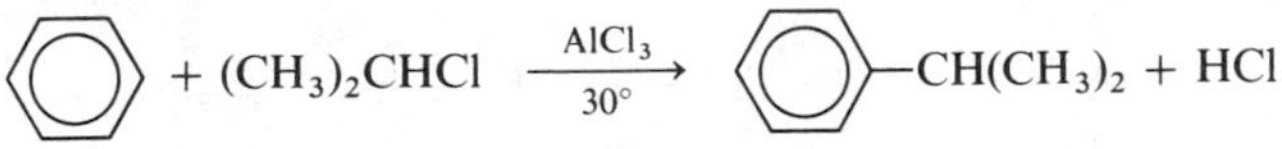

$$+ (CH_3)_2CHCl \xrightarrow[30°]{AlCl_3} -CH(CH_3)_2 + HCl$$

isopropylbenzene
(cumene)

Acylation:

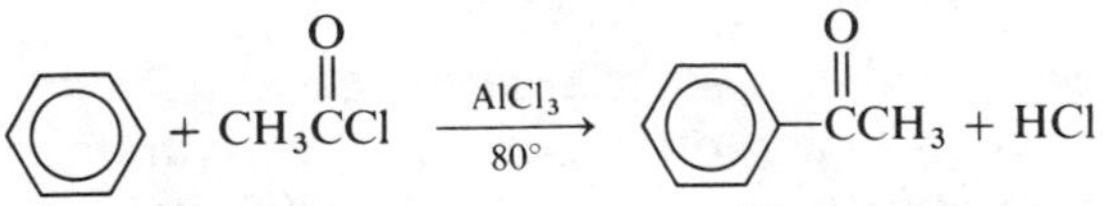

$$+ CH_3\overset{O}{\overset{\|}{C}}Cl \xrightarrow[80°]{AlCl_3} \overset{O}{\overset{\|}{C}}CH_3 + HCl$$

acetophenone
97%

Sulfonation:

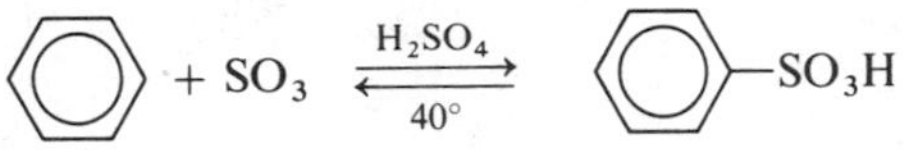

$$+ SO_3 \underset{40°}{\overset{H_2SO_4}{\rightleftarrows}} -SO_3H$$

benzenesulfonic acid
50%

The preceding examples show **monosubstitution** of the benzene ring. Further substitution is possible:

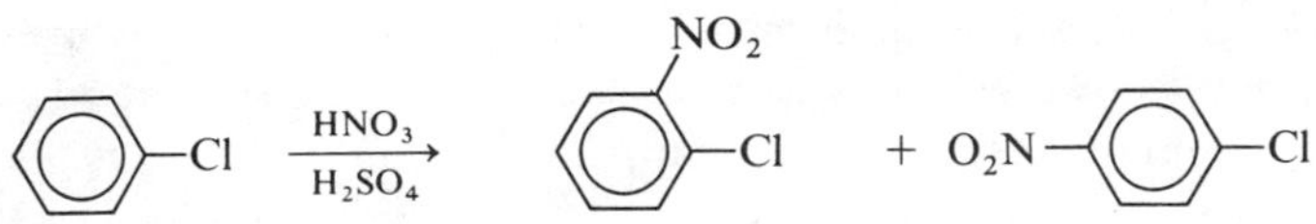

chlorobenzene   *o*-chloronitrobenzene   *p*-chloronitrobenzene

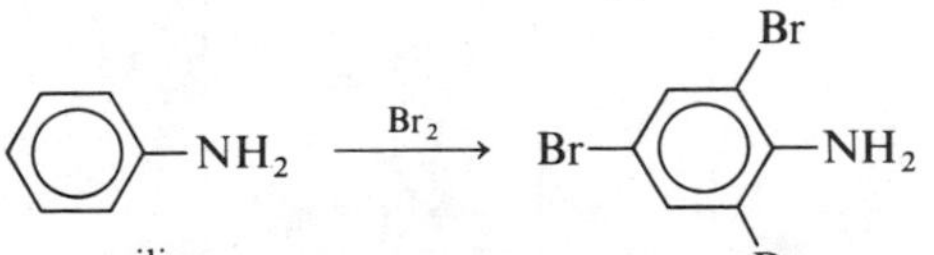

aniline

2,4,6-tribromoaniline

We will first consider the mechanism of monosubstitution (that is, the first substitution), and then the mechanism of further substitution, leading to disubstituted and more highly substituted benzenes.

Section 10.9

The First Substitution

In each of the monosubstitution reactions shown, a Lewis acid is used as a catalyst. The Lewis acid undergoes reaction with the reagent (such as Br_2 or HNO_3) to generate an electrophile, which is the actual agent of substitution. For example, $AlCl_3$ can remove a chloride ion from a secondary or tertiary alkyl chloride to yield a carbocation. Or H_2SO_4 (a very strong acid) can remove a *hydroxyl* group from nitric acid to yield the nitronium ion, $^+NO_2$.

Formation of electrophiles by Lewis acids:

$$R\text{—}Cl + AlCl_3 \longrightarrow R^+ + AlCl_4^-$$

$$HO\text{—}NO_2 + H_2SO_4 \longrightarrow {}^+NO_2 + HSO_4^- + H_2O$$

The electrophile is attracted to the pi electrons of benzene and may displace a proton to give the substitution product.

A. Aromatic Bromination

We will discuss the mechanism of **aromatic bromination** first. The catalyst in aromatic bromination is $FeBr_3$ (often generated *in situ* from Fe and Br_2). The function of the catalyst is to generate the electrophile Br^+. This may occur by direct reaction and fission of the Br—Br bond. More likely, Br_2 is not completely cleaved upon reaction with the $FeBr_3$ catalyst, but is polarized. (For the sake of simplicity, we will show Br^+ as the electrophile.)

$$Br\text{—}Br + FeBr_3 \rightleftharpoons \underset{polarized}{\overset{\delta+ \quad \delta-}{Br\text{—}Br\text{---}FeBr_3}} \rightleftharpoons \underset{cleaved}{Br^+ + FeBr_4^-}$$

electrophilic

When an electrophile such as Br^+ collides with the electrons of the aromatic pi cloud, a pair of the pi electrons forms a sigma bond with the electrophile. The result is a type of carbocation called a **benzenonium ion**. This step is the slow step, and therefore the rate-determining step, in the reaction. (We will use Kekulé formulas here. Also, we will show the benzene hydrogens so that you can count electrons and see more clearly what is happening.)

Step 1 (slow):

benzene

intermediate
benzenonium ion

Like other carbocations, the benzenonium ion undergoes rapid reaction; it loses a proton to a base in the reaction mixture. The product is bromobenzene, a product in which the aromatic character of the ring has been recaptured.

Step 2 (*fast*):

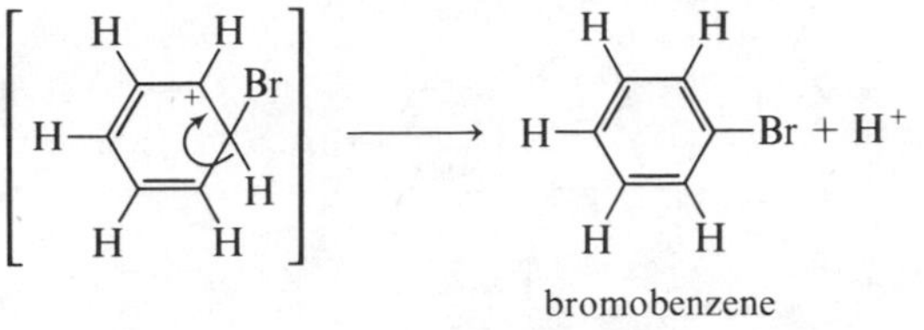

bromobenzene

The third step in the reaction mechanism (which is concurrent with the loss of H^+) is the regeneration of the Lewis acid catalyst. The proton released in Step 2 undergoes reaction with the $FeBr_4^-$ ion to yield HBr and $FeBr_3$.

$$H^+ + FeBr_4^- \rightleftharpoons FeBr_3 + HBr$$

Ignoring the function of the catalyst, we may write an equation for the overall reaction of the aromatic bromination of benzene:

benzene   intermediate   bromobenzene
              benzenonium ion

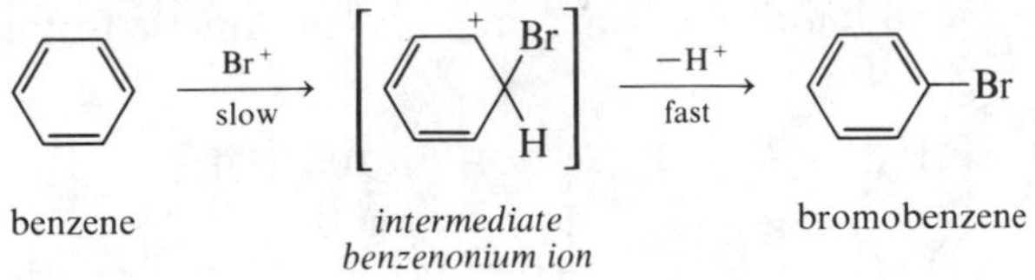

Sample Problem

Write resonance structures for the intermediate benzenonium ion in the aromatic bromination of benzene.

Solution:

$\left(\text{The intermediate is often represented as}\right.$ $\left.\right)$

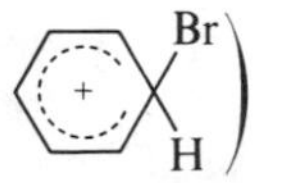

Note the similarity between an electrophilic aromatic substitution reaction and an E1 reaction. In an E1 reaction, an intermediate carbocation eliminates a proton to form an alkene.

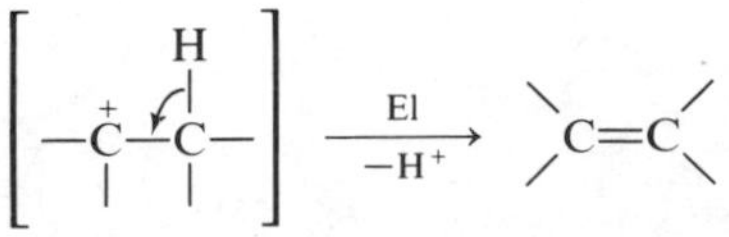

An alkyl carbocation also can undergo reaction with an anion in an S_N1 reaction. However, the intermediate benzenonium ion does *not* undergo this reaction with an anion. The addition of the anion would destroy the aromaticity and the resultant resonance-stabilization of the benzene ring.

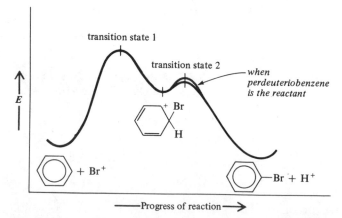

B.   Isotope Effect

Recall from Section 5.10A that a C—D bond is stronger than a C—H bond. If the breaking of a C—H bond is part of the rate-determining step of a reaction, the rate of reaction for a C—D compound is slower than the rate for the corresponding C—H compound.

If, as we have said, the rate-determining step of electrophilic aromatic substitution is the formation of the benzenonium ion, then reaction of deuteriated benzene would proceed at the *same rate* as the reaction of normal benzene. Experiments have shown this to be true; benzene and perdeuteriobenzene undergo electrophilic bromination at the same rate, and no kinetic isotope effect is observed.

Figure 10.10.   Energy diagram for the bromination of benzene.

Step 2 in the reaction mechanism, loss of H^+ or D^+, does involve breaking of the C—H or C—D bond. Undoubtedly, the rate of elimination of D^+ is slower than that of H^+, but in either case the second step is so fast compared to Step 1 that no change in overall rate of reaction is observed. This fact may be illustrated with an energy diagram (see Figure 10.10).

C.   *Mechanisms of Other Substitutions*

Other electrophilic aromatic substitution reactions proceed through a series of steps similar to those in aromatic bromination.

Nitration:

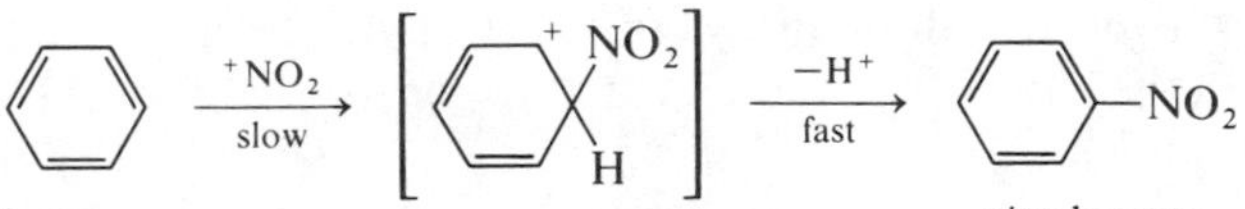

benzene   a benzenonium   nitrobenzene
                 ion

Alkylation:

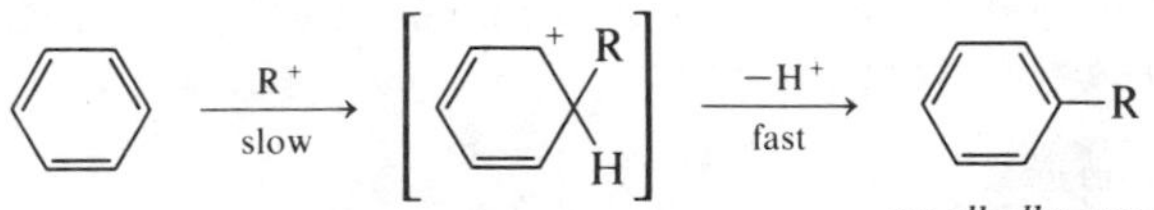

an alkylbenzene

Sulfonation:

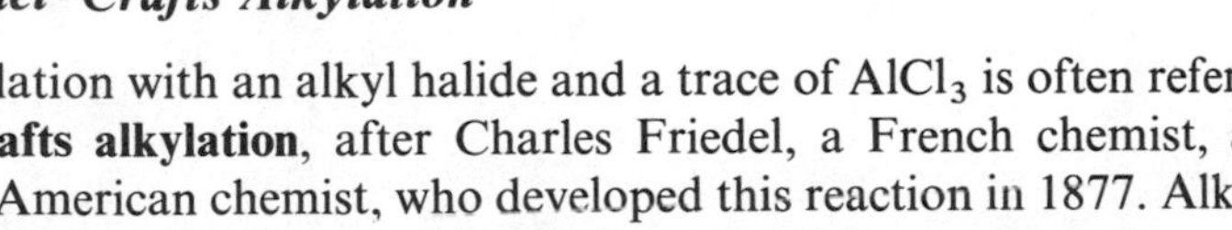

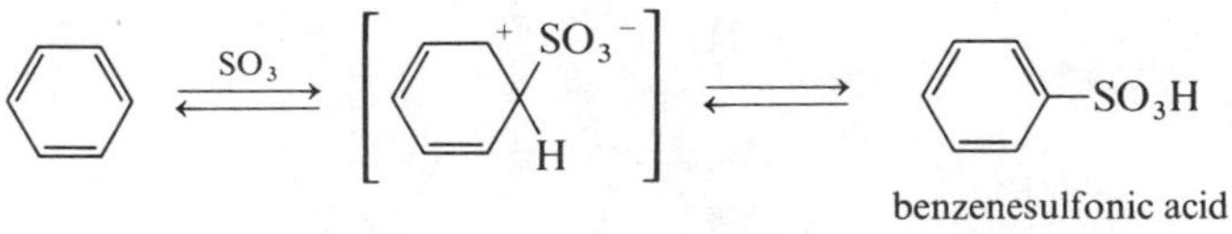

benzenesulfonic acid

D.   *Friedel–Crafts Alkylation*

Alkylation with an alkyl halide and a trace of $AlCl_3$ is often referred to as a **Friedel–Crafts alkylation**, after Charles Friedel, a French chemist, and James Crafts, an American chemist, who developed this reaction in 1877. Alkylation deserves special mention because it is widely used and because certain problems may arise in its use.

One problem in Friedel–Crafts alkylations is that the substitution of an alkyl group on the benzene ring activates the ring so that a *second* substitution may also occur. (We will discuss ring activation and second substitutions later in this chapter.) To suppress this second reaction, an excess of the aromatic compound is commonly used.

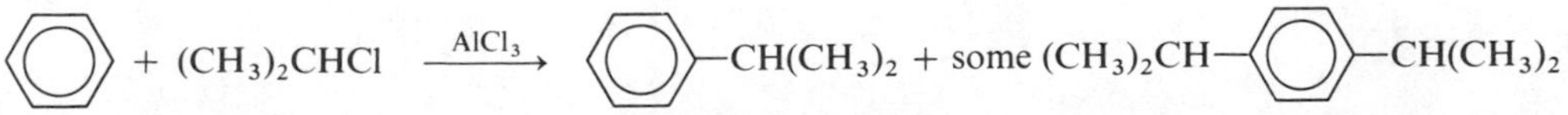

excess   isopropyl   isopropylbenzene   *p*-diisopropylbenzene
              chloride

Another problem in Friedel–Crafts alkylations is that the attacking electro-phile may undergo rearrangement by 1,2-shifts of H or R.

$$\text{C}_6\text{H}_6 + \text{CH}_3\text{CH}_2\text{CH}_2\text{Cl} \xrightarrow[25°]{\text{AlCl}_3} \text{C}_6\text{H}_5\text{--CH(CH}_3)_2 + \text{C}_6\text{H}_5\text{--CH}_2\text{CH}_2\text{CH}_3$$

n-propyl chloride   isopropylbenzene   *n*-propylbenzene
70%   30%

$$\text{C}_6\text{H}_6 + \text{CH}_3\overset{\text{CH}_3}{\underset{}{\text{CHCH}_2\text{Cl}}} \xrightarrow[25°]{\text{AlCl}_3} \text{C}_6\text{H}_5\text{--C(CH}_3)_3 \text{ and } no \text{ C}_6\text{H}_5\text{--CH}_2\text{CH(CH}_3)_2$$

isobutyl chloride   *t*-butylbenzene   isobutylbenzene
100%

The rearrangements shown are of primary alkyl halides, which do not readily form carbocations. In these cases, reaction probably proceeds through an RX—AlCl$_3$ complex.

$$\text{CH}_3\text{CH}_2\text{CH}_2\text{--Cl} + \text{AlCl}_3 \rightleftharpoons \text{CH}_3\text{CH}_2\overset{\delta+}{\text{CH}_2}\text{--}\overset{\delta-}{\text{Cl}}\text{---AlCl}_3$$

n-propyl chloride   *a complex*

This complex may (1) undergo reaction with benzene to yield the nonrearranged product, or (2) undergo rearrangement to a secondary or tertiary carbocation, which leads to the rearranged product.

No rearrangement:

n-propylbenzene

Rearrangement:

$$\text{CH}_3\overset{\overset{\text{H}}{|}}{\text{CHCH}_2}\text{--Cl} \text{---AlCl}_3 \xrightarrow{-\text{AlCl}_4^-} [\text{CH}_3\overset{+}{\text{CHCH}_3}] \xrightarrow{} \text{C}_6\text{H}_5\text{--CH(CH}_3)_2$$

a 2° carbocation   isopropylbenzene

Friedel–Crafts alkylations may also be accomplished with alkenes in the presence of HCl and AlCl$_3$. The mechanism is similar to alkylation with an alkyl halide and proceeds by way of the more stable carbocation.

$$\text{CH}_3\text{CH}=\text{CH}_2 + \text{HCl} + \text{AlCl}_3 \longrightarrow [\text{CH}_3\overset{+}{\text{CHCH}_3}] + \text{AlCl}_4^-$$

propene   *more stable*
2° carbocation

isopropylbenzene
85%

Sample Problem

Predict the major product of the reaction of neopentyl chloride and benzene with $AlCl_3$ catalyst.

Solution:

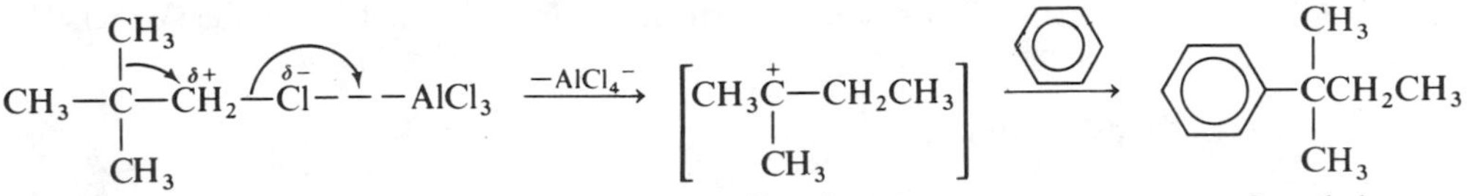

rearrangement of complex — *a 3° carbocation* — 2-methyl-2-phenylbutane

Sample Problem

Suggest a synthesis for diphenylmethane from benzene.

Solution:

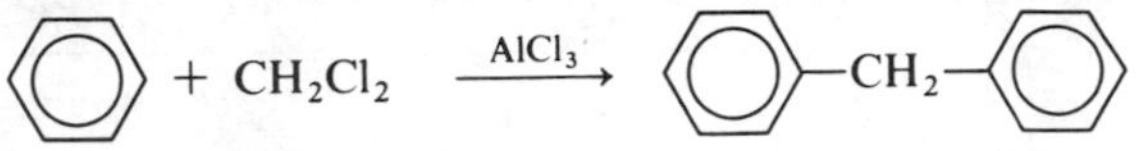

excess — methylene chloride — diphenylmethane

E. *Friedel–Crafts Acylation*

The RCO— group or the ArCO— group is called an **acyl group**. Substitution of an acyl group on an aromatic ring by reaction with an acid halide is called an **aromatic acylation reaction**, or a **Friedel–Crafts acylation**. This reaction is often the method of choice for preparing an aryl ketone. The carbonyl group of the aryl ketone may be reduced to a CH_2 group (Section 11.14C). By the combination of a Friedel–Crafts acylation and reduction, an alkylbenzene may be prepared without rearrangement of the alkyl group.

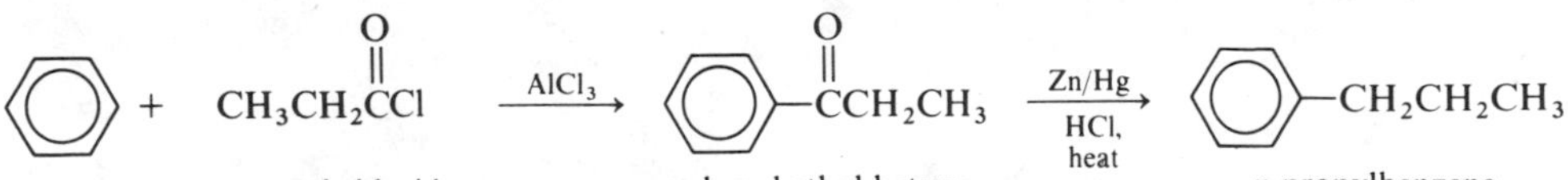

propanoyl chloride *an acid halide* — phenyl ethyl ketone 90% — *n*-propylbenzene 80%

The mechanism of the Friedel-Crafts acylation reaction is similar to that of the other electrophilic aromatic substitution reactions. The attacking electrophile may be either an **acylium ion** or a complex between the acid chloride and $ALCl_3$. In either case, a partially positive carbon is the electrophilic center that attacks the benzene ring.

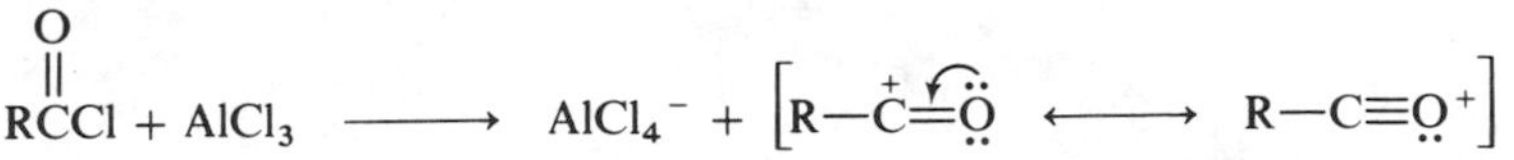

an acylium ion

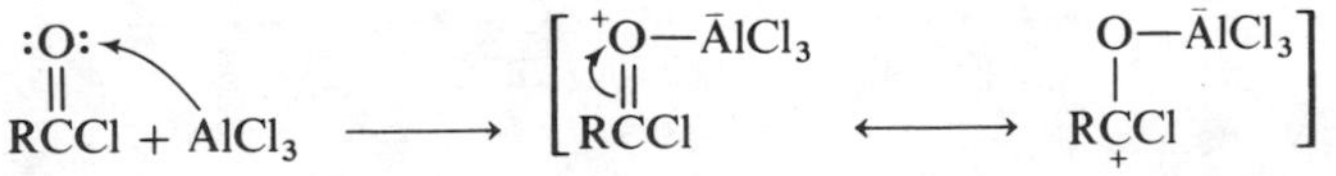

a complex

STUDY PROBLEMS

10.6 Give mechanisms for the reactions of the two preceding electrophiles (the acylium ion and the acid chloride–aluminum chloride complex) with benzene to yield ketones.

10.7 Predict the major organic products (structures and names) of the reaction of benzene with the following mixtures:

(a) $CH_3Cl + AlCl_3$ (b) $CH_3CH_2CH_2CH_2Cl + AlCl_3$

(c) $(CH_3)_2CHCH_2\overset{\displaystyle O}{\overset{\displaystyle \|}{C}}Cl + AlCl_3$

10.8 Show by equations how the following products could be obtained by electrophilic substitution reactions with benzene: (a) *t*-butylbenzene, and   (b) isobutylbenzene.

F. Sulfonation

The sulfonation of benzene with fuming sulfuric acid ($H_2SO_4 + SO_3$) yields benzenesulfonic acid. Unlike the other electrophilic substitution reactions of benzene, sulfonation is a readily reversible reaction and shows a moderate kinetic isotope effect. Perdeuteriobenzene undergoes sulfonation at about half the rate of ordinary benzene.

From these data, we conclude that the intermediate benzenonium ion in sulfonation can revert to benzene or go on to benzenesulfonic acid with almost equal ease (or the reaction would not be readily reversible). Also, the rates of reaction of Step 1 and Step 2 must be more nearly equal than for other electro-

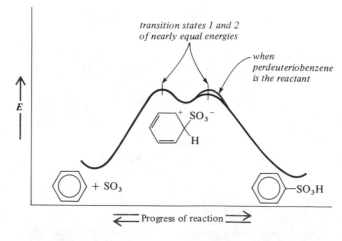

Figure 10.11.   Energy diagram for the sulfonation of benzene.

philic aromatic substitution reactions (or the reaction would not show a kinetic isotope effect).

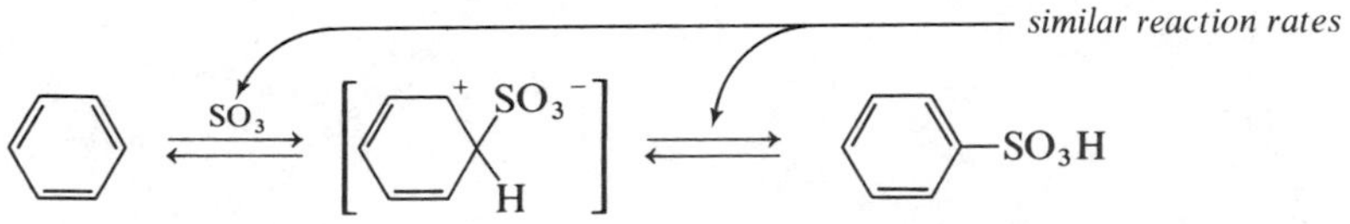

benzenesulfonic acid

Figure 10.11 shows an energy diagram for the sulfonation of benzene. Note that the energies of the transition states of Steps 1 and 2 are roughly the same.

Section 10.10

The Second Substitution

A substituted benzene may undergo substitution of a second group. Some substituted benzenes undergo reaction *more easily* than benzene itself, while other substituted benzenes undergo reaction *less easily*. For example, aniline undergoes electrophilic substitution a million times faster than benzene. Nitrobenzene, on the other hand, undergoes reaction at approximately one-millionth the rate of benzene! (Rather than allowing a reaction to proceed over a much longer period of time, a chemist commonly uses stronger reagents and higher temperatures for a less reactive compound.)

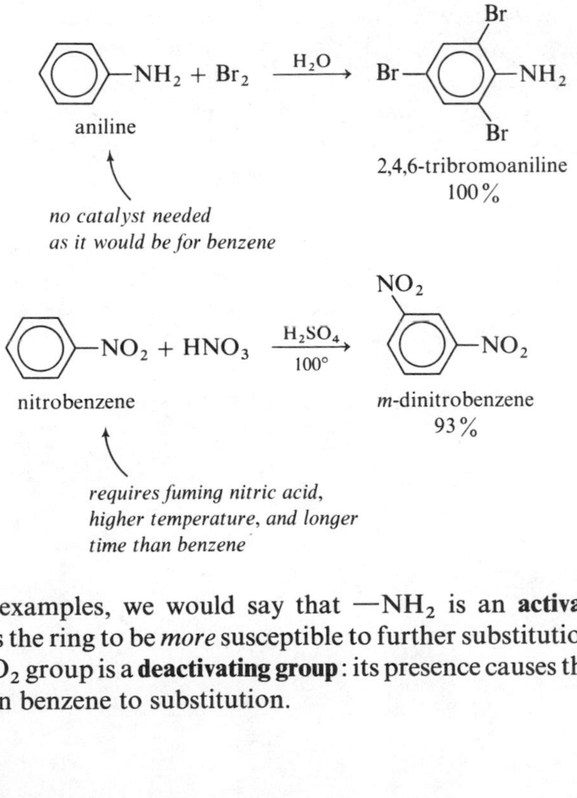

aniline

no catalyst needed as it would be for benzene

2,4,6-tribromoaniline
100%

nitrobenzene

requires fuming nitric acid, higher temperature, and longer time than benzene

m-dinitrobenzene
93%

In these examples, we would say that —NH_2 is an **activating group**: its presence causes the ring to be *more* susceptible to further substitution. On the other hand, the —NO_2 group is a **deactivating group**: its presence causes the ring to be *less* susceptible than benzene to substitution.

Besides the differences in reaction rates of substituted benzenes, the *position* of the second attack varies:

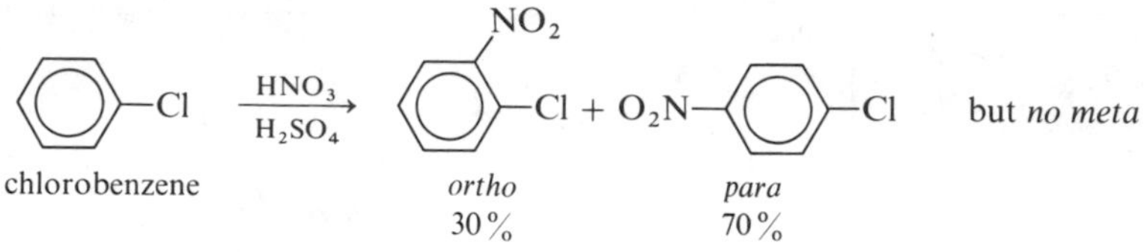

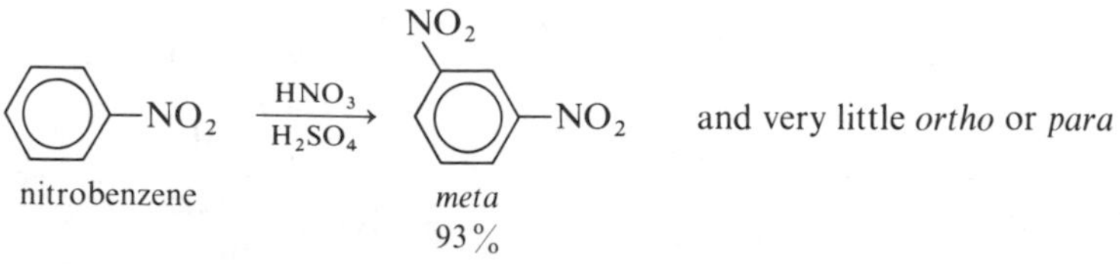

chlorobenzene   *ortho*   *para*   but *no meta*

30%   70%

nitrobenzene   *meta*   and very little *ortho* or *para*

93%

STUDY PROBLEM

10.9 If chlorobenzene were nitrated at equal rates at each possible position of substitution, what would be the ratio of *o-*, *m-*, and *p*-products?

Chlorobenzene is nitrated in the *ortho-* and *para*-positions, but not in the *meta*-position. However, nitrobenzene undergoes a second nitration in the *meta*-position; very little substitution at the *ortho-* or *para*-positions occurs. These examples show that the nature of the incoming group has no effect on its own positioning on the ring. The position of second substitution is determined by the group that is already on the ring.

To differentiate between these two types of substituent, Cl is called an ***ortho*, *para*-director**, while NO$_2$ is called a ***meta*-director**. Any substituent on a benzene ring is either an *o,p*-director or a *m*-director (see Table 10.5).

Table 10.6 contains a summary of commonly encountered benzene substituents classified as *activating* or *deactivating* and as *o,p-directors* or *m-directors*. Note that all *o,p*-directors except the halogens are also activating groups. All *m*-directors are deactivating. Also note that all *o,p*-directors except aryl and alkyl

Table 10.5. *Orientation of the Nitro Group in Aromatic Nitration*

	Approximate percents of products		
Reactant	*o*	*p*	*m*
C_6H_5OH	50	50	—
$C_6H_5CH_3$	60	40	—
C_6H_5Cl	30	70	—
C_6H_5Br	40	60	—
$C_6H_5NO_2$	6	—	94
$C_6H_5CO_2H$	20	—	80

Table 10.6. *Effect of the First Substituent on the Second Substitution*

	o,p-Directors	*m*-Directors (all deactivating)	
increasing activation (↑)	$-\ddot{N}H_2, -\ddot{N}HR, -\ddot{N}R_2$	$-\overset{\overset{\displaystyle O}{\|\|}}{C}R$	
	$-\ddot{O}H$	$-CO_2R$	
	$-\ddot{O}R$	$-SO_3H$	
		$-CHO$	
	$-\ddot{N}H\overset{\overset{\displaystyle O}{\|\|}}{C}R$	$-CO_2H$	increasing deactivation
	$-C_6H_5$ (aryl)	$-CN$	
	$-R$ (alkyl)	$-NO_2$	
	$-\ddot{\underset{..}{X}}:$ (*deactivating*)	$-NR_3{}^+$	(↓)

groups have an unshared pair of electrons on the atom attached to the ring. None of the *m*-directors have an unshared pair of electrons on the atom attached to the ring.

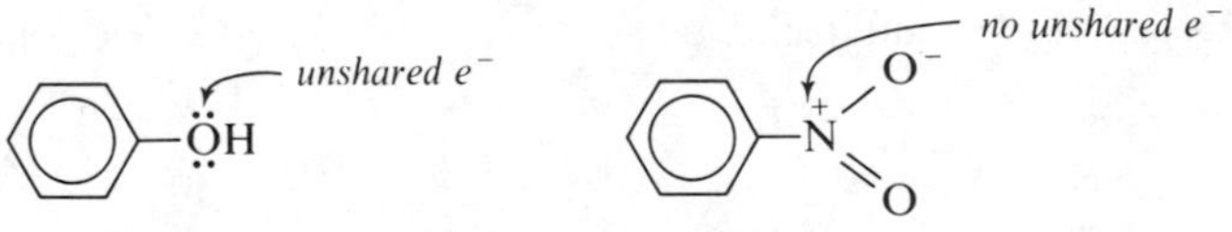

o,p-director,
activating

m-director,
deactivating

Sample Problem

What would be the major organic products of second substitution in each of the following reactions?

(a) C_6H_5Cl $\xrightarrow{HNO_3, H_2SO_4}$

(b) $C_6H_5NO_2$ $\xrightarrow{Br_2, FeBr_3}$

(c) C_6H_5OH $\xrightarrow{SO_3, H_2SO_4}$

(d) $C_6H_5CH_3$ $\xrightarrow[AlCl_3, HCl]{CH_2=CH_2}$

Solution:

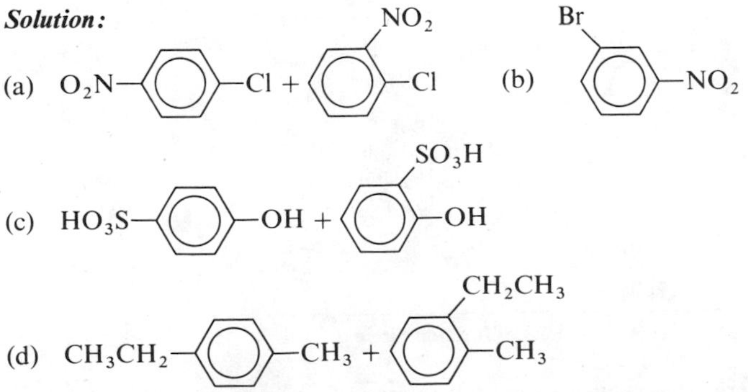

(a)

(b)

(c)

(d)

A. Mechanism of the Second Substitution with an o,p-Director

Why are most o,p-directors activating groups? Why do they direct incoming groups to the o- and p-positions? To answer these questions, let us consider aniline, a compound with the o,p-directing NH_2 group on the ring. The resonance structures for aniline show that the NH_2 group is *electron-releasing by resonance*, even though N is an electronegative atom.

unshared pair of e^- donated

The result of the resonance-stabilization of aniline is that the ring is partially negative and is highly attractive to an incoming electrophile. All positions (o-, m-, and p-) on the aniline ring are activated to electrophilic substitution; however, the o- and p-positions are more highly activated than the m-position. The resonance structures above show that the o- and p-positions carry partial negative charges, while the m-position does not.

The amino group in aniline activates the benzene ring toward substitution to such an extent that (1) no Lewis acid catalyst is needed, and (2) it is very difficult to obtain a monobromoaniline. Aniline quickly undergoes reaction to form the 2,4,6-tribromoaniline (both o-positions and the p-position brominated).

The mechanism of the bromination of aniline is similar to the mechanism of the bromination of benzene itself.

aniline   *a benzenonium ion*   *p*-bromoaniline

The difference between the bromination of aniline and that of benzene lies in the stabilization of the intermediate benzenonium ion. A substituted benzenonium ion is resonance-stabilized just as is the unsubstituted benzenonium ion, but in the case of aniline, the amino group can increase the stabilization. An increased stabilization of the intermediate means a transition state of lower energy in Step 1 (see Figure 10.12) and therefore a faster rate of reaction.

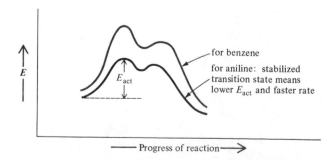

Figure 10.12.   Energy diagrams for the bromination of aniline and benzene.

Resonance structures for the p-intermediate:

added stabilization

In the intermediate for *m*-substitution, the nitrogen of the amino group cannot help share the positive charge. (Draw the Kekulé structures for the *m*-substituted intermediate and verify this statement for yourself.) Therefore, the intermediate for *m*-substitution is of higher energy than are the intermediates leading to either *o*- or *p*-substituted products. Because this intermediate is of higher energy, its transition state also has a higher energy, and the rate of reaction at the *m*-position is lower.

The amino group, along with —OH, —OR, —NHCOR, and phenyl groups, activates the benzene ring toward electrophilic substitution by donating a pair of electrons to the ring through resonance. Substitution occurs at the *o*- and *p*-positions because the group helps share the positive charge in the intermediate.

STUDY PROBLEMS

10.10 Give the resonance structures for the intermediate in the nitration of phenol to yield *o*-nitrophenol.

10.11 The benzene ring in acetanilide (Table 10.1, page 455) is *less* reactive toward electrophilic substitution than the ring in aniline. Suggest a reason for this lesser activation by the —NHCCH$_3$ group.
$$\overset{\displaystyle \|}{\underset{\displaystyle O}{}}$$

Halogens are different from the other *o*, *p*-directors. They direct an incoming group *ortho* or *para*, but they *deactivate* the ring to electrophilic substitution. A halogen substituent on the benzene ring directs an incoming group to the *o*- or *p*-position for the same reason the amino or hydroxyl group does. The halogen can donate electrons and help share the positive charge in the intermediate.

But why does a halogen deactivate the ring? A halogen, oxygen, or nitrogen withdraws electronic charge from the ring by the inductive effect. We would expect that any electronegative group would decrease the electron density of the ring and would make the ring less attractive to an incoming electrophile.

e⁻ withdrawal should deactivate the ring (and does deactivate the ring when X is Cl, Br, I)

In phenol or aniline, the effect of ring deactivation by electron withdrawal is counterbalanced by the release of electrons by resonance. Why is the same effect not observed in halobenzenes? In phenol or aniline, the resonance structures of the intermediate that confer added stability arise from overlap of $2p$ orbitals of carbon and $2p$ orbitals of N or O. These $2p$ orbitals are about the same size, and overlap is maximal.

In chlorobenzene, bromobenzene, or iodobenzene, the overlap in the intermediate is $2p–3p$, $2p–4p$, or $2p–5p$, respectively. The overlap is between orbitals of different size and is not so effective. The intermediate is less stabilized, the transition-state energy is higher, and the rate of reaction is lower. (Fluorobenzene, with $2p–2p$ overlap in the intermediate, is more reactive than the other halobenzenes toward electrophilic substitution.)

In summary, OH, NH_2, or a halogen determines the orientation of an incoming group by *donating electrons* by resonance and by adding resonance-stabilization to *o*- and *p*-intermediates. For OH and NH_2, electron release by resonance activates the ring toward electrophilic substitution. Electron release by resonance is less effective for Cl, Br, or I than it is for OH or NH_2. Chlorobenzene, bromobenzene, and iodobenzene contain deactivated rings because the electron-withdrawal by these substituents is relatively more effective.

An *alkyl group* does not have unshared electrons to donate for resonance-stabilization. However, an alkyl group is electron-releasing by the inductive effect, a topic we discussed in Section 5.7D. Because an alkyl group releases electrons to the benzene ring, the ring gains electron density and becomes more attractive toward an incoming electrophile.

R groups activate because they are e^--releasing

To see why alkyl groups direct incoming electrophiles to *o*- and *p*-positions, we must again look at the intermediates.

The intermediates for *o*- or *p*-substitution both have resonance structures in which the positive charge is adjacent to the R group. These structures are especially important contributors to resonance-stabilization because the R group can help delocalize the positive charge by electron release and lower the energy of the transition state leading to these intermediates. The situation is directly analogous to that of an R group stabilizing a carbocation. The resonance structures for the intermediate in *m*-substitution have no such contributor. The *m*-intermediate is of higher energy. Attack on an alkylbenzene occurs *ortho* and *para* at a rate that is much faster than attack at a *meta* position.

Sample Problem

Which compound would you expect to undergo aromatic nitration more readily, $C_6H_5CH_3$ or $C_6H_5CCl_3$?

Solution: While the CH_3 group is electron-releasing and activates the ring, the CCl_3 group is strongly *electron-withdrawing* because of the influence of the electronegative chlorines. $C_6H_5CH_3$ has an activated ring; $C_6H_5CCl_3$ has a *deactivated* ring and undergoes substitution more slowly.

STUDY PROBLEM

10.12 Give the major organic products of the reaction of each of the following compounds with isopropyl chloride and $AlCl_3$. Indicate the relative order of the reaction rates.

    (a) bromobenzene   (b) phenol   (c) toluene   (d) benzene

B. Mechanism of the Second Substitution with a meta-Director

In benzene substituted with a *meta*-director (such as NO_2 or CO_2H), the atom attached to the benzene ring has no unshared pair of electrons and carries a positive or a partial positive charge. It is easy to see why the *m*-directors are deactivating. Each one is *electron-withdrawing* and cannot donate electrons by resonance. Each one decreases the electron density of the ring and makes it less attractive to an incoming electrophile. The energy of the Step-1 transition state is higher than it would be for unsubstituted benzene.

A *meta*-director does not activate the *m*-position toward electrophilic substitution. A *meta*-director *deactivates all positions in the ring*, but it deactivates the *m*-position less than the other positions. The resonance structures for attack at the various positions show that the *o*- and *p*-intermediates are destabilized by the nearness of two positive charges. The *m*-intermediate has no such destabilizing resonance structure. The following resonance structures are for the bromination of nitrobenzene:

favored: no adjacent + charges

C.   *Summary of Substituent Effects*

A substituent that is electron-releasing activates a benzene ring and is an *o,p*-director.

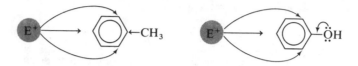

A halogen is an *o, p*-director because it releases electrons by resonance, but it deactivates the ring by its electron-withdrawing inductive effect.

A *meta*-director deactivates all positions on the ring by electron withdrawal and deactivates the *o*- and *p*-positions especially by resonance-destabilization.

Section 10.11

The Third Substitution

What if a benzene ring has two substituents already? Where does a third substituent go? The answer is easy if two groups reinforce each other and both direct the incoming group to the same position.

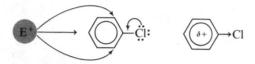

What if the two groups conflict in their directive influence? In this case, the *most powerful activator is the directing group* (see Table 10.6). For example, OH is a more powerful activator than CH_3. If OH and CH_3 conflict in the directions they give to an incoming group, the incoming group goes *o* or *p* to the OH group.

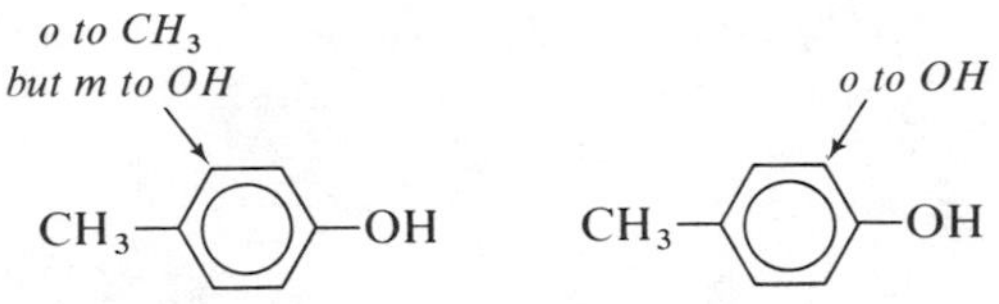

o to CH₃ but m to OH — CH₃—⬡—OH — *not favored*

o to OH — CH₃—⬡—OH — *favored*

In *p*-methylphenol, the OH group has a much greater activating effect than the CH₃ group. The OH directs an incoming electrophile *ortho* or *para* to itself, even though that position is *meta* to the CH₃ group. (In the example, the *para* position is already occupied by the CH₃ group.)

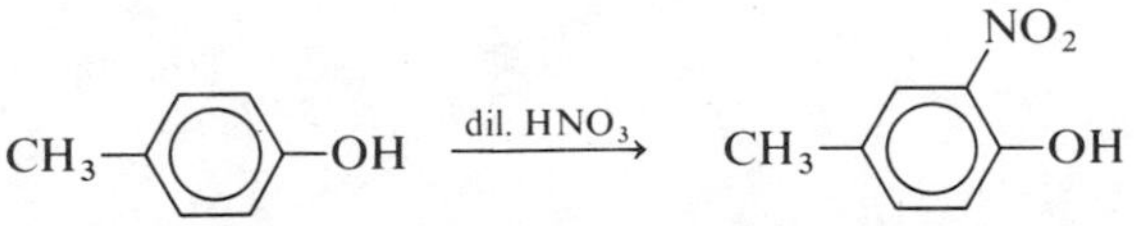

CH₃—⬡—OH $\xrightarrow{\text{dil. HNO}_3}$ CH₃—⬡(NO₂)—OH

p-methylphenol
(*p*-cresol)

4-methyl-2-nitrophenol
only substitution product

STUDY PROBLEM

10.13 Predict the products of the next substitution:

(a) 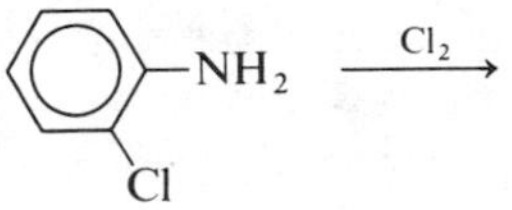 ⬡(Cl)—NH₂ $\xrightarrow{\text{Cl}_2}$

(b) 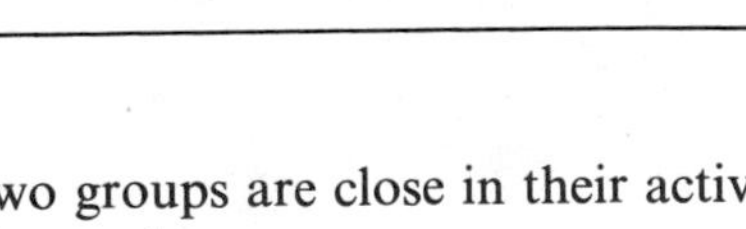 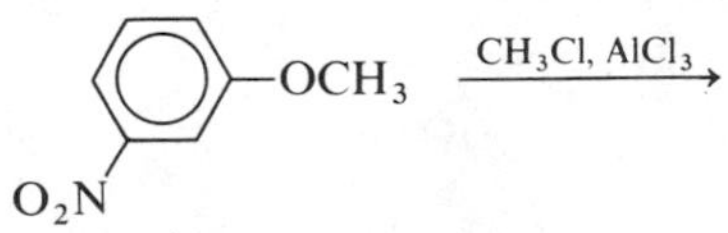 O₂N—⬡—OCH₃ $\xrightarrow{\text{CH}_3\text{Cl, AlCl}_3}$

(c) 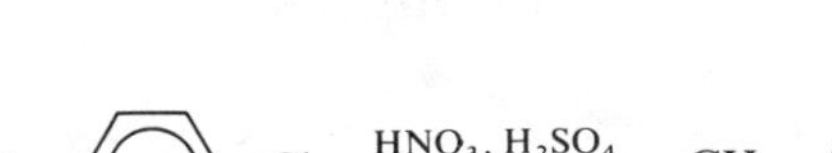 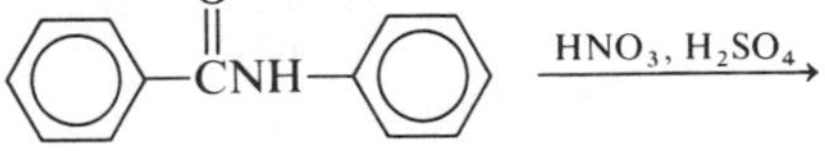 ⬡—C(=O)NH—⬡ $\xrightarrow{\text{HNO}_3,\ \text{H}_2\text{SO}_4}$

If two groups are close in their activating ability, mixtures of products are usually the result.

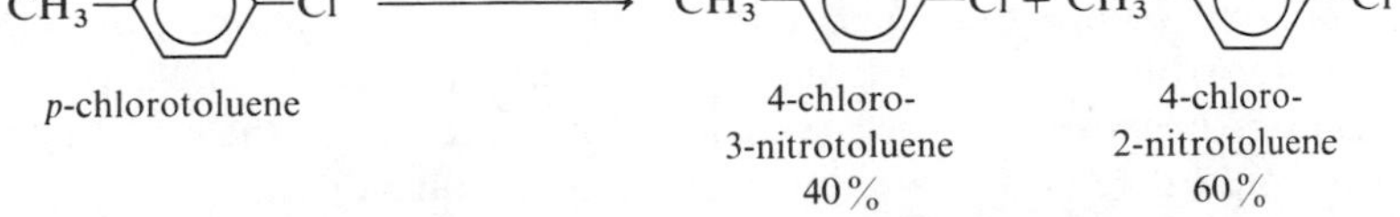

CH₃—⬡—Cl $\xrightarrow{\text{HNO}_3,\ \text{H}_2\text{SO}_4}$ CH₃—⬡(NO₂)—Cl + CH₃—⬡(NO₂)—Cl

p-chlorotoluene

4-chloro-3-nitrotoluene
40%

4-chloro-2-nitrotoluene
60%

If two *deactivating* groups are on a ring, regardless of their positions, it may be difficult to effect a third substitution. *m*-Dinitrobenzene cannot be nitrated with concentrated HNO_3 and H_2SO_4 because the ring is highly deactivated. 2,4-Dinitrotoluene, however, may accept a third nitro group. (Why?)

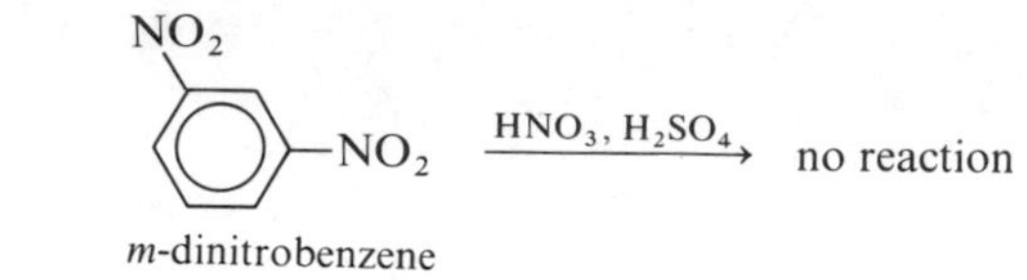

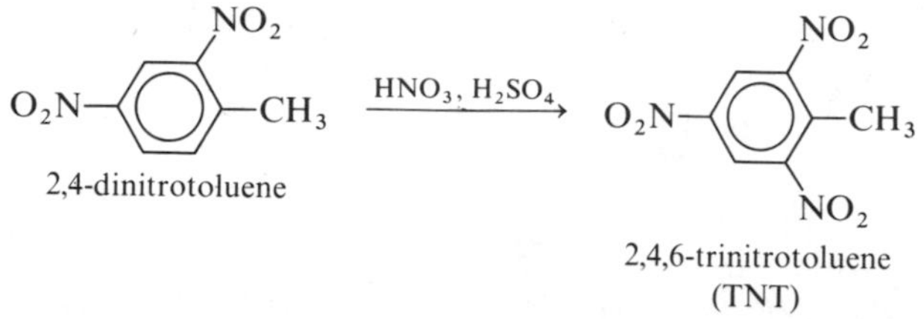

m-dinitrobenzene $\xrightarrow{HNO_3, H_2SO_4}$ no reaction

2,4-dinitrotoluene $\xrightarrow{HNO_3, H_2SO_4}$ 2,4,6-trinitrotoluene (TNT)

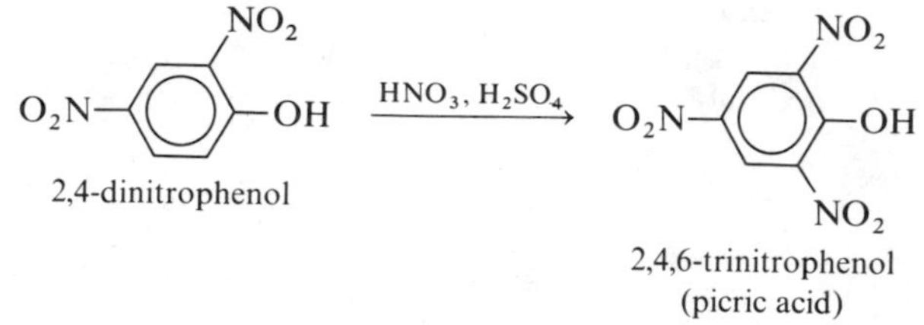

2,4-dinitrophenol $\xrightarrow{HNO_3, H_2SO_4}$ 2,4,6-trinitrophenol (picric acid)

If two groups on a ring are *meta* to each other (even if the ring is activated), the ring usually does not undergo substitution in the position between them. The lack of reactivity of this position is probably due to steric hindrance.

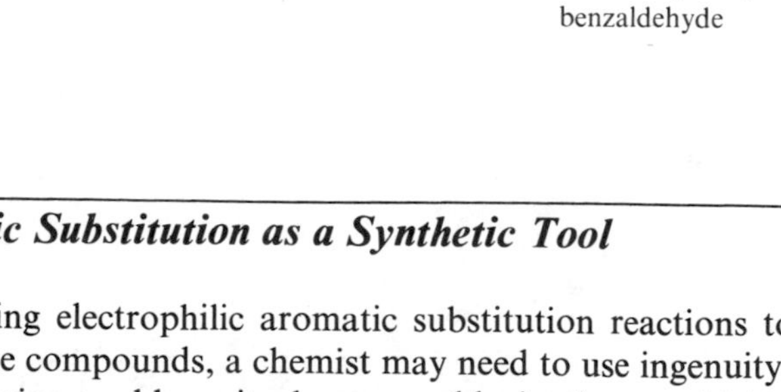

m-hydroxybenzaldehyde $\xrightarrow{Br_2, FeBr_3}$ 6-bromo-3-hydroxy-benzaldehyde

Section 10.12

Aromatic Substitution as a Synthetic Tool

When using electrophilic aromatic substitution reactions to prepare substituted benzene compounds, a chemist may need to use ingenuity. For example, if we are preparing *m*-chloronitrobenzene, chlorination would be a poor choice as the first step because this reaction places an *o,p*-director on the ring. Subsequent nitration would give *o*- and *p*-chloronitrobenzene but not the desired *m*-chloronitrobenzene. It would be best to start with nitration because the nitro group is a *meta*-director. In synthetic work with substituted benzenes, the *order of substitution reactions* is of importance.

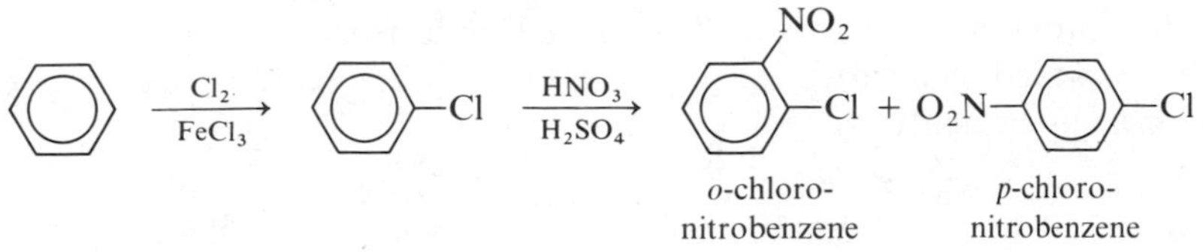

o-chloro-
nitrobenzene

p-chloro-
nitrobenzene

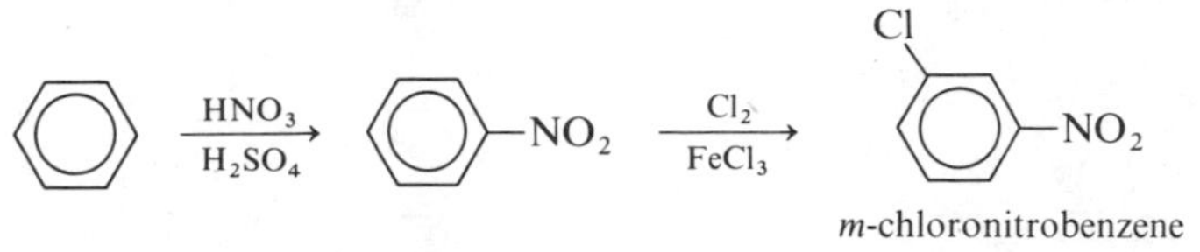

m-chloronitrobenzene

Conversion of one group to another may also be necessary. The nitro group is easily reduced to an amino group with a mixture of iron filings and HCl. This reaction gives a route to *m*-substituted anilines. Benzene may be first nitrated, then subjected to *m*-substitution, and finally the nitro group may be reduced to an amino group. In the reaction shown, an amine salt (with a protonated —NH$_2$ group) is the product. Treatment with a base generates the amine.

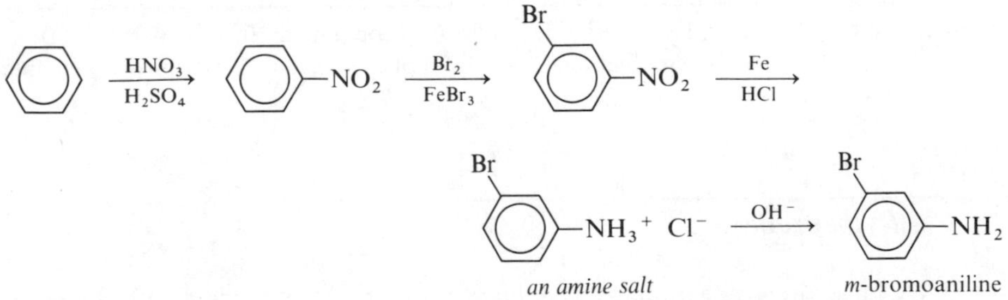

an amine salt

m-bromoaniline

Knowledge of individual chemical characteristics of aromatic compounds is often required for successful solutions of synthetic problems. For example, aniline does not undergo Friedel–Crafts reactions because an amino group (a basic group) undergoes reaction with Lewis acids.

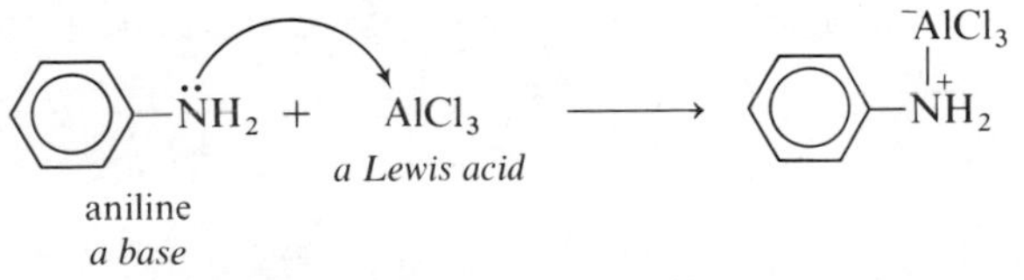

aniline
a base

a Lewis acid

Nitrobenzene also does not undergo Friedel–Crafts reactions; in this case, lack of reaction is due to deactivation of the ring by the electron-withdrawing nitro group.

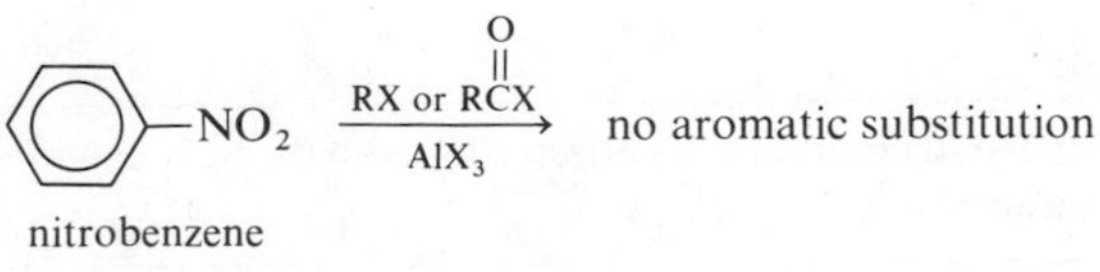

no aromatic substitution

nitrobenzene

The sulfonic acid group is easily removed from an aromatic ring and therefore may be displaced by a variety of reagents. Phenols, for example, can be prepared from arylsulfonic acids.

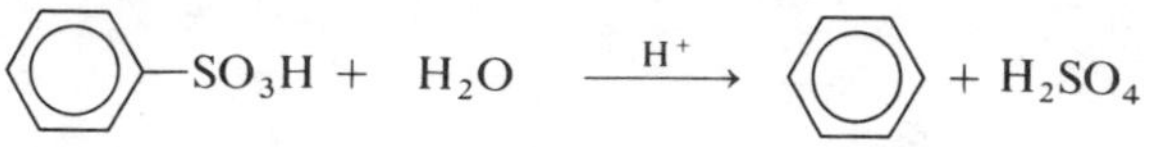

benzenesulfonic   *as steam*   benzene
acid

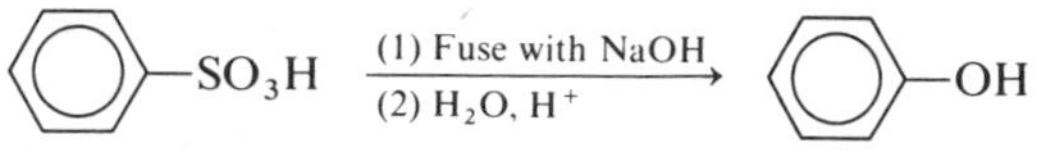

phenol

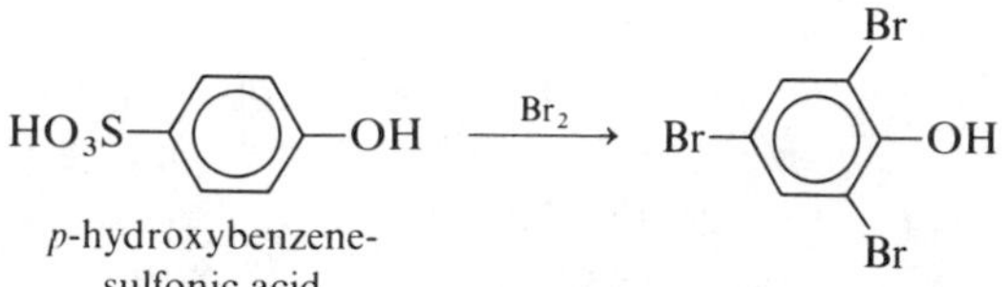

p-hydroxybenzene-   2,4,6-tribromophenol
sulfonic acid

STUDY PROBLEM

10.14 Show how you would synthesize the following compounds from benzene: (a) *m*-chloroaniline; (b) *n*-pentylbenzene; (c) 1,2-diphenylethane; (d) triphenylmethane.

Section 10.13

Alkylbenzenes

We have already seen many instances in which the benzene ring has a large effect on its substituents. For example, phenol is more acidic than an alcohol (Section 7.19), and a benzyl halide, unlike other primary alkyl halides, undergoes S_N1 reactions (Section 5.8). Let us now look at how a benzene ring affects the reactivities of some other groups attached to it; we will begin with the alkylbenzenes.

The alkyl groups attached to a benzene ring are no different from other alkyl groups, with one important exception: part of the alkyl group forms the benzylic position.

Benzylic positions:

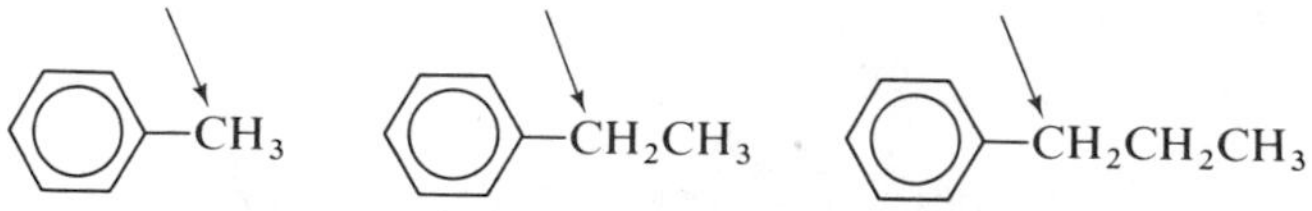

A benzyl cation, a benzyl free radical, and a benzyl carbanion are all resonance-stabilized by the benzene ring. Consequently, the benzylic position is a site of attack in many reactions.

STUDY PROBLEM

10.15 Give the resonance structures of the intermediates in the S_N1 reaction of benzyl bromide with KOH in water.

Although an alkene is readily oxidized by such reagents as hot $KMnO_4$ solution, a benzene ring is not oxidized under these laboratory conditions. However, the *alkyl group* of an alkylbenzene may be oxidized. Because of the reactivity of the benzylic position, alkylbenzenes all give the same product, benzoic acid.

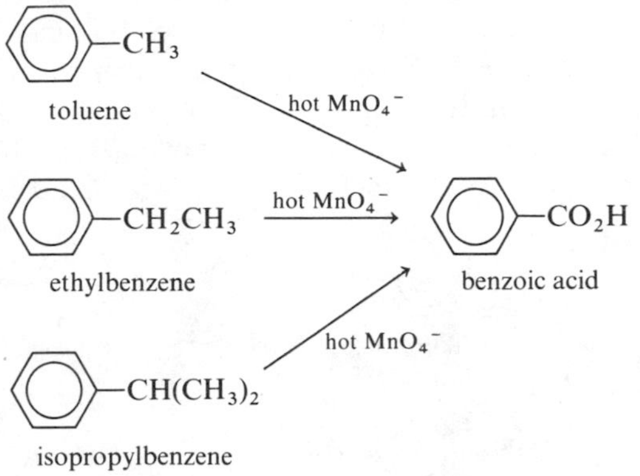

STUDY PROBLEM

10.16 (a) Predict the product of the reaction of *o*-xylene (*o*-dimethylbenzene) with hot $KMnO_4$ solution.

  (b) What would be the oxidation product of tetralin with hot $KMnO_4$ solution?

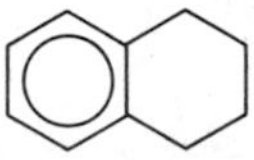

tetralin

Free-radical halogenation is another reaction that takes place preferentially at the benzylic position (Section 6.8B). (Note that the conditions of free-radical halogenation are different from those for electrophilic aromatic halogenation, which is an ionic reaction, not a free-radical reaction.)

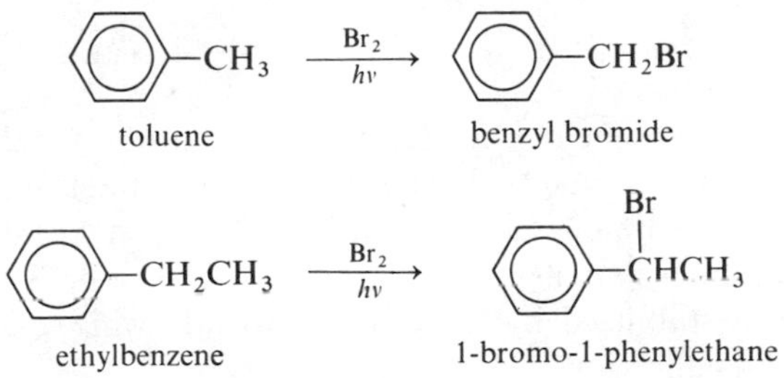

Section 10.14

Halobenzenes and Nucleophilic Aromatic Substitution

In Chapter 5, we mentioned that aryl halides do not undergo the substitution and elimination reactions characteristic of alkyl halides because of the extra strength of a bond from an sp^2 carbon.

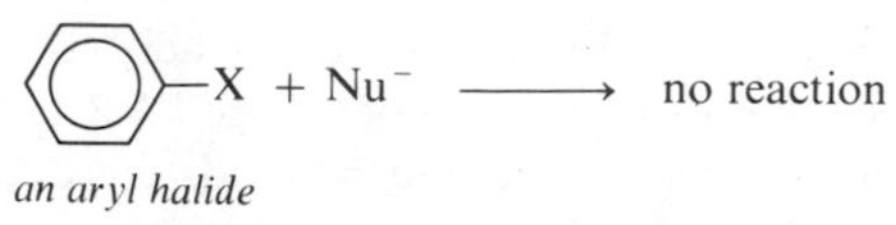

$$\text{an aryl halide} \quad \langle\bigcirc\rangle\text{--X} + \text{Nu}^- \longrightarrow \text{no reaction}$$

Under certain circumstances, chlorobenzene and other aryl halides do undergo nucleophilic substitution (but not by an S_N1 or S_N2 path). The reactivity of aryl halides toward nucleophiles is *enhanced by the presence of electron-withdrawing substituents on the ring.* This is the opposite of a substituent's effect in electrophilic aromatic substitution. Here, an electron-withdrawing substituent makes the ring less rich in electrons and more attractive to an attacking nucleophile.

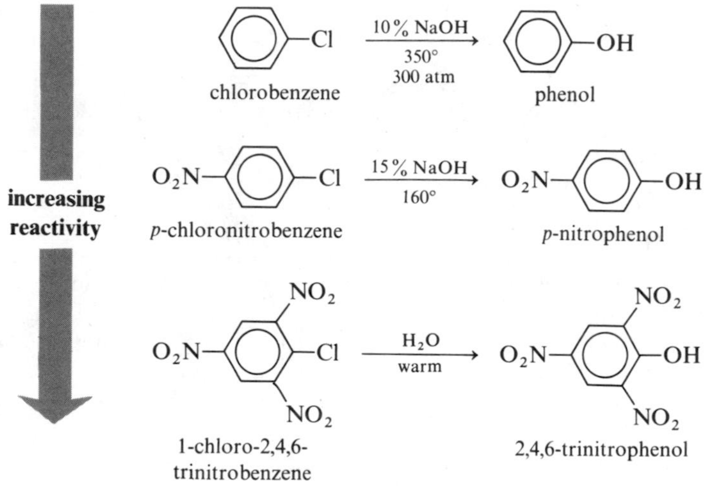

increasing reactivity

chlorobenzene $\xrightarrow[\substack{350° \\ 300 \text{ atm}}]{10\% \text{ NaOH}}$ phenol

p-chloronitrobenzene $\xrightarrow[160°]{15\% \text{ NaOH}}$ p-nitrophenol

1-chloro-2,4,6-trinitrobenzene $\xrightarrow[\text{warm}]{H_2O}$ 2,4,6-trinitrophenol

Other nucleophiles besides OH^- and H_2O can also undergo reaction with activated aryl chlorides.

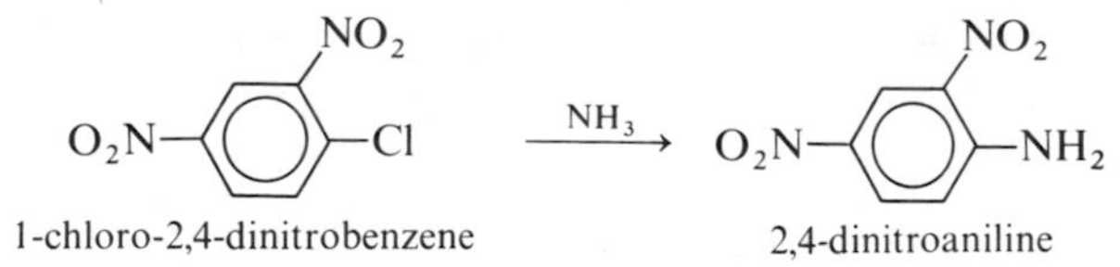

1-chloro-2,4-dinitrobenzene $\xrightarrow{NH_3}$ 2,4-dinitroaniline

The mechanism of nucleophilic aromatic substitution is thought to proceed by one of two routes. The first is through a carbanion intermediate. If the ring is activated toward nucleophilic substitution by an electron-withdrawing group, the reaction proceeds by a two-step mechanism: (1) addition of the nucleophile to form a carbanion (stabilized by the electron-withdrawing group), and (2) subsequent loss of the halide ion.

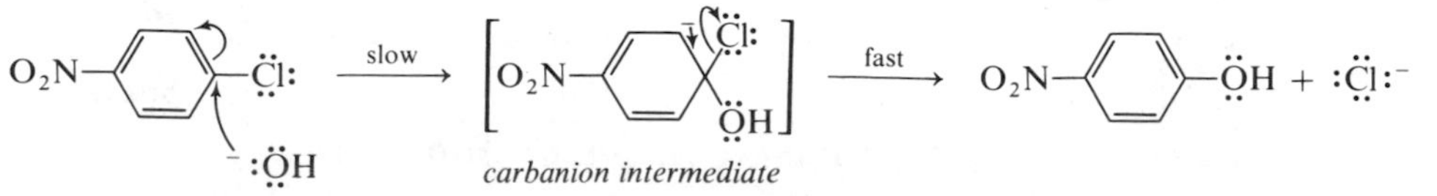

carbanion intermediate

Although the carbanion intermediate is unstable and reactive, it is stabilized to some extent by resonance and by dispersal of the negative charge by the electron-withdrawing group. Resonance structures of this intermediate show that an electron-withdrawing *o-* or *p-*substituent lends more stability to the carbanion inter-mediate than does a *meta-*substituent. When the substituent is *o-* or *p-*, the negative charge is adjacent to the electron-withdrawing group in one resonance structure. In the case of the nitro group, added stability is gained because the nitro group helps disperse the negative charge by resonance.

Resonance structures for p-substituted intermediate:

added stabilization

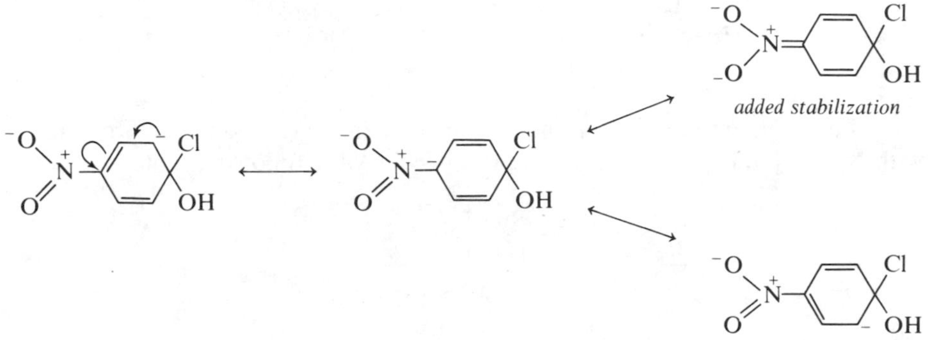

For m-substituted intermediate (no added stabilization):

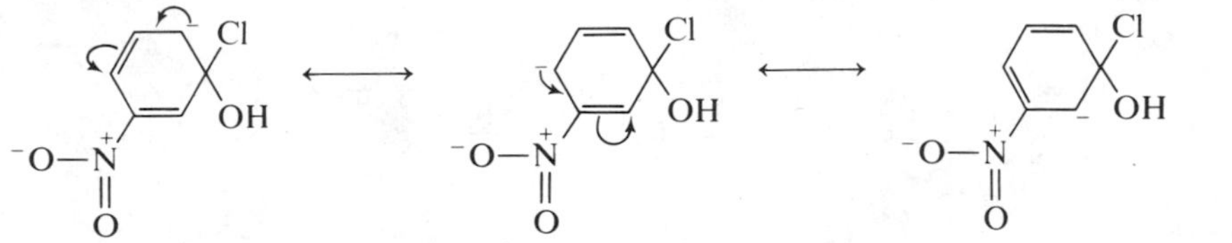

STUDY PROBLEM

10.17 Give the resonance structures for the carbanion intermediate in the reaction of sodium hydroxide and *o-*chloronitrobenzene.

If there is no electron-withdrawing substituent on the ring, nucleophilic aromatic substitution is more difficult and proceeds by the second mechanistic sequence. In these cases, the mechanism is thought to proceed through a **benzyne** intermediate.

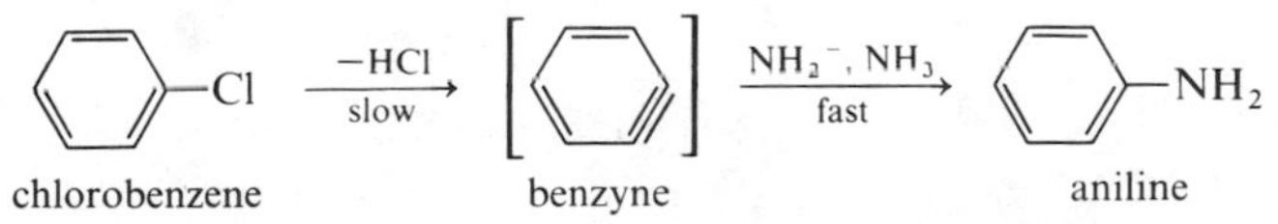

chlorobenzene   benzyne   aniline

The structure of benzyne is not like that of an alkyne. The two ring carbons that have a triple bond between them are joined by an sp^2–sp^2 sigma bond and *p–p* overlap (the aromatic pi cloud). These two bonds are the same as in benzene. The third bond is the side-to-side overlap of two sp^2 orbitals, the ones that originally were used in the bonds to H and X. Figure 10.13 shows this overlap. Because of the rigid geometry of the ring and the unfavorable angles of normal sp^2 orbitals, this overlap cannot be very good. The new bond is very weak, and benzyne is a highly reactive intermediate.

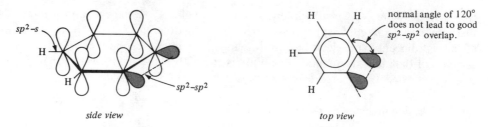

Figure 10.13.   The bonding in the benzyne intermediate.

The formation of the benzyne intermediate in the reaction of chlorobenzene with $NaNH_2$ in liquid NH_3 is thought to occur by the following route:

benzyne

Benzyne undergoes a rapid addition of a nucleophile to yield a carbanion that can abstract a proton from NH_3 to yield the product (aniline, here) and another NH_2^- ion.

a carbanion

SUMMARY

An **aromatic compound** is a type of compound that gains substantial stabilization by pi-electron delocalization. To be aromatic, a compound must be cyclic and planar. Each ring atom must have a p orbital perpendicular to the plane of the ring, and the p orbitals must contain $(4n + 2)$ pi electrons **(Hückel rule)**.

Benzene and other aromatics undergo **electrophilic aromatic substitution reactions**:

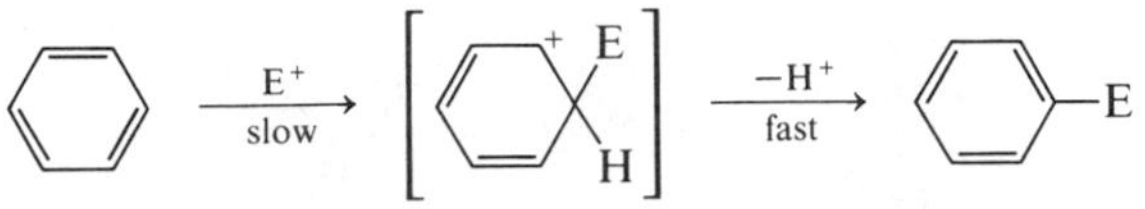

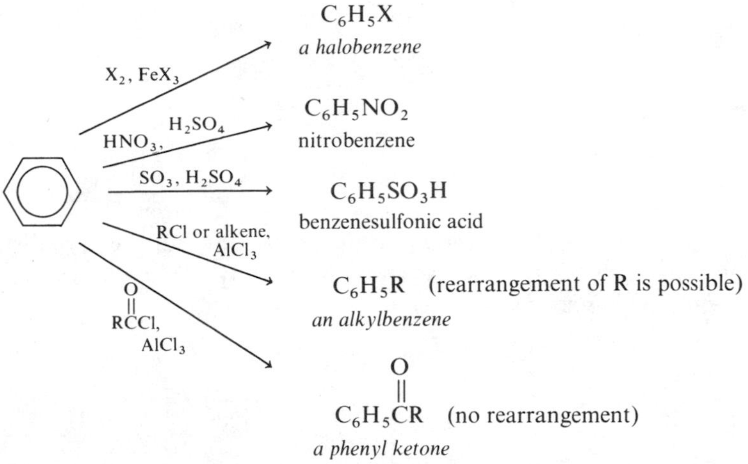

$$\text{benzene} \xrightarrow[\text{slow}]{E^+} \left[\text{arenium ion} \right] \xrightarrow[\text{fast}]{-H^+} \text{C}_6\text{H}_5\text{--E}$$

$$\text{benzene}$$

$$\xrightarrow{X_2,\ FeX_3} \quad C_6H_5X \quad \textit{a halobenzene}$$

$$\xrightarrow[H_2SO_4]{HNO_3,} \quad C_6H_5NO_2 \quad \textit{nitrobenzene}$$

$$\xrightarrow{SO_3,\ H_2SO_4} \quad C_6H_5SO_3H \quad \textit{benzenesulfonic acid}$$

$$\xrightarrow[AlCl_3]{RCl\ or\ alkene,} \quad C_6H_5R \quad \text{(rearrangement of R is possible)} \quad \textit{an alkylbenzene}$$

$$\xrightarrow[AlCl_3]{RCCl,} \quad \overset{O}{\underset{\parallel}{C_6H_5CR}} \quad \text{(no rearrangement)} \quad \textit{a phenyl ketone}$$

A second substitution results in o- and p-isomers or else m-isomers, depending on the first substituent (see Table 10.6). The o,p-directors (except R) have electrons that can be donated to the ring by resonance.

Electron release by resonance:

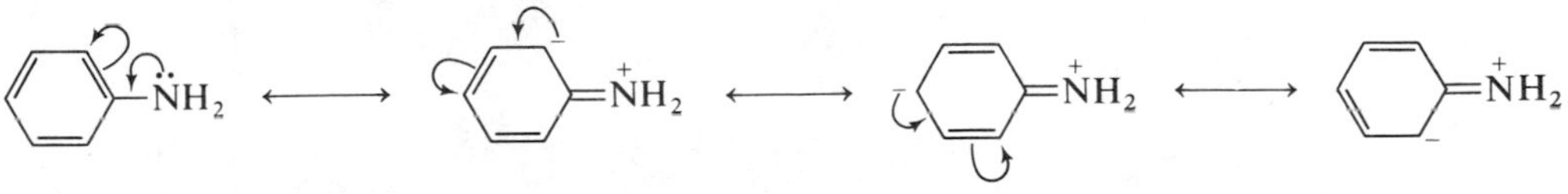

Electron release by inductive effect:

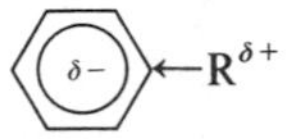

All o,p-directors except X activate the entire ring toward electrophilic substitution. The o- and p-positions are the preferred positions of substitution because of added resonance-stabilization of their intermediates.

Aromaticity, Benzene, and Substituted Benzenes

All *m*-directors and **X** *deactivate* the ring toward further electrophilic substitution by electron withdrawal.

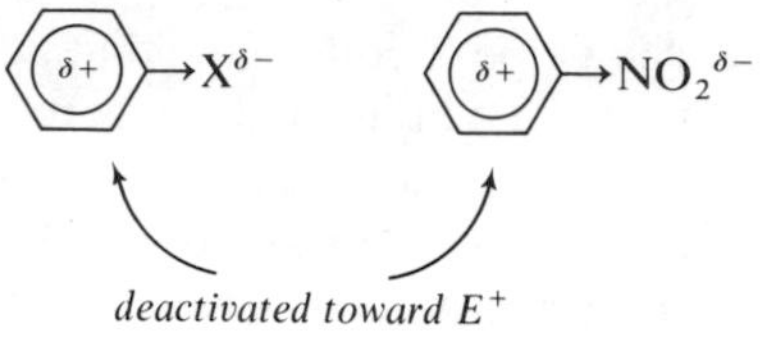

deactivated toward E^+

Alkylbenzenes contain a benzylic position that is active toward many reagents:

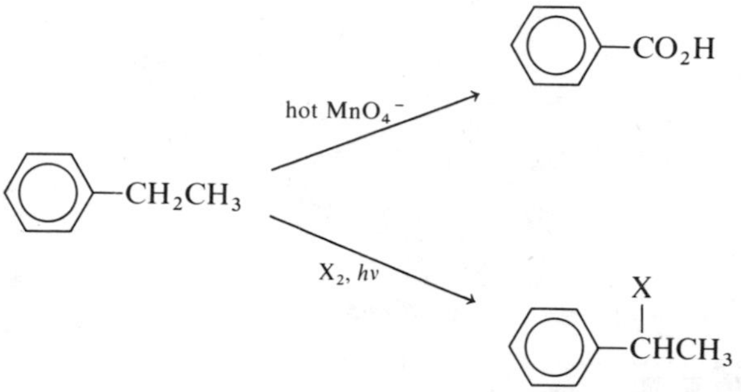

Halobenzenes do not undergo S_N1 or S_N2 reactions, but **X** can be displaced in **nucleophilic aromatic substitution reactions**, especially if the ring is activated by electron-withdrawing groups such as NO_2,

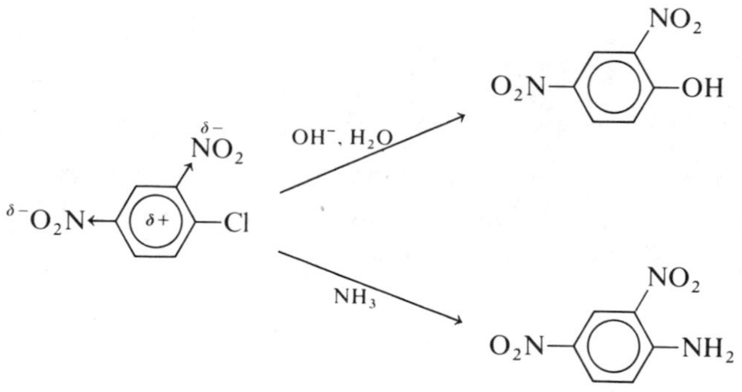

STUDY PROBLEMS

10.18 Draw the structure of each of the following compounds: (a) *o*-dideuteriobenzene; (b) 1,3,5-trichlorobenzene; (c) *m*-bromotoluene; (d) *p*-bromonitrobenzene; (e) 4-bromo-2,3-dinitrotoluene; (f) *m*-chlorobenzoic acid; (g) isopropylbenzene.

10.19 Name each of the following compounds:

(a) $C_6H_5CH{=}CH_2$ (b) 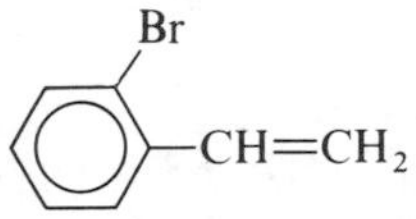 [structure with Br] —CH=CH$_2$ (c) $(C_6H_5)_3CH$

(d) 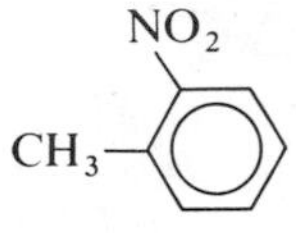 CH$_3$—[structure with NO$_2$] (e) 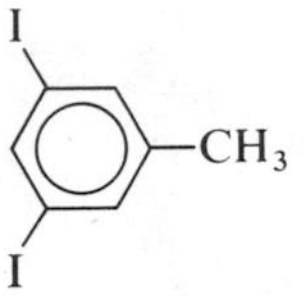 [structure with I, I] —CH$_3$ (f) 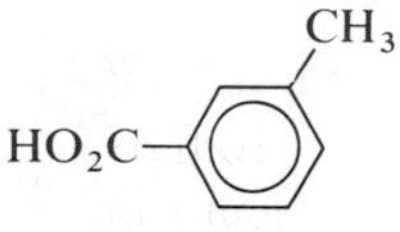 HO$_2$C—[structure with CH$_3$]

(g) 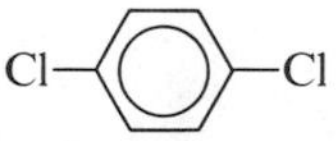 Cl—[structure]—Cl (h) $C_6H_5CH_2I$ (i) $C_6H_5CH{=}CHCH{=}CHC_6H_5$

10.20 Give the structures and the names of all the isomeric: (a) monobromoanilines; (b) monochlorophenols; and (c) dinitrotoluenes.

10.21 Which of the following compounds could be aromatic? (*Hint*: The Hückel rule may be extrapolated to structures with more than one ring.)

(a) [structure]

(b) [structure] azulene

(c) [structure] cyclooctatetraene dianion

[14]annulene

(d) 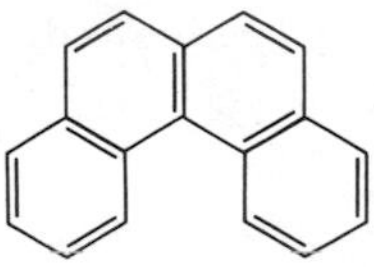 [structure]

(e) 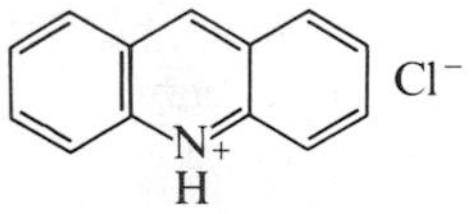 [structure] Cl$^-$

10.22 Naphthalene undergoes electrophilic aromatic substitution at the α-position:

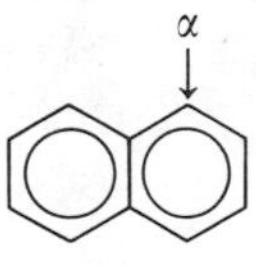

[structure] α

Predict the organic product of the monosubstitution reactions of naphthalene with each of the following sets of reagents:

(a) Br$_2$, FeBr$_3$ (b) HNO$_3$, H$_2$SO$_4$
(c) ClCH$_2$CH$_3$, AlCl$_3$ (d) CH$_2$=CH$_2$, AlCl$_3$, HCl

(e) CH$_3$CCl, AlCl$_3$ [with O double-bonded above the C]

Aromaticity, Benzene, and Substituted Benzenes

10.23 What is the electrophilic agent in aromatic (a) nitration; (b) chlorination; (c) sulfonation; (d) acylation with acetyl chloride; and (e) alkylation with isobutyl chloride? In each case, write an equation that shows how the electrophile is formed.

10.24 Nitrobenzene is sometimes used as a solvent for Friedel–Crafts alkylations. Why does the reaction of nitrobenzene not interfere with the desired reaction?

10.25 Friedel–Crafts acylation reactions may be accomplished with acid anhydrides as well as with acid halides:

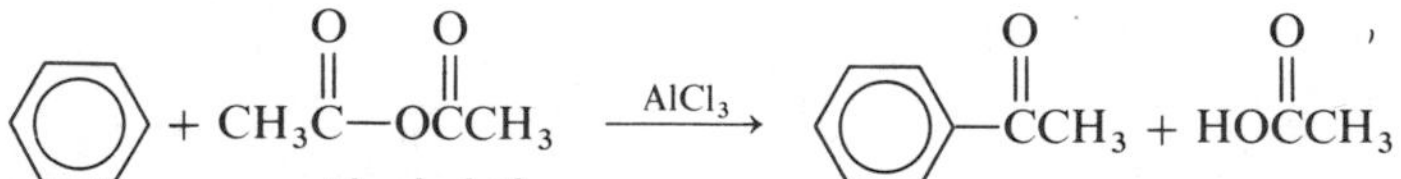

$$\text{benzene} + CH_3\overset{O}{\overset{\|}{C}}{-}O\overset{O}{\overset{\|}{C}}CH_3 \xrightarrow{AlCl_3} \text{benzene}{-}\overset{O}{\overset{\|}{C}}CH_3 + HO\overset{O}{\overset{\|}{C}}CH_3$$

an acid anhydride

Predict the products of the following reactions:

(a) naphthalene + $CH_3\overset{O}{\overset{\|}{C}}O\overset{O}{\overset{\|}{C}}CH_3 \xrightarrow{AlCl_3}$

(b) benzene + [succinic anhydride] $\xrightarrow{AlCl_3}$

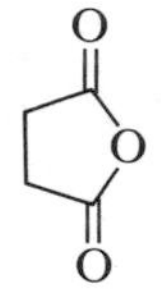

(c) benzene + [phthalic anhydride] $\xrightarrow{AlCl_3}$

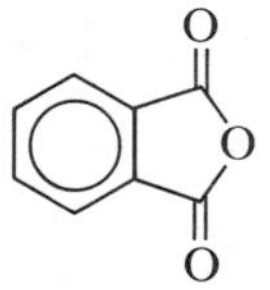

10.26 Which one of each of the following pairs is more reactive toward aromatic bromination?

(a) acetanilide ($C_6H_5NH\overset{O}{\overset{\|}{C}}CH_3$) or benzene
(b) bromobenzene or toluene
(c) *p*-xylene (*p*-dimethylbenzene) or *p*-toluic acid (*p*-methylbenzoic acid)
(d) *m*-dinitrobenzene or *m*-nitrotoluene
(e) chlorobenzene or *m*-dichlorobenzene
(f) toluene or phenol
(g) phenol or chlorobenzene

10.27 Label each of the following groups as an *o,p*-director or as a *m*-director:

(a) 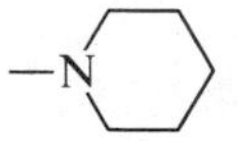 $-N\langle$ (b) 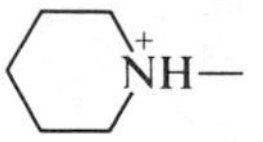 $\langle\overset{+}{N}H-$ (c) $-OC_6H_5$

(d) $-\overset{O}{\overset{\|}{C}}NHCH_3$ (e) $-\overset{O}{\overset{\|}{C}}C_6H_5$ (f) 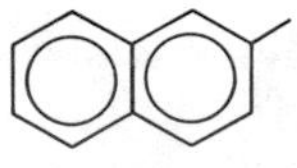 [naphthalene with methyl]

(g) $-O\overset{O}{\overset{\|}{C}}CH_3$ (h) $-\overset{O}{\overset{\|}{C}}OCH_3$ (i) 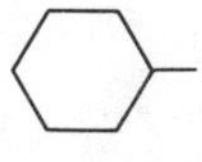 [cyclohexyl]

10.28 Predict the major organic products:

    (a)   ethylbenzene + Cl_2 $\xrightarrow{FeCl_3}$

    (b)   ethylbenzene + Br_2 $\xrightarrow{hv}$

    (c)   styrene + $KMnO_4$ $\xrightarrow{heat}$

    (d)   toluene + 1-chloropropane $\xrightarrow{AlCl_3}$

    (e)   toluene + propene $\xrightarrow[HCl]{AlCl_3}$

    (f)   toluene + fuming H_2SO_4 $\longrightarrow$

    (g)   styrene + excess H_2 $\xrightarrow[200°, \, 100 \text{ atm}]{Ni}$

    (h)   propylbenzene + cyclohexene $\xrightarrow[\text{(a Lewis acid)}]{HF}$

    (i)   styrene + HBr $\longrightarrow$

    (j)   styrene + Br_2 $\longrightarrow$

10.29 Predict the major organic products:

    (a) $C_6H_5CH_2CH_2CH_2\overset{\displaystyle O}{\overset{\|}{C}}Cl$ $\xrightarrow{AlCl_3}$

    (b)   toluene + isobutyl chloride $\xrightarrow{AlCl_3}$

    (c)   benzene + 1-chloro-2-butene $\xrightarrow{AlCl_3}$

10.30 Ring monobromination of a diethylbenzene gives three isomeric bromodiethyl-benzenes (two formed in minor amounts). Give the structures of the diethylbenzene and the brominated products.

10.31 Predict the major products of aromatic monochlorination of (a) chlorobenzene; (b) o-dichlorobenzene; (c) m-bromochlorobenzene; (d) m-xylene; (e) acetophenone (see Table 10.1); and (f) (trichloromethyl)benzene ($C_6H_5CCl_3$).

10.32 Predict the major products of aromatic mononitration of the following compounds:

    (a) 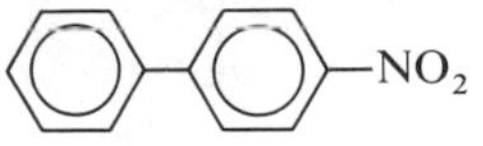   [biphenyl]—NO_2 (b) 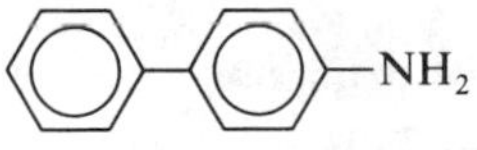   [biphenyl]—NH_2

    (c) 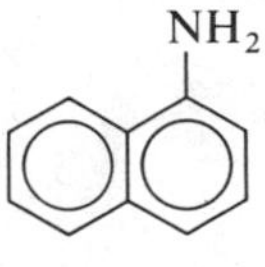   [naphthalene]—NH_2 (d) 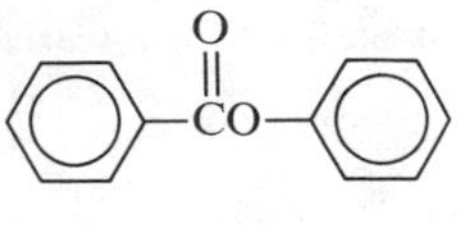   [benzophenone]

    (e) 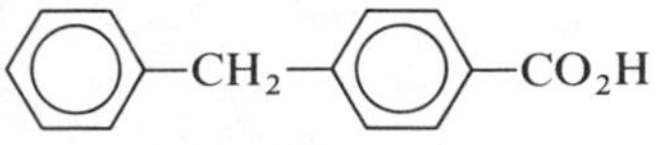   [phenyl]—CH_2—[phenyl]—CO_2H (f) 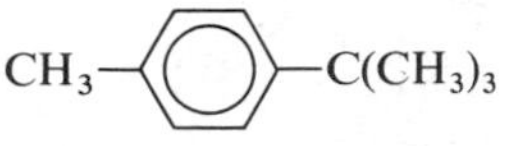 CH_3—[phenyl]—$C(CH_3)_3$

    (g) 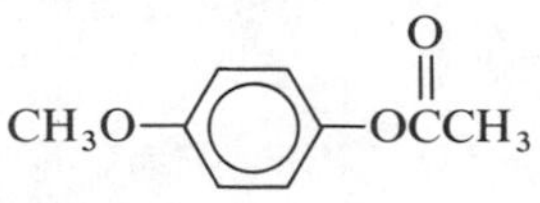 CH_3O—[phenyl]—$O\overset{\displaystyle O}{\overset{\|}{C}}CH_3$

10.33 Starting with a monosubstituted benzene, show how each of the following compounds can be prepared:

(a) 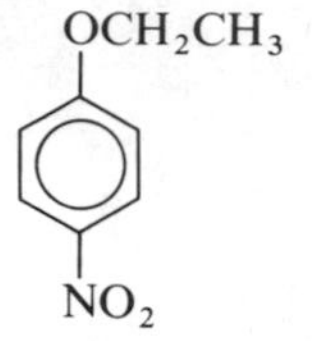 [benzene ring with OCH_2CH_3 at top and NO_2 at bottom (para)]   (b) 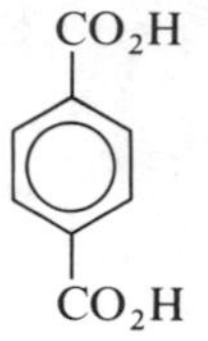 [benzene ring with CO_2H at top and CO_2H at bottom (para)]   (c) 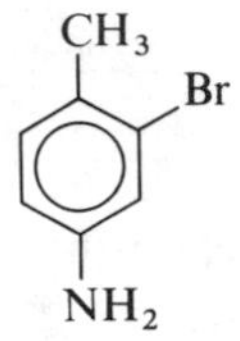 [benzene ring with CH_3 at top, Br at upper right, NH_2 at bottom]

10.34 How would you synthesize each of the following compounds from benzene (assuming that you can separate *o*- and *p*-isomers)?   (a) *p*-chlorobenzoic acid: (b) *o*-nitrotoluene;   (c) 1,1-diphenylethane;   (d) *p*-bromobenzenesulfonic acid;   (e) *m*-bromobenzoic acid;   (f) *p*-bromonitrobenzene;   (g) phenol.

10.35 What ions are formed when triphenylmethanol is treated with concentrated H_2SO_4? Suggest a reason for the formation of these ions.

10.36 Suggest syntheses for the three nitrobenzoic acids from toluene.

10.37 Suggest a laboratory technique for effecting each of the following conversions:

(a)   propylbenzene to 1-phenyl-1-propene

(b) 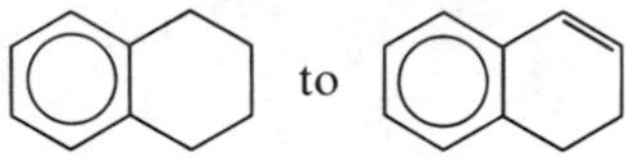   [decalin structure]   to   [octahydronaphthalene structure]

(c)   toluene   to $C_6H_5CH_2OCH_3$

10.38 Complete the following equations:

(a) 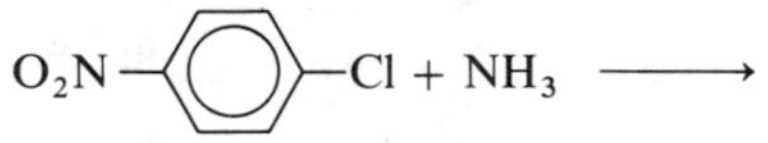 O_2N—[benzene ring]—$Cl + NH_3 \longrightarrow$

(b) 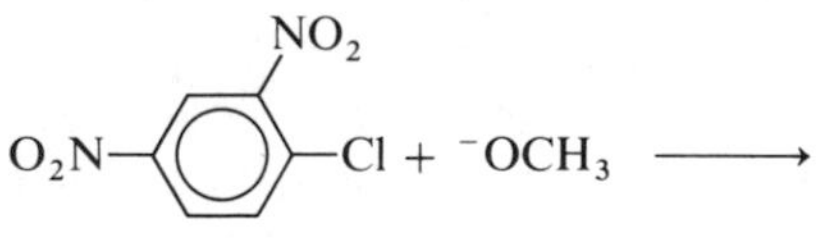 O_2N—[benzene ring with NO_2]—$Cl + {}^-OCH_3 \longrightarrow$

(c) 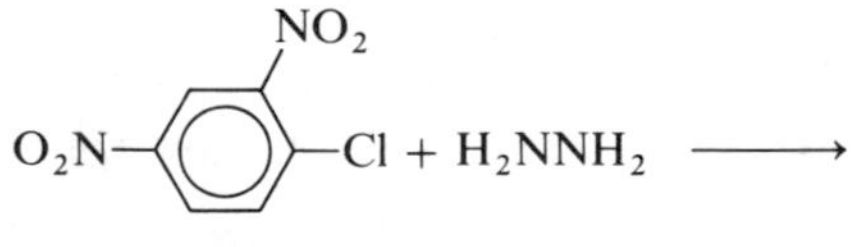 O_2N—[benzene ring with NO_2]—$Cl + H_2NNH_2 \longrightarrow$

10.39 Predict the major organic product of the reaction of benzene with ICl (with iron filings added as catalyst).

10.40 Suggest mechanisms for the following reactions:

(a)   benzene + $\overset{\overset{\text{O}}{\|}}{\text{FCH}} \xrightarrow{\text{BF}_3}$ benzaldehyde $\left(C_6H_5\overset{\overset{\text{O}}{\|}}{\text{CH}} \right)$

(b)   *p*-xylene $\xrightarrow[\text{AlCl}_3]{\text{HCl}}$ a mixture of *o*-, *m*-, and *p*-xylenes

10.41 Suggest a mechanism for the following reaction:

$$C_6H_5C(CH_3)_3 + Br_2 \xrightarrow{\text{AlBr}_3} C_6H_5Br + (CH_3)_2C{=}CH_2$$

10.42 Suggest a structure for a compound, C_7H_6BrCl, that yields *m*-chlorobenzoic acid upon oxidation.

10.43 The following reaction is called a **Claisen rearrangement**. Suggest a mechanism for this reaction.

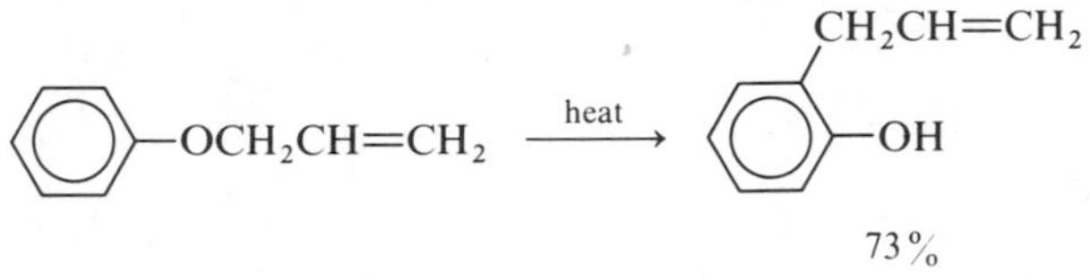

73%

10.44 In an experiment designed to test the existence of benzyne as an intermediate in nucleophilic aromatic substitution, chlorobenzene was treated with sodamide ($NaNH_2$) in liquid ammonia. The chlorobenzene was labeled with carbon-14 at the C—Cl position.

(a) If this reaction proceeds in accordance with the benzyne mechanism, what would be the distribution of carbon-14 in the product aniline—that is, at what positions and in what percentages would carbon-14 be found?

(b) What would be the distribution of carbon-14 if the reaction proceeds by simple nucleophilic displacement?

10.45 There are three dibromobenzenes; they melt at 87°, 6°, and −7°, respectively. The dibromo isomer that melts at 87° yields only one mononitrodibromobenzene. The dibromo isomer that melts at 6° yields two mononitrodibromobenzenes. The dibromo isomer that melts at −7° yields three mononitrodibromobenzenes. Using these data, assign the structures of the three dibromobenzenes.

10.46 **Michler's ketone** is used as an intermediate in the dye industry. It is synthesized from phosgene ($Cl_2C{=}O$) and an excess of *N,N*-dimethylaniline with a $ZnCl_2$ catalyst. Suggest a structure for Michler's ketone.

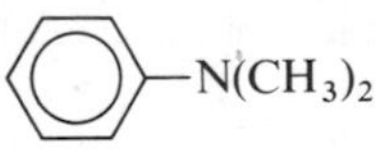

N,N-dimethylaniline

10.47 When bromobenzene is chlorinated, two isomeric compounds (A and B, C_6H_4BrCl) can be isolated. Bromination of A gives a number of isomeric products of the composition $C_6H_3Br_2Cl$, while bromination of B yields two isomers (C and D) of the composition $C_6H_3Br_2Cl$. Compound C is identical with one of the compounds obtained from the bromination of A; however, D is different from any of the isomeric compounds obtained from the bromination of A. Give the structures of A, B, C, and D.

10.48 Suggest a reason for the fact that aniline (with a pK_b of 9.4) is about one-millionth as basic as cyclohexylamine, $C_6H_{11}NH_2$ ($pK_b = 3.3$).

10.49 Would you expect *p*-nitroaniline to be more or less basic than aniline? Why?

10.50 Reaction of *o*-chlorotoluene with KNH_2 in liquid NH_3 yields a mixture of *o*- and *m*-$CH_3C_6H_4NH_2$. The *p*-isomer is not observed. A similar reaction with *p*-chlorotoluene gives *m*- and *p*-$CH_3C_6H_4NH_2$, but not the *o*-isomer. Finally, *m*-chlorotoluene gives all three isomers. Write equations for these reactions (with intermediates).

10.51 Benzene was treated with Br_2 and $FeBr_3$ to yield two isomeric products, A and B ($C_6H_4Br_2$). The infrared spectra of the products are given in Figure 10.14. What are the structures of A and B?

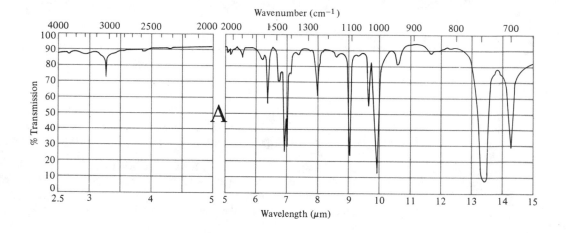

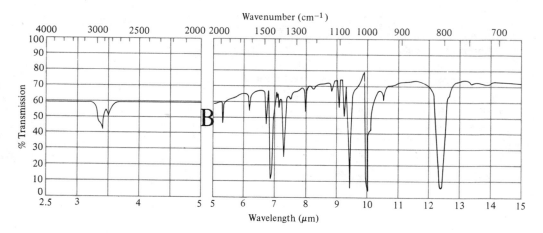

Figure 10.14. Infrared spectra for Problem 10.51.

10.52 A compound C_6H_5Cl was treated with HNO_3 and H_2SO_4. The products of this reaction were then treated with Fe and HCl. The nmr spectrum of one of the products of this reaction is given in Figure 10.15. What is the structure of this component? What would be the structures of the other components of the product mixture?

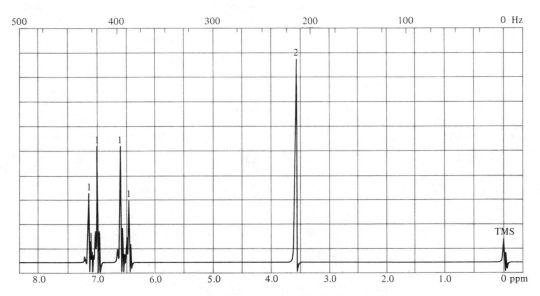

Figure 10.15. Nmr spectrum for Problem 10.52.

10.53 A compound with the formula $C_{15}H_{14}O$ gives the nmr spectrum shown in Figure 10.16. Its infrared spectrum shows strong absorption at about 1750 cm^{-1} (5.75 μm). What is the structure of the compound?

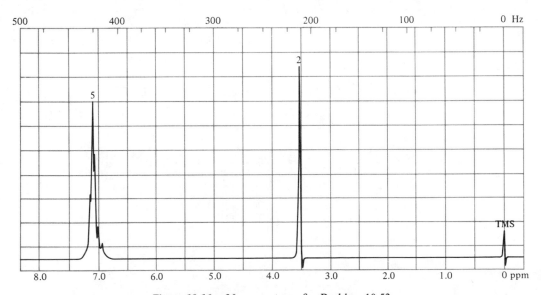

Figure 10.16. Nmr spectrum for Problem 10.53.

10.54 One of the isomeric cresols (methylphenols) was treated with NaOH and methyl iodide. The nmr spectrum of the product is shown in Figure 10.17. What are the structures of the cresol and the product?

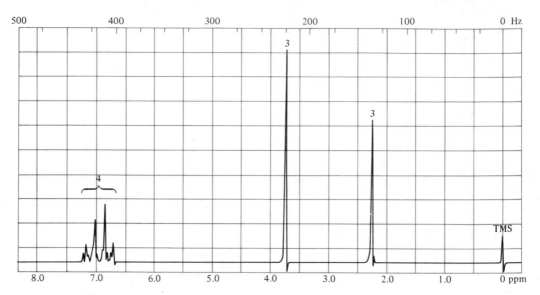

Figure 10.17. Nmr spectrum for Problem 10.54.

10.55 Upon treatment with HNO_3, a monosubstituted aromatic compound yielded two isomeric products, A and B. Treatment of A with NaOH followed by CH_3I gave C. In an identical manner, compound B yielded compound D. The infrared spectra of A, B, C, and D are given in Figure 10.18. Reaction of C with Fe and HCl, followed by treatment with base, yielded E. Following this same procedure, compound D yielded compound F. The nmr spectra of E and F are given in Figure 10.19. What are the structures of the original compound, A, B, C, D, E, and F?

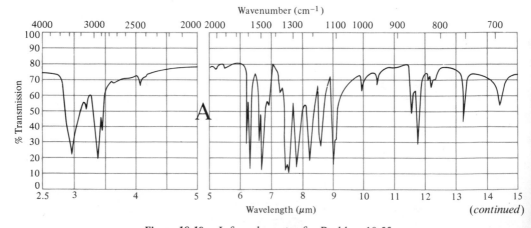

Figure 10.18. Infrared spectra for Problem 10.55.

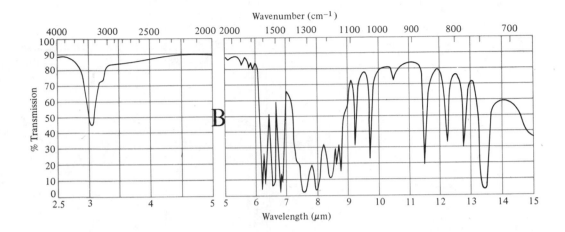

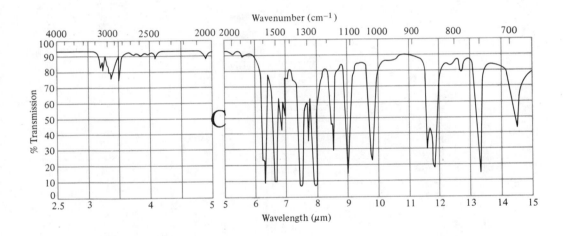

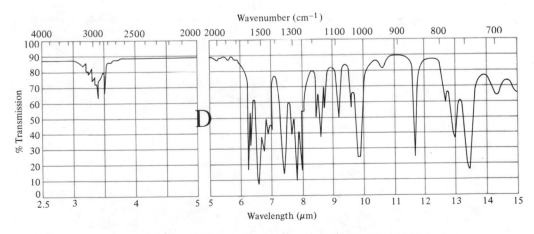

Figure 10.18 (continued). Infrared spectra for Problem 10.55.

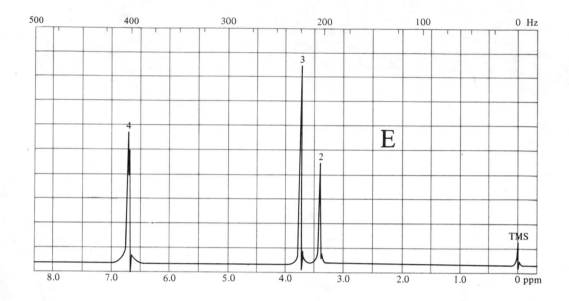

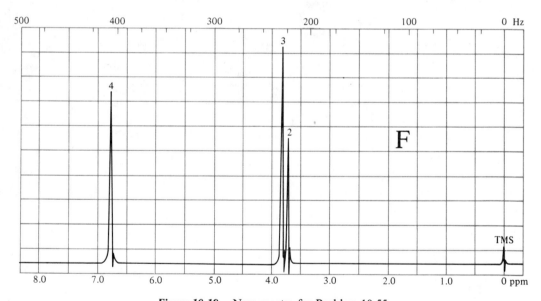

Figure 10.19. Nmr spectra for Problem 10.55.

Chapter 11

Aldehydes and Ketones

Aldehydes and ketones are but two of many classes of organic compounds that contain carbonyl groups. A **ketone** has *two alkyl (or aryl) groups* attached to the carbonyl carbon, while an **aldehyde** has *one alkyl (or aryl) group and one hydrogen* attached to the carbonyl carbon.

$$\begin{matrix} & O \\ & \parallel \\ R-&C-H \quad \text{or} \quad RCHO \end{matrix} \qquad \begin{matrix} & O \\ & \parallel \\ R-&C-R \quad \text{or} \quad RCOR \end{matrix}$$

an aldehyde   *a ketone*

Other carbonyl compounds, such as carboxylic acids or esters, have electronegative groups connected to the carbonyl carbon; consequently, their chemistry is slightly different from that of aldehydes and ketones. These other carbonyl compounds will be covered in later chapters.

Section 11.1

Nomenclature of Aldehydes and Ketones

In the IUPAC system, the name of an aldehyde is derived from the name of the parent alkane by changing the final **-e** to **-al**. No number is needed; the —CHO group always contains carbon 1.

$$\begin{matrix} O \\ \parallel \\ CH_3CH \end{matrix} \qquad \begin{matrix} O \\ \parallel \\ CH_3CHCH \\ | \\ Cl \end{matrix} \qquad \begin{matrix} O \\ \parallel \\ CH_2{=}CHCH \end{matrix}$$

IUPAC: ethanal   2-chloropropanal   propenal

Ketones are named by changing the **-e** of the alkane name to **-one**. A number is used where necessary:

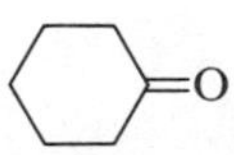

$$\begin{matrix} O \\ \parallel \\ CH_3CCH_2CH_2CH_3 \end{matrix} \qquad \begin{matrix} O \quad\quad O \\ \parallel \quad\quad \parallel \\ CH_3CCH_2CCH_3 \end{matrix}$$

IUPAC: cyclohexanone   2-pentanone   2,4-pentanedione

Table 11.1. Trivial Names for Some Carboxylic Acids and Aldehydes

Carboxylic acid		Aldehyde	
$\overset{O}{\overset{\|}{HCOH}}$	formic acid	$\overset{O}{\overset{\|}{HCH}}$	formaldehyde
$\overset{O}{\overset{\|}{CH_3COH}}$	acetic acid	$\overset{O}{\overset{\|}{CH_3CH}}$	acetaldehyde
$\overset{O}{\overset{\|}{CH_3CH_2COH}}$	propionic acid	$\overset{O}{\overset{\|}{CH_3CH_2CH}}$	propionaldehyde
$\overset{O}{\overset{\|}{CH_3CH_2CH_2COH}}$	butyric acid	$\overset{O}{\overset{\|}{CH_3CH_2CH_2CH}}$	butyraldehyde
⬡–$\overset{O}{\overset{\|}{COH}}$	benzoic acid	⬡–$\overset{O}{\overset{\|}{CH}}$	benzaldehyde

Trivial names for the common aldehydes and ketones are widely used. Aldehydes are named after the parent carboxylic acids with the *-oic acid* or *-ic acid* changed to *-aldehyde*. Table 11.1 lists a few examples.

Propanone is usually called *acetone*, while the other simple ketones are sometimes named by a functional-group name. The alkyl or aryl groups attached to the carbonyl group are named, then the word *ketone* is added:

$$\overset{O}{\overset{\|}{CH_3CCH_3}} \qquad \overset{O}{\overset{\|}{CH_3CCH_2CH_3}} \qquad \overset{O}{\overset{\|}{(CH_3)_2CHCC(CH_3)_3}}$$

trivial: acetone   methyl ethyl ketone   isopropyl *t*-butyl ketone
IUPAC: propanone   butanone   2,2,4-trimethyl-3-pentanone

Other positions in a molecule in relation to the carbonyl group may be referred to by Greek letters. The carbon adjacent to the C=O is called the **alpha** (α) carbon. The next carbon is **beta** (β), then **gamma** (γ), **delta** (δ), and so forth, according to the Greek alphabet. Occasionally, **omega** (ω), the last letter in the Greek alphabet, is used to designate the terminal carbon of a long chain, regardless of the actual length of the chain. The groups (or atoms) attached to an α carbon are called α groups; those attached to the β carbon are called β groups.

$$\overset{O}{\overset{\|}{CH_3CH_2CH_2CH}} \qquad \overset{O\quad O}{\overset{\|\quad\|}{CH_3CCH_2CCH_3}} \qquad \overset{Br}{\overset{\|}{CH_3CHCHO}}$$

       α carbon   *a β-diketone*   *an α-bromoaldehyde*
       β carbon

$$\overset{O}{\overset{\|}{BrCH_2CH_2CH_2CH_2CC_6H_5}} \qquad \overset{O}{\overset{\|}{Br(CH_2)_{10}CCH_3}} \qquad \overset{O}{\overset{\|}{Br(CH_2)_{25}CCH_2CH_3}}$$

all are ω-bromoketones

The Greek-letter designations may be used in the trivial names of carbonyl compounds, but *not in the IUPAC names* because this latter practice would be mixing two systems of nomenclature.

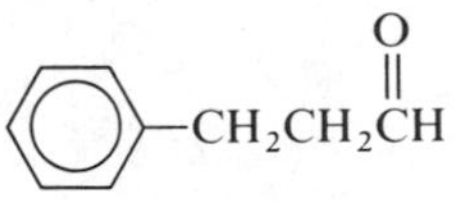

β-phenylpropionaldehyde
(or 3-phenylpropanal)

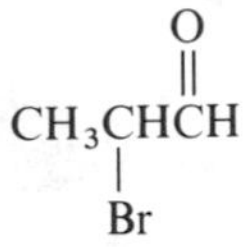

α-bromopropionaldehyde
(or 2-bromopropanal)

Section 11.2

Preparation of Aldehydes and Ketones

The most common way of preparing a simple aldehyde or ketone is by the *oxidation of an alcohol.* These oxidations were discussed in Section 7.17.

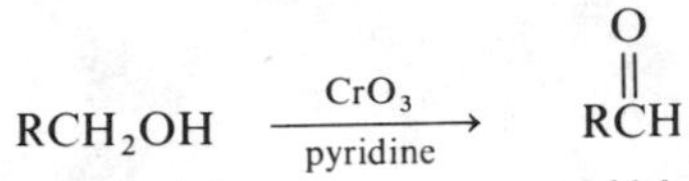

a 1° alcohol → *an aldehyde*

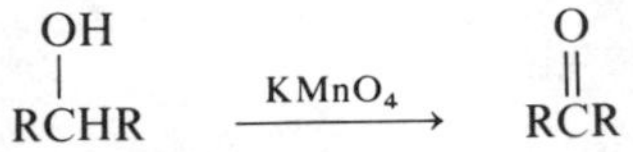

a 2° alcohol → *a ketone*

Aryl ketones can be prepared by *Friedel–Crafts acylation reactions* (Section 10.9E).

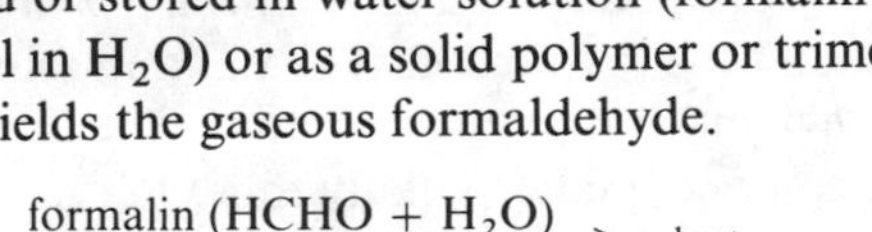

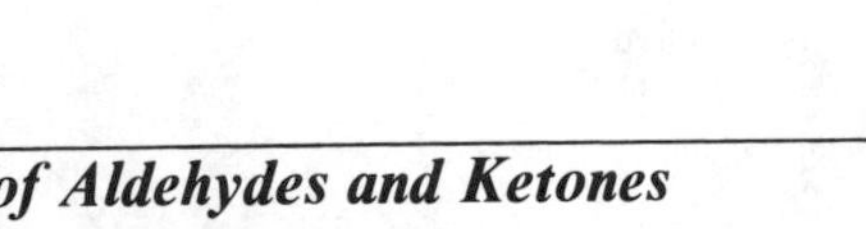

an aryl ketone

One of the more important aldehydes, *formaldehyde*, which is used as a reagent and as a preservative for biological specimens, is a gas. However, it is conveniently shipped or stored in water solution (formalin = 37% formaldehyde and 7–15% methanol in H_2O) or as a solid polymer or trimer. Heating any one of these preparations yields the gaseous formaldehyde.

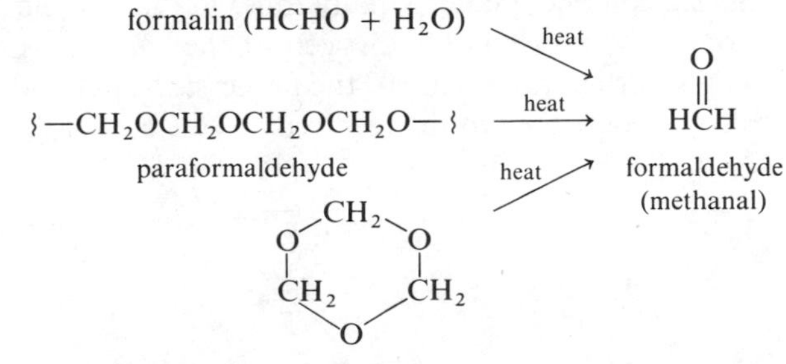

trioxane
mp 62°C

 Acetaldehyde, with a boiling point near room temperature (20°), is also conveniently stored or shipped in a cyclic trimer or tetramer form. Acetaldehyde is used as an intermediate in industrial syntheses of acetic acid, acetic anhydride (Section 13.4A), and other compounds.

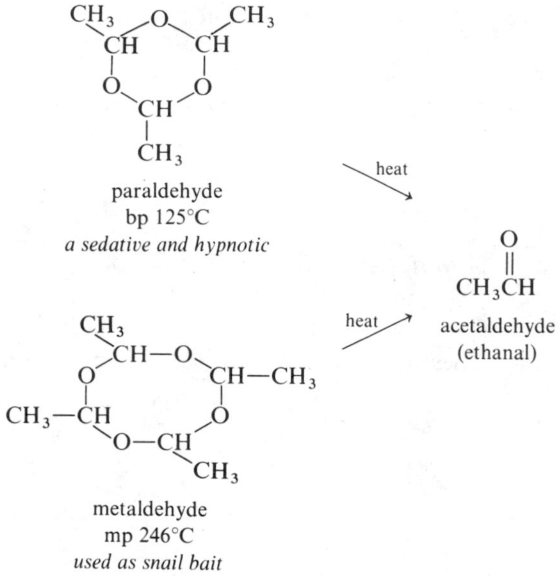

paraldehyde
bp 125°C
a sedative and hypnotic

heat

$$CH_3CH$$
acetaldehyde
(ethanal)

heat

metaldehyde
mp 246°C
used as snail bait

Section 11.3

The Carbonyl Group

 The carbonyl group consists of an sp^2 carbon atom joined to an oxygen atom by a sigma bond and by a pi bond. (See Figure 2.21, page 62, for the orbital picture.) The sigma bonds of the carbonyl group lie in a *plane* with bond angles of approximately 120° around the sp^2 carbon. The pi bond joining the C and the O lies above and below the plane of these sigma bonds. The carbonyl group is *polar*, the electrons in the sigma bond, and especially those in the pi bond, being drawn toward the electronegative oxygen. The oxygen of the carbonyl group has *two filled orbitals*. All these structural features—the flatness, the pi bond, the polarity, and the filled orbitals—contribute to the reactivity of the carbonyl group.

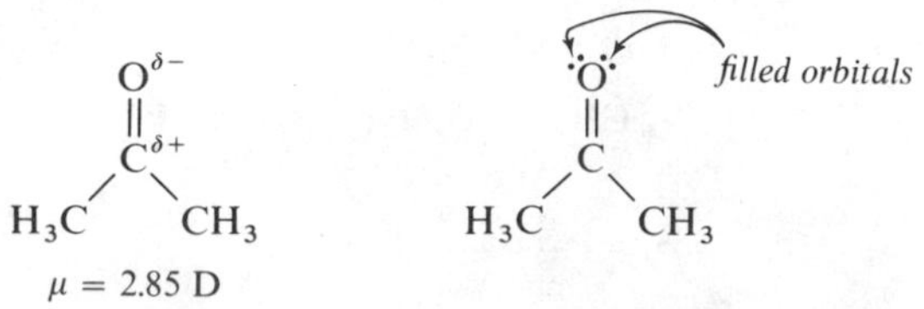

filled orbitals

$\mu = 2.85$ D

Isolated carbon–carbon double bonds are nonpolar. For reaction, an electrophile is needed to attack the pi-bond electrons. However, the carbon–oxygen double bond is polar even without electrophilic attack. A carbonyl compound may be attacked either by a nucleophile or by an electrophile.

Many reactions of carbonyl groups involve an initial protonation of the oxygen. This protonation enhances the positive charge of the carbonyl carbon so that this carbon is more easily attacked by weaker nucleophiles.

resonance structures for
a protonated carbonyl group

Physical Properties of Aldehydes and Ketones

The unique features of the carbonyl group influence the physical properties of the aldehydes and ketones. Because they are polar, and therefore undergo intermolecular dipole–dipole attractions, aldehydes and ketones have higher boiling points than nonpolar compounds of similar molecular weight (see Table 11.2). To a limited extent, aldehydes and ketones can solvate ions (for example, NaI is soluble in acetone).

$$
\begin{array}{ccc}
\overset{\displaystyle CH_3}{\underset{\displaystyle |}{}} & \overset{\displaystyle O}{\underset{\displaystyle \|}{}} & \overset{\displaystyle OH}{\underset{\displaystyle |}{}} \\
CH_3CHCH_3 & CH_3CCH_3 & CH_3CHCH_3 \\
\text{bp } -12° & \text{bp } 56° & \text{bp } 82.5°
\end{array}
$$

Because of the filled orbitals on the oxygen, a carbonyl compound can undergo hydrogen bonding (but not with another carbonyl compound that has no acidic hydrogens available for hydrogen bonding).

$$
\begin{array}{cc}
:\!O\!:\,-\,-\,-\,H\!-\!O & \\
\| & | \\
R\!-\!C\!-\!R & H
\end{array}
$$

The result of this ability to form hydrogen bonds is that the aldehydes and ketones of low molecular weight, like alcohols, are soluble in water (Table 11.2). However, since they cannot undergo hydrogen bonding with themselves, the boiling points are substantially lower than those of corresponding alcohols.

Table 11.2.   Physical Properties of Some Aldehydes and Ketones

Trivial name	Structure	Bp, °C	Solubility in H_2O
aldehydes:			
formaldehyde	HCHO	-21	∞
acetaldehyde	CH_3CHO	20	∞
propionaldehyde	CH_3CH_2CHO	49	16 g/100 ml
butyraldehyde	$CH_3CH_2CH_2CHO$	76	7 g/100 ml
benzaldehyde	C_6H_5CHO	178	slightly
ketones:			
acetone	$CH_3\overset{\displaystyle O}{\overset{\|}{C}}CH_3$	56	∞
methyl ethyl ketone	$CH_3\overset{\displaystyle O}{\overset{\|}{C}}CH_2CH_3$	80	26 g/100 ml
acetophenone	$C_6H_5\overset{\displaystyle O}{\overset{\|}{C}}CH_3$	202	insoluble
benzophenone	$C_6H_5\overset{\displaystyle O}{\overset{\|}{C}}C_6H_5$	306	insoluble

Section 11.5

Spectral Properties of Aldehydes and Ketones

A.   Infrared Spectra

The infrared spectrum is useful in the detection of a carbonyl group in a ketone or an aldehyde. (Characteristic absorption bands are listed in Table 11.3.) However, carbonyl groups are also found in other compounds (carboxylic acids, esters, and so forth). For this reason, the fact that a carbonyl group is present does not mean that an unknown is necessarily an aldehyde or a ketone.

For aldehydes, corroborating evidence may be found in both the infrared and nmr spectra because of the unique absorption of the aldehyde hydrogen. Ketones, unfortunately, cannot be positively identified by spectral methods. The usual procedure is to eliminate the other carbonyl compounds as possibilities. If a carbonyl compound is not an aldehyde, carboxylic acid, ester, amide, etc., it is probably a ketone.

The $C=O$ absorption of both aldehydes and ketones appears somewhere near 1700 cm^{-1} (about 5.8 μm). If the carbonyl group is in conjugation with a double bond or benzene ring, the position of absorption is shifted to a slightly lower frequency (about 1675 cm^{-1}, or 6 μm, for ketones). Figure 11.1 shows the infrared spectra of 1-phenyl-2-propanone (nonconjugated) and 1-phenyl-1-propanone (conjugated).

Table 11.3. **Characteristic Infrared Absorption of Alde-**
hydes and Ketones

Type of vibration	Position of absorption	
	cm^{-1}	μm
aldehydes:		
C—H stretching of —CHO	2695–2830	3.5–3.7
C=O stretching	1720–1740	5.7–5.8
ketones:		
C=O stretching	1666–1754	5.7–6

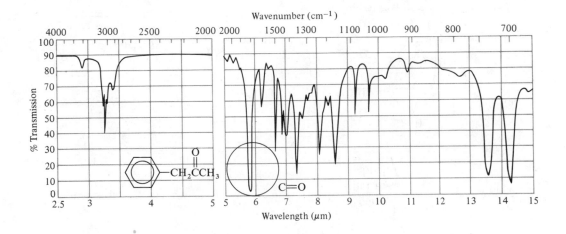

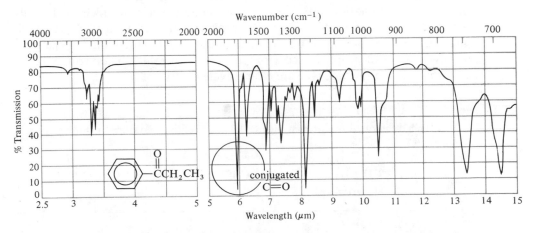

Figure 11.1. Infrared spectra of 1-phenyl-2-propanone and 1-phenyl-1-propanone, illustrating the slight shift of C=O absorption to lower frequency (longer wavelength) by conjugation.

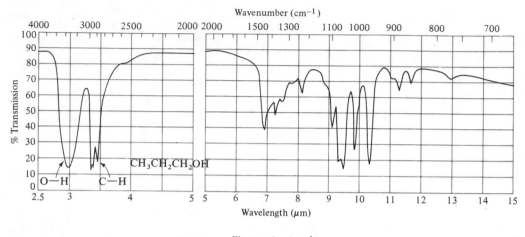

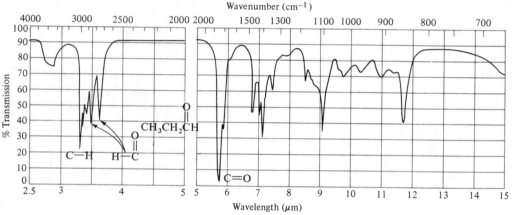

Figure 11.2. Infrared spectra of 1-propanol and propanal, illustrating the absorption of aldehydes.

The C—H stretching of the aldehyde group, which gives absorption just to the right of the aliphatic C—H absorption, is characteristic of an aldehyde. Usually two peaks are found in this region. The peak at higher frequency, closer to aliphatic C—H absorption, is often obscured by the C—H absorption. Compare the infrared spectra of propanal and 1-propanol in Figure 11.2. The two C—H absorption peaks of the aldehyde are clearly evident.

STUDY PROBLEM

11.1 Match the infrared spectrum in Figure 11.3 to one of the following structures:

$$
\text{(a)} \quad \underset{\displaystyle \|}{\overset{\displaystyle O}{C_6H_5\overset{\|}{C}CH_2CH_3}} \qquad \text{(b)} \quad (CH_3)_2CHCH_2CH_2\overset{\overset{\displaystyle O}{\displaystyle \|}}{C}H \qquad \text{(c)} \quad \underset{\displaystyle CH_3}{\overset{\displaystyle O}{C_6H_5\overset{\|}{C}HCH}}
$$

B. Nmr Spectra

The electrons in a carbonyl group, like those in a double bond or an aromatic pi cloud, are set in motion by an external magnetic field. The resulting induced

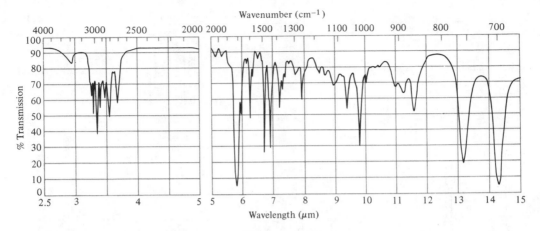

Figure 11.3. Infrared spectrum for Problem 11.1.

molecular field has a profound effect upon the nmr absorption of the aldehyde proton. You will recall from Section 8.8B that nmr absorption for an aldehyde proton is shifted far downfield (9–10 ppm, offset from the usual spectral range). This large shift arises from the additive effects of both anisotropic deshielding by the pi electrons and inductive deshielding by the electropositive carbon of the carbonyl group.

The α hydrogens of either aldehydes or ketones are not affected to such a large extent by the carbonyl group. The nmr absorption for the α protons (2.1–2.6 ppm) appears slightly downfield from that of other CH absorption (about 1.5 ppm) because of electron withdrawal by the electronegative oxygen atom. The effects of this deshielding by the inductive effect are evident in the nmr spectra of butanal (Figure 11.4) and 1-phenylpropanone (Figure 11.5). In an aldehyde, the splitting

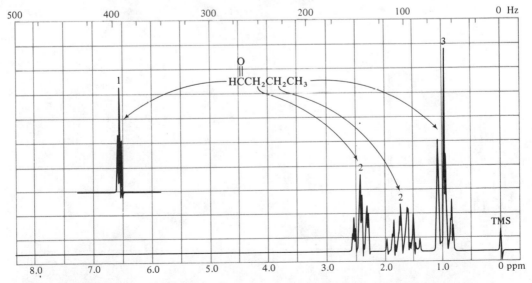

Figure 11.4. Nmr spectrum of butanal, showing the relative chemical shifts of α, β, and γ protons and the aldehyde proton.

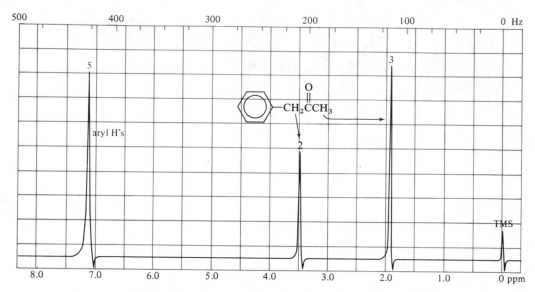

Figure 11.5. Nmr spectrum of 1-phenyl-2-propanone.

of the aldehyde proton may sometimes be used to determine the number of α hydrogens. The spectrum of butanal shows a triplet for the —CHO proton, an indication of two α hydrogens.

STUDY PROBLEM

11.2   The nmr spectrum in Figure 11.6 is of an aldehyde. Which of the following aldehydes is it?

(a)   CH₃—〈 〉—CH (with O double bond)   (b)   〈 〉—CH₂CH (with O double bond)   (c)   〈 〉—CH (with O double bond)

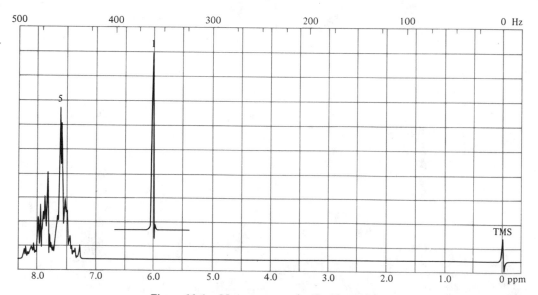

Figure 11.6.   Nmr spectrum for Problem 11.2.

Addition of Reagents to the Carbonyl Group

The focal point of reactivity in aldehydes and ketones is the pi bond of the carbonyl group. Like alkenes, aldehydes and ketones undergo addition of reagents to the pi bond.

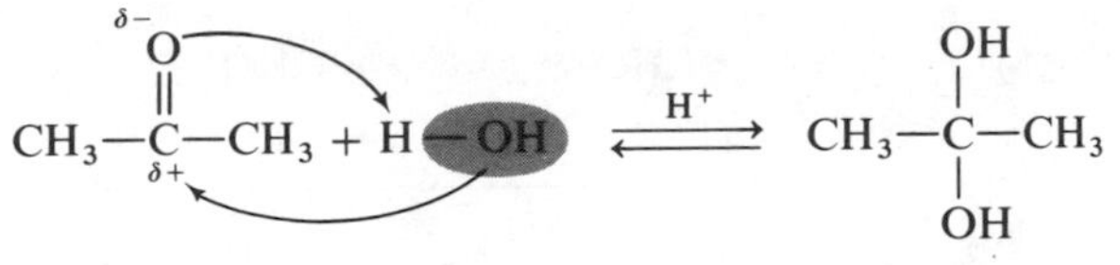

$$CH_3-\underset{\delta+}{\overset{\overset{\delta-}{O}}{C}}-CH_3 + H-OH \xrightleftharpoons{H^+} CH_3-\underset{OH}{\overset{OH}{C}}-CH_3$$

a hydrate

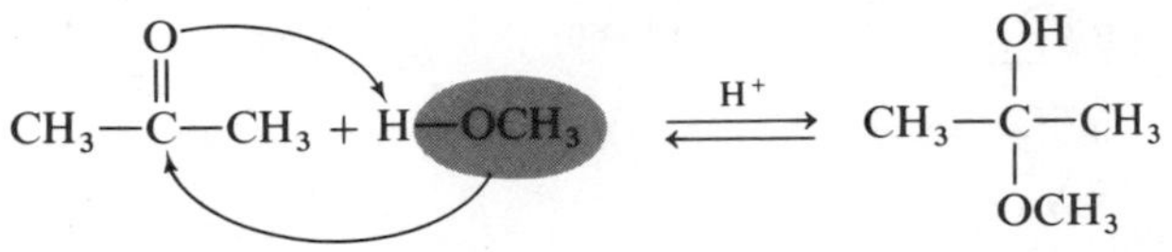

$$CH_3-\overset{\overset{O}{\|}}{C}-CH_3 + H-OCH_3 \xrightleftharpoons{H^+} CH_3-\underset{OCH_3}{\overset{OH}{C}}-CH_3$$

a hemiketal

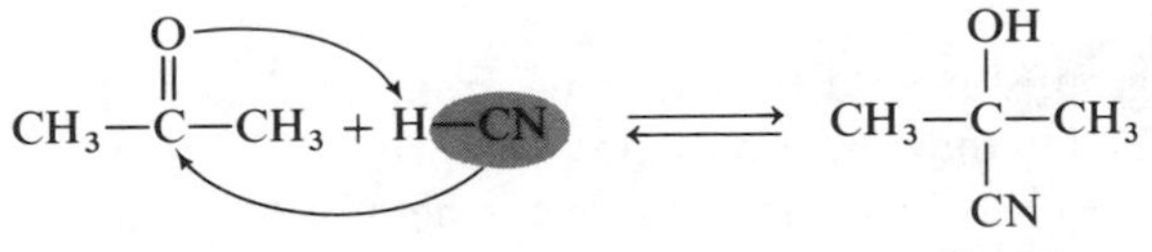

$$CH_3-\overset{\overset{O}{\|}}{C}-CH_3 + H-CN \rightleftharpoons CH_3-\underset{CN}{\overset{OH}{C}}-CH_3$$

a cyanohydrin

General:
$$R-\overset{\overset{O}{\|}}{C}-R + H-A \rightleftharpoons R-\underset{A}{\overset{OH}{C}}-R$$

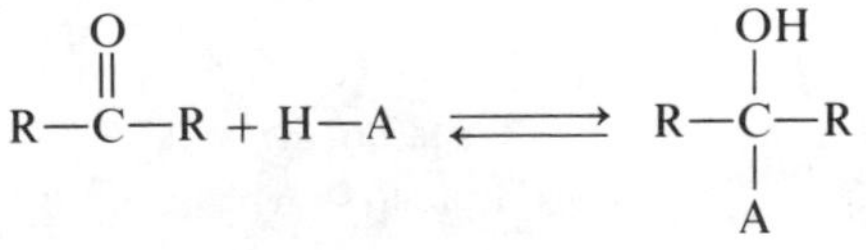

The relative reactivities of aldehydes and ketones in addition reactions may be attributed partly to the *amount of positive charge on the carbonyl carbon*. A greater positive charge means a higher reactivity. If this partial positive charge is dispersed throughout the molecule, then the carbonyl compound is more stable and less reactive.

The carbonyl group is stabilized by adjacent alkyl groups, which are electron-releasing. A ketone, with two R groups, is about 7 kcal/mole more stable than an aldehyde, with only one R group. Formaldehyde, with no alkyl groups, is the most reactive of the aldehydes and ketones.

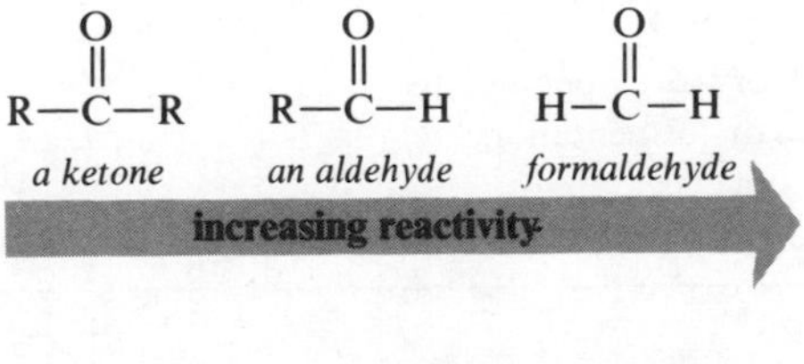

$$\underset{a\ ketone}{R-\overset{\overset{O}{\|}}{C}-R} \qquad \underset{an\ aldehyde}{R-\overset{\overset{O}{\|}}{C}-H} \qquad \underset{formaldehyde}{H-\overset{\overset{O}{\|}}{C}-H}$$

increasing reactivity

Sample Problem

List the following aldehydes in terms of increasing reactivity: CH_3CHO, $ClCH_2CHO$, Cl_2CHCHO, Cl_3CCHO.

Solution: Cl is *electron-withdrawing*. The carbonyl carbon becomes *increasingly positive* and *increasingly reactive* as more Cl atoms are added to the α carbon. Therefore, the order of reactivity is as already shown, with CH_3CHO being the least reactive and Cl_3CCHO being the most reactive.

$$CH_3 \rightarrow \overset{\delta+}{C}HO \qquad Cl_3C \leftarrow \overset{\delta+}{C}HO$$

$$\textit{stabilized} \qquad\qquad \textit{destabilized}$$

Steric factors also play a role in the relative reactivities of aldehydes and ketones. An addition reaction of the carbonyl group leads to an increase in steric hindrance around the carbonyl carbon.

$$\underset{\substack{\text{R} \quad \text{R}}}{\overset{\substack{sp^2,\ less\ hindered \\[4pt] O \\ \parallel \\ C}}{\diagdown \diagup}} + CH_3CH_2OH \underset{}{\overset{H^+}{\rightleftharpoons}} \overset{\substack{sp^3,\ more\ hindered \\[4pt] OH}}{\underset{\substack{| \\ OCH_2CH_3}}{R-C-R}}$$

Bulky groups around the carbonyl group lead to more steric hindrance in the product (and in the transition state). The product is of higher energy because of steric repulsions. A more hindered ketone is therefore less reactive than an aldehyde or a less hindered ketone.

$$\underset{\textit{an ethyl ketone}}{\overset{\overset{\textstyle O}{\parallel}}{CH_3CH_2CH_2CCH_2CH_3}} \qquad \underset{\textit{a methyl ketone}}{\overset{\overset{\textstyle O}{\parallel}}{CH_3CH_2CH_2CCH_3}} \qquad \underset{\textit{an aldehyde}}{\overset{\overset{\textstyle O}{\parallel}}{CH_3CH_2CH_2CH}}$$

$$\xrightarrow{\textbf{increasing reactivity}}$$

STUDY PROBLEM

11.3 An aldehyde or ketone undergoes a reversible acid-catalyzed reaction with ethanol:

$$\overset{\overset{\textstyle O}{\parallel}}{R-C-R} + CH_3CH_2OH \overset{H^+}{\rightleftharpoons} \underset{\underset{\textstyle OCH_2CH_3}{|}}{\overset{\overset{\textstyle OH}{|}}{R-C-R}}$$

A series of compounds is treated with ethanol and a trace of H_2SO_4, and the reaction mixtures are allowed to come to equilibrium. Of each of the following pairs of compounds, which compound yields the greater percentage of addition product in the equilibrium mixture?

(a) 3-pentanone   or   cyclopentanone
(b) 2-pentanone   or   3-pentanone
(c) 2-pentanone   or   pentanal
(d) 2-chlorocyclopentanone   or   2-methylcyclopentanone

Reaction with Water

Water can add to a carbonyl group to form a 1,1-diol, called a **gem-diol**, or **hydrate**. The reaction is reversible, and the equilibrium generally lies on the carbonyl side.

$$CH_3-\overset{\overset{\displaystyle O}{\|}}{C}-CH_3 + H_2O \;\rightleftharpoons\; CH_3-\overset{\overset{\displaystyle OH}{|}}{\underset{\underset{\displaystyle OH}{|}}{C}}-CH_3$$

acetone　　　　　　　　　　　　　*a hydrate*

Stable hydrates are known, but they are the exception rather than the rule. *Chloral hydrate* (a hypnotic and chief ingredient of the "Mickey Finn") is an example of a stable hydrate. *Formalin* also contains a stable hydrate of formaldehyde.

$$Cl_3C\overset{\overset{\displaystyle O}{\|}}{C}H + H_2O \;\rightleftharpoons\; Cl_3CCH(OH)_2$$

chloral　　　　　　　　　　chloral hydrate

$$H\overset{\overset{\displaystyle O}{\|}}{C}H \;\; + H_2O \;\rightleftharpoons\; HCH(OH)_2$$

formaldehyde　　　　　　　*in formalin*

Both formaldehyde and chloral are more reactive than most other aldehydes or ketones because the carbonyl carbon in each has a fairly large amount of positive charge. In formaldehyde, there are no alkyl groups to help disperse the positive charge. In chloral, the strongly electron-withdrawing Cl_3C- group enhances the positive charge by removing electron density.

Let us compare the equilibrium constants for the hydration reactions of chloral (with a more positive carbonyl carbon) and acetone (with the positive charge more dispersed). The equilibrium constants differ by a factor of 10^6!

$$Cl_3C\overset{\overset{\displaystyle O}{\|}}{C}H + H_2O \;\rightleftharpoons\; Cl_3C\overset{\overset{\displaystyle OH}{|}}{\underset{\underset{\displaystyle OH}{|}}{C}}H \qquad K = \frac{[Cl_3CH(OH)_2]}{[Cl_3CHO][H_2O]} = 3000$$

$$CH_3\overset{\overset{\displaystyle O}{\|}}{C}CH_3 + H_2O \;\rightleftharpoons\; CH_3\overset{\overset{\displaystyle OH}{|}}{\underset{\underset{\displaystyle OH}{|}}{C}}CH_3 \qquad K = \frac{[CH_3C(OH)_2CH_3]}{[CH_3COCH_3][H_2O]} = 0.002$$

STUDY PROBLEM

11.4 Which of the following structures would you predict to form stable hydrates?

$$
\text{(a)} \quad Cl_3CCCCl_3 \ (\overset{O}{\overset{\|}{})}
$$

(b) 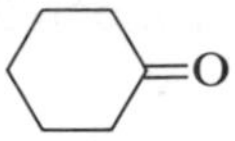 [cyclohexanone structure] =O

(c) C_6H_5CHO

$$
\text{(d)} \quad (CH_3)_3CCCH_2CH_3 \ (\overset{O}{\overset{\|}{})}
$$

Section 11.8

Reaction with Alcohols

Like water, an alcohol can add to a carbonyl group. In most cases, the equilibrium lies on the aldehyde or ketone side of the equation, just as in the reaction with water.

The product of addition of one molecule of an alcohol to an aldehyde is called a **hemiacetal**, while the product of addition of *two* molecules of alcohol (with the loss of H_2O) is called an **acetal**. (**Hemiketal** and **ketal** are the corresponding terms used for ketone products.) All these reactions are catalyzed by a trace of strong acid.

General:

$$
\underset{\substack{an\ aldehyde}}{\overset{O}{\overset{\|}{RCH}}} \underset{\xrightleftharpoons{}}{\overset{ROH,\ H^+}{}} \underset{\substack{a\ hemiacetal \\ (OH\ and\ OR\ on\ C)}}{\overset{OR}{\underset{OH}{RCH}}} \underset{\xrightleftharpoons{}}{\overset{ROH,\ H^+}{}} \underset{\substack{an\ acetal \\ (two\ OR's\ on\ C)}}{\overset{OR}{\underset{OR}{RCH}}} + H_2O
$$

$$
\underset{\substack{acetaldehyde \\ (ethanal)}}{\overset{O}{\overset{\|}{CH_3CH}}} \underset{\xrightleftharpoons{}}{\overset{CH_3CH_2OH,\ H^+}{}} \underset{\substack{a\ hemiacetal}}{\overset{OCH_2CH_3}{\underset{OH}{CH_3CH}}} \underset{\xrightleftharpoons{}}{\overset{CH_3CH_2OH,\ H^+}{}} \underset{\substack{an\ acetal}}{\overset{OCH_2CH_3}{\underset{OCH_2CH_3}{CH_3CH}}} + H_2O
$$

Sample Problem

Give the structures of the organic compounds present in a methanol solution of cyclohexanone that contains a trace of HCl.

Solution:

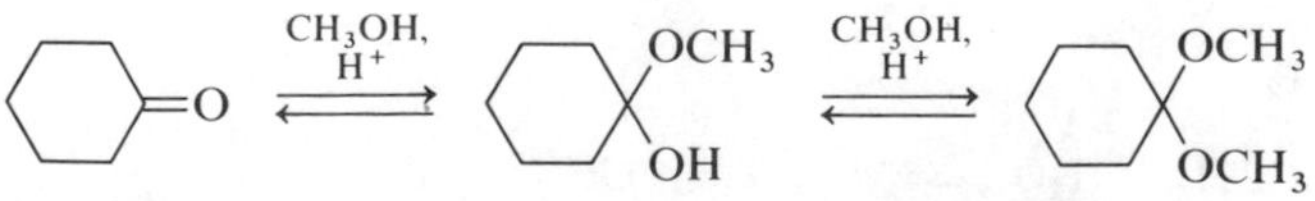

[cyclohexanone] =O $\underset{\xrightleftharpoons{}}{\overset{CH_3OH,\ H^+}{}}$ [cyclohexane ring with OCH_3 and OH] *hemiketal* $\underset{\xrightleftharpoons{}}{\overset{CH_3OH,\ H^+}{}}$ [cyclohexane ring with OCH_3 and OCH_3] *ketal*

STUDY PROBLEMS

11.5   Which of the following structures contains a hemiacetal or hemiketal group, and which contains an acetal or ketal group? Circle each group.

(a) 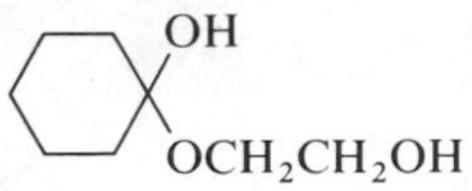 [structure: cyclohexane ring with OH and OCH₂CH₂OH groups]   (b) 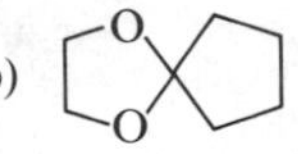 [bicyclic structure with two O atoms]   (c) 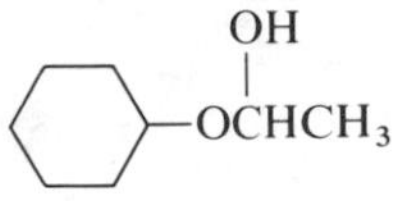 [structure: cyclohexane ring with OH and —OCHCH₃]

11.6   Give the structures of the alcohol and the aldehyde or ketone that are needed to prepare each of the compounds shown in the preceding problem.

The mechanism for the reversible reactions of aldehydes or ketones with alcohols is typical of the mechanisms for many acid-catalyzed addition reactions of carbonyl compounds: a series of protonations and deprotonations of oxygen-containing groups.

Protonation:

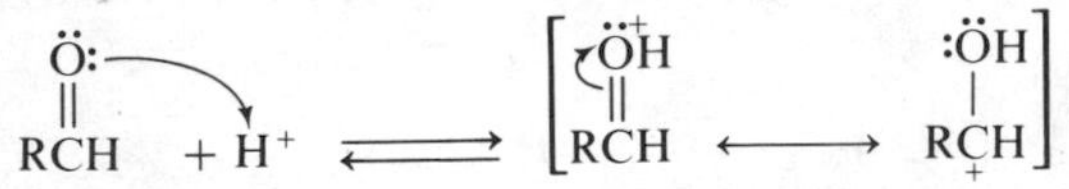

$$RCH + H^+ \rightleftharpoons \left[\overset{+}{\ddot{O}H} \text{ resonance } :\ddot{O}H \right]$$

an aldehyde   *resonance structures for*
                               a protonated aldehyde

Attack of ROH:

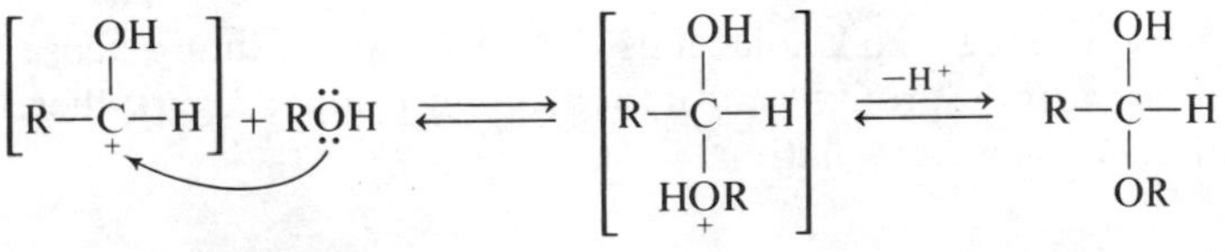

a protonated   *a hemiacetal*
hemiacetal

In the mechanism for acetal formation from the hemiacetal, again protonation and deprotonation, along with loss of water, are the major reaction steps. Acetal formation from a hemiacetal is therefore a two-step *substitution* of an OR group for an OH group.

Protonation and loss of water:

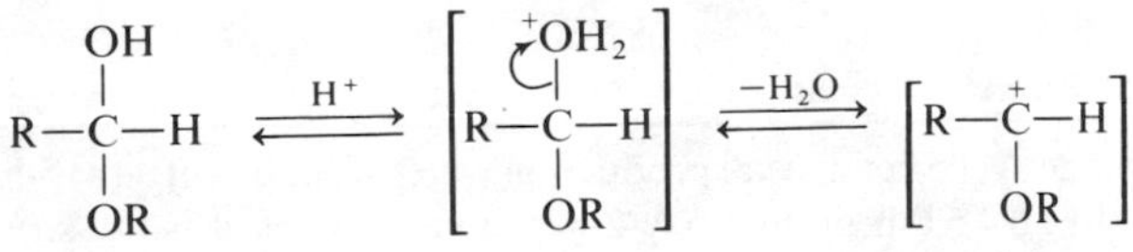

a hemiacetal   *a carbocation*

Attack of ROH:

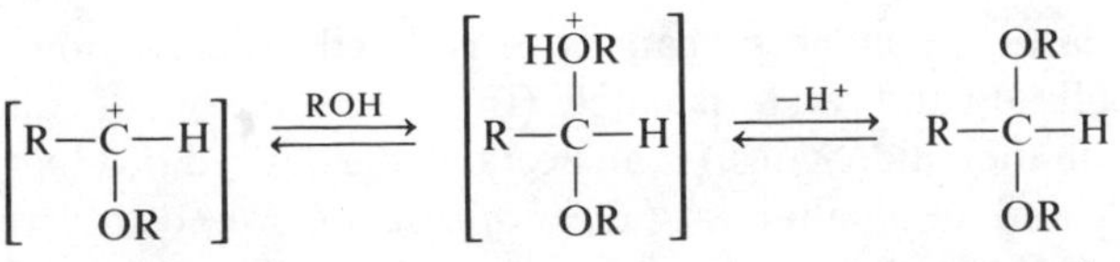

an acetal

STUDY PROBLEM

11.7   An intermediate in the formation of an acetal is a carbocation. Would you expect this hemiacetal carbocation to be more or less stabilized than a comparable aliphatic carbocation? Why?

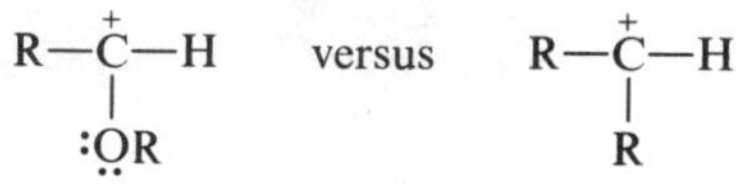

$$R—\overset{+}{\underset{\overset{|}{:\!\underset{\cdot\cdot}{O}R}}{C}}—H \qquad versus \qquad R—\overset{+}{\underset{\overset{|}{R}}{C}}—H$$

In the equilibrium between an aldehyde, a hemiacetal, and an acetal, the aldehyde is generally favored. In an equilibrium mixture, we would usually find a large amount of aldehyde and only small amounts of hemiacetal and acetal. There is one important exception to this generality. A molecule that has an OH group γ or δ (1,4 or 1,5) to an aldehyde or ketone carbonyl group undergoes an intramolecular reaction to form a five- or six-membered hemiacetal ring. *These cyclic hemiacetals are favored over the open-chain aldehyde forms.*

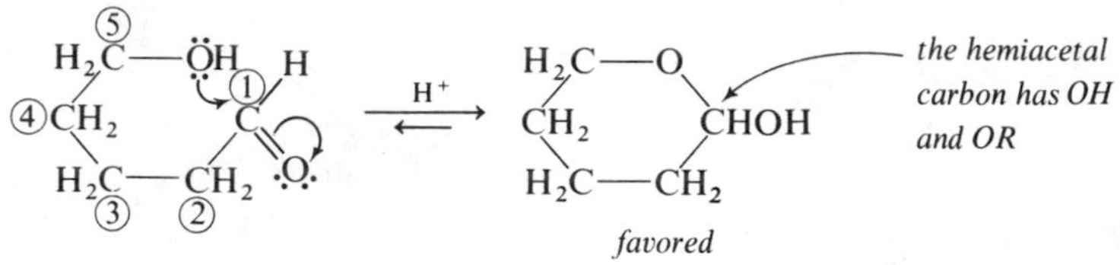

the hemiacetal carbon has OH and OR

favored

The reason that cyclic hemiacetals are important is that glucose and other sugars contain hydroxyl groups γ and δ to carbonyl groups; sugars, therefore, form cyclic hemiacetals in water solution.

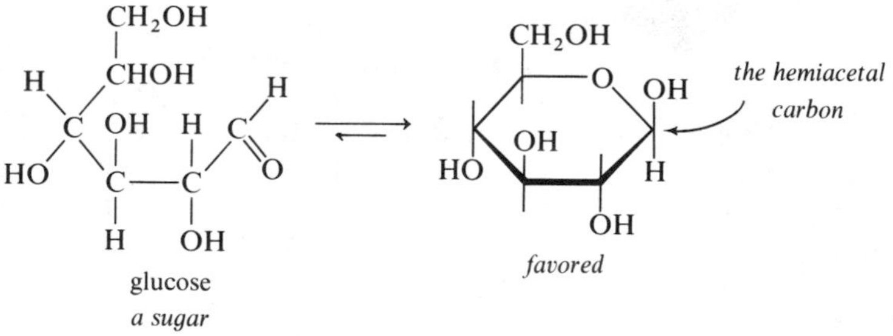

the hemiacetal carbon

glucose
a sugar

favored

STUDY PROBLEM

11.8   Predict the cyclic hemiacetal products in water solutions of   (a) 5-hydroxy-2-hexanone, and   (b) 1,3,4,5,6-pentahydroxy-2-hexanone. (This last is the structure of *fructose*, or *grape sugar*.)

In most cases, a hemiacetal cannot be isolated. Acetals, however, are stable in nonacidic solution and can be isolated. (In acidic solution, of course, they are in equilibrium with their aldehydes.) If an acetal is the desired product from reaction of an aldehyde and an alcohol, an *excess of alcohol* is used to drive the series of reaction steps to that product. *Removing water* as it is formed also helps drive the reversible reactions to the acetal side. Best results in this type of reaction are obtained when the acetal is *cyclic*:

$$\underset{\substack{\text{acetaldehyde}}}{CH_3\overset{\overset{O}{\|}}{C}H} + \underset{\substack{\text{ethylene glycol} \\ \text{(1,2-ethanediol)}}}{HOCH_2CH_2OH} \xrightleftharpoons{H^+} \underset{\substack{\text{a cyclic acetal}}}{CH_3\overset{\overset{O-CH_2}{\diagdown}}{C}H\overset{|}{\underset{O-CH_2}{\diagup}}} + H_2O$$

A **blocking group** is a group used to prevent a functional group from reacting while a reaction is carried out on another part of the molecule. A blocking group must be inert to the desired reaction, yet must be easy to remove when the desired reaction is completed. If a desired reaction can be carried out under alkaline conditions, acetals and ketals are effective blocking groups for aldehydes and ketones. For example, by blocking an aldehyde group as an acetal, we can oxidize a double bond in the same molecule without oxidizing the aldehyde to a carboxylic acid.

Blocking:

$$\underset{\substack{\text{propenal} \\ \text{(acrolein)}}}{CH_2{=}CH\overset{\overset{O}{\|}}{C}H} + \underset{\substack{HOCH_2 \\ | \\ HOCH_2}}{} \xrightleftharpoons{H^+} \underset{\substack{\text{an acetal}}}{CH_2{=}CH\overset{\overset{O-CH_2}{\diagdown}}{C}H\overset{|}{\underset{O-CH_2}{\diagup}}} + H_2O$$

Oxidation of double bond and regeneration of aldehyde:

$$CH_2{=}CH\overset{\overset{O}{\diagdown}}{C}H\overset{}{\underset{O}{\diagup}} \xrightarrow[\text{cold}]{MnO_4^-,\,OH^-} \overset{OH\;OH}{\underset{}{CH_2CH-CH}}\overset{\overset{O}{\diagdown}}{\underset{O}{\diagup}} \xrightleftharpoons{H_2O,\,H^+} \underset{\substack{\text{2,3-dihydroxypropanal} \\ \text{(glyceraldehyde)}}}{\overset{OH\;OH\quad O}{CH_2CH-CH}}$$

Reaction with Hydrogen Cyanide

Hydrogen cyanide (bp 26°) can be considered to be either a gas or a low-boiling liquid. In normal laboratory operations, it is used as a gas, but by use of a special apparatus it can be used as a liquid (and, in some cases, even as a solvent). Often, HCN is generated directly in a reaction mixture from KCN or NaCN and a strong acid. Hydrogen cyanide is toxic and is particularly insidious because the human nose can detect its odor only at levels that may be lethal.

Like water and alcohols, hydrogen cyanide can add to the carbonyl group of an aldehyde or a ketone. The product in either case is referred to as a **cyanohydrin**.

$$\underset{\substack{\text{acetaldehyde}}}{CH_3\overset{\overset{\ddot{O}:}{\|}}{C}H} + H{-}CN \;\rightleftharpoons\; \underset{\substack{\text{acetaldehyde} \\ \text{cyanohydrin} \\ 75\%}}{CH_3\overset{\overset{:\ddot{O}H}{|}}{C}H\overset{|}{\underset{CN}{}}}$$

$$General: \quad R-\overset{\overset{\displaystyle O}{\|}}{C}-R + HCN \;\rightleftharpoons\; R-\overset{\overset{\displaystyle OH}{|}}{\underset{\underset{\displaystyle CN}{|}}{C}}-R$$

an aldehyde
or ketone

a cyanohydrin

Hydrogen cyanide ($pK_a = 9.3$) is too weak an acid to add directly to a carbonyl group. Successful addition requires slightly alkaline reaction conditions. In this way, the concentration of cyanide ion is increased, and addition proceeds by nucleophilic attack of CN^- upon the carbonyl group.

$$HCN + OH^- \;\rightleftharpoons\; H_2O + CN^-$$

$$R-\overset{\overset{\displaystyle O}{\|}}{C}-H \;\rightleftharpoons\; R-\overset{\overset{\displaystyle O^-}{|}}{\underset{\underset{\displaystyle CN}{|}}{C}}-H \;\overset{HCN}{\rightleftharpoons}\; R-\overset{\overset{\displaystyle OH}{|}}{\underset{\underset{\displaystyle CN}{|}}{C}}-H + CN^-$$

Cyanohydrins are useful synthetic intermediates. For example, the CN group can be hydrolyzed to a carboxyl group, or it can be reduced to a CH_2NH_2 group. (Reactions of the CN group will be discussed in Chapter 13.)

$$(CH_3)_2\overset{\overset{\displaystyle OH}{|}}{C}CN \quad \overset{H_2O, \; H^+}{\nearrow} \quad (CH_3)_2\overset{\overset{\displaystyle OH}{|}}{C}CO_2H$$

acetone cyanohydrin

$(CH_3)_2\overset{\overset{\displaystyle OH}{|}}{C}CO_2H$
2-hydroxy-2-methylpropanoic acid
an α-hydroxy acid

$\overset{[H]}{\searrow}$

$(CH_3)_2\overset{\overset{\displaystyle OH}{|}}{C}CH_2NH_2$
1-amino-2-methyl-2-propanol
a β-amino alcohol

The millipede (*Apheloria corrigata*) carries its own poison-gas generator in the form of *mandelonitrile*, a cyanohydrin stored in its defensive glands. When the millipede is attacked, the cyanohydrin is mixed with an enzyme that causes a rapid dissociation to a mixture of benzaldehyde and HCN, which is squirted on the predator to ward off the attack.

$$C_6H_5\overset{\overset{\displaystyle OH}{|}}{C}HCN \;\overset{enzyme}{\longrightarrow}\; C_6H_5\overset{\overset{\displaystyle O}{\|}}{C}H \; + HCN$$

mandelonitrile

benzaldehyde

In plants of the genus *Prunus* (which includes plums, apricots, cherries, and peaches), cyanohydrins are biosynthesized and stored as sugar derivatives in the kernels of the pits. Amygdalin and Laetrile are the best known of these cyanohydrins. (These two compounds are closely related structurally; indeed, amygdalin is often sold as Laetrile.) Because these cyanohydrins can be hydrolyzed enzymatically to HCN, the pits of cherries and other *Prunus* species should not be eaten in quantity.

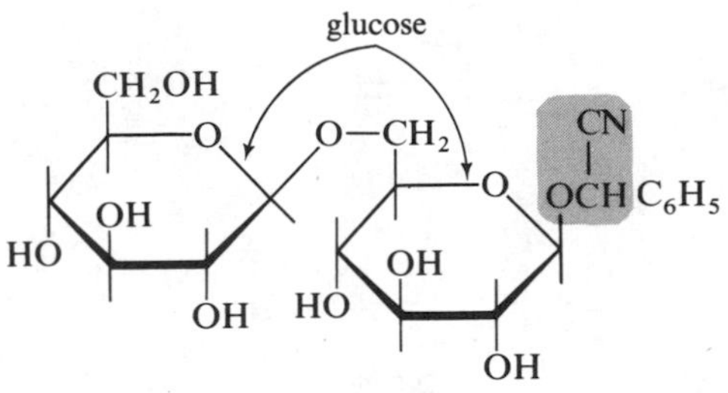

glucose

glucuronic acid

CH$_2$OH

CN

OCH C$_6$H$_5$

OH

HO

OH

OH HO

OH

OH

amygdalin

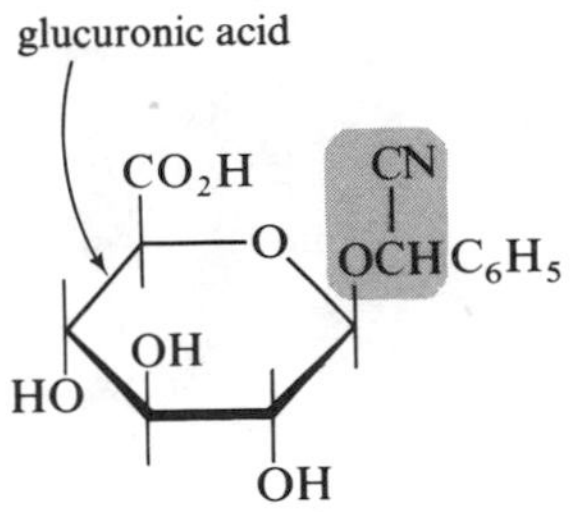

CO$_2$H

CN

OCH C$_6$H$_5$

OH

HO

OH

Laetrile

STUDY PROBLEMS

11.9 List the following carbonyl compounds in terms of increasing reactivity toward HCN (least reactive first):

(a) $(C_6H_5)_2C{=}O$ (b) $C_6H_5\overset{\displaystyle O}{\overset{\|}{C}}H$ (c) $C_6H_5\overset{\displaystyle O}{\overset{\|}{C}}CH_3$

11.10 Suggest a method of synthesis for lactic acid, $CH_3CH(OH)CO_2H$, from ethanol and HCN.

Section 11.10

Reaction with Ammonia and Amines

A. Imines

Ammonia is a nucleophile and, like other nucleophiles, can attack the carbon of the carbonyl group of either an aldehyde or a ketone. The reaction is catalyzed by a trace of acid. For the moment, we may view the first step in the reaction as a simple addition of ammonia across the carbonyl group. The product of the addition is unstable and eliminates water to form an **imine**, a compound that contains the C=N grouping.

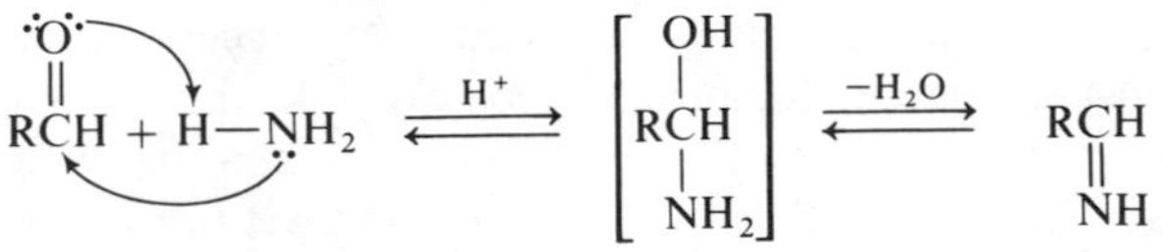

$$RCH + H-NH_2 \;\underset{}{\overset{H^+}{\rightleftharpoons}}\; \left[\begin{array}{c} OH \\ | \\ RCH \\ | \\ NH_2 \end{array}\right] \;\underset{}{\overset{-H_2O}{\rightleftharpoons}}\; \begin{array}{c} RCH \\ \| \\ NH \end{array}$$

an imine

Unsubstituted imines formed from NH_3 are unstable and polymerize on standing. However, if a *primary amine* (RNH_2) is used instead of ammonia, a more stable, substituted imine (sometimes called a **Schiff base**) is formed. Aromatic aldehydes (such as benzaldehyde) or arylamines (such as aniline) give the most stable imines, but other aldehydes, ketones, and primary amines may be used.

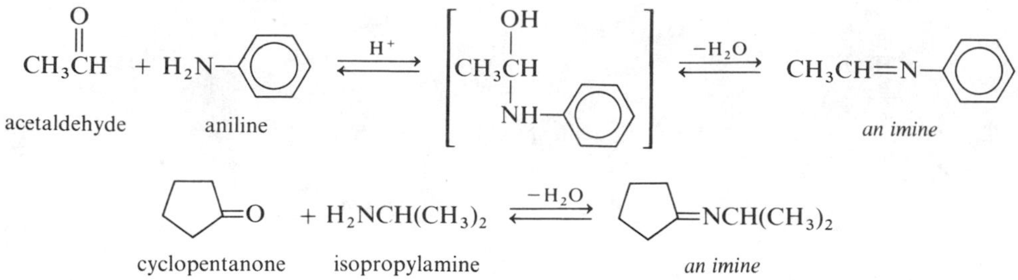

STUDY PROBLEMS

11.11 Why does an arylamine yield a more stable imine than isopropylamine?

11.12 What is the geometry of $CH_3CH{=}NCH_3$? Would you expect this compound to have any stereoisomeric forms?

The steps in the mechanism of imine formation consist of initial protonation of the carbonyl oxygen, attack by the nucleophilic amine (the rate-determining step), a proton shift, and, finally, loss of water and a proton.

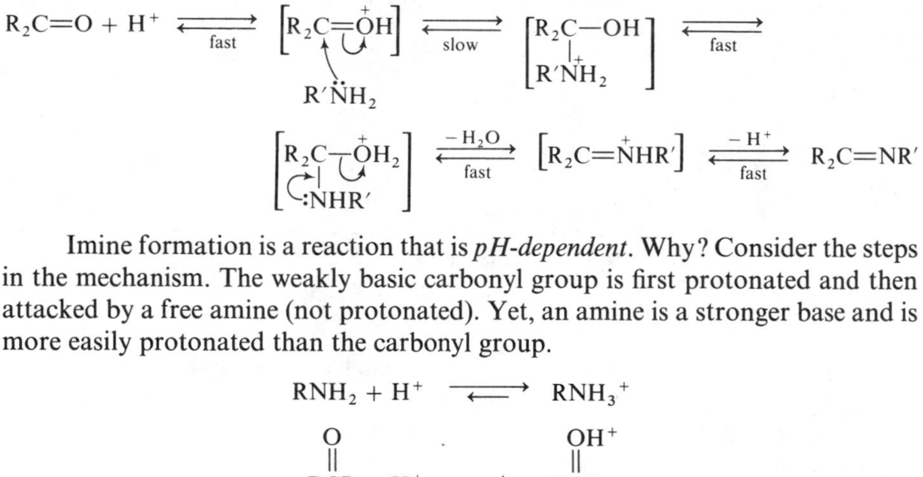

Imine formation is a reaction that is *pH-dependent*. Why? Consider the steps in the mechanism. The weakly basic carbonyl group is first protonated and then attacked by a free amine (not protonated). Yet, an amine is a stronger base and is more easily protonated than the carbonyl group.

Therefore, the reaction requires a careful balance of pH. The solution must be acidic enough that some carbonyl groups are protonated, but not so acidic that all of the amino groups are protonated. At high acid concentration, all the amine molecules are in the nonreactive protonated form. At the other extreme of low acid concentration, none of the carbonyl compound is in the reactive protonated form. In between these two extremes is the optimum pH (about pH 3–4) at which the rate of reaction is greatest. At this pH, some of the amine is protonated, but some is free. Although most of the carbonyl compound is free, some is protonated and susceptible to attack.

Imines are important intermediates in the biosynthesis of α-amino acids, $RCH(NH_2)CO_2H$, which are used by an organism in the synthesis of proteins. If a diet does not contain the required proportions of necessary amino acids, an organism can, in some cases, convert an unneeded amino acid to a desired amino acid in a **transamination reaction**. The process involves the transfer of an amino group from the unneeded amino acid to a keto acid.

Transamination:

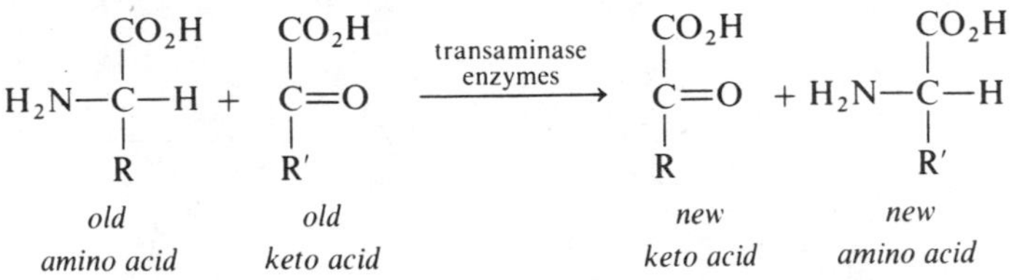

The reaction is thought to proceed through a series of imine intermediates:

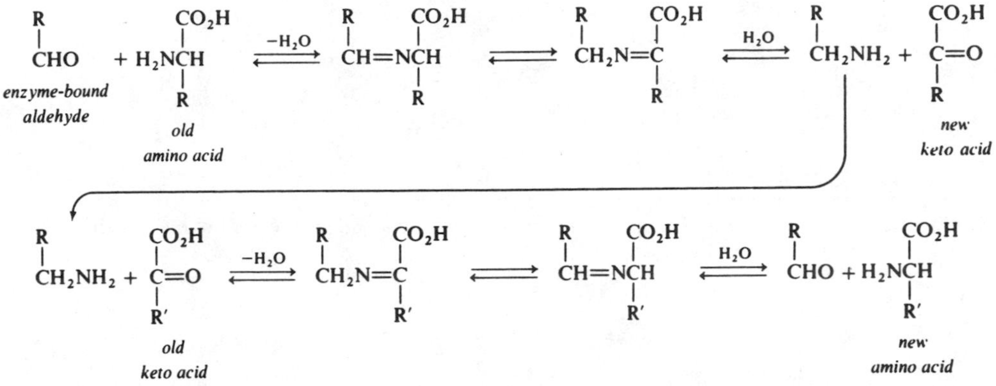

STUDY PROBLEM

11.13 How would you prepare each of the following imines from a carbonyl compound?

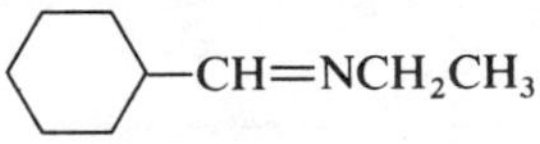

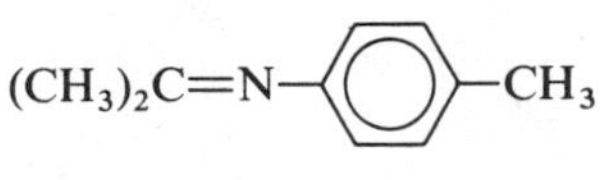

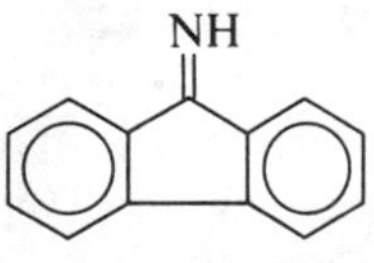

B. Enamines

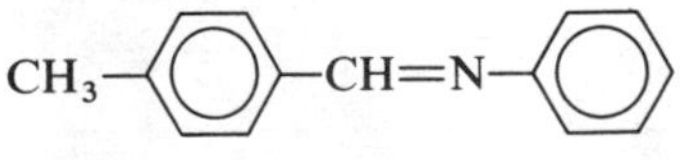

With primary amines, aldehydes and ketones yield imines. With *secondary* amines (R_2NH), aldehydes and ketones yield **iminium ions**, which undergo further reaction to **enamines** (vinylamines). The enamine is formed by loss of a proton from a carbon atom β to the nitrogen, which results in a double bond between the α and β carbon atoms.

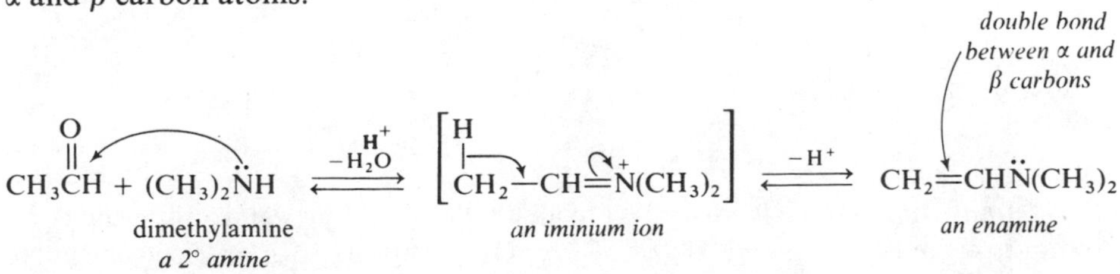

STUDY PROBLEM

11.14 Predict the product of the reaction of cyclohexanone with:

(a) CH_3NH_2 (b) $(CH_3)_2NH$ (c)  NH

Sample Problem

Give the enamine product of the following reaction:

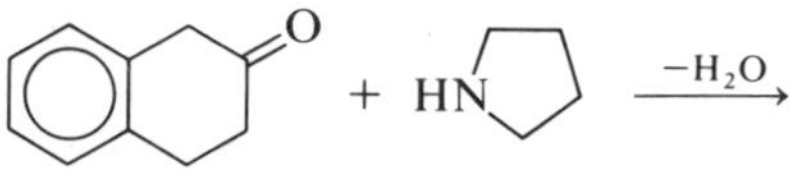

Solution:

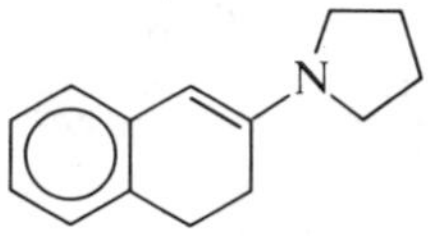

STUDY PROBLEM

11.15 In the preceding sample problem, the double bond in the enamine could have been formed as follows:

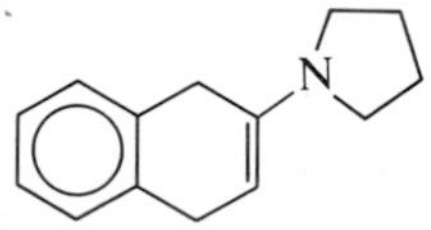

Suggest a reason why the double bond is *not* formed in this position.

Section 11.11

Reaction with Hydrazine and Related Compounds

Imines are easily hydrolyzed (cleaved by water). The initial step of hydrolysis is protonation of the imine nitrogen. If an *electronegative group* is attached to the imine nitrogen, the basicity of the nitrogen is reduced and the hydrolysis is suppressed.

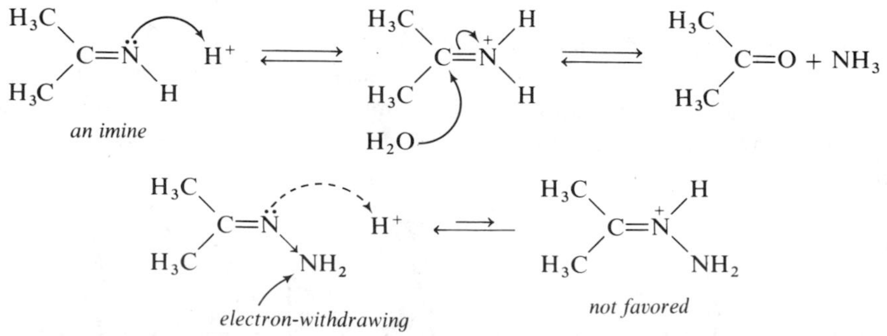

Imine-type products formed from aldehydes or ketones and a nitrogen compound of the type $H_2N—NH_2$ or $H_2N—OH$ (reagents with an electronegative

Table 11.4. *Some Nitrogen Compounds that Form Stable Substitution Products with Aldehydes and Ketones*

Name	*Structure*	*Product with RCHO*
hydroxylamine	$HONH_2$	$RCH{=}NOH$ *an oxime*
hydrazine	H_2NNH_2	$RCH{=}NNH_2$ *a hydrazone*
phenylhydrazine	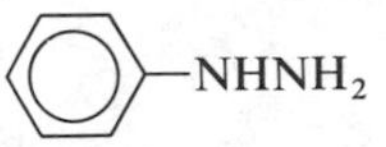 ⬡—$NHNH_2$	$RCH{=}NNHC_6H_5$ *a phenylhydrazone*
2,4-dinitro-phenylhydrazine	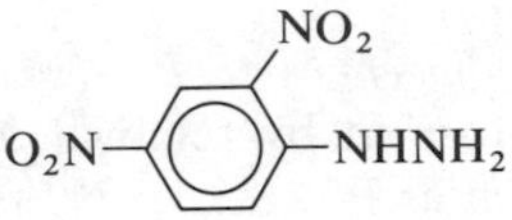 O_2N—⬡(NO_2)—$NHNH_2$	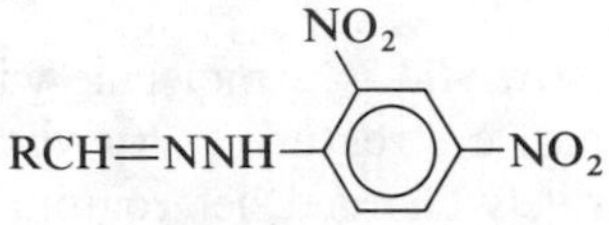 $RCH{=}NNH$—⬡(NO_2)—NO_2 *a 2,4-dinitrophenylhydrazone*
semicarbazide	$H_2NNHCNH_2$ (O)	$RCH{=}NNHCNH_2$ (O) *a semicarbazone*

group attached to the N) are quite stable. Table 11.4 lists the variety of nitrogen compounds that undergo reaction with aldehydes and most ketones to form stable imine-type products.

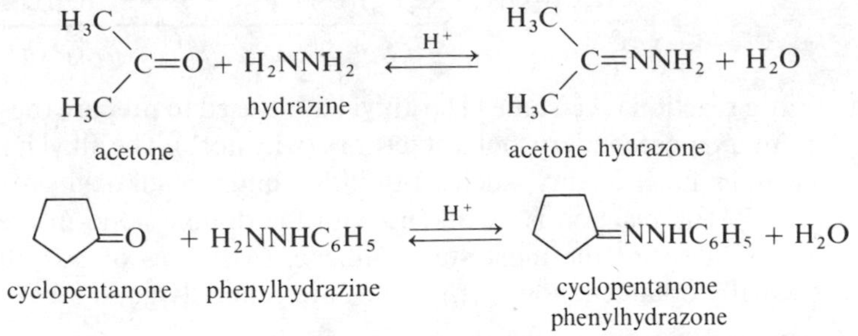

$$\underset{\text{acetone}}{(H_3C)_2C{=}O} + \underset{\text{hydrazine}}{H_2NNH_2} \underset{}{\overset{H^+}{\rightleftharpoons}} \underset{\text{acetone hydrazone}}{(H_3C)_2C{=}NNH_2} + H_2O$$

$$\underset{\text{cyclopentanone}}{\text{⬠=O}} + \underset{\text{phenylhydrazine}}{H_2NNHC_6H_5} \overset{H^+}{\rightleftharpoons} \underset{\substack{\text{cyclopentanone} \\ \text{phenylhydrazone}}}{\text{⬠=NNHC}_6H_5} + H_2O$$

The hydrazones and other products listed in Table 11.4, especially the high-molecular-weight 2,4-dinitrophenylhydrazones, or DNP's, are generally solids. Before the wide use of spectrometers, these derivatives were used extensively for identification purposes. A liquid ketone of unknown structure could be converted to the solid DNP, purified by crystallization, and its melting point compared to those of DNP's of known structure.

STUDY PROBLEM

11.16 Predict the product of the reaction of: (a) butanone with semicarbazide; (b) cyclohexanone with 2,4-dinitrophenylhydrazine; and (c) acetophenone ($C_6H_5COCH_3$) with hydrazine.

Section 11.12

The Wittig Reaction

In 1954, George Wittig reported a general synthesis of alkenes from carbonyl compounds using *phosphonium ylids*. This synthesis is called the **Wittig reaction**.

$$
\underset{\substack{\text{an aldehyde} \\ \text{or ketone}}}{\overset{R}{\underset{R}{\diagdown}}C=O} + \underset{\text{a phosphonium ylid}}{(C_6H_5)_3P=\overset{R'}{\underset{R'}{C}}} \longrightarrow \underset{\text{an alkene}}{\overset{R}{\underset{R}{\diagdown}}C=\overset{R'}{\underset{R'}{C}}} + (C_6H_5)_3PO
$$

from the ylid

An **ylid** is a molecule with *adjacent* $+$ *and* $-$ *charges* (see the following resonance structures). An ylid is formed by removal of a proton vicinal to a positively charged heteroatom (such as P^+, S^+, or N^+). The phosphonium ylid for a Wittig reaction is prepared by (1) nucleophilic substitution (S_N2) of an alkyl halide with triphenylphosphine (a good nucleophile, a weak base), and (2) treatment with base, a reaction in which the intermediate phosphonium salt eliminates a proton to form the ylid.

$$
\underset{\text{triphenylphosphine}}{(C_6H_5)_3P:} + \overset{R'}{\underset{R'}{CH}}\!\!-\!\!X \xrightarrow[S_N2]{-X^-} \underset{\text{a phosphonium salt}}{(C_6H_5)_3\overset{+}{P}\!\!-\!\!\overset{H}{C}R'_2} \xrightarrow{^-OCH_2CH_3}
$$

$$
CH_3CH_2OH + \underbrace{(C_6H_5)_3\overset{+}{P}\!\!-\!\!\overset{..}{\overset{-}{C}}R'_2 \longleftrightarrow (C_6H_5)_3P=CR'_2}_{\text{resonance structures for the ylid}}
$$

The Wittig reaction is versatile. The alkyl halide used to prepare the ylid may be methyl, primary, or secondary, but not tertiary (why not?). The alkyl halide may also contain other functionality, such as double bonds or alkoxyl groups. The product of the Wittig reaction is an alkene with the double bond in the desired position, even if it is not the most stable alkene. (Mixtures of *cis-* and *trans-* isomers are usually obtained, however.) Yields are generally good (about 70%).

$$
\underset{\text{cyclohexanone}}{\bigcirc\!\!=\!\!O} + (C_6H_5)_3P=C(CH_3)_2 \longrightarrow \underset{\substack{\text{isopropylidene-} \\ \text{cyclohexane}}}{\bigcirc\!\!=\!\!C(CH_3)_2} + (C_6H_5)_3PO
$$

$$
\underset{\text{benzaldehyde}}{\bigcirc\!\!-\!\!\overset{\overset{O}{\|}}{CH}} + (C_6H_5)_3P=CH_2 \longrightarrow \underset{\text{styrene}}{\bigcirc\!\!-\!\!CH=CH_2} + (C_6H_5)_3PO
$$

$$
\underset{\text{acetone}}{CH_3\overset{\overset{O}{\|}}{C}CH_3} + (C_6H_5)_3P=CHCH=CH_2 \longrightarrow \underset{\text{4-methyl-1,3-pentadiene}}{(CH_3)_2C=CHCH=CH_2} + (C_6H_5)_3PO
$$

The mechanism of the Wittig reaction is still being investigated. A currently accepted theory is that the carbonyl group undergoes nucleophilic attack by the negative carbon of the ylid.

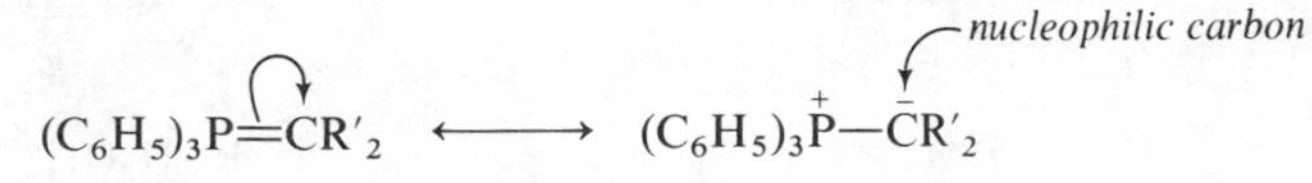

$$(C_6H_5)_3P{=}CR'_2 \longleftrightarrow (C_6H_5)_3\overset{+}{P}{-}\overset{-}{C}R'_2$$

nucleophilic carbon

resonance structures

Addition to carbonyl:

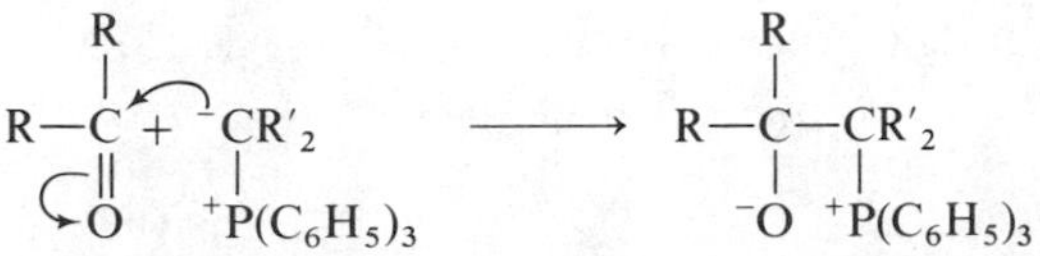

$$\begin{array}{c} R \\ | \\ R{-}C{+}\ ^-CR'_2 \\ || \quad | \\ O \quad ^+P(C_6H_5)_3 \end{array} \longrightarrow \begin{array}{c} R \\ | \\ R{-}C{-}CR'_2 \\ | \quad | \\ ^-O \quad ^+P(C_6H_5)_3 \end{array}$$

a betaine

The addition product of the ylid and aldehyde or ketone is a **betaine** (a molecule having *nonadjacent* opposite charges). The betaine undergoes elimination of triphenylphosphine oxide to form the alkene.

Elimination to alkene:

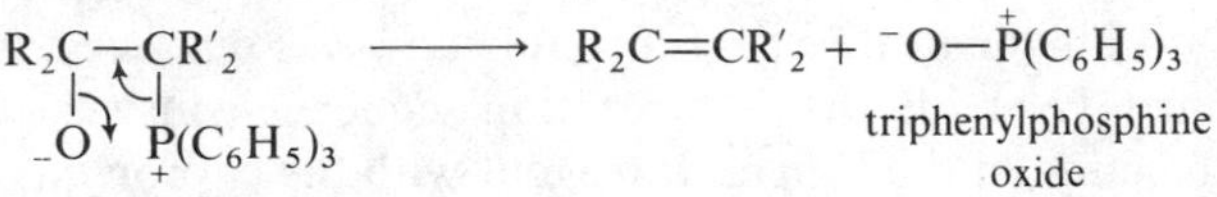

$$\begin{array}{c} R_2C{-}CR'_2 \\ | \quad | \\ ^-O \quad P(C_6H_5)_3 \\ \quad\quad + \end{array} \longrightarrow R_2C{=}CR'_2 + {}^-O{-}\overset{+}{P}(C_6H_5)_3$$

triphenylphosphine
oxide

STUDY PROBLEMS

11.17 (a) Suggest a Wittig reaction for the synthesis of methylenecyclohexane.
(b) What product would you obtain if you tried to make this compound by the dehydration of 1-methyl-1-cyclohexanol?

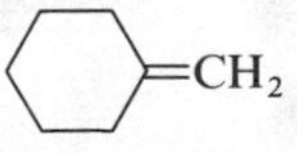

$$\text{⬡}{=}CH_2$$

methylenecyclohexane

11.18 What alkyl halide and what carbonyl compound would you use to prepare each of the following compounds by a Wittig reaction?

(a) $C_6H_5CH{=}CHCH_2CH_3$ (b) 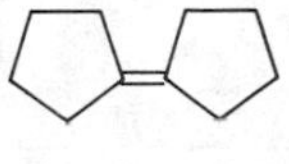 ⬠⬠ (c) 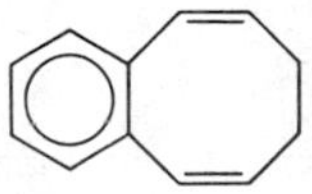 ⬡⬡

Section 11.13

Reaction with Grignard Reagents

The reaction of a Grignard reagent with a carbonyl compound is another example of a nucleophilic addition to the positive carbon of a carbonyl group.

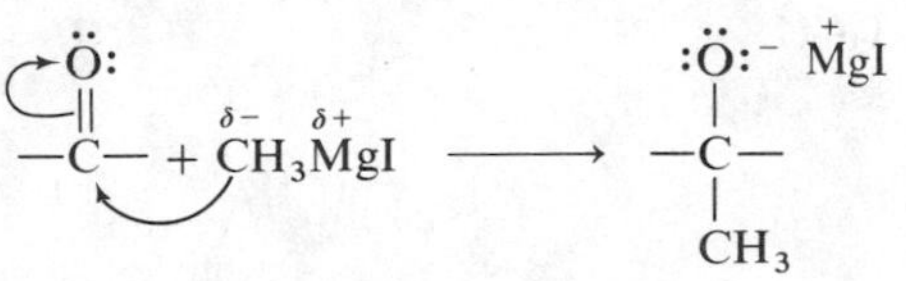

$$\begin{array}{c} \ddot{O}: \\ || \\ {-}C{-}\ +\ \overset{\delta-}{C}H_3\overset{\delta+}{M}gI \end{array} \longrightarrow \begin{array}{c} :\ddot{O}:^-\ \overset{+}{M}gI \\ | \\ {-}C{-} \\ | \\ CH_3 \end{array}$$

Aldehydes and Ketones

Table 11.5. *Grignard Products from Aldehydes and Ketones*

Reactants	Products after hydrolysis

$$RMgX \;+\; \underset{\text{formaldehyde}}{H\overset{\overset{\displaystyle O}{\|}}{C}H} \;\longrightarrow\; \underset{\text{a } 1^\circ \text{ alcohol}}{RCH_2OH}$$

$$RMgX \;+\; \underset{\text{other aldehydes}}{R'\overset{\overset{\displaystyle O}{\|}}{C}H} \;\longrightarrow\; \underset{\text{a } 2^\circ \text{ alcohol}}{R\overset{\overset{\displaystyle OH}{|}}{C}HR'}$$

$$RMgX + \underset{\text{ketones}}{R'\overset{\overset{\displaystyle O}{\|}}{C}R'} \;\longrightarrow\; \underset{\text{a } 3^\circ \text{ alcohol}}{R'_2\overset{\overset{\displaystyle OH}{|}}{C}R}$$

Reaction of a Grignard reagent with an aldehyde or a ketone provides an excellent method for the synthesis of alcohols and was discussed in that context earlier (Sections 6.13 and 7.4B). The reaction sequence consists of two separate steps: (1) the reaction of the Grignard reagent with the carbonyl compound, and (2) hydrolysis of the resulting magnesium alkoxide to yield the alcohol. Table 11.5 summarizes the reactions of formaldehyde, other aldehydes, and ketones with RMgX.

$$R'MgX + R\overset{\overset{\displaystyle O}{\|}}{C}R \;\longrightarrow\; \underset{\substack{\text{a magnesium} \\ \text{alkoxide}}}{R\overset{\overset{\displaystyle OMgX}{|}}{\underset{\underset{\displaystyle R'}{|}}{C}}R} \;\xrightarrow{H_2O,\ H^+}\; \underset{\text{an alcohol}}{R\overset{\overset{\displaystyle OH}{|}}{\underset{\underset{\displaystyle R'}{|}}{C}}R} \;+\; HOMgX$$

Sample Problem

Suggest *two* synthetic routes to 2-butanol from an aldehyde or ketone and a Grignard reagent.

Solution: In the synthesis of 2-butanol, either (1) CH_3MgX and CH_3CH_2CHO may be used, or (2) CH_3CH_2MgX and CH_3CHO may be used. In the laboratory, the choice would depend on a number of factors, including availability and cost of the appropriate alkyl halides and aldehydes.

$$\underset{\displaystyle \underset{\text{from } CH_3MgI}{\Big\uparrow} \qquad \underset{\text{from } HCCH_2CH_3}{\nwarrow}}{CH_3\overset{\overset{\displaystyle OH}{|}}{C}HCH_2CH_3} \qquad\qquad \underset{\displaystyle \underset{\text{from } CH_3CH}{\nearrow} \qquad \underset{\text{from } BrMgCH_2CH_3}{\Big\uparrow}}{CH_3\overset{\overset{\displaystyle OH}{|}}{C}H{-}CH_2CH_3}$$

from CH_3MgI from $H\overset{\overset{\displaystyle O}{\|}}{C}CH_2CH_3$ from $CH_3\overset{\overset{\displaystyle O}{\|}}{C}H$ from $BrMgCH_2CH_3$

The two sequences to 2-butanol:

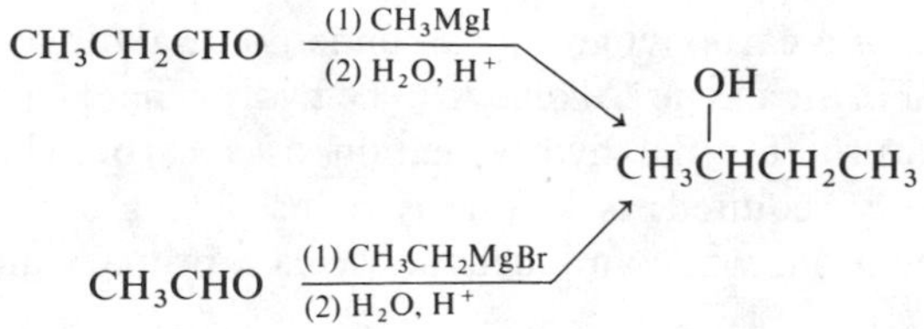

$$CH_3CH_2CHO \xrightarrow[\text{(2) } H_2O, H^+]{\text{(1) } CH_3MgI}$$

$$\begin{array}{c} OH \\ | \\ CH_3CHCH_2CH_3 \end{array}$$

$$CH_3CHO \xrightarrow[\text{(2) } H_2O, H^+]{\text{(1) } CH_3CH_2MgBr}$$

Sample Problem

Suggest three different Grignard reactions leading to 2-phenyl-2-butanol.

Solution:

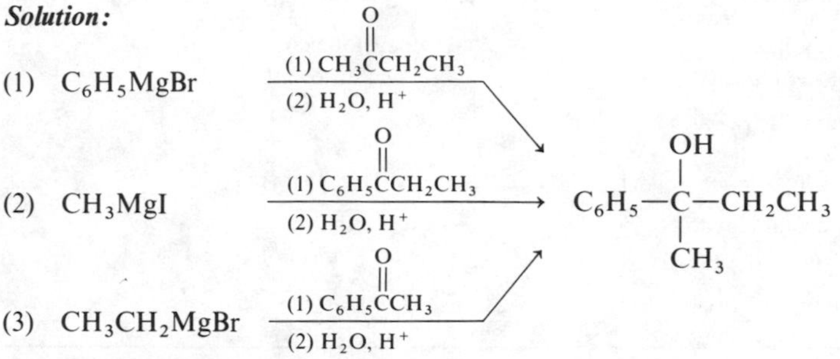

(1) C_6H_5MgBr $\xrightarrow[\text{(2) } H_2O, H^+]{\text{(1) } CH_3\overset{\displaystyle O}{\overset{\displaystyle \|}{C}}CH_2CH_3}$

(2) CH_3MgI $\xrightarrow[\text{(2) } H_2O, H^+]{\text{(1) } C_6H_5\overset{\displaystyle O}{\overset{\displaystyle \|}{C}}CH_2CH_3}$ $\quad C_6H_5-\overset{\displaystyle OH}{\underset{\displaystyle CH_3}{\overset{\displaystyle |}{\underset{\displaystyle |}{C}}}}-CH_2CH_3$

(3) CH_3CH_2MgBr $\xrightarrow[\text{(2) } H_2O, H^+]{\text{(1) } C_6H_5\overset{\displaystyle O}{\overset{\displaystyle \|}{C}}CH_3}$

STUDY PROBLEMS

11.19 What Grignard reagent would you use to effect the following conversions?   (a) form-aldehyde to benzyl alcohol;   (b) cyclohexanone to 1-propyl-1-cyclohexanol.

11.20 Which of the following compounds could *not* be used as a carbonyl starting material in a Grignard synthesis? (*Hint*: See Section 6.15.)

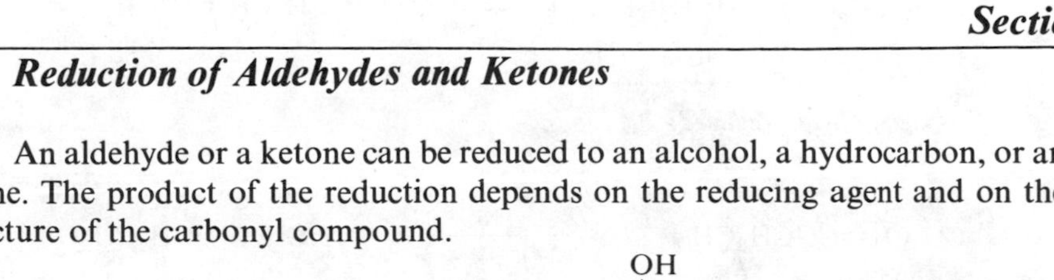

(a) $\begin{array}{cc} OH & O \\ | & \| \\ CH_3CHCH_2CH \end{array}$
(b) $\begin{array}{cc} O & O \\ \| & \| \\ CH_3CCH_2COH \end{array}$
(c) $\begin{array}{c} O \\ \| \\ C_6H_5CH_2CH_2CH \end{array}$

(d) $H_2N-\langle\bigcirc\rangle-\overset{\displaystyle O}{\overset{\displaystyle \|}{CH}}$
(e) $\begin{array}{c} O \\ \| \\ HCCH_2CH_2CH_2CH \end{array}$
(f) $\langle\bigcirc\rangle=O$

Section 11.14

Reduction of Aldehydes and Ketones

An aldehyde or a ketone can be reduced to an alcohol, a hydrocarbon, or an amine. The product of the reduction depends on the reducing agent and on the structure of the carbonyl compound.

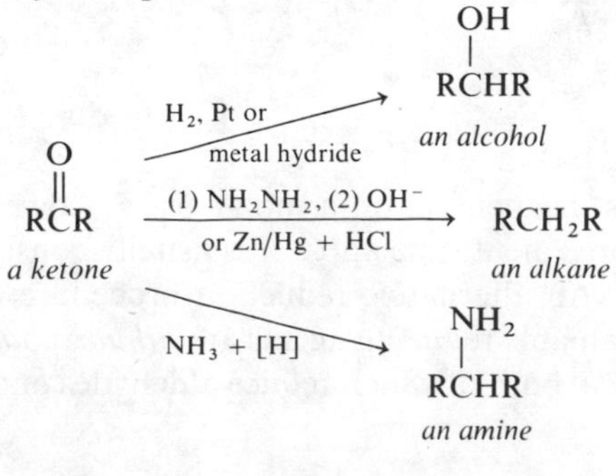

$$\begin{array}{c} O \\ \| \\ RCR \\ \textit{a ketone} \end{array}
\begin{cases}
\xrightarrow[\text{metal hydride}]{H_2, \text{ Pt or}} & \begin{array}{c} OH \\ | \\ RCHR \\ \textit{an alcohol} \end{array} \\[2em]
\xrightarrow[\text{or Zn/Hg + HCl}]{\text{(1) } NH_2NH_2, \text{ (2) } OH^-} & \begin{array}{c} RCH_2R \\ \textit{an alkane} \end{array} \\[2em]
\xrightarrow{NH_3 + [H]} & \begin{array}{c} NH_2 \\ | \\ RCHR \\ \textit{an amine} \end{array}
\end{cases}$$

A. Hydrogenation

The pi bond of a carbonyl group can undergo catalytic hydrogenation, just as can the pi bond in an alkene. Alkenes can be hydrogenated at low pressure and at room temperature; for the hydrogenation of a carbonyl group, heat and pressure are usually required. A ketone is reduced to a secondary alcohol by catalytic hydrogenation, while an aldehyde yields a primary alcohol. Yields are excellent (90–100%).

$$\text{cyclohexanone} + H_2 \xrightarrow[50°, \ 65 \ atm]{Ni} \text{cyclohexanol}$$

cyclohexanone · *a ketone*   cyclohexanol · *a 2° alcohol*

$$\overset{O}{\overset{\|}{CH_3CH}} + H_2 \xrightarrow[heat, \ pressure]{Ni} CH_3CH_2OH$$

acetaldehyde   ethanol
an aldehyde   *a 1° alcohol*

STUDY PROBLEM

11.21 2-Heptanol can be obtained by two Grignard reactions as well as by a hydrogenation reaction. Write the equations for the three sets of reactions that would lead to this alcohol.

If both a double bond and a carbonyl group are present in a structure, the double bond may be hydrogenated, leaving the carbonyl intact, or both may be hydrogenated. However, the carbonyl group cannot be hydrogenated independently of the double bond. If it is desired to reduce a carbonyl group while leaving a double bond intact, a metal hydride reduction is the method of choice.

$C=C$ *reduced* (*but not* $C=O$):

$$CH_3CH{=}CHCH_2\overset{O}{\overset{\|}{CH}} + H_2 \xrightarrow[25°]{Ni} CH_3CH_2CH_2CH_2\overset{O}{\overset{\|}{CH}}$$

3-pentenal   pentanal

$C=C$ *and* $C=O$ *reduced*:

$$CH_3CH{=}CHCH_2\overset{O}{\overset{\|}{CH}} + 2 \ H_2 \xrightarrow[heat, \ pressure]{Ni} CH_3CH_2CH_2CH_2CH_2OH$$

3-pentenal   1-pentanol

B. Metal Hydrides

Hydrogen gas is inexpensive on a molar basis; however, a hydrogenation reaction is rather inconvenient. The apparatus usually consists of gas tanks and a metal pressure vessel. An alternative reduction procedure involves the use of a metal hydride. Two valuable reducing agents are *lithium aluminum hydride* (LAH) and *sodium borohydride*, both of which reduce aldehydes and ketones to alcohols.

$$\text{Li}^+ \quad \text{H}-\overset{\overset{\displaystyle H}{|}}{\underset{\underset{\displaystyle H}{|}}{\text{Al}}}=\text{H} \qquad\qquad \text{Na}^+ \quad \text{H}-\overset{\overset{\displaystyle H}{|}}{\underset{\underset{\displaystyle H}{|}}{\text{B}}}=\text{H}$$

lithium aluminum hydride   sodium borohydride

$$\underset{\text{butanone}}{\overset{\displaystyle O}{\overset{\displaystyle \|}{CH_3CH_2CCH_3}}} \quad\xrightarrow[\text{(2) } H_2O]{\text{(1) LiAlH}_4}\quad \underset{\text{2-butanol}}{\overset{\displaystyle OH}{\overset{\displaystyle |}{CH_3CH_2CHCH_3}}}$$

These two metal hydrides are quite different in their reactivities. LAH is a powerful reducing agent that reduces not only aldehydes and ketones, but also carboxylic acids, esters, amides, and nitriles. LAH undergoes violent reaction with water; reductions are usually carried out in a solvent such as anhydrous ether.

Sodium borohydride is a milder reducing agent. $NaBH_4$ reduces aldehydes and ketones, but not other unsaturated groups. Its reactions may be carried out in an aqueous alcohol as the solvent. For simple reductions of aldehydes and ketones, the milder $NaBH_4$ is the preferred reagent; it is certainly more convenient to use because of its lack of reactivity toward water.

Neither LAH nor $NaBH_4$ reduces alkenyl double bonds in most cases. Consequently, a structure that contains both a double bond and a carbonyl group can be reduced selectively at the carbonyl position. In this respect, the metal hydrides are complementary to hydrogen gas as reducing agents.

C=O reduced (but not C=C):

$$\underset{\text{3-pentenal}}{\overset{\displaystyle O}{\overset{\displaystyle \|}{CH_3CH=CHCH_2CH}}} \quad\xrightarrow[\text{(2) } H_2O,\ H^+]{\text{(1) NaBH}_4}\quad \underset{\text{3-penten-1-ol}}{CH_3CH=CHCH_2CH_2OH}$$

STUDY PROBLEMS

11.22 Show how each of the following alcohols could be prepared by the $NaBH_4$ reduction of an aldehyde or ketone:

(a) $CH_3CH_2CH_2OH$ (b) ⬡—OH   (c) ⬡—$\overset{\overset{\displaystyle OH}{|}}{CH}CH_3$

11.23 When glucose (page 543) is treated with $NaBH_4$, then with aqueous acid, an artificial sweetener called *sorbitol* results. What is the structure of sorbitol?

Metal hydrides react by transferring a negative hydride ion to the positive carbon of a carbonyl group, just as a Grignard reagent transfers R to the carbonyl group.

$$\overset{\displaystyle O}{\overset{\displaystyle \|}{R-C-R}} + H-\overset{\overset{\displaystyle H}{|}}{\underset{\underset{\displaystyle \textbf{H}}{|}}{B}}=H \longrightarrow \overset{\displaystyle O^-}{\underset{\underset{\displaystyle H}{|}}{\overset{\overset{\displaystyle |}{R-C-R}}{}}} + BH_3 \qquad \textit{three more H's}$$

Each hydride ion can reduce one carbonyl group. Therefore, one mole of LAH or NaBH$_4$ can reduce *four* moles of aldehyde or ketone, theoretically. After the reaction is completed, treatment with water or aqueous acid liberates the alcohol from its salt.

Step 1:
$$4 \ \overset{\overset{\text{O}}{\|}}{\text{RCR}} + \text{NaBH}_4 \longrightarrow \text{Na}^+ \ {}^-\text{B}\left(\text{OCHR}\overset{\overset{\text{R}}{|}}{}\right)_4$$

Step 2:
$$\underset{\underset{\text{RCHR}}{|}}{\overset{\overset{\text{O}^-}{|}}{}} + \text{H}^+ \longrightarrow \underset{\underset{\text{RCHR}}{|}}{\overset{\overset{\text{OH}}{|}}{}}$$

Camphor is a bridged, cyclic compound with a ketone group. Reduction of camphor with LAH leads to 90% of the isomer in which the OH group is *cis* to the bridge. Why is this so? Let us look at the structure of camphor. Note that the bridge provides substantial steric hindrance on one side of the carbonyl group—on top, as it is shown here.

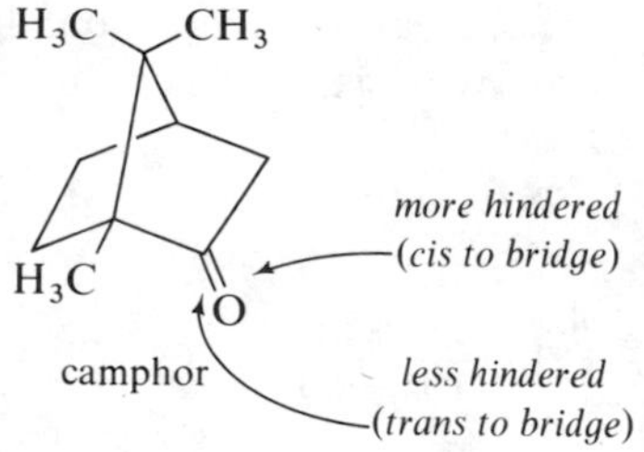

When a ketone is reduced by LAH, it is not just a tiny hydride ion attacking; it is the relatively bulky AlH$_4{}^-$ ion. There is evidence that the electropositive, metallic portion of the metal hydride ion forms a complex with the carbonyl oxygen while the hydride ion is transferred to the carbonyl carbon. A look at the likely structure of the transition state shows how AlH$_4{}^-$ attacks the *less hindered* side of the camphor structure—that is, AlH$_4{}^-$ attacks the carbonyl group from the side that is *trans* to the bridge. The resultant OH group is then formed *cis* to the bridge.

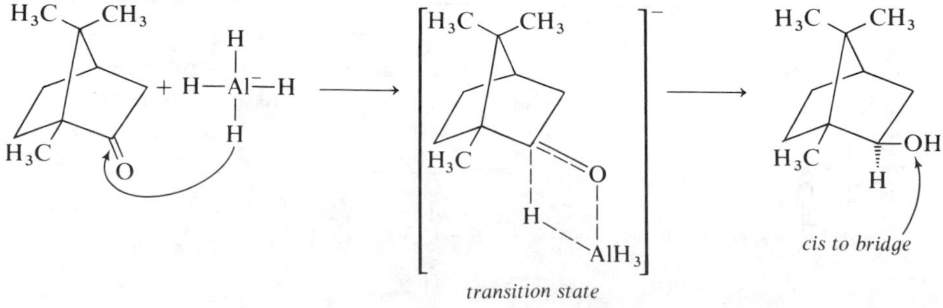

transition state

When a *cis*-3-alkyl-4-*t*-butylcyclohexanone is subjected to a reaction with LAH, the predominant product is that in which the OH is *cis* to the *t*-butyl group and the alkyl group. Suggest a reason.

Solution: The equatorial *t*-butyl group forces the R group into the axial position (see Section 4.5). The transition state leading to an equatorial OH shows more steric hindrance (1,3-diaxial interactions) than that leading to the axial OH. Therefore, the transition state leading to an axial OH is of lower energy and is favored, and the *cis*-product results.

To equatorial:

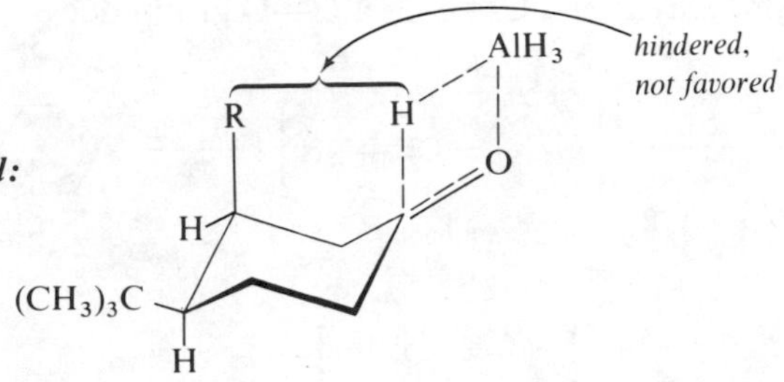

To axial:

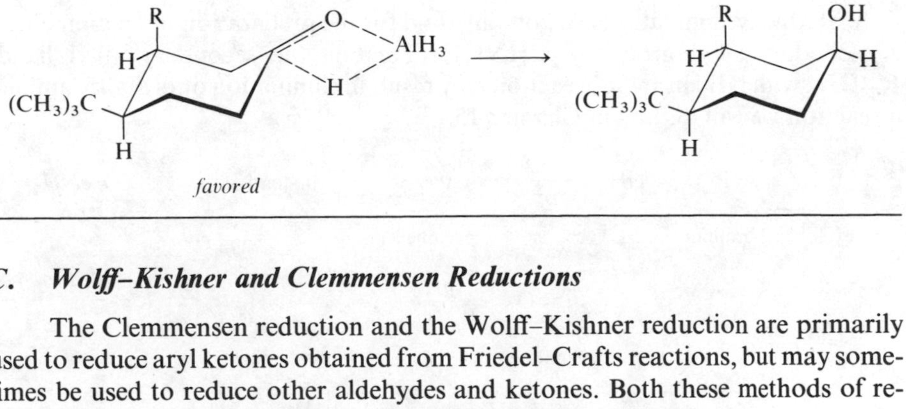

favored

C. Wolff–Kishner and Clemmensen Reductions

The Clemmensen reduction and the Wolff–Kishner reduction are primarily used to reduce aryl ketones obtained from Friedel–Crafts reactions, but may sometimes be used to reduce other aldehydes and ketones. Both these methods of reduction result in the conversion of a C=O group to a CH_2 group.

In the Wolff–Kishner reduction, the aldehyde or ketone is first converted to a hydrazone by reaction with hydrazine. The hydrazone is then treated with a strong base, such as potassium *t*-butoxide in dimethyl sulfoxide as solvent. The reaction is therefore limited to carbonyl compounds that are stable in base.

Wolff–Kishner reduction:

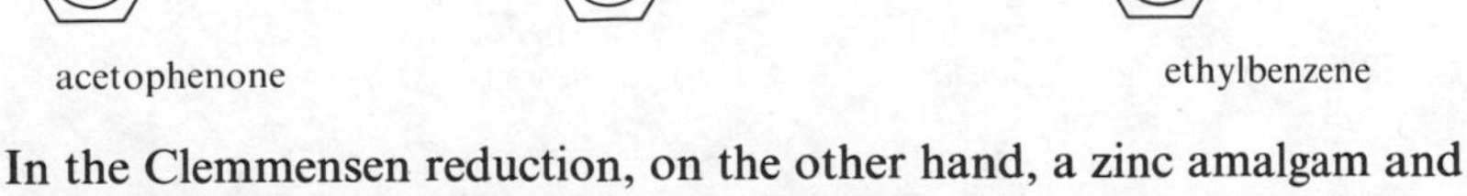

acetophenone

ethylbenzene

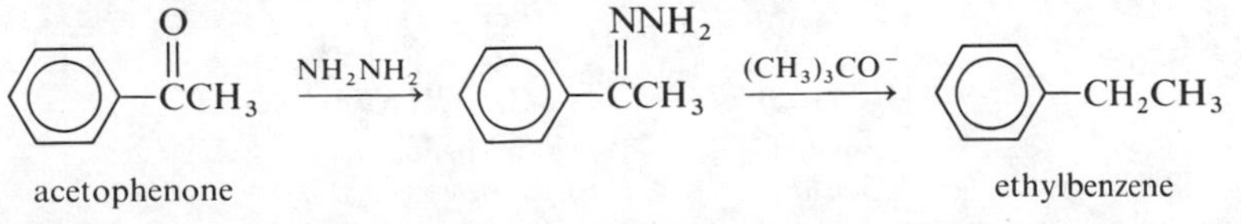

In the Clemmensen reduction, on the other hand, a zinc amalgam and concentrated HCl are used; these reagents would be the reagents of choice for a compound unstable in base but stable in acid.

Clemmensen reduction:

$$\text{C}_6\text{H}_5-\overset{\overset{\displaystyle O}{\|}}{\text{C}}\text{CH}_3 \xrightarrow[\text{HCl}]{\text{Zn/Hg}} \text{C}_6\text{H}_5-\text{CH}_2\text{CH}_3$$

D. Reductive Amination

If an amine is the desired reduction product, the carbonyl compound is treated with ammonia or a primary amine to form the imine in the presence of hydrogen and a catalyst. The imine C=N group then undergoes catalytic hydrogenation in the same way that a C=C or a C=O group does.

$$\text{C}_6\text{H}_5-\overset{\overset{\displaystyle O}{\|}}{\text{C}}\text{H} \xrightarrow{\text{NH}_3} \left[\text{C}_6\text{H}_5-\text{CH}=\text{NH}\right] \xrightarrow{\text{H}_2,\ \text{Ni}} \text{C}_6\text{H}_5-\text{CH}_2\text{NH}_2$$

benzaldehyde   *an imine*   benzylamine
85%

$$\text{CH}_3\text{CH}_2\overset{\overset{\displaystyle O}{\|}}{\text{C}}\text{CH}_3 \xrightarrow{\text{CH}_3\text{NH}_2} \left[\text{CH}_3\text{CH}_2\overset{\overset{\displaystyle NCH_3}{\|}}{\text{C}}\text{CH}_3\right] \xrightarrow{\text{H}_2,\ \text{Ni}} \text{CH}_3\text{CH}_2\overset{\overset{\displaystyle NHCH_3}{|}}{\text{C}}\text{HCH}_3$$

butanone   *an imine*   *N*-methyl-2-butylamine

Reductive amination is a good method for the preparation of an amine with a secondary alkyl group: $R_2\text{CHNH}_2$. (Treating the secondary alkyl halide $R_2\text{CHX}$ with NH_3 in an S_N2 reaction may result in elimination or in dialkylamines, a reaction we will discuss in Chapter 15.)

$$\text{cyclohexyl}-\text{Br} + \text{NH}_3 \xrightarrow{\text{E2}} \text{cyclohexene} \quad \text{instead of} \quad \text{cyclohexyl}-\text{NH}_2$$

cyclohexyl bromide   cyclohexene

$$\text{cyclohexyl}=\text{O} \xrightarrow[\text{H}_2,\ \text{Ni}]{\text{NH}_3} \text{cyclohexyl}-\text{NH}_2$$

cyclohexanone   cyclohexylamine

Section 11.15

Oxidation of Aldehydes and Ketones

Ketones are not easily oxidized, but aldehydes are very easily oxidized to carboxylic acids. Almost any reagent that oxidizes an alcohol also oxidizes an aldehyde (see Section 7.17C). Permanganate or dichromate salts are the most popular oxidizing agents, but are by no means the only reagents that can be used.

$$\text{CH}_3\text{CH}_2\overset{\overset{\displaystyle O}{\|}}{\text{C}}\text{H} \xrightarrow{\text{KMnO}_4} \text{CH}_3\text{CH}_2\overset{\overset{\displaystyle O}{\|}}{\text{C}}\text{OH}$$

propanal   propanoic acid
an aldehyde   *a carboxylic acid*

$$\text{CH}_3\overset{\overset{\displaystyle O}{\|}}{\text{C}}\text{CH}_3 \xrightarrow{\text{KMnO}_4} \text{no reaction}$$

acetone
a ketone

In addition to oxidation by permanganate or dichromate, aldehydes are oxidized by very mild oxidizing agents, such as Ag^+ or Cu^{2+}. **Tollens reagent** (an alkaline solution of the silver–ammonia complex ion) is used as a test for aldehydes. The aldehyde is oxidized to a carboxylate anion; the Ag^+ in the Tollens reagent is reduced to Ag metal. A positive test is indicated by the formation of a silver mirror on the wall of the test tube. With the widespread use of spectroscopy, the Tollens test is no longer the test of choice for an aldehyde, but mirrors are sometimes still made this way.

$$\underset{\text{Tollens reagent}}{\overset{\displaystyle O}{\overset{\displaystyle \|}{RCH}} + Ag(NH_3)_2{}^+} \xrightarrow{OH^-} \underset{\text{mirror}}{\overset{\displaystyle O}{\overset{\displaystyle \|}{RCO^-}} + Ag}$$

Section 11.16

Reactivity of the Alpha Hydrogens

A carbon–hydrogen bond is usually stable, nonpolar, and certainly not acidic. But the presence of a carbonyl group results in an *acidic alpha hydrogen*. If a hydrogen is alpha to *two* carbonyl groups, it is acidic enough that salts can be formed by treatment with an alkoxide. The pK_a of ethyl acetoacetate ($CH_3COCH_2CO_2CH_2CH_3$) is 11; it is more acidic than ethanol ($pK_a = 16$) or water ($pK_a = 15$). Treatment of this β-dicarbonyl compound with sodium ethoxide (or any strong base, such as NaH or $NaNH_2$) yields the sodium salt. (Sodium hydroxide is usually not used with keto esters because the ester groups undergo hydrolysis in NaOH and water. This reaction will be discussed in Section 13.5C.)

α to one C=O
$$\underset{\substack{\text{acetone} \\ pK_a = 20}}{CH_3\overset{\displaystyle O}{\overset{\displaystyle \|}{C}}CH_3}$$

α to two C=O groups
$$\underset{\substack{\text{ethyl acetoacetate} \\ pK_a = 11}}{CH_3\overset{\displaystyle O}{\overset{\displaystyle \|}{C}}CH_2\overset{\displaystyle O}{\overset{\displaystyle \|}{C}}OCH_2CH_3}$$

$$\underset{H}{\overset{\displaystyle O}{\overset{\displaystyle \|}{CH_2\overset{\displaystyle}{C}CH_3}}} + Na^+\ {}^-OCH_2CH_3 \rightleftarrows \underset{\text{not favored}}{Na^+\ {}^-CH_2\overset{\displaystyle O}{\overset{\displaystyle \|}{C}}CH_3 + CH_3CH_2OH}$$

$$\underset{H}{CH_3\overset{\displaystyle O}{\overset{\displaystyle \|}{C}}CH\overset{\displaystyle O}{\overset{\displaystyle \|}{C}}OCH_2CH_3} + Na^+\ {}^-OCH_2CH_3 \rightleftarrows \underset{\substack{Na^+ \\ \text{favored}}}{CH_3\overset{\displaystyle O}{\overset{\displaystyle \|}{C}}CH\overset{\displaystyle O}{\overset{\displaystyle \|}{C}}OCH_2CH_3 + CH_3CH_2OH}$$

Why is a hydrogen alpha to a carbonyl group acidic? The answer is twofold. First, the alpha carbon is adjacent to one (or two) partially positive carbon atoms. The alpha carbon, too, partakes of some of this positive charge (inductive effect by electron-withdrawal), and C—H bonds are consequently weakened.

$$\overset{\displaystyle O}{\overset{\displaystyle \|}{-C}}\leftarrow\overset{\delta+}{CH_2}\rightarrow\overset{\displaystyle O}{\overset{\displaystyle \|}{C}}-$$

Second, and more important, is the resonance-stabilization of the **enolate ion**, the anion formed when the proton is lost. From the resonance structures, we can see that the negative charge is carried by the carbonyl oxygens as well as by the α carbon. This delocalization of the charge stabilizes the enolate ion and favors its formation.

Adjacent to one carbonyl group:

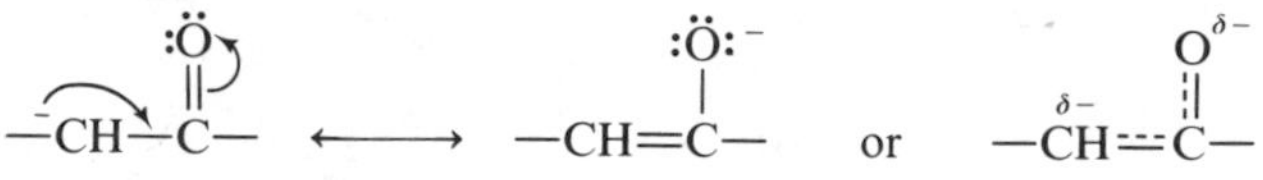

Adjacent to two carbonyl groups:

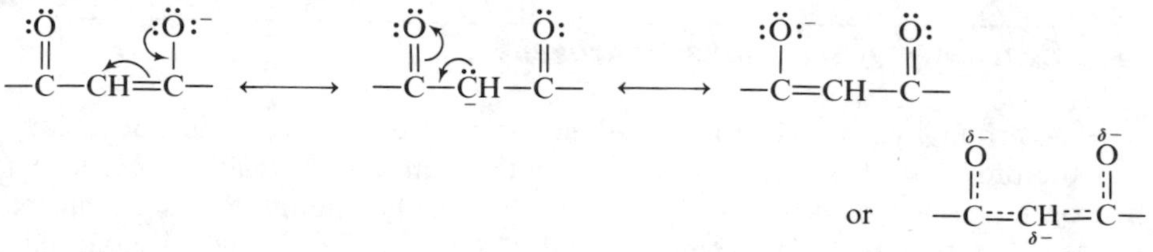

STUDY PROBLEM

11.24 Give the resonance structures of the enolate ions formed when the following diones are treated with sodium ethoxide:

(a) 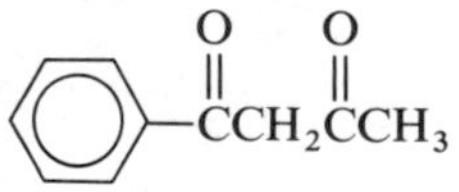   (b) 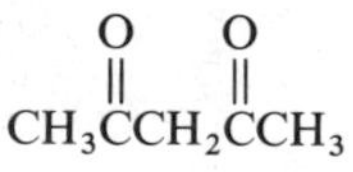 $CH_3CCH_2CCH_3$ (with two O double bonds)

Section 11.17

Tautomerism

Even if a strong base is not present, the acidity of the alpha hydrogen may be evident. A carbonyl compound with an acidic alpha hydrogen may exist in two forms called **tautomers**: a **keto** tautomer and an **enol** tautomer. The keto tautomer of a carbonyl compound has the expected carbonyl structure. The enol tautomer, which is a vinyl alcohol (*-ene* + *-ol*), is formed by transfer of an acidic hydrogen from the α carbon to the carbonyl oxygen. Because a hydrogen atom is in different positions, the two tautomeric forms are not resonance structures, but are two different structures in equilibrium. (Remember that resonance structures vary only in the positions of *electrons*.)

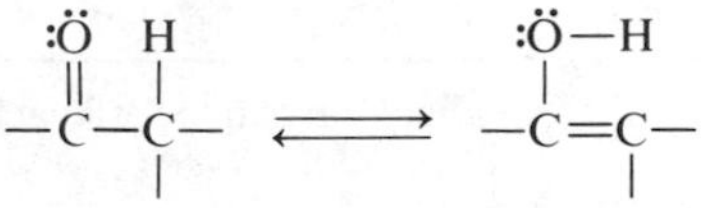

$$\overset{:\ddot{O}}{\underset{keto\ form}{\overset{\|}{-C}-\overset{H}{\underset{|}{C}}-}} \quad \rightleftharpoons \quad \overset{:\ddot{O}-H}{\underset{enol\ form}{\overset{|}{-C}=\overset{}{C}-}}$$

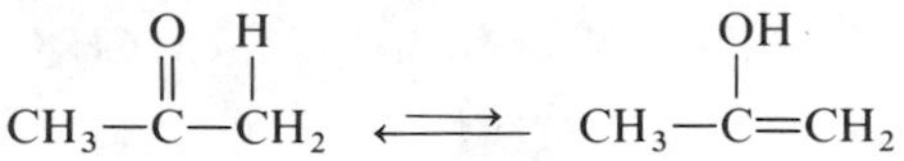

$$\underset{\substack{keto\ form \\ of\ acetone}}{CH_3-\overset{O}{\overset{\|}{C}}-\overset{H}{\underset{|}{C}H_2}} \quad \rightleftharpoons \quad \underset{\substack{enol\ form \\ of\ acetone}}{CH_3-\overset{OH}{\overset{|}{C}}=CH_2}$$

STUDY PROBLEM

11.25 Which of each of the following pairs are tautomers, and which are resonance structures?

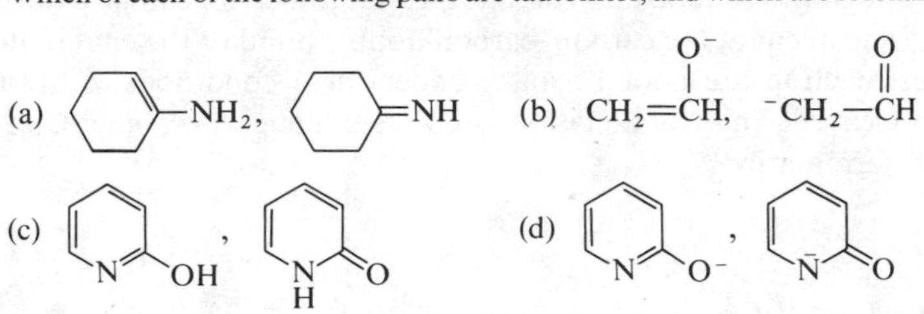

(a) [structure] —NH$_2$, [structure] =NH   (b) $CH_2=\overset{O^-}{\underset{|}{C}H}$, $^-CH_2-\overset{O}{\overset{\|}{C}}H$

(c) [structure] , [structure]   (d) [structure] , [structure]

The relative quantities of enol versus keto in a pure liquid may be determined by infrared or nmr spectroscopy. Acetone exists primarily in the keto form (99.99%). Most other simple aldehydes and ketones also exist primarily in their keto forms; however, 2,4-pentanedione (acetoacetone) exists as 80% enol! How can this tremendous difference be explained? Let us consider the structures of the 2,4-pentanedione tautomers:

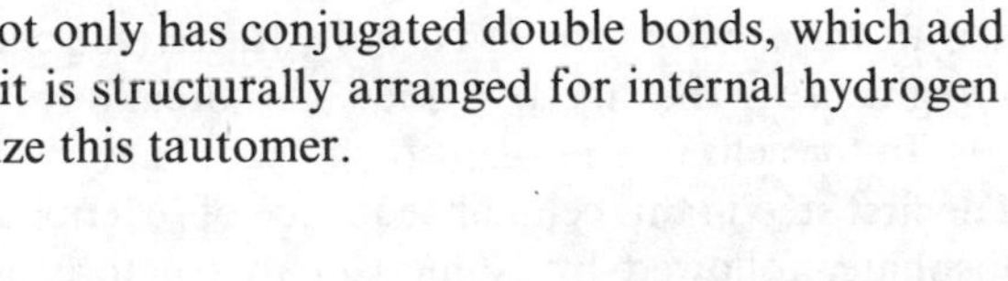

$$\underset{\substack{keto\ form \\ 20\%}}{} \quad \rightleftharpoons \quad \underset{\substack{enol\ form \\ 80\%}}{}$$

The enol form not only has conjugated double bonds, which add a small amount of stability, but it is structurally arranged for internal hydrogen bonding, which also helps stabilize this tautomer.

Sample Problem

Suggest reasons why 1,2-cyclohexanedione exists 100% in an enol form.

Solution:

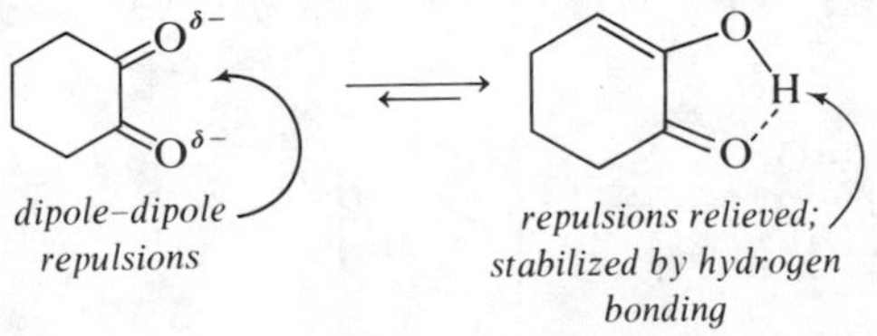

dipole–dipole repulsions   *repulsions relieved; stabilized by hydrogen bonding*

STUDY PROBLEM

11.26 Write the structures of the principal tautomers of each of the following carbonyl compounds:

$$\text{(a) } CH_3\overset{O}{\underset{\|}{C}}CH_2\overset{O}{\underset{\|}{C}}H \qquad \text{(b) } CH_3\overset{O}{\underset{\|}{C}}\overset{O}{\underset{\|}{C}}\underset{\underset{CH_3}{|}}{C}HCCH_3 \qquad \text{(c) } CH_3\overset{O}{\underset{\|}{C}}-\!\!\!\!\!\!\bigcirc\!\!\!\!\!\!=O$$

Tautomerism can affect the reactivity of a compound. An exception to the generality that ketones are not easily oxidized is the oxidation of a ketone with at least one α hydrogen. A ketone that can undergo tautomerism can be oxidized by a strong oxidizing agent at the carbon–carbon double bond of the enol tautomer. Yields in this reaction are poor because, under these conditions, other C—C bonds may be cleaved. This reaction is not used in synthetic work, but is used often in structure determinations.

$$CH_3CH_2CH_2-\overset{O}{\underset{\|}{C}}-CH_2CH_3 \;\rightleftharpoons$$

3-hexanone

$$CH_3CH_2CH\overset{OH}{=}CCH_2CH_3 \quad \xrightarrow[\text{heat}]{\text{conc. HNO}_3} \quad 2\ CH_3CH_2CO_2H$$

propanoic acid

$$+$$

$$CH_3CH_2CH_2\overset{OH}{C}=CHCH_3 \quad \xrightarrow[\text{heat}]{\text{conc. HNO}_3}$$

CH₃CH₂CH₂CO₂H

butanoic acid

+

CH₃CO₂H

acetic acid

A. Tautomerism in Carbohydrate Metabolism

The first step in the metabolism of carbohydrates (starches and sugars) is their breakdown to glucose in the digestive tract. This breakdown is the hydrolysis of the acetal bonds. In the cells of an organism, glucose is eventually converted to CO_2 and H_2O. The first step in this cellular sequence of reactions is the formation of glucose 6-phosphate, followed by isomerism to fructose 6-phosphate. The isomerism reaction is simply an enzyme-catalyzed tautomerism that proceeds by way of an *enediol intermediate*, an intermediate that can lead to two carbonyl products.

$$\begin{array}{c} HC\!=\!O \\ | \\ HCOH \\ | \end{array} \;\rightleftharpoons\; \left[\begin{array}{c} HCOH \\ \| \\ COH \\ | \end{array}\right] \;\rightleftharpoons\; \begin{array}{c} H_2COH \\ | \\ C\!=\!O \\ | \end{array}$$

an aldehyde   *an enediol*   *a ketone*

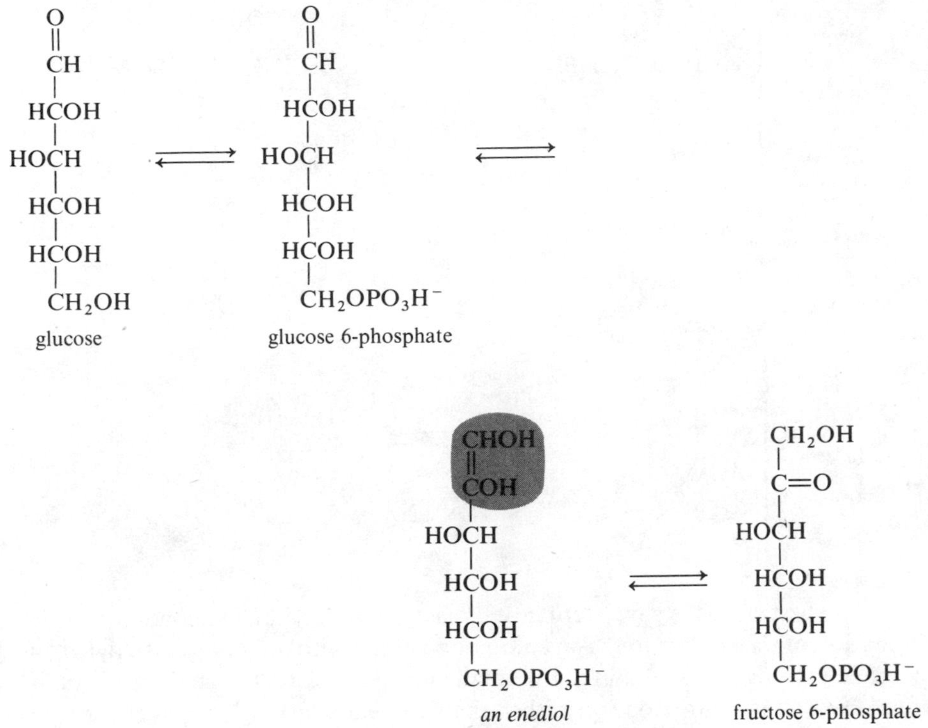

$$
\begin{array}{ccc}
\underset{\underset{\displaystyle CH}{\|}}{O} & & \underset{\underset{\displaystyle CH}{\|}}{O} \\
| & & | \\
HCOH & & HCOH \\
| & & | \\
HOCH & \rightleftharpoons & HOCH & \rightleftharpoons \\
| & & | \\
HCOH & & HCOH \\
| & & | \\
HCOH & & HCOH \\
| & & | \\
CH_2OH & & CH_2OPO_3H^- \\
\text{glucose} & & \text{glucose 6-phosphate}
\end{array}
$$

$$
\begin{array}{ccc}
\underset{\underset{\displaystyle COH}{\|}}{CHOH} & & CH_2OH \\
| & & \| \\
 & & C{=}O \\
HOCH & & | \\
| & & HOCH \\
HCOH & \rightleftharpoons & HCOH \\
| & & | \\
HCOH & & HCOH \\
| & & | \\
CH_2OPO_3H^- & & CH_2OPO_3H^- \\
\textit{an enediol} & & \text{fructose 6-phosphate}
\end{array}
$$

STUDY PROBLEM

11.27 After fructose 6-phosphate is formed, it is converted enzymatically to the 1,6-diphosphate, which in turn is cleaved into two three-carbon compounds:

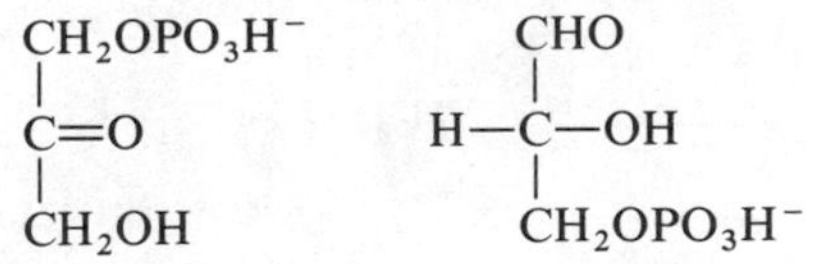

$$
\begin{array}{cc}
CH_2OPO_3H^- & CHO \\
| & | \\
C{=}O & H{-}C{-}OH \\
| & | \\
CH_2OH & CH_2OPO_3H^- \\
\text{dihydroxyacetone} & \text{glyceraldehyde} \\
\text{phosphate} & \text{3-phosphate}
\end{array}
$$

Before being carried on to the next step, the dihydroxyacetone phosphate is also converted to glyceraldehyde 3-phosphate. Suggest an intermediate in this conversion.

Section 11.18

Alpha Halogenation

Aldehydes and ketones are readily halogenated at the α carbon. The reaction requires either alkaline conditions or an acidic catalyst. (Note that base is a *reactant*, whereas acid is a *catalyst*.)

In base

$$\underset{\text{acetone}}{CH_3\overset{\overset{\displaystyle O}{\|}}{C}CH_3} + Br_2 + OH^- \longrightarrow \underset{\text{bromoacetone}}{BrCH_2\overset{\overset{\displaystyle O}{\|}}{C}CH_3} + Br^- + H_2O$$

cyclohexanone $=O + Br_2 + OH^- \longrightarrow =O + Br^- + H_2O$
Br
2-bromo-
cyclohexanone

In acid

$$CH_3\overset{\overset{\displaystyle O}{\|}}{C}CH_3 + Br_2 \xrightarrow{H^+} BrCH_2\overset{\overset{\displaystyle O}{\|}}{C}CH_3 + HBr$$

$=O + Br_2 \xrightarrow{H^+} =O + HBr$
Br

The first step (the slow step) in the reaction under alkaline conditions is the formation of the enolate ion. The anion of a ketone with only one carbonyl group is a much stronger base than the hydroxide ion. Therefore, the acid–base equilibrium favors the hydroxide ion rather than the enolate ion. Nonetheless, a *few* enolate ions exist in alkaline solution. As these few anions are used up, more are generated to go on to Step 2. In Step 2, the enolate ion quickly undergoes reaction with halogen to yield the α-halogenated ketone and a halide ion.

In base:

   Step 1 (slow):

$$CH_3\overset{\overset{\displaystyle O}{\|}}{C}CH_3 + OH^- \underset{-H_2O}{\longleftrightarrow} \left[CH_3\overset{\overset{\displaystyle O}{\|}}{C}CH_2 \longleftrightarrow CH_3\overset{\overset{\displaystyle O^-}{|}}{C}=CH_2 \right]$$

resonance structures for the enolate ion

   Step 2 (fast):

$$CH_3\overset{\overset{\displaystyle O}{\|}}{C}CH_2 + Br\!-\!Br \longrightarrow CH_3\overset{\overset{\displaystyle O}{\|}}{C}CH_2Br + Br^-$$

STUDY PROBLEMS

11.28 Upon which species does the rate of base-promoted α halogenation depend? Would the reaction follow first-order or second-order kinetics?

11.29 One of the disadvantages of base-promoted α halogenation of a ketone is that a second halogen atom is introduced more easily than the first.

$$CH_3\overset{\overset{\displaystyle O}{\|}}{C}CH_2Br + Br_2 + OH^- \longrightarrow CH_3\overset{\overset{\displaystyle O}{\|}}{C}CHBr_2 + Br^- + H_2O$$

Give the steps in the mechanism of the second halogenation and suggest a reason why this reaction has a faster rate than that of the first halogenation.

Alpha halogenation in acid usually gives higher yields than the reaction in base. The acid-catalyzed reaction proceeds by way of the enol, the formation of which is the rate-determining step. The carbon–carbon double bond of the enol undergoes electrophilic addition, just like any carbon–carbon double bond, to form the more stable carbocation. In this case, the more stable carbocation is the one in which the positive charge is on the carbon of the carbonyl group (because this intermediate is resonance-stabilized). This carbocation intermediate quickly loses a proton and forms the ketone, which is now halogenated in the alpha position.

In acid:

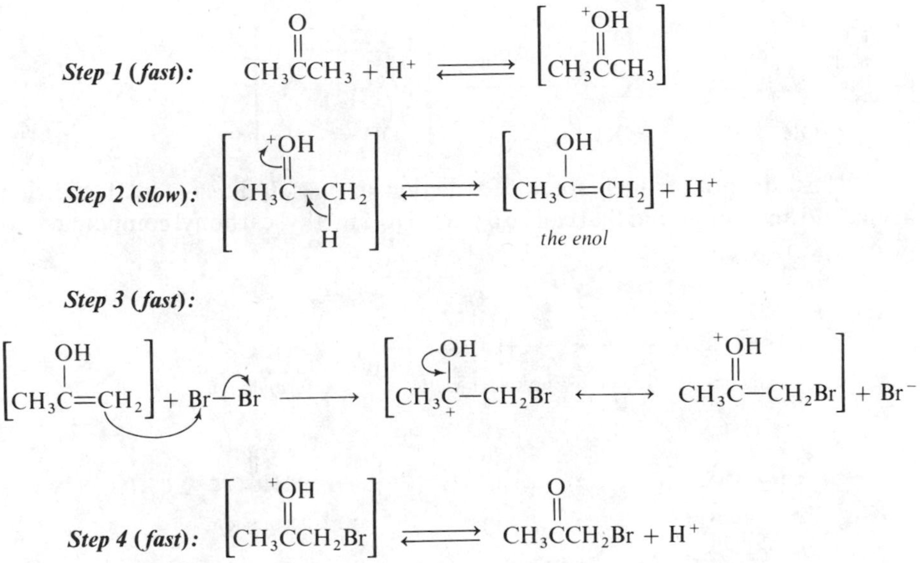

Step 1 (*fast*):
$$CH_3CCH_3 + H^+ \rightleftharpoons \left[CH_3CCH_3 \right]$$

Step 2 (*slow*):
$$\left[CH_3C{-}CH_2 \atop H \right] \rightleftharpoons \left[CH_3C{=}CH_2 \right] + H^+$$
the enol

Step 3 (*fast*):
$$\left[CH_3C{=}CH_2 \right] + Br{-}Br \longrightarrow \left[CH_3C{-}CH_2Br \right] \longleftrightarrow CH_3C{-}CH_2Br + Br^-$$

Step 4 (*fast*):
$$\left[CH_3CCH_2Br \right] \rightleftharpoons CH_3CCH_2Br + H^+$$

STUDY PROBLEM

11.30 (a) What species are involved in the rate-determining step of acid-catalyzed α halogenation of acetone?

(b) What would be the relative rates of α bromination and α iodination?

A. Haloform Reaction

Alpha halogenation is the basis of a chemical test, called the **iodoform test**, for methyl ketones. The methyl group of a methyl ketone is iodinated stepwise until the yellow solid iodoform (CHI_3) is formed.

Iodoform test:

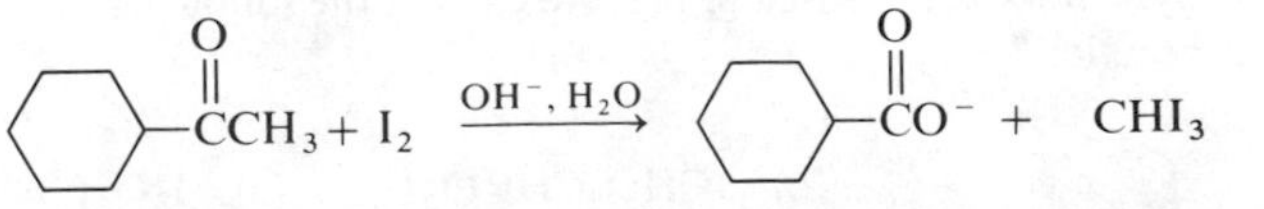

| cyclohexyl methyl ketone | cyclohexyl-carboxylate ion | iodoform *yellow solid* |

Steps in the reaction:

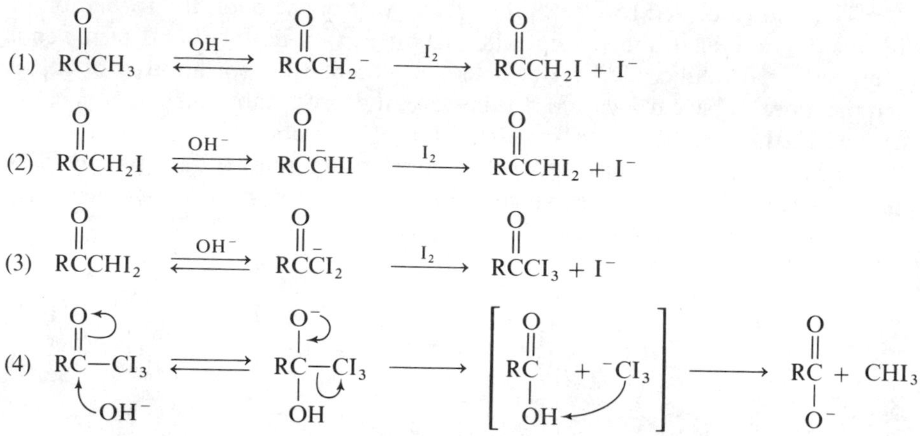

(1) $\underset{\text{RCCH}_3}{\overset{\text{O}}{\|}} \quad \xrightleftharpoons{\text{OH}^-} \quad \underset{\text{RCCH}_2^-}{\overset{\text{O}}{\|}} \quad \xrightarrow{\text{I}_2} \quad \underset{\text{RCCH}_2\text{I} + \text{I}^-}{\overset{\text{O}}{\|}}$

(2) $\underset{\text{RCCH}_2\text{I}}{\overset{\text{O}}{\|}} \quad \xrightleftharpoons{\text{OH}^-} \quad \underset{\text{RCCHI}}{\overset{\text{O}}{\|}} \quad \xrightarrow{\text{I}_2} \quad \underset{\text{RCCHI}_2 + \text{I}^-}{\overset{\text{O}}{\|}}$

(3) $\underset{\text{RCCHI}_2}{\overset{\text{O}}{\|}} \quad \xrightleftharpoons{\text{OH}^-} \quad \underset{\text{RCCI}_2}{\overset{\text{O}}{\|}} \quad \xrightarrow{\text{I}_2} \quad \underset{\text{RCCI}_3 + \text{I}^-}{\overset{\text{O}}{\|}}$

(4) $\underset{\overset{|}{\text{OH}^-}}{\overset{\text{O}}{\overset{\|}{\text{RC}{-}\text{CI}_3}}} \rightleftharpoons \underset{\overset{|}{\text{OH}}}{\overset{\text{O}^-}{\overset{|}{\text{RC}{-}\text{CI}_3}}} \longrightarrow \left[\underset{\overset{|}{\text{OH}}}{\overset{\text{O}}{\overset{\|}{\text{RC}}}} + {}^-\text{CI}_3\right] \longrightarrow \underset{\overset{|}{\text{O}^-}}{\overset{\text{O}}{\overset{\|}{\text{RC}}}} + \text{CHI}_3$

The test is not uniquely specific for methyl ketones. Iodine is a mild oxidizing agent, and any compound that can be oxidized to a methyl carbonyl compound also gives a positive test.

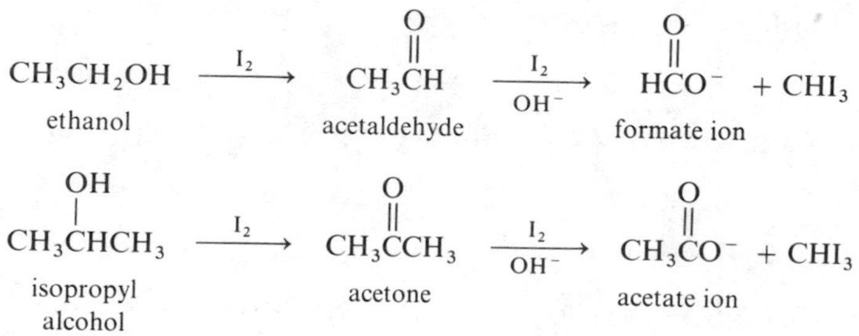

$$\underset{\text{ethanol}}{\text{CH}_3\text{CH}_2\text{OH}} \xrightarrow{\text{I}_2} \underset{\text{acetaldehyde}}{\overset{\text{O}}{\overset{\|}{\text{CH}_3\text{CH}}}} \xrightarrow[\text{OH}^-]{\text{I}_2} \underset{\text{formate ion}}{\overset{\text{O}}{\overset{\|}{\text{HCO}^-}}} + \text{CHI}_3$$

$$\underset{\substack{\text{isopropyl} \\ \text{alcohol}}}{\overset{\text{OH}}{\overset{|}{\text{CH}_3\text{CHCH}_3}}} \xrightarrow{\text{I}_2} \underset{\text{acetone}}{\overset{\text{O}}{\overset{\|}{\text{CH}_3\text{CCH}_3}}} \xrightarrow[\text{OH}^-]{\text{I}_2} \underset{\text{acetate ion}}{\overset{\text{O}}{\overset{\|}{\text{CH}_3\text{CO}^-}}} + \text{CHI}_3$$

Bromine and chlorine also undergo reaction with methyl ketones to yield bromoform (CHBr_3) and chloroform (CHCl_3), respectively. "Haloform" is the general term used to describe CHX_3; hence this reaction is often referred to as the **haloform reaction**. Because bromoform and chloroform are nondistinctive liquids, their formations are not useful for test purposes. However, the reaction of a methyl ketone with any of these halogens provides a method for the conversion of these compounds to carboxylic acids.

STUDY PROBLEMS

11.31 Which of the following compounds gives a positive iodoform test?

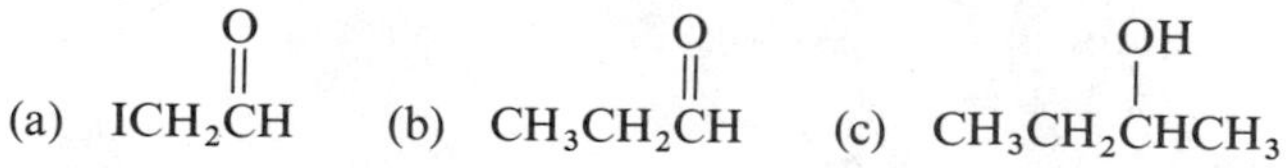

(a) $\underset{\text{ICH}_2\text{CH}}{\overset{\text{O}}{\overset{\|}{}}}$ (b) $\underset{\text{CH}_3\text{CH}_2\text{CH}}{\overset{\text{O}}{\overset{\|}{}}}$ (c) $\underset{\text{CH}_3\text{CH}_2\text{CHCH}_3}{\overset{\text{OH}}{\overset{|}{}}}$

11.32 What methyl ketone can be used to prepare each of the following carboxylic acids by a haloform reaction?

(a) 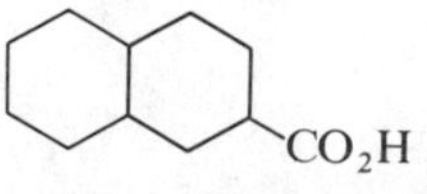 CO_2H (b) $(\text{CH}_3)_2\text{CHCO}_2\text{H}$ (c)  $\text{HO}_2\text{C}{-}\langle\bigcirc\rangle{-}\text{CO}_2\text{H}$

Section 11.19

1,4-Addition to α,β-Unsaturated Carbonyl Compounds

A. Electrophilic 1,4-Addition

When an alkene undergoes reaction with HCl, the reaction proceeds by electrophilic attack of H^+ to yield the more stable carbocation, followed by attack of Cl^-.

$$CH_3CH=CH_2 \xrightarrow{H^+} [CH_3\overset{+}{C}HCH_3] \xrightarrow{Cl^-} CH_3\overset{\displaystyle Cl}{\underset{\displaystyle |}{C}}HCH_3$$

propene   2-chloropropane

An α,β-unsaturated aldehyde or ketone has a carbon–carbon double bond in conjugation with a carbonyl group. The carbon–carbon double bond in an alkene is nonpolar. However, a carbon–carbon double bond in conjugation with a carbonyl group is *polar*, as the following resonance structures indicate.

$$CH_2=CH-\overset{\ddot{O}:}{\overset{\|}{C}H} \longleftrightarrow CH_2=CH-\overset{:\ddot{O}:^-}{\underset{+}{\overset{|}{C}H}} \longleftrightarrow {}^+CH_2-CH=\overset{:\ddot{O}:^-}{\overset{|}{C}H}$$

The resonance structures show that the β carbon, as well as the carbonyl carbon, carries a partial positive charge while the carbonyl oxygen carries a partial negative charge.

$$CH_2=CH-\overset{O^{\delta-}}{\overset{\|}{C}H}$$

β carbon is δ+   carbonyl carbon is δ+

Because the C=C grouping in an α,β-unsaturated carbonyl compound is polarized, the mechanism for electrophilic addition is somewhat different from that for electrophilic addition to an isolated, nonpolar, alkene double bond. Let us consider a few examples of electrophilic addition reactions of α,β-unsaturated carbonyl compounds; then we will discuss the mechanism.

$$CH_2=CH\overset{O}{\overset{\|}{C}}H + HCl \longrightarrow \overset{Cl}{\underset{|}{C}}H_2CH_2\overset{O}{\overset{\|}{C}}H$$

propenal   3-chloropropanal
(acrolein)   (β-chloropropionaldehyde)

$$CH_3CH=CH\overset{O}{\overset{\|}{C}}CH_3 + H_2O \xrightarrow{H^+} CH_3\overset{OH}{\underset{|}{C}}HCH_2\overset{O}{\overset{\|}{C}}CH_3$$

3-penten-2-one   4-hydroxy-2-pentanone

2-cyclohexen-1-one   + HBr ⟶   3-bromocyclohexanone

Note that in each reaction, the nucleophilic part of the reagent (not H^+) becomes bonded to the β carbon. The reason for this is that the β carbon has a partial positive charge. The initial attack by H^+ occurs not at this positive carbon, but at the partially negative oxygen of the carbonyl group.

$$\overset{\delta+}{CH_2}=CH\overset{O^{\delta-}}{\underset{\|}{C}}H \qquad H^+$$

The protonated intermediate is resonance-stabilized. In this intermediate, the β carbon still carries a partial positive charge and can be attacked by a nucleophile.

Protonation:

$$CH_2=CH\overset{O}{\underset{\|}{C}}H \underset{}{\overset{H^+}{\rightleftharpoons}} \left[CH_2=CH\overset{+OH}{\underset{\|}{C}}H \longleftrightarrow CH_2=CH-\overset{OH}{\underset{\underset{+}{|}}{C}}H \longleftrightarrow \overset{+}{C}H_2CH=\overset{OH}{\underset{|}{C}}H \right]$$

resonance-stabilized

Attack of Nu⁻:

$$\left[{}^+CH_2CH=\overset{OH}{\underset{|}{C}}H \right] + Cl^- \longrightarrow \left[ClCH_2CH=\overset{OH}{\underset{|}{C}}H \right] \underset{}{\overset{}{\rightleftharpoons}} ClCH_2CH_2\overset{O}{\underset{\|}{C}}H$$

an enol

Note that this reaction is a **1,4-addition**, the same type of addition observed with conjugated dienes. The difference is that the initial addition product is an enol, which undergoes tautomerism to the final keto form.

You might wonder why the nucleophile cannot also attack the carbonyl carbon (which also carries a partial positive charge in the intermediate). This attack on the carbonyl carbon can also occur, but the product is unstable and reverts to starting material. This is a concurrent, but nonproductive, side reaction.

$$\left[CH_2=CH\overset{OH}{\underset{\underset{+}{|}}{C}}H \right] + Cl^- \rightleftharpoons \left[CH_2=CHCH\overset{O \rightharpoondown H}{\underset{|}{\underset{Cl}{}}} \right] \rightleftharpoons CH_2=CH\overset{O}{\underset{\|}{C}}H + HCl$$

B. Nucleophilic 1,4-Addition

The pi bond of an alkene is not normally attacked by a nucleophile unless there has been prior attack by an electrophile. However, a double bond in conjugation with a carbonyl group is polarized. In this case, nucleophilic addition can occur at *either the C=C double bond or at the C=O double bond* (at either of the two partially positive carbons).

$$CH_2=CH\overset{O}{\underset{\|}{C}}CH_3 + {}^-CN \overset{HCN}{\longrightarrow} CH_2=CH\overset{OH}{\underset{\underset{CN}{|}}{C}}CH_3 \quad or \quad CH_2-CH_2\overset{O}{\underset{\|}{C}}CH_3$$
$$\underset{CN}{|}$$

Let us look at the mechanism of each reaction. First, we will consider the attack of the cyanide ion (from HCN and dilute base) on the carbonyl group. In this case, the nucleophilic CN^- attacks the partially positive carbon of the carbonyl group. The reaction is no different from cyanohydrin formation by an ordinary ketone.

Attack of CN^- on the carbonyl carbon:

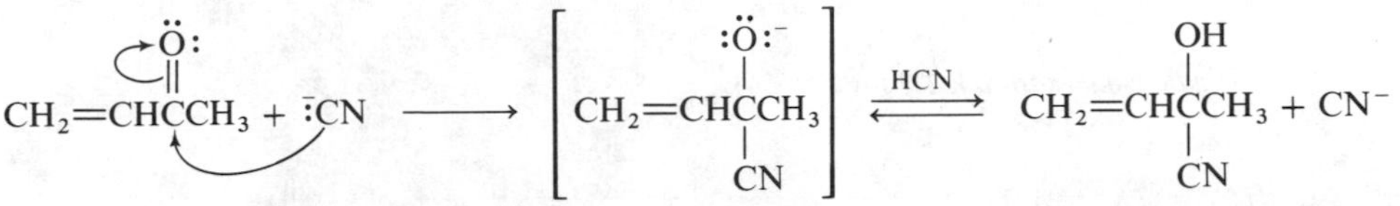

$$CH_2{=}CHCCH_3 + \ddot{:}CN \longrightarrow \left[CH_2{=}CHCCH_3 \right] \overset{HCN}{\rightleftharpoons} CH_2{=}CHCCH_3 + CN^-$$

Now we will consider attack of the nucleophilic CN^- on the β carbon. This reaction is a 1,4-addition of CN^- and H^+ to the conjugated system. The product of the 1,4-addition is an enol, which forms the product ketone.

Attack of CN^- on the β carbon:

$$CH_2{=}CH{-}CCH_3 \rightleftharpoons \left[CH_2{-}CH{-}CCH_3 \longleftrightarrow CH_2{-}CH{=}CCH_3 \right] \overset{HCN}{\longrightarrow}$$

$$CN^- + \left[CH_2{-}CH{=}CCH_3 \right] \rightleftharpoons CH_2CH_2CCH_3$$

an enol

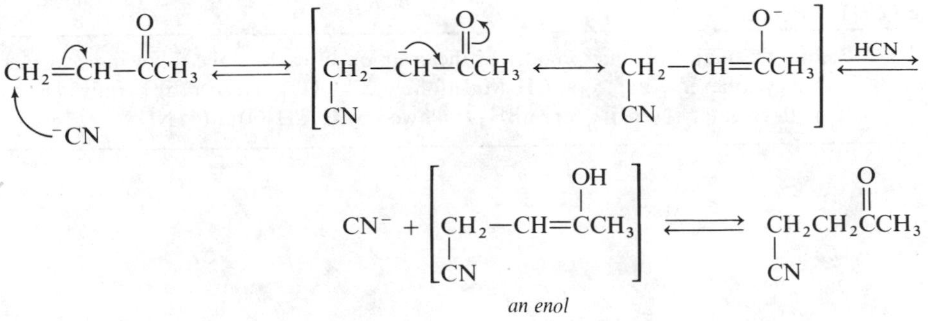

Which of the two addition reactions occurs? Sometimes both do, and a mixture of products results. In most cases, however, one product or the other predominates. Steric hindrance around the double bond or the carbonyl group may lead to preferred attack at the nonhindered position. Aldehydes, less hindered than ketones, usually undergo carbonyl attack.

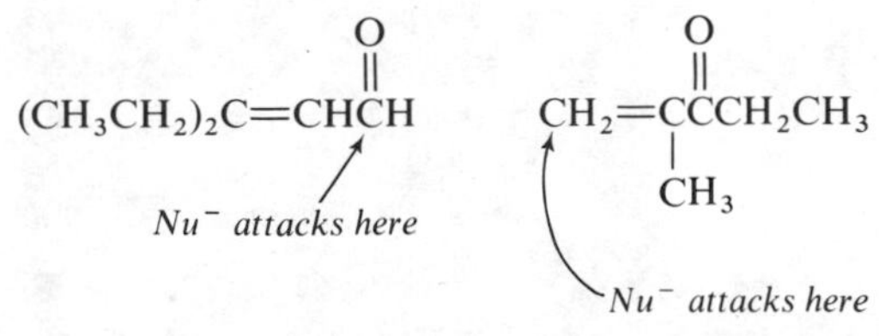

$$(CH_3CH_2)_2C{=}CHCH \qquad CH_2{=}CCCH_2CH_3$$

Nu⁻ attacks here CH_3

Nu⁻ attacks here

A highly basic nucleophile (such as RMgX or LiAlH₄) attacks preferentially at the carbonyl group, while a weaker base (such as CN^- or R_2NH) usually attacks at the carbon–carbon double bond.

Stronger bases attack 1,2 (at C=O):

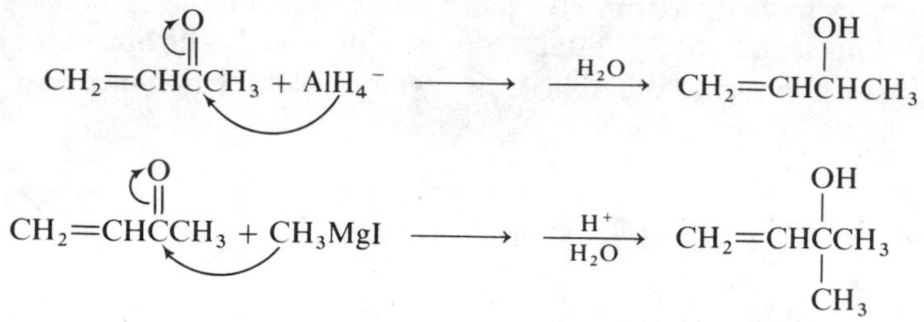

$$CH_2=CHCCH_3 + AlH_4^- \longrightarrow \xrightarrow{H_2O} CH_2=CHCHCH_3 \quad (OH)$$

$$CH_2=CHCCH_3 + CH_3MgI \longrightarrow \xrightarrow[H_2O]{H^+} CH_2=CHCCH_3 \quad (OH, CH_3)$$

Weaker bases attack 1,4 (at C=C):

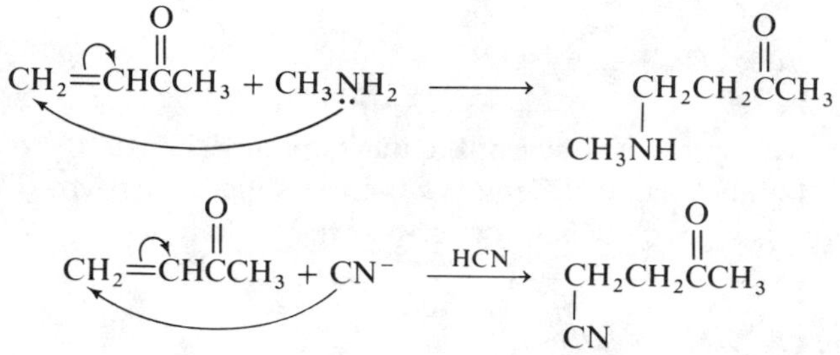

$$CH_2=CHCCH_3 + CH_3NH_2 \longrightarrow CH_2CH_2CCH_3 \quad (CH_3NH)$$

$$CH_2=CHCCH_3 + CN^- \xrightarrow{HCN} CH_2CH_2CCH_3 \quad (CN)$$

STUDY PROBLEM

11.33 Predict the major organic product of the reaction of each of the following reagents with 2-cyclohexen-1-one: (a) CH_3MgI (followed by H^+, H_2O); (b) 1 equivalent of H_2 with Ni catalyst (25°); (c) $NaBH_4$ (followed by H^+, H_2O); (d) NH_3.

SUMMARY

The carbonyl group is *planar* and *polar*, and the oxygen has *two filled orbitals*. The carbonyl group may undergo *electrophilic* or *nucleophilic* attack.

$$\overset{\delta+}{\underset{}{\diagup}}\overset{\delta-}{C{=}\ddot{O}:} \quad E^+ \longrightarrow \overset{}{\diagup}C{=}\overset{+}{\ddot{O}}E \qquad \overset{}{\diagup}C{=}\ddot{O}: \quad Nu^- \longrightarrow -\overset{|}{\underset{|}{C}}-\ddot{O}:^- \quad Nu$$

Because of (1) *inductive stabilization* of the partial positive charge on the carbonyl carbon, and (2) *steric hindrance*, ketones are less reactive than aldehydes:

$$\underset{RCR}{\overset{O}{\underset{\|}{}}} < \underset{RCH}{\overset{O}{\underset{\|}{}}} < \underset{HCH}{\overset{O}{\underset{\|}{}}}$$

Many reactions of aldehydes and ketones are simple *additions* to the C=O double bond:

$$\underset{a\ ketone}{\overset{O}{\underset{\|}{RCR}}} + H{-}OH \overset{H^+}{\rightleftharpoons} \underset{}{\overset{OH}{\underset{|}{RCR}}} \quad a\ hydrate$$
$$\underset{}{\overset{|}{OH}}$$

$$+ H{-}OR' \overset{H^+}{\rightleftharpoons} \underset{}{\overset{OH}{\underset{|}{RCR}}} \quad a\ hemiketal$$
$$\underset{}{\overset{|}{OR'}}$$

$$+ H{-}CN \rightleftharpoons \underset{}{\overset{OH}{\underset{|}{RCR}}} \quad a\ cyanohydrin$$
$$\underset{}{\overset{|}{CN}}$$

$$+ R'{-}MgX \longrightarrow \underset{}{\overset{OMgX}{\underset{|}{RCR}}} \overset{H^+, H_2O}{\longrightarrow} \underset{}{\overset{OH}{\underset{|}{RCR}}} \quad a\ 3°\ alcohol$$
$$\underset{}{\overset{|}{R'}} \qquad \underset{}{\overset{|}{R'}}$$

$$+ H_2 \overset{Ni}{\underset{heat,\ pressure}{\longrightarrow}} \underset{}{\overset{OH}{\underset{|}{RCR}}} \quad a\ 2°\ alcohol$$
$$\underset{}{\overset{|}{H}}$$

$$+ BH_4^- \longrightarrow \underset{}{\overset{OBH_3^-}{\underset{|}{RCR}}} \overset{H^+, H_2O}{\longrightarrow} \underset{}{\overset{OH}{\underset{|}{RCR}}} \quad a\ 2°\ alcohol$$
$$\underset{}{\overset{|}{H}} \qquad \underset{}{\overset{|}{H}}$$

Substitution reactions of aldehydes and ketones are the result of initial addition reactions followed by elimination.

$$\underset{\text{a }1°\text{ amine}}{\overset{\text{O}}{\underset{\|}{\text{RCR}}} + \text{R}'\text{NH}_2} \overset{\text{H}^+}{\rightleftharpoons} \left[\underset{\text{NHR}'}{\overset{\text{OH}}{\underset{|}{\overset{|}{\text{RCR}}}}}\right] \overset{-\text{H}_2\text{O}}{\rightleftharpoons} \underset{\text{an imine}}{\overset{\text{O}}{\underset{\|}{\underset{\text{NR}'}{\text{RCR}}}}}$$

$$\underset{\text{a }2°\text{ amine}}{\overset{\text{O}}{\underset{\|}{\text{RCCH}_2\text{R}}} + \text{R}'_2\text{NH}} \overset{\text{H}^+}{\rightleftharpoons} \left[\underset{\text{NR}'_2}{\overset{\text{OH}}{\underset{|}{\overset{|}{\text{RC}-\text{CH}_2\text{R}}}}}\right] \overset{-\text{H}_2\text{O}}{\rightleftharpoons} \underset{\text{an enamine}}{\underset{\text{NR}'_2}{\overset{|}{\text{RC}=\text{CHR}}}}$$

$$\overset{\text{O}}{\underset{\|}{\text{RCR}}} + \text{H}_2\text{NNH}_2 \overset{\text{H}^+}{\rightleftharpoons} \left[\underset{\text{NHNH}_2}{\overset{\text{OH}}{\underset{|}{\overset{|}{\text{RCR}}}}}\right] \overset{-\text{H}_2\text{O}}{\rightleftharpoons} \underset{\text{a hydrazone}}{\overset{\text{O}}{\underset{\|}{\underset{\text{NNH}_2}{\text{RCR}}}}}$$

$$\text{R}_2\text{C}=\text{O} + (\text{C}_6\text{H}_5)_3\overset{+}{\text{P}}-\overset{-}{\text{C}}\text{R}'_2 \longrightarrow \left[\underset{\text{R}_2\text{C}-\text{CR}'_2}{\overset{\text{O}^-\ \overset{+}{\text{P}}(\text{C}_6\text{H}_5)_3}{\underset{|}{\overset{|\quad\ |}{}}}}\right] \overset{-(\text{C}_6\text{H}_5)_3\text{PO}}{\longrightarrow} \underset{\text{an alkene}}{\text{R}_2\text{C}=\text{CR}'_2}$$

Because the carbonyl group is polar and because its pi electrons can participate in resonance-stabilization, an α *hydrogen is acidic*, especially if it is α to two carbonyl groups.

$$\overset{\text{O}}{\underset{\|}{\text{CH}_3\text{CH}}} + \text{OH}^- \rightleftharpoons \overset{\text{O}}{\underset{\|}{{}^-\text{CH}_2\text{CH}}} + \text{H}_2\text{O}$$

acidic

$$\overset{\text{O}\ \ \text{O}}{\underset{\|\ \ \ \|}{\text{CH}_3\text{CCH}_2\text{CCH}_3}} + \text{OH}^- \rightleftharpoons \overset{\text{O}\ \ \ \text{O}}{\underset{\|\ \ -\ \|}{\text{CH}_3\text{CCHCCH}_3}} + \text{H}_2\text{O}$$

$$\underset{\text{keto tautomer}}{\overset{\text{O}\ \ \text{H}\ \ \text{O}}{\underset{\|\ \ |\ \ \|}{\text{CH}_3\text{C}-\text{CH}-\text{CCH}_3}}} \rightleftharpoons \underset{\text{enol tautomer}}{\overset{\text{OH}\ \ \ \ \text{O}}{\underset{|\ \ \ \ \ \|}{\text{CH}_3\text{C}=\text{CH}-\text{CCH}_3}}}$$

Ketones may be halogenated in the alpha position.

$$\overset{\text{O}}{\underset{\|}{\text{RCH}_2\text{CR}}} \xrightarrow[\text{H}^+\text{ or OH}^-]{\text{X}_2} \underset{\text{X}}{\overset{\text{O}}{\underset{|}{\overset{\|}{\text{RCHCR}}}}}$$

When a C=C double bond is in conjugation with C=O, addition reactions may occur 1,2 or 1,4.

Electrophilic:

$$\overset{\text{O}}{\underset{\|}{\text{R}_2\text{C}=\text{CH}-\text{CR}}} \xrightarrow[1,4]{\text{HCl}} \left[\underset{\text{Cl}}{\overset{\text{OH}}{\underset{|}{\overset{|}{\text{R}_2\text{C}-\text{CH}=\text{CR}}}}}\right] \rightleftharpoons \underset{\text{Cl}}{\overset{\text{O}}{\underset{|}{\overset{\|}{\text{R}_2\text{C}-\text{CH}_2-\text{CR}}}}}$$

Nucleophilic:

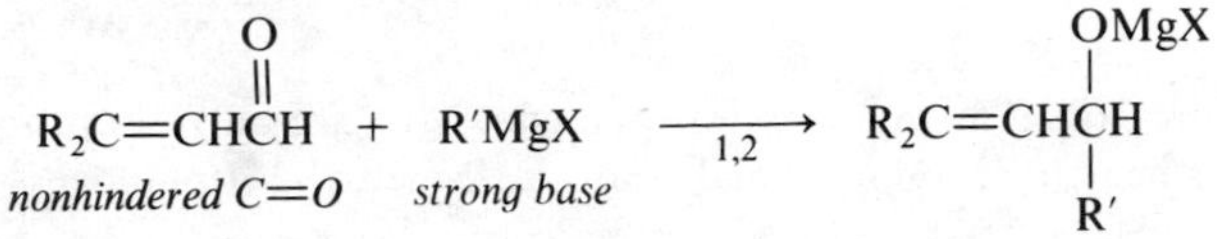

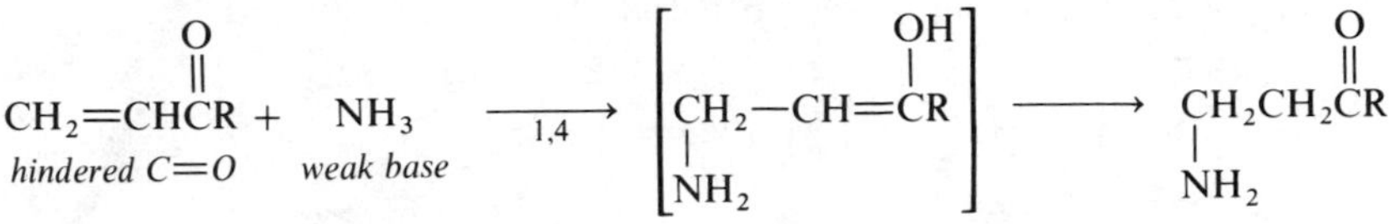

$$R_2C{=}CHCH\overset{\overset{\displaystyle O}{\|}}{} + \underset{\text{strong base}}{R'MgX} \xrightarrow{1,2} R_2C{=}CHC\overset{\overset{\displaystyle OMgX}{|}}{\underset{\underset{\displaystyle R'}{|}}{H}}$$

nonhindered C=O

$$CH_2{=}CHCR\overset{\overset{\displaystyle O}{\|}}{} + \underset{\text{weak base}}{NH_3} \xrightarrow{1,4} \left[CH_2\overset{\overset{\displaystyle }{}}{\underset{\underset{\displaystyle NH_2}{|}}{-}}CH{=}C\overset{\overset{\displaystyle OH}{|}}{R} \right] \longrightarrow CH_2CH_2C\overset{\overset{\displaystyle O}{\|}}{R}$$

hindered C=O

STUDY PROBLEMS

11.34 Write the structures for: (a) 2-methyl-1-cyclopentanone; (b) *sec*-butyl isopropyl ketone; (c) bromoacetone; (d) 2-iodopentanal; and (e) 2-methyl-3-heptanone.

11.35 Give an acceptable name for each of the following structures:

(a) 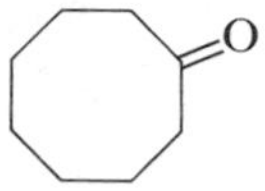 [structure]   (b) 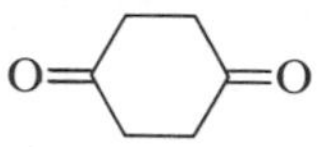 $O=\langle\rangle=O$

(c) $C_6H_5CH_2CHO$ (d) $(CH_3)_2CHCCH_2CH_2CH_3$ with O double bond

(e) $BrCH_2CH_2CH_2CHO$ (f) $(CH_3)_2CHCHO$

11.36 Give formulas for: (a) a β-ketoaldehyde; (b) an α,β-unsaturated ketone; (c) an α-bromoaldehyde; (d) a β-hydroxyketone.

11.37 Tell whether each of the following equations represents an *electrophilic* attack or a *nucleophilic* attack on the carbonyl group:

(a) $CH_3\overset{O}{\underset{\parallel}{C}}CH_3 + H^+ \rightleftharpoons CH_3\overset{+OH}{\underset{\parallel}{C}}CH_3$

(b) $CH_3\overset{O}{\underset{\parallel}{C}}CH_3 + CH_3CH_2MgI \longrightarrow CH_3\underset{\underset{CH_2CH_3}{|}}{\overset{\overset{OMgI}{|}}{C}}CH_3$

(c) $CH_3CH_2CHO + Li^+ \ AlH_4^- \longrightarrow \left[\begin{matrix}CH_3CH_2CH===O\\ | \qquad\qquad |\\ H ---- AlH_3\end{matrix}\right]^- Li^+$

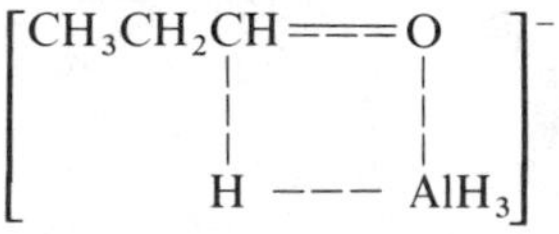

11.38 Which of the following aldehydes would form the most stable hydrate? the least stable?

(a) $BrCH_2CHO$ (b) Br_2CHCHO (c) Br_3CCHO

11.39 Write the equation for hydrate formation by Br_2CHCHO.

11.40 Write equations for the reactions leading to the hemiacetal and acetal of: (a) propanal and methanol; (b) acetone and ethylene glycol; (c) 5-hydroxy-2-hexanone and methanol.

11.41 Each of the following compounds is dissolved in water to which a trace of HCl has been added. Give the structures of any other compounds (besides HCl, water, and the compound in question) that would be found in each solution.

(a) 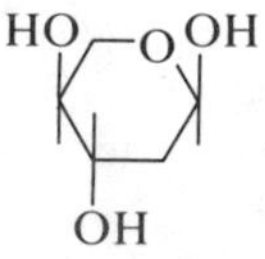 [structure]   (b) 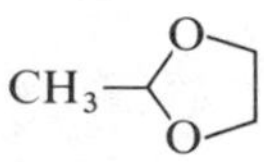 CH_3-[structure]   (c) 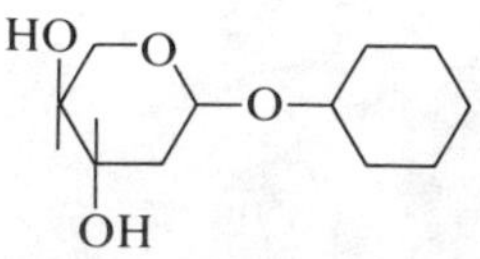 [structure]

11.42 Write equations for the reactions of acetone with (a) semicarbazide, and (b) 2,4-dinitrophenylhydrazine.

11.43 Write equations for the reactions of: (a) benzaldehyde with ⟨benzene ring⟩—NH_2, and (b) propanal with $(CH_3)_2NH$.

11.44 Show how you would prepare the following compounds:

(a) $CH_3CH_2CH{=}CHN(CH_2CH_3)_2$ (b)

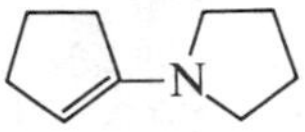

(c) $CH_3CH_2CH{=}NC_6H_5$

11.45 Predict the major organic products:

(a) 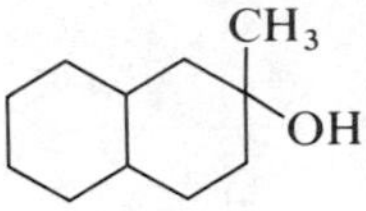 $\xrightarrow[\text{warm}]{H_2SO_4}$

(b) 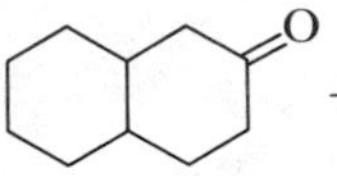 $+ (C_6H_5)_3P{=}CH_2 \longrightarrow$

11.46 Complete the following equations:

(a) 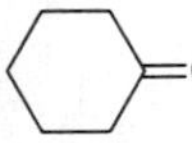 $={}O + (CH_3)_2C(CH_2OH)_2 \underset{\longleftarrow}{\overset{H^+}{\rightleftharpoons}}$

(b) 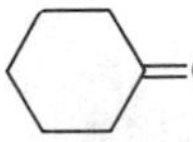 $={}O + H_2NOH \underset{\longleftarrow}{\overset{H^+}{\rightleftharpoons}}$

(c) 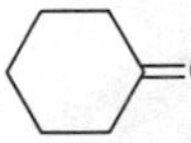 $={}O \xrightarrow[\text{(2) } H_2O, H^+]{\text{(1) } NaC{\equiv}CCH_3}$

(d) 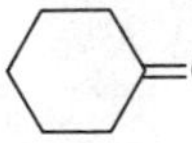 $={}O + HSCH_2CH_2SH \underset{\longleftarrow}{\overset{H^+}{\rightleftharpoons}}$

11.47 Complete the following equations:

(a) 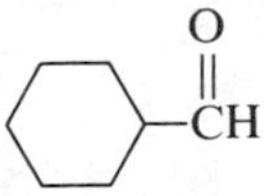 $-\overset{\overset{\displaystyle O}{\|}}{C}H + HCN \rightleftharpoons$

(b) 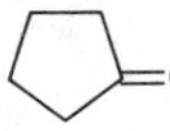 $={}O + NaCN + H_2SO_4 \rightleftharpoons$

(c) 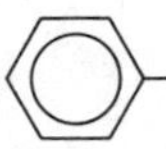 $-CHO + CH_3NH_2 \rightleftharpoons$

(d) 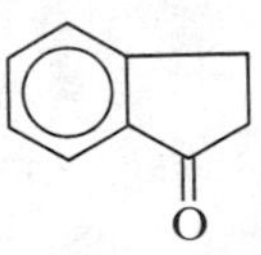 $+ C_6H_5NH_2 \rightleftharpoons$

(e) 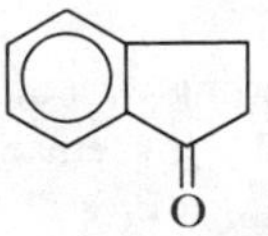 $+ HN$⟨ring⟩ $\rightleftharpoons$

11.48 Give the product of the reaction of cyclopentanone with:

  (a) Br_2 in acetic acid
  (b) $NaBH_4$, followed by H^+, H_2O
  (c) phenylhydrazine with H^+
  (d) $(CH_3)_2CHMgBr$, followed by H^+, H_2O
  (e) $(C_6H_5)_3P{=}C(CH_3)_2$
  (f) hydrazine, followed by heating in NaOH solution

11.49 List the following compounds in terms of reactivity toward 2,4-dinitrophenylhydrazine (least reactive first): (a) 2-pentanone; (b) 3-pentanone; (c) pentanal.

11.50 How would you effect the following conversions by Wittig reactions? (Start with alkyl halides.)

  (a)

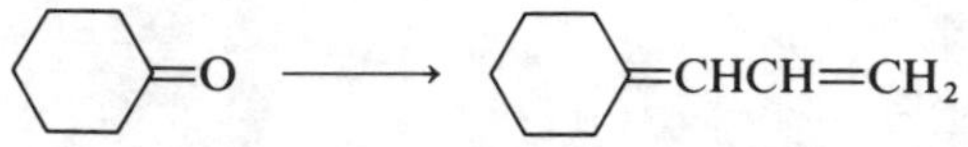

  (b) $(C_6H_5)_2C{=}O \longrightarrow (C_6H_5)_2C{=}CH_2$

  (c) 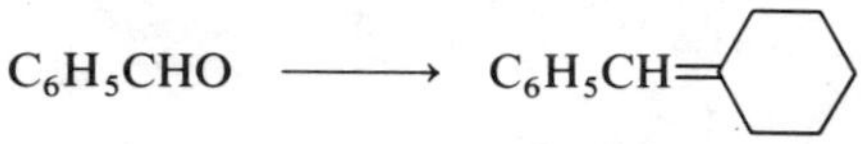 $C_6H_5CHO \longrightarrow C_6H_5CH{=}$

  (d)

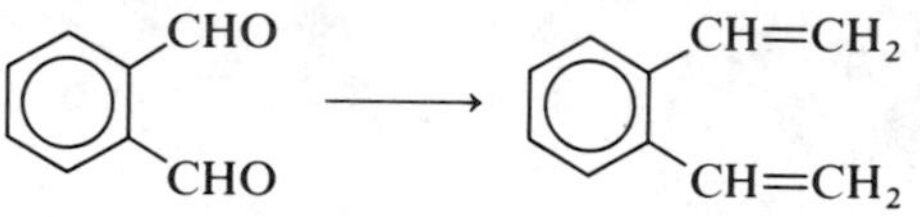

  (e)

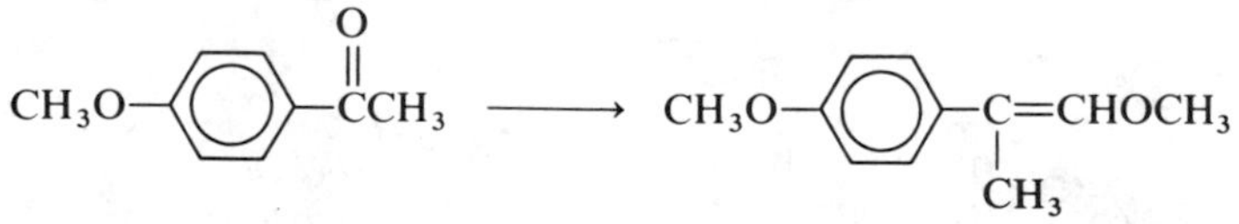

11.51 Predict the major organic products:

  (a)

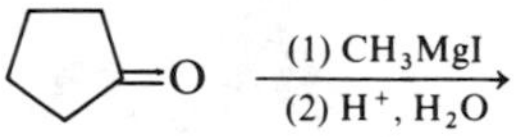

  (b)

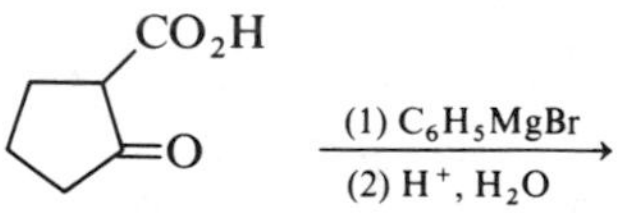

  (c) 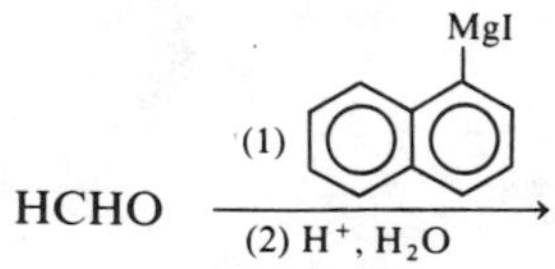 HCHO

11.52 Suggest a synthetic path leading to 2-phenyl-2-propanol, starting with isopropyl alcohol and bromobenzene as the only organic starting materials.

11.53 Suggest a synthesis for each of the following compounds, starting with methyl iodide and other appropriate reagents: (a) 3-methyl-3-pentanol; (b) ethanol; (c) 2-pentanol.

11.54 Predict the organic products:

(a) $\underset{\text{O}}{\overset{\displaystyle\|}{CH_3CCH_3}} + NH_3 \xrightarrow{\text{H}_2,\ \text{Pt}}$

(b) $\underset{\text{O}}{\overset{\displaystyle\|}{CH_3CCH_3}} + HOCH_2CH_2NH_2 \xrightarrow{\text{H}_2,\ \text{Pt}}$

(c) 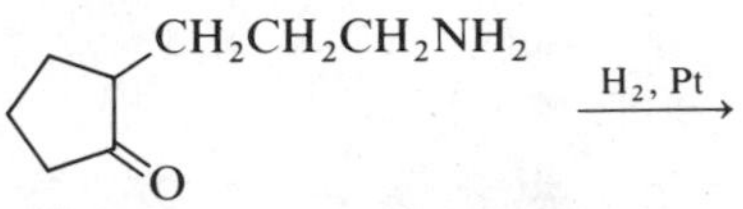   (cyclopentanone with $CH_2CH_2CH_2NH_2$ substituent) $\xrightarrow{\text{H}_2,\ \text{Pt}}$

(d) $CH_3CH_2CHO \xrightarrow[\text{heat, pressure}]{\text{H}_2,\ \text{Pt}}$

(e) $OHCCH_2CH_2CHO \xrightarrow[\text{heat, pressure}]{\text{excess H}_2,\ \text{Pt}}$

(f) 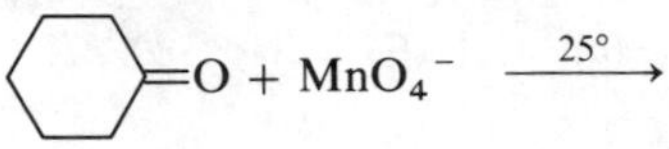   (cyclohexane)$=O + MnO_4^- \xrightarrow{25°}$

(g) 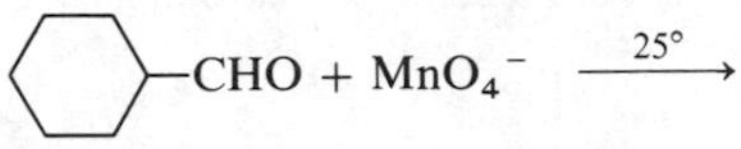   (cyclohexane)$-CHO + MnO_4^- \xrightarrow{25°}$

(h) 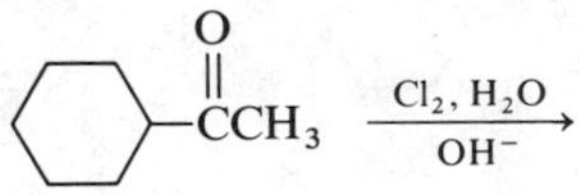   (cyclohexane)$-\overset{\text{O}}{\overset{\displaystyle\|}{C}}CH_3 \xrightarrow[\text{OH}^-]{\text{Cl}_2,\ \text{H}_2\text{O}}$

11.55 Which of the following compounds would give a positive Tollens test?

(a) CH_3CHO (b) $\underset{\text{O}}{\overset{\displaystyle\|}{CH_3CCH_3}}$ (c) 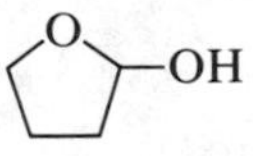   (tetrahydrofuran ring)$-OH$ (d) 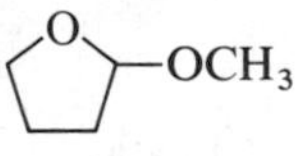   (tetrahydrofuran ring)$-OCH_3$

11.56 Circle the most acidic H in each of the following structures:

(a) $CH_3CH_2CH_2\overset{\text{O}}{\overset{\displaystyle\|}{C}}OCH_2CH_3$ (b) 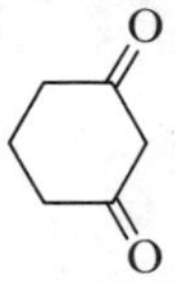   (1,3-cyclohexanedione)   (c) $CH_3\overset{\text{O}}{\overset{\displaystyle\|}{C}}\underset{\underset{CH_3}{|}}{CH}\overset{\text{O}}{\overset{\displaystyle\|}{C}}CH_2CH_3$

(d) 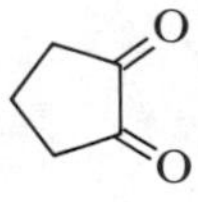   (1,2-cyclopentanedione)

11.57 Rank the following compounds in terms of increasing acidity (least acidic first):
(a) 2,4-pentanedione;   (b) butanal;   (c) water.

11.58 Complete the following equations for acid–base reactions:

(a) $CH_2\left(\overset{\overset{\displaystyle O}{\parallel}}{C}OCH_2CH_3\right)_2 + {}^-OCH_2CH_3 \rightleftharpoons$

(b) $CH_3\overset{\overset{\displaystyle O}{\parallel}}{C}H + OH^- \rightleftharpoons$

(c) 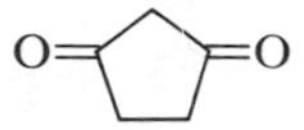 $O=\langle\rangle=O + CO_3{}^{2-} \rightleftharpoons$

(d) $(C_6H_5)_2CH\overset{\overset{\displaystyle O}{\parallel}}{C}OCH_2CH_3 + Na^+ \ {}^-OCH_2CH_3 \rightleftharpoons$

11.59 Each of the following compounds is about as acidic as a β-diketone. Show the resonance structures for the anions of each that would account for this acidity.

(a) CH_3NO_2 (b) $CH_3\overset{\overset{\displaystyle O}{\parallel}}{C}CH_2CN$ (c) $C_6H_5CH_2\overset{\overset{\displaystyle O}{\parallel}}{C}H$

11.60 Write equations that illustrate tautomerism of the following carbonyl compounds:

(a) 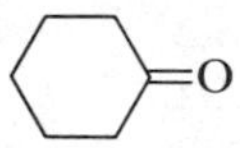 [cyclohexanone structure] $=O$ (b) 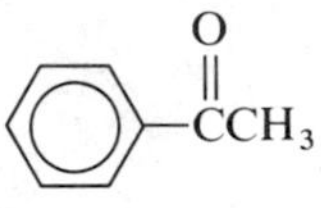 [benzene ring]$-\overset{\overset{\displaystyle O}{\parallel}}{C}CH_3$ (c) [1,3-cyclohexanedione structure]   (d) 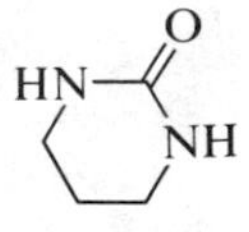 [cyclic structure with HN, O, NH]

11.61 Nitrosocyclohexane undergoes tautomerism. Write the equation that illustrates this reaction.

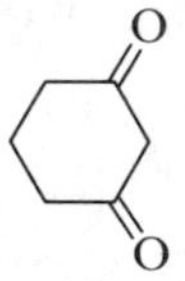

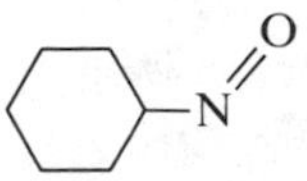

[cyclohexane]$-N\overset{\diagup O}{}$

nitrosocyclohexane

11.62 Predict the organic products:

(a) 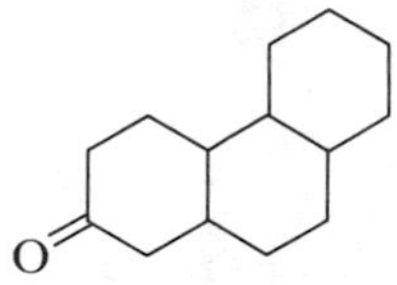 [fused ring ketone structure] $+ Cl_2 \xrightarrow{H^+}$

(b) 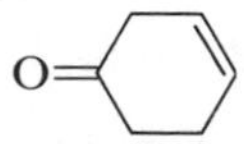 $O=\langle\rangle + Cl_2 \xrightarrow{CCl_4}$

(c) 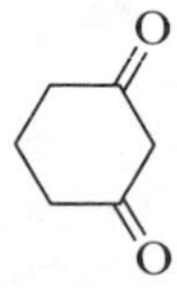 [1,3-cyclohexanedione structure] $+ Br_2 \xrightarrow{H^+}$

(d) 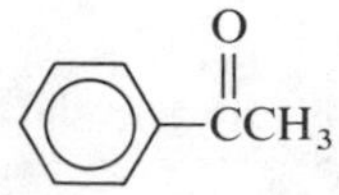 [benzene ring]$-\overset{\overset{\displaystyle O}{\parallel}}{C}CH_3 + Cl_2 \xrightarrow{H^+}$

11.63 What would be observed if each of the following compounds were placed in a test tube and a solution of I_2 in dilute aqueous NaOH were added?

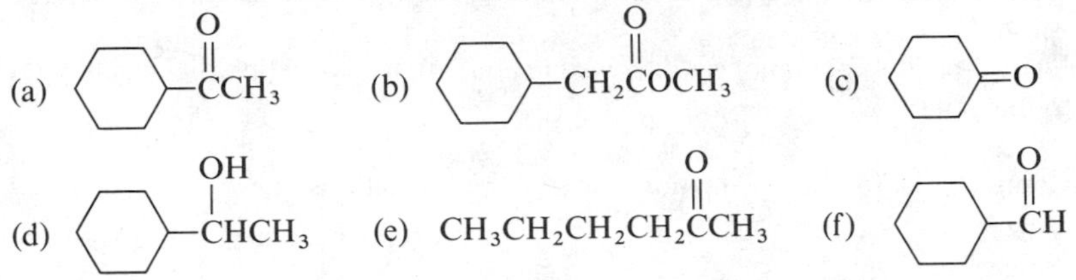

(a) cyclohexyl—CCH_3, O

(b) benzyl—CH_2COCH_3, O

(c) cyclohexyl=O

(d) cyclohexyl—$CHCH_3$, OH

(e) $CH_3CH_2CH_2CH_2CCH_3$, O

(f) cyclohexyl—CH, O

11.64 How would you differentiate the following pairs of compounds by simple chemical tests?

(a) cyclohexanone and cyclohexanol
(b) 2-pentanone and 3-pentanone
(c) pentanal and 2-pentanone
(d) 2-pentene and 2-pentanone

11.65 Suggest a reagent for effecting each of the following conversions:

(a) CH_2=CHCOCH$_2$CH$_3$ $\longrightarrow$ ClCH$_2$CH$_2$COCH$_2$CH$_3$

(b) cyclohexenyl—CCH_3 $\longrightarrow$ cyclohexyl with CN and CCH_3 (O)

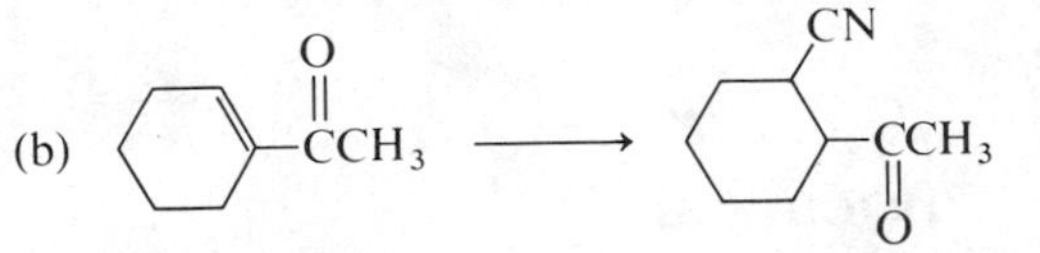

(c) CH_2=CHCCH$_2$CH$_3$ $\longrightarrow$ CH$_3$CH$_2$NHCH$_2$CH$_2$CCH$_2$CH$_3$

11.66 Complete the following equations:

(a) CH_3CH=CHCOCH$_2$CH$_3$ + HI $\longrightarrow$

(b) cyclohexenyl=O + H$_2$O $\xrightarrow{H_2SO_4}$

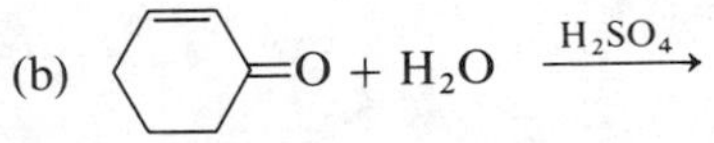

(c) CH_2=CHCCH$_3$ + HBr $\longrightarrow$

(d) CH_2=CHCH$_2$CH$_2$CCH$_3$ + HCl $\longrightarrow$

(e) decalone + CH_3NH_2 $\longrightarrow$

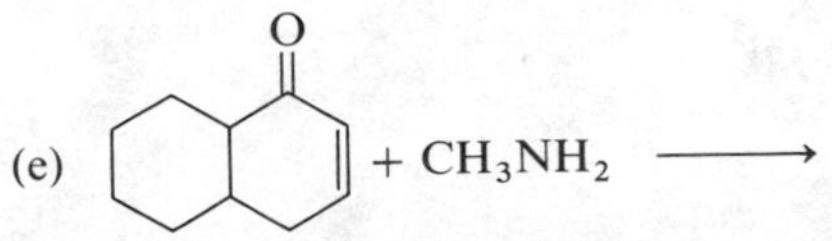

11.67 Suggest a technique by which ^{18}O-labeled aldehydes and ketones might be used to determine the relative rates of hydrate formation.

11.68 3-Phenyl-2-butanone can form two enols, but one is preferred. Which one? If 3-phenyl-2-butanone is dissolved in D_2O with an acidic or basic catalyst, then recovered, it is found to contain deuterium in its structure at primarily one location. Which location?

11.69 If (R)-3-phenyl-2-butanone is dissolved in aqueous acid or base, what would you expect to happen to it?

11.70 Complete the following equations for acid–base reactions:

(a) $\overset{\displaystyle O}{\overset{\|}{CH_3CH_2CCH_3}}$ + excess D_2O $\overset{^-OD}{\rightleftharpoons}$

(b) $\overset{\displaystyle O}{\overset{\|}{CH_3CCH_3}}$ + $^-N(CH_2CH_3)_2$ $\rightleftharpoons$

(c) (S)-$\overset{\displaystyle CH_3}{\overset{|}{CH_3CH_2CHCH_2CHO}}$ + OH^- $\rightleftharpoons$

(d) (S)-$\overset{\displaystyle CH_3}{\overset{|}{CH_3CH_2CH_2CHCHO}}$ + OH^- $\rightleftharpoons$

11.71 *Glutaraldehyde* forms a cyclic hydrate that contains one equivalent of water. What is its structure, and how is it formed? (*Hint*: If *one* aldehyde group is hydrated, what reaction might the molecule undergo?)

$$\overset{\displaystyle O \qquad\quad O}{\overset{\|\qquad\quad\;\|}{HC(CH_2)_3CH}}$$

glutaraldehyde
used as an antiseptic

11.72 Benzene undergoes reaction with formaldehyde and HCl in the presence of zinc chloride to yield benzyl chloride. Write a mechanism for this reaction.

$$C_6H_6 + \overset{\displaystyle O}{\overset{\|}{HCH}} + HCl \xrightarrow{ZnCl_2} C_6H_5CH_2Cl$$

11.73 Suggest a mechanism for the following reaction:

$$CH_2{=}CHCHO + NH_2NH_2 \longrightarrow$$

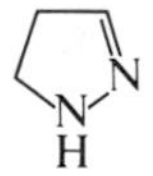

11.74 Suggest a technique by which the Grignard reagent of 3-bromopropanal could be made.

11.75 The sugar *ribose* is found in nucleic acids in its five-membered-ring acetal form. Show by equations how ribose reacts with methanol to yield a five-membered-ring acetal.

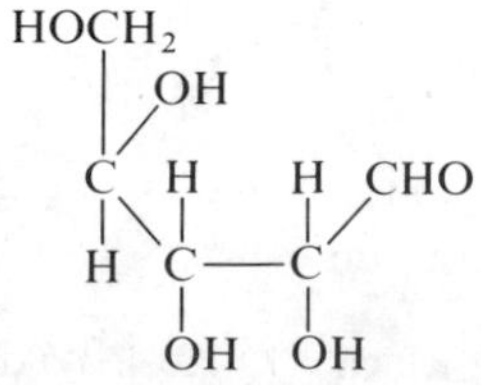

ribose

11.76 The following structure is that of *puberulic acid*, an antibiotic found in *Penicillium puberulum*. When treated with dilute acid, it readily forms a cation. Give the structure of the cation (and its resonance structures).

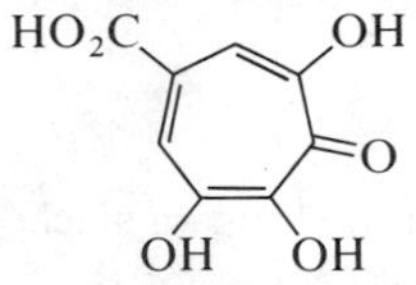

puberulic acid

11.77 Suggest a reason for the following observations:

$$CH_3CH_2OCH_2CH_3 \xrightarrow{\text{dilute HCl}} \text{no reaction}$$

$$CH_3CH(OCH_2CH_3)_2 \underset{\xleftarrow{\text{dilute HCl}}}{} CH_3\overset{\overset{\text{O}}{\|}}{C}H + 2\ CH_3CH_2OH$$

11.78 *Civetone* is an active ingredient of *civet*, a mixture isolated from the scent glands of the African civet cat and used in perfumes. Civetone, which has the formula $C_{17}H_{30}O$, shows strong absorption in the infrared spectrum at 1700 cm^{-1} (5.8 μm) and shows no offset downfield absorption in the nmr spectrum. Treatment of civetone with Br_2 in CCl_4 yields a single dibromide A, $C_{17}H_{30}Br_2O$. Oxidation of civetone with $KMnO_4$ solution yields a diacid B, $C_{17}H_{30}O_5$. Oxidation of civetone with hot, concentrated HNO_3 yields principally $HO_2C(CH_2)_7CO_2H$ and $HO_2C(CH_2)_6CO_2H$. Hydrogenation of civetone (Pd catalyst, no heat or pressure), followed by oxidation with hot HNO_3, yields a diacid $HO_2C(CH_2)_{15}CO_2H$. What are the structures of civetone, A, and B?

11.79 *Muscone* ($C_{16}H_{30}O$) is the active ingredient of *musk*, which is obtained from the scent glands of the male musk deer and is also used in perfumes. Muscone is oxidized by hot HNO_3 to a mixture of diacids, two of which are

$$\underset{\text{CH}_3}{HO_2C(CH_2)_{11}\overset{\overset{\text{CH}_3}{|}}{C}HCH_2CO_2H} \quad \text{and} \quad HO_2C(CH_2)_{12}\overset{\overset{\text{CH}_3}{|}}{C}HCO_2H.$$

Reduction of muscone with a zinc–mercury amalgam and HCl yields methylcyclopentadecane:

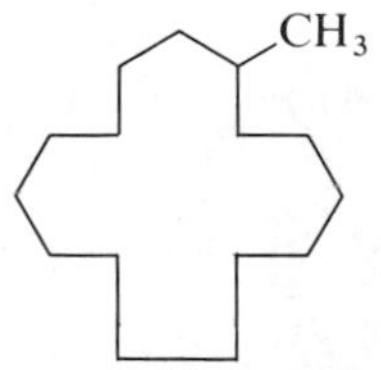

What is the structure of muscone?

11.80 Explain why compound A forms two enols, while compound B forms only one. (Include the enol structures in your answer.)

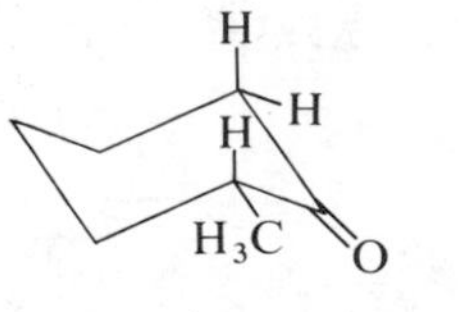

A 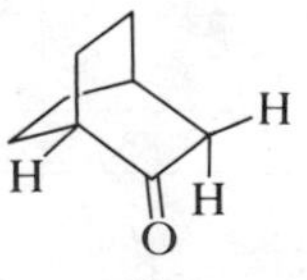   B

11.81 Predict the major organic product:

$$CH_2{=}\underset{\underset{CH_3}{|}}{C}\overset{\overset{O}{\|}}{C}CH_3 \ + \ {}^-CH(\overset{\overset{O}{\|}}{C}OCH_2CH_3)_2 \ \xrightarrow{\text{cold, dil. HCl}}$$

11.82 The formation of a hemiacetal from an aldehyde and an alcohol is catalyzed by base, as well as by acid. The mechanism for the acid-catalyzed reaction was presented in Section 11.8. Suggest a mechanism for the base-catalyzed reaction of acetaldehyde and methanol.

11.83 An acetal can be formed in acidic solution, but not in base. Why not?

11.84 Give equations for the mechanism of base-promoted chlorination of (R)-1-phenyl-2-methyl-1-butanone.

11.85 Match each of the spectra in Figure 11.7 with one of the following structures:

(a) $(CH_3)_3CCHO$ (b) [furan]$C{=}C\underset{\underset{CHO}{|}}{\overset{\overset{H}{|}}{}}$ (c) $NCCH_2CH_2\underset{\underset{CH_3}{|}}{\overset{\overset{CH_3}{|}}{C}}CHO$

(d) $(CH_3)_2N{-}[\text{benzene ring}]{-}CHO$ (e) $(CH_3)_2N{-}[\text{benzene ring}]{-}CH_2CHO$

11.86 Compound A has a molecular weight of 132. Treatment of A with $NaBH_4$ in aqueous methanol yields Compound B. The nmr spectrum of A and the infrared spectrum of B are shown in Figure 11.8 (page 564). What are the structures of A and B?

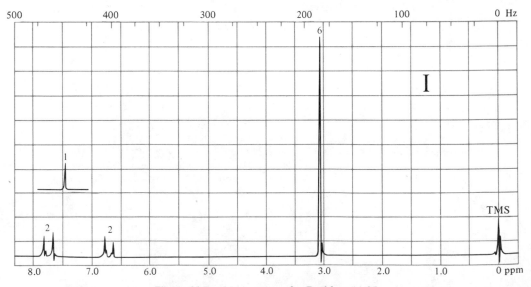

Figure 11.7. Nmr spectra for Problem 11.85.

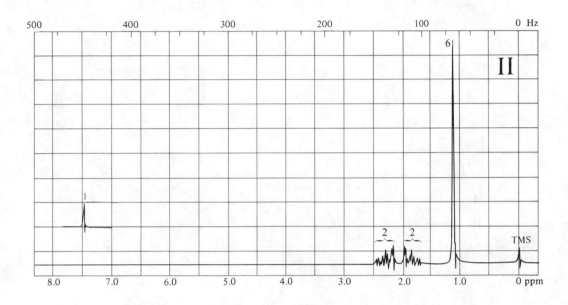

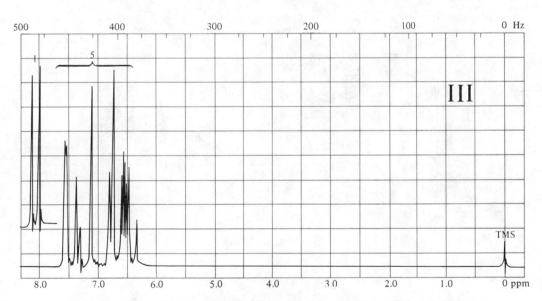

Figure 11.7 (continued).   Nmr spectra for Problem 11.85.

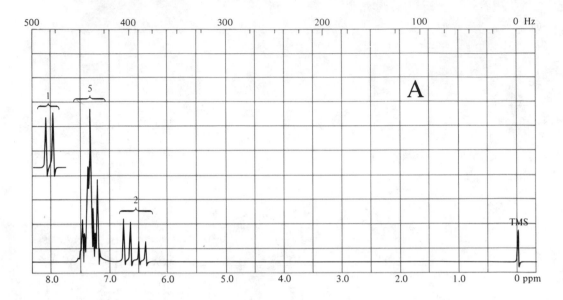

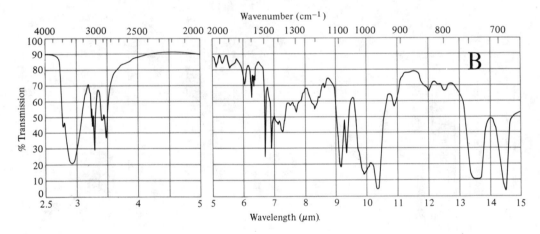

Figure 11.8. Spectra for Problem 11.86.

Chapter 12

Carboxylic Acids

A **carboxylic acid** is an organic compound containing the **carboxyl group**, $-CO_2H$. The carboxyl group contains a carbonyl group and a hydroxyl group; the interactions of these two groups lead to a chemical reactivity that is unique to carboxylic acids.

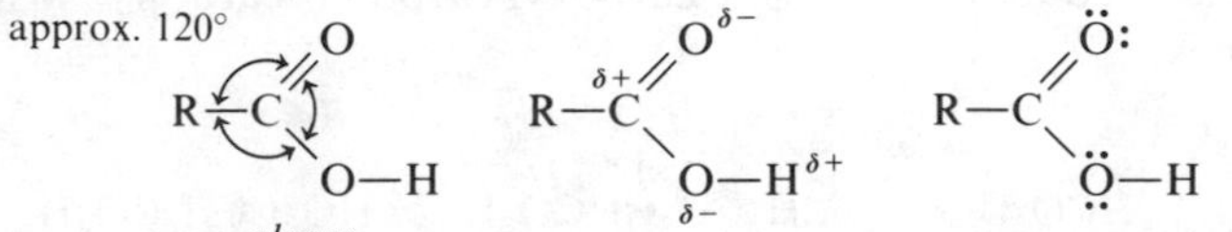

Because the carboxyl group is polar and nonhindered, its reactions are not affected to a great extent by the rest of the molecule. All of the following carboxylic acids undergo similar reactions:

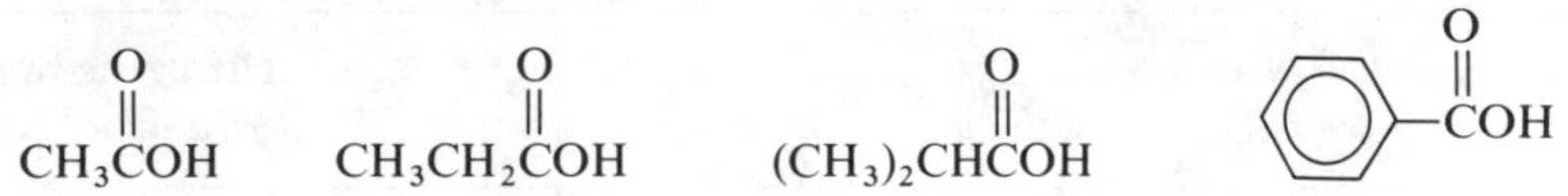

CH_3COH	CH_3CH_2COH	$(CH_3)_2CHCOH$	benzoic acid
IUPAC: ethanoic acid	propanoic acid	2-methylpropanoic acid	
trivial: acetic acid	propionic acid	isobutyric acid	

The most notable chemical property of carboxylic acids is their acidity. Ranked against the mineral acids, such as HCl or HNO_3 (pK_a values about 1 or smaller), the carboxylic acids are weak acids (pK_a values typically about 5). However, the carboxylic acids are more acidic than alcohols or phenols, primarily because of resonance-stabilization of the carboxylate anion, $RCO_2{}^-$. A *p*-orbital picture of the carboxylate ion is shown in Figure 12.1.

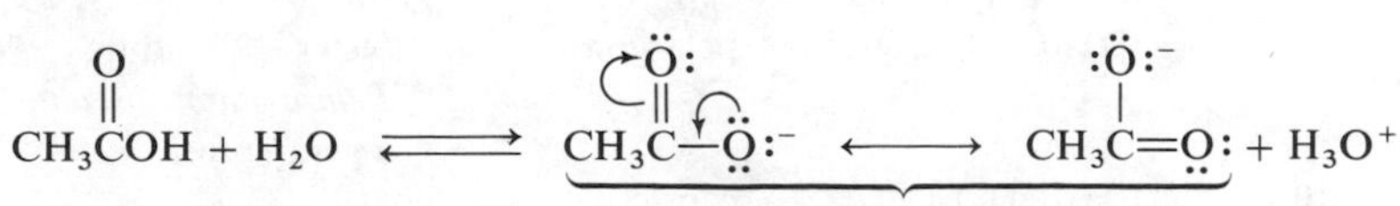

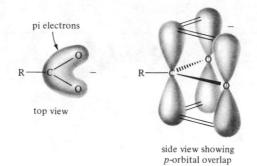

pi electrons

R—C

top view

side view showing
p-orbital overlap

Figure 12.1.   Bonding in the carboxylate ion, $RCO_2{}^-$.

Section 12.1

Nomenclature of Carboxylic Acids

The IUPAC name of an aliphatic carboxylic acid is that of the alkane parent with the -**e** changed to -**oic acid**. The carboxyl carbon is carbon 1, just as the aldehyde carbon is.

	Cl	
HCO_2H	$CH_3CH_2CHCO_2H$	$HO_2CCH_2CO_2H$
IUPAC: methanoic acid	2-chlorobutanoic acid	propanedioic acid

For the first four carboxylic acids, the trivial names are used more often than the IUPAC names. (See Table 12.1.) The name **formic acid** comes from *formica* (Latin for "ants"): in medieval times, alchemists obtained formic acid

Table 12.1.   Trivial Names of the First Ten Carboxylic Acids

Number of carbons	Structure	Trivial name	Occurrence and derivation of name
1	HCO_2H	formic	ants (L. *formica*)
2	CH_3CO_2H	acetic	vinegar (L. *acetum*)
3	$CH_3CH_2CO_2H$	propionic	milk, butter, and cheese (Gr. *protos*, first; *pion*, fat)
4	$CH_3(CH_2)_2CO_2H$	butyric	butter (L. *butyrum*)
5	$CH_3(CH_2)_3CO_2H$	valeric	valerian root (L. *valere*, to be strong)
6	$CH_3(CH_2)_4CO_2H$	caproic	goat (L. *caper*)
7	$CH_3(CH_2)_5CO_2H$	enanthic	(Gr. *œnanthe*, vine blossom)
8	$CH_3(CH_2)_6CO_2H$	caprylic	goat
9	$CH_3(CH_2)_7CO_2H$	pelargonic	Its ester is found in *Pelargonium roseum*, a geranium.
10	$CH_3(CH_2)_8CO_2H$	capric	goat

by distilling red ants! **Acetic acid** is from the Latin *acetum*, "vinegar." In its pure form, it is called *glacial* acetic acid. The term "glacial" arises from the fact that pure acetic acid is a viscous liquid that solidifies into an icy-looking solid. The name for **propionic acid** literally means "first fat." Propionic acid is the first carboxylic acid (the one of lowest molecular weight) to exhibit some of the properties of **fatty acids**, which are carboxylic acids obtained from the hydrolysis of fats (discussed in Section 19.1). **Butyric acid** is found in rancid butter (Latin, *butyrum*).

Some other commonly encountered carboxylic acids and names follow:

CH_3—⬡—CO_2H ⬡(with CO_2H and CO_2H)   ⬡—CO_2H $CH_2{=}CHCO_2H$

p-toluic acid   *o*-phthalic acid   cyclohexanecarboxylic acid   acrylic acid

As with aldehydes and ketones, Greek letters may be used in the trivial names of carboxylic acids to refer to a position in the molecule relative to the carboxyl group.

$$CH_3CH_2CO_2H$$

β carbon   *α carbon*

$$\overset{Br}{\underset{|}{CH_3CH_2CHCO_2H}}$$

α-bromobutyric acid
(2-bromobutanoic acid)

It is sometimes convenient to refer to the RCO— group as an **acyl group** and to $RCO_2{}^-$ as an **acyloxy group**. For example, the *acylation* of benzene is the substitution of a RCO— group on the aromatic ring.

$$\overset{O}{\overset{\|}{RC{-}}} \qquad \overset{O}{\overset{\|}{RCO{-}}}$$

an acyl group   *an acyloxy group*

$$\overset{O}{\overset{\|}{CH_3C{-}}} \qquad ⬡{-}\overset{O}{\overset{\|}{C{-}}} \qquad \overset{O}{\overset{\|}{CH_3CO{-}}}$$

acetyl group   benzoyl group   acetoxy group
(Ac—)   (Bz—)   (AcO—)

STUDY PROBLEMS

12.1 Give IUPAC names for the following carboxylic acids:

(a) $CH_2{=}CHCO_2H$ (b) $HO_2CCH_2CH_2CH_2CO_2H$ (c) $\underset{\underset{CH_3}{|}}{BrCHCO_2H}$

12.2 Give trivial names for

(a) $\underset{\underset{Br}{|}}{CH_3CHCO_2H}$ and (b) $HOCH_2CH_2CO_2H$.

Section 12.2

Physical Properties of Carboxylic Acids

The carboxyl group is ideally structured for forming two hydrogen bonds between a pair of molecules. A pair of hydrogen-bonded carboxylic acid molecules is often referred to as a **carboxylic acid dimer**. Because of the strength of these hydrogen bonds (a total of about 10 kcal/mole for the two hydrogen bonds), carboxylic acids are found as dimers to a limited extent even in the vapor phase.

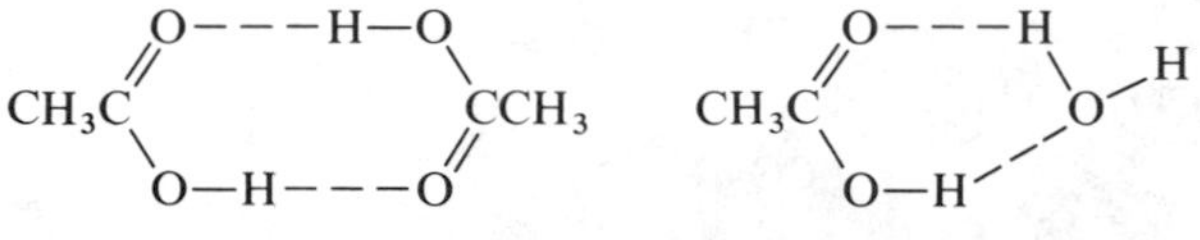

a carboxylic acid dimer   hydrogen bonds with H_2O

STUDY PROBLEM

12.3   Show the principal hydrogen bonds between molecules of each of the following compounds:

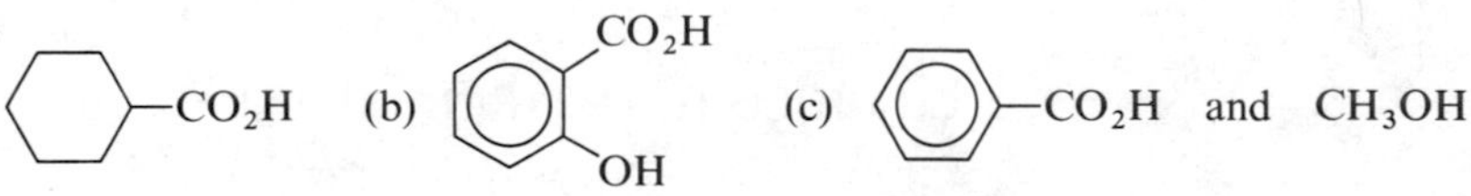

The physical properties of carboxylic acids reflect the strong hydrogen bonding between carboxylic acid molecules. The melting points and boiling points are relatively high. The infrared spectra of carboxylic acids also show the effects of hydrogen bonding (see Section 12.3A). The lower-molecular-weight acids are water-soluble, as well as soluble in organic solvents. The melting points, boiling points, and water-solubilities of some carboxylic acids are listed in Table 12.2.

A notable property (not a physical property, but a physiological one) of the lower-molecular-weight carboxylic acids is their odor. Formic and acetic acids

Table 12.2. Physical Properties of Some Carboxylic Acids

Name	Structure	Mp, °C	Bp, °C	Solubility in H_2O at 20°C
formic	HCO_2H	8	100.5	∞
acetic	CH_3CO_2H	16.6	118	∞
propionic	$CH_3CH_2CO_2H$	−22	141	∞
butyric	$CH_3(CH_2)_2CO_2H$	−6	164	∞
valeric	$CH_3(CH_2)_3CO_2H$	−34	187	3.7 g/100 ml
caproic	$CH_3(CH_2)_4CO_2H$	−3	205	1.0 g/100 ml
cyclohexane-carboxylic	$C_6H_{11}CO_2H$	31	233	0.2 g/100 ml
benzoic	$C_6H_5CO_2H$	122	250	0.3 g/100 ml

have pungent odors. Propionic acid has a pungent odor reminiscent of rancid fat. The odor of rancid butter arises in part from butyric acid. Caproic acid smells like a goat. (Goat sweat, incidentally, contains caproic acid.) Valeric acid (from the Latin *valere*, "to be strong") is not a strong acid, but it does have a strong odor somewhere in between that of rancid butter and goat sweat. The odors of the aliphatic carboxylic acids of ten and more carbons diminish, probably because of their lack of volatility.

Section 12.3

Spectral Properties of Carboxylic Acids

A. Infrared Spectra

Carboxylic acids, either as pure liquids or in solution at concentrations in excess of about 0.01 M, exist primarily as hydrogen-bonded dimers rather than as discrete monomers. The infrared spectrum of a carboxylic acid is therefore the spectrum of the dimer. Because of the hydrogen bonding, the O—H stretching absorption of carboxylic acids is very broad and very intense. This O—H absorption starts around 4000 cm^{-1} (2.5 μm) and slopes into the region of aliphatic carbon–hydrogen absorption (see Figure 12.2). The broadness of the carboxylic acid O—H band can often obscure both aliphatic and aromatic C—H absorption, as well as any other OH or NH absorption in the spectrum.

The carbonyl absorption is observed at about 1700–1720 cm^{-1} (5.8–5.86 μm) and is of moderately strong intensity. Conjugation shifts this absorption to shorter frequencies: 1680–1710 cm^{-1} (5.8–5.95 μm).

The fingerprint region in an infrared spectrum of a carboxylic acid often shows C—O stretching and O—H bending (see Table 12.3). Another O—H bending vibration of the dimer results in a broad absorption near 925 cm^{-1} (10.8 μm).

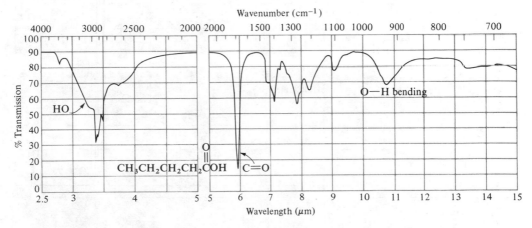

Figure 12.2. Infrared spectrum of pentanoic acid.

Table 12.3.   Characteristic Infrared Absorption for Carboxylic Acids

	Position of absorption	
Type of vibration	cm^{-1}	μm
O—H stretching	2860–4000	2.5–3.5
C=O stretching	1700–1720	5.8–5.86
C—O stretching	1210–1330	7.5–8.26
O—H bending	1300–1440	6.94–7.71
O—H bending (dimer)	~925	~10.8

B.   Nmr Spectra

In the nmr spectrum, the absorption of the acidic proton of a carboxylic acid is seen as a singlet far downfield at about 10–13 ppm, offset from the usual spectral range. The alpha protons are only slightly affected by the C=O group; their absorption is slightly downfield (about 2.2 ppm) because of the inductive effect of the partially positive carbonyl carbon. There is no unique splitting pattern associated with the carboxylic acid group because the carboxyl proton is not vicinal to any other protons. (See Figure 12.3.)

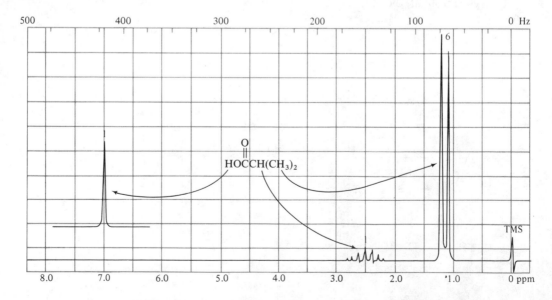

Figure 12.3.   Nmr spectrum of 2-methylpropanoic acid.

Section 12.4

Preparation of Carboxylic Acids

The numerous synthetic paths that lead to carboxylic acids may be grouped into three types of reaction: (1) *hydrolysis of the derivatives of the carboxylic acids*; (2) *oxidation reactions*; and (3) *Grignard reactions*.

A. Hydrolysis of Derivatives of Carboxylic Acids

Hydrolysis of carboxylic acid derivatives results from the attack of water or OH⁻ on the carbonyl (or —CN) carbon of the derivative. We will discuss each of these reactions in detail in Chapter 13.

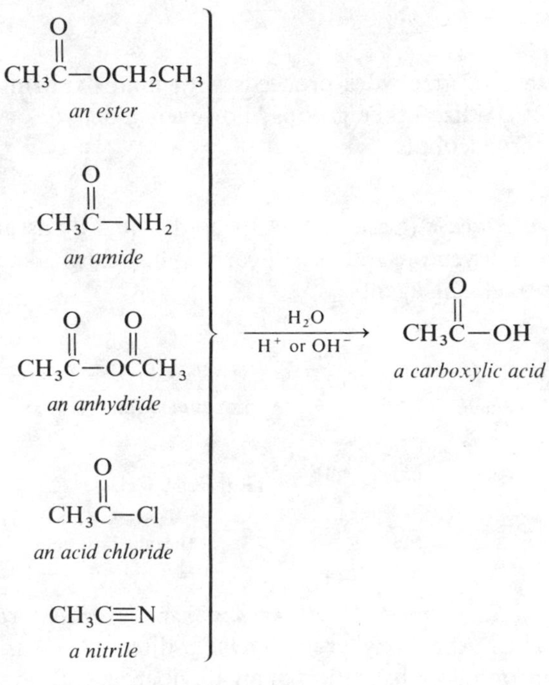

$$
\left.
\begin{array}{l}
\underset{an\ ester}{CH_3\overset{\displaystyle O}{\overset{\|}{C}}-OCH_2CH_3} \\[2em]
\underset{an\ amide}{CH_3\overset{\displaystyle O}{\overset{\|}{C}}-NH_2} \\[2em]
\underset{an\ anhydride}{CH_3\overset{\displaystyle O}{\overset{\|}{C}}-\overset{\displaystyle O}{\overset{\|}{C}}CH_3} \\[2em]
\underset{an\ acid\ chloride}{CH_3\overset{\displaystyle O}{\overset{\|}{C}}-Cl} \\[2em]
\underset{a\ nitrile}{CH_3C\equiv N}
\end{array}
\right\}
\xrightarrow[\mathrm{H^+\ or\ OH^-}]{\mathrm{H_2O}}
\underset{a\ carboxylic\ acid}{CH_3\overset{\displaystyle O}{\overset{\|}{C}}-OH}
$$

B. Oxidation

Oxidation of a variety of compounds leads to carboxylic acid products.

$$
\underset{a\ 1°\ alcohol}{CH_3CH_2OH} \xrightarrow{[O]} CH_3CO_2H
$$

$$
\underset{an\ aldehyde}{CH_3CHO} \xrightarrow{[O]} CH_3CO_2H
$$

$$
\underset{an\ alkene}{CH_3CH=CHCH_3} \xrightarrow{[O]} CH_3CO_2H
$$

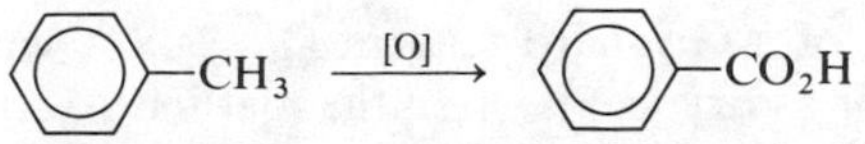

$$
\underset{an\ alkylbenzene}{C_6H_5-CH_3} \xrightarrow{[O]} C_6H_5-CO_2H
$$

Oxidation of Primary Alcohols and Aldehydes to yield carboxylic acids was discussed in Sections 7.17C and 11.15, respectively. The principal limitation of alcohol-oxidation is that the necessary strength of the oxidizing agent precludes the presence of another oxidizable functional group in the molecule (unless it is protected by a blocking group, such as the dibromide of an alkene or an acetal of an aldehyde). Even with this limitation, the oxidation of primary alcohols is the most common oxidative procedure for obtaining carboxylic acids because alcohols are often available.

$$RCH_2OH \xrightarrow[\text{heat}]{MnO_4^-} RCO_2H$$

no double bond, aldehyde, benzyl group, or other —OH group

The oxidation of aldehydes proceeds with mild oxidizing agents (such as Ag^+) that do not oxidize other groups; however, aldehydes are not as readily available as primary alcohols.

Oxidation of Alkenes (Section 9.14) is used primarily as an analytical tool, but also can be employed in synthesis of carboxylic acids. Like alcohols, alkenes require vigorous oxidizing agents.

$$CH_3CH_2CH{=}CH_2 \xrightarrow[\text{heat}]{MnO_4^-} CH_3CH_2CO_2H + CO_2 + H_2O$$

1-butene   propanoic acid

$$\text{cyclohexene} \xrightarrow[\text{heat}]{MnO_4^-} HO_2CCH_2CH_2CH_2CH_2CO_2H$$

adipic acid
(hexanedioic acid)

Oxidation of Substituted Alkylbenzenes is an excellent route to the substituted benzoic acids. A carboxyl group is a *meta*-director, but an alkyl group is an *o,p*-director. Electrophilic substitution of an alkylbenzene, followed by oxidation, yields *o*- and *p*-substituted benzoic acids.

$$O_2N-\underset{\text{2,4-dinitrotoluene}}{\underset{NO_2}{\bigcirc}}-CH_3 \xrightarrow[\text{heat}]{MnO_4^-} O_2N-\underset{\text{2,4-dinitrobenzoic acid}}{\underset{NO_2}{\bigcirc}}-CO_2H$$

C. Grignard Reactions

The reaction of a Grignard reagent (1°, 2°, 3°, vinyl, or aryl) with carbon dioxide (as a gas or as dry ice) is often the method of choice for preparing a carboxylic acid.

Grignard reactions:

$$(CH_3)_3CMgCl \xrightarrow[\text{(2) } H_2O,\ H^+]{\text{(1) } CO_2} (CH_3)_3CCO_2H$$

t-butylmagnesium   2,2-dimethylpropanoic acid
chloride   80%

$$\langle\bigcirc\rangle\!-\!MgBr \xrightarrow[\text{(2) } H_2O,\ H^+]{\text{(1) } CO_2} \langle\bigcirc\rangle\!-\!CO_2H$$

phenylmagnesium   benzoic acid
bromide   85%

In the reaction of RMgX with CO_2, the partially negative carbon of the Grignard reagent adds to the partially positive carbon of CO_2, just as in the reaction with a ketone. The magnesium carboxylate salt precipitates so that further addition does not occur. In a subsequent step, treatment with aqueous acid liberates the carboxylic acid.

Step 1:
$$O{=}\overset{\delta+}{C}{=}O + \overset{\delta-}{R}{-}MgX \longrightarrow O{=}\underset{\underset{R}{|}}{C}{-}O^-\ {}^+MgX$$

Step 2:
$$RCO_2^-\ {}^+MgX + H_2O \xrightarrow{H^+} RCO_2H + HOMgX$$

D. Summary of Synthetic Methods

Let us summarize the common synthetic routes to carboxylic acids from a different viewpoint—that of what happens to the molecule as a whole. Synthesis from an alkyl halide by way of the nitrile or Grignard reagent leads to a carboxylic acid with *one more carbon* than in the alkyl halide.

Chain-lengthening:

$$1° RX \xrightarrow[S_N2]{CN^-} RCN \xrightarrow{H_2O,\ H^+} RCO_2H$$

$$\underset{\substack{1°,\ 2°,\ 3°,\\ \text{vinyl, or aryl}}}{RX} \xrightarrow{Mg} RMgX \xrightarrow[\text{(2) } H_2O,\ H^+]{\text{(1) } CO_2} RCO_2H$$

Oxidation of a primary alcohol (or aldehyde) does not affect the length of the carbon chain, nor does hydrolysis of a carboxylic acid derivative.

Same number of carbons:

$$RCH_2OH \xrightarrow[\text{heat}]{MnO_4^-} RCO_2H$$

$$\overset{O}{\overset{\|}{R{C}OR'}} \xrightarrow{H^+,\ H_2O} \overset{O}{\overset{\|}{R{C}OH}} + R'OH$$

Oxidation of an alkene (unless the alkene is cyclic) causes fragmentation of the parent chain.

$$RCH{=}CR_2 \xrightarrow[\text{heat}]{MnO_4^-} RCO_2H + O{=}CR_2$$

STUDY PROBLEM

12.4 Considering only nitrile formation and Grignard reactions, propose a feasible route for each of the following conversions:

(a) $HOCH_2CH_2Cl \longrightarrow HOCH_2CH_2CO_2H$

(b) $(CH_3)_3CCH_2Cl \longrightarrow (CH_3)_3CCH_2CO_2H$

(c) 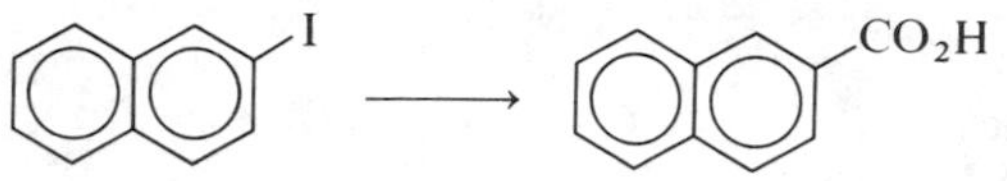 $\longrightarrow$

(d)  $\longrightarrow$

Section 12.5

Acidity of Carboxylic Acids

Carboxylic acids, sulfonic acids (RSO_3H), and monoalkyl sulfates ($ROSO_3H$) are the only classes of organic compounds more acidic than carbonic acid (H_2CO_3). Of these three classes, carboxylic acids are by far the most common.

	RCH_3	RNH_2	$RC{\equiv}CH$	ROH	H_2O	$ArOH$	H_2CO_3	RCO_2H
approx. pK_a:	45	35	25	18	15	10	6.4	5

increasing acid strength →

Because it is more acidic than carbonic acid, a carboxylic acid undergoes an acid–base reaction with sodium bicarbonate as well as with stronger bases such as NaOH.

$$\underset{\text{acetic acid}}{CH_3\overset{\displaystyle O}{\overset{\|}{C}}OH} + OH^- \longrightarrow \underset{\text{acetate ion}}{CH_3\overset{\displaystyle O}{\overset{\|}{C}}O^-} + H_2O$$

$$CH_3\overset{\displaystyle O}{\overset{\|}{C}}OH + HCO_3^- \longrightarrow CH_3\overset{\displaystyle O}{\overset{\|}{C}}O^- + [H_2CO_3] \longrightarrow H_2O + CO_2$$

While carboxylic acids undergo reaction with sodium bicarbonate, phenols require the stronger base NaOH, and alcohols require a yet stronger base, such as $NaNH_2$.

In NaHCO$_3$: $RCO_2H \xrightarrow{HCO_3^-} RCO_2^- + CO_2 + H_2O$

$ArOH$ and $ROH \xrightarrow{HCO_3^-}$ no appreciable reaction

In NaOH: $RCO_2H \xrightarrow{OH^-} RCO_2^- + H_2O$

$ArOH \xrightarrow{OH^-} ArO^- + H_2O$

$ROH \xrightarrow{OH^-}$ no appreciable reaction

This difference between phenols and carboxylic acids in reactivity toward NaOH and $NaHCO_3$ is the basis of a simple classification and separation procedure. If a water-insoluble compound dissolves in NaOH solution, but not in $NaHCO_3$ solution, it is likely to be a phenol. On the other hand, if the compound dissolves in *both* NaOH and $NaHCO_3$ solution, it is probably a carboxylic acid.

A carboxylic acid can be extracted from a mixture of water-insoluble organic compounds with sodium bicarbonate solution. The acid forms a sodium salt and becomes water-soluble, while the other organic compounds remain insoluble. The free carboxylic acid is obtained from the water solution by acidification.

When used either as a test or as a separation procedure, the reaction with sodium bicarbonate has its limitations. If the hydrocarbon portion of the carboxylic acid is long, the compound fails to dissolve in $NaHCO_3$ solution and may even fail to dissolve in NaOH solution. In addition, some phenols, such as the nitrophenols, have acid strengths comparable to those of carboxylic acids; these phenols dissolve in $NaHCO_3$ as well as in NaOH solutions.

STUDY PROBLEMS

12.5 An aldehyde obtained from a storeroom is probably contaminated with some carboxylic acid (from air oxidation of the aldehyde). Describe in words how you would remove the unwanted acid.

12.6 You are confronted with an ether solution containing a mixture of heptanoic acid, α-naphthol, and octanol. How would you separate these three components?

α-naphthol

A. Neutralization Equivalent

The **equivalent weight** of an acid, or its **neutralization equivalent**, is the number of grams of the acid that undergoes reaction with 1.0 equivalent of OH^-. The neutralization equivalent is determined by titrating a known weight of the acid with a standardized solution of sodium hydroxide. The endpoint is often determined by the color change of an indicator such as phenolphthalein; however, a pH meter gives more reliable results.

$$RCO_2H + OH^- \longrightarrow RCO_2^- + H_2O$$

At the endpoint, the number of equivalents of base added—the normality of the base times its volume in liters, or (NV)—is equal to the number of equivalents of acid. From the weight of the sample of acid and its number of equivalents, the neutralization equivalent can be calculated.

$$NV = \text{no. of equivalents of } OH^- = \text{no. of equivalents of acid}$$

$$\text{neutralization equivalent of acid} = \frac{\text{wt. in g of acid}}{\text{no. of equivalents of acid}}$$

Example: A 0.528-g sample of a carboxylic acid requires 24.00 ml of 0.100 N NaOH to be neutralized.

$$\text{equivalents acid} = \text{equivalents OH}^-$$
$$= NV$$
$$= (0.100 \text{ eq./liter})(0.0240 \text{ liter})$$
$$= 0.00240 \text{ eq.}$$

$$\text{neutralization equivalent} = \frac{\text{wt. in g}}{\text{no. of equivalents}}$$

$$= \frac{0.528}{0.00240}$$

$$= 220$$

If a carboxylic acid has only one acidic proton per molecule, the neutralization equivalent equals the molecular weight. If an acid has *two* acidic protons, the neutralization equivalent is only *half* the molecular weight,

	$\bigcirc\!-\!CO_2H$	$HO_2C\!-\!\bigcirc\!-\!CO_2H$
neutralization equivalent:	122.1	83.0
molecular weight:	122.1	166.1

STUDY PROBLEMS

12.7 A 0.200-g sample of an unknown acid requires 13.00 ml of 0.201 N sodium hydroxide solution to reach neutrality. What is the neutralization equivalent of the acid?

12.8 What are the equivalent weights of:

(a) acetic acid
(b) succinic acid ($HO_2CCH_2CH_2CO_2H$)
(c) hydroxyacetic acid?

Section 12.6

Salts of Carboxylic Acids

The reaction of a carboxylic acid with a base results in a *salt*. An organic salt has many of the physical properties of its inorganic counterparts. Like NaCl or KNO_3, an organic salt is high-melting, water-soluble, and odorless.

$$HCO_2H \ + \ Na^+ \ OH^- \ \longrightarrow \ HCO_2^- \ Na^+ \ + \ H_2O$$

formic acid   sodium formate

$$\bigcirc\!-\!CO_2H \ + \ Na^+ \ HCO_3^- \ \longrightarrow \ \bigcirc\!-\!CO_2^- \ Na^+ \ + \ H_2O \ + \ CO_2$$

cyclohexane-   sodium cyclohexanecarboxylic acid   carboxylate

The carboxylate anion is named by changing the **-ic acid** ending of the carboxylic acid name to **-ate**. In the name of the salt, the name of the cation precedes the name of the anion as a separate word.

$$CH_3CO_2H \qquad CH_3CO_2^- \ Na^+$$

acetic acid   sodium acetate

benzoic acid   ammonium benzoate

$$HO_2CCH_2CH_2\overset{\displaystyle NH_2}{\overset{|}{C}}HCO_2H \qquad HO_2CCH_2CH_2\overset{\displaystyle NH_2}{\overset{|}{C}}HCO_2^- \ Na^+$$

glutamic acid   monosodium glutamate
an amino acid found in proteins   *a flavor enhancer* (MSG)

The carboxylate ion is a weak base and can act as a nucleophile. Esters, for example, may be prepared by the S_N2 reaction of primary alkyl halides and carboxylates (see Chapter 5).

$$CH_3CO_2^- \ + \ \overset{\displaystyle CH_3}{\overset{|}{C}}H_2{-}Br \ \xrightarrow{\ S_N2\ } \ CH_3CO_2{-}CH_2CH_3 \ + \ Br^-$$

acetate ion   ethyl bromide   ethyl acetate
                                                      an ester

Section 12.7

How Structure Affects Acid Strength

Acid strength is a term describing the extent of ionization of an acid: the greater the amount of ionization, the more hydrogen ions are formed, and the stronger is the acid. The strength of an acid is expressed as its K_a or its pK_a (see Table 12.4). (You may want to review the discussion of K_a and pK_a in Section 1.10

Table 12.4. **pK_a Values for Some Carboxylic Acids**

Name	Structure	pK_a
formic	HCO_2H	3.75
acetic	CH_3CO_2H	4.75
propionic	$CH_3CH_2CO_2H$	4.87
butyric	$CH_3(CH_2)_2CO_2H$	4.81
trimethylacetic	$(CH_3)_3CCO_2H$	5.02
fluoroacetic	FCH_2CO_2H	2.66
chloroacetic	$ClCH_2CO_2H$	2.81
bromoacetic	$BrCH_2CO_2H$	2.87
iodoacetic	ICH_2CO_2H	3.13
dichloroacetic	Cl_2CHCO_2H	1.29
trichloroacetic	Cl_3CCO_2H	0.7
α-chloropropionic	$CH_3CHClCO_2H$	2.8
β-chloropropionic	$ClCH_2CH_2CO_2H$	4.1
lactic	$CH_3\overset{\displaystyle OH}{\overset{|}{C}}HCO_2H$	3.87
vinylacetic	$CH_2{=}CHCH_2CO_2H$	4.35

before proceeding.) In this section, we will discuss the general structural features that affect the acid strength of an organic compound. Our emphasis will be on carboxylic acids, but we will not limit the discussion to just these compounds.

The reaction of a weak acid with water is reversible. The equilibrium lies on the lower-energy side of the equation. Any structural feature that *stabilizes the anion* with respect to its conjugate acid *increases the acid strength* by driving the equilibrium to the H^+ and anion (A^-) side.

$$HA + H_2O \rightleftharpoons H_3O^+ + A^- \quad \overset{lower\ energy\ means}{stronger\ acid}$$

The principal factors that affect the stability of A^-, and thus the acid strength of HA, are: (1) electronegativity of A^-; (2) size of A^-; (3) hybridization of A^-; (4) inductive effect of other atoms or groups attached to the negative atom in A^-; (5) resonance-stabilization of A^-; and (6) solvation of A^-. We will discuss each of these features in turn.

A. *Electronegativity*

A more electronegative atom holds its bonding electrons more tightly than does a less electronegative atom. In comparisons of anions, the anion of greater electronegativity is the more stable anion. Therefore, in a series of compounds, we observe that the strongest acid is the one that yields the most electronegative anion upon ionization.

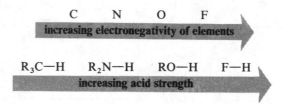

Just the reverse is true when we consider the base strength of the resulting anions. The anion of a very weak acid is a very strong base, while the anion of a stronger acid is a weaker base.

$$
\begin{array}{cccc}
R_3C^- & R_2N^- & RO^- & F^-
\end{array}
$$
increasing base strength ⟵

Consider, for example, the ionization reactions of ethanol and HF in water. As an element, F is more electronegative than O; thus, a fluoride ion is better able to carry a negative charge than is the alkoxide ion. Although HF is a weak acid, it is a much stronger acid than ethanol. Conversely, the fluoride ion is a weaker base than the ethoxide ion.

$$CH_3CH_2OH + H_2O \rightleftharpoons CH_3CH_2O^- + H_3O^+$$

$\quad$ *weaker acid* $\qquad\qquad\qquad\qquad$ *stronger base*

$\quad$ $pK_a = 16$

$$HF + H_2O \rightleftharpoons F^- + H_3O^+$$

$\quad$ *stronger acid* $\qquad\qquad\qquad\qquad$ *weaker base*

$\quad$ $pK_a = 3.45$

B. Size

A larger atom is better able to disperse a negative charge than is a smaller atom. Dispersal of a charge results in stabilization. Thus, as the size of an atom attached to H increases in a series of compounds, the stability of the anion increases, and so does acid strength.

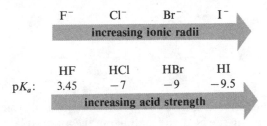

$$F^- \qquad Cl^- \qquad Br^- \qquad I^-$$
increasing ionic radii

$$\begin{array}{cccc} HF & HCl & HBr & HI \\ pK_a: \quad 3.45 & -7 & -9 & -9.5 \end{array}$$
increasing acid strength

C. Hybridization

In Section 9.1, we discussed why an alkyne with a $\equiv$CH group is weakly acidic. The increasing s character of the hybrid orbitals of carbon in the series $sp^3 \rightarrow sp^2 \rightarrow sp$ means increasing electronegativity of the carbon, and thus increasing polarity of the CH bond and increasing acid strength. A greater electronegativity of the atom bonded to H also enhances anion stability and thus the acidity of the compound. For these reasons, an alkynyl proton is more acidic than an alkenyl proton, which, in turn, is more acidic than the proton of an alkane.

$$\begin{array}{ccc} CH_3CH_3 & CH_2{=}CH_2 & CH{\equiv}CH \\ \text{approx. } pK_a: \quad 43 & 36 & 26 \end{array}$$
increasing acid strength

Again, the strongest acid of the series yields the anion that is the weakest base.

$$CH_3CH_2^- \qquad CH_2{=}CH^- \qquad CH{\equiv}C^-$$
increasing base strength

D. Inductive Effect

So far, we have discussed how the atom bonded directly to a hydrogen affects acid strength. However, other parts of a molecule can also affect acid strength. Compare the pK_a values for acetic acid and chloroacetic acid:

$$\begin{array}{cc} CH_3CO_2H & ClCH_2CO_2H \\ \text{acetic acid} & \text{chloroacetic acid} \\ pK_a = 4.75 & pK_a = 2.81 \end{array}$$

As an acid, chloroacetic acid is one hundred times stronger than acetic acid! This enhanced acidity arises from the inductive effect of the electronegative chlorine. In the nonionized carboxylic acid, the electron-withdrawing Cl decreases the electron density of the α carbon. The result is a relatively high-energy structure with adjacent positive charges.

$$\overset{\delta-}{Cl}\!\leftarrow\!\underset{\delta+}{CH_2}\!-\!\overset{\overset{\textstyle O}{\|}}{\underset{\delta+}{C}}OH \qquad \begin{array}{l}\textit{adjacent } \delta+ \textit{ charges}\\ \textit{destabilize acid}\end{array}$$

The presence of the chlorine, however, *reduces* the energy of the anion. In this case, the negative charge of the carboxylate group is partially dispersed by the nearby $\delta+$ charge.

$$\underset{\delta-}{Cl}\!\leftarrow\!\underset{\delta+}{CH_2}\!\leftarrow\!\overset{\overset{\textstyle O}{\|}}{C}\!-\!O^- \qquad \begin{array}{l}\textit{nearby } \delta+ \textit{ and}\\ -\textit{ charges stabilize anion}\end{array}$$

The effect of an electronegative group near the carboxyl group is to strengthen the acid by destabilizing the acid and stabilizing the anion relative to each other.

$$\underset{\textit{less stable}}{ClCH_2\overset{\overset{\textstyle O}{\|}}{C}OH} + H_2O \;\rightleftarrows\; \underset{\textit{more stable}}{ClCH_2\overset{\overset{\textstyle O}{\|}}{C}O^-} + H_3O^+$$

A list of groups in order of their electron-withdrawal power follows:

$$CH_3-\quad H-\quad CH_2\!=\!CH-\quad C_6H_5-\quad HO-\quad CH_3O-\quad I-\quad Br-\quad Cl-$$

increasing power of electron-withdrawal →

The pK_a values of the following carboxylic acids reflect the differences in electron-withdrawal by groups attached to $-CH_2CO_2H$:

$CH_3CH_2CO_2H$	CH_3CO_2H	$CH_2{=}CHCH_2CO_2H$	$C_6H_5CH_2CO_2H$	$HOCH_2CO_2H$	$ClCH_2CO_2H$
pK_a: 4.87	4.75	4.35	4.31	3.87	2.81

increasing acid strength →

The inductive effect is additive. Dichloroacetic acid is a stronger acid than is chloroacetic acid, and trichloroacetic acid is the strongest of the three.

$ClCH_2CO_2H$	Cl_2CHCO_2H	Cl_3CCO_2H
chloroacetic acid	dichloroacetic acid	trichloroacetic acid
p$K_a = 2.81$	p$K_a = 1.29$	p$K_a = 0.7$

The influence of the inductive effect upon acid strength diminishes with an increasing number of atoms between the carboxyl group and the electronegative group. 2-Chlorobutanoic acid is a substantially stronger acid than butanoic acid itself; however, 4-chlorobutanoic acid has a pK_a value very close to that of the unsubstituted acid.

$$\overset{\qquad\overset{\textstyle Cl}{|}\qquad}{CH_3CH_2CHCO_2H} \qquad \overset{\quad\overset{\textstyle Cl}{|}\qquad}{CH_3CHCH_2CO_2H} \qquad \overset{\overset{\textstyle Cl}{|}\qquad}{CH_2CH_2CH_2CO_2H} \qquad CH_3CH_2CH_2CO_2H$$

pK_a: 2.9   4.0   4.5   4.8

decreasing acid strength as distance between $-$Cl and $-CO_2H$ increases →

STUDY PROBLEM

12.9 Which is the stronger acid: (a) phenylacetic acid or bromoacetic acid? (b) dibromoacetic acid or bromoacetic acid? (c) 2-iodopropanoic acid or 3-iodopropanoic acid?

E. Resonance-Stabilization

Alcohols, phenols, and carboxylic acids all contain —OH groups. Yet these classes of compounds vary dramatically in acid strength. The differences may be attributed directly to the resonance-stabilization (or lack of it) of the anion with respect to its conjugate acid.

ROH   ArOH   RCO$_2$H

approx. pK_a: 18   10   5

In the case of *alcohols*, the anion is not resonance-stabilized. The negative charge of an alkoxide ion resides entirely on the oxygen and is not delocalized. At the opposite end of the scale are the *carboxylic acids*. The negative charge of the carboxylate ion is equally shared by two electronegative oxygen atoms. *Phenols* are intermediate between carboxylic acids and alcohols in acidity. The oxygen of a phenoxide ion is adjacent to the aromatic ring and the negative charge is partially delocalized by the aromatic pi cloud.

An alcohol: CH$_3$CH$_2$O$^-$ *no resonance-stabilization*

A phenol:

major contributor

A carboxylic acid:

equal contributors

F. Solvation

The solvation of the anion can play a major role in the acidity of a compound. By associating with an anion, solvent molecules stabilize the anion by helping disperse the negative charge through dipole–dipole interactions. Any factor that increases the degree of solvation of the anion increases the acidity of that compound in solution. For example, water has a greater ability to solvate ions than does ethanol. A water solution of a carboxylic acid is more acidic than an ethanol solution by a factor of about 10^5!

G. Acid Strengths of Substituted Benzoic Acids

You might expect that resonance-stabilization by the aromatic pi cloud would play a large role in the relative acid strengths of benzoic acid and substituted benzoic acids—however, this is not the case. The negative charge of the carboxylate ion is shared by the two carboxylate oxygen atoms but cannot be effectively delocalized by the aromatic ring. (The oxygens of the carboxylate anion are not directly adjacent to the aromatic ring; resonance structures in which the negative charge is delocalized by the ring cannot be drawn.)

Even though the negative charge of the benzoate ion is not delocalized by the benzene ring, benzoic acid is a stronger acid than phenol. In the benzoate ion, the negative charge is equally shared by two electronegative oxygen atoms. In the phenoxide ion, however, most of the negative charge resides on the single oxygen atom.

Because the benzene ring does not participate in resonance-stabilization of the carboxylate group, substituents on a benzene ring influence acidity primarily by the inductive effect. Regardless of the position of substitution, an *electron-withdrawing* group usually enhances the acidity of a benzoic acid (see Table 12.5).

Table 12.5. pK_a Values for Some Benzoic Acids

Acid[a]	Position of substitution versus pK_a		
	ortho	*meta*	*para*
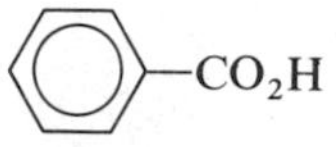 ⬡—CO$_2$H	4.2	4.2	4.2
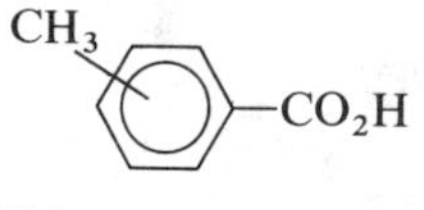 CH$_3$⬡—CO$_2$H	3.9	4.3	4.4
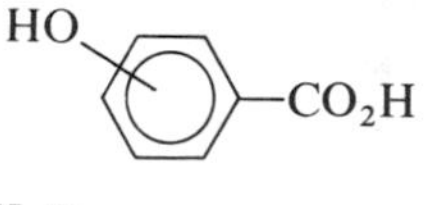 HO⬡—CO$_2$H	3.0	4.1	4.5
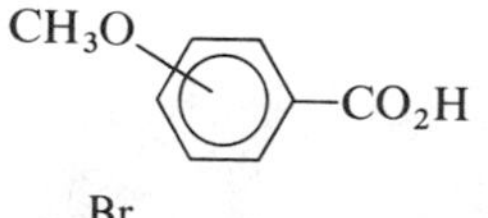 CH$_3$O⬡—CO$_2$H	4.1	4.1	4.5
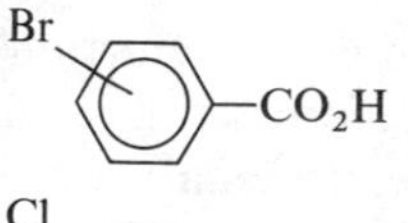 Br⬡—CO$_2$H	2.9	3.8	4.0
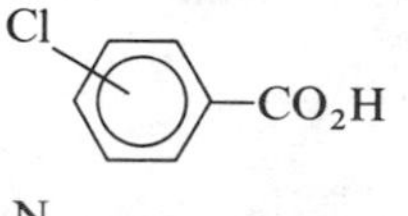 Cl⬡—CO$_2$H	2.9	3.8	4.0
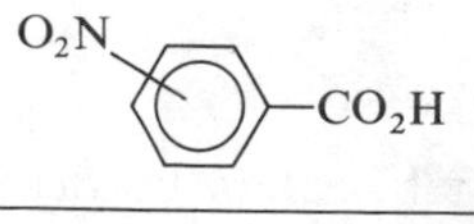 O$_2$N⬡—CO$_2$H	2.2	3.5	3.4

[a] A bond to the center of a benzene ring denotes an unspecified position of substitution.

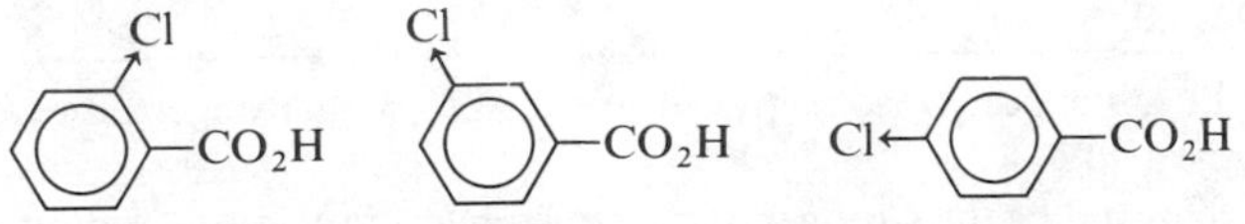

all are stronger acids than benzoic acid

The reasons that an electronegative substituent increases the acid strength are again destabilization of the acid and stabilization of the anion.

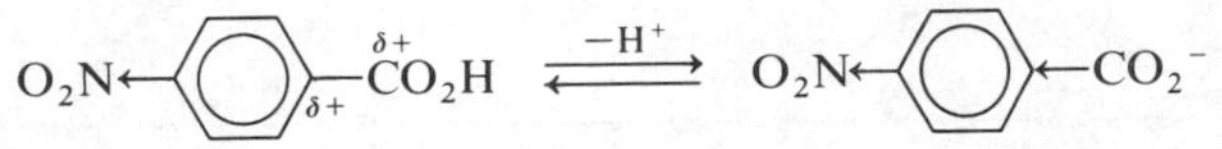

destabilized by electron-withdrawal   *stabilized by electron-withdrawal*

An *electron-releasing* alkyl substituent that is *m-* or *p-* to the carboxyl group decreases the acid strength of a benzoic acid. By releasing electrons, the substituent stabilizes the nonionized acid and destabilizes the anion.

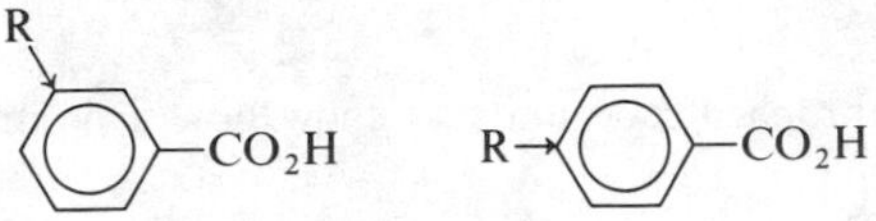

m- or p-alkyl group decreases acid strength

Almost all *ortho*-substituents (whether electron-releasing or electron-withdrawing) increase the acid strength of a benzoic acid. The reasons for this ***ortho*-effect**, as it is called, are probably a combination of both steric and electronic factors.

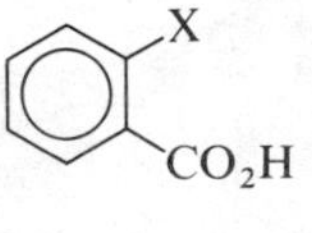

o-substituents increase acid strength

Sample Problem

In Table 12.5 you will notice that *p*-hydroxybenzoic acid is a weaker acid than benzoic acid, even though the hydroxyl group is electron-withdrawing. Suggest a reason for this. (*Hint:* write resonance structures for the anion showing the delocalization of unshared electrons on the OH oxygen by the benzene ring.)

Solution: The lowering of the acid strength is an example of resonance-destabilization of the benzoate anion. The key is in the circled structure, in which the negative charge is *adjacent* to the $-CO_2^-$ group. This resonance structure lends high energy to the anion.

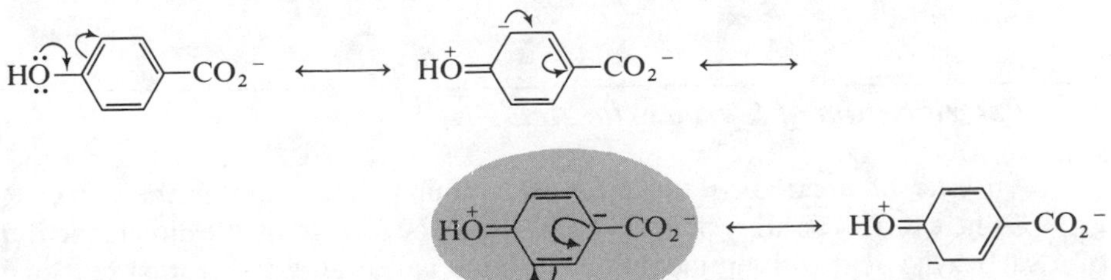

STUDY PROBLEMS

12.10 (a) Would you expect *m*-isopropylbenzoic acid to be a stronger or a weaker acid than benzoic acid?

(b) Which would be the stronger acid, *m*-nitrobenzoic acid or 3,5-dinitrobenzoic acid?

12.11 The pK_a of *o*-methoxybenzoic acid is 4.1. It is a stronger acid than benzoic acid because of the *ortho*-effect. However, *o*-hydroxybenzoic acid (salicylic acid) is ten times stronger an acid than the methoxy acid—its pK_a is 3.0. Write the structures of the two anions and suggest why the hydroxyl group has the greater stabilizing effect.

Sample Problem

The acid strength of a phenol is also affected by substituents on the ring:

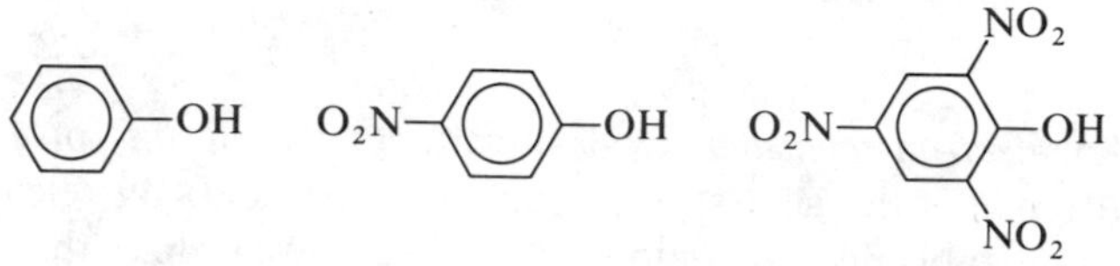

	phenol	*p*-nitrophenol	picric acid
approx. pK_a:	10	7	0.4

Write resonance structures for the *p*-nitrophenoxide ion that show how a *p*-nitro group stabilizes the anion.

Solution:

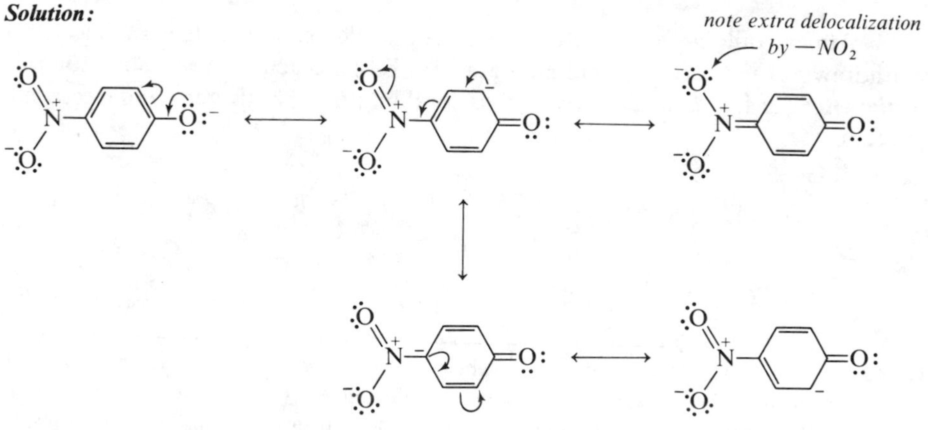

STUDY PROBLEM

12.12 Rank the following hydrocarbons in order of increasing acidity of the methyl hydrogen (weakest acid first): (a) diphenylmethane; (b) triphenylmethane; (c) toluene; (d) methane.

Section 12.8

Esterification of Carboxylic Acids

An **ester of a carboxylic acid** is a compound that contains the —CO$_2$R group, where R may be alkyl or aryl. An ester may be formed by the direct reaction of a carboxylic acid with an alcohol, a reaction called an **esterification reaction**. Esterification is acid-catalyzed and reversible.

$$\text{General:} \quad \underset{\substack{\text{a carboxylic acid}}}{\overset{\overset{\displaystyle O}{\|}}{\text{RCOH}}} + \underset{\substack{\text{an alcohol}}}{\text{R'OH}} \underset{}{\overset{H^+,\ heat}{\rightleftharpoons}} \underset{\substack{\text{an ester}}}{\overset{\overset{\displaystyle O}{\|}}{\text{RCOR'}}} + H_2O$$

$$\underset{\substack{\text{acetic acid}}}{\overset{\overset{\displaystyle O}{\|}}{CH_3COH}} + \underset{\substack{\text{ethanol}}}{CH_3CH_2OH} \overset{H^+,\ heat}{\rightleftharpoons} \underset{\substack{\text{ethyl acetate}}}{\overset{\overset{\displaystyle O}{\|}}{CH_3COCH_2CH_3}} + H_2O$$

The rate at which a carboxylic acid is esterified depends primarily upon the steric hindrance in both the alcohol and the carboxylic acid. The acid strength of the carboxylic acid plays only a minor role in the rate at which the ester is formed.

Reactivity of alcohols toward esterification:

$$CH_3OH > 1° > 2° > 3°$$

Reactivity of carboxylic acids toward esterification:

$$HCO_2H > CH_3CO_2H > RCH_2CO_2H > R_2CHCO_2H > R_3CCO_2H$$

Like many reactions of aldehydes and ketones, esterification of a carboxylic acid proceeds through a series of protonation and deprotonation steps. The carbonyl oxygen is protonated, the nucleophilic alcohol attacks the positive carbon, and elimination of water yields the ester.

We may summarize the mechanism in the following way:

$$\underset{\substack{\text{a carboxylic}\\\text{acid}}}{\overset{\overset{\displaystyle O}{\|}}{RCOH}} + R'OH \overset{H^+}{\rightleftharpoons} \left[\overset{\overset{\displaystyle OH}{|}}{\underset{\underset{\displaystyle OR'}{|}}{R-C-OH}} \right] \rightleftharpoons \underset{\substack{\text{an ester}}}{\overset{\overset{\displaystyle O}{\|}}{RCOR'}} + H_2O$$

Note that in an esterification reaction, it is the C—O bond of the carboxylic acid that is broken and not the O—H bond of the acid nor the C—O bond of the alcohol. Evidence for the mechanism is the reaction of a labeled alcohol such as $CH_3^{18}OH$ with a carboxylic acid. In this case, the ^{18}O stays with the methyl group.

STUDY PROBLEM

12.13 Write the complete mechanism for the esterification of acetic acid with $CH_3^{18}OH$.

The esterification reaction is reversible. To obtain a high yield of an ester, we must shift the equilibrium to the ester side. One technique for accomplishing this is to use an excess of one of the reactants (the cheaper one). Another technique is to remove one of the products from the reaction mixture (for example, by the azeotropic distillation of water).

As the amount of steric hindrance in the intermediate increases, the rate of ester formation and the yield of ester drop. If bulky esters are to be prepared, it is better to use another route, such as the reaction of an alcohol with an acid chloride, which is more reactive than the carboxylic acid (see Section 13.5B).

Phenyl esters $(RCO_2C_6H_5)$ are not generally prepared directly from phenols and carboxylic acids because the equilibrium favors the acid–phenol side rather than the ester side. Phenyl esters, like bulky esters, can be obtained by using the more reactive acid derivatives.

STUDY PROBLEMS

12.14 Predict the esterification products of: (a) *p*-toluic acid and isopropyl alcohol; (b) terephthalic acid $(p\text{-}HO_2C—C_6H_4—CO_2H)$ and excess ethanol; (c) acetic acid and (R)-2-butanol.

12.15 4-Hydroxybutanoic acid spontaneously forms a cyclic ester, or *lactone*. What is the structure of this lactone?

Section 12.9

Reduction of Carboxylic Acids

The carbonyl carbon of a carboxylic acid is at the highest oxidation state it can attain and still be part of an organic molecule. (The next higher oxidation state is in CO_2.) Other than combustion or oxidation by very strong reagents, such as hot $H_2SO_4\text{–}CrO_3$ (cleaning solution), the carboxylic acid group is inert toward further oxidative reaction.

Surprisingly, the carboxylic acid group is also inert toward most common reducing agents (such as hydrogen plus catalyst). This inertness made necessary the development of alternative reduction methods, such as conversion of the carboxylic acid to an ester and then reduction of the ester. However, the introduction of lithium aluminum hydride (LAH) in the late 1940's simplified the reduction because LAH reduces a carboxyl group directly to a —CH_2OH group. (Other carbonyl functionality in the molecule is, of course, reduced as well; see Section 11.14.)

$$CH_3CO_2H \xrightarrow[\text{(2) } H_2O]{\text{(1) LiAlH}_4} CH_3CH_2OH$$

acetic acid   ethanol

benzoic acid   benzyl alcohol

STUDY PROBLEM

12.16 Give the structures for the LAH reduction products of:

(a) ⬡—CO_2H (b) O=⬡—CO_2H

Section 12.10

Polyfunctional Carboxylic Acids

Dicarboxylic acids and carboxylic acids containing other functional groups often show unique chemical properties. In this section, we will consider a few of the more important of these polyfunctional carboxylic acids. Hydroxy acids will be mentioned in Chapter 13, and amino acids will be discussed in Chapter 18.

A. Acidity of Dibasic Acids

A **dibasic acid** is one that undergoes reaction with *two equivalents of base*. The term **diprotic acid** (two acidic protons) would perhaps be a better term to describe such a compound. In general, dibasic carboxylic acids have a chemistry similar to that of the monocarboxylic acids, but let us examine a few of the differences.

With any dibasic acid (inorganic or organic), the first hydrogen ion is removed more easily than the second. Thus, K_1 (the acidity constant for the ionization of the first H^+) is larger than K_2 (that for the ionization of the second H^+), and the value for pK_1 is smaller than that for pK_2. The difference between pK_1 and pK_2 decreases with distance between the carboxyl groups. (Why?) The first and second pK_a values for a few diacids are listed in Table 12.6.

$$HO_2CCH_2CO_2H + H_2O \rightleftharpoons HO_2CCH_2CO_2^- + H_3O^+$$

malonic acid
$pK_1 = 2.83$

$$HO_2CCH_2CO_2^- + H_2O \rightleftharpoons {}^-O_2CCH_2CO_2^- + H_3O^+$$

$pK_2 = 5.69$

Table 12.6. pK_a Values for Some Diacids

Name[a]	Structure	pK_1	pK_2
oxalic	HO_2C-CO_2H	1.2	4.2
malonic	$HO_2CCH_2CO_2H$	2.8	5.7
succinic	$HO_2C(CH_2)_2CO_2H$	4.2	5.6
glutaric	$HO_2C(CH_2)_3CO_2H$	4.3	5.4
adipic	$HO_2C(CH_2)_4CO_2H$	4.4	5.4
pimelic	$HO_2C(CH_2)_5CO_2H$	4.5	5.4
o-phthalic	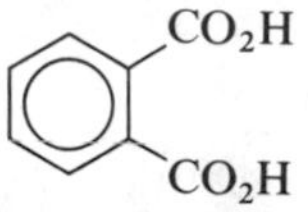	2.9	5.5

[a] To memorize the names of the diacids with two to seven carbons, note that the first letters (o, m, s, g, a, p) fit the phrase: "Oh my, such good apple pie." (o-Phthalic acid is, of course, not part of the homologous series.)

B. Anhydride Formation by Dibasic Acids

An **anhydride of a carboxylic acid** has the structure of two carboxylic acid molecules joined together with the loss of water.

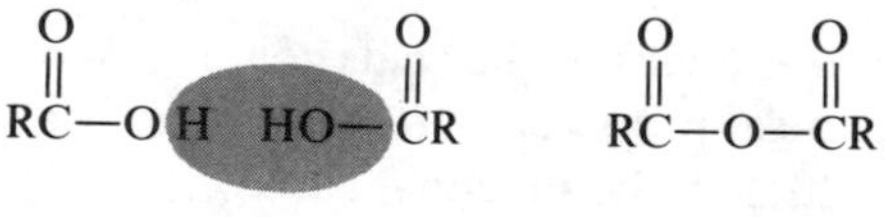

two carboxylic acids   *an anhydride*

Although it would seem reasonable at first glance, heating most carboxylic acids does *not* result in the anhydride. (The reactions that *do* lead to anhydrides will be discussed in Section 13.4.) Exceptions are dicarboxylic acids that can form five- or six-membered cyclic anhydrides. These diacids yield anhydrides when heated to 200°–300°.

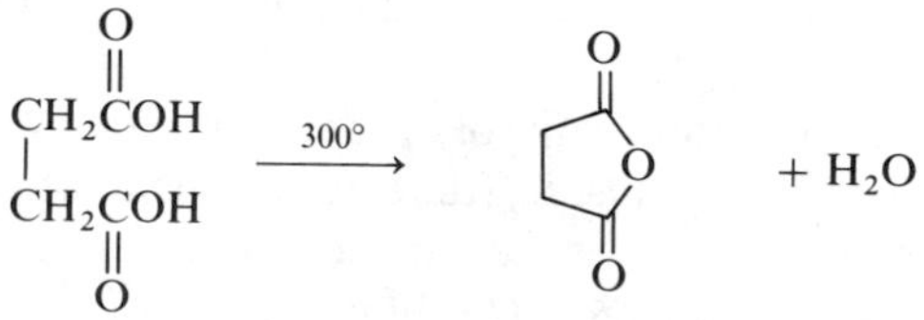

succinic acid   succinic anhydride

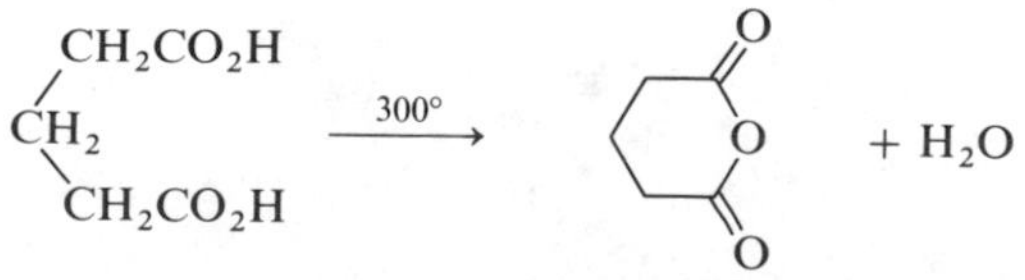

glutaric acid   glutaric anhydride

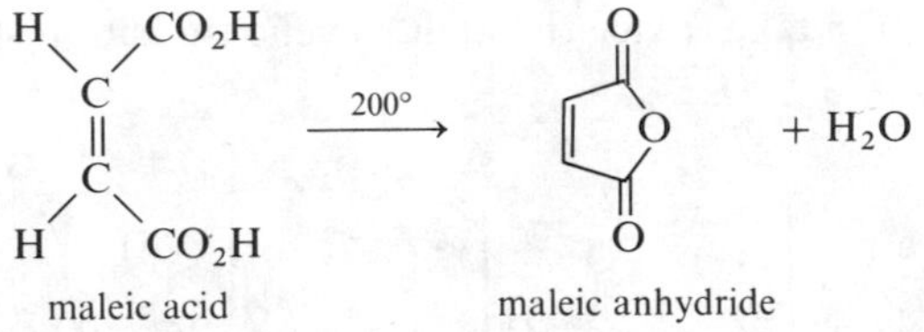

maleic acid   maleic anhydride

A five- or six-membered cyclic anhydride may also be synthesized by heating the appropriate diacid with acetic anhydride. This reaction is the result of an equilibrium between a more stable, cyclic anhydride with a less stable, open-chain anhydride. Removing the acetic acid by distillation helps drive the reaction to completion.

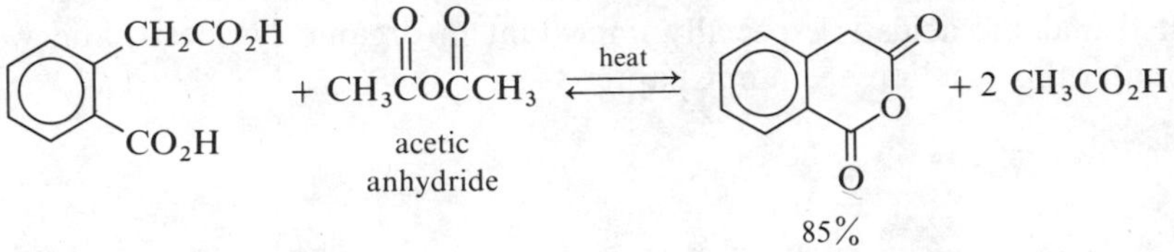

STUDY PROBLEMS

12.17 *o*-Phthalic acid (Table 12.6) forms a cyclic anhydride when heated at 200°. What is its structure?

12.18 When adipic acid (hexanedioic acid) is heated with a strong dehydrating agent such as P_2O_5, a cyclic anhydride is not formed. Instead, a polymeric product is obtained. What is the structure of this polymer?

C. Decarboxylation of β-Keto Acids and β-Diacids

Simply heating most carboxylic acids does not result in any chemical reaction. However, a carboxylic acid with a β carbonyl group undergoes **decarboxylation** (loss of CO_2) when heated. (The temperature necessary varies with the individual compound.)

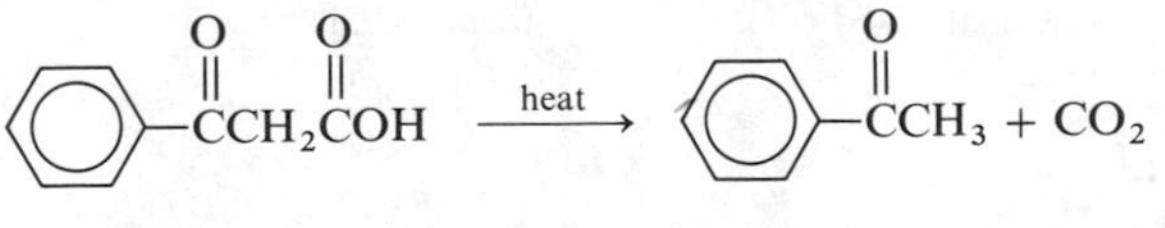

Decarboxylation takes place through a cyclic transition state:

$$RC \underset{H_2}{\overset{O \cdots H \cdots O}{\diagdown C \diagup}} C=O \longrightarrow \left[RC \underset{H_2}{\overset{O \cdots H \cdots O}{\diagdown C \diagup}} C=O \right] \longrightarrow \left[RC \overset{OH}{\diagdown} \overset{\overset{O}{\parallel}}{\underset{CH_2}{C}} \overset{O}{\diagup} \right] \xrightarrow{-CO_2} RC \overset{O}{\overset{\parallel}{C}} CH_3$$

transition state   an enol

Note that the cyclic transition state requires only a carbonyl group beta to the carboxyl group. This carbonyl group need not necessarily be a keto group. A β-diacid also undergoes decarboxylation when heated. Decarboxylation of substituted malonic acids is especially important in organic synthesis, and we will encounter this reaction again in Chapter 14.

$$H{-}\overset{O}{\overset{\parallel}{OC}}{-}\underset{CH_2CH_3}{\overset{O}{\overset{\parallel}{CHCOH}}} \xrightarrow{\text{heat}} CH_3CH_2CH_2\overset{O}{\overset{\parallel}{COH}} + CO_2$$

ethylmalonic acid   butanoic acid

STUDY PROBLEM

12.19 Write the mechanism for the decarboxylation of ethylmalonic acid.

A few α-carbonyl acids, such as oxalic acid, can also undergo decarboxylation. The decarboxylation of α-keto acids is common in biological systems in which enzymes catalyze the reaction. In the enzymatic decarboxylation of pyruvic acid, the resultant acetyl group undergoes thioesterification with coenzyme A (Section 13.8). The carbon dioxide is then eliminated by the respiratory system.

$$HO\overset{O}{\overset{\parallel}{C}}{-}\overset{O}{\overset{\parallel}{CO}}H \xrightarrow{150°} HCO_2H + CO_2$$

oxalic acid   formic acid

$$CH_3\overset{O}{\overset{\parallel}{C}}{-}\overset{O}{\overset{\parallel}{CO}}H + HSCoA \xrightarrow{\text{enzymes}} CH_3\overset{O}{\overset{\parallel}{C}}SCoA + CO_2 + 2H^+ + 2e^-$$

pyruvic acid   coenzyme A   acetylcoenzyme A
formed in glucose
metabolism

STUDY PROBLEM

12.20 Predict the product when each of the following acids is heated:

(a) $CH_2(CO_2H)_2$

(b) $CH_3\overset{\displaystyle O}{\overset{\|}{C}}CHCO_2H$
  $\quad\quad\quad\quad |$
  $\quad\quad\quad\quad CH_3$

(c) $CH_3CH_2\overset{\displaystyle O}{\overset{\|}{C}}CHCO_2H$
  $\quad\quad\quad\quad\quad\quad |$
  $\quad\quad\quad\quad\quad\quad CH_2CH_3$

(d) $CH_3\overset{\displaystyle O}{\overset{\|}{C}}CH_2CH_2CH_2CO_2H$

D. α,β-Unsaturated Carboxylic Acids

An isolated double bond in an unsaturated carboxylic acid behaves independently of the carboxyl group. A *conjugated* double bond and carboxyl group, however, may undergo typical electrophilic 1,4-addition reactions. These reactions take place in the same fashion as those of α,β-unsaturated aldehydes or ketones (Section 11.19).

1,4-Addition of HCl:

$$CH_3CH{=}CHCO_2H \xrightarrow{\text{H}^+} \left[CH_3\overset{+}{C}HCH_2CO_2H\right] \xrightarrow{\text{Cl}^-} CH_3\overset{\text{Cl}}{\overset{|}{C}}HCH_2CO_2H$$

2-butenoic acid   3-chlorobutanoic acid

Because of the polarizing effect of the carbonyl group, an α,β-unsaturated acid can undergo nucleophilic attack as well. Again, these reactions are similar to those of α,β-unsaturated aldehydes and ketones. The addition is also a 1,4-addition.

$$CN^- + CH_2{=}CH{-}\overset{\displaystyle O}{\overset{\|}{C}}{-}OH \longrightarrow \left[NCCH_2CH{=}\overset{O^-}{\overset{|}{C}}OH\right] \rightleftharpoons NCCH_2CH_2\overset{\displaystyle O}{\overset{\|}{C}}O^-$$

an enol

$$\ddot{N}H_3 + \underset{HO_2C}{\overset{H}{\diagdown}}C{=}C\underset{H}{\overset{CO_2H}{\diagup}} \longrightarrow {}^-O_2C\overset{{}^+NH_3}{\overset{|}{C}}HCH_2CO_2H$$

aspartic acid
*an amino acid found
in proteins*

fumaric acid

STUDY PROBLEM

12.21 A double bond in conjugation with an aldehyde or ketone may undergo nucleophilic attack at the β position by a Grignard reagent (Section 11.19). What products would you expect from the reaction of 2-pentenoic acid with phenylmagnesium bromide? (Be careful; check Section 6.15.)

SUMMARY

Carboxylic acids (RCO_2H) undergo hydrogen bonding to form **dimers**, a structural feature that has an effect on their physical and spectral properties.

Carboxylic acids may be synthesized by: (1) the *hydrolysis of their derivatives* (esters, amides, anhydrides, acid halides, or nitriles); (2) *oxidation of primary alcohols, aldehydes, alkenes, or alkylbenzenes*; and (3) *Grignard reactions* of RMgX and CO_2.

Carboxylic acids are one of the few general classes of organic compounds that is more acidic than H_2CO_3; carboxylic acids undergo reaction with HCO_3^-. **Carboxylate salts** result from the reaction of a carboxylic acid with base.

$$RCO_2H \ + \ NaOH \ \longrightarrow \ RCO_2^- \ Na^+ + H_2O$$

a carboxylic   *a base*   *a sodium*
acid   *carboxylate*

The strength of an acid is determined by the relative stabilities of the acid and its anion. Acid strength is affected by *electronegativity* (HF > ROH > R_2NH > RH); by *size* (HI > HBr > HCl > HF); and by *hybridization* ($\equiv$CH > $=$CH$_2$ > $-$CH$_3$). The *inductive effect* of electron-withdrawing groups causes an increase in acid strength ($ClCH_2CO_2H > CH_3CO_2H$). *Resonance-stabilization* of the anion also strengthens an acid ($RCO_2H > ArOH > ROH$). The anion of an acid can be partially stabilized by *solvation*—more solvation strengthens an acid.

The strength of a benzoic acid is determined largely by inductive effects because the $-CO_2^-$ group does not enter into resonance with the aromatic ring. Electron-withdrawing substituents strengthen the acid, while electron-releasing groups weaken the acid. Substitution at the *o*-position almost always increases acid strength.

A carboxylic acid may be **esterified** by reaction with an alcohol:

$$RCO_2H \ + \ R'OH \ \underset{}{\overset{H^+}{\rightleftharpoons}} \ RCO_2R' + H_2O$$

a carboxylic   *an alcohol*   *an ester*
acid

Carboxylic acids are not readily oxidized. Reduction with LAH, followed by hydrolysis, leads to a primary alcohol.

$$RCO_2H \ \xrightarrow[\text{(2) } H_2O]{\text{(1) LiAlH}_4} \ RCH_2OH$$

a 1° alcohol

A dibasic acid yields the **anhydride** when heated if a five- or six-membered ring can be formed.

β-Keto acids or β-diacids undergo **decarboxylation**.

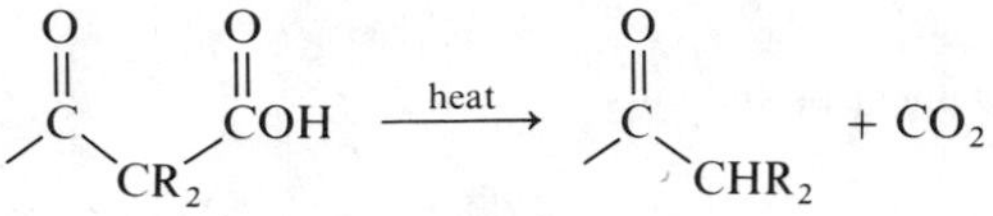

$$\underset{CR_2}{\overset{O}{\underset{\|}{C}}}\!\!\!\!\overset{O}{\underset{\|}{C}}OH \quad \xrightarrow{\text{heat}} \quad \underset{CHR_2}{\overset{O}{\underset{\|}{C}}} + CO_2$$

α,β-Unsaturated carboxylic acids can undergo **1,4-addition reactions** with electrophiles and with nucleophiles.

$$CH_2{=}CHCO_2H + H{-}Nu \longrightarrow \underset{\underset{Nu}{|}}{CH_2CH_2CO_2H}$$

$$CH_2{=}CHCO_2H + Nu^- \longrightarrow \underset{\underset{Nu}{|}}{CH_2CH_2CO_2^-}$$

STUDY PROBLEMS

12.22 Name the following acids and salts:

(a) $(CH_3)_3CCO_2H$

(b) 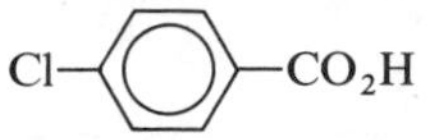 $Cl-\langle\bigcirc\rangle-CO_2H$

(c) $CH_3CH_2CHBrCHBrCO_2H$

(d) $(CH_3CH_2CO_2)_2Mg$

(e) $\begin{matrix} CO_2^- \\ | \\ CO_2^- \end{matrix} \ Ca^{2+}$

(f) $CH_3CHBrCO_2^- \ Na^+$

12.23 Give the structures for: (a) 4-iodobutanoic acid; (b) potassium formate; (c) disodium *o*-phthalate; (d) sodium benzoate; and (e) *m*-methylbenzoic acid.

12.24 Give the structure of each of the following groups: (a) propionyl group; (b) butyryl group; (c) *m*-nitrobenzoyl group.

12.25 Explain why benzoic acid boils at 250°C, but its ester ethyl benzoate boils at 213°C.

12.26 Show the principal types of hydrogen bonding (there may be more than one type) that occur in each of the following systems: (a) an aqueous solution of propanoic acid; (b) a solution of propanoic acid in acetic acid; (c) an aqueous solution of lactic acid, $CH_3CH(OH)CO_2H$.

12.27 Show how you could synthesize butanoic acid from each of the following compounds:

(a) 1-bromopropane

(b) 1-butanol

(c) butanal

(d) 4-octene

(e) $CH_3CH_2CH_2CO_2CH_2CH_3$

(f)  $CH_3CH_2CH_2CO_2-\langle\bigcirc\rangle$

12.28 Suggest reagents for the following conversions:

(a) $H_2NCH_2CH_2CH_2Br \longrightarrow {}^+H_3NCH_2CH_2CH_2CO_2^-$

(b) $(CH_3)_3CBr \longrightarrow (CH_3)_3CCO_2H$

(c) $CH_3CH_2OH \longrightarrow \begin{matrix} CH_3CHCO_2H \\ | \\ OH \end{matrix}$

(d) $BrCH_2CH_2CH_2Br \longrightarrow HO_2CCH_2CH_2CH_2CO_2H$

(e) 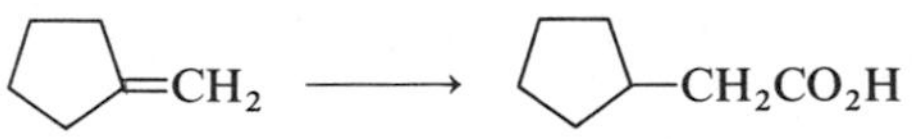 $\langle\bigcirc\rangle=CH_2 \longrightarrow \langle\bigcirc\rangle-CH_2CO_2H$

(f) $C_6H_5Br \longrightarrow C_6H_5CO_2H$

(g) 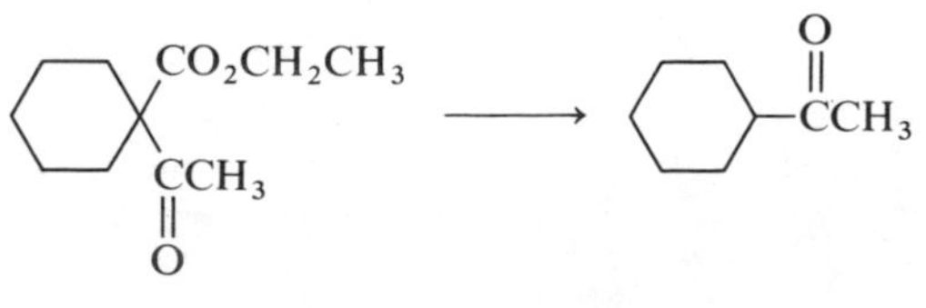 $\langle\bigcirc\rangle\begin{matrix} CO_2CH_2CH_3 \\ \diagdown \\ CCH_3 \\ \| \\ O \end{matrix} \longrightarrow \langle\bigcirc\rangle-\overset{\overset{\displaystyle O}{\|}}{C}CH_3$

12.29 Predict the major organic products:

(a) + excess NaOH $\longrightarrow$

(b) $C_6H_5CH_2Cl + CH_3CH_2\overset{\overset{O}{\|}}{C}O^-\ Na^+$. $\longrightarrow$

(c) $CH_3CO_2H + CH_3O^- \longrightarrow$

(d) $CH_3CO_2H + CH_3NH_2 \longrightarrow$

(e) $CH_3CO_2^- + ClCH_2CO_2H \longrightarrow$

(f) $HO_2CCH_2CO_2H + 1$ equivalent $NaHCO_3 \longrightarrow$

(g) + 2 equivalents $NaHCO_3 \longrightarrow$

(h) $C_6H_5CO_2H + CH_3I + CO_3^{2-} \longrightarrow$

12.30 Predict the products:

(a) $C_6H_5CO_2H + LiOH \longrightarrow$

(b) $C_6H_5OH + LiOH \longrightarrow$

(c) $-OH + LiOH \longrightarrow$

12.31 If a 0.200 M solution of pentanoic acid has a hydrogen-ion concentration of 0.00184 M, what is the dissociation constant (K_a) of the acid? (*Hint*: See Section 1.10.)

12.32 A mixture contains *p*-ethylphenol, benzoic acid, and benzaldehyde. The mixture is dissolved in ether and washed with an aqueous solution of $NaHCO_3$. The bicarbonate solution is Solution A. The mixture is then washed with an aqueous solution of NaOH (Solution B) and finally with water (Solution C). The remaining ether solution is Solution D. Identify the main organic components in Solutions A, B, C, and D.

12.33 How would you separate each of the following pairs of compounds?

(a) octanoic acid and ethyl octanoate
(b) phenol and phenyl propanoate
(c) phenol and cyclohexanol

12.34 What is the neutralization equivalent of each of the following acids?

(a) $\overset{\overset{OH}{|}}{C}H_3CHCO_2H$ (b) $HO\overset{\overset{CH_2CO_2H}{|}}{\underset{\underset{CH_2CO_2H}{|}}{C}}CO_2H$ (c) $\overset{\overset{O}{\|}}{\underset{\underset{CH_2CO_2H}{|}}{C}}CO_2H$

    lactic acid   citric acid   oxaloacetic acid

12.35 A 0.250-g sample of an unknown acid is titrated with a standardized NaOH solution that is 0.307 M. The volume of the NaOH solution required to neutralize the acid is 11.00 ml. What is the neutralization equivalent of the acid?

12.36 Which of the following acids could be the acid in Problem 12.35?

(a) $CH_3CH_2CH_2CO_2H$ (b) $CH_3CH_2CO_2H$

(c) $HO_2CCH_2CO_2H$ (d) $HO_2CCH_2CH_2CH_2CH_2CO_2H$

(e)

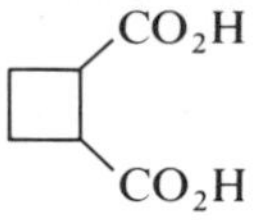

12.37 Calculate the pK_a for each of the following acids (see Section 1.10):

(a) cis-C_6H_5CH=$CHCO_2H$, $K_a = 1.3 \times 10^{-4}$
(b) $trans$-C_6H_5CH=$CHCO_2H$, $K_a = 3.65 \times 10^{-5}$

12.38 The pH of a 0.010 M solution of an acid was found to be 2.5. Calculate the K_a of this acid.

12.39 How do you account for the following acidities?

$$FCH_2CO_2H \qquad ClCH_2CO_2H \qquad BrCH_2CO_2H$$
$$pK_a = 2.66 \qquad pK_a = 2.81 \qquad pK_a = 2.87$$

12.40 List the following compounds in order of increasing acid strength (least acidic first):

(a) $CH_3CH_2CHBrCO_2H$ (b) $CH_3CHBrCH_2CO_2H$
(c) $CH_3CH_2CH_2CO_2H$ (d) $CH_3CH_2CH_2CH_2OH$
(e) C_6H_5OH (f) H_2CO_3
(g) Br_3CCO_2H (h) H_2O

12.41 Which one of each of the following pairs of carboxylic acids is the stronger acid?
(a) benzoic acid or *p*-bromobenzoic acid;   (b) benzoic acid or *m*-bromobenzoic acid;
(c) *m*-bromobenzoic acid or 3,5-dibromobenzoic acid.

12.42 Arrange the following compounds in order of increasing acidity (weakest acid first). Give a reason for your answer.

      p-nitrophenol   *p*-methylphenol   phenol

12.43 Which of the following acids is most acidic? least acidic?

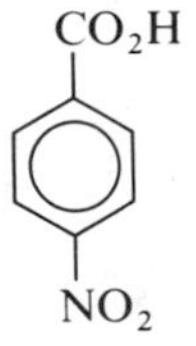

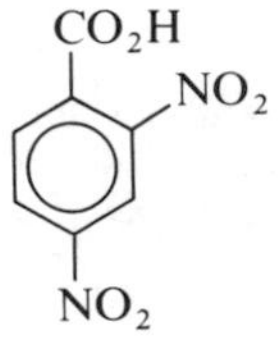

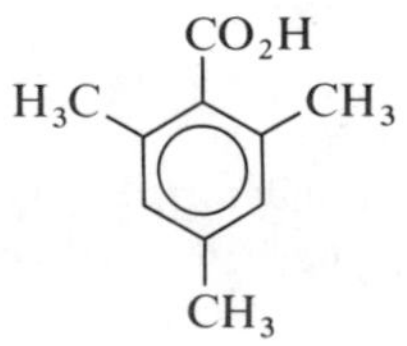

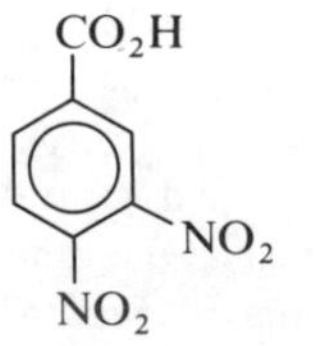

12.44 In each pair, which is the stronger base?

(a) $CH_3CH=CH^-$ or $CH_3C\equiv C^-$

(b) Cl^- or $CH_3CO_2^-$

(c) $ClCH_2CO_2^-$ or $Cl_2CHCO_2^-$

(d) $(CH_3)_3CO^-$ or $(CH_3)_3CCO_2^-$

(e) $CH_3CHClCO_2^-$ or $ClCH_2CH_2CO_2^-$

(f) 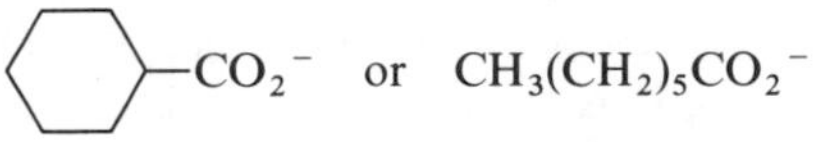 $-CO_2^-$ or $CH_3(CH_2)_5CO_2^-$

(g) 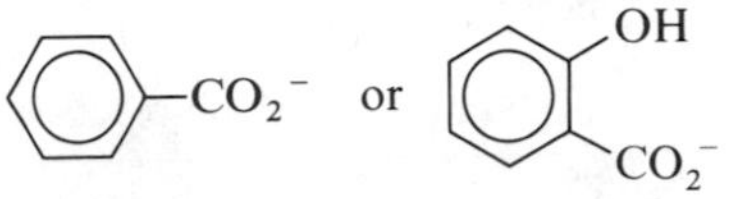 $-CO_2^-$ or

(h) 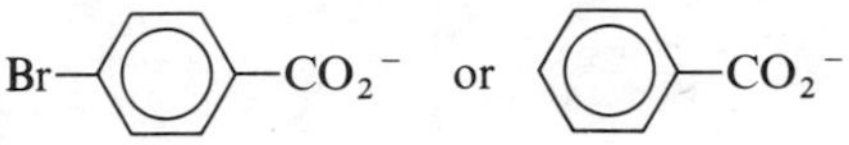 $Br-$$-CO_2^-$ or $-CO_2^-$

12.45 Suggest reasons why *o*-phthalic acid has a pK_1 of 2.9 and a pK_2 of 5.5, while terephthalic acid has a pK_1 of 3.5 and a pK_2 of 4.8.

o-phthalic acid   terephthalic acid

12.46 Complete the following equations, giving the organic products:

(a) $-CO_2H + (CH_3)_2CHOH \xrightarrow[\text{heat}]{H^+}$

(b) $-CO_2H + HOCH_2CH_2OH \xrightarrow[\text{heat}]{H^+}$

(c) $\xrightarrow[\text{(2) H}_2\text{O}]{\text{(1) LiAlH}_4}$

(d) $\xrightarrow[\text{(2) H}_2\text{O, H}^+]{\text{(1) NaBH}_4, \text{OH}^-}$

(e) $HCO_2H + $$-OH \xrightarrow[\text{heat}]{H^+}$

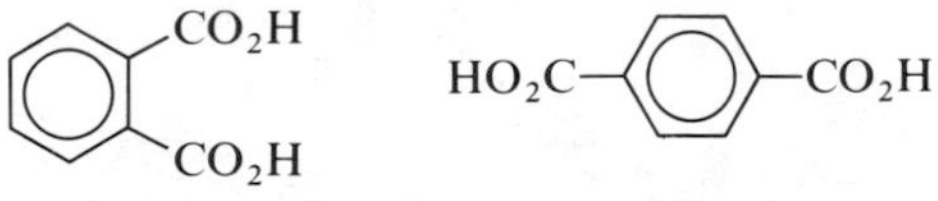

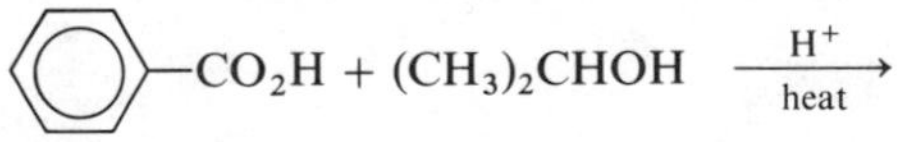

(f) 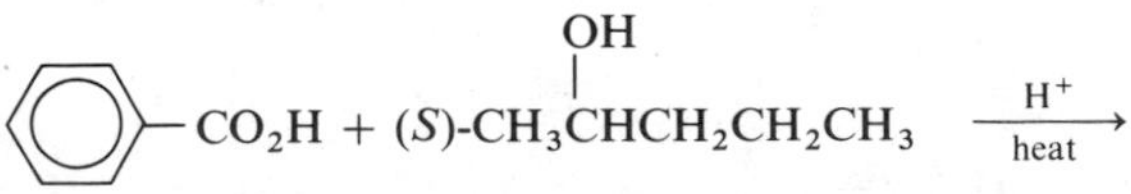 $-CO_2H + (S)\text{-}CH_3\overset{\overset{\displaystyle OH}{|}}{C}HCH_2CH_2CH_3 \xrightarrow[\text{heat}]{H^+}$

(g) 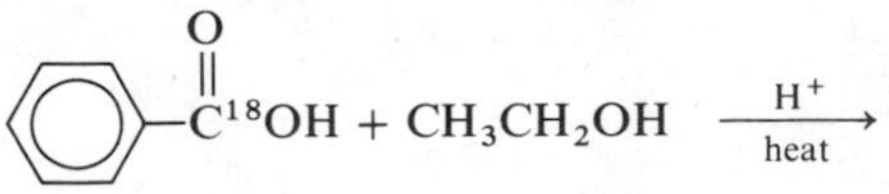 $-\overset{\overset{\displaystyle O}{||}}{C}{}^{18}OH + CH_3CH_2OH \xrightarrow[\text{heat}]{H^+}$

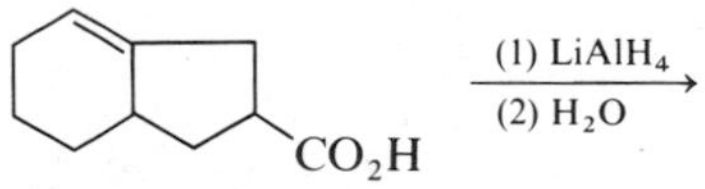

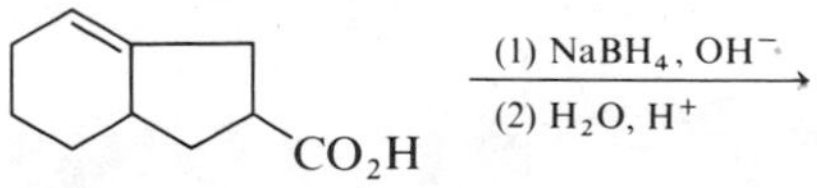

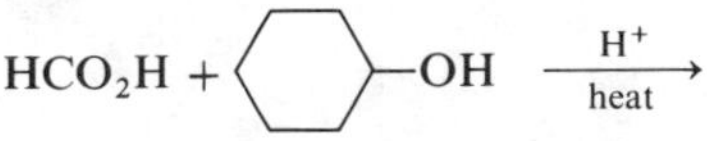

12.47 List the following acids and alcohols in order of increasing rates of reaction leading to the esters (slowest first):

  (a) acetic acid with methanol and HCl
  (b) cyclohexanecarboxylic acid with *t*-butyl alcohol and HCl
  (c) cyclohexanecarboxylic acid with ethanol and HCl

12.48 Predict the products of LAH reduction of: (a) propanoic acid; (b) 2-chloropropanoic acid; (c) propenoic acid; and (d) 3-hydroxypropanoic acid.

12.49 Racemic 2-bromopropanoic acid undergoes reaction with (R)-2-butanol to produce an ester mixture. (a) What are the structures (stereochemistry included) of the esters? (b) Are these esters enantiomers or diastereomers?

12.50 What would be the major organic product of each of the following reactions?

(a) 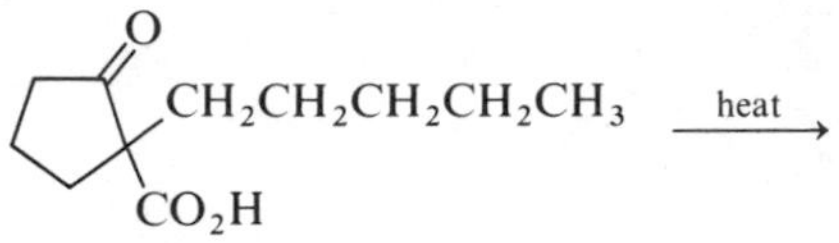 cyclopentanone ring with $CH_2CH_2CH_2CH_2CH_3$ and CO_2H $\xrightarrow{\text{heat}}$

(b) 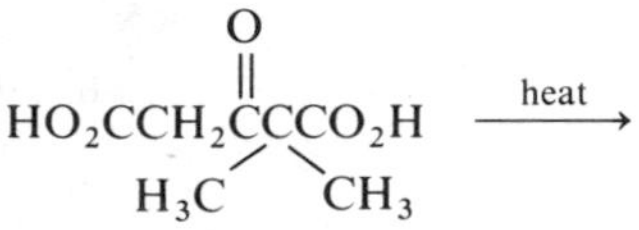 $HO_2CCH_2\overset{O}{\overset{\|}{C}}CCO_2H$ with H_3C and CH_3 $\xrightarrow{\text{heat}}$

(c) benzo-cycloheptene ring with CO_2H, $=O$, CO_2H $\xrightarrow{\text{heat}}$

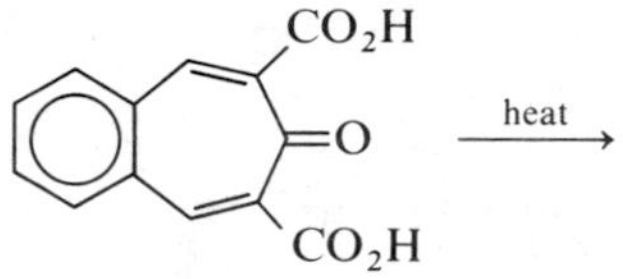

12.51 Maleic acid (page 589) forms a cyclic anhydride when heated. Its geometric isomer, fumaric acid, undergoes no reaction under the same conditions. Why not?

12.52 Predict the major organic products:

  (a) a concentrated solution (inert solvent) of $HOCH_2(CH_2)_8CO_2H$ $\xrightarrow[\text{heat}]{\text{H}^+}$

  (b) a dilute solution (inert solvent) of $HOCH_2(CH_2)_8CO_2H$ $\xrightarrow[\text{heat}]{\text{H}^+}$

(c) 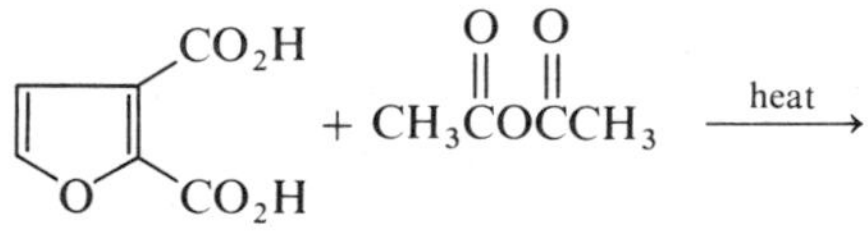 furan ring with CO_2H, CO_2H $+ CH_3\overset{O}{\overset{\|}{C}}O\overset{O}{\overset{\|}{C}}CH_3$ $\xrightarrow{\text{heat}}$

(d) 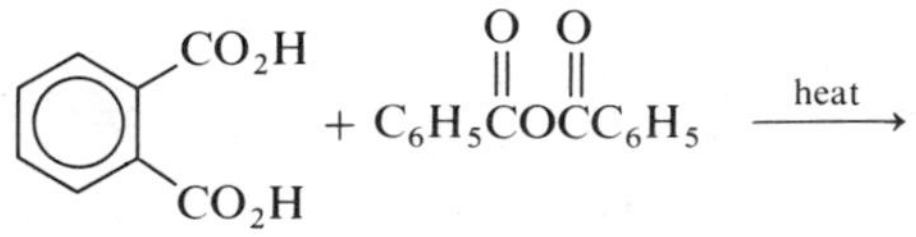 benzene ring with CO_2H, CO_2H $+ C_6H_5\overset{O}{\overset{\|}{C}}O\overset{O}{\overset{\|}{C}}C_6H_5$ $\xrightarrow{\text{heat}}$

(e) $CH_3\overset{O}{\overset{\|}{C}}CH_2CO_2CH_2CH_3$ $\xrightarrow[\text{heat}]{\text{H}_2\text{O, H}^+}$

(f) 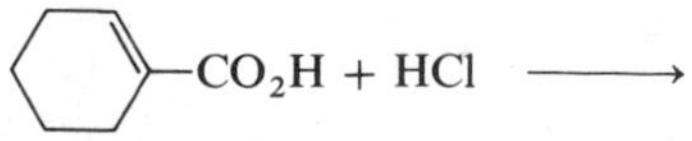 cyclohexene ring $-CO_2H + HCl$ $\longrightarrow$

(g) 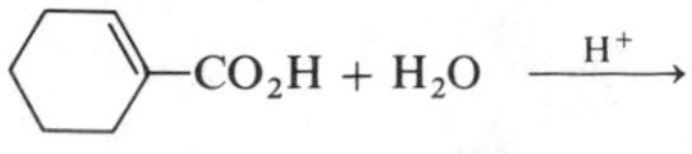 cyclohexene ring $-CO_2H + H_2O$ $\xrightarrow{\text{H}^+}$

12.53 One of the steps in the biological oxidation of glucose to CO_2 and H_2O is the β decarboxylation of oxalosuccinic acid. What is the product of the decarboxylation?

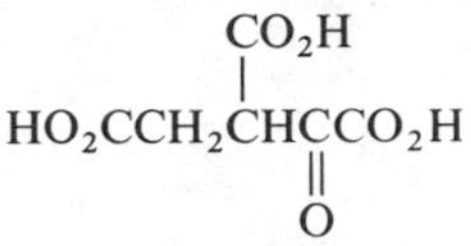

$$\underset{\text{oxalosuccinic acid}}{HO_2CCH_2\overset{\displaystyle \overset{CO_2H}{|}}{C}H\overset{\displaystyle \underset{||}{O}}{C}CO_2H}$$

12.54 Suggest a mechanism for the following reaction:

$$C_6H_5CCl_3 \xrightarrow[\text{(2) } H_2O, H^+]{\text{(1) } OH^-, \text{ heat}} C_6H_5CO_2H$$

12.55 Propose mechanisms for the following reactions:

(a) $CH_3\overset{\displaystyle \overset{O}{||}}{C}OH + H_2{}^{18}O \xrightleftharpoons{H^+} CH_3\overset{\displaystyle \overset{O}{||}}{C}-{}^{18}OH + H_2O$

(b) 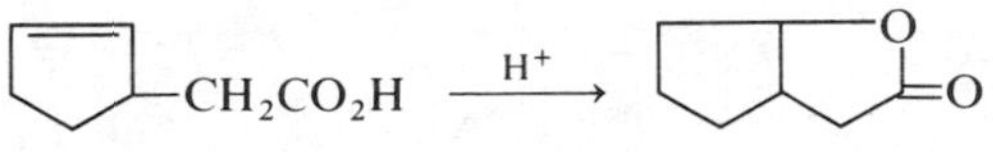 $-CH_2CO_2H \xrightarrow{H^+}$

(c) 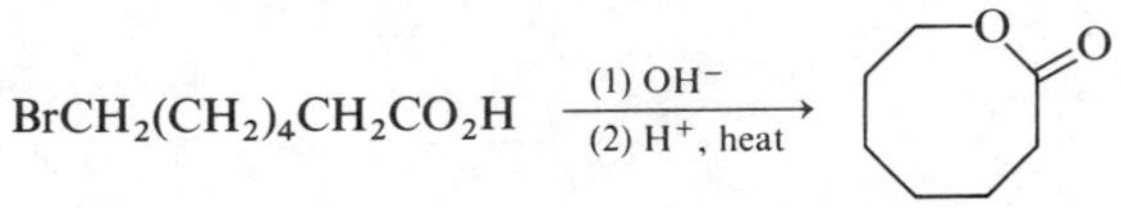 $BrCH_2(CH_2)_4CH_2CO_2H \xrightarrow[\text{(2) } H^+, \text{ heat}]{\text{(1) } OH^-}$

12.56 *Dacron* is a synthetic polymer that can be made by the reaction of terephthalic acid (Problem 12.45) and 1,2-ethanediol. What is the structure of Dacron?

12.57 Compound A, $C_4H_6O_4$, yields compound B, $C_3H_6O_2$, when heated. The neutralization equivalent of A is 60 ± 1, while that of B is 75 ± 1. What are the structures of A and B?

12.58 With ${}^{14}CH_3I$ as the only source of ${}^{14}C$, show how you would prepare the following labeled compounds:

(a) $CH_3CH_2CO_2{}^{14}CH_3$ (b) ${}^{14}CH_3CO_2H$ (c) ${}^{14}CH_3OH$

(d) $C_6H_5{}^{14}CO_2H$

12.59 Write equations that show how benzoic acid can be converted into each of the following compounds:

(a) 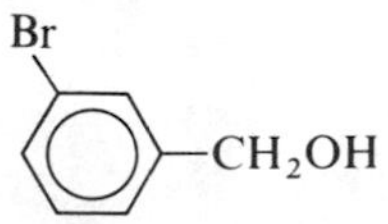 $-CH_2OH$ (b) 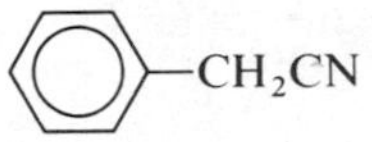 $-CH_2CN$ (c) 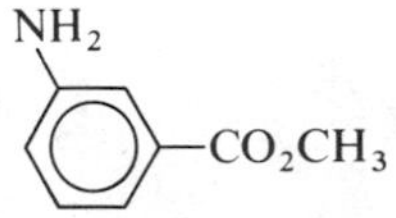 $-CO_2CH_3$

12.60 Compound A, $C_4H_6O_4$, yielded Compound B, $C_4H_4O_3$, when heated. When A was treated with an excess of methanol and a trace of sulfuric acid, Compound C, $C_6H_{10}O_4$, was obtained. Upon treatment with $LiAlH_4$ followed by hydrolysis, Compound A yielded Compound D, $C_4H_{10}O_2$. What are the structures of Compounds A, B, C, and D?

12.61 The salt of a carboxylic acid does not show carbonyl absorption at 1660–2000 cm^{-1} (5–6 μm) in the infrared spectrum. Explain.

12.62 The nmr and infrared spectra of Compound A ($C_8H_8O_2$) are shown in Figure 12.4. When A is treated with hot $KMnO_4$ solution, Compound B ($C_8H_8O_3$) is obtained. The nmr and infrared spectra of B are also shown in Figure 12.4. What are the structures of A and B?

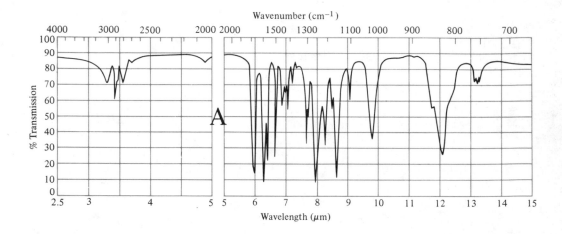

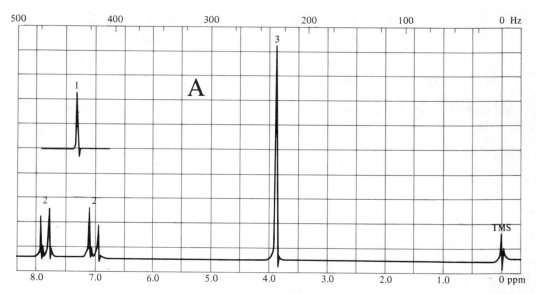

Figure 12.4.   Spectra for Problem 12.62.

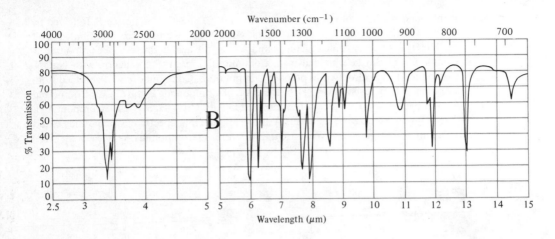

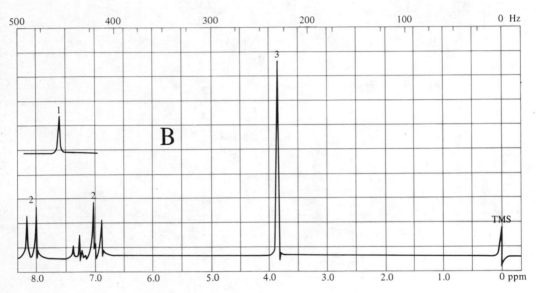

Figure 12.4 (continued). Spectra for Problem 12.62.

12.63 Compound A can be obtained by the reaction of CO_2 with Compound B, followed by hydrolysis. Compound A can also be obtained when Compound C is treated with $Ag(NH_3)_2{}^+$. Another route to Compound A is by the acid hydrolysis of Compound D. Compound D can be obtained from Compound E by an S_N2 reaction with NaCN. Compound E was also used to prepare Compound B. Compound E was obtained from Compound F by reaction with HBr. Reaction of Compounds B and C gave Compound G after hydrolysis. Treatment of Compound G with CrO_3/H_2SO_4 gave Compound H. The infrared spectra of Compounds A and G and the nmr spectra of Compounds F and H are given in Figure 12.5. What are the structures of Compounds A–H?

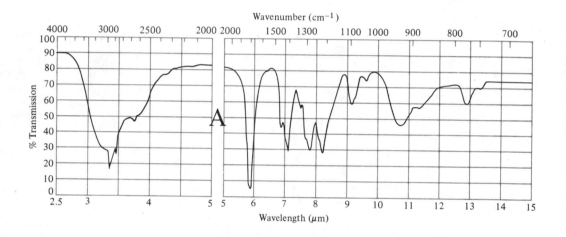

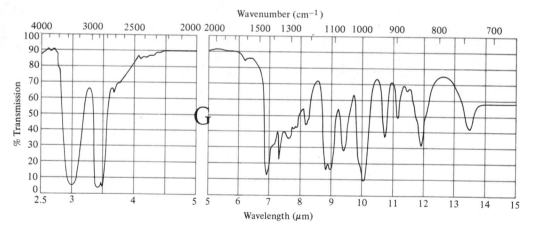

Figure 12.5. Spectra for Problem 12.63.

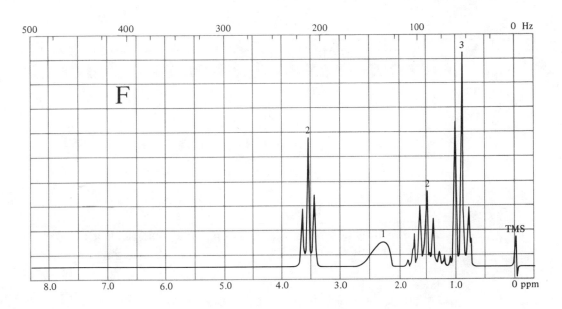

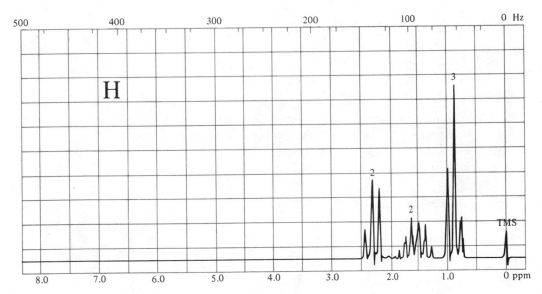

Figure 12.5 (continued). Spectra for Problem 12.63.

Chapter 13

Derivatives of Carboxylic Acids

A **derivative of a carboxylic acid** is a compound that yields a carboxylic acid upon reaction with water.

$$\underset{\text{ethyl acetate}}{CH_3\overset{\overset{\displaystyle O}{\|}}{C}OCH_2CH_3} + H_2O \;\underset{}{\overset{H^+,\,heat}{\rightleftharpoons}}\; \underset{\text{acetic acid}}{CH_3\overset{\overset{\displaystyle O}{\|}}{C}OH} + HOCH_2CH_3$$

$$\underset{\text{acetamide}}{CH_3\overset{\overset{\displaystyle O}{\|}}{C}NH_2} + H_2O + H^+ \;\overset{heat}{\longrightarrow}\; CH_3\overset{\overset{\displaystyle O}{\|}}{C}OH + NH_4{}^+$$

In this chapter, we will discuss acid halides, acid anhydrides, esters, amides, and nitriles. Table 13.1 shows some representative examples of these compounds. Note that all the derivatives except nitriles contain **acyl groups**, RCO—. In each case, an electronegative atom is attached to the carbonyl carbon of the acyl group. For this reason, the chemistry of each of these classes of compounds is similar.

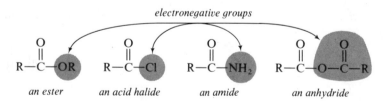

an ester   *an acid halide*   *an amide*   *an anhydride*

Carboxylic acids and some of their derivatives are found in nature. Fats are triesters, waxes are monoesters, and proteins are polyamides, to name just a few. Acid halides are never found in nature, and anhydrides are found only rarely. One example of a naturally occurring anhydride is *cantharidin*, a cyclic anhydride found in Spanish flies. Cantharidin is an irritant of the urinary tract. The dried flies were used by the ancient Greeks and Romans as an aphrodisiac.

cantharidin

Table 13.1.   *Some Derivatives of Carboxylic Acids*

Class	Examples	
	Structure	*Trivial name*
acid halide	CH_3COCl	acetyl chloride
	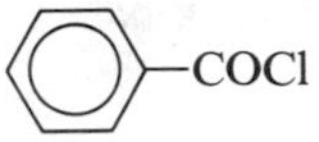 ⬡—COCl	benzoyl chloride
acid anhydride	$(CH_3CO)_2O$	acetic anhydride
	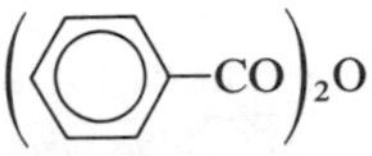 (⬡—CO)$_2$O	benzoic anhydride
ester	$CH_3CO_2CH_2CH_3$	ethyl acetate
	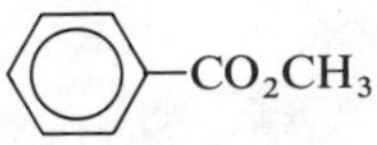 ⬡—CO_2CH_3	methyl benzoate
amide	CH_3CONH_2	acetamide
	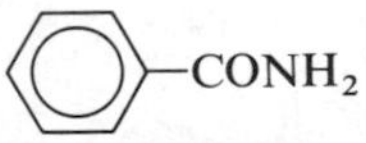 ⬡—$CONH_2$	benzamide
nitrile	CH_3CN	acetonitrile
	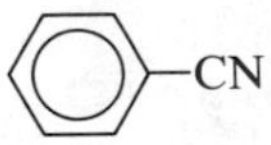 ⬡—CN	benzonitrile

Reactivity of Carboxylic Acid Derivatives

Why are carboxylic acids, esters, and amides commonly found in nature, while acid halides and anhydrides are not? Why are the carboxylic acid derivatives different from aldehydes or ketones? We may answer these questions by considering the relative reactivities of carboxylic acid derivatives and how they undergo reaction.

The derivatives of carboxylic acids contain *leaving groups* attached to the acyl carbons, whereas aldehydes and ketones do not. Reagents *add* to the carbonyl group of ketones and aldehydes, but *substitute* for the leaving groups of acid derivatives:

$$\textit{Addition:} \quad CH_3\overset{\displaystyle O}{\overset{\|}{C}}CH_3 \;\underset{}{\overset{HCN}{\rightleftharpoons}}\; CH_3-\overset{\displaystyle OH}{\underset{\displaystyle CN}{\overset{|}{\underset{|}{C}}}}-CH_3$$

Substitution:

$$CH_3\overset{O}{\overset{\|}{C}}-Cl \xrightarrow{H_2O} CH_3\overset{O}{\overset{\|}{C}}-OH + HCl$$

good leaving group

In Chapter 5, we mentioned that the attacking nucleophile in a substitution reaction should be a stronger base than the leaving group. Halide ions are good leaving groups because they are very weak bases.

$$HO^- + \underset{R}{CH_2}-Cl \longrightarrow \underset{R}{HOCH_2} + \underset{\substack{weaker\ base \\ than\ OH^-}}{Cl^-}$$

The reactivity of carbonyl compounds toward substitution at the carbonyl carbon may be directly attributed to the basicity of the leaving group:

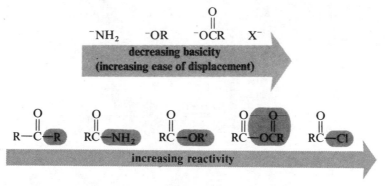

$^-NH_2 \quad {}^-OR \quad {}^-O\overset{O}{\overset{\|}{C}}R \quad X^-$

**decreasing basicity
(increasing ease of displacement)**

$$R-\overset{O}{\overset{\|}{C}}-R \quad RC\overset{O}{\overset{\|}{}}-NH_2 \quad RC\overset{O}{\overset{\|}{}}-OR' \quad RC\overset{O}{\overset{\|}{}}-O\overset{O}{\overset{\|}{C}}R \quad RC\overset{O}{\overset{\|}{}}-Cl$$

increasing reactivity

Acid chlorides and acid anhydrides, with good leaving groups, are readily attacked by water. Therefore, we would not expect to find these compounds in the cells of plants or animals. Because of their high reactivity, however, these acid derivatives are invaluable in the synthesis of other organic compounds. A relatively nonreactive carboxylic acid may be converted to one of these more reactive derivatives and then converted to a ketone, an ester, or an amide (Figure 13.1).

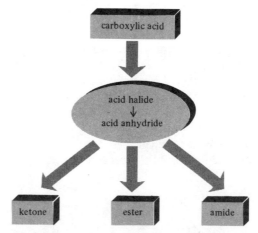

Figure 13.1. The synthetic relationship of acid halides and anhydrides to the other carboxylic acid derivatives.

Esters and amides are relatively stable toward water. In the laboratory, these compounds require an acid or a base and, usually, heating to undergo reaction. In nature, enzymes can perform the functions of acid or base and heat.

STUDY PROBLEM

13.1 Both acetyl chloride and vinyl chloride have a chlorine atom attached to an sp^2 carbon. Suggest a reason why acetyl chloride is quite reactive, while vinyl chloride is almost inert to substitution reactions.

$$CH_3\overset{\overset{\displaystyle O}{\|}}{C}{-}Cl \qquad CH_2{=}CH{-}Cl$$

  acetyl chloride   vinyl chloride
                    (chloroethene)

Section 13.2

Spectral Properties of Carboxylic Acid Derivatives

The nmr spectra of carboxylic acid derivatives provide little information about the functionality in these compounds. The signals for α hydrogens of these carbonyl compounds are shifted slightly downfield from the signals for ordinary aliphatic hydrogens because of deshielding by the partially positive carbonyl carbon atom. Note that the α hydrogens of an acid chloride exhibit a greater chemical shift than those of the other acid derivatives. This large chemical shift arises from the greater ability of the Cl (compared to O or N) to withdraw electron density from nearby bonds.

$$CH_3CN \quad CH_3\overset{\overset{\displaystyle O}{\|}}{C}OCH_3 \quad CH_3\overset{\overset{\displaystyle O}{\|}}{C}NH_2 \quad CH_3\overset{\overset{\displaystyle O}{\|}}{C}OH \quad CH_3\overset{\overset{\displaystyle O}{\|}}{C}Cl$$

δ in ppm: 2.00   2.03   2.08   2.10   2.67

increasing chemical shift for α hydrogens →

The infrared spectra of acid derivatives provide more information about the type of functional group than do nmr spectra. With the exception of the nitriles, the principal distinguishing feature of the infrared spectra of all the carboxylic acid derivatives is the carbonyl absorption found at about 1620–1820 cm^{-1} (5.5–6 μm). The positions of carbonyl absorption for the various acid derivatives are summarized in Table 13.2. Anhydrides and esters also show C—O absorption in the region of 1050–1250 cm^{-1} (8–9.5 μm).

$$\overset{\overset{\displaystyle O}{\|}}{R}CCl \quad \overset{\overset{\displaystyle O}{\|}}{R}CNH_2 \qquad \overset{\overset{\displaystyle O}{\|}}{R}C{-}OR \quad \overset{\overset{\displaystyle O}{\|}}{R}C{-}O{-}\overset{\overset{\displaystyle O}{\|}}{C}R$$

show C=O   *also show C—O*

Derivatives of Carboxylic Acids

Table 13.2. Infrared Carbonyl Absorption for Carboxylic Acid Derivatives

		Position of absorption	
Class	*Structure*	cm^{-1}	μm
acid chloride	$\overset{\displaystyle O}{\overset{\|\|}{RCCl}}$	1785–1815	5.51–5.60
acid anhydride	$\overset{\displaystyle O\ \ O}{\overset{\|\|\ \ \|\|}{RCOCR}}$	1740–1870 (usually two peaks)	5.35–5.75
ester	$\overset{\displaystyle O}{\overset{\|\|}{RCOR}}$	1735–1750	5.71–5.76
amide	$\overset{\displaystyle O}{\overset{\|\|}{RCNH_2}}$	1626–1786	5.60–6.15

A. Acid Chlorides

The carbonyl infrared absorption of acid chlorides is observed at slightly higher frequencies than that of other acid derivatives. There is no other distinguishing feature in the infrared spectrum that signifies "This is an acid chloride." See Figure 13.2 for the infrared spectrum of a typical acid chloride.

B. Anhydrides

A carboxylic acid anhydride, which has two C=O groups, generally exhibits a *double carbonyl peak* in the infrared spectrum. Anhydrides also exhibit a C—O stretching band around $1100\ cm^{-1}$ (9 μm). Figure 13.3 shows the infrared spectrum of a typical aliphatic anhydride.

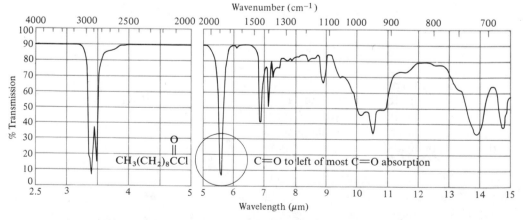

Figure 13.2. Infrared spectrum of decanoyl chloride.

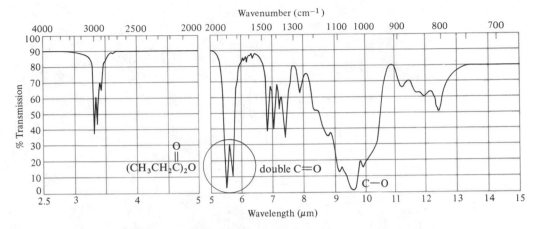

Figure 13.3. Infrared spectrum of propanoic anhydride.

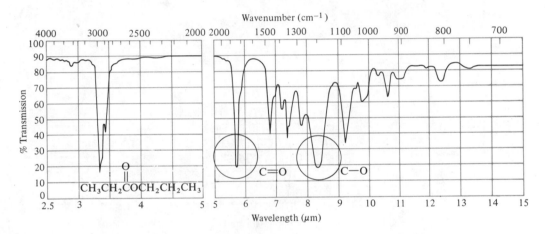

Figure 13.4. Infrared spectrum of propyl propanoate.

C. Esters

The carbonyl infrared absorption of aliphatic esters is observed at about 1740 cm^{-1} (5.75 μm). However, conjugated esters (either α,β-unsaturated esters of α-aryl esters) absorb at slightly lower frequencies, about 1725 cm^{-1} (5.8 μm). Esters also exhibit C—O stretching absorption in the fingerprint region. See Figure 13.4 for the spectrum of a typical ester.

D. Amides

The position of absorption of the carbonyl group of an amide is variable and depends upon the extent of hydrogen bonding between molecules. The infrared spectrum of a pure liquid amide (maximum hydrogen bonding) shows a carbonyl peak called the **amide I bond** around 1650 cm^{-1} (6.0 μm). (The spectra in Figure 13.5 show this C=O peak.) As the sample is diluted with a nonhydrogen-bonding

Derivatives of Carboxylic Acids

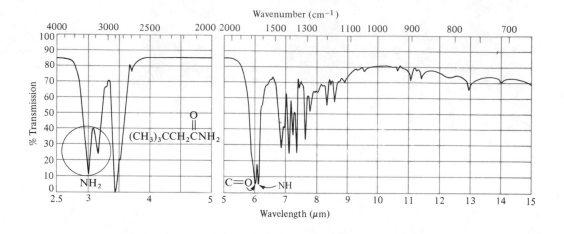

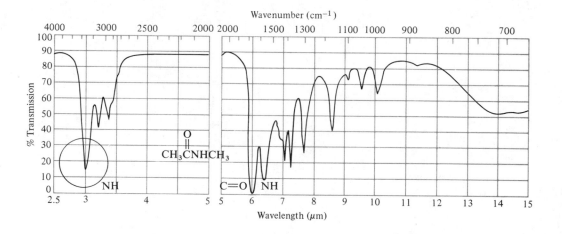

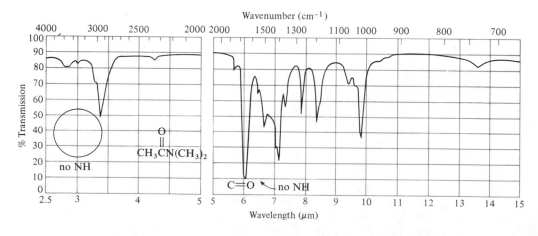

Figure 13.5. Infrared spectra of a 1° amide (top), a 2° amide (center), and a 3° amide (bottom).

solvent, the extent of the hydrogen bonding diminishes, and the $C=O$ absorption is shifted to a higher frequency (1700 cm^{-1}; 5.88 μm).

The **amide II band** appears between 1515–1670 cm^{-1} (6.0–6.6 μm), just to the right of the $C=O$ absorption. This absorption arises from NH bending. Therefore, a disubstituted, or tertiary, amide does not show an amide II band.

The NH stretching vibrations give rise to absorption to the left of aliphatic CH absorption at 3125–3570 cm^{-1} (2.8–3.2 μm). (This is about the same region where the NH of amines and OH absorb.) *Primary amides* (RCONH$_2$) show a double peak in this region. *Secondary amides* (RCONHR), with only one NH bond, show a single peak. *Tertiary amides* (RCONR$_2$), with no NH, show no absorption in this region. Figure 13.5 shows the infrared spectra of the three types of amides; compare the NH stretching and bending absorptions of these three compounds.

E. Nitriles

The $C\equiv N$ absorption is found in the triple-bond region of the infrared spectrum (2200–2300 cm^{-1}; 4.3–4.5 μm) and is medium to weak in intensity (see Figure 13.6).

STUDY PROBLEM

13.2 An unknown has the molecular formula $C_4H_5O_2N$. Its infrared and nmr spectra are given in Figure 13.7 (page 612). What is the structure of the unknown?

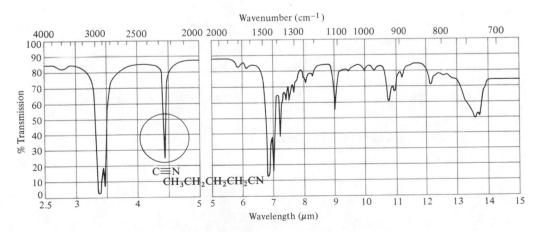

Figure 13.6. Infrared spectrum of pentanenitrile.

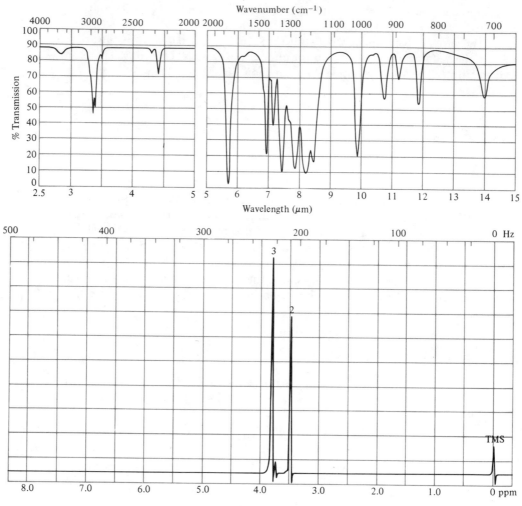

Figure 13.7.   Spectra for Problem 13.2.

Section 13.3

Acid Halides

Because acid chlorides are the most economical and therefore the most popular of the acid halides, we will limit our discussion to just these compounds. Other acid halides undergo reactions similar to those of the acid chlorides.

A.   Nomenclature of Acid Chlorides

Acid chlorides are named after the parent carboxylic acid with the **-ic acid** ending changed to **-yl chloride**.

$$\underset{\text{CH}_3\text{CCl}}{\overset{\overset{\displaystyle O}{\|}}{}} \qquad \underset{\text{CH}_3\text{CH}_2\text{CCl}}{\overset{\overset{\displaystyle O}{\|}}{}} \qquad \underset{\text{CH}_3\text{CH}_2\text{CH}_2\text{CCl}}{\overset{\overset{\displaystyle O}{\|}}{}}$$

IUPAC:	ethanoyl chloride	propanoyl chloride	butanoyl chloride
trivial:	acetyl chloride	propionyl chloride	butyryl chloride

B. Preparation of Acid Chlorides

Acid chlorides may be obtained directly from their parent carboxylic acids by reaction with thionyl chloride ($SOCl_2$) or some other active halogenating agent, such as phosphorus trichloride (PCl_3):

$$\underset{\substack{\text{a carboxylic} \\ \text{acid}}}{RCOH} + SOCl_2 \longrightarrow \underset{\substack{\text{an acid} \\ \text{halide}}}{RCCl} + HCl + SO_2$$

$$3\ RCOH + PCl_3 \longrightarrow RCCl + H_3PO_3$$

Note the similarity between these reactions and the corresponding reactions of alcohols (Section 7.9).

$$CH_3CH_2OH + SOCl_2 \longrightarrow CH_3CH_2Cl + SO_2 + HCl$$

$$CH_3COH + SOCl_2 \longrightarrow CH_3CCl + SO_2 + HCl$$

STUDY PROBLEM

13.3 Write an equation for the preparation of each of the following acid chlorides:

(a) CH_3CH_2CCl (b) $ClC{-}CCl$ (c) $C_6H_5CH_2CCl$

(d) 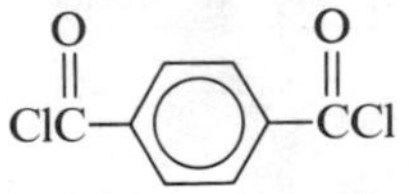 $ClC{-}\bigcirc{-}CCl$

C. Reactions of Acid Chlorides

The acid halides are the most reactive of all the derivatives of carboxylic acids. The halide ion is a good leaving group. Attached to the positive carbon of a carbonyl group, it is displaced even more easily than when it is attached to an alkyl carbon. In the following general mechanism for the reaction of an acid chloride with a nucleophile, note that displacement of Cl^- is not a simple displacement like an S_N2 reaction. Rather, the reaction consists of two steps: (1) *addition of the nucleophile to the carbonyl group*, followed by (2) *elimination of the chloride ion*.

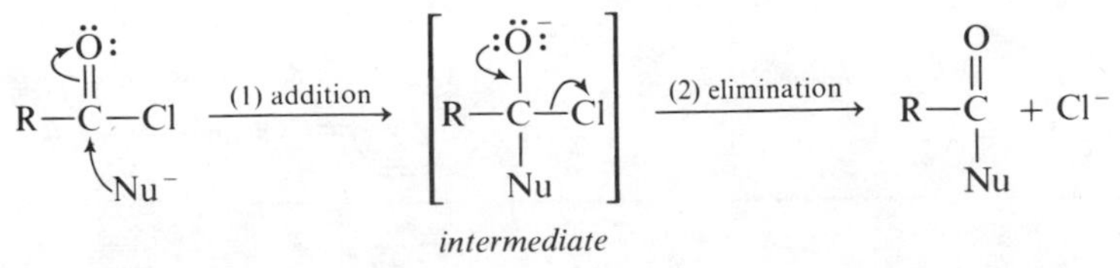

$$R{-}\overset{\ddot{O}:}{\underset{Nu^-}{C}}{-}Cl \xrightarrow{\text{(1) addition}} \left[R{-}\overset{:\ddot{O}:^-}{\underset{Nu}{C}}{-}Cl \right] \xrightarrow{\text{(2) elimination}} R{-}\overset{O}{\underset{Nu}{C}} + Cl^-$$

intermediate

Derivatives of Carboxylic Acids

Hydrolysis   Cleavage by water, called **hydrolysis**, is a typical reaction of an acid chloride with a nucleophile.

Nucleophilic attack and elimination of Cl⁻ :

$$CH_3\overset{O}{\overset{\|}{C}}Cl + H_2O \longrightarrow \left[CH_3\overset{O^-}{\underset{{}^+OH_2}{\overset{|}{C}}}Cl \right] \longrightarrow CH_3\overset{O}{\overset{\|}{C}} + Cl^-$$
$$\qquad\qquad\qquad\qquad\qquad\qquad\qquad\qquad\qquad {}^+OH_2$$

Loss of a proton: $CH_3\overset{O}{\underset{{}^+OH_2}{\overset{\|}{C}}} \rightleftharpoons CH_3\overset{O}{\underset{OH}{\overset{\|}{C}}} + H^+$

Overall reaction: $CH_3\overset{O}{\overset{\|}{C}}Cl + H_2O \longrightarrow CH_3\overset{O}{\overset{\|}{C}}OH + HCl$
acetyl chloride   acetic acid

Although all acid chlorides undergo acidic and alkaline hydrolysis to yield carboxylic acids, their rates of reaction vary. An acid chloride that has a bulky alkyl group attached to the carbonyl group undergoes reaction more slowly than an acid chloride with a small alkyl group. For example, acetyl chloride reacts almost explosively with water, but butanoyl chloride requires gentle reflux.

The effect of the size of the alkyl group on the reaction rate is one of *solubility in water* rather than steric hindrance. An acid chloride with a small alkyl group is more soluble and undergoes reaction faster. An increase in the size of the alkyl portion of the molecule renders the acid chloride less water-soluble; the reaction is slower. If hydrolysis of a variety of acid chlorides is carried out in an inert solvent that dissolves both the acid chloride and water, the rates of hydrolysis are similar.

$$CH_3CH_2CH_2\overset{O}{\overset{\|}{C}}Cl \qquad CH_3CH_2\overset{O}{\overset{\|}{C}}Cl \qquad CH_3\overset{O}{\overset{\|}{C}}Cl$$

increasing rate of hydrolysis in pure H₂O ⟶

Sample Problem

Suggest a reason why benzoyl chloride is less reactive toward nucleophilic attack than most aliphatic acid chlorides.

Solution: Conjugation of the carbonyl group can slow the rate of hydrolysis by dispersal of the positive charge on the carbonyl carbon. (A less positive carbon is less attractive to a nucleophile.)

+ *charge delocalized*

STUDY PROBLEMS

13.4 Suggest a mechanism for the hydrolysis of butanoyl chloride in dilute, aqueous NaOH.

13.5 Suggest a reason why an acid halide cannot be prepared from an ester and HCl.

Reaction with Alcohols Acid chlorides undergo reaction with alcohols to yield esters and HCl in a reaction that is directly analogous to hydrolysis. The reaction of an organic compound with an alcohol is referred to as **alcoholysis**. Alcoholysis of acid chlorides is valuable for the synthesis of hindered esters or phenyl esters.

$$\underset{\text{acetyl chloride}}{CH_3\overset{\overset{\displaystyle O}{\|}}{C}Cl} + \underset{\text{methanol}}{CH_3OH} \longrightarrow \underset{\text{methyl acetate}}{CH_3\overset{\overset{\displaystyle O}{\|}}{C}OCH_3} + HCl$$

It is usually wise to remove HCl from the reaction mixture as it is formed. The reason is that HCl can undergo reaction with the alcohol and produce alkyl chlorides or alkenes and water. A tertiary amine or pyridine is usually added as a scavenger for HCl.

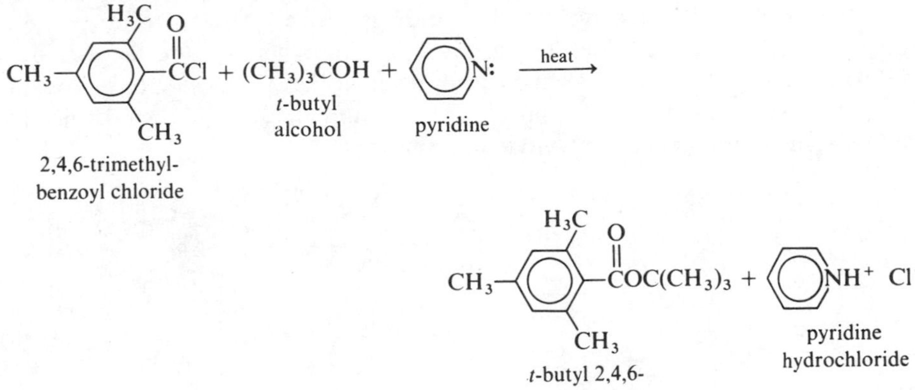

2,4,6-trimethyl-benzoyl chloride + *t*-butyl alcohol + pyridine $\xrightarrow{\text{heat}}$ *t*-butyl 2,4,6-trimethylbenzoate 79% + pyridine hydrochloride

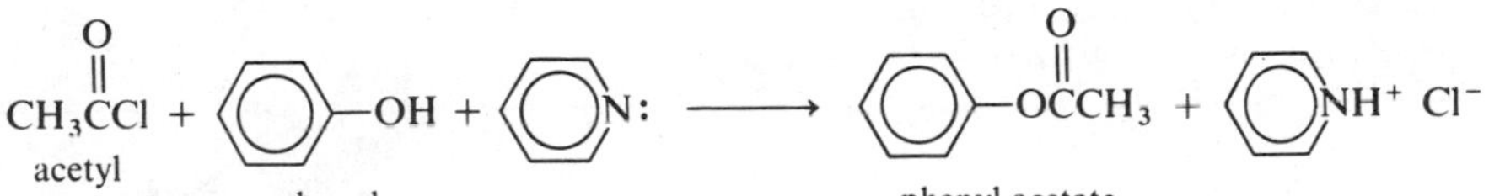

acetyl chloride + phenol + pyridine $\longrightarrow$ phenyl acetate + pyridine hydrochloride

STUDY PROBLEM

13.6 Write the mechanism for the reaction of butanoyl chloride with phenol in the presence of pyridine.

Reaction with Ammonia and Amines Ammonia and amines are good nucleophiles. Like other nucleophiles, they undergo reaction with acid chlorides. The organic product of the reaction is an *amide*. As protons are lost in the deprotonation step, they react with the basic NH_3 or amine. For this reason, at least two equivalents of NH_3 or amine must be used.

Derivatives of Carboxylic Acids

$$CH_3\overset{\displaystyle O}{\overset{\|}{C}}Cl + \quad NH_3 \longrightarrow CH_3\overset{\displaystyle O}{\overset{\|}{C}}NH_2 + HCl \quad \overset{NH_3}{\longrightarrow} NH_4^+ \ Cl^-$$

ammonia   *a 1° amide*

$$CH_3\overset{\displaystyle O}{\overset{\|}{C}}Cl + 2\ CH_3NH_2 \longrightarrow CH_3\overset{\displaystyle O}{\overset{\|}{C}}NHCH_3 + CH_3NH_3^+ \ Cl^-$$

methylamine   *a 2° amide*
a 1° amine

$$CH_3\overset{\displaystyle O}{\overset{\|}{C}}Cl + 2\ (CH_3)_2NH \longrightarrow CH_3\overset{\displaystyle O}{\overset{\|}{C}}N(CH_3)_2 + (CH_3)_2NH_2^+ \ Cl^-$$

dimethylamine   *a 3° amide*
a 2° amine

If an amine is expensive, a chemist may not want to use an excess in the reaction with acid chloride. Only one mole of amine is needed to undergo reaction with acid chloride; a second mole is wasted when it is acting merely as a scavenger for HCl. In this case, the chemist will use another base to remove the HCl. For example, an inexpensive tertiary amine might be used. (A tertiary amine is reactive toward HCl, but cannot form an amide with an acid chloride. Why not?)

If an acid halide (such as benzoyl chloride) is not very reactive toward water, aqueous NaOH may be added to remove HX. The reactants and the aqueous NaOH form two layers. As HX is formed, it undergoes reaction with NaOH in the water layer. This reaction of an acid chloride and an amine in the presence of NaOH solution is called the **Schotten–Baumann reaction**.

benzoyl   piperidine
chloride

an amide
80%

to H₂O layer

STUDY PROBLEM

13.7   The Schotten–Baumann reaction is not applicable if the acid chloride and amine are water-soluble. What products would you expect from a mixture of acetyl chloride, methylamine, NaOH, and H_2O?

Conversion to Anhydrides   Carboxylate ions are nucleophiles, and carboxylate salts (RCO_2Na) can be used for displacement of the chloride of acid chlorides. The product of the reaction is an acid anhydride.

$$CH_3(CH_2)_5\overset{\displaystyle O}{\overset{\|}{C}}Cl + CH_3(CH_2)_5\overset{\displaystyle O}{\overset{\|}{C}}O^- \longrightarrow CH_3(CH_2)_5\overset{\displaystyle O}{\overset{\|}{C}}O\overset{\displaystyle O}{\overset{\|}{C}}(CH_2)_5CH_3 + Cl^-$$

heptanoyl chloride   heptanoate ion   heptanoic anhydride
60%

STUDY PROBLEM

13.8   Write the mechanism for the reaction of sodium acetate and benzoyl chloride.

Conversion to Aryl Ketones   Acid halides are usually the reagents of choice for Friedel–Crafts acylation reactions (Section 10.9E). This reaction is a route to aryl alkyl ketones without rearrangement of the alkyl side chain. (Recall that similar *alkylations* go through alkyl carbocations and that rearrangements are common.)

$$\text{benzene} + \underset{\substack{\text{propanoyl} \\ \text{chloride}}}{CH_3CH_2\overset{\displaystyle O}{\overset{\|}{C}}Cl} \xrightarrow{\text{AlCl}_3} \underset{\substack{\text{1-phenyl-1-propanone} \\ 90\%}}{\overset{\displaystyle O}{\overset{\|}{C}}CH_2CH_3} + HCl$$

STUDY PROBLEM

13.9 Without referring to Chapter 10, tell how you would prepare isobutylbenzene from benzene.

Reaction with Organometallic Compounds   An acid chloride undergoes reaction with a variety of nucleophiles, including organometallic compounds. Reaction of an acid chloride with a Grignard reagent first yields a ketone, which then undergoes further reaction with the Grignard reagent to yield a *tertiary alcohol* after hydrolysis. (If an excess of the acid halide is used and temperatures of about −25° are maintained, the intermediate ketone may be isolated.)

$$\underset{\substack{\text{an acid chloride}}}{R-\overset{\displaystyle O}{\overset{\|}{C}}-Cl} \xrightarrow{R'MgX} \underset{\substack{\text{a ketone}}}{R-\overset{\displaystyle O}{\overset{\|}{C}}-R'} \xrightarrow{R'MgX} R-\overset{\displaystyle OMgX}{\underset{\displaystyle R'}{\overset{\|}{C}}}-R' \xrightarrow{H_2O, H^+} \underset{\substack{\text{a 3° alcohol}}}{R-\overset{\displaystyle OH}{\underset{\displaystyle R'}{\overset{\|}{C}}}-R'}$$

$$\underset{\substack{\text{benzoyl chloride}}}{\overset{\displaystyle O}{\overset{\|}{C}}Cl} \xrightarrow[\text{(2) H}_2\text{O, H}^+]{\text{(1) 2 CH}_3\text{MgI}} \underset{\substack{\text{2-phenyl-2-propanol} \\ \text{a 3° alcohol}}}{\overset{\displaystyle OH}{\underset{\|}{C}}(CH_3)_2}$$

A suitable organometallic reagent for preparing a ketone from an acid chloride is the **cadmium reagent**, an organocadmium compound prepared from a Grignard reagent and cadmium chloride.

Formation of a cadmium reagent:

$$2\ RMgX + CdCl_2 \longrightarrow \underset{\substack{\text{a cadmium} \\ \text{reagent}}}{R_2Cd}\ + MgCl_2 + MgX_2$$

Cadmium is less electropositive than magnesium; therefore, the C—Cd bond is less polar than the C—Mg bond. For this reason, cadmium reagents are less reactive than Grignard reagents.

$$\underset{\text{more negative}}{\overset{\delta-\quad\ \delta+}{R-MgX}} \qquad \underset{\text{less negative}}{\overset{\delta-\quad\ \delta+\quad\ \delta-}{R-Cd-R}}$$

Cadmium reagents do not undergo reaction with ketones, but they do undergo reaction with acid halides and offer an excellent method of ketone synthesis.

Reaction with acid halide:

$$R_2Cd + R'\overset{O}{\overset{\|}{C}}Cl \longrightarrow R'-\overset{O}{\overset{\|}{C}}-R + RCdCl$$

a ketone

Two examples of ketone syntheses with cadmium reagents follow. In the second example, note that the acid halide contains an ester group. This synthesis would not have been successful if a Grignard reagent had been used because the ester group would also react with the Grignard reagent.

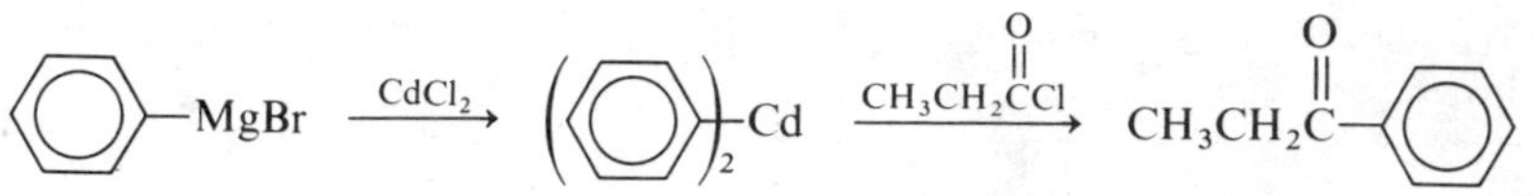

a phenyl ketone

$$CH_3CH_2CH_2MgBr \xrightarrow{CdCl_2} (CH_3CH_2CH_2)_2Cd \xrightarrow{CH_3O\overset{O}{\overset{\|}{C}}CH_2CH_2\overset{O}{\overset{\|}{C}}Cl}$$

$$CH_3O\overset{O}{\overset{\|}{C}}CH_2CH_2\overset{O}{\overset{\|}{C}}CH_2CH_2CH_3$$

a keto ester
75%

Secondary and tertiary alkylcadmium reagents are unstable; therefore, an organocadmium reagent is useful only when R is methyl, primary, or phenyl. A more general route to ketones is the use of **lithium dialkylcuprates**. (In Section 6.14, we described the use of these agents and alkyl halides in alkane synthesis.) Like cadmium reagents, cuprates undergo reaction with acid halides to yield ketones.

$$CH_3I \xrightarrow{Li} CH_3Li \xrightarrow{CuI} LiCu(CH_3)_2$$

a lithium dialkylcuprate

$$LiCu(CH_3)_2 + (CH_3)_3C\overset{O}{\overset{\|}{C}}-Cl \longrightarrow (CH_3)_3C\overset{O}{\overset{\|}{C}}-CH_3$$

t-butyl methyl ketone
(3,3-dimethyl-2-butanone)

STUDY PROBLEM

13.10 Show by equations how you would prepare the following ketones from alkyl halides and acid chlorides by way of a cadmium reagent and by way of a cuprate:

(a) (b)

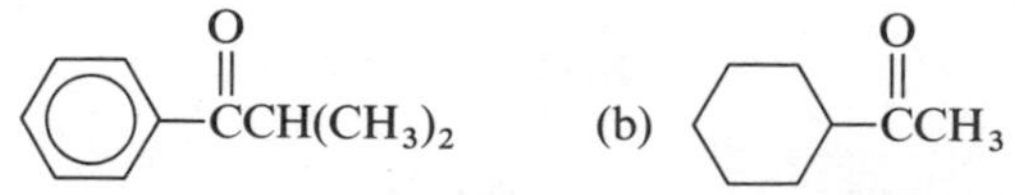

Reduction Reduction of acid chlorides with lithium aluminum hydride yields primary alcohols. Since primary alcohols also can be obtained by LAH reduction of the parent acids, this reaction finds little synthetic use.

The partial reduction of an acid chloride to an aldehyde can be effected, and this reaction is very useful. (A carboxylic acid itself is not readily reduced to an aldehyde.) A milder reducing agent than LAH is required to reduce RCOCl to RCHO instead of to RCH$_2$OH. A suitable reagent is **lithium tri-*t*-butoxyaluminum hydride**, which is obtained from *t*-butyl alcohol and LAH. This reducing reagent is less reactive than LAH because of both steric hindrance and electron-withdrawal by the oxygen atoms.

Preparation of reducing agent:

$$3 \; (CH_3)_3COH + LiAlH_4 \longrightarrow Li^+ \; H\text{---}\overset{\displaystyle OC(CH_3)_3}{\underset{\displaystyle OC(CH_3)_3}{\overset{|}{\underset{|}{Al}}}}\text{---}OC(CH_3)_3 + 3 \; H_2$$

t-butyl alcohol

lithium tri-*t*-butoxy-
aluminum hydride

Reaction with RCOCl:

benzoyl chloride

benzaldehyde
an aldehyde

Alpha Halogenation Ketones can be halogenated in the α position by treatment with X$_2$ and H$^+$ or OH$^-$. This reaction, which was discussed in Section 11.18, proceeds by way of the enol. Carboxylic acids do not undergo α halogenation because they do not tautomerize readily. On the other hand, acid halides do undergo tautomerization easily and therefore undergo α halogenation. Halogenation of a carboxylic acid proceeds smoothly when a catalytic amount of PCl$_3$ is added to the reaction mixture. The PCl$_3$ converts a small proportion of the acid to the acid chloride, which undergoes α halogenation. The α-halogenated acid chloride undergoes exchange of the acyl halogen atom with the carboxylic acid to yield more acid chloride, which can then also be halogenated. This reaction is called the **Hell–Volhard–Zelinsky reaction**.

α Halogenation:

Formation of α-halo acid:

$$\underset{\text{chloroacetic acid}}{ClCH_2\overset{\overset{\displaystyle O}{\|}}{C}Cl + CH_3\overset{\overset{\displaystyle O}{\|}}{C}OH \;\rightleftharpoons\; ClCH_2\overset{\overset{\displaystyle O}{\|}}{C}OH + CH_3\overset{\overset{\displaystyle O}{\|}}{C}Cl}$$

Some other examples of α halogenation of carboxylic acids (by way of acid halides) follow:

$$\underset{\text{propanoic acid}}{CH_3CH_2CO_2H} + Cl_2 \xrightarrow{\;PCl_3\;} \underset{\substack{\text{2-chloropropanoic}\\\text{acid}}}{CH_3\overset{\overset{\displaystyle Cl}{|}}{C}HCO_2H} + HCl$$

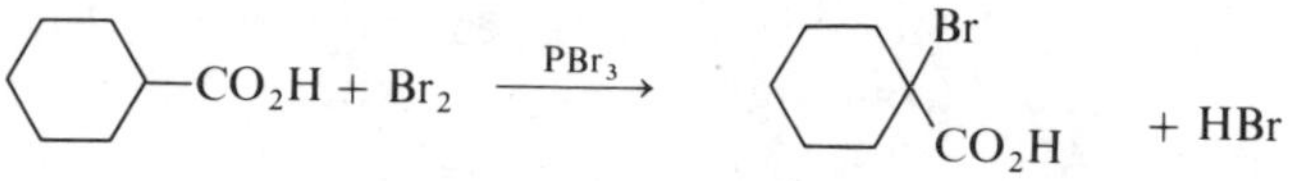

cyclohexane-
carboxylic acid   1-bromo-1-cyclohexane-
carboxylic acid

STUDY PROBLEM

13.11 Give the organic product of each of the following reactions:

(a) $(CH_3)_2CHCO_2H + Cl_2 \xrightarrow{\;PCl_3\;}$

(b) 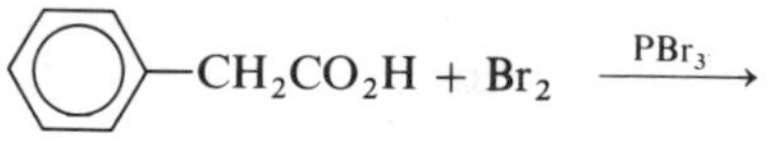 $-CH_2CO_2H + Br_2 \xrightarrow{\;PBr_3\;}$

Section 13.4

Anhydrides of Carboxylic Acids

An **anhydride of a carboxylic acid** has the structure of two carboxylic acid molecules with a molecule of water removed. (*Anhydride* means "without water.")

$$CH_3\overset{\overset{\displaystyle O}{\|}}{C}O\,H \quad HO\,\overset{\overset{\displaystyle O}{\|}}{C}CH_3 \xrightarrow{\;-H_2O\;} \underset{\textit{an anhydride}}{CH_3\overset{\overset{\displaystyle O}{\|}}{C}O\overset{\overset{\displaystyle O}{\|}}{C}CH_3}$$

A. Nomenclature of Anhydrides

Symmetrical anhydrides are those in which the two acyl groups are the same. They are named after the parent carboxylic acid followed by the word **anhydride**.

$$CH_3\overset{\overset{\displaystyle O}{\|}}{C}O\overset{\overset{\displaystyle O}{\|}}{C}CH_3 \qquad CH_3CH_2\overset{\overset{\displaystyle O}{\|}}{C}O\overset{\overset{\displaystyle O}{\|}}{C}CH_2CH_3$$

IUPAC:	ethanoic anhydride	propanoic anhydride
trivial:	acetic anhydride	propionic anhydride

Unsymmetrical anhydrides are named by the word **anhydride** preceded by the names of the *two* parent acids.

$$\underset{\begin{array}{cc} & \end{array}}{CH_3\overset{\displaystyle O}{\overset{\|}{C}}O\overset{\displaystyle O}{\overset{\|}{C}}CH_2CH_3}$$

IUPAC:	ethanoic propanoic anhydride
trivial:	acetic propionic anhydride

STUDY PROBLEM

13.12 Give a suitable name for each of the following anhydrides:

(a) $CH_3CH_2CH_2CH_2\overset{\displaystyle O}{\overset{\|}{C}}O\overset{\displaystyle O}{\overset{\|}{C}}CH_2CH_2CH_2CH_3$ (b) $\left(C_6H_5\overset{\displaystyle O}{\overset{\|}{C}}\right)_2O$

(c) $C_6H_5\overset{\displaystyle O}{\overset{\|}{C}}O\overset{\displaystyle O}{\overset{\|}{C}}CH_3$

B.   Preparation of Anhydrides

With few exceptions, acid anhydrides cannot be formed directly from their parent carboxylic acids, but must be prepared from the more reactive derivatives of carboxylic acids. One route to an anhydride is from an acid chloride with a carboxylate, a reaction mentioned on page 616.

$$\underset{\text{an acid chloride}}{R\overset{\displaystyle O}{\overset{\|}{C}}-Cl} \quad + \quad \underset{\text{a carboxylate}}{{}^{-}O\overset{\displaystyle O}{\overset{\|}{C}}R'} \longrightarrow \underset{\text{an anhydride}}{R\overset{\displaystyle O}{\overset{\|}{C}}-O\overset{\displaystyle O}{\overset{\|}{C}}R' + Cl^{-}}$$

Another route to an anhydride is by treatment of the carboxylic acid with acetic anhydride. A reversible reaction occurs between a carboxylic acid and an anhydride. The equilibrium can be shifted to the right by distilling the acetic acid as it is formed. This reaction has also been mentioned previously (Section 12.10B).

$$2 \underset{\text{benzoic acid}}{\bigcirc -CO_2H} + \underset{\text{acetic anhydride}}{CH_3\overset{\displaystyle O}{\overset{\|}{C}}O\overset{\displaystyle O}{\overset{\|}{C}}CH_3} \rightleftharpoons \underset{\text{benzoic anhydride}}{\bigcirc -\overset{\displaystyle O}{\overset{\|}{C}}O\overset{\displaystyle O}{\overset{\|}{C}}-\bigcirc} + \underset{\text{acetic acid}}{2\ CH_3CO_2H\uparrow}$$

A five- or six-membered cyclic anhydride can be formed by heating the appropriate diacid (see Section 12.10B).

$$\underset{\substack{\text{succinic acid} \\ \textit{a diacid}}}{\overset{\displaystyle CH_2CO_2H}{\underset{\displaystyle CH_2CO_2H}{|}}} \xrightarrow{\text{heat}} \underset{\substack{\text{succinic anhydride} \\ \textit{a cyclic anhydride}}}{\left[\text{cyclic structure}\right]} + H_2O$$

Derivatives of Carboxylic Acids

C. Reactions of Anhydrides

Like acid halides, acid anhydrides are more reactive than carboxylic acids and may be used to synthesize ketones, esters, or amides. Acid anhydrides undergo reactions with the same nucleophiles that the acid chlorides react with; however, the rates of reaction are slower. (A carboxylate ion is not quite as good a leaving group as a halide ion.) Note that the other product in these reactions is a carboxylic acid or, when the reaction mixture is alkaline, its anion.

$$RC\overset{O}{\underset{}{\|}}-O\overset{O}{\underset{}{\|}}CR + Nu^{-} \xrightarrow{\text{addition}} \left[RC\overset{O^-}{\underset{Nu}{\|}}-O\overset{O}{\underset{}{\|}}CR \right] \xrightarrow{\text{elimination}} RC\overset{O}{\underset{Nu}{\|}} + {}^{-}O\overset{O}{\underset{}{\|}}CR$$

intermediate

Hydrolysis Anhydrides undergo reaction with water to yield carboxylic acids. The rate of reaction, like the rate of hydrolysis of an acid chloride, depends on the solubility of the anhydride in water.

$$CH_3\overset{O}{\underset{}{\|}}COC\overset{O}{\underset{}{\|}}CH_3 + H_2O \longrightarrow 2\ CH_3\overset{O}{\underset{}{\|}}COH$$

acetic anhydride　　　　　　　　　　　acetic acid

General:　$RC\overset{O}{\underset{}{\|}}OC\overset{O}{\underset{}{\|}}R' + H_2O \longrightarrow RCO_2H + R'CO_2H$

an anhydride　　　　　　　　　*carboxylic acids*

Reaction with Alcohols and Phenols The reaction of an anhydride with either an alcohol or a phenol yields an ester. The reaction is particularly useful with the commercially available acetic anhydride, which results in acetates.

$$CH_3\overset{O}{\underset{}{\|}}COC\overset{O}{\underset{}{\|}}CH_3 + CH_3CH_2OH + \langle\bigcirc\rangle N: \longrightarrow CH_3\overset{O}{\underset{}{\|}}COCH_2CH_3 + CH_3CO_2^{-}\ H\overset{+}{N}\langle\bigcirc\rangle$$

acetic　　　　　ethanol　　　　　　　　　　　　　　　　ethyl acetate
anhydride　　　　　　　　　pyridine

$$CH_3\overset{O}{\underset{}{\|}}COC\overset{O}{\underset{}{\|}}CH_3 + \langle\bigcirc\rangle-OH + \langle\bigcirc\rangle N: \longrightarrow CH_3\overset{O}{\underset{}{\|}}CO-\langle\bigcirc\rangle + CH_3CO_2^{-}\ H\overset{+}{N}\langle\bigcirc\rangle$$

phenol　　　　　　　　　　　　　　　　　　　　phenyl acetate

STUDY PROBLEM

13.13 Both *aspirin* and *heroin* are made by the treatment of an alcohol or phenol with acetic anhydride. Write the equations for the preparations of these two drugs from the following compounds:

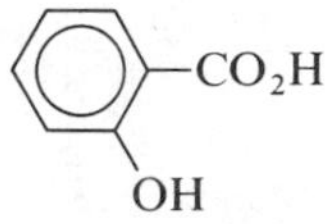

salicylic acid
used to prepare aspirin

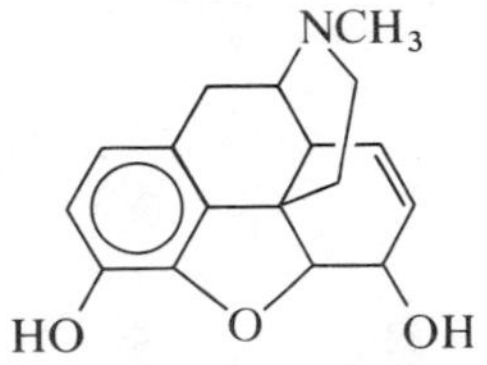

morphine
used to prepare heroin

Reaction with Ammonia and Amines Ammonia, primary amines, and secondary amines undergo reaction with anhydrides to yield *amides*. Again, acetic anhydride is the most popular anhydride used in this reaction. Ammonia and acetic anhydride yield acetamide, while amines and acetic anhydride give substituted acetamides. One mole of amine is consumed in neutralization of the acetic acid formed in the reaction.

$$CH_3\overset{O}{\overset{||}{C}}O\overset{O}{\overset{||}{C}}CH_3 + 2\ NH_3 \longrightarrow CH_3\overset{O}{\overset{||}{C}}NH_2 + CH_3CO_2{}^-\ NH_4{}^+$$

ammonia   acetamide

$$CH_3\overset{O}{\overset{||}{C}}O\overset{O}{\overset{||}{C}}CH_3 + 2\ RNH_2 \longrightarrow CH_3\overset{O}{\overset{||}{C}}NHR + CH_3CO_2{}^-\ RNH_3{}^+$$

a 1° amine   *an N-alkyl-acetamide*

$$CH_3\overset{O}{\overset{||}{C}}O\overset{O}{\overset{||}{C}}CH_3 + 2\ R_2NH \longrightarrow CH_3\overset{O}{\overset{||}{C}}NR_2 + CH_3CO_2{}^-\ R_2NH^+$$

a 2° amine   *an N,N-dialkyl-acetamide*

Sample Problem

Predict the product of reaction of one equivalent of succinic anhydride with two equivalents of ammonia.

Solution:

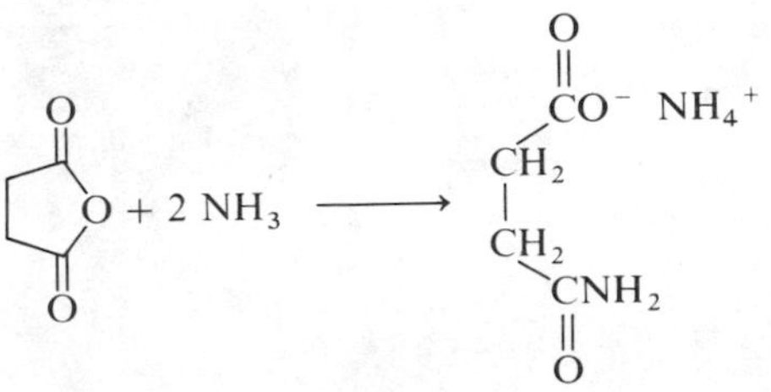

STUDY PROBLEM

13.14 Give the structures of all principal organic products:

$$\text{naphthalene-NH}_2 + CH_3\overset{O}{\overset{\|}{C}}O\overset{O}{\overset{\|}{C}}CH_3 + \text{pyridine} \longrightarrow$$

Section 13.5

Esters of Carboxylic Acids

Esters, one of the most useful classes of organic compounds, may be converted to a variety of other compounds (see Figure 13.8). Esters are common in nature. Volatile esters lend pleasant aromas to many fruits and perfumes. Fats and waxes are esters (Sections 19.1 and 19.3). Esters are also used for synthetic polymers: for example, Dacron is a polyester. Table 13.3 lists some representative esters. You might find it interesting to compare the odors of some of these esters to the odors of carboxylic acids, Section 12.2.

A. Nomenclature of Esters

The name of an ester consists of two words. The first word is the name of the **alkyl group** attached to the ester oxygen. The second word is derived from the

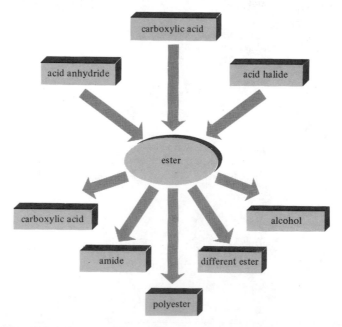

Figure 13.8. The synthetic relationship of esters to other compounds.

Table 13.3. Names, Odors, and Boiling Points of Selected Esters

Trivial name	*Structure*	*Odor*	*Bp, °C*
methyl acetate	$CH_3CO_2CH_3$	pleasant	57.5
ethyl acetate	$CH_3CO_2CH_2CH_3$	pleasant	77
propyl acetate	$CH_3CO_2CH_2CH_2CH_3$	like pears	102
butyl acetate	$CH_3CO_2(CH_2)_3CH_3$	like bananas	126
amyl acetate	$CH_3CO_2(CH_2)_4CH_3$	like pears	148
butyl butyrate	$CH_3(CH_2)_2CO_2(CH_2)_3CH_3$	like pineapple	166
isobutyl propionate	$CH_3CH_2CO_2CH_2CH(CH_3)_2$	like rum	137
methyl salicylate	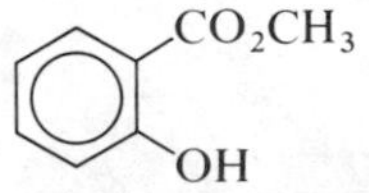	like wintergreen	220

carboxylic acid name with **-ic acid** changed to **-ate**. Note the similarity between the name of an ester and that of a carboxylate salt.

$$CH_3CH_2\overset{O}{\overset{\|}{C}}O{-}H \qquad CH_3CH_2\overset{O}{\overset{\|}{C}}O^-\ Na^+ \qquad CH_3CH_2\overset{O}{\overset{\|}{C}}O{-}CH_3$$

	an acid	*a salt*	*an ester*
IUPAC:	propanoic acid	sodium propanoate	methyl propanoate
trivial:	propionic acid	sodium propionate	methyl propionate

B. *Preparation of Esters*

Most methods for ester synthesis have been covered elsewhere in this text. In this section, we will provide a summary of these methods. One additional reaction, that of a carboxylic acid with diazomethane, will be discussed here.

From carboxylic acids and alcohols (Section 12.8):

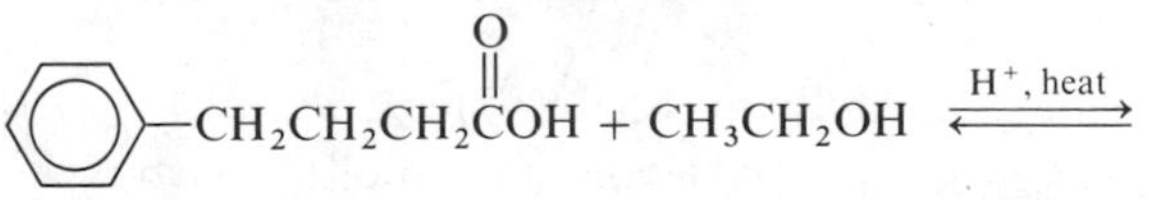

4-phenylbutanoic acid ethanol

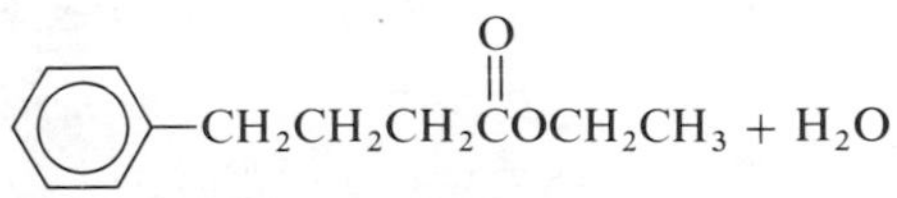

ethyl 4-phenylbutanoate
85%

From acid halides and alcohols (for hindered systems and for phenols) (Section 13.3):

$$Cl\overset{O}{\overset{\|}{C}}CH_2\overset{O}{\overset{\|}{C}}Cl + 2\,(CH_3)_3COH \longrightarrow (CH_3)_3CO\overset{O}{\overset{\|}{C}}CH_2\overset{O}{\overset{\|}{C}}OC(CH_3)_3 + 2\,HCl$$

malonyl chloride *t*-butyl alcohol di-*t*-butyl malonate
80%

From an anhydride and an alcohol or phenol (Section 13.4):

phthalic anhydride

2-butanol

2-butyl hydrogen phthalate
97%

From a carboxylate and a primary alkyl halide (Section 12.6):

$$CH_3CO^- + \text{benzyl chloride} \longrightarrow \text{benzyl acetate} + Cl^-$$

acetate ion   benzyl chloride

benzyl acetate
93%

From a carboxylic acid and diazomethane:

$$\text{cyclohexanecarboxylic acid} + CH_2N_2 \xrightarrow{\text{ether}} \text{methyl cyclohexanecarboxylate} + N_2$$

cyclohexane-
carboxylic acid

diazomethane

methyl cyclohexane-
carboxylate
100%

With the exception of the diazomethane reaction, the preceding esterification reactions usually give good, but not quantitative, yields. The reaction of a carboxylic acid with diazomethane usually gives a quantitative yield (eliminating the need for purification of the product ester). Diazomethane (CH_2N_2), which has been mentioned earlier (Section 9.12), is a toxic, explosive gas; it is almost always prepared just prior to the time it is needed. Despite these disadvantages, diazomethane is often the reagent of choice. For example, if a chemist wishes to esterify a few milligrams of a carboxylic acid for spectral analysis or if, for any reason, he wants a near-quantitative yield of an ester, he would probably choose to make the methyl ester with diazomethane.

How does esterification with diazomethane occur? The carbon of diazomethane carries a partial negative charge, and the acidic proton of the carboxylic acid is removed by this carbanion-like structure. Then nitrogen (N_2), one of the best leaving groups known, is displaced by the carboxylate anion to yield the methyl ester.

Resonance structures of CH_2N_2:

$$CH_2{=}\overset{+}{N}{=}\overset{..}{N}{:}^- \longleftrightarrow {}^-{:}CH_2{-}\overset{+}{N}{\equiv}N{:}$$

Reaction with RCO_2H:

$$RCO{-}H \quad {}^-CH_2{-}N_2{}^+ \longrightarrow \left[RCO^- \quad CH_3{-}\overset{+}{N_2} \right] \longrightarrow RCOCH_3 + N_2$$

a methyl ester

STUDY PROBLEMS

13.15 Using the reactions outlined in this section, show the various ways in which methyl benzoate can be prepared.

13.16 The structure of acetylsalicylic acid (aspirin) follows. How would you prepare this compound from methyl salicylate (Table 13.3)?

$$
\underset{\text{aspirin}}{
\begin{array}{c}
\text{O} \\
\parallel \\
\text{C6H4}
\end{array}
}
$$

aspirin

C. Reactions of Esters

In *acidic solution*, the carbonyl oxygen of an ester may be protonated. The partially positive carbon can then be attacked by a weak nucleophile such as water.

Protonation:

$$
\begin{array}{ccc}
\overset{\text{O}}{\underset{\parallel}{R-C-OR}} & \xrightarrow{H^+} & \left[\overset{+\text{OH}}{\underset{\parallel}{R-C-OR}} \longleftrightarrow \overset{\text{OH}}{\underset{|}{R-\underset{+}{C}-OR}} \right] \; Nu^-
\end{array}
$$

resonance structures
for a protonated ester

The carbonyl oxygen is protonated rather than the alkoxyl oxygen because the carbonyl oxygen of an ester is the more basic of the two. From the resonance structures of the protonated ester, you can see that this resulting cation is resonance-stabilized. (The cation formed by protonation of the alkoxyl oxygen is not resonance-stabilized.)

In an *alkaline solution*, the carbon of the carbonyl group of an ester may be attacked by a good nucleophile without prior protonation. This is the same addition–elimination path as for nucleophilic attack on acid chlorides or anhydrides.

$$
\underset{\delta+}{\overset{\text{O}}{\underset{\parallel}{R-C-OR}}} + Nu^- \xrightarrow{\text{addition}} \left[\overset{\text{O}^-}{\underset{\underset{Nu}{|}}{R-C-OR}} \right] \xrightarrow{\text{elimination}} \overset{\text{O}}{\underset{\underset{Nu}{|}}{R-C}} + {}^-OR
$$

intermediate

Acid Hydrolysis The esterification of a carboxylic acid with an alcohol (Section 12.8) is a reversible reaction. When a carboxylic acid is esterified, an excess of the alcohol is used. To cause the reverse reaction—that is, *acid-catalyzed hydrolysis of an ester to a carboxylic acid*—an excess of water is used. The excess of water shifts the equilibrium to the carboxylic acid side of the equation.

Esterification:

O
‖
〈 〉—COH + CH₃OH ⇌(H⁺, heat) 〈 〉—COCH₃ + H₂O
‖
O

benzoic acid   methanol   methyl benzoate
                (excess)

Hydrolysis:

O
‖
〈 〉—COCH₃ + H₂O ⇌(H⁺, heat) 〈 〉—COH + CH₃OH
‖
O

methyl benzoate   *excess*   benzoic acid   methanol

If water labeled with oxygen-18 is used in the hydrolysis, the labeled oxygen ends up in the carboxylic acid.

$$\underset{\|}{O} \qquad \underset{\|}{O}$$

$$RCOR + H_2{}^{18}O \;\overset{H^+, heat}{\rightleftharpoons}\; RC^{18}OH + ROH$$

$$\overset{\curvearrowleft}{no\ {}^{18}O}$$

The reason for this is that the water attacks the *carbonyl group*. The RO bond is not broken in the hydrolysis.

O   *this bond is broken*
‖
RC—O—R

              this bond is not broken

The following mechanism accounts for this observation. Note that the first step is *protonation* (only one resonance structure is shown), followed by *addition of H₂O*, then *elimination of R′OH*, followed by *deprotonation.*

$$\underset{\|}{O}\atop RC{-}OR' \;\overset{H^+}{\rightleftharpoons}\; \left[\begin{matrix}OH\\|\\RC{-}OR'\\+\end{matrix}\right] \;\overset{H_2{}^{18}O}{\rightleftharpoons}\; \left[\begin{matrix}OH\\|\\RC{-}OR'\\|\\{}^{18}OH_2\\+\end{matrix}\right] \;\rightleftharpoons$$

$$\left[\begin{matrix}:\ddot{O}H\\|\\RC{-}O^+R'\\|\ \ \ |\\{}^{18}OH\ \ H\end{matrix}\right] \;\overset{-R'OH}{\rightleftharpoons}\; \left[\begin{matrix}{}^+OH\\\|\\RC\\\|\\{}^{18}OH\end{matrix} \longleftrightarrow \begin{matrix}OH\\|\\RC\\\|\\{}^{18}\overset{+}{O}H\end{matrix}\right] \;\overset{-H^+}{\rightleftharpoons}\; \begin{matrix}O\\\|\\RC\\|\\{}^{18}OH\end{matrix} \quad or \quad \begin{matrix}OH\\|\\RC\\\|\\{}^{18}O\end{matrix}$$

resonance structures
for protonated acid

A simplified mechanism for ester hydrolysis may be written:

$$\underset{\|}{O}\atop RCOR' + H_2O \;\overset{H^+}{\rightleftharpoons}\; \left[\begin{matrix}OH\\|\\R{-}C{-}OR'\\|\\OH\end{matrix}\right] \;\rightleftharpoons\; \underset{\|}{O}\atop RCOH \;+\; HOR'$$

an ester   *a carboxylic*   *an alcohol*
                                           acid

STUDY PROBLEM

13.17 What would you expect as acid-hydrolysis products of the following labeled ester?

$$\underset{\text{CH}_3\text{C}^{18}\text{OCH}_2\text{CH}_3}{\overset{\displaystyle\text{O}}{\overset{\|}{}}}$$

Alkaline Hydrolysis (Saponification) Hydrolysis of an ester in base, or **saponification**, is an *irreversible reaction*. Because it is irreversible, saponification often gives better yields of carboxylic acid and alcohol than does acid hydrolysis. Because the reaction occurs in base, the product of saponification is the carboxylate salt. The free acid is generated when the solution is acidified.

Saponification:

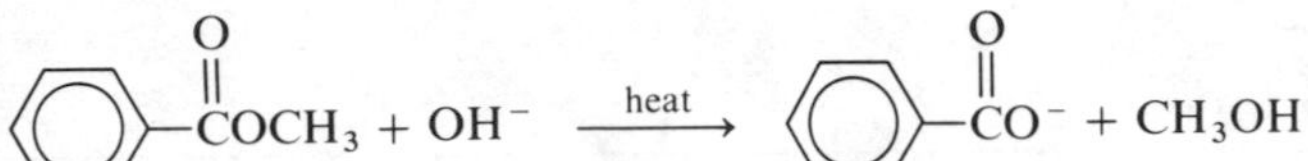

methyl benzoate   benzoate ion

Acidification:

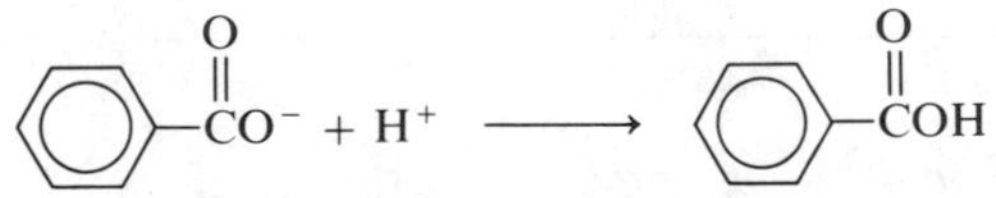

benzoic acid

A large body of evidence has been accumulated to support the following mechanistic scheme, which is typical of nucleophilic attack on a carboxylic acid derivative.

Step 1 (addition of OH⁻) (slow):

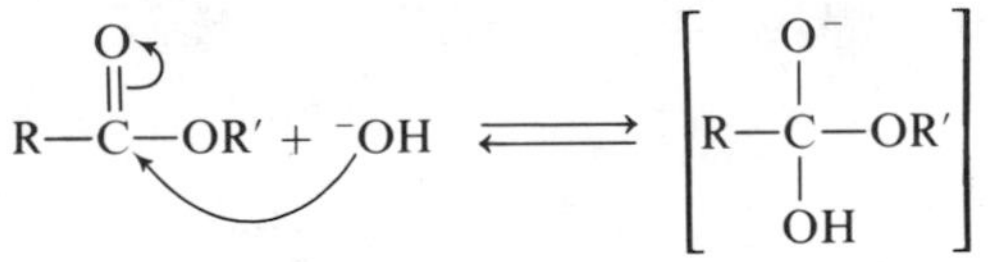

Step 2 (elimination of ⁻OR′ and proton transfer) (fast):

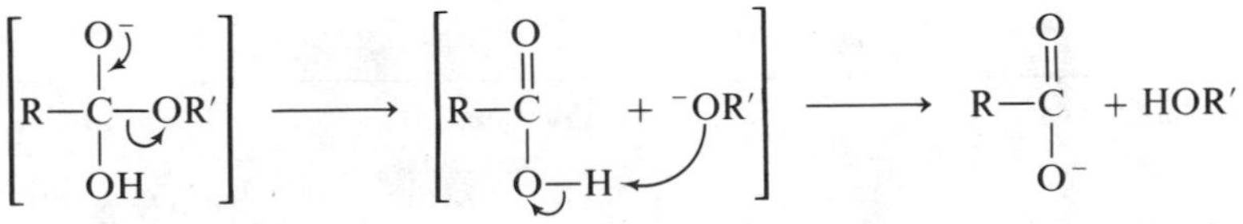

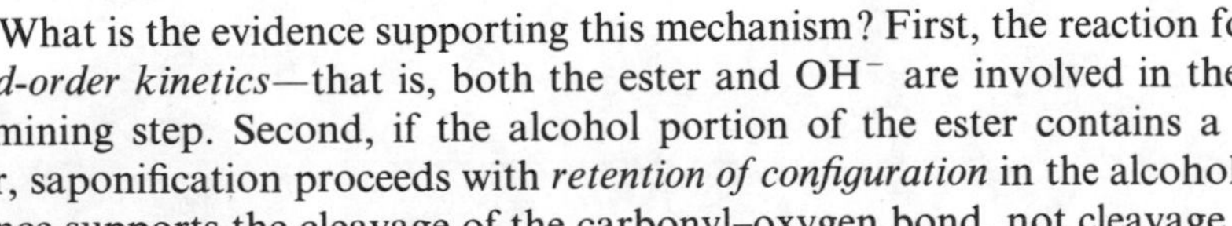

What is the evidence supporting this mechanism? First, the reaction follows *second-order kinetics*—that is, both the ester and OH⁻ are involved in the rate-determining step. Second, if the alcohol portion of the ester contains a chiral center, saponification proceeds with *retention of configuration* in the alcohol. This evidence supports the cleavage of the carbonyl–oxygen bond, not cleavage of the alkyl–oxygen bond.

chiral center

$$\text{(benzene ring)}-\overset{\overset{\displaystyle O}{||}}{C}-O\overset{\overset{CH_2CH_3}{|}}{\underset{\underset{CH_3}{|}}{C}}\text{.....}H \xrightarrow[\text{H}_2\text{O}]{\text{OH}^-} \text{(benzene ring)}-\overset{\overset{\displaystyle O}{||}}{C}OH + HO\overset{\overset{CH_2CH_3}{|}}{\underset{\underset{CH_3}{|}}{C}}\text{.....}H$$

(*R*)-2-butyl benzoate   benzoic acid   (*R*)-2-butanol

if this bond were cleaved, we
would expect racemization or inversion

$$\text{(benzene ring)}-\overset{\overset{\displaystyle O}{||}}{C}-O-\overset{\overset{CH_2CH_3}{|}}{\underset{\underset{CH_3}{|}}{C}}\text{.....}H$$

no racemization or inversion observed;
this bond is cleaved

STUDY PROBLEM

13.18 Predict the products of saponification of $CH_3\overset{\overset{\displaystyle}{}}{\underset{\underset{\displaystyle O}{||}}{C}}{}^{18}OCH_2CH_3$.

The word *saponification* comes from the word "soap." Soaps, which are synthesized by the saponification of fats, will be discussed at greater length in Chapter 19.

$$\begin{array}{l} CH_2O\overset{\overset{\displaystyle O}{||}}{C}(CH_2)_{14}CH_3 \\ | \\ CHO\overset{\overset{\displaystyle O}{||}}{C}(CH_2)_{14}CH_3 \;\; + \; 3\,NaOH \longrightarrow \\ | \\ CH_2O\overset{\overset{\displaystyle O}{||}}{C}(CH_2)_{14}CH_3 \end{array} \qquad \begin{array}{l} CH_2OH \\ | \\ CHOH \;\; + \; 3\,CH_3(CH_2)_{14}\overset{\overset{\displaystyle O}{||}}{C}O^-\;Na^+ \\ | \\ CH_2OH \end{array}$$

tripalmitin   glycerol   sodium palmitate
a fat, or triglyceride   *a soap*

Sample Problem

Which has a faster rate of saponification,   (a) ethyl benzoate or   (b) ethyl *p*-nitrobenzoate?

Solution: (b) has the faster rate because it has an electron-withdrawing nitro group. The transition state leading to the intermediate in Step 1 is more stabilized by dispersal of the negative charge:

$$O_2N \leftarrow \text{(benzene ring)} \leftarrow \overset{\overset{\displaystyle O^-}{|}}{\underset{\underset{\displaystyle OH}{|}}{C}}-OCH_2CH_3$$

STUDY PROBLEM

13.19 Write the equation for the saponification with aqueous NaOH of each of the following esters:

(a) ⟨benzene⟩—$CO_2CH_2CH_3$ (b) [cyclic carbonate with O—C(=O)—O]

(c) [chroman-2-one structure]   (d) [quinoxaline structure with $CH_2CO_2CH_2CH_3$ and OH]

Transesterification Exchange of the alcohol portion of an ester can be accomplished in acidic or basic solution by a reversible reaction between the ester and an alcohol. These **transesterification reactions** are directly analogous to hydrolysis in acid or base. Because the reactions are reversible, an excess of the initial alcohol is generally used.

$$\text{⟨C}_6\text{H}_5\text{C(=O)}\text{—OCH}_3 + CH_3CH_2OH \underset{}{\overset{H^+ \text{ or } CH_3CH_2O^-}{\rightleftharpoons}} \text{⟨C}_6\text{H}_5\text{C(=O)}\text{—OCH}_2CH_3 + CH_3OH}$$

methyl benzoate   *excess*   ethyl benzoate

STUDY PROBLEM

13.20 Suggest a mechanism for the transesterification reaction of ethyl acetate with (a) methanol and HCl, and (b) methanol and sodium methoxide.

Reaction with Ammonia Esters undergo reaction with aqueous ammonia to yield amides. The reaction is slow compared to the reactions of acid halides or anhydrides with ammonia. This slowness of the ester reaction can be an advantage because the reaction of an acid chloride with an amine can sometimes be violent. The ester route to amides is also the reaction of choice when a chemist desires an amide with another functional group that would not be stable toward an acid chloride. Such a case is illustrated in our second example.

$$ClCH_2\overset{O}{\overset{||}{C}}OCH_2CH_3 + NH_3 \xrightarrow[1\,hr]{0°} ClCH_2\overset{O}{\overset{||}{C}}NH_2 + CH_3CH_2OH$$

ethyl chloroacetate   chloroacetamide
                                   80%

$$CH_3\underset{OH}{\overset{}{C}}H\overset{O}{\overset{||}{C}}OCH_2CH_3 + NH_3 \xrightarrow[24\,hr]{25°} CH_3\underset{OH}{\overset{}{C}}H\overset{O}{\overset{||}{C}}NH_2 + CH_3CH_2OH$$

ethyl 2-hydroxypropanoate   2-hydroxypropanamide
(ethyl lactate)   70%

STUDY PROBLEM

13.21 What products would arise from the reaction of 2-hydroxypropanoic acid (lactic acid) with $SOCl_2$?

Reduction Esters can be reduced by catalytic hydrogenation, sometimes called **hydrogenolysis of esters**, or by lithium aluminum hydride. An older technique is the reaction of the ester with sodium metal in ethanol. Regardless of the reducing agent, a pair of alcohols (with at least one being primary) results from the reduction of an ester.

General:

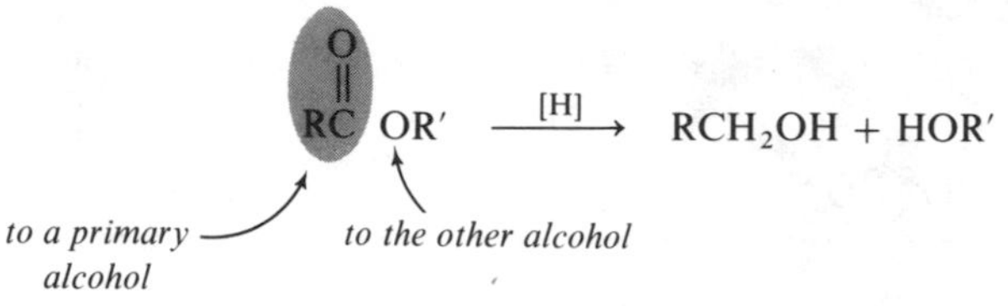

$$RC\!-\!OR' \xrightarrow{[H]} RCH_2OH + HOR'$$

to a primary alcohol — *to the other alcohol*

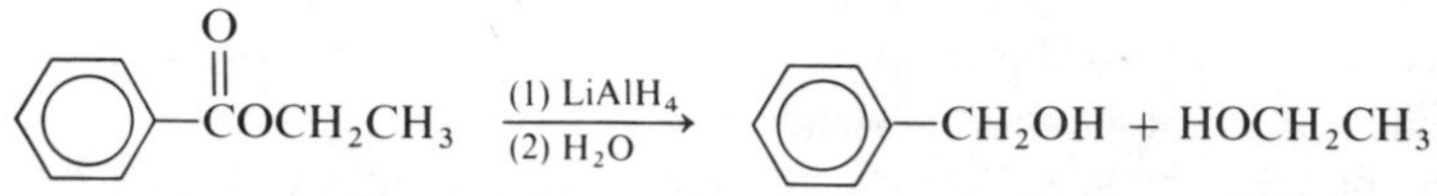

ethyl benzoate $\xrightarrow[(2)\ H_2O]{(1)\ LiAlH_4}$ benzyl alcohol + ethanol
90%

$$CH_3(CH_2)_8COCH_2CH_3 \xrightarrow[CH_3CH_2OH]{Na} CH_3(CH_2)_8CH_2OH + HOCH_2CH_3$$
ethyl decanoate — 1-decanol — ethanol — 70%

$$CH_3CH_2OC(CH_2)_4COCH_2CH_3 \xrightarrow[255°,\ 200\ atm]{H_2\ CuCr_2O_4\ catalyst} HOCH_2(CH_2)_4CH_2OH + CH_3CH_2OH$$
diethyl adipate (diethyl hexanedioate) — 1,6-hexanediol — ethanol — 90%

STUDY PROBLEM

13.22 Show by equations how you would prepare $CH_3(CH_2)_{14}CH_2OH$ from tripalmitin (page 630).

Reaction with Grignard Reagents The reaction of esters with Grignard reagents is an excellent technique for the preparation of *tertiary alcohols with two identical R groups.*

General:

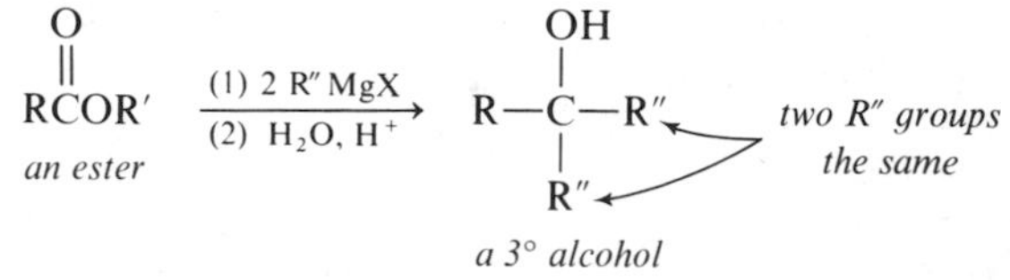

$$RCOR' \xrightarrow[(2)\ H_2O,\ H^+]{(1)\ 2\ R''MgX} R\!-\!\underset{R''}{\overset{OH}{C}}\!-\!R''$$
an ester — *two R″ groups the same* — *a 3° alcohol*

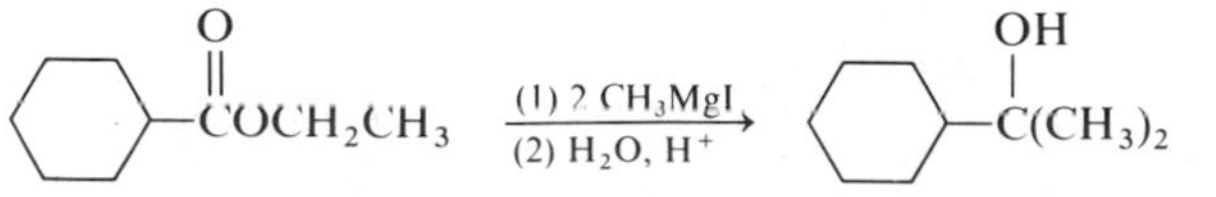

ethyl cyclohexane-carboxylate $\xrightarrow[(2)\ H_2O,\ H^+]{(1)\ 2\ CH_3MgI}$ 2-cyclohexyl-2-propanol ($C(CH_3)_2$)

The reaction of a Grignard reagent with an ester is similar to the reaction of a Grignard reagent with an aldehyde or ketone—that is, the nucleophilic carbon of the Grignard reagent attacks the positive carbon of the carbonyl group. In the case of an ester, as in the case of an acid halide (page 617), *two* equivalents of Grignard reagent attack the carbonyl carbon atom. To see why this is so, let us consider the reaction stepwise. First, the negative carbon of the Grignard reagent attacks the carbon of the carbonyl group. The product of this step has a hemiketal-like structure that loses an alkoxyl group to yield a ketone.

Initial attack:

$$R-\overset{\overset{O}{\|}}{C}-OR' + \overset{\delta-}{C}H_3-\overset{\delta+}{M}gX \longrightarrow \left[R-\overset{\overset{O^- \ ^+MgX}{|}}{\underset{CH_3}{C}}-OR' \right] \longrightarrow \left[R-\overset{\overset{O}{\|}}{\underset{CH_3}{C}} \right] + R'OMgX$$

a type of hemiketal   *a ketone*

The ketone then undergoes a *second* reaction with the Grignard reagent. The rate of the second reaction is greater than that of the first; hence the ketone cannot be isolated.

Second attack and hydrolysis:

$$\left[R-\overset{\overset{O}{\|}}{C}-CH_3 \right] + CH_3-MgX \longrightarrow R-\overset{\overset{OMgX}{|}}{\underset{CH_3}{C}}-CH_3 \xrightarrow{H_2O, H^+} R-\overset{\overset{OH}{|}}{\underset{CH_3}{C}}-CH_3 + HOMgX$$

a 3° alcohol

STUDY PROBLEMS

13.23 Show by equations how you would prepare the following alcohols from methyl propanoate: (a) 2-methyl-2-butanol, and (b) 3-ethyl-3-pentanol.

13.24 Predict the product of the reaction of ethyl formate with ethylmagnesium bromide, followed by work-up with aqueous acid.

Section 13.6

Lactones

A molecule that contains a carboxylic acid group and a hydroxyl group can undergo an intramolecular esterification to yield a cyclic ester called a **lactone**.

4-hydroxybutanoic
acid
a γ-hydroxy acid

4-hydroxybutanoic
acid lactone
(γ-butyrolactone)

5-hydroxypentanoic
acid
a δ-hydroxy acid

5-hydroxypentanoic
acid lactone
(δ-valerolactone)

With γ- or δ-hydroxy acids, which form lactones that are five- or six-membered rings, the cyclization is so facile that the hydroxy acids often cannot

Table 13.4. *Composition of Equilibrium Mixtures of Hydroxy Acid versus Lactone*

Hydroxy acid	Lactone	% Acid	% Lactone
$HOCH_2CH_2CO_2H$	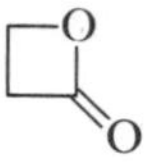	100	0
$HOCH_2CH_2CH_2CO_2H$	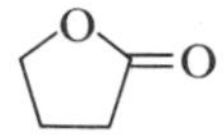	27	73
$HOCH_2(CH_2)_2CH_2CO_2H$	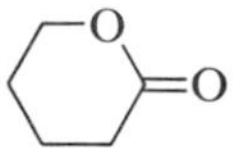	9	91
$HOCH_2(CH_2)_3CH_2CO_2H$	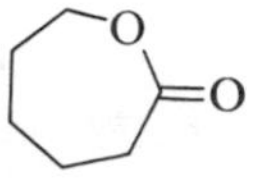	100	0

be isolated. Although the reaction is catalyzed by acid or base, even a trace of acid from the glassware is sufficient to catalyze lactone formation if a five- or six-membered ring is the product. The percentages of hydroxy acid and lactone in some equilibrium mixtures in aqueous acid are shown in Table 13.4.

STUDY PROBLEM

13.25 Lactic acid (2-hydroxypropanoic acid) does not form a lactone. However, when it is heated, it yields a dimeric cyclic ester called a **lactide**. What is the structure of this lactide?

Carboxylic acids with hydroxyl groups in positions other than the γ- or δ-positions are stable and do not cyclize spontaneously. (Compare the percents of lactone in the equilibrium mixtures of the hydroxy acids in Table 13.4.) However, the lactones of these hydroxy acids may be synthesized under the usual conditions for esterification. In these cases, a *dilute solution* of hydroxy acid in an inert solvent is used. An intramolecular reaction is favored by dilute solution because collisions between molecules are less apt to occur. If the solution is *concentrated*, then the hydroxy acid molecules undergo reaction with each other to yield a **polyester**. In either case, a solvent such as benzene allows the product water to be distilled as an azeotrope and drives the reaction toward the lactone (or polyester).

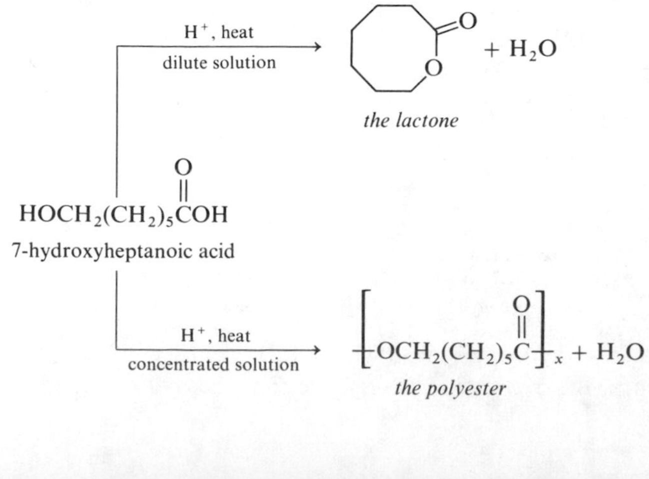

Polyesters

The synthetic fiber **Dacron** is a polyester made by a transesterification reaction of dimethyl terephthalate and ethylene glycol. The reason that polymer-formation can occur is that the reactants are *bifunctional*, and thus each reactant can undergo reaction with two other molecules.

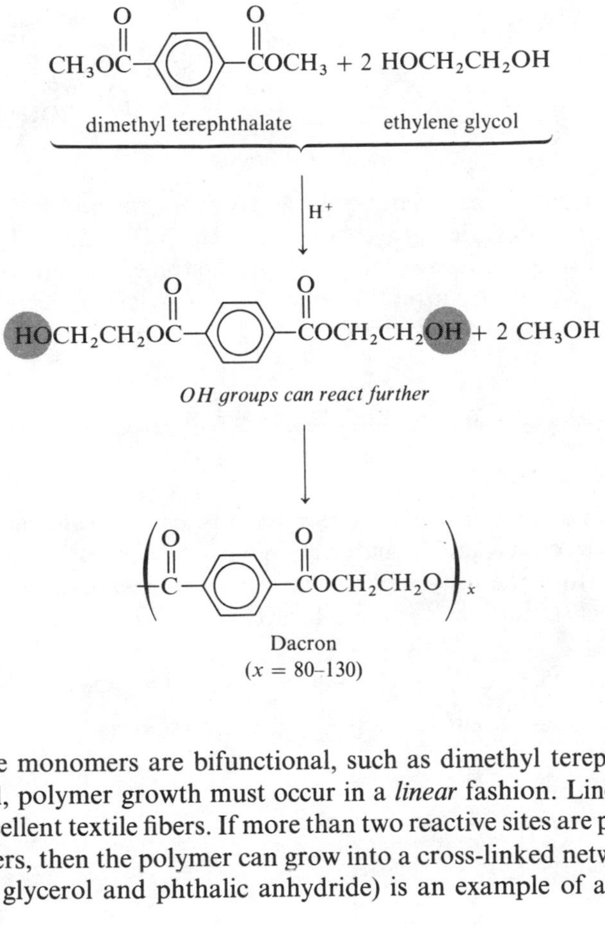

$$CH_3O\overset{O}{\overset{\|}{C}}-\underset{\text{dimethyl terephthalate}}{\underbrace{\bigcirc}}-\overset{O}{\overset{\|}{C}}OCH_3 + 2\ \underset{\text{ethylene glycol}}{\underbrace{HOCH_2CH_2OH}}$$

$$\Big\downarrow H^+$$

$$HOCH_2CH_2O\overset{O}{\overset{\|}{C}}-\bigcirc-\overset{O}{\overset{\|}{C}}OCH_2CH_2OH + 2\ CH_3OH$$

OH groups can react further

$$\left(\overset{O}{\overset{\|}{C}}-\bigcirc-\overset{O}{\overset{\|}{C}}OCH_2CH_2O\right)_x$$

Dacron
($x = 80$–130)

When the monomers are bifunctional, such as dimethyl terephthalate and ethylene glycol, polymer growth must occur in a *linear* fashion. Linear polymers often make excellent textile fibers. If more than two reactive sites are present in one of the monomers, then the polymer can grow into a cross-linked network. **Glyptal** (a polymer of glycerol and phthalic anhydride) is an example of a cross-linked polyester.

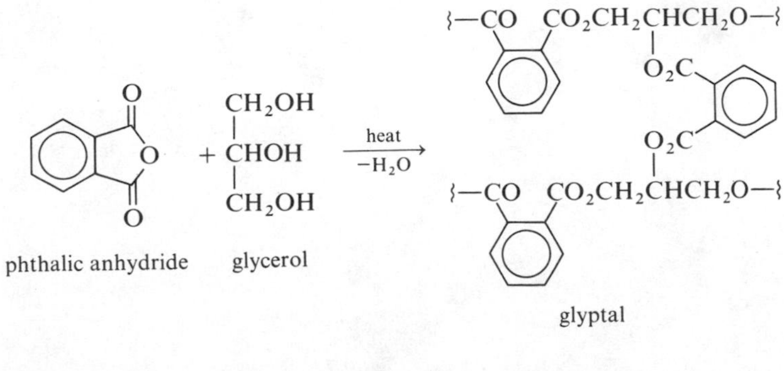

phthalic anhydride   glycerol

glyptal

Section 13.8

Thioesters

Esters with the $\overset{\overset{\displaystyle O}{\displaystyle \|}}{RCS}-$ unit are called **thioesters**. **Acetylcoenzyme A**, which is important in biological reactions, is a thioester.

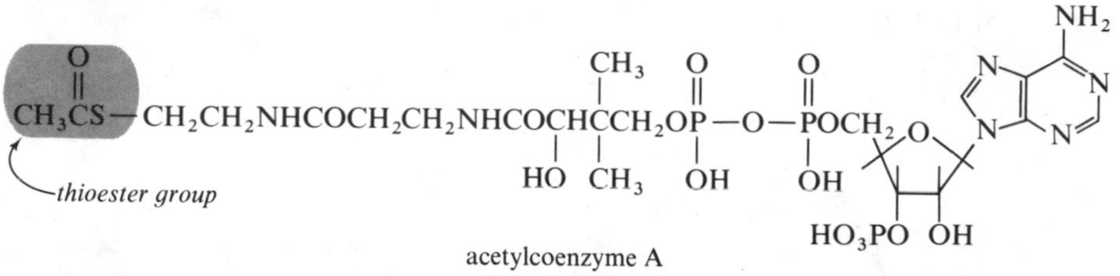

acetylcoenzyme A
($CH_3CO-SCoA$)

In an organism, acetylcoenzyme A has two principal functions. The first function is that of an **acylating agent** (a reagent that places an acyl group, $RCO-$, in a molecule). The following example shows the transfer of an acetyl group from acetylcoenzyme A to a phosphate group. In this reaction, acetylcoenzyme A is hydrolyzed to the thiol **coenzyme A**.

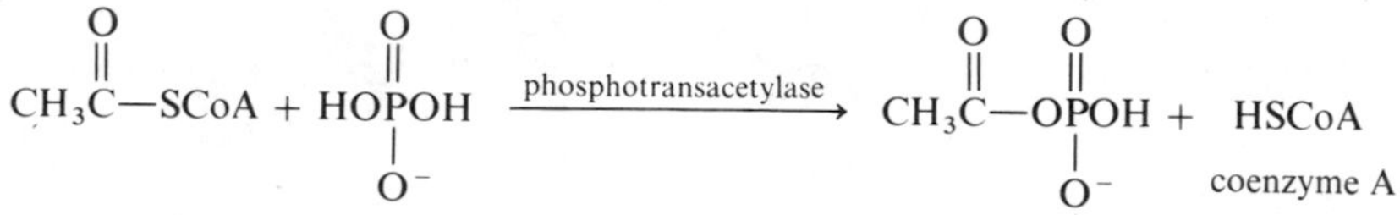

The second function of acetylcoenzyme A is that of an **alkylating agent**. The α hydrogen of a thioester is acidic and can be removed rather easily by the appropriate enzyme. Therefore, the acetyl carbon in acetylcoenzyme A can act as a nucleophile and can attack a carbonyl group. (This type of reaction will be discussed in Chapter 14.)

Loss of proton:

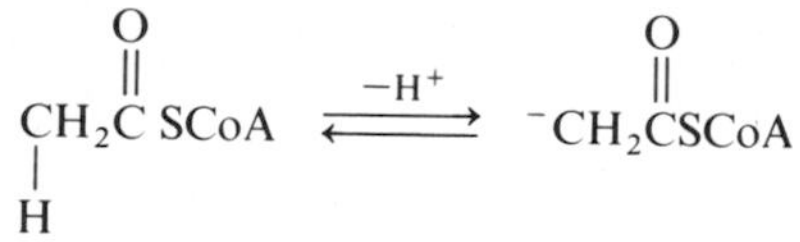

Nucleophilic attack and thioester hydrolysis:

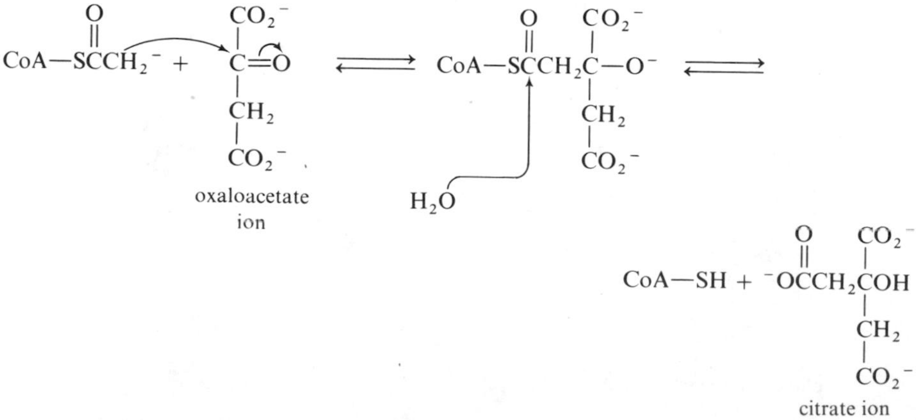

oxaloacetate
ion

citrate ion

Section 13.9

Amides

A.   Nomenclature of Amides

An **amide** is a compound that has a trivalent nitrogen attached to a carbonyl group. An amide is named from the parent carboxylic acid with the **-oic** (or **-ic**) **acid** ending changed to **-amide**.

$$\underset{\text{acetamide}}{\underset{\text{ethanamide}}{CH_3\overset{\displaystyle O}{\overset{\|}{C}}NH_2}} \qquad \underset{\text{butyramide}}{\underset{\text{butanamide}}{CH_3CH_2CH_2\overset{\displaystyle O}{\overset{\|}{C}}NH_2}}$$

IUPAC:	ethanamide
trivial:	acetamide

Amides with alkyl substituents on the nitrogen have their names preceded by *N*-alkyl, where *N* refers to the nitrogen atom.

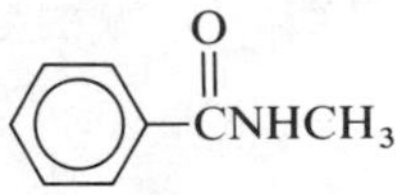

N-methylbenzamide   *N,N*-dimethylformamide

A few amides of interest follow; the amide groups are circled:

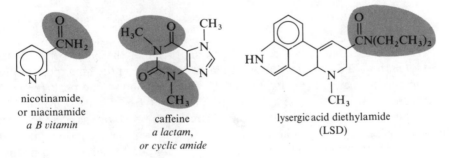

nicotinamide,
or niacinamide
a B vitamin

caffeine
*a lactam,
or cyclic amide*

lysergic acid diethylamide
(LSD)

B.   Preparation of Amides

Amides are synthesized from derivatives of carboxylic acids and ammonia or the appropriate amine. These reactions have been discussed previously in this chapter.

From acid chlorides (Section 13.3C):

$$R\overset{\displaystyle O}{\overset{\|}{C}}Cl + 2\,NH_3 \longrightarrow R\overset{\displaystyle O}{\overset{\|}{C}}NH_2 + NH_4Cl$$

From acid anhydrides (Section 13.4C):

$$R\overset{\displaystyle O}{\overset{\|}{C}}O\overset{\displaystyle O}{\overset{\|}{C}}R + 2\,NH_3 \longrightarrow R\overset{\displaystyle O}{\overset{\|}{C}}NH_2 + RCO^-\ NH_4^+$$

From esters (Section 13.5C):

$$\underset{\text{RCOR}' + \text{NH}_3}{\overset{O}{\overset{\|}{}}} \longrightarrow \underset{\text{RCNH}_2 + \text{R}'\text{OH}}{\overset{O}{\overset{\|}{}}}$$

C. Reactions of Amides

An amide contains a nitrogen that has a pair of unshared electrons in a filled orbital. It would be reasonable to expect amides to undergo reaction with acids, as do amines; however, they do not. Amides are *very* weak bases with pK_b values of 15–16. (By contrast, methylamine has a pK_b of 3.34.) The resonance structures for an amide show why the nitrogen of an amide is neither particularly basic nor nucleophilic.

$$\underset{\text{methylamine}}{\text{CH}_3\ddot{\text{N}}\text{H}_2} + \text{dilute HCl} \longrightarrow \underset{\substack{\text{methylammonium} \\ \text{chloride}}}{\text{CH}_3\text{NH}_3{}^+ \ \text{Cl}^-}$$

$$\underset{\text{acetamide}}{\overset{O}{\overset{\|}{\text{CH}_3\ddot{\text{C}}\ddot{\text{N}}\text{H}_2}}} + \text{dilute HCl} \longrightarrow \text{no appreciable salt formation}$$

Resonance structures for an amide:

$$\underset{}{\overset{O}{\overset{\|}{\text{R—C—}\ddot{\text{N}}\text{H}_2}}} \longleftrightarrow \underset{}{\overset{O^-}{\overset{|}{\text{R—C}=\overset{+}{\text{N}}\text{H}_2}}} \quad \begin{array}{l}\textit{less basic than} \\ \textit{an amine nitrogen}\end{array}$$

The effect of the partial double-bond character of the bond between the carbonyl carbon and the nitrogen of an amide is evident in the nmr spectrum of *N,N*-dimethylformamide (Figure 13.9). The spectrum shows one peak for *each* methyl group. If the two methyl groups underwent free rotation around the C—N bond, they would be equivalent and would give rise to one singlet. The fact that there are two methyl singlets shows that the two methyl groups are *not equivalent*. The restricted rotation around the C—N bond results in two methyl groups, each in a different magnetic environment. (The energy barrier for rotation around the C—N bond in an amide has been found to be 18 kcal/mole.)

$$\underset{\text{H}}{\overset{\text{O}}{\underset{}{\text{C}=\!=\text{N}}}}\overset{\text{CH}_3}{\underset{\text{CH}_3}{}} \quad \begin{array}{l}\text{restricted rotation} \\ \text{cis to oxygen} \\ \text{trans to oxygen}\end{array}$$

Hydrolysis   Like esters, amides may be hydrolyzed in either acidic or alkaline solution. In either case, the acid or base is a reactant, not a catalyst, and must be used in a 1:1 molar ratio or in excess. Neither type of hydrolysis reaction is reversible.

In acid:

$$\underset{\textit{N,N}\text{-dimethylpropanamide}}{\overset{O}{\overset{\|}{\text{CH}_3\text{CH}_2\text{CN}(\text{CH}_3)_2}}} + \text{H}_2\text{O} + \text{H}^+ \longrightarrow \underset{\substack{\text{propanoic} \\ \text{acid}}}{\text{CH}_3\text{CH}_2\text{CO}_2\text{H}} + \underset{\substack{\text{dimethyl-} \\ \text{ammonium ion}}}{\text{H}_2\overset{+}{\text{N}}(\text{CH}_3)_2}$$

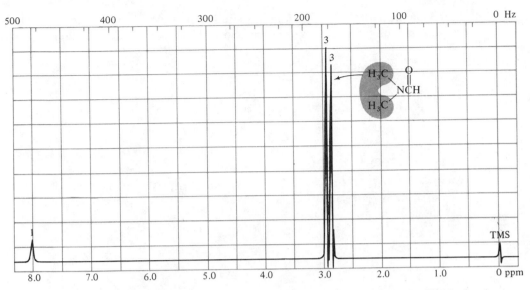

Figure 13.9. The nmr spectrum of *N,N*-dimethylformamide, showing a pair of peaks for the *N*-methyl groups.

In base:

$$CH_3CH_2\overset{\overset{\displaystyle O}{\|}}{C}N(CH_3)_2 + OH^- \longrightarrow CH_3CH_2\overset{\overset{\displaystyle O}{\|}}{C}O^- + HN(CH_3)_2$$

propanoate ion   dimethylamine

Hydrolysis of an amide in acidic solution proceeds in a fashion similar to hydrolysis of an ester. The carbonyl oxygen is protonated, the carbonyl carbon is attacked by H_2O, and an amine is expelled. This amine then undergoes reaction with H^+ to yield the amine salt. The formation of the amine salt explains (1) why H^+ is a reactant, not a catalyst, and (2) why the reverse reaction does not proceed. (Although R_3N is a nucleophile, R_3NH^+ is not, and it cannot attack the carbonyl group.)

In acid:

Alkaline hydrolysis of an amide is similar to saponification of an ester. The products are the carboxylate salt of the acid and a free amine or ammonia.

In base:

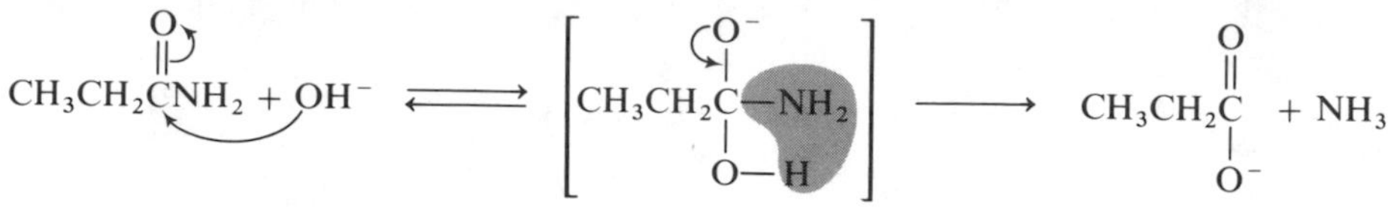

$$CH_3CH_2CNH_2 + OH^- \rightleftharpoons \left[CH_3CH_2C{-}NH_2 \right] \longrightarrow CH_3CH_2C + NH_3$$

STUDY PROBLEMS

13.26 The following structure represents a portion of a polyamide molecule, similar in structure to a protein. What would be the alkaline hydrolysis products? What would be the acid hydrolysis products?

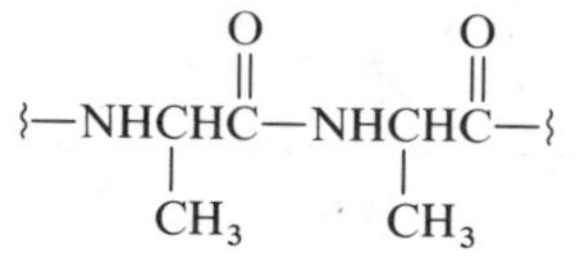

$$\{-NHCHC{-}NHCHC-\}$$

13.27 What would be the hydrolysis products of (a) nicotinamide (page 637) in acid? (b) LSD (page 637) in base? and (c) the following lactam in base?

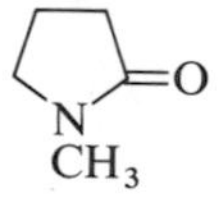

Section 13.10

Polyamides

There can be no question that the most important polyamides are the *proteins*. Chapter 18 is devoted to this subject. The most notable example of a man-made polyamide is the synthetic polyamide **nylon 66**, which is prepared from adipic acid (a diacid) and hexamethylenediamine (a diamine). As in the synthesis of the polyester Dacron, the result of the reaction of two types of bifunctional molecules is a linear polymer.

$$x\ HO_2C(CH_2)_4CO_2H + x\ H_2NCH_2(CH_2)_4CH_2NH_2 \xrightarrow[-H_2O]{heat} \left[C(CH_2)_4C{-}NH(CH_2)_6NH \right]_x$$

adipic acid   hexamethylenediamine   nylon 66

Nylon 66 is but one member of the family of synthetic nylons. Nylon 66 is made from a *six-carbon* diacid and *six-carbon* diamine. **Nylon 6**, on the other hand, is prepared from caprolactam, a monomer that contains the acid and amine in the same molecule (with *six carbons*). In this reaction, caprolactam undergoes ring opening with water; then, in the polymerization, water is eliminated.

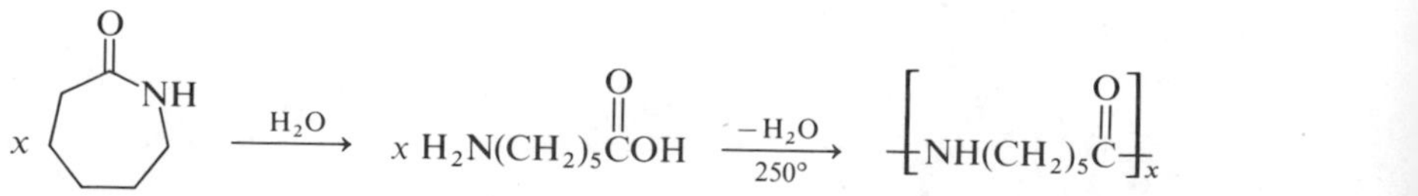

$$x \xrightarrow{H_2O} x\ H_2N(CH_2)_5COH \xrightarrow[250°]{-H_2O} \left[NH(CH_2)_5C \right]_x$$

caprolactam   nylon 6

Section 13.11

Compounds Related to Amides

Some types of compounds that are related to amides are shown in Table 13.5. **Urea** is one of the most important amide relatives. Excess nitrogen from the metabolism of proteins is excreted by the higher animals as urea. Some lower animals excrete ammonia, while reptiles and birds excrete **guanidine**. Both guanidine and urea, as well as ammonia, are widely used as nitrogen fertilizers and as starting materials for synthetic polymers and drugs.

$$\underset{\text{urea}}{H_2N-\overset{\displaystyle O}{\overset{\|}{C}}-NH_2} \qquad \underset{\text{a substituted urea}}{R_2N-\overset{\displaystyle O}{\overset{\|}{C}}-NR_2} \qquad \underset{\text{guanidine}}{H_2N-\overset{\displaystyle NH}{\overset{\|}{C}}-NH_2}$$

Urea is used for the synthesis of barbiturates (used as sedatives) by reaction with α-substituted diethyl malonates. This reaction is similar to the reaction of an ester with an amine to yield an amide.

Table 13.5.   Some Types of Compounds Related to Amides

Partial structure	Class of compound	Example
$-\overset{\displaystyle O}{\overset{\|}{C}}N\diagdown^{\diagup}$	amide	$CH_3\overset{\displaystyle O}{\overset{\|}{C}}NH_2$
$-\overset{\displaystyle O}{\overset{\|}{C}}N\diagdown^{\diagup}$ in ring	lactam	(cyclic structure)
$-\overset{\displaystyle O}{\overset{\|}{C}}N\overset{\displaystyle O}{\overset{\|}{C}}-$	imide	(cyclic structure)
$\diagdown_{\diagup}N\overset{\displaystyle O}{\overset{\|}{C}}N\diagdown^{\diagup}$	urea	$H_2N\overset{\displaystyle O}{\overset{\|}{C}}NH_2$
$\diagdown_{\diagup}N\overset{\displaystyle O}{\overset{\|}{C}}O-$	carbamate, or urethane	$H_2N\overset{\displaystyle O}{\overset{\|}{C}}OCH_3$
$-\overset{\displaystyle O}{\underset{\displaystyle O}{\overset{\|}{\underset{\|}{S}}}}N\diagdown^{\diagup}$	sulfonamide	$\text{Ph}-\overset{\displaystyle O}{\underset{\displaystyle O}{\overset{\|}{\underset{\|}{S}}}}NH_2$

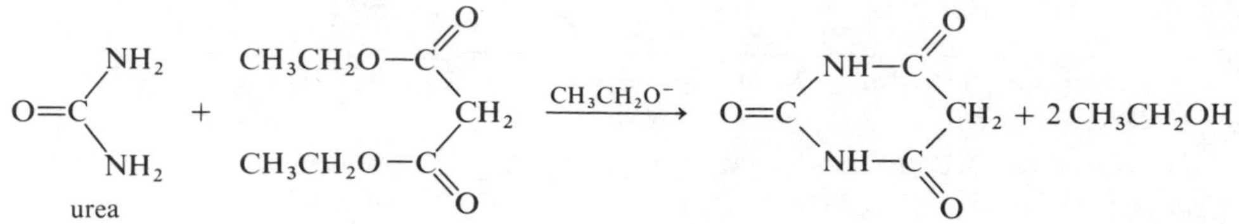

urea   diethyl malonate   barbituric acid
        not substituted

STUDY PROBLEM

13.28 What two reactants would you use to synthesize each of the following barbiturates?

(a)

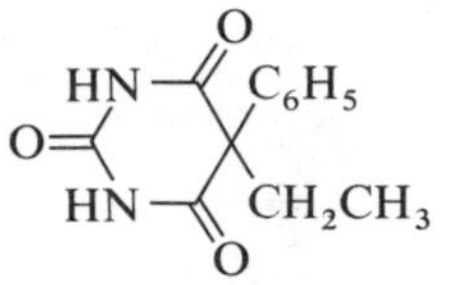

phenobarbital

(b)

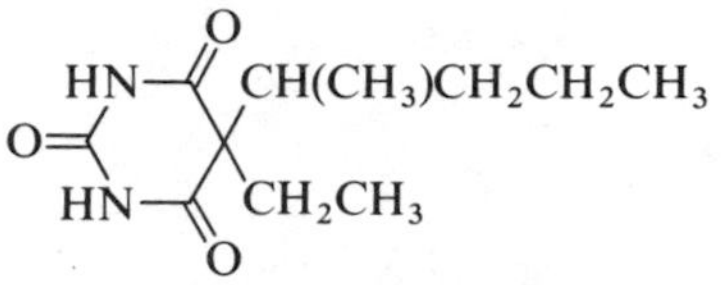

pentobarbital
(Nembutal)

(c)

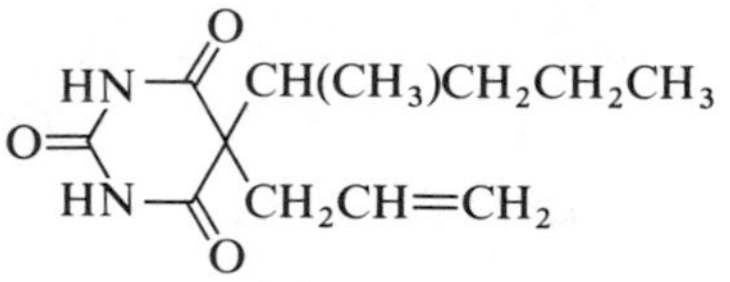

Seconal

An **imide**, a compound with the $-\overset{O}{\overset{\|}{C}}NH\overset{O}{\overset{\|}{C}}-$ group, is the nitrogen analog of an acid anhydride. Like amides, an imide can be made from ammonia and an acid anhydride.

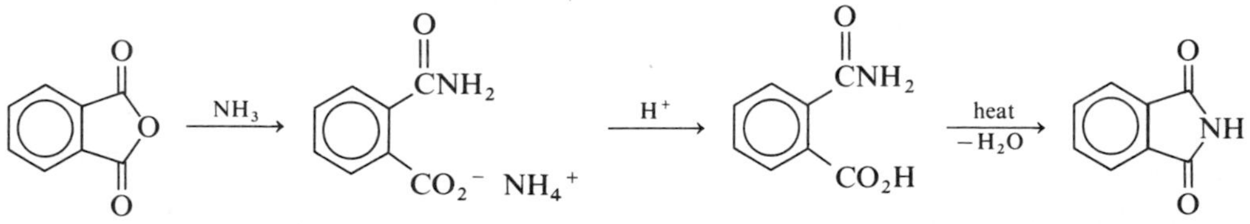

phthalic
anhydride

phthalimide
a cyclic imide

A **carbamate**, or **urethane**, is a compound in which the $-NH_2$, $-NHR$, or $-NR_2$ group is attached to an ester carbonyl group. A carbamate is related to a carbonate structure, with one O replaced by N.

$$RO-\overset{O}{\overset{\|}{C}}-OR \qquad H_2N-\overset{O}{\overset{\|}{C}}-OR$$

a carbonate   *a carbamate*

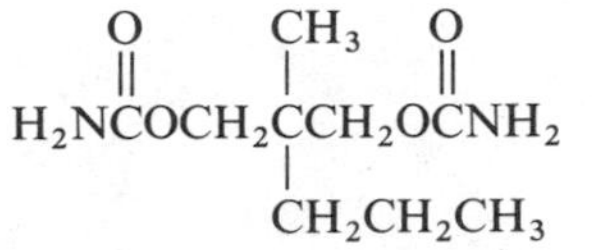

$$\underset{\substack{\text{meprobamate}\\ \textit{a dicarbamate used as}\\ \textit{a tranquilizer (Miltown, Equanil)}}}{\overset{\displaystyle O \qquad CH_3 \quad O}{\overset{\displaystyle \| \qquad\quad | \qquad \|}{H_2NCOCH_2\underset{\displaystyle |}{\underset{\displaystyle CH_2CH_2CH_3}{C}}CH_2OCNH_2}}}$$

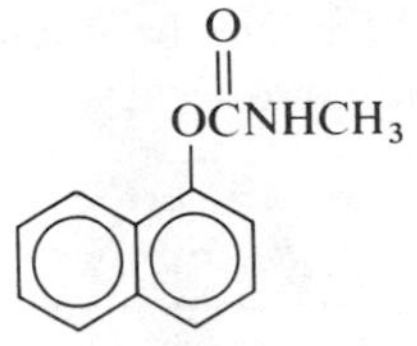

1-naphthyl-*N*-methylcarbamate
(Sevin)
a biodegradable insecticide

One way in which a carbamate may be prepared is by the action of an alcohol or phenol on an **isocyanate**, a compound containing the —N=C=O group.

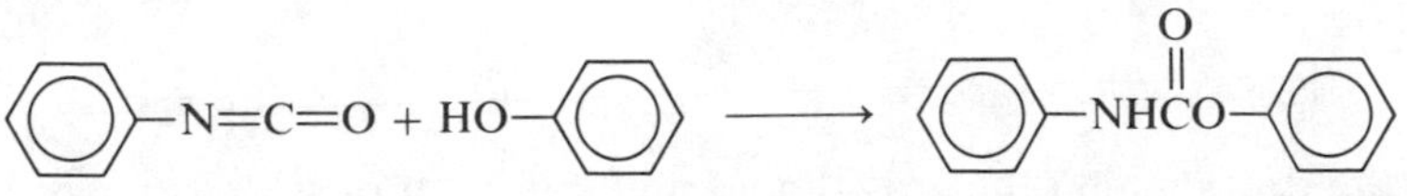

phenyl isocyanate   phenol   phenyl *N*-phenylcarbamate

An analogous reaction is used to make **polyurethanes** (used for polyurethane foam insulation, for example). As in the formation of other polymers mentioned in this chapter, bifunctional starting materials must be used. (The foaming effect in polyurethane foam is achieved by adding a low-boiling liquid, such as methylene chloride or trichlorofluoromethane, that vaporizes during the polymerization.)

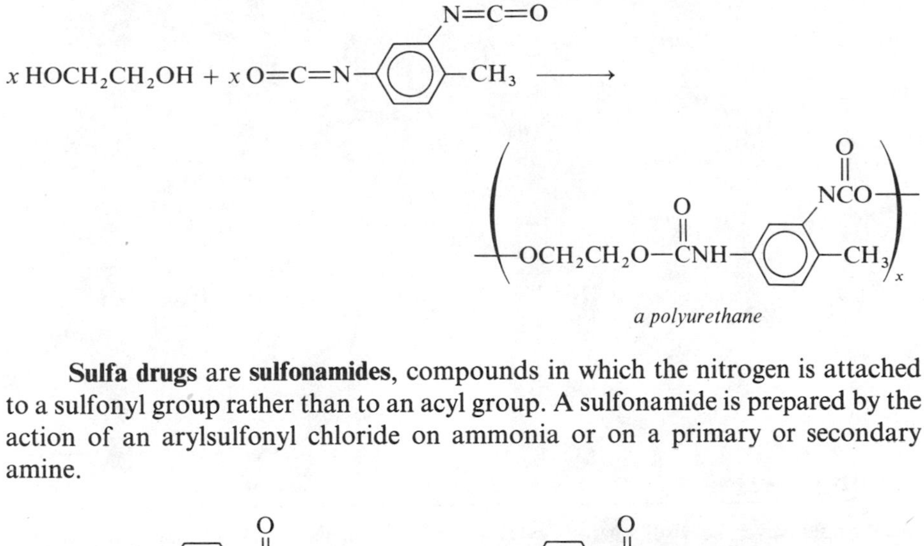

a polyurethane

Sulfa drugs are **sulfonamides**, compounds in which the nitrogen is attached to a sulfonyl group rather than to an acyl group. A sulfonamide is prepared by the action of an arylsulfonyl chloride on ammonia or on a primary or secondary amine.

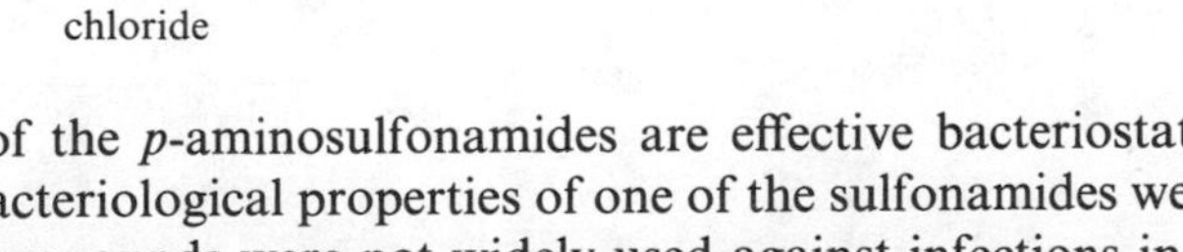

benzenesulfonyl
chloride

an amine

a sulfonamide

Many of the *p*-aminosulfonamides are effective bacteriostatic agents. Although the bacteriological properties of one of the sulfonamides were observed in 1909, these compounds were not widely used against infections in humans until around 1940. Because of bacterial resistance and of undesirable side effects, sulfa drugs have been largely supplanted in human medicine by the antibiotics (such as the penicillins and tetracyclines).

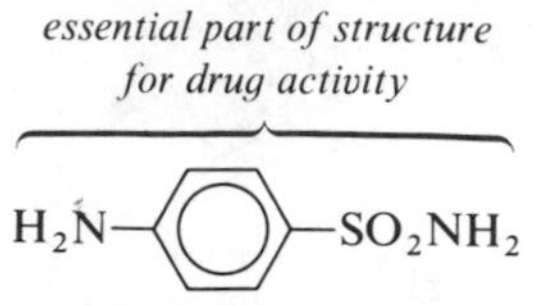

essential part of structure for drug activity

H_2N—⟨O⟩—SO_2NH_2

sulfanilamide

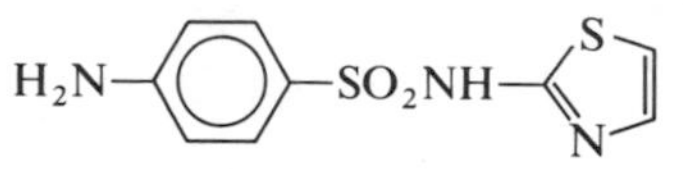

H_2N—⟨O⟩—SO_2NH—C⟨S,N⟩

sulfathiazole

H_2N—⟨O⟩—SO_2NH—⟨N–N⟩—OCH_3

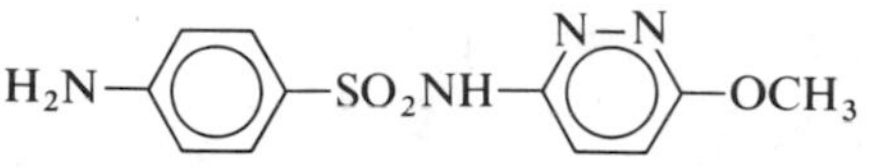

sulfamethoxypyridazine

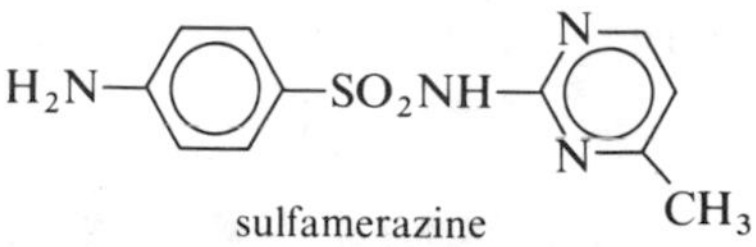

H_2N—⟨O⟩—SO_2NH—⟨N,N⟩—CH_3

sulfamerazine

Sulfa drugs inhibit the growth and multiplication of some types of bacteria that require *p*-aminobenzoic acid (PABA) for the biosynthesis of folic acids. The sulfa drugs are hydrolyzed *in vivo* to sulfanilamide, which is mistaken for PABA by certain bacterial enzymes. In effect, the sulfonamide is incorporated in place of PABA and blocks the further synthesis of folic acids. Sulfa drugs are not effective against all bacteria because some strains do not require PABA and some strains can synthesize their own PABA, which successfully competes against the sulfonamide for inclusion into folic acids.

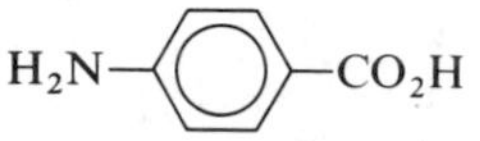

H_2N—⟨O⟩—CO_2H

p-aminobenzoic acid
(PABA)

from PABA

folic acid structure

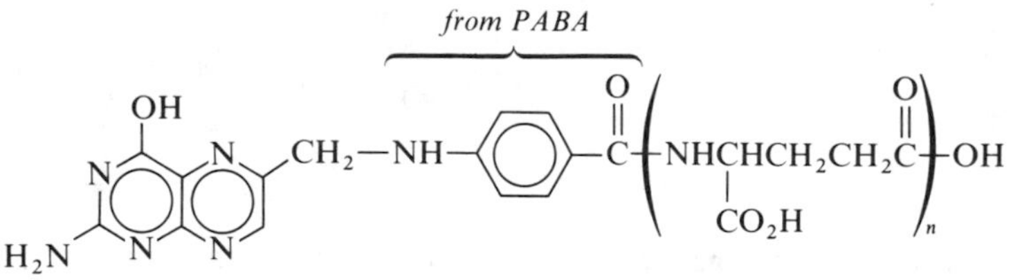

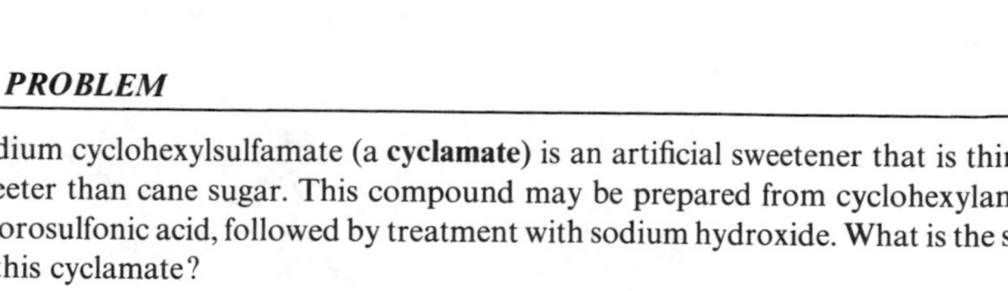

folic acid

STUDY PROBLEM

13.29 Sodium cyclohexylsulfamate (a **cyclamate**) is an artificial sweetener that is thirty times sweeter than cane sugar. This compound may be prepared from cyclohexylamine and chlorosulfonic acid, followed by treatment with sodium hydroxide. What is the structure of this cyclamate?

⟨cyclohexyl⟩—NH_2 + HOSCl (O,O) $\longrightarrow$ $\xrightarrow{OH^-}$

cyclohexylamine   chlorosulfonic acid

Section 13.12

Nitriles

A. Nomenclature of Nitriles

Nitriles are organic compounds containing the C≡N group. They are also sometimes called *cyano compounds* or *cyanides*. In the IUPAC system, the number of carbon atoms, including that in the CN group, determines the alkane parent. The alkane name is suffixed with **-nitrile**.

$$CH_3C{\equiv}N \qquad CH_3CH_2C{\equiv}N$$

IUPAC: ethanenitrile   propanenitrile

Some nitriles are named after the trivial names of their carboxylic acid parent with the **-ic acid** changed to **-nitrile**, or to **-onitrile** if the parent name lacks an *o-*.

$$\underset{\text{acetic acid}}{CH_3\overset{\displaystyle O}{\overset{\|}{C}}OH} \qquad \underset{\text{acetonitrile}}{CH_3CN} \qquad \underset{\text{benzoic acid}}{\bigcirc\!\!-\!\overset{\displaystyle O}{\overset{\|}{C}}OH} \qquad \underset{\text{benzonitrile}}{\bigcirc\!\!-\!CN}$$

STUDY PROBLEM

13.30 Give the structures of   (a) pentanenitrile, and   (b) butyronitrile.

B. Bonding in Nitriles

The cyano group contains a triple bond—one sigma bond and two pi bonds (Figure 13.10). Although the nitrogen has a pair of unshared electrons, a nitrile is a very weak base. The pK_b of a nitrile is about 24, while the pK_b of NH_3 is about 4.5 (about 20 powers of ten difference). The lack of basicity of a —CN: group results from the unshared electrons being in an *sp* orbital. The greater amount of *s* character in an *sp* orbital (compared to that in an sp^2 or sp^3 orbital) means that these *sp* electrons are more tightly held and less available for bonding to a proton.

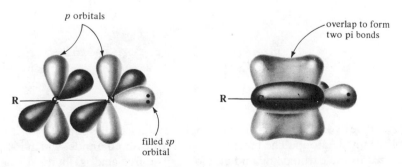

Figure 13.10.   The bonding in a nitrile, RC≡N:.

C. Preparation of Nitriles

Hydrogen cyanide (HCN) is an extremely weak acid (pK_a about 10). For this reason, the CN^- ion (from NaCN, for example) is a fairly strong base and is a good nucleophile for S_N2 displacement of a halide ion from an alkyl halide. This reaction is the principal route to nitriles; however, because of elimination reactions, high yields are obtained only with *primary alkyl halides*.

$$CH_3CH_2CH_2CH_2Br + CN^- \xrightarrow{S_N2} CH_3CH_2CH_2CH_2CN + Br^-$$

1-bromobutane   pentanenitrile
a 1° alkyl halide   90%

Aryl nitriles are best obtained through the **diazonium salts**, compounds that will be discussed in Section 15.12.

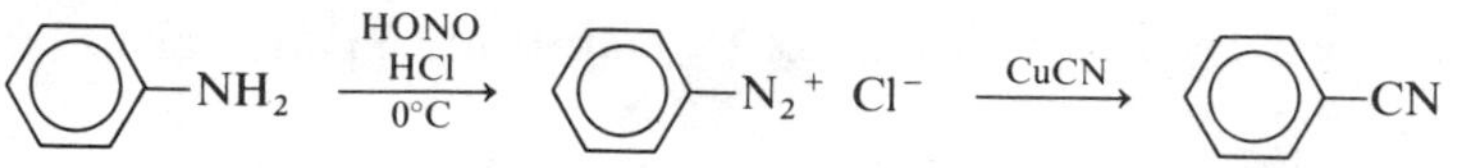

aniline   benzenediazonium   benzonitrile
                 chloride

D. Reactions of Nitriles

Hydrolysis   Nitriles are included as carboxylic acid derivatives because their hydrolysis yields carboxylic acids. The hydrolysis of a nitrile may be carried out by heating with either dilute acid or base.

$$CH_3CH_2CH_2CH_2CN + 2 H_2O + H^+ \xrightarrow{heat} CH_3CH_2CH_2CH_2CO_2H + NH_4^+$$

pentanenitrile   pentanoic acid
                                  85%

In acidic hydrolysis, the weakly basic nitrogen is protonated and then water attacks the electropositive carbon atom. The reaction goes through an amide, which is further hydrolyzed to the carboxylic acid and ammonia. Because the ammonia undergoes reaction with hydrogen ions, an excess of acid must be used.

In acid:

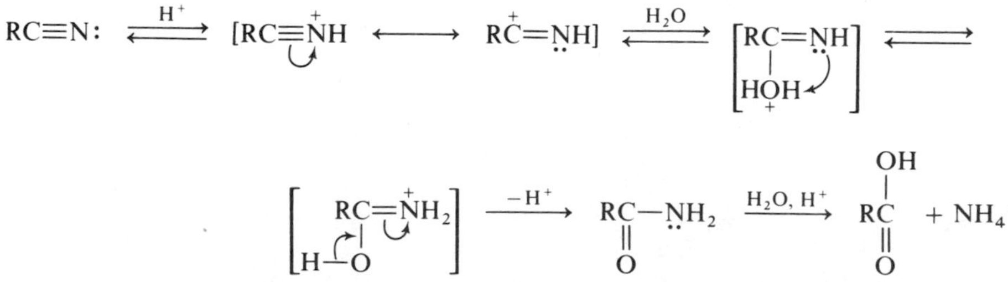

intermediate
amide

Alkaline hydrolysis occurs by nucleophilic attack on the partially positive carbon of the nitrile group. The reaction again results in an amide, which is further hydrolyzed to the carboxylate and ammonia. The free acid is obtained when the solution is acidified.

In base:

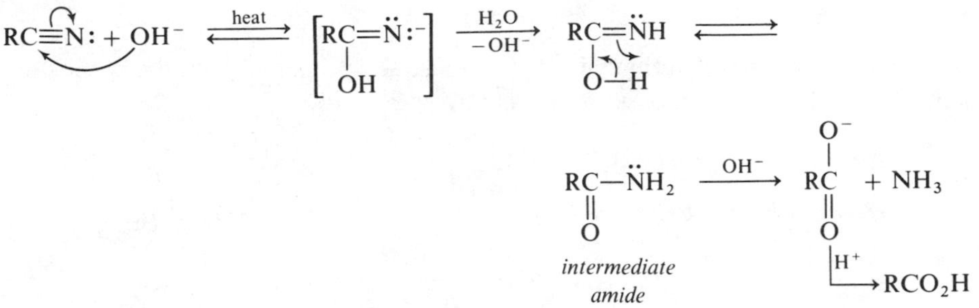

$$RC\equiv N: + OH^- \xrightleftharpoons{heat} \left[\begin{matrix} RC=\ddot{N}:^- \\ | \\ OH \end{matrix} \right] \xrightarrow[-OH^-]{H_2O} \begin{matrix} RC=\ddot{N}H \\ | \\ O-H \end{matrix} \rightleftharpoons$$

$$\begin{matrix} RC-\ddot{N}H_2 \\ \| \\ O \end{matrix} \xrightarrow{OH^-} \begin{matrix} O^- \\ | \\ RC \\ \| \\ O \end{matrix} + NH_3$$

intermediate amide

$$\xrightarrow{H^+} RCO_2H$$

Reduction Nitriles can be reduced to *primary amines* of the type RCH_2NH_2 either by catalytic hydrogenation or by lithium aluminum hydride.

General:

$$RC\equiv N \xrightarrow{[H]} RCH_2NH_2$$

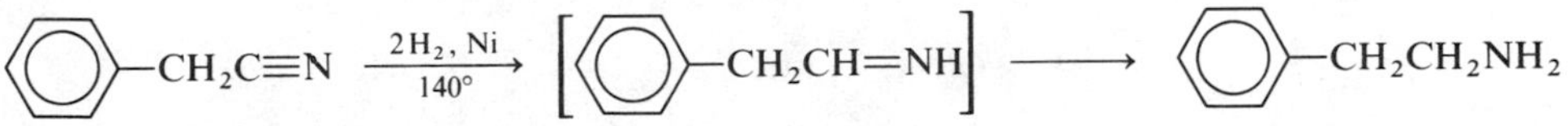

$$\bigcirc-CH_2C\equiv N \xrightarrow[140°]{2H_2,\ Ni} \left[\bigcirc-CH_2CH=NH \right] \longrightarrow \bigcirc-CH_2CH_2NH_2$$

phenylacetonitrile

(2-phenylethyl)amine
70%

$$CH_3CH_2CH_2C\equiv N \xrightarrow[(2)\ H_2O]{(1)\ LiAlH_4} CH_3CH_2CH_2CH_2NH_2$$

butanenitrile

n-butylamine
85%

SUMMARY

The **derivatives of carboxylic acids** are usually prepared from the carboxylic acids themselves or from other more reactive derivatives:

Acid chlorides: $\quad RCO_2H + SOCl_2 \longrightarrow RCOCl$

Acid anhydrides: $\quad RCOCl + RCO_2^- \longrightarrow RCO-O-COR$

Esters: $\quad RCO_2H + R'OH \underset{}{\overset{H^+}{\rightleftarrows}} RCO_2R' + H_2O$

$\qquad\qquad RCOCl + R'OH \longrightarrow RCO_2R' + HCl$

$\qquad RCO-O-COR + R'OH \longrightarrow RCO_2R' + HO_2CR$

$\qquad\qquad RCO_2R'' + R'OH \xrightarrow{H^+ \text{ or } ^-OR'} RCO_2R' + R''OH$

$\qquad\qquad RCO_2H + CH_2N_2 \longrightarrow RCO_2CH_3 + N_2$

Amides: $\quad RCOCl + R_2NH \longrightarrow RCONR_2$

$\qquad RCO-O-COR + R_2NH \longrightarrow RCONR_2$

$\qquad\qquad RCO_2R' + R_2NH \longrightarrow RCO_2NR_2 + R'OH$

Nitriles: $\quad RCH_2X + CN^- \longrightarrow RCH_2CN + X^-$

$\qquad ArNH_2 \xrightarrow[0°]{HONO,\ HCl} ArN_2^+\ Cl^- \xrightarrow{CuCN} ArCN$

The reactions of the carboxylic acid derivatives with nucleophiles are similar. Differences arise from differences in reactivity.

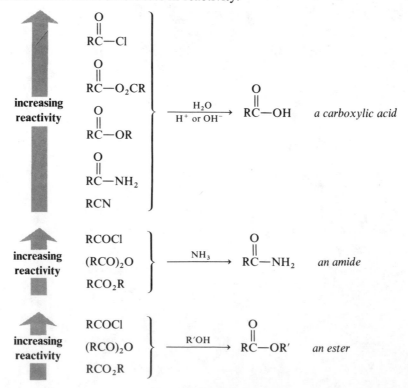

In addition to these reactions, the more reactive acid halides undergo Friedel–Crafts reactions with aromatic compounds and also undergo reaction with cadmium reagents or lithium dialkylcuprates to yield ketones.

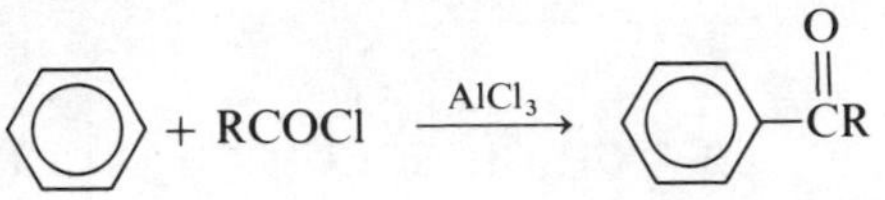

$$\bigcirc + RCOCl \xrightarrow{AlCl_3} \bigcirc-\overset{\overset{O}{\|}}{C}R \qquad \textit{an aryl ketone}$$

$$RCOCl \xrightarrow[(2) \ H_2O, \ H^+]{(1) \ R_2'Cd} R\overset{\overset{O}{\|}}{C}R' \qquad \textit{a ketone}$$

Esters undergo reaction with Grignard reagents to yield tertiary alcohols.

$$RCO_2R \xrightarrow[(2) \ H_2O, \ H^+]{(1) \ R'MgX} R\overset{\overset{OH}{|}}{C}R'_2 \qquad \textit{a 3° alcohol}$$

All the derivatives may be reduced by catalytic hydrogenation or by LAH; the reductions of esters and nitriles are shown:

$$RCO_2R' \xrightarrow{[H]} RCH_2OH + HOR' \qquad \textit{alcohols}$$

$$RCN \xrightarrow{[H]} RCH_2NH_2 \qquad \textit{a 1° amine}$$

STUDY PROBLEMS

13.31 Name the following compounds:

(a) 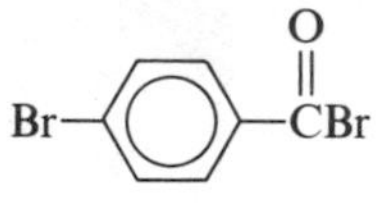 Br—⟨○⟩—CBr (with O double-bonded to C)

(b) $CH_3CH_2COCCH_2CH_2CH_2CH_3$ (with two C=O groups)

(c) $C_6H_5CN(CH_2CH_3)_2$ (with C=O)

(d) $CH_3CH_2CH_2CH_2CH_2CN$

(e) 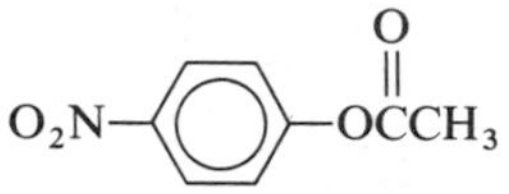 O_2N—⟨○⟩—$OCCH_3$ (with C=O)

(f) 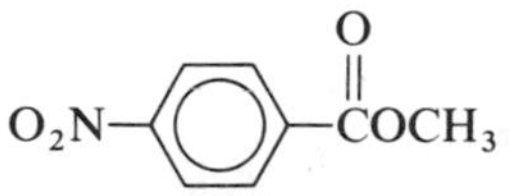 O_2N—⟨○⟩—$COCH_3$ (with C=O)

(g) 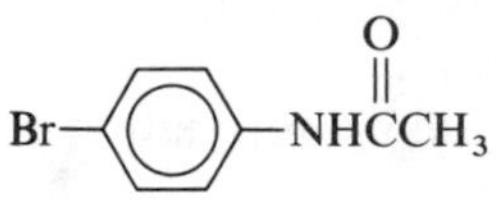 Br—⟨○⟩—$NHCCH_3$ (with C=O)

13.32 Give structures for the following compounds:

(a) 5-hydroxy-2-octenoic acid lactone (b) *N,N*-diethylpropanamide
(c) *N,N'*-dimethylurea (the *N* and *N'* refer to two different nitrogens)
(d) 2-methylpentanenitrile (e) ethyl 2-aminopropanoate
(f) β-chlorobutyronitrile (g) benzoic formic anhydride

13.33 List the following compounds in order of increasing bond moment of the indicated bond:

(a) $CH_3C{-}OCH_3$ (with C=O)

(b) $CH_3C{-}CH_3$ (with C=O)

(c) $CH_3C{-}Cl$ (with C=O)

(d) $CH_3C{-}NH_2$ (with C=O)

13.34 What would be the products of the reaction of each of the following reagents with acetic anhydride? (a) cyclohexanol; (b) *p*-bromophenol; (c) piperidine (page 616); (d) sodium ethoxide in ethanol; (e) aqueous NaOH.

13.35 Give the organic product of the reaction with benzoyl chloride of each of the reagents in Problem 13.34.

13.36 Predict the organic products and the relative rates of reaction for each of the following acid derivatives toward alkaline hydrolysis in 1*N* NaOH:

(a) $C_6H_5CO_2CH_2CH_3$

(b) $C_6H_5CNHCH_2CH_3$ (with C=O)

(c) C_6H_5CCl (with C=O)

(d) $C_6H_5COCCH_2CH_3$ (with two C=O groups)

13.37 Predict the organic products and the relative rates of reaction for each of the following esters toward sodium ethoxide in ethanol:

(a) 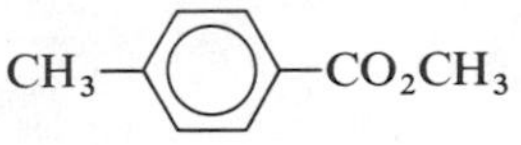 CH_3—⟨◯⟩—CO_2CH_3 (b) 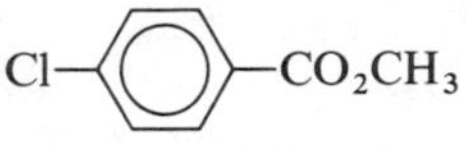 Cl—⟨◯⟩—CO_2CH_3

(c) 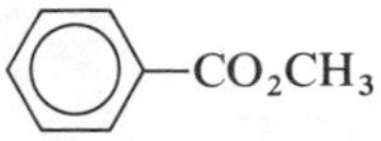 ⟨◯⟩—CO_2CH_3

13.38 Show by equations how you would convert ethyl acetate to: (a) acetic acid; (b) ethanol; (c) *t*-butyl alcohol; (d) acetophenone $\left(\begin{matrix} & O \\ & \| \\ C_6H_5CCH_3 \end{matrix} \right)$; (e) sodium acetate; (f) *N*-methylacetamide.

13.39 Would acid hydrolysis or saponification be the method of choice for the conversion of 2-butenyl acetate to acetic acid and 2-buten-1-ol? Why?

13.40 The following ketones can be prepared by the reaction of an acid chloride with either a cadmium reagent or a lithium dialkylcuprate. There may be more than one cadmium reagent or cuprate that could be used. Write the equations showing the various methods of preparing these ketones.

(a) $C_6H_5CH_2\overset{\overset{\displaystyle O}{\|}}{C}CH_2CH_3$ (b) $(CH_3)_2CH\overset{\overset{\displaystyle O}{\|}}{C}CH_2CH_3$

(c) $(CH_3)_2CHCH_2\overset{\overset{\displaystyle H_3C}{|}}{\underset{\underset{\displaystyle CH_3}{|}}{C}}{-}\overset{\overset{\displaystyle O}{\|}}{C}C_6H_5$

13.41 *Phosgene*, $Cl\overset{\overset{\displaystyle O}{\|}}{C}Cl$, is a toxic gas that was used as a war gas in World War I. Phosgene undergoes the usual reactions of an acid chloride, but can undergo these reactions twice. Predict the product of the reaction of phosgene with each of the following reagents: (a) excess H_2O; (b) excess ethanol; (c) 1.0 equivalent ethanol; (d) 1.0 equivalent ethanol, followed by 1.0 equivalent NH_3.

13.42 Predict the products of the reactions of (a) acetic anhydride with (*R*)-2-octylamine, and (b) benzoic anhydride with $(CH_3)_2CH^{18}OH$.

13.43 Would you expect a methyl ester or a *t*-butyl ester to be saponified more readily? Explain.

13.44 When 2,4,6-trimethylbenzoic acid is heated with ethanol and a trace of H_2SO_4, no ester is obtained. Suggest a reason.

13.45 *Kodel* is the name of a fiber formed by the following transesterification reaction:

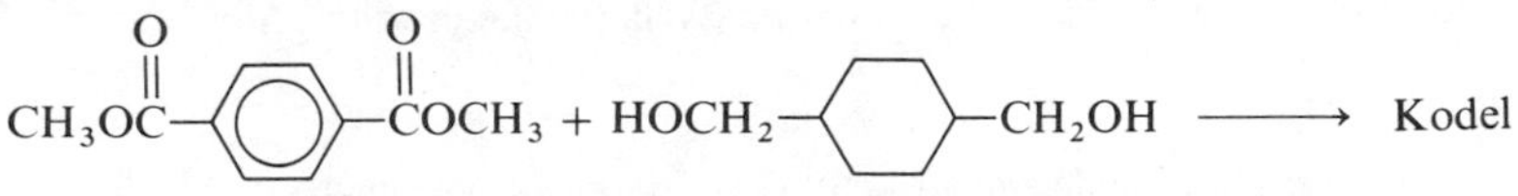

$CH_3O\overset{\overset{\displaystyle O}{\|}}{C}$—⟨◯⟩—$\overset{\overset{\displaystyle O}{\|}}{C}OCH_3$ + $HOCH_2$—⟨◯⟩—CH_2OH $\longrightarrow$ Kodel

dimethyl terephthalate   1,4-di(hydroxymethyl)-
                                cyclohexane

(a) What is the structure of Kodel?
(b) How could the starting diol be prepared from dimethyl terephthalate?

13.46 Complete the following equations:

(a) 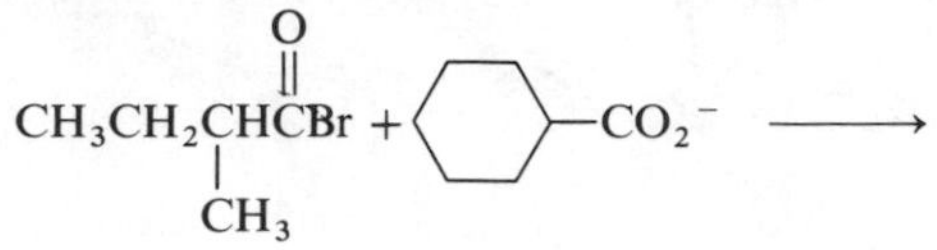 $CH_3CH_2\overset{\overset{\displaystyle O}{\|}}{C}HCBr + \langle\rangle-CO_2^- \longrightarrow$
$|$
CH_3

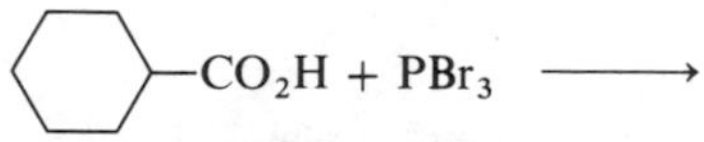

(b) $\langle\rangle-CO_2H + PBr_3 \longrightarrow$

(c) $\langle\rangle-CO_2H + \langle\rangle-OH \xrightarrow[\text{heat}]{H_2SO_4}$

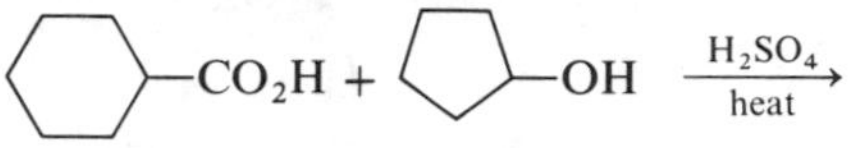

(d) 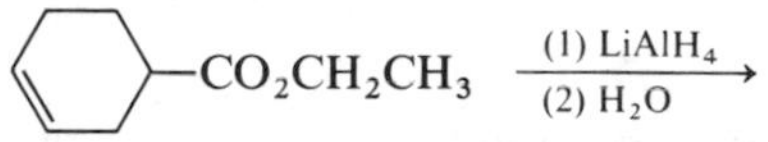 $\langle\rangle-CO_2CH_2CH_3 \xrightarrow[(2)\ H_2O]{(1)\ LiAlH_4}$

(e) $CH_3CH_2CH_2CO_2H + SOCl_2 \longrightarrow$

(f) 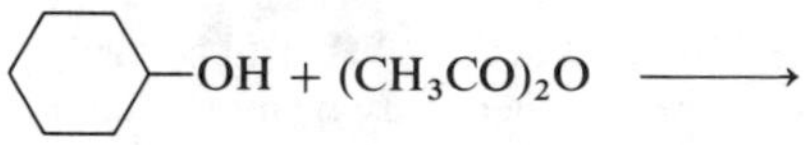 $\langle\rangle-OH + (CH_3CO)_2O \longrightarrow$

(g) $CH_3CH_2O\overset{\overset{\displaystyle O}{\|}}{C}OCH_2CH_3 + D_2O \xrightarrow{D^+}$

(h) $CH_3CH_2\overset{\overset{\displaystyle O}{\|}}{C}Cl + (CH_3CH=CH)_2Cd \longrightarrow$

(i) $CH_3CH_2\overset{\overset{\displaystyle O}{\|}}{C}Cl + LiCu[CH(CH_3)_2]_2 \longrightarrow$

13.47 Write the equation for the preparation of each of the following compounds from acetic anhydride and other appropriate reagents:

(a) $CH_3\overset{\overset{\displaystyle O}{\|}}{C}NHCH(CH_3)_2$

(b) 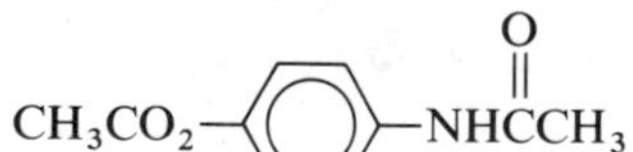 $CH_3CO_2-\langle\rangle-NH\overset{\overset{\displaystyle O}{\|}}{C}CH_3$

(c) $\begin{matrix} CH_3CO_2 & & O_2CCH_3 \\ CH_3CO_2 & O & CH_2O_2CCH_3 \end{matrix}$

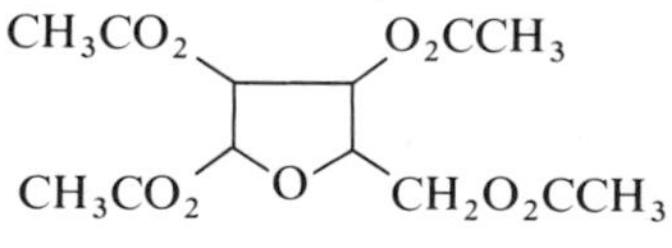

(d) 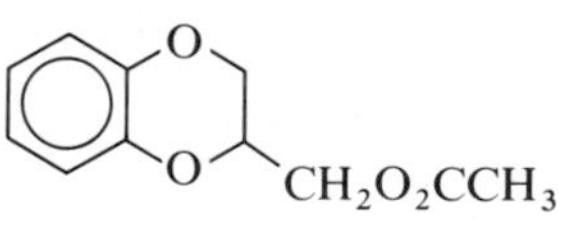 structure with $CH_2O_2CCH_3$

13.48 What is the structure of nylon 44? Suggest a laboratory synthesis.

13.49 Aniline is treated with acetic anhydride. What is the product? Suggest a mechanism.

13.50 An amide, like an aldehyde or ketone, is capable of tautomerism:

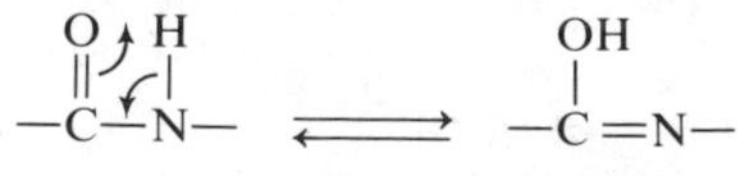

$$-\overset{\overset{\displaystyle O}{\|}}{C}-\overset{\overset{\displaystyle H}{|}}{N}- \;\rightleftharpoons\; -\overset{\overset{\displaystyle OH}{|}}{C}=N-$$

amide form   *"enol" form*

Show all tautomeric enol forms for each of the following cyclic structures, all of which are found in nucleic acids:

(a) 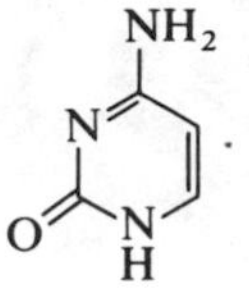 cytosine (b) 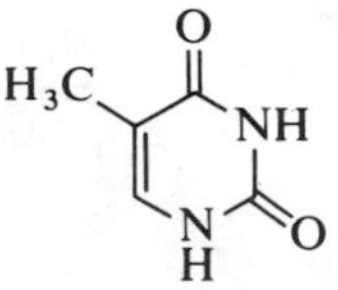 thymine (c) 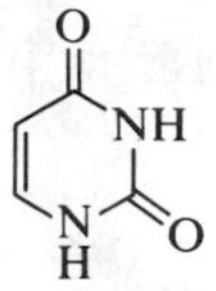 uracil (d) 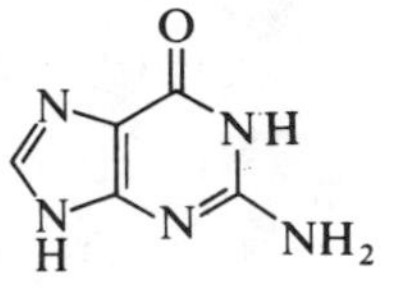 guanine

13.51 Suggest a practical method for the synthesis of:

(a) hexanoic acid from 1-bromopentane
(b) 2-hydroxyhexanoic acid from pentanal
(c) β-phenylethylamine ($C_6H_5CH_2CH_2NH_2$) from benzyl bromide
(d) *p*-tolyl methyl ketone from toluene
(e) *N*-cyclohexylacetamide from acetic acid

13.52 Propose chemical tests for distinguishing between the following pairs:

(a) benzoic acid and methyl benzoate
(b) ethyl benzoate and *N*-ethylbenzamide
(c) benzoic acid and benzoyl chloride

13.53 Predict the product of catalytic hydrogenation (high temperature and pressure) of each of the following compounds:

(a) $CH_3CH_2CO_2\overset{\underset{\displaystyle CH_3}{|}}{C}HCH_2CH{=}CH_2$ (b) 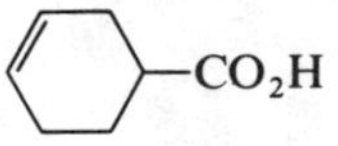 [cyclohexene]—CO_2H

(c) $CH_3CH_2\overset{\underset{\displaystyle ||}{O}}{C}NHCH_3$ (d) 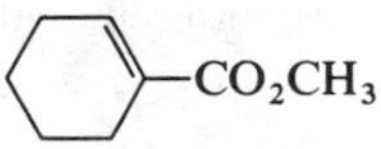 [cyclohexene]—CO_2CH_3

13.54 Give the structures of the major organic products:

(a) $(CH_3)_2CHCO_2H + CH_3CH_2Br \xrightarrow{HCO_3^-}$

(b) cholesterol (page 889) + $\left(CH_3\overset{\underset{\displaystyle ||}{O}}{C}\right)_2O \longrightarrow$

(c) 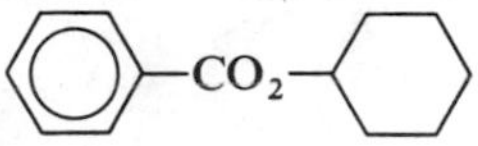 [benzene]—CO_2—[cyclohexyl] + $CH_3CH_2OH \xrightarrow{CH_3CH_2O^-}$

(d) $CH_3\overset{\underset{\displaystyle ||}{O}}{C}CH_2CO_2CH_3 \xrightarrow[\text{(2) } H_2O]{\text{(1) LiAlH}_4}$

(e) $CH_3CH_2\overset{\underset{\displaystyle ||}{O}}{C}N(CH_3)_2 + H_2O + HBr \xrightarrow{heat}$

(f) $CH_3CH_2\overset{\underset{\displaystyle ||}{O}}{C}N(CH_3)_2 + KOH \xrightarrow[\text{heat}]{H_2O}$

13.55 Give the structure of the polyamide from the polymerization of methyl 2-aminoacetate.

13.56 Complete the following equations:

(a) $(R)\text{-}C_6H_5CO_2\overset{\overset{\displaystyle CH_3}{|}}{C}HCH_2CH_2CH_3 + OH^- \xrightarrow[\text{heat}]{H_2O}$

(b) $(CH_3)_3\overset{\overset{\displaystyle O}{\|}}{C}CNH_2 + D_2O \xrightarrow[\text{heat}]{OD^-}$

(c) 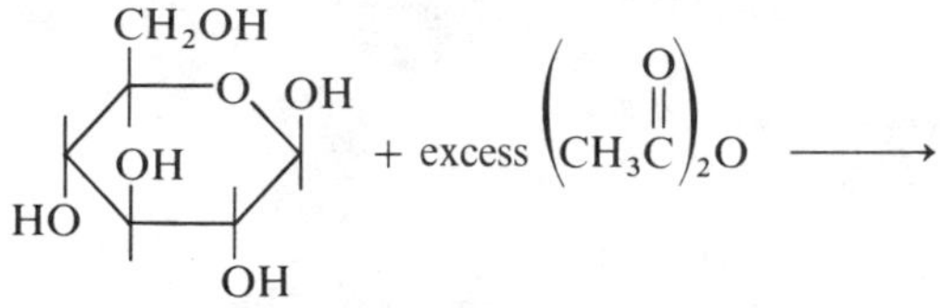 $+ \text{ excess } \left(CH_3\overset{\overset{\displaystyle O}{\|}}{C}\right)_2O \longrightarrow$

(d) 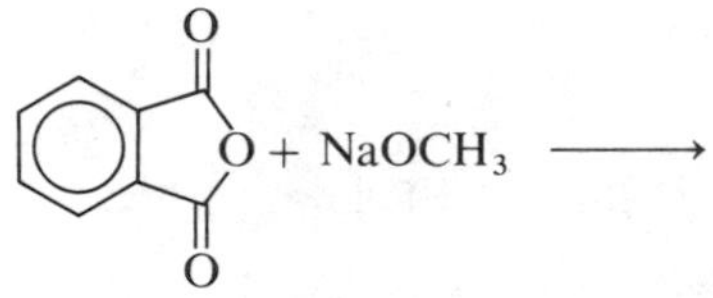 $+ NaOCH_3 \longrightarrow$

(e) $CH_3CH_2CH_2\overset{\overset{\displaystyle O}{\|}}{C}Cl + (CH_3CH_2CH_2)_2Cd \longrightarrow$

(f) 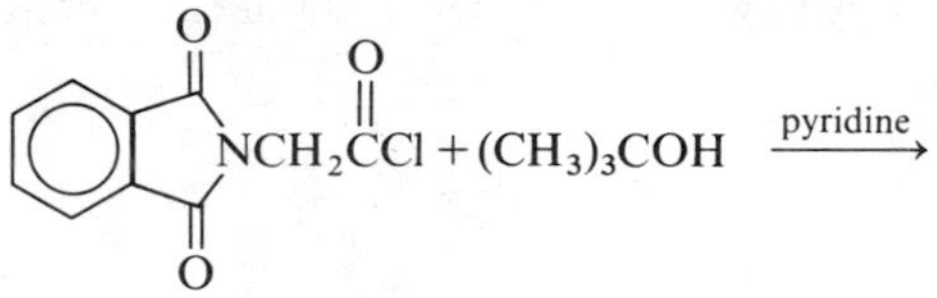 $+ (CH_3)_3COH \xrightarrow{\text{pyridine}}$

13.57 Give the products of each of the following reactions and the mechanisms for their formation:

(a) $CH_3\overset{\overset{\displaystyle OH}{|}}{C}HCO_2CH_3 + \text{dil. HCl} \xrightarrow{\text{heat}}$

(b) $(CH_3)_2CHCO_2CH_3 + \text{dil. NaOH} \xrightarrow{\text{heat}}$

13.58 The reaction of phosgene ($Cl_2C{=}O$) with ethylene glycol (1,2-ethanediol) can lead to two products: one is cyclic and one is polymeric. What are the structures of these products?

13.59 γ-Butyrolactone (page 633) is heated with a dilute solution of HCl in $H_2{}^{18}O$. What organic compounds could be isolated from the product mixture?

13.60 Urea is hydrolyzed by aqueous HCl to yield NH_4Cl and CO_2. Suggest a mechanism.

13.61 Suggest a mechanism for the following reaction:

$$CH_2{=}CHCH_2CH_2CO_2H \xrightarrow[H_2O]{Br_2} BrCH_2\text{—}\underset{}{\overset{}{\text{(lactone)}}}{=}O$$

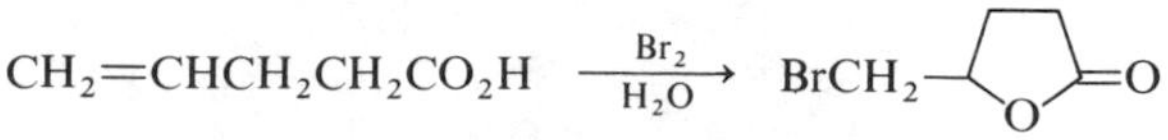

13.62 *o*-Phthalic acid (page 567) does not give an acid chloride when treated with $SOCl_2$. Instead, the half-acid chloride undergoes an intramolecular reaction to yield another product. What is this product and how is it formed?

13.63 When Compound A is subjected to acid hydrolysis, no ^{18}O is found in the product acetic acid. However, when Compound B is subjected to acid hydrolysis, some acetic acid containing ^{18}O is isolated. Explain these observations.

$$\underset{\textbf{A}}{CH_3\overset{\overset{O}{\|}}{C}{}^{18}OCH_2CH_3} \qquad \underset{\textbf{B}}{CH_3\overset{\overset{O}{\|}}{C}{}^{18}OC(CH_3)_3}$$

13.64 The acid $\overset{\overset{O}{\|}}{H}CCH_2CH_2CO_2H$ was treated with HCN. The product has the molecular formula $C_5H_5O_2N$. What was this product? Suggest a route for its formation.

13.65 Fill in the blanks and provide the structures for Compounds A–D:

n-Propyl bromide was treated with _____(1)_____ to yield Compound A. Upon _____(2)_____, Compound A was converted to Compound B, which in turn yielded Compound C upon reaction with _____(3)_____. Treatment of Compound B with _____(4)_____, followed by reaction with Compound C, yielded Compound D. The infrared spectra of Compounds A–D are given in Figure 13.11.

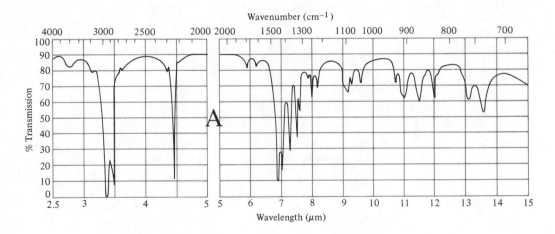

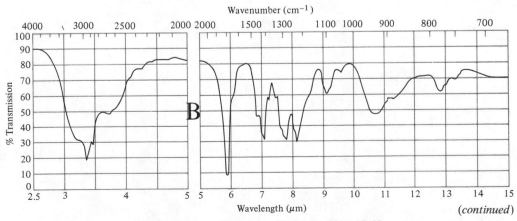

Figure 13.11. Infrared spectra for Problem 13.65.

(*continued*)

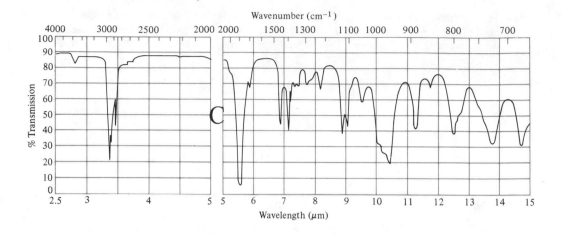

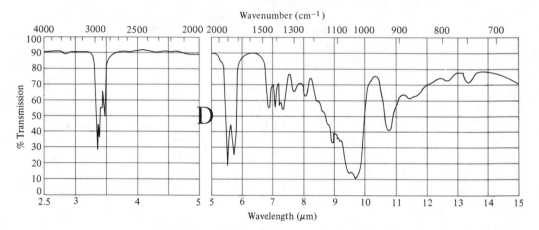

Figure 13.11 (continued). Infrared spectra for Problem 13.65.

13.66 When treated with HCN and OH⁻, Compound A, $C_5H_8O_2$, yielded Compound B, $C_6H_9NO_2$. Hydrolysis of B gave Compound C, $C_6H_{10}O_4$. Treatment of C with acetic anhydride yielded Compound D, $C_6H_8O_3$. The nmr spectrum of A is given in Figure 13.12. What are the structures of Compounds A–D?

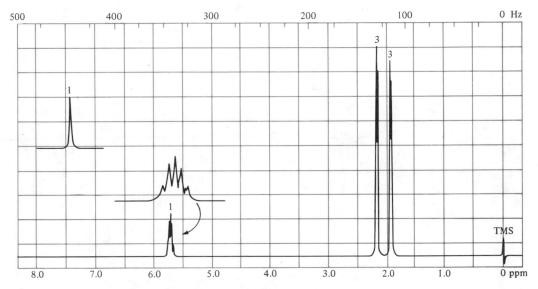

Figure 13.12. Nmr spectrum for Problem 13.66.

13.67 Upon reaction with excess CH_3OH and an acidic catalyst, Compound A yields Compound B. Reduction of either Compound A or Compound B with $LiAlH_4$ yields Compound C. Reaction of Compound A with $SOCl_2$ yields Compound D, which can be converted to Compounds B and E by appropriate reagents. Compound E can also be obtained from Compound B by reactions with the same reagent used to convert D to E. The nmr spectrum for Compound C and the infrared spectra for Compounds B, D, and E are given in Figure 13.13. What are the structures of Compounds A–E?

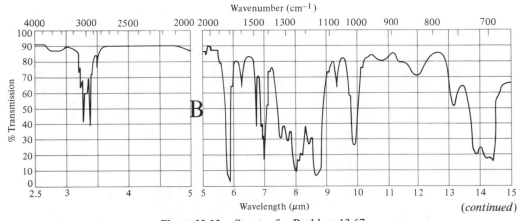

Figure 13.13. Spectra for Problem 13.67.

(continued)

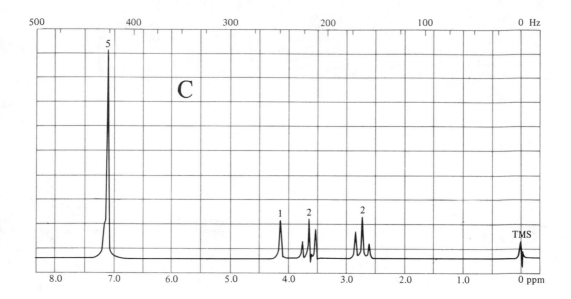

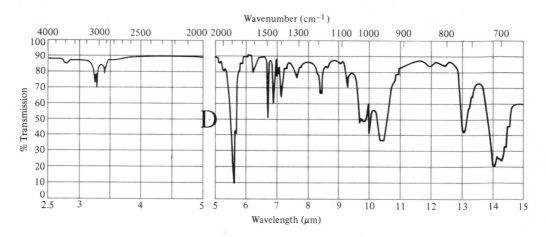

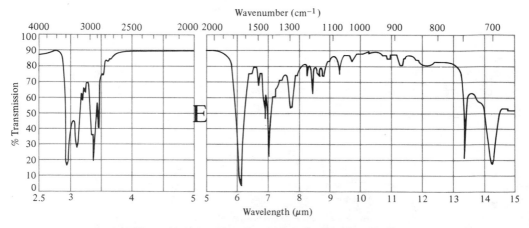

Figure 13.13 (continued). Spectra for Problem 13.67.

Chapter 14

Enolates and Carbanions:
Building Blocks for Organic Synthesis

Nucleophilic reagents undergo reaction with compounds that contain partially positive carbon atoms.

$$Nu^- + \overset{\delta+}{R}-\overset{\delta-}{X} \longrightarrow Nu-R + X^-$$

$$Nu^- + R-\overset{\overset{\displaystyle O^{\delta-}}{\|}}{\underset{\delta+}{C}}-R \longrightarrow R-\overset{\overset{\displaystyle O^-}{|}}{\underset{\underset{\displaystyle Nu}{|}}{C}}-R$$

Reagents that contain **nucleophilic carbon atoms**, carbon atoms with carbanion character, also attack partially positive carbon atoms. As an example, a **Grignard reagent**, which has a partially negative carbon atom, attacks carbonyl groups.

$$CH_3\overset{\delta-}{CH_2}\overset{\delta+}{MgBr} + CH_3\overset{\overset{\displaystyle O}{\|}}{C}CH_3 \longrightarrow CH_3\overset{\overset{\displaystyle O^- \ ^+MgBr}{|}}{\underset{\underset{\displaystyle CH_2CH_3}{|}}{C}}CH_3$$

The attack of one carbon upon another results in a new carbon–carbon bond. Reagents like Grignard reagents with nucleophilic carbon atoms allow a chemist to synthesize compounds with complex carbon skeletons from simple compounds.

Grignard reagents are but one of many reagents with nucleophilic carbons that are available to the organic chemist. Another versatile class of reagents for building complex molecules are the **enolates**. Recall from Section 11.16 that a hydrogen α to a carbonyl group is acidic and can be removed by a strong base. The resulting enolate anion contains a partially negative carbon atom.

$$\underset{\substack{\text{diethyl malonate}}}{\overset{\displaystyle CH_3CH_2O\overset{\overset{\displaystyle O}{\|}}{C}}{\underset{\displaystyle CH_3CH_2O\underset{\underset{\displaystyle O}{\|}}{C}}{\diagdown\!\!\!\diagup CH_2}} + \underset{\text{sodium ethoxide}}{Na^+ \ ^-OCH_2CH_3} \ \rightleftharpoons \ \underset{\substack{\text{diethyl sodium malonate}\\ \textit{an enolate}}}{\overset{\displaystyle CH_3CH_2O\overset{\overset{\displaystyle O}{\|}}{C}}{\underset{\displaystyle CH_3CH_2O\underset{\underset{\displaystyle O}{\|}}{C}}{\diagdown\!\!\!\diagup CH^-}} Na^+ + \underset{\text{ethanol}}{CH_3CH_2OH}$$

Enolates can enter into a number of organic reactions. One is S_N2 displacement of a halide ion from a methyl or primary alkyl halide. This reaction is called an **alkylation reaction** because an alkyl group becomes attached to a carbon of the enolate. A typical alkylation reaction is the reaction of the enolate of diethyl malonate with an alkyl halide:

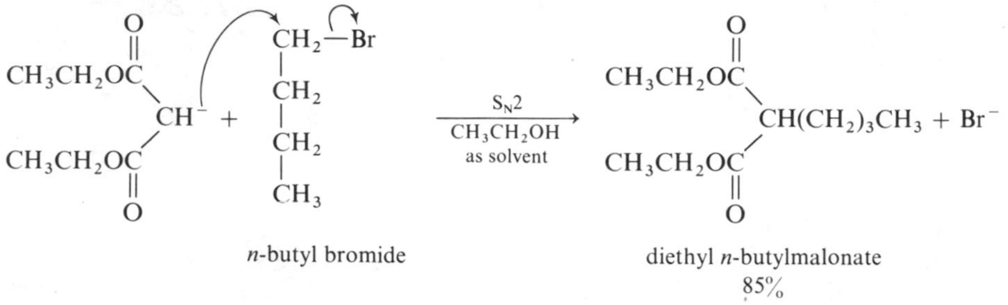

n-butyl bromide diethyl *n*-butylmalonate
85%

An alkylation reaction is just one technique for the synthesis of complex carbon skeletons using enolates as nucleophiles. However, before we begin a discussion of the synthetic utility of enolates, let us consider their formation.

Section 14.1

Acidity of the Alpha Hydrogen

A hydrogen that is α to a carbonyl group is acidic primarily because of resonance-stabilization of the product anion.

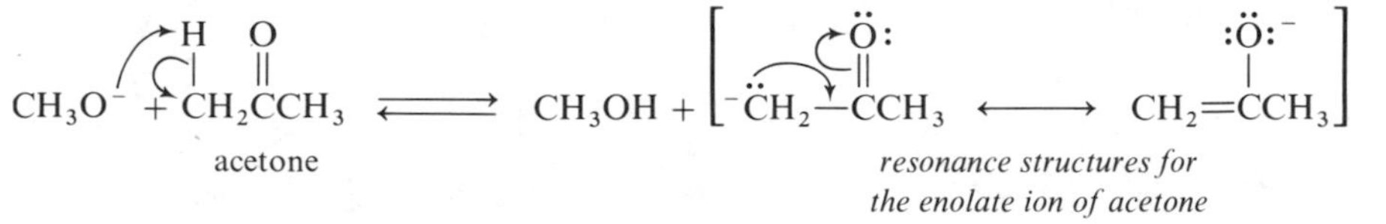

acetone

resonance structures for
the enolate ion of acetone

Because of the resonance-stabilization in the enolate ion of acetone, acetone is a far stronger acid than an alkane. (However, acetone is only one ten-thousandth as strong an acid as ethanol.)

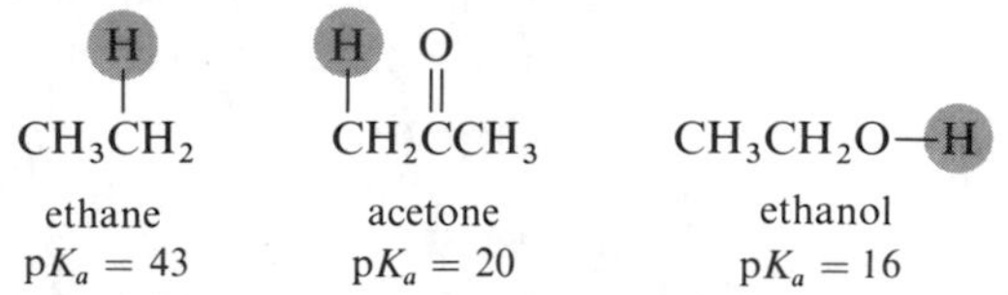

ethane	acetone	ethanol
$pK_a = 43$	$pK_a = 20$	$pK_a = 16$

The alpha hydrogen of an ester is less easily removed than that of an aldehyde or ketone because the carbonyl oxygen is already participating in delocalization. In an ester, the carbonyl oxygen already carries a partial negative charge from delocalization of the electrons on the alkoxyl oxygen. Therefore, the carbonyl group is somewhat less able to delocalize the anionic negative charge of the enolate. The resonance structures for a typical ester, ethyl acetate, follow:

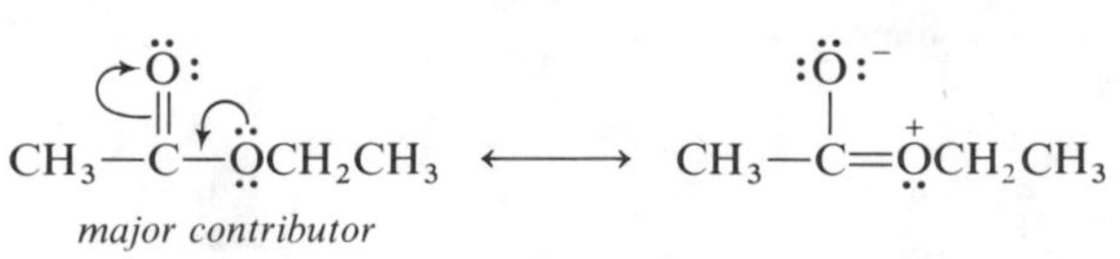

major contributor

Because the α hydrogen of an ester is less easily removed, a simple ester is less acidic than a ketone.

$$\underset{\substack{\uparrow \\ \text{H}}}{\text{CH}_2}\underset{\substack{\| \\ \text{O}}}{\text{C}}\text{OCH}_2\text{CH}_3$$

ethyl acetate
$\text{p}K_a = 25$

A hydrogen alpha to a single carbonyl group is less acidic than that of an alcohol; therefore, treatment of an aldehyde, ketone, or ester with an alkoxide results in a very low concentration of enolate ions. If we want a reasonably high concentration of the enolate, we must use a much stronger base, such as NaNH_2 or NaH.

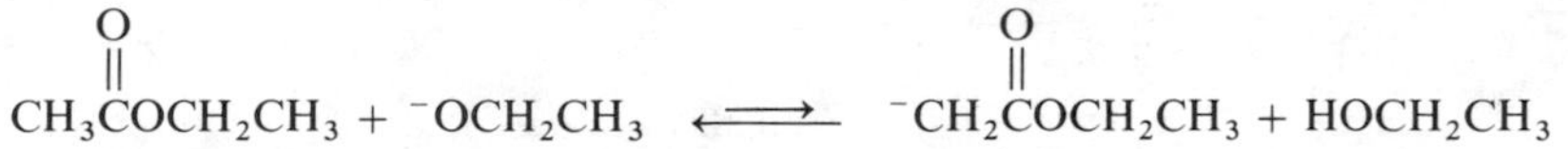

$$\underset{\substack{\| \\ \text{O}}}{\text{CH}_3\text{C}}\text{OCH}_2\text{CH}_3 + {}^-\text{OCH}_2\text{CH}_3 \;\rightleftharpoons\; {}^-\underset{\substack{\| \\ \text{O}}}{\text{CH}_2\text{C}}\text{OCH}_2\text{CH}_3 + \text{HOCH}_2\text{CH}_3$$

| ethyl acetate | *not favored* | ethanol |
| $\text{p}K_a = 25$ | | $\text{p}K_a = 16$ |

$$\underset{\substack{\| \\ \text{O}}}{\text{CH}_3\text{C}}\text{OCH}_2\text{CH}_3 + {}^-\text{NH}_2 \;\rightleftharpoons\; {}^-\underset{\substack{\| \\ \text{O}}}{\text{CH}_2\text{C}}\text{OCH}_2\text{CH}_3 + \text{NH}_3$$

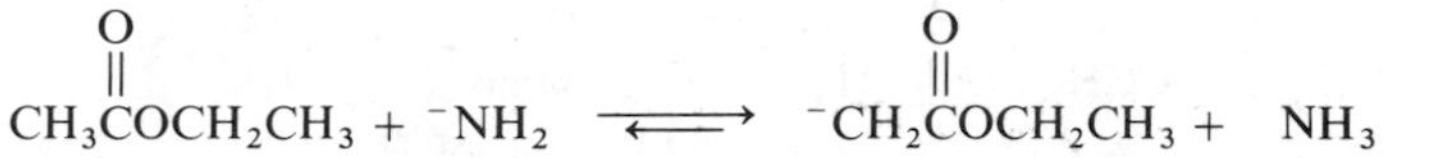

| $\text{p}K_a = 25$ | *favored* | $\text{p}K_a = 35$ |

If a hydrogen is alpha to two carbonyl groups, the negative charge on the anion can be delocalized by both C=O groups. Such a hydrogen is *more acidic than that of an alcohol*. A high concentration of enolate may be obtained by treatment of a β-dicarbonyl compound with an alkoxide. Table 14.1 (page 662) lists the $\text{p}K_a$ values for some compounds with hydrogens alpha to one and two carbonyl groups.

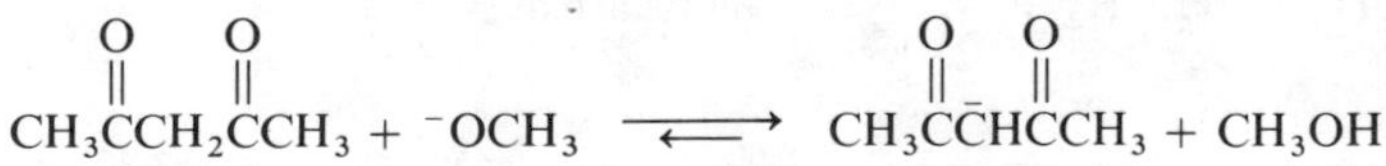

$$\underset{\substack{\| \;\; \| \\ \text{O} \;\; \text{O}}}{\text{CH}_3\text{C}\text{CH}_2\text{C}\text{CH}_3} + {}^-\text{OCH}_3 \;\rightleftharpoons\; \underset{\substack{\| \;\; \| \\ \text{O} \;\; \text{O}}}{\text{CH}_3\text{C}\text{CH}\text{C}\text{CH}_3} + \text{CH}_3\text{OH}$$

| 2,4-pentanedione | *favored* | $\text{p}K_a = 15.5$ |
| $\text{p}K_a = 9$ | | |

Resonance structures of the enolate ion:

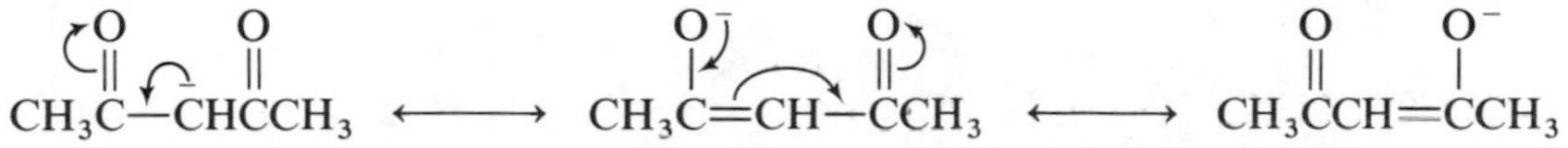

Not only a carbonyl group, but any strongly electron-withdrawing group, enhances the acidity of an alpha hydrogen. Some other compounds that are more acidic than ethanol are:

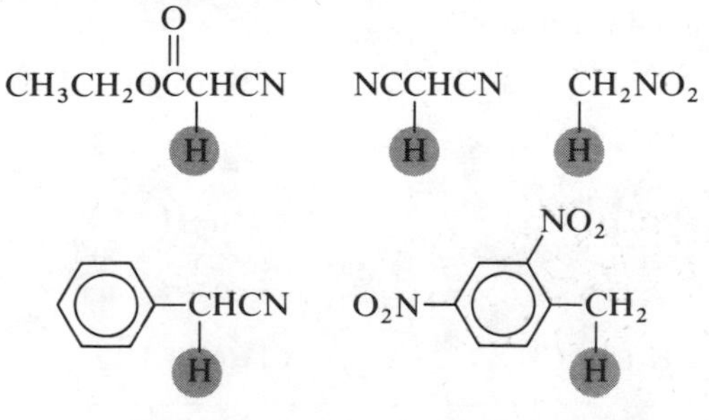

Table 14.1. pK_a Values for Some Carbonyl Compounds

Structure	Name	Approx. pK_a
O O ‖ ‖ CH$_3$CCHCCH$_3$ H	2,4-pentanedione (acetoacetone)	9
O O ‖ ‖ CH$_3$CCHCOCH$_2$CH$_3$ H	ethyl acetoacetate (acetoacetic ester)	11
O O ‖ ‖ CH$_3$CCCOCH$_2$CH$_3$ R H	an alkylacetoacetic ester	13
O O ‖ ‖ CH$_3$CH$_2$OCCHCOCH$_2$CH$_3$ H	diethyl malonate (malonic ester)	13
O ‖ CH$_2$CCH$_3$ H	acetone	20
O ‖ CH$_2$COCH$_2$CH$_3$ H	ethyl acetate	25

STUDY PROBLEMS

14.1 Which of the indicated hydrogens are acidic?

(a) CH$_3$CH=CHCHO   (b) C$_6$H$_5$CHO   (c) CH$_3$CH$_2$CO$_2$CH$_2$CH$_3$

(d) C$_6$H$_5$CH$_2$NO$_2$

14.2 Write an equation to show the acid–base reaction, if any, of each of the following compounds with sodium ethoxide:

(a) CH$_3$CH$_2$CHO

(b) (CH$_3$)$_2$CHCO$_2$CH$_2$CH$_3$

(c) (CH$_3$)$_3$CCO$_2$CH$_2$CH$_3$

(d) O$_2$N—⬡—CH$_2$CH$_3$ (with NO$_2$ substituent)

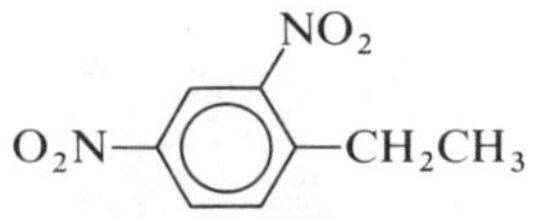

(e) CH$_3$CH$_2$CCH$_2$CO$_2$CH$_2$CH$_3$ (with O double bond on third carbon)

(f) CH$_2$(CO$_2$H)$_2$

Section 14.2

Alkylation of Malonic Ester

One of the more powerful tools at the disposal of the synthetic organic chemist is the reaction of an enolate with an alkyl halide. In this section, we will emphasize the *alkylation of malonic ester*. In general, the end products from alkylation of malonic ester are α-*substituted acetic acids*. In the following example, the R group comes from RX. (In the discussions that follow, we will use $-C_2H_5$ to represent the ethyl group.)

General:

$$CH_2(CO_2C_2H_5)_2 \xrightarrow[\text{(2) RX}]{\text{(1) Na}^+ \ ^-OC_2H_5} RCH(CO_2C_2H_5)_2 \xrightarrow[\text{heat}]{H_2O, H^+} \overset{\text{from RX}}{RCH_2\overset{\overset{\text{O}}{\|}}{C}OH}$$

   diethyl malonate   a diethyl   an α-substituted
   (malonic ester)   alkylmalonate   acetic acid

$$CH_2(CO_2C_2H_5)_2 \xrightarrow[\text{(2) CH}_3\text{CH}_2\text{Br}]{\text{(1) Na}^+ \ ^-OC_2H_5} CH_3CH_2CH(CO_2C_2H_5)_2 \xrightarrow[115°]{H_2O, H^+} \overset{\text{from RX}}{CH_3CH_2CH_2CO_2H}$$

   diethyl malonate   diethyl ethylmalonate   butanoic acid
                                                     80%

A malonic ester alkylation consists of three separate reactions: (1) preparation of the enolate; (2) the actual alkylation; and (3) hydrolysis of the ester, followed by decarboxylation of the resulting β-dicarboxylic acid.

Preparation of the enolate:

$$CH_2(CO_2C_2H_5)_2 + Na^+ \ ^-OC_2H_5 \rightleftharpoons Na^+ \ ^-CH(CO_2C_2H_5)_2 + HOC_2H_5$$

Alkylation:

$$CH_3CH_2\!-\!Br + \ ^-CH(CO_2C_2H_5)_2 \longrightarrow CH_3CH_2\!-\!CH(CO_2C_2H_5)_2 + Br^-$$

Hydrolysis and decarboxylation:

$$CH_3CH_2CH(CO_2C_2H_5)_2 \xrightarrow[\text{heat}]{H_2O, H^+} CH_3CH_2\overset{\overset{CO_2H}{\diagup}}{\underset{\underset{CO_2H}{\diagdown}}{CH}} \xrightarrow[\text{heat}]{-CO_2} CH_3CH_2CH_2CO_2H$$

While there are many chemical reactions involved in this sequence, the laboratory procedure is quite simple because all the reactions can occur in the same reaction vessel. One reactant is added after another, and the final product is isolated as the last step. (Sometimes the intermediate alkylated ester is purified prior to hydrolysis and decarboxylation in order to simplify the final purification.) Let us discuss each of the steps in this reaction in more detail.

A.   Formation of the Enolate

The enolate of malonic ester is usually prepared by treatment of the ester with sodium ethoxide. Therefore, step 1 is the dissolving of sodium metal in anhydrous ethanol (not the common 95% ethanol). (Why not?) Excess ethanol serves as the solvent for the reaction. Step 2 is the addition of diethyl malonate. The ethoxide ion is a stronger base than the enolate ion; therefore, the acid–base equilibrium lies on the side of the resonance-stabilized enolate anion.

$$Na + C_2H_5OH \longrightarrow Na^+ \; {}^-OC_2H_5 + \tfrac{1}{2}H_2\uparrow$$

$$C_2H_5O\overset{\overset{\textstyle O}{\|}}{C}CH_2\overset{\overset{\textstyle O}{\|}}{C}OC_2H_5 + {}^-OC_2H_5 \rightleftharpoons C_2H_5O\overset{\overset{\textstyle O}{\|}}{C}\overset{-}{C}H\overset{\overset{\textstyle O}{\|}}{C}OC_2H_5 + HOC_2H_5$$

favored

STUDY PROBLEM

14.3   Predict what would occur if a chemist added diethyl malonate to a solution of *sodium methoxide* in *methanol*.

B.   Alkylation

The alkylation reaction is a typical S_N2 displacement by a nucleophile. Methyl and primary alkyl halides give the best yields, with secondary alkyl halides giving lower yields because of competing elimination reactions. (Tertiary alkyl halides give exclusively elimination products, and aryl halides are nonreactive in S_N2 reactions.)

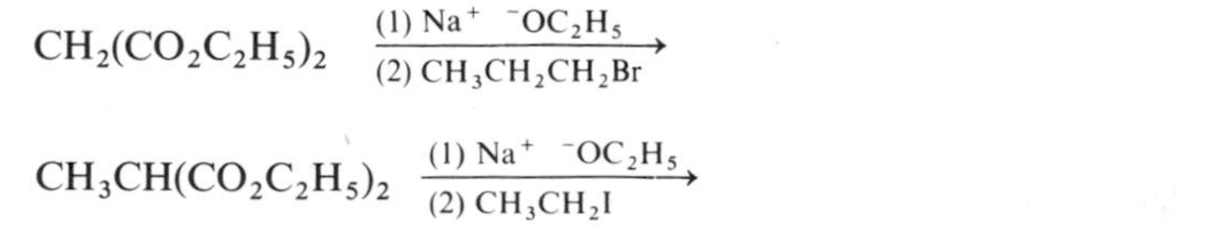

$$(C_2H_5O_2C)_2CH^- + \underset{\underset{\textstyle CH_3}{|}}{CH_2}{-}Br \xrightarrow{S_N2} (C_2H_5O_2C)_2CH\underset{\underset{\textstyle CH_3}{|}}{CH_2} + Br^-$$

STUDY PROBLEM

14.4   Predict the products of the following reactions:

(a) $CH_2(CO_2C_2H_5)_2 \xrightarrow[\text{(2) } CH_3CH_2CH_2Br]{\text{(1) } Na^+ \; {}^-OC_2H_5}$

(b) $CH_3CH(CO_2C_2H_5)_2 \xrightarrow[\text{(2) } CH_3CH_2I]{\text{(1) } Na^+ \; {}^-OC_2H_5}$

The product of the alkylation still contains an acidic hydrogen:

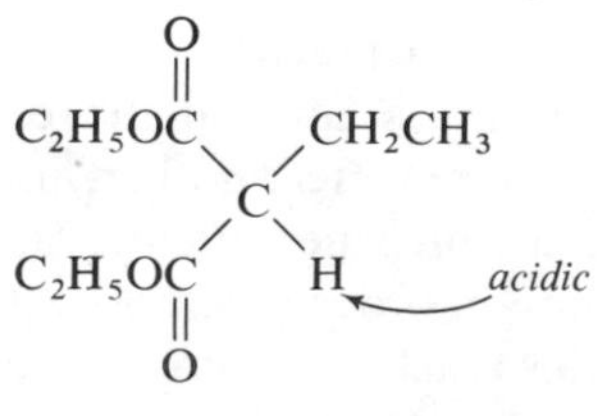

$$C_2H_5O\overset{\overset{\textstyle O}{\|}}{C}\diagdown\underset{C_2H_5O\overset{\underset{\textstyle O}{\|}}{C}\diagup}{\overset{\diagup CH_2CH_3}{\underset{\diagdown H}{C}}} \qquad \leftarrow acidic$$

This second hydrogen can be removed by base, and a *second* R group can be substituted on the malonic ester. This second R group may be the same as, or different from, the first.

$$CH_3CH_2CH(CO_2C_2H_5)_2 \xrightarrow{Na^+ \ ^-OC_2H_5}$$

diethyl ethylmalonate

$$CH_3CH_2\bar{C}(CO_2C_2H_5)_2 \xrightarrow{CH_3I} \overset{\overset{\displaystyle CH_3}{\displaystyle |}}{CH_3CH_2C(CO_2C_2H_5)_2}$$

an enolate   diethyl
ethylmethylmalonate

C. Hydrolysis and Decarboxylation

We have mentioned previously that a compound with a carboxyl group beta to a carbonyl group undergoes decarboxylation when heated. The mechanism for decarboxylation was shown in Section 12.10C. If malonic ester (substituted or not) is hydrolyzed in hot acidic solution, a β-diacid is formed and may undergo decarboxylation. (Sometimes decarboxylation does not occur until the diacid is distilled.)

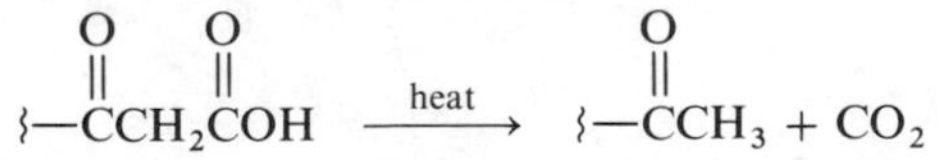

$$\overset{O \quad O}{\underset{\| \quad \|}{\}-CCH_2COH}} \xrightarrow{heat} \overset{O}{\underset{\|}{\}-CCH_3 + CO_2}}$$

Hydrolysis and decarboxylation:

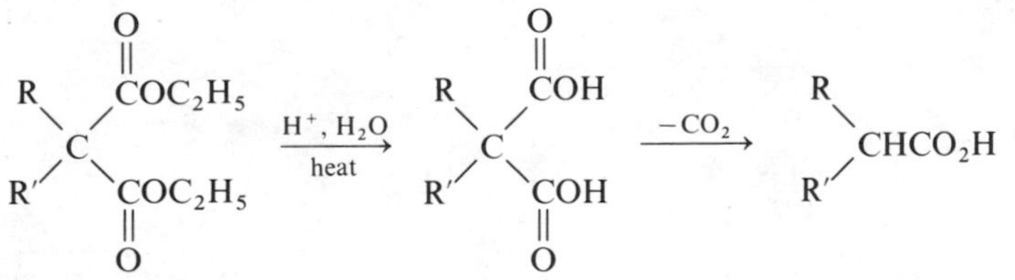

an α-disubstituted   *an α-disubstituted*
malonic ester   *acetic acid*

What if a chemist does not want a decarboxylation product, but wants a diacid? A diacid may be prepared by *saponification of the diester in base, followed by acidification*. This way, the carboxylic acid itself is not subjected to heat and is less likely to undergo decarboxylation.

Saponification and acidification:

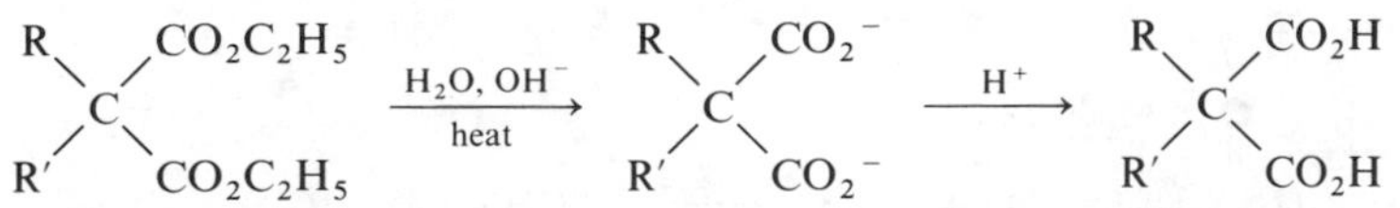

an α-disubstituted
malonic acid

STUDY PROBLEMS

14.5 Give equations for the following reactions:

(a) saponification of diethyl propylmalonate, followed by treatment with cold HCl
(b) acid hydrolysis of diethyl dimethylmalonate

14.6 Give the mechanism for the decarboxylation of methylmalonic acid.

Section 14.3

Alkylation of Acetoacetic Ester

Alkylation reactions are not limited to the enolate of diethyl malonate. Other enolates also undergo S_N2 reaction with methyl or primary alkyl halides to yield alkylated products. Another commonly used enolate is that obtained from ethyl acetoacetate (acetoacetic ester). The end product of alkylation of acetoacetic ester is an *α-substituted acetone*.

General:

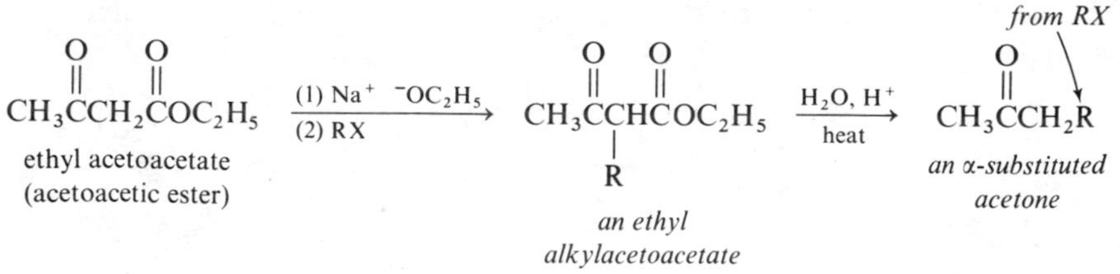

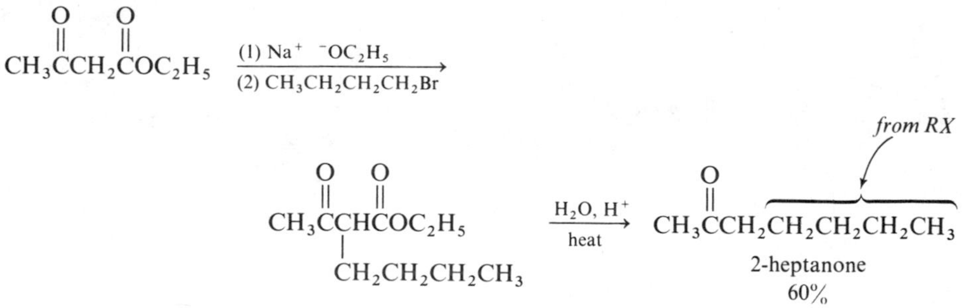

$$\underset{\substack{\text{ethyl acetoacetate}\\ \text{(acetoacetic ester)}}}{CH_3CCH_2COC_2H_5} \xrightarrow[\text{(2) RX}]{\text{(1) Na}^+ \ ^-OC_2H_5} \underset{\substack{R\\ \textit{an ethyl}\\ \textit{alkylacetoacetate}}}{CH_3CCHCOC_2H_5} \xrightarrow[\text{heat}]{H_2O, H^+} \underset{\substack{\textit{an α-substituted}\\ \textit{acetone}}}{CH_3CCH_2R}$$

from RX

$$CH_3CCH_2COC_2H_5 \xrightarrow[\text{(2) CH}_3\text{CH}_2\text{CH}_2\text{CH}_2\text{Br}]{\text{(1) Na}^+ \ ^-OC_2H_5}$$

from RX

$$\underset{CH_2CH_2CH_2CH_3}{CH_3CCHCOC_2H_5} \xrightarrow[\text{heat}]{H_2O, H^+} \underset{\substack{\text{2-heptanone}\\ 60\%}}{CH_3CCH_2CH_2CH_2CH_2CH_3}$$

The steps in an acetoacetic ester synthesis are similar to those for a malonic ester synthesis.

Preparation of the enolate:

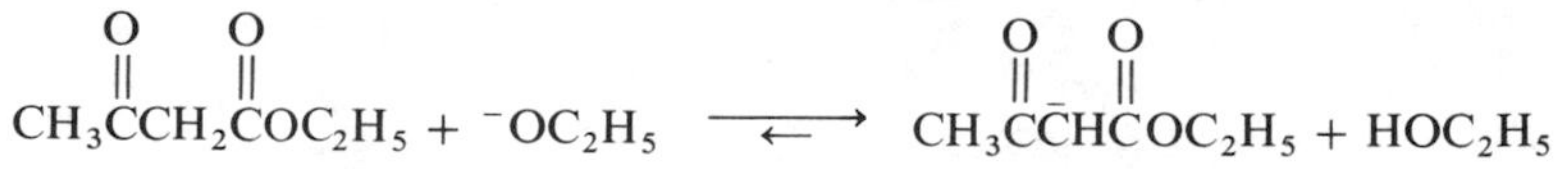

$$CH_3CCH_2COC_2H_5 + {}^-OC_2H_5 \leftrightarrows CH_3CCHCOC_2H_5 + HOC_2H_5$$

Alkylation:

$$CH_3CCHCOC_2H_5 + R\text{—}X \xrightarrow{S_N2} \underset{R}{CH_3CCHCOC_2H_5} + X^-$$

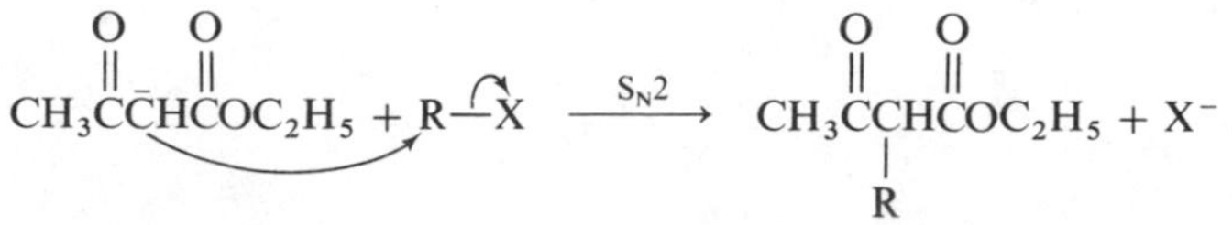

Hydrolysis and decarboxylation:

$$\underset{\overset{|}{R}}{CH_3\overset{\overset{O}{\|}}{C}CH\overset{\overset{O}{\|}}{C}OC_2H_5} \xrightarrow[\text{heat}]{H_2O, H^+} \underset{\overset{|}{R}}{CH_3\overset{\overset{O}{\|}}{C}CH\overset{\overset{O}{\|}}{C}OH} \xrightarrow[\text{heat}]{-CO_2} CH_3\overset{\overset{O}{\|}}{C}CH_2R$$

STUDY PROBLEMS

14.7 Fill in the blanks:

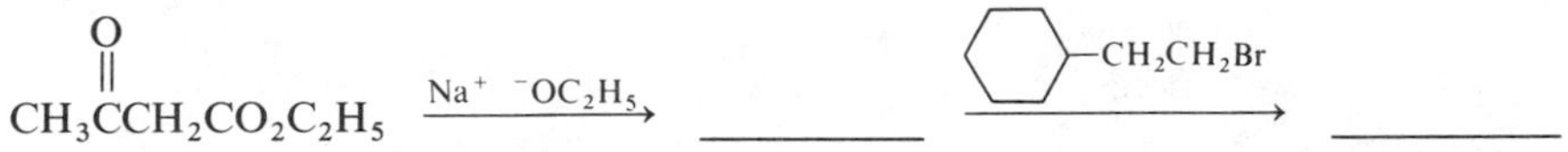

$$CH_3\overset{\overset{O}{\|}}{C}CH_2CO_2C_2H_5 \xrightarrow{Na^+ {}^-OC_2H_5} \underline{\qquad} \xrightarrow{\langle\!\!\!\text{⬡}\!\!\!\rangle - CH_2CH_2Br} \underline{\qquad}$$

14.8 Predict the major organic products:

(a) ethyl acetoacetate $\xrightarrow[\text{(2) CH}_3\text{I}]{\text{(1) Na}^+ \ {}^-\text{OC}_2\text{H}_5}$

(b) [the product from (a)] $\xrightarrow[\text{(2) CH}_3\text{I}]{\text{(1) Na}^+ \ {}^-\text{OC}_2\text{H}_5}$

(c) [the product from (b)] $\xrightarrow[\substack{\text{heat}\\ -\text{CO}_2}]{\text{H}_2\text{O, H}^+}$

Section 14.4

Syntheses Using Alkylation Reactions

In general, the products of alkylation reactions of malonic ester or acetoacetic ester are substituted acetic acids or substituted acetones.

From malonic ester:

$$R-CH_2CO_2H \qquad or \qquad \underset{R'}{\overset{R}{\diagdown}}CHCO_2H$$

From acetoacetic ester:

$$R-CH_2\overset{\overset{O}{\|}}{C}CH_3 \qquad or \qquad \underset{R'}{\overset{R}{\diagdown}}CH\overset{\overset{O}{\|}}{C}CH_3$$

However, we can also obtain diacids, diesters, keto acids, and keto esters. The assorted products that may be obtained from alkylation of malonic ester or acetoacetic ester are summarized in Figure 14.1.

It is comparatively easy to predict the products of a reaction when we are given the reactants. It is somewhat more difficult to decide upon specific reactants to use in a synthesis problem. Remember to work the problem backwards: if you

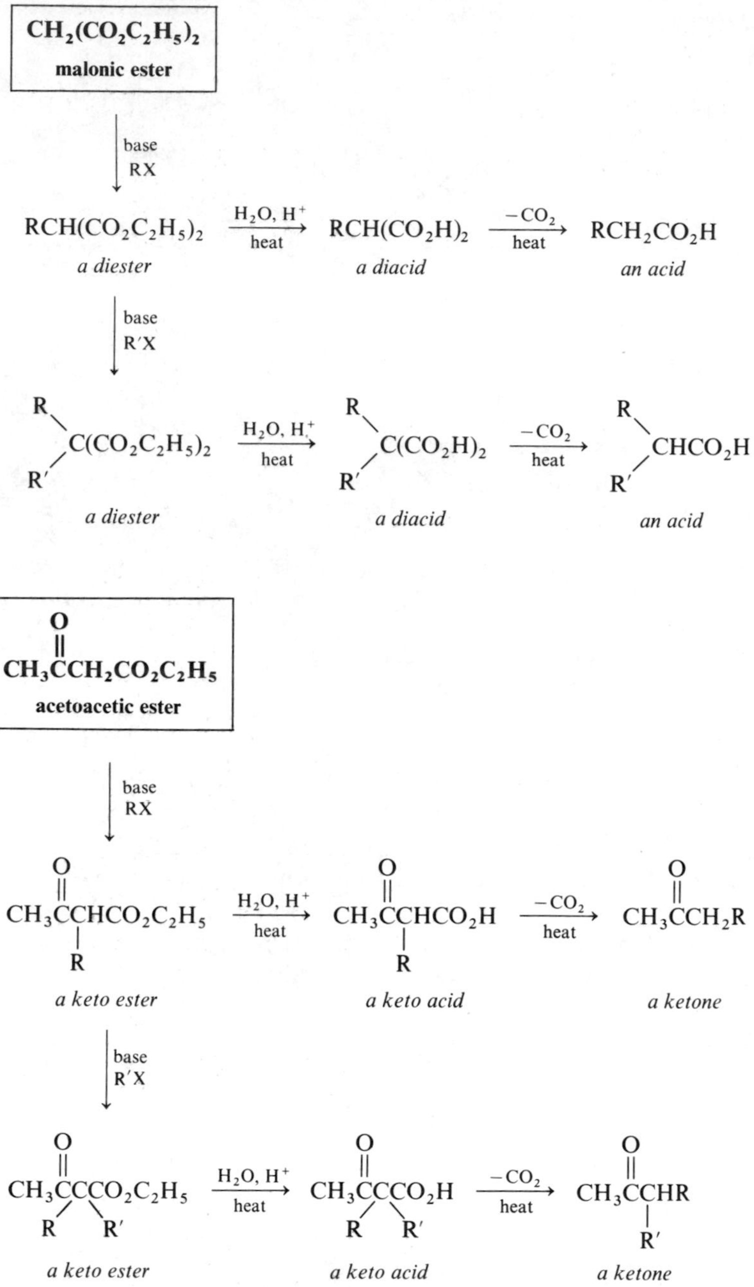

$$CH_2(CO_2C_2H_5)_2$$
malonic ester

$\downarrow$ base
  RX

$$RCH(CO_2C_2H_5)_2 \xrightarrow[\text{heat}]{H_2O,\ H^+} RCH(CO_2H)_2 \xrightarrow[\text{heat}]{-CO_2} RCH_2CO_2H$$

a diester *a diacid* *an acid*

$\downarrow$ base
  R′X

$$\begin{array}{c} R \\ \diagdown \\ \diagup \\ R' \end{array} C(CO_2C_2H_5)_2 \xrightarrow[\text{heat}]{H_2O,\ H^+} \begin{array}{c} R \\ \diagdown \\ \diagup \\ R' \end{array} C(CO_2H)_2 \xrightarrow[\text{heat}]{-CO_2} \begin{array}{c} R \\ \diagdown \\ \diagup \\ R' \end{array} CHCO_2H$$

a diester *a diacid* *an acid*

$$\overset{\displaystyle O}{\overset{\|}{CH_3CCH_2CO_2C_2H_5}}$$
acetoacetic ester

$\downarrow$ base
  RX

$$\overset{\displaystyle O}{\overset{\|}{CH_3C\underset{\underset{R}{|}}{C}HCO_2C_2H_5}} \xrightarrow[\text{heat}]{H_2O,\ H^+} \overset{\displaystyle O}{\overset{\|}{CH_3C\underset{\underset{R}{|}}{C}HCO_2H}} \xrightarrow[\text{heat}]{-CO_2} \overset{\displaystyle O}{\overset{\|}{CH_3CCH_2R}}$$

a keto ester *a keto acid* *a ketone*

$\downarrow$ base
  R′X

$$\overset{\displaystyle O}{\overset{\|}{CH_3C\underset{\underset{R\quad R'}{|\quad |}}{C}CO_2C_2H_5}} \xrightarrow[\text{heat}]{H_2O,\ H^+} \overset{\displaystyle O}{\overset{\|}{CH_3C\underset{\underset{R\quad R'}{|\quad |}}{C}CO_2H}} \xrightarrow[\text{heat}]{-CO_2} \overset{\displaystyle O}{\overset{\|}{CH_3C\underset{\underset{R'}{|}}{C}HR}}$$

a keto ester *a keto acid* *a ketone*

Figure 14.1. Products from the alkylations of malonic ester and acetoacetic ester.

are asked to synthesize a compound by an alkylation reaction, first decide what dicarbonyl compound you would need, then pick the alkyl halide.

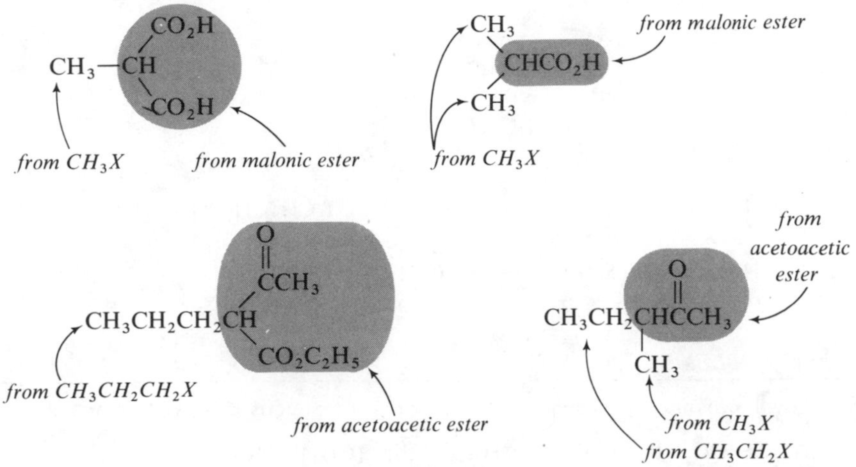

$$CH_3-\underset{\overset{|}{CO_2H}}{\overset{\overset{|}{CO_2H}}{CH}}$$

from CH_3X *from malonic ester*

$$\underset{\overset{|}{CH_3}}{\overset{\overset{|}{CH_3}}{CHCO_2H}}$$ *from malonic ester*

from CH_3X

$$CH_3CH_2CH_2\underset{\overset{|}{CO_2C_2H_5}}{\overset{\overset{\overset{O}{||}}{CCH_3}}{CH}}$$

from $CH_3CH_2CH_2X$

from acetoacetic ester

$$CH_3CH_2\underset{\overset{|}{CH_3}}{\overset{\overset{O}{||}}{CHCCH_3}}$$

from acetoacetic ester

from CH_3X
from CH_3CH_2X

Example: If you were asked to write the equations for the synthesis of 3-methyl-2-pentanone, you would:

(1) *write the structure;*
(2) *decide what β-dicarbonyl compound you would need;* and
(3) *decide what alkyl halides would have to be used for the substitution.*

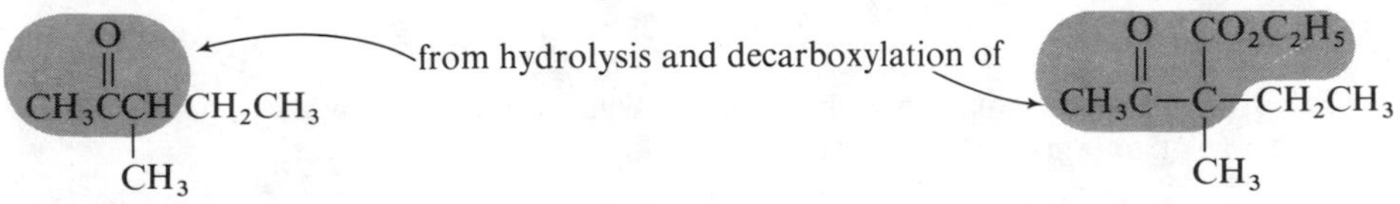

$$\underset{\overset{|}{CH_3}}{\overset{\overset{O}{||}}{CH_3CCH}}CH_2CH_3$$

— from hydrolysis and decarboxylation of →

$$CH_3C-\underset{\overset{|}{CH_3}}{\overset{\overset{O\quad CO_2C_2H_5}{||\quad\;\;|}}{C}}-CH_2CH_3$$

It is evident that the β-dicarbonyl starting material is acetoacetic ester. The alkyl halides needed are CH_3X and CH_3CH_2X. Now, equations for the steps in the synthesis may be written:

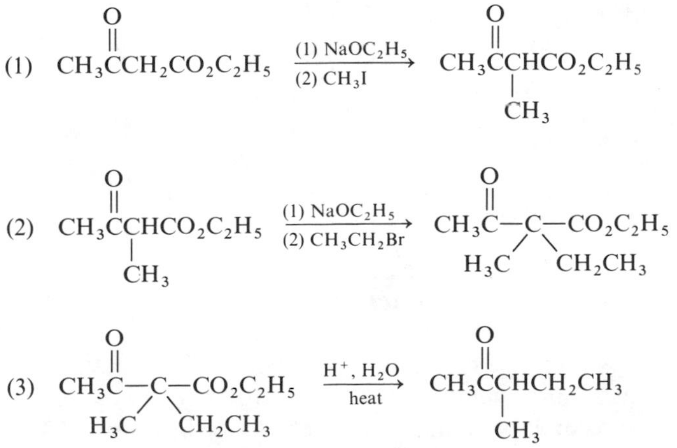

(1) $CH_3\overset{\overset{O}{||}}{C}CH_2CO_2C_2H_5 \xrightarrow[\text{(2) } CH_3I]{\text{(1) } NaOC_2H_5} CH_3\overset{\overset{O}{||}}{C}\underset{\overset{|}{CH_3}}{CHCO_2C_2H_5}$

(2) $CH_3\overset{\overset{O}{||}}{C}\underset{\overset{|}{CH_3}}{CHCO_2C_2H_5} \xrightarrow[\text{(2) } CH_3CH_2Br]{\text{(1) } NaOC_2H_5} CH_3\overset{\overset{O}{||}}{C}-\underset{\overset{|}{H_3C}\quad\overset{|}{CH_2CH_3}}{C}-CO_2C_2H_5$

(3) $CH_3\overset{\overset{O}{||}}{C}-\underset{H_3C\quad CH_2CH_3}{C}-CO_2C_2H_5 \xrightarrow[\text{heat}]{H^+, H_2O} CH_3\overset{\overset{O}{||}}{C}\underset{\overset{|}{CH_3}}{CHCH_2CH_3}$

Sample Problem

Suggest a reaction sequence leading to 3-phenylpropanoic acid.

from benzyl bromide

Solution: $\bigcirc$—$CH_2$$CH_2CO_2H$ ←*from malonic ester*

(1) $CH_2(CO_2C_2H_5)_2 \xrightarrow{Na^+ \ ^-OC_2H_5} \ ^-CH(CO_2C_2H_5)_2$

(2) $C_6H_5CH_2Br + \ ^-CH(CO_2C_2H_5)_2 \xrightarrow{-Br^-} C_6H_5CH_2CH(CO_2C_2H_5)_2$

(3) $C_6H_5CH_2CH(CO_2C_2H_5)_2 \xrightarrow[\text{heat}]{H_2O, \ H^+} C_6H_5CH_2CH_2CO_2H$

STUDY PROBLEMS

14.9 Show how you could synthesize the following compounds by alkylation reactions:

(a) $CH_3CH_2CH_2CH_2CH(CO_2H)_2$ (b) $(CH_3)_2CHCO_2H$

(c) $CH_3\overset{\overset{\displaystyle O}{\|}}{C}CHCH_2CH_2CH_3$
                 $\underset{\displaystyle CH_3}{|}$

14.10 Suggest a synthesis for the following ester from malonic ester:

$$\underset{\displaystyle CH_2CO_2C_2H_5}{\overset{\displaystyle CH(CO_2C_2H_5)_2}{|}}$$

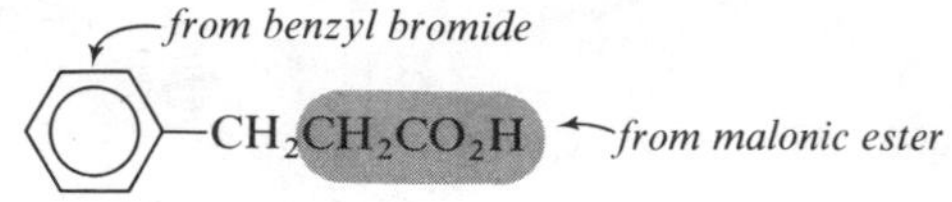

14.11 Give a synthetic route to each of the following compounds by alkylation reactions. Show all intermediate products.

(a) $CH_3\overset{\overset{\displaystyle O}{\|}}{C}\overset{}{C}HC\overset{\overset{\displaystyle O}{\|}}{}CH_3$ (b) $CH_3CH_2CH_2CH(CN)_2$
             $\underset{\displaystyle CH_3}{|}$

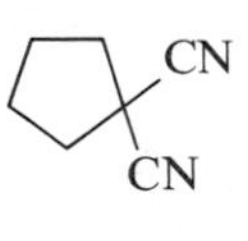

(c)   (cyclopentane ring with CN, CN)   (d)   (cyclohexane-1,3-dione ring)—$CH_2CH(CH_3)_2$

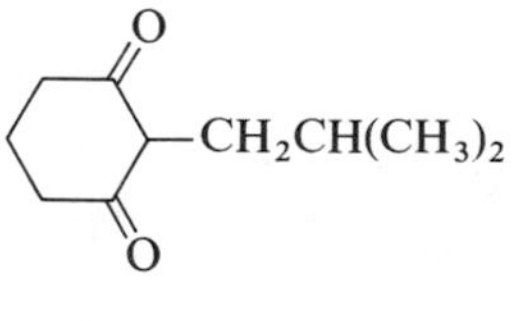

Section 14.5

Alkylation and Acylation of Enamines

Another type of organic compound containing a nucleophilic carbon that can undergo alkylation reactions is an **enamine**. In Section 11.10B, we discussed the formation of enamines from secondary amines and aldehydes or ketones.

Formation of an enamine:

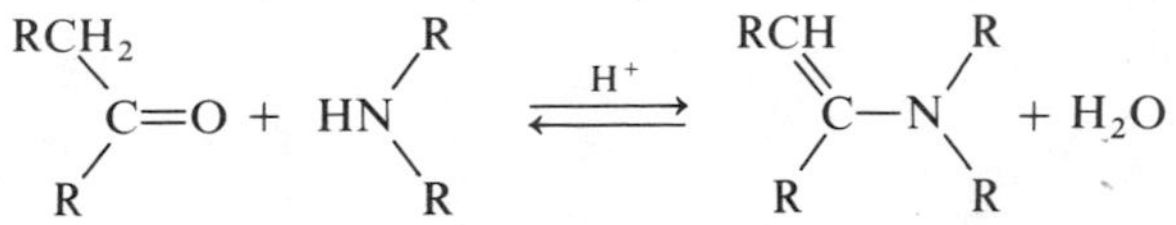

$$\underset{\underset{R}{|}}{\overset{\overset{RCH_2}{|}}{C}}=O \;+\; HN\overset{R}{\underset{R}{\diagup}} \;\underset{\longleftarrow}{\overset{H^+}{\rightleftharpoons}}\; \underset{\underset{R}{|}}{\overset{\overset{RCH}{\|}}{C}}-N\overset{R}{\underset{R}{\diagup}} \;+\; H_2O$$

a ketone   a 2° amine   an enamine

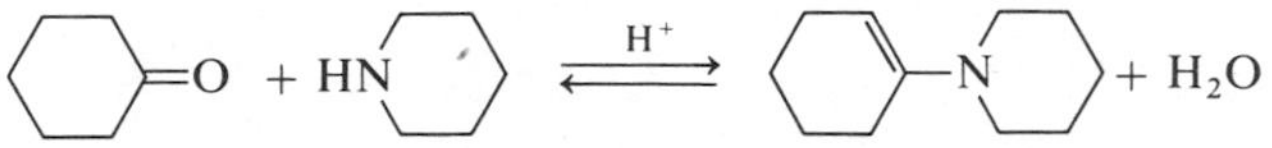

$$\bigcirc\!\!=\!O \;+\; HN\!\!\bigcirc \;\underset{\longleftarrow}{\overset{H^+}{\rightleftharpoons}}\; \bigcirc\!\!-\!N\!\!\bigcirc \;+\; H_2O$$

cyclohexanone   piperidine   an enamine

The nitrogen of an enamine has an unshared pair of electrons. These electrons are, in a sense, in an *allylic position* and consequently are in conjugation with the double bond. Resonance structures for the enamine show that the carbon β to the nitrogen has a partial negative charge.

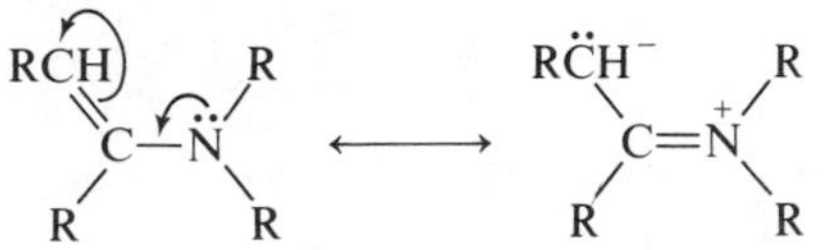

$$\underset{\underset{R}{|}}{\overset{\overset{RCH}{\big\rfloor}}{C}}-\overset{..}{N}\overset{R}{\underset{R}{\diagup}} \;\longleftrightarrow\; \underset{\underset{R}{|}}{\overset{\overset{R\overset{..}{C}H^-}{\|}}{C}}=\overset{+}{N}\overset{R}{\underset{R}{\diagup}}$$

resonance structures for an enamine

This β carbon has carbanion character and can act as a nucleophile. For example, when an enamine is treated with an alkyl halide, such as CH_3I, the enamine displaces the halogen of the alkyl halide in an S_N2 reaction. The result is alkylation of the enamine at the position that is β to the nitrogen.

Alkylation:

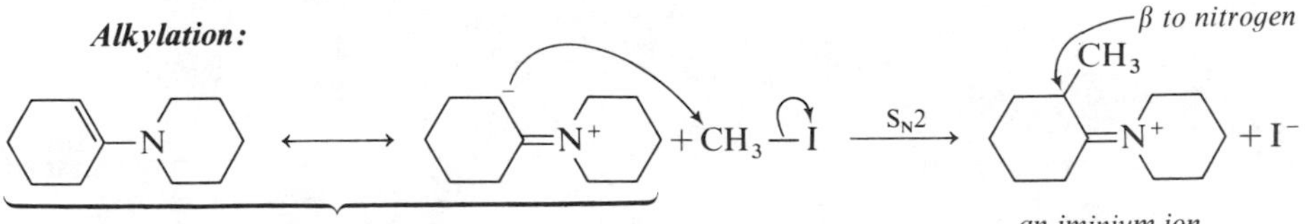

$$\bigcirc\!\!-\!N\!\!\bigcirc \;\longleftrightarrow\; \bigcirc\!\!=\!\!\overset{+}{N}\!\!\bigcirc \;+\;CH_3\!\!-\!\!I \;\xrightarrow{S_N2}\; \underset{}{\overset{CH_3}{\bigcirc}}\!\!=\!\!\overset{+}{N}\!\!\bigcirc \;+\;I^-$$

                                                    β to nitrogen

the enamine   *an iminium ion*

The product iminium ion is readily hydrolyzed to a ketone. The net result of the entire reaction sequence is alkylation of a ketone in the α position.

Hydrolysis:

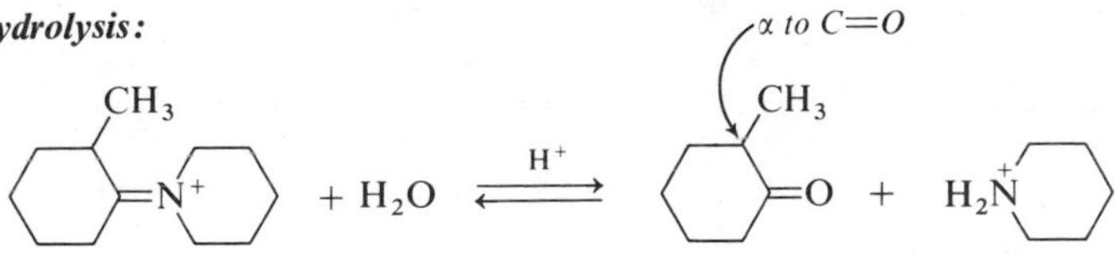

$$\underset{}{\overset{CH_3}{\bigcirc}}\!\!=\!\!\overset{+}{N}\!\!\bigcirc \;+\; H_2O \;\underset{\longleftarrow}{\overset{H^+}{\rightleftharpoons}}\; \underset{}{\overset{CH_3}{\bigcirc}}\!\!=\!O \;+\; H_2\overset{+}{N}\!\!\bigcirc$$

                                            α to C=O

the iminium ion   2-methyl-1-   piperidinium ion
                                          cyclohexanone
                                          a ketone

A generalized sequence for an enamine synthesis follows:

Preparation of enamine:

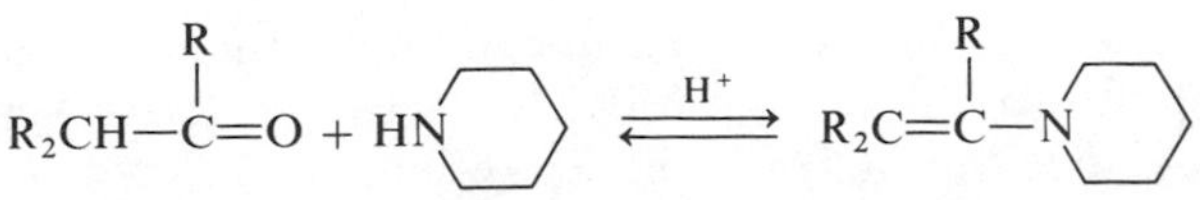

$$R_2CH-\overset{\overset{R}{|}}{C}=O \;+\; HN\!\!\bigcirc \;\underset{\longleftarrow}{\overset{H^+}{\rightleftharpoons}}\; R_2C=\overset{\overset{R}{|}}{C}-N\!\!\bigcirc$$

Substitution reaction:

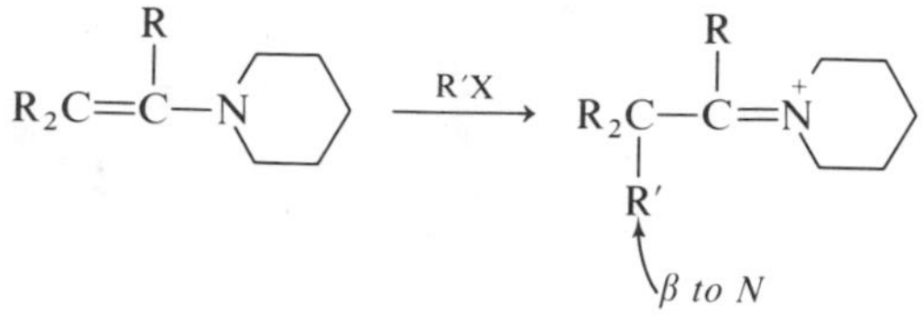

Hydrolysis:

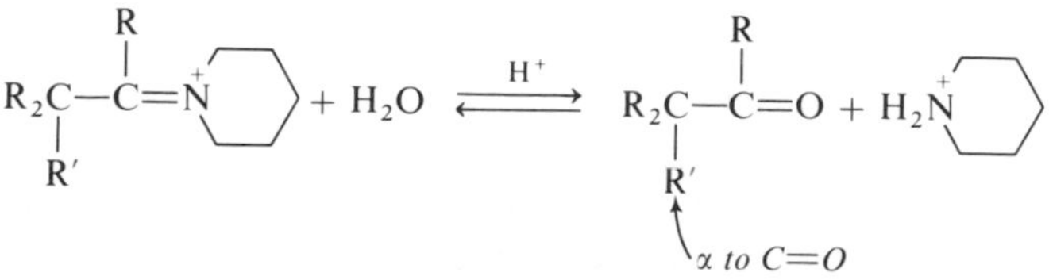

Give the steps in the preparation of the following ketone, using an enamine synthesis with piperidine as the amine.

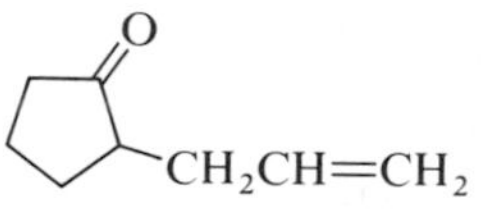

Solution:

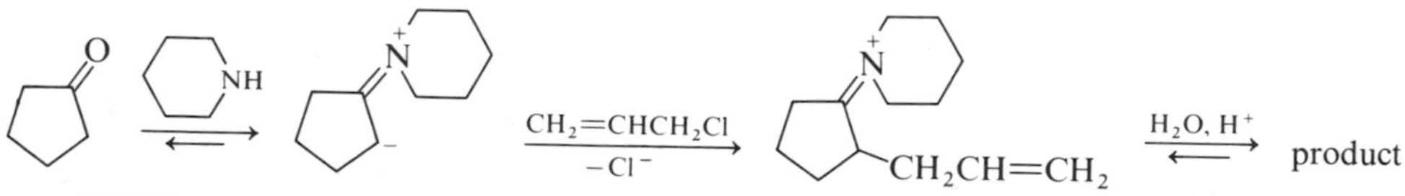

The alkylation step in an enamine synthesis is an S_N2 reaction with a rather weak nucleophile. (Why?) It is not surprising then that only the most reactive halogen compounds are suitable as alkylating agents. These compounds include allyl halides, benzyl halides, α-halocarbonyl compounds, and methyl iodide. (Alkyl halides other than CH_3I are attacked by the enamine nitrogen, rather than by the carbon.)

Some reactive halides:

CH_3CCl	$CH_2=CHCH_2Cl$	$C_6H_5CH_2Cl$	$BrCH_2CCH_3$	CH_3I
acetyl chloride	allyl chloride	benzyl chloride	bromoacetone	methyl iodide

The reactions of enamines with α-halocarbonyl compounds and acid halides follow similar paths to that of alkylation. In each case, the final product (after hydrolysis) is a ketone substituted at the α position.

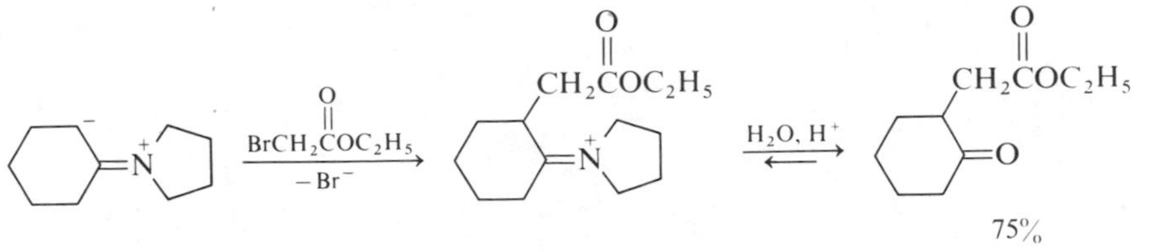

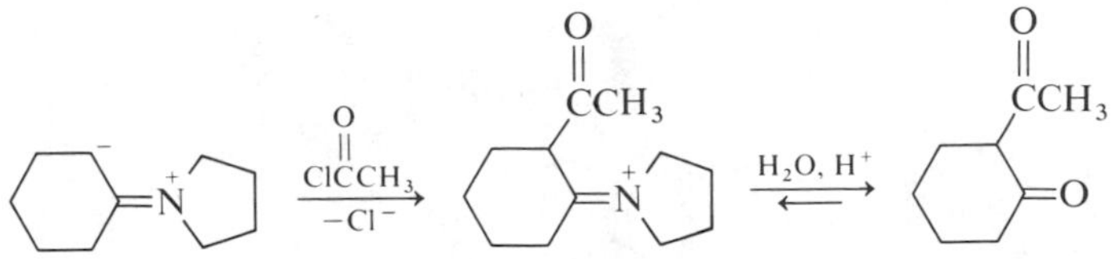

75%

How would you prepare the following compound by an enamine synthesis?

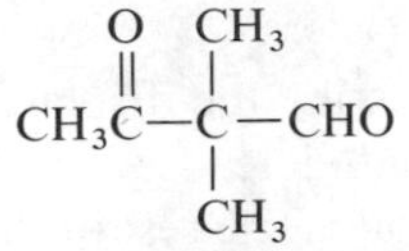

Solution:

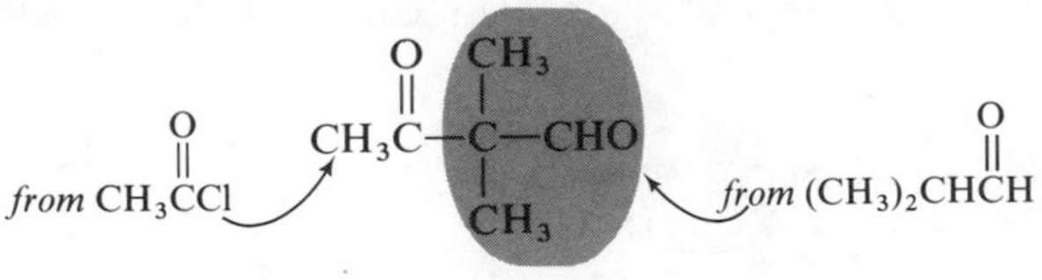

from CH_3CCl *from* $(CH_3)_2CHCH$

Reaction sequence:

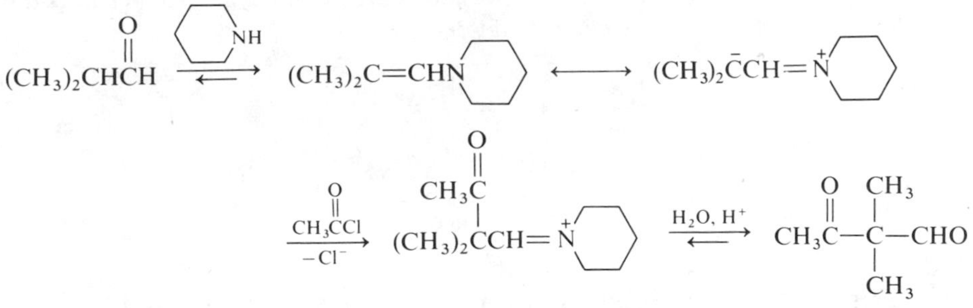

STUDY PROBLEMS

14.12 Suggest a mechanism for the hydrolysis of the iminium ion in the preceding sample problem.

14.13 Enamine syntheses are generally carried out using a cyclic amine as the secondary amine. Suggest a reason for this.

Three cyclic amines used in enamine syntheses:

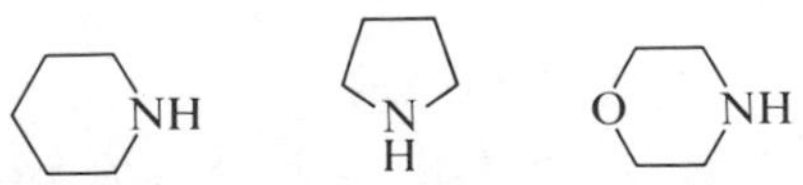

piperidine   pyrrolidine   morpholine

14.14 Predict the products:

$$\text{(cyclohexanone)} \quad \xrightarrow[\text{pyrrolidine}]{} \quad \xrightarrow{C_6H_5CH_2Br} \quad \xrightarrow[\text{H}_2\text{O, H}^+]{}$$

14.15 Write equations showing how the following compound may be prepared by an enamine synthesis:

$$\begin{array}{c} \text{O} \\ \| \\ \text{CH}_2\text{CCH}_3 \end{array}$$

Section 14.6

Aldol Condensations

So far, we have been discussing the displacement of halide ions by nucleophiles. A reagent with a nucleophilic carbon atom can also attack the partially positive carbon of a carbonyl group. The rest of this chapter will be devoted to the reactions of enolates and related anions with carbonyl compounds.

$$\text{Nu}^- + \begin{array}{c} \text{O} \\ \| \\ -\text{C}- \end{array} \longrightarrow \begin{array}{c} \text{O}^- \\ | \\ -\text{C}- \\ | \\ \text{Nu} \end{array}$$

When an aldehyde is treated with a base, the resulting enolate ion can undergo reaction at the carbonyl group of another molecule of aldehyde. The result is the *addition of one molecule of aldehyde to another.*

from one aldehyde

$$2 \begin{array}{c} \text{O} \\ \| \\ \text{CH}_3\text{CH} \end{array} \xrightarrow{\text{OH}^-} \begin{array}{c} \text{OH} \quad \text{O} \\ | \qquad \| \\ \text{CH}_3\text{CH}-\text{CH}_2\text{CH} \end{array}$$

acetaldehyde   3-hydroxybutanal
(aldol)
50%

This reaction is called an **aldol condensation reaction**. The word "aldol," derived from *ald*ehyde and alcoh*ol*, describes the product. A **condensation reaction** is one in which two or more molecules combine into a larger molecule with or without the loss of a small molecule (such as water). The aldol condensation is an addition reaction in which no small molecule is lost.

How does an aldol condensation proceed? If acetaldehyde is treated with dilute aqueous sodium hydroxide, a low concentration of enolate ions is formed. The reaction is reversible—as enolate ions undergo reaction, more are formed.

$$\begin{array}{c} \text{O} \\ \| \\ \text{CH}_3\text{CH} \end{array} + \text{OH}^- \rightleftharpoons \left[\begin{array}{cc} \text{O} & \text{O}^- \\ \| & | \\ {}^-\text{CH}_2\text{CH} \longleftrightarrow \text{CH}_2\!=\!\text{CH} \end{array} \right] + \text{H}_2\text{O}$$

resonance structures for
the enolate ion

The enolate ion undergoes reaction with another acetaldehyde molecule by adding to the carbonyl carbon to form an alkoxide ion.

$$CH_3\overset{\overset{\displaystyle O}{\|}}{C}H + {}^-CH_2\overset{\overset{\displaystyle O}{\|}}{C}H \rightleftharpoons \left[CH_3\overset{\overset{\displaystyle O^-}{|}}{C}H-CH_2\overset{\overset{\displaystyle O}{\|}}{C}H\right]$$

an alkoxide ion

Because alkoxides are stronger bases than water, the alkoxide abstracts a proton from water to yield the product aldol.

$$\left[CH_3\overset{\overset{\displaystyle O^-}{|}}{C}HCH_2\overset{\overset{\displaystyle O}{\|}}{C}H\right] + H_2O \rightleftharpoons CH_3\overset{\overset{\displaystyle OH}{|}}{C}HCH_2\overset{\overset{\displaystyle O}{\|}}{C}H + OH^-$$

α hydrogens

aldol

The aldol product still has a carbonyl group with α hydrogens. Can it undergo further reaction to form trimers? tetramers? polymers? Yes, these materials are by-products of the reaction. For simplicity, we will show only the dimer products and ignore the fact that other, higher-molecular-weight products may also be formed.

We have shown the aldol condensation for acetaldehyde. Other aldehydes also undergo this self-addition. Ketones undergo aldol condensations at a lower rate; the equilibrium does not favor the ketone-condensation product. (Why not?) Although there are a number of laboratory procedures that can be used to induce ketone condensations of the aldol type, the reaction is not as useful with ketones as it is with aldehydes. Therefore, we will concentrate our present discussion on aldehydes.

Note that the reacting aldehyde must have an α hydrogen and that the product is, in each case, a *β*-**hydroxy aldehyde**.

Other examples of aldol condensations:

$$CH_3CH_2\overset{\overset{\displaystyle O}{\|}}{C}H + CH_3CH_2\overset{\overset{\displaystyle O}{\|}}{C}H \overset{OH^-}{\rightleftharpoons} CH_3CH_2\overset{\overset{\displaystyle OH}{|}}{C}H-\overset{\overset{\displaystyle}{|}}{\underset{\underset{\displaystyle CH_3}{|}}{C}}H\overset{\overset{\displaystyle O}{\|}}{C}H$$

propanal

an aldol

cyclohexanecarboxaldehyde

an aldol

Sample Problem

Show how you could prepare 3-hydroxy-2,2,4-trimethylpentanal by an aldol condensation.

Solution: Write the structure and indicate the position of condensation.

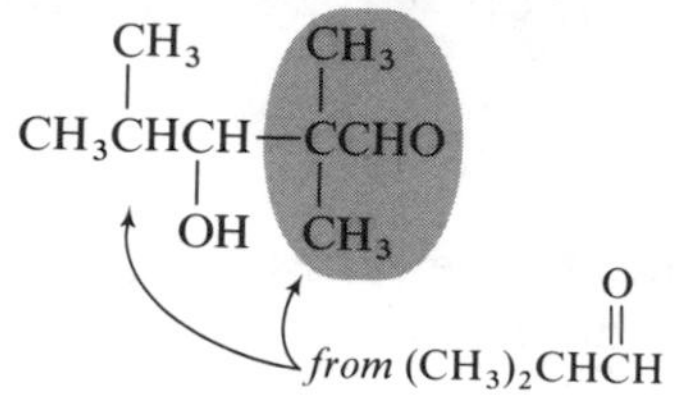

$$
\begin{array}{cc}
CH_3 & CH_3 \\
| & | \\
CH_3CHCH\!-\!CCHO & \\
| & | \\
OH & CH_3 \\
\end{array}
$$

$$from\ (CH_3)_2CHCH$$

Write the equation.

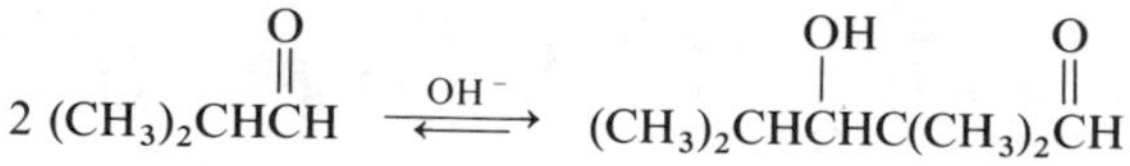

$$
2\ (CH_3)_2CHCH \xrightarrow[]{OH^-} (CH_3)_2CHCHC(CH_3)_2CH
$$

STUDY PROBLEMS

14.16 Which of the following aldehydes can undergo self-condensations?

(a) 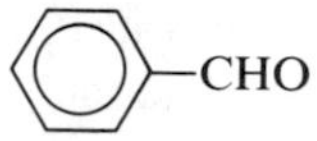 ⬡—CHO   (b) HCHO   (c) $(CH_3CH_2)_2CHCHO$

(d) $(CH_3)_3CCHO$

14.17 Predict the product of the self-condensation of: (a) butanal;   (b) acetone; and   (c) 3-methylbutanal.

A.   Dehydration of the Aldols

A β-hydroxy carbonyl compound undergoes dehydration readily because the double bond in the product is in conjugation with the carbonyl group. Therefore, an **α,β-unsaturated aldehyde** may be readily obtained as the product of an aldol condensation.

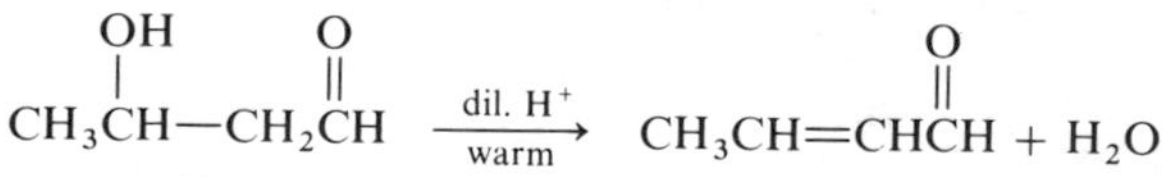

$$
\underset{\text{aldol}}{CH_3CH\!-\!CH_2CH} \xrightarrow[\text{warm}]{\text{dil. }H^+} \underset{\substack{\text{crotonaldehyde} \\ \text{(2-butenal)}}}{CH_3CH\!=\!CHCH} + H_2O
$$

$$
\xrightarrow[\text{warm}]{\text{dil. }H^+}
$$

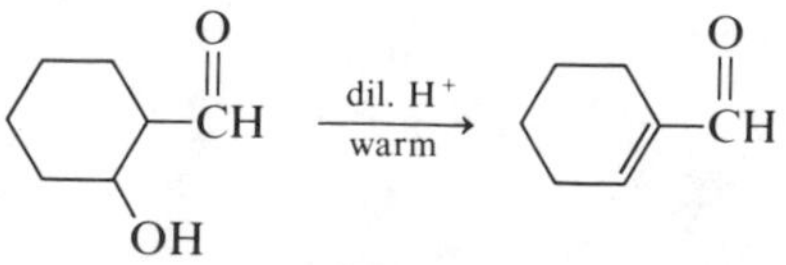

When dehydration leads to a double bond in conjugation with an aromatic ring, dehydration is often spontaneous.

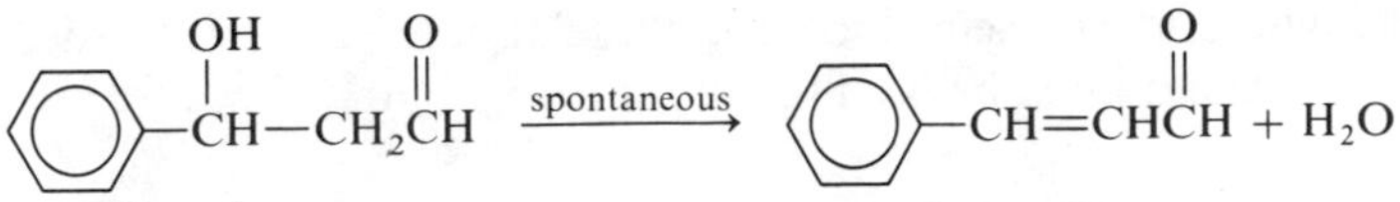

3-hydroxy-3-
phenylpropanal

cinnamaldehyde
(3-phenylpropenal)

B. Crossed Aldol Condensations

An aldehyde with no α hydrogens cannot form an enolate ion and thus cannot dimerize in an aldol condensation. However, if such an aldehyde is mixed with an aldehyde that *does* have an alpha hydrogen, a condensation between the two can occur. This reaction is called a **crossed aldol condensation**. A crossed aldol condensation is most useful when only one of the carbonyl compounds has an α hydrogen; otherwise, mixtures of products result.

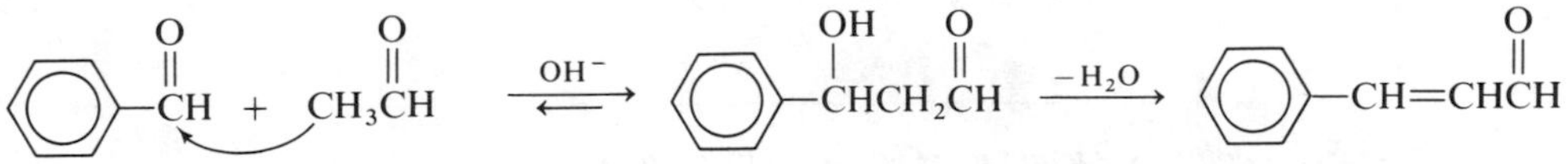

benzaldehyde   acetaldehyde
(*no α hydrogens*)

cinnamaldehyde

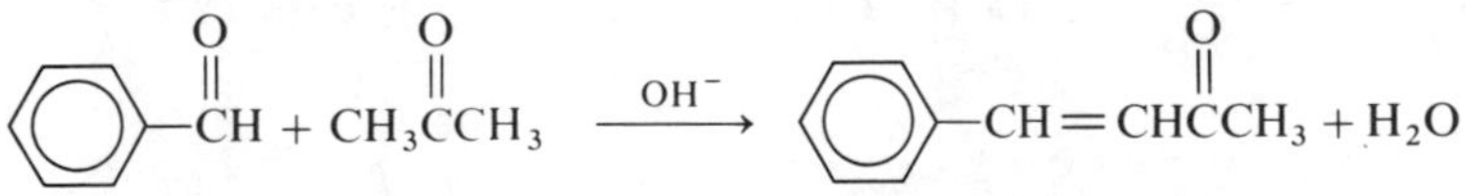

acetone

4-phenyl-3-buten-2-one
90%

2,2-dimethyl-
propanal

3-hydroxy-4,4-
dimethylpentanal

STUDY PROBLEM

14.18 Predict the major products:

(a) $C_6H_5CHO + CH_3CH_2CH_2CHO \xrightarrow{OH^-}$

(b) $C_6H_5CHO + CH_3CH_2\overset{O}{\overset{\|}{C}}CH_2CH_3 \xrightarrow{OH^-}$

C. Syntheses Using Aldol Condensations

In an aldol condensation, two types of product can result: (1) β-hydroxy aldehydes or ketones, and (2) α,β-unsaturated aldehydes or ketones (see Figure 14.2). In a synthetic problem, look for these functionalities and decide which aldehydes or ketones must be used for the starting materials.

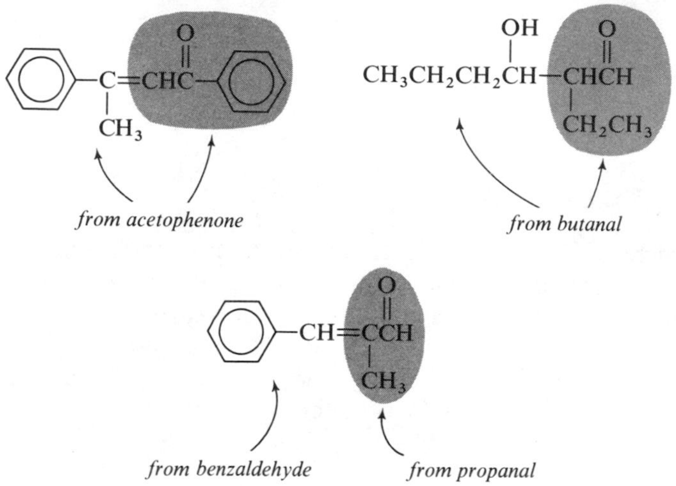

from acetophenone   *from butanal*

from benzaldehyde   *from propanal*

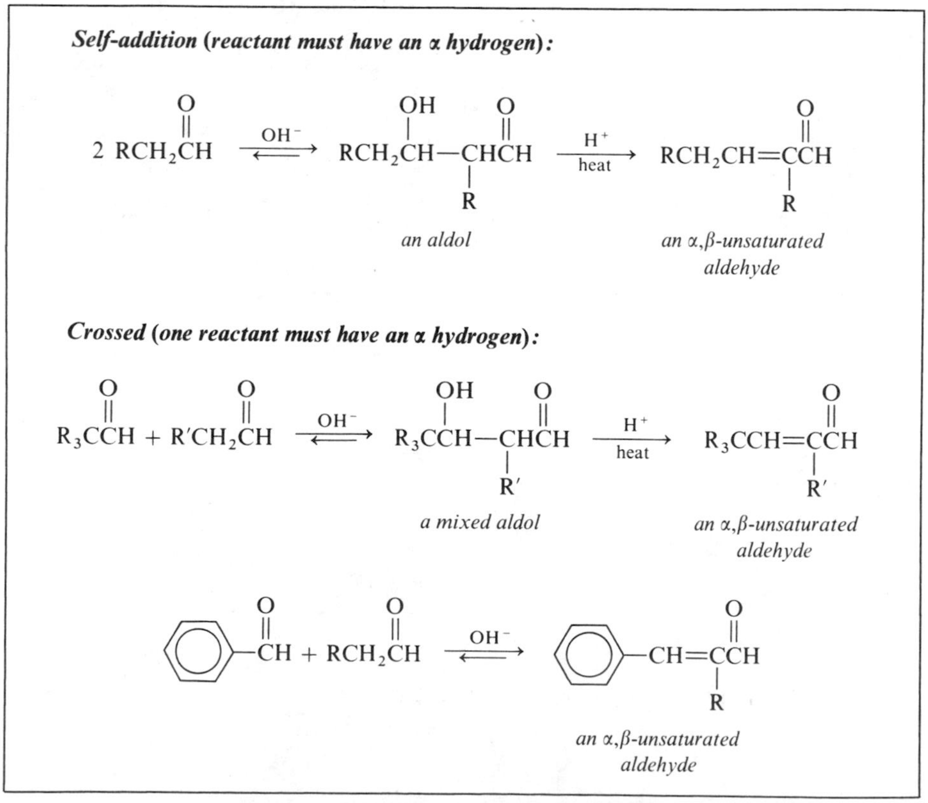

Figure 14.2. Products from aldol condensations.

Sample Problem

The following ketone can be prepared in 90% yield by a crossed aldol condensation:

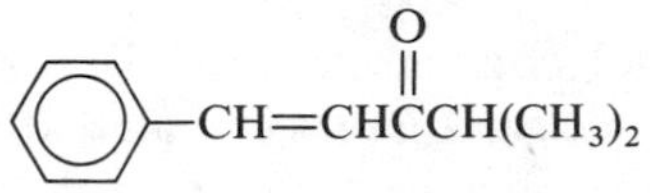

$$C_6H_5-CH=CHCCH(CH_3)_2$$ (with C=O)

What organic reactants are needed?

Solution: $C_6H_5CH=CHCCH(CH_3)_2$

from C_6H_5CH (with C=O)   *from* $CH_3CCH(CH_3)_2$ (with C=O)

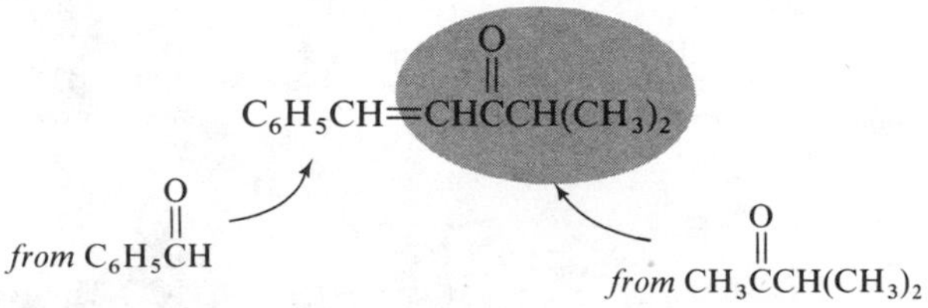

Sample Problem

How would you make the following conversion?

$$CH_3CCH_3 \longrightarrow CH_2=CHCCH_3$$

acetone   3-buten-2-one

Solution: $CH_2=CHCCH_3$

from HCHO   *from* CH_3CCH_3

$$HCH + CH_3CCH_3 \xrightarrow{OH^-} CH_2-CH_2CCH_3 \xrightarrow[\substack{heat \\ -H_2O}]{H^+} CH_2=CHCCH_3$$

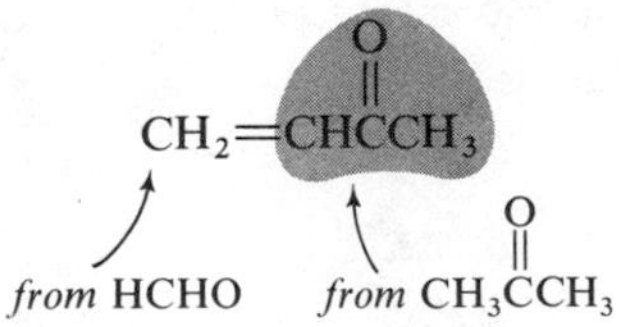

(with OH on first carbon)

STUDY PROBLEM

14.19 Suggest syntheses for the following compounds from aldehydes or ketones:

(a) $C_6H_5CH=CCHO$
        |
        CH_3

(b) 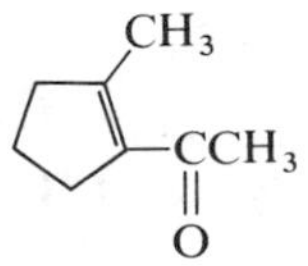 (cyclopentene ring with CH_3 and CCH_3 with C=O)

(c) (furan ring)$-CH=CHCH$ with C=O

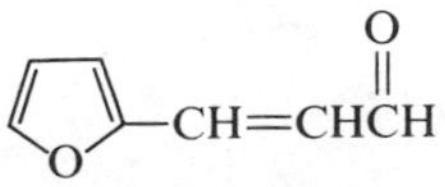

(d) 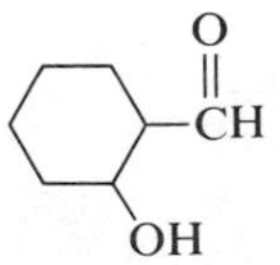 (cyclohexane ring with CH (C=O) and OH)

Section 14.7

Reactions Related to the Aldol Condensation

We have shown aldol condensations and crossed aldol condensations; however, for this type of condensation to occur, all that is needed is one compound with a carbonyl group plus one compound with an acidic hydrogen. The **Knoevenagel condensation** is the reaction of an aldehyde with a compound that has an acidic α hydrogen.

Knoevenagel condensation:

$$
\underset{\substack{\text{benzaldehyde}}}{\overset{\overset{\displaystyle O}{\overset{\|}{\text{—}\text{CH}}}}{\bigcirc\!\!\!\!\bigcirc}} + \underset{\text{malonic acid}}{CH_2(CO_2H)_2} \xrightarrow[\text{heat}]{NH_3} \underset{\substack{\text{cinnamic acid}\\ \text{(3-phenylpropenoic acid)}\\ 85\%}}{\bigcirc\!\!\!\!\bigcirc\text{—}CH\!\!=\!\!CHCO_2H} + H_2O + CO_2
$$

If ammonia or an amine is used as a base, malonic acid itself may be used, as in the preceding example. Under these conditions, diethyl malonate and similar compounds also give good yields of α,β-unsaturated products.

A variation of the Knoevenagel reaction allows the less reactive ketones to undergo condensation with the more acidic ethyl cyanoacetate ($pK_a = 9$, compared to $pK_a = 11$ for diethyl malonate).

$$
\bigcirc\!\!=\!\!O + \underset{\substack{\text{ethyl}\\ \text{cyanoacetate}}}{\overset{\overset{\displaystyle CN}{\diagup}}{\underset{\diagdown}{CH_2}}} \xrightarrow[\substack{\text{benzene}\\ \text{heat}}]{\substack{NH_4{}^+\ {}^-O_2CCH_3\\ \text{glacial } CH_3CO_2H}} \underset{80\%}{\bigcirc\!\!=\!\!\overset{\overset{\displaystyle CN}{\diagup}}{\underset{\diagdown}{C}}} + H_2O
$$

with $CO_2C_2H_5$ groups as shown.

Sample Problem

Suggest a technique for the preparation of $C_6H_5CH\!=\!CHNO_2$.

Solution:

$$C_6H_5CH\!=\!CHNO_2$$

from benzaldehyde   *from nitromethane*

$$
\underset{}{C_6H_5\overset{\overset{\displaystyle O}{\|}}{C}H} + CH_3NO_2 \underset{}{\overset{OH^-}{\rightleftarrows}} C_6H_5CH\!=\!CHNO_2 + H_2O
$$

How would you prepare the following compound?

$$\text{C}_6\text{H}_5-\text{CH}=\overset{\overset{\text{CN}}{|}}{\text{C}}-\text{C}_6\text{H}_5$$

Solution:

$$\text{C}_6\text{H}_5\text{CH}=\overset{\overset{\text{CN}}{|}}{\text{C}}\text{C}_6\text{H}_5$$

from $\text{C}_6\text{H}_5\text{CHO}$ ⟋ ⟍ *from* $\text{C}_6\text{H}_5\text{CH}_2\text{CN}$

$$\overset{\overset{\text{O}}{||}}{\text{C}_6\text{H}_5\text{CH}} + \overset{\overset{\text{CN}}{|}}{\text{CH}_2\text{C}_6\text{H}_5} \xrightarrow{\text{OH}^-} \text{C}_6\text{H}_5\text{CH}=\overset{\overset{\text{CN}}{|}}{\text{C}}\text{C}_6\text{H}_5 + \text{H}_2\text{O}$$

STUDY PROBLEM

14.20 Suggest synthetic routes to the following compounds:

(a) $(\text{CH}_3\text{CH}_2)_2\text{C}=\overset{\overset{\text{O}}{||}}{\underset{\underset{\text{CN}}{|}}{\text{C}}}\text{COC}_2\text{H}_5$ (b) ⬡$=\text{C}(\text{CN})_2$

Section 14.8

Cannizzaro Reaction

An aldehyde with no α hydrogen cannot undergo self-addition to yield an aldol product.

$$\overset{\overset{\text{O}}{||}}{\text{C}_6\text{H}_5-\text{CH}} \quad \text{or} \quad \overset{\overset{\text{O}}{||}}{\text{HCH}} \xrightarrow{\text{OH}^-} \text{no aldol product}$$

benzaldehyde   formaldehyde

If an aldehyde with no α hydrogen is heated with concentrated hydroxide solution, a disproportionation reaction occurs in which one half of the aldehyde molecules are oxidized to a carboxylic acid and one half are reduced to an alcohol. This reaction is known as the **Cannizzaro reaction**. Aldehydes with α hydrogens do not undergo this reaction; under these conditions, they undergo an aldol condensation.

$$2 \; \overset{\overset{\text{O}}{||}}{\text{C}_6\text{H}_5-\text{CH}} \xrightarrow[\text{heat}]{\text{conc. KOH}} \overset{\overset{\text{O}}{||}}{\text{C}_6\text{H}_5-\text{CO}^-} + \text{C}_6\text{H}_5-\text{CH}_2\text{OH}$$

benzoate ion   benzyl alcohol

$$2 \; \overset{\overset{\text{O}}{||}}{\text{HCH}} \xrightarrow[\text{heat}]{\text{conc. KOH}} \overset{\overset{\text{O}}{||}}{\text{HCO}^-} + \text{CH}_3\text{OH}$$

formate ion   methanol

The Cannizzaro reaction is initiated by attack of ⁻OH on the carbonyl carbon, followed by a hydride transfer.

Attack by ⁻OH:

$$\underset{}{\overset{O}{\underset{\|}{HC}}}-H + {}^{-}OH \longrightarrow \underset{OH}{\overset{O^-}{\underset{|}{HC}}}-H$$

Hydride transfer:

$$\underset{OH}{\overset{O^-}{\underset{|}{HC}}}-H \quad \overset{H}{\underset{H}{\diagdown}}C=O \longrightarrow \left[\underset{OH}{\overset{O}{\underset{\|}{HC}}} + CH_3O^- \right] \longrightarrow \underset{O^-}{\overset{O}{\underset{|}{HC}}} + CH_3OH$$

Section 14.9

Ester Condensations

Esters with alpha hydrogens can undergo self-condensation reactions to yield **β-keto esters**. An ester condensation is similar to an aldol condensation; the difference is that the —OR group of an ester can act as a leaving group. The result is therefore *substitution* (whereas aldol condensations are *additions*). Simple ester condensations, such as the following examples, are called **Claisen condensations**. (Note the naming of the keto ester products.)

$$2\ \overset{O}{\underset{\|}{CH_3COC_2H_5}} \xrightarrow{Na^+\ {}^-OC_2H_5} \overset{O}{\underset{\|}{CH_3C}}-CH_2\overset{O}{\underset{\|}{C}}OC_2H_5 + C_2H_5OH$$

ethyl acetate

ethyl acetoacetate
(ethyl 3-oxobutanoate)
75%

$$2\ \overset{O}{\underset{\|}{CH_3CH_2COC_2H_5}} \xrightarrow{Na^+\ {}^-OC_2H_5} \overset{O}{\underset{\|}{CH_3CH_2C}}-\underset{CH_3}{\overset{O}{\underset{|}{CH}}}\overset{O}{\underset{\|}{C}}OC_2H_5 + C_2H_5OH$$

ethyl propanoate

ethyl 2-methyl-3-oxopentanoate
45%

Let us look at the stepwise reaction. First is the *formation of the enolate of the ester* by an acid–base reaction with the alkoxide ion. (An alkoxide, rather than a hydroxide, is used as the base to prevent saponification of the ester; see Section 13.5C.) As in the aldol condensation, a low concentration of enolate is formed because the enolate (with only one carbonyl) is a stronger base than the alkoxide ion.

Enolate formation:

$$\overset{O}{\underset{\|}{CH_3COC_2H_5}} + {}^-OC_2H_5 \rightleftharpoons \left[\overset{O}{\underset{\|}{{}^-CH_2COC_2H_5}} \longleftrightarrow \overset{O^-}{\underset{|}{CH_2=COC_2H_5}} \right] + C_2H_5OH$$

ethyl acetate

resonance structures for enolate ion

The nucleophilic carbon then attacks the carbonyl group in a typical carbonyl *addition reaction*. This addition of the enolate is followed by *elimination of ROH*:

Attack on carbonyl group:

$$CH_3\overset{O}{\overset{\|}{C}}OC_2H_5 + {}^-CH_2CO_2C_2H_5 \longrightarrow \left[CH_3\overset{O^-}{\overset{|}{C}}OC_2H_5 \atop CH_2CO_2C_2H_5 \right]$$

Loss of ROH:

$$\left[CH_3\overset{O^-}{\overset{|}{C}}{-}OC_2H_5 \atop CH_2CO_2C_2H_5 \right] \longrightarrow \left[CH_3\overset{O}{\overset{\|}{C}} \atop CH_2CO_2C_2H_5 \right. \left. + \; {}^-OC_2H_5 \right] \rightleftharpoons$$

$$CH_3\overset{O}{\overset{\|}{C}}\bar{C}HCO_2C_2H_5 + HOC_2H_5$$

the enolate of
ethyl acetoacetate

The product β-keto ester is more acidic than an alcohol because it has hydrogens that are α to two carbonyl groups. Therefore, the product of the condensation is the enolate salt of the β-keto ester. The β-keto ester itself is produced when the reaction mixture is acidified with cold, dilute mineral acid.

$$CH_3\overset{O}{\overset{\|}{C}}\bar{C}HCO_2C_2H_5 \xrightarrow{H^+} CH_3\overset{O}{\overset{\|}{C}}CH_2CO_2C_2H_5$$

ethyl acetoacetate
a β-keto ester

A β-keto ester may be hydrolyzed in acidic solution, in which case decarboxylation may occur.

Hydrolysis and decarboxylation:

$$CH_3\overset{O}{\overset{\|}{C}}CH_2CO_2C_2H_5 \xrightarrow[-C_2H_5OH]{H^+, H_2O, heat} CH_3\overset{O}{\overset{\|}{C}}CH_2CO_2H \xrightarrow[heat]{-CO_2} CH_3\overset{O}{\overset{\|}{C}}CH_3$$

a β-keto ester   *a ketone*

Sample Problem

Predict the product of the ester condensation of methyl butanoate with sodium methoxide as the base, followed by acidification.

Solution:

(1) Write the structure of the starting ester, and determine the structure of the enolate ion.

$$CH_3CH_2CH_2\overset{O}{\overset{\|}{C}}OCH_3 + {}^-OCH_3 \rightleftharpoons CH_3CH_2\overset{-}{C}H\overset{O}{\overset{\|}{C}}OCH_3 + CH_3OH$$

(2)   Give the equation for nucleophilic attack on the carbonyl group and loss of ROH.

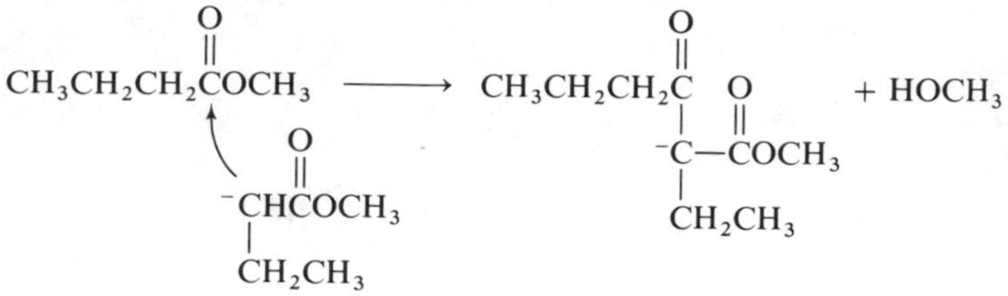

$$CH_3CH_2CH_2\overset{\displaystyle O}{\overset{\|}{C}}OCH_3 \longrightarrow CH_3CH_2CH_2\overset{\displaystyle O}{\overset{\|}{C}}\,O + HOCH_3$$

with attacking group $^-CHCOCH_3$ bearing CH_2CH_3, and product side showing $^-C-COCH_3$ bearing CH_2CH_3

(3)   Acidify:

$$\xrightarrow{H^+} CH_3CH_2CH_2\overset{\displaystyle O}{\overset{\|}{C}}\overset{\displaystyle O}{\underset{\underset{\displaystyle CH_2CH_3}{|}}{\overset{\|}{C}}}HCOCH_3$$

(4)   Write the equation for the overall reaction:

$$2\ CH_3CH_2CH_2\overset{\displaystyle O}{\overset{\|}{C}}OCH_3 \xrightarrow[\text{(2) H}^+]{\text{(1) Na}^+\ ^-OCH_3} CH_3CH_2CH_2\overset{\displaystyle O}{\overset{\|}{C}}\overset{\displaystyle O}{\underset{\underset{\displaystyle CH_2CH_3}{|}}{\overset{\|}{C}}}HCOCH_3$$

STUDY PROBLEM

14.21 Predict the major organic product:

(a) $C_6H_5CH_2CO_2C_2H_5 \xrightarrow[\text{(2) H}^+]{\text{(1) Na}^+\ ^-OC_2H_5}$

(b)   [the product from (a)] $\xrightarrow[\text{heat}]{H_2O,\ H^+}$

Sample Problem

A Claisen-like condensation, called a **Dieckmann ring closure**, is used to prepare the following cyclic ketone from a diester. What is the structure of the diester?

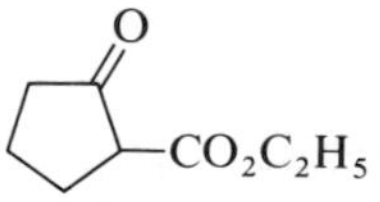

Solution: Since the keto group arises from attack of an alpha carbon, the ring must be closed at the following position:

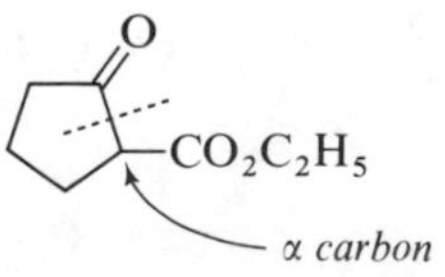

Therefore, the starting diester must be diethyl adipate.

$$
\underset{\substack{\text{diethyl adipate} \\ \text{(diethyl hexanedioate)}}}{\overset{\displaystyle \overset{O}{\overset{\|}{C}OC_2H_5}}{\underset{\displaystyle CH_2}{\underset{\displaystyle H_2C \quad CH_2CO_2C_2H_5}{H_2C}}}}
\quad \underset{\longrightarrow}{\overset{^-OC_2H_5}{\rightleftharpoons}} \quad
\underset{\displaystyle CH_2}{\underset{\displaystyle H_2C \quad \overset{-}{C}HCO_2C_2H_5}{\overset{\displaystyle \overset{O}{\overset{\|}{C}OC_2H_5}}{H_2C}}}
\quad \xrightarrow{-C_2H_5OH} \quad \xrightarrow{H^+}
$$

$$
\underset{\displaystyle CH_2}{\underset{\displaystyle H_2C \quad CHCO_2C_2H_5}{\overset{\displaystyle H_2C-C}{\overset{\displaystyle \overset{O}{\|}}{}}}}
$$

STUDY PROBLEM

14.22 Give the equations for the preparation of the following cyclic compounds from open-chain starting materials:

(a) [cyclohexanone with $-CO_2H$ substituent]   (b) [cyclopentanone with H_3C, CH_3 and $-CO_2CH_3$ substituents]

A. Crossed Claisen Condensations

Two different esters may be used in the Claisen condensation. Best results (that is, avoidance of mixtures) are obtained if only one of the esters has an alpha hydrogen.

$$
\underset{\text{no } \alpha \text{ hydrogen}}{C_6H_5-\overset{O}{\overset{\|}{C}}OCH_3} + CH_3CH_2CO_2CH_3 \xrightarrow[\text{(2) H}^+]{\text{(1) Na}^+ \ ^-OCH_3} \underset{\substack{CH_3 \\ 45\%}}{C_6H_5-\overset{O}{\overset{\|}{C}}\overset{|}{C}HCO_2CH_3} + CH_3OH
$$

$$
\underset{\text{no } \alpha \text{ hydrogen}}{H\overset{O}{\overset{\|}{C}}OC_2H_5} + CH_3CO_2C_2H_5 \xrightarrow[\text{(2) H}^+]{\text{(1) Na}^+ \ ^-OC_2H_5} H\overset{O}{\overset{\|}{C}}CH_2CO_2C_2H_5 + C_2H_5OH
$$

Crossed Claisen condensations may be successfully carried out between ketones and esters. The α hydrogen of the ketone is removed preferentially because ketones are more acidic than esters. For this reason, the crossed Claisen is favored over a self-Claisen condensation of the ester.

$$
\underset{\text{ethyl benzoate}}{C_6H_5-\overset{O}{\overset{\|}{C}}OC_2H_5} + \underset{\text{acetone}}{CH_3\overset{O}{\overset{\|}{C}}CH_3} \xrightarrow[\text{(2) H}^+]{\text{(1) Na}^+ \ ^-OC_2H_5} \underset{\substack{\text{1-phenyl-1,3-butanedione} \\ 40\%}}{C_6H_5-\overset{O}{\overset{\|}{C}}-CH_2\overset{O}{\overset{\|}{C}}CH_3} + C_2H_5OH
$$

Sample Problem

A mixture of acetone and diethyl oxalate $(C_2H_5O_2C\!-\!CO_2C_2H_5)$ is added to a mixture of sodium ethoxide in ethanol. After the reaction is completed, the mixture is treated with cold, dilute HCl. A condensation product is isolated from the mixture in 60% yield. What is the product?

Solution:

$$(1) \quad CH_3\overset{O}{\overset{\|}{C}}CH_3 + {}^-OC_2H_5 \rightleftharpoons {}^-CH_2\overset{O}{\overset{\|}{C}}CH_3 + HOC_2H_5$$

$$(2) \quad C_2H_5O\overset{O}{\overset{\|}{C}}\!-\!\overset{O}{\overset{\|}{C}}OC_2H_5 + {}^-CH_2\overset{O}{\overset{\|}{C}}CH_3 \xrightarrow{\quad} \xrightarrow{H^+}$$

$$\underbrace{C_2H_5O\overset{O}{\overset{\|}{C}}\!-\!\overset{O}{\overset{\|}{C}}}_{from\ diethyl\ oxalate}\!-\!\underbrace{CH_2\overset{O}{\overset{\|}{C}}CH_3}_{from\ acetone} + HOC_2H_5$$

STUDY PROBLEM

14.23 Predict the products:

(a) $\quad C_2H_5O_2C\!-\!CO_2C_2H_5 + CH_3CO_2C_2H_5 \xrightarrow[\ (2)\ H^+\ ]{\ (1)\ Na^+\ ^-OC_2H_5\ }$

(b) $\quad \overset{}{\bigcirc}\!\!=\!\!O + CH_3CO_2C_2H_5 \xrightarrow[\ (2)\ H^+\ ]{\ (1)\ Na^+\ ^-OC_2H_5\ }$

B. Syntheses Using Ester Condensations

Since the product of an ester condensation between two esters is a β-keto ester (or a ketone after hydrolysis and decarboxylation), the decision of which starting materials to use is not difficult. The keto group comes from one starting ester; the ester group with its attachment comes from the other starting ester. The different types of products from ester condensations are summarized in Figure 14.3.

$$CH_3CH_2CH_2\overset{O}{\overset{\|}{C}}\!-\!\underset{\underset{CH_2CH_3}{|}}{CHCO_2C_2H_5}$$

from ethyl butanoate

$$\bigcirc\!\!-\!\overset{O}{\overset{\|}{C}}\!-\!\underset{\underset{CH_2CH_3}{|}}{CHCO_2H} \qquad \bigcirc\!\!-\!\overset{O}{\overset{\|}{C}}\!-\!CH_2CH_2CH_3$$

from ethyl benzoate   *from ethyl butanoate*   *from ethyl benzoate*

from ethyl butanoate (after decarboxylation)

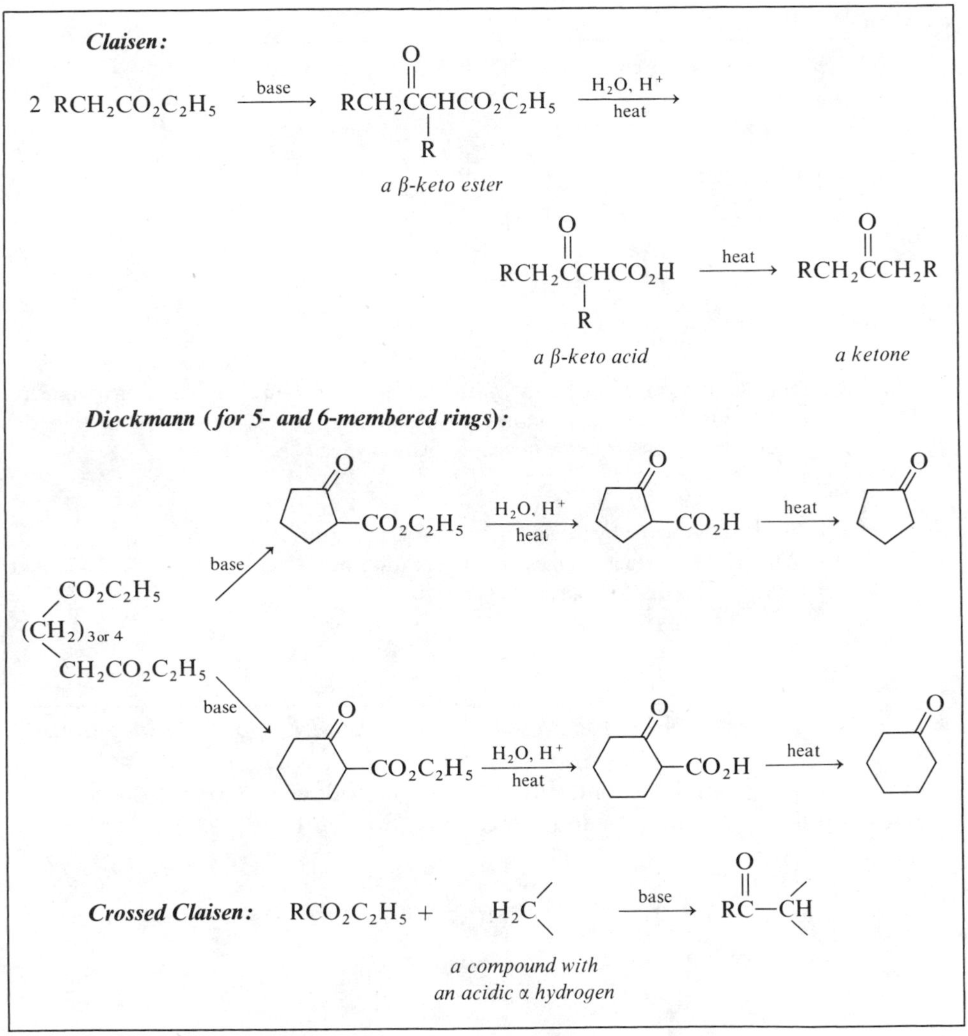

Claisen:

$$2 \ RCH_2CO_2C_2H_5 \xrightarrow{\text{base}} RCH_2\overset{\overset{\displaystyle O}{\|}}{C}\underset{\underset{\displaystyle R}{|}}{CH}CO_2C_2H_5 \xrightarrow[\text{heat}]{H_2O,\ H^+}$$

a β-keto ester

$$RCH_2\overset{\overset{\displaystyle O}{\|}}{C}\underset{\underset{\displaystyle R}{|}}{CH}CO_2H \xrightarrow{\text{heat}} RCH_2\overset{\overset{\displaystyle O}{\|}}{C}CH_2R$$

a β-keto acid   *a ketone*

Dieckmann (for 5- and 6-membered rings):

Crossed Claisen: $RCO_2C_2H_5$ + $H_2C\big\langle$ $\xrightarrow{\text{base}}$ $R\overset{\overset{\displaystyle O}{\|}}{C}-CH\big\langle$

*a compound with
an acidic α hydrogen*

Figure 14.3.   Products of ester condensations.

What reactants would you need to prepare the following compound by an ester condensation?

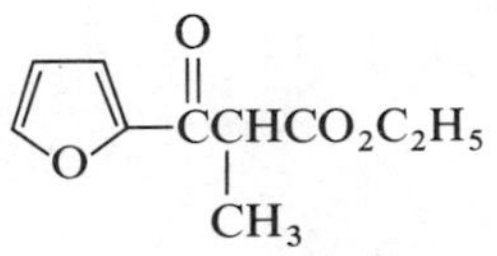

Solution:

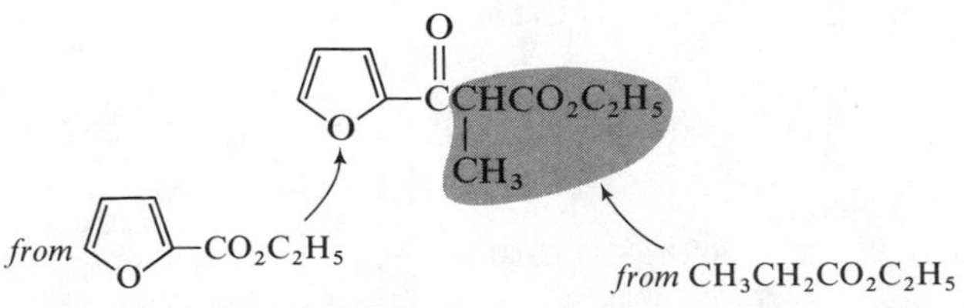

STUDY PROBLEMS

14.24 Give equations for preparations of the following compounds:

(a) [structure: a cyclohexanone ring with CH_3 at top and CO_2H at bottom, $=O$ on the ring]

(b) [structure: benzene ring]$-\overset{\overset{\displaystyle O}{\|}}{C}CH_2CO_2H$

(c) [structure: benzene ring]$-\overset{\overset{\displaystyle O}{\|}}{C}CH(CN)_2$

(d) $(CH_3)_3C\overset{\overset{\displaystyle O}{\|}}{C}CH_2\overset{\overset{\displaystyle O}{\|}}{C}CH_3$

14.25 Ester condensations are used for the synthesis of hydrocarbon chains in living organisms. Fatty acids, for example, are synthesized from acetyl groups by way of the thioester acetylcoenzyme A, the structure of which was shown in Section 13.8.

(a) Indicate the acidic hydrogens in the abbreviated structure $CH_3\overset{\overset{\displaystyle O}{\|}}{C}SCoA$.

(b) What is the product of an ester condensation between two molecules of acetylcoenzyme A? (Use the abbreviated structure.)

Section 14.10

Nucleophilic Addition to α,β-Unsaturated Carbonyl Compounds

A double bond in conjugation with a carbonyl group is susceptible to nucleophilic attack in a 1,4-addition reaction (Section 11.19).

$$CH_2{=}CH{-}\overset{\overset{\displaystyle O}{\|}}{C}CH_3 + :NH_3 \longrightarrow \left[\begin{array}{c} \overset{\displaystyle O^-}{|} \\ CH_2{-}CH{=}CCH_3 \\ \overset{\displaystyle |}{^+NH_3} \end{array} \right] \longrightarrow CH_2CH_2\overset{\overset{\displaystyle O}{\|}}{C}CH_3 \atop | \atop NH_2$$

an enol

If an α,β-unsaturated carbonyl compound can undergo nucleophilic attack, we might expect that an enolate ion could add to the double bond. Indeed, it does. This useful synthetic reaction is called a **Michael addition**.

$$CH_2{=}CH{-}\overset{\overset{\displaystyle O}{\|}}{C}H + {}^-CH(CO_2C_2H_5)_2 \rightleftharpoons \left[\begin{array}{c} \overset{\displaystyle O^-}{|} \\ CH_2{-}CH{=}CH \\ \overset{\displaystyle |}{CH(CO_2C_2H_5)_2} \end{array} \right] \overset{H^+}{\rightleftharpoons} CH_2CH_2\overset{\overset{\displaystyle O}{\|}}{C}H \atop | \atop CH(CO_2C_2H_5)_2$$

an enol ⟶ 50%

[benzene ring]$-CH{=}CH{-}\overset{\overset{\displaystyle O}{\|}}{C}OC_2H_5 + {}^-CH(CO_2C_2H_5)_2 \rightleftharpoons$

$$\left[[benzene ring]{-}CH{-}CH{=}\overset{\overset{\displaystyle O^-}{|}}{C}OC_2H_5 \atop \quad\quad | \atop \quad CH(CO_2C_2H_5)_2 \right] \overset{H^+}{\rightleftharpoons} [benzene ring]{-}CHCH_2\overset{\overset{\displaystyle O}{\|}}{C}OC_2H_5 \atop | \atop CH(CO_2C_2H_5)_2$$

98%

The product of the last example shown is a triester. Saponification, followed by acidification, gives a triacid. Under the conditions of acid hydrolysis, decarboxylation may occur.

Hydrolysis and decarboxylation:

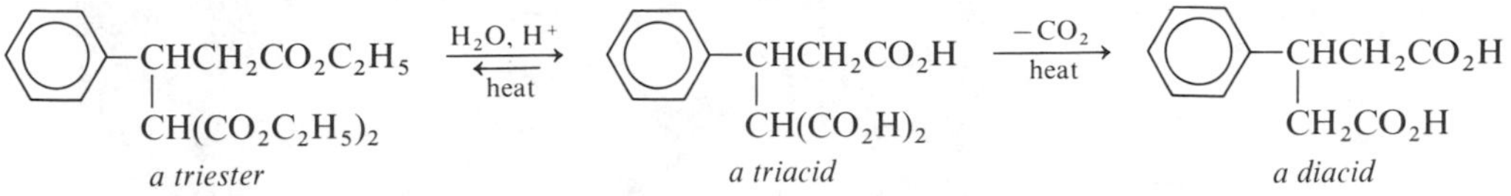

In the decarboxylation of the triacid, it is the malonic acid grouping that loses CO_2. (Why?) This group is circled in the following equation.

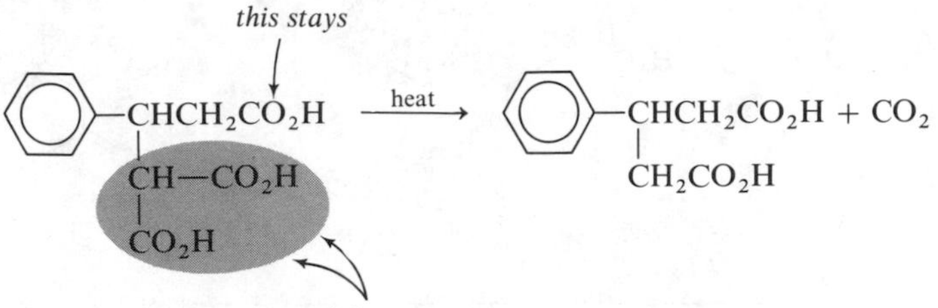

The types of products that we can obtain from simple Michael additions are shown in Figure 14.4. Michael additions in combination with other condensations are exceedingly useful in laboratory syntheses of complex cyclic compounds, such

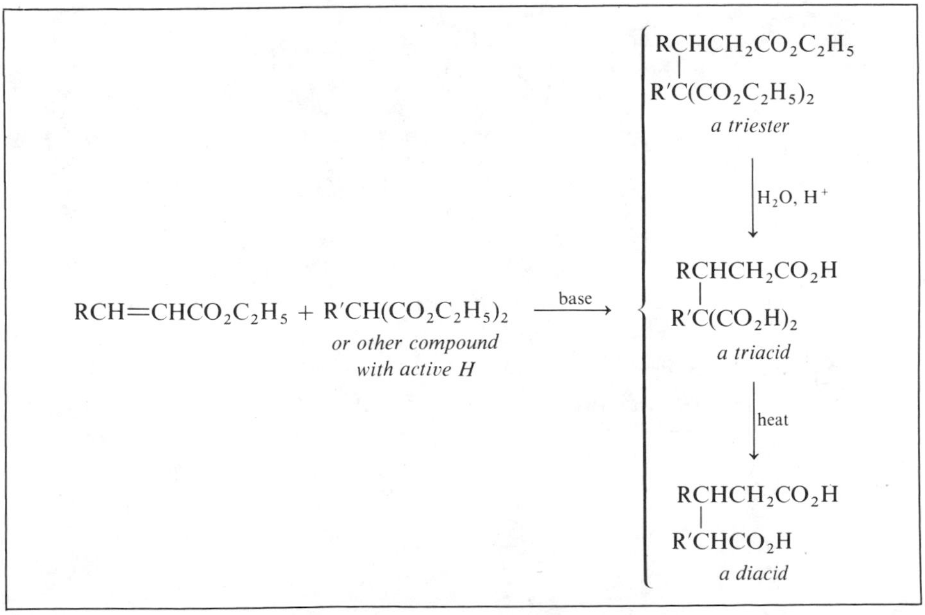

Figure 14.4. Products of Michael additions of malonic ester with an α,β-unsaturated ester.

as steroids. A portion of one such synthesis is shown. This particular ring-forming sequence (Michael plus aldol) is called a **Robinson annelation**.

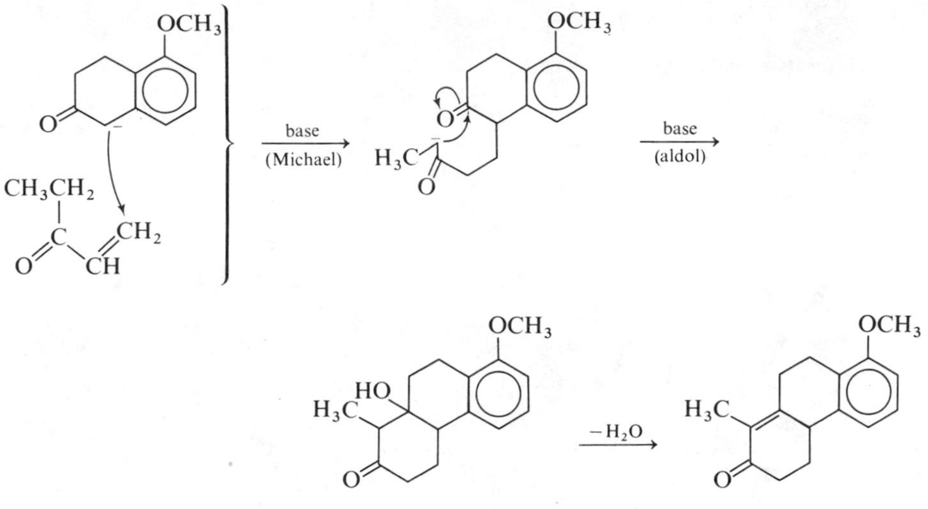

Sample Problem

Show by equations how you would prepare the following keto acid by a Michael addition:

$$\underset{\text{O}}{\overset{\text{O}}{\parallel}}$$
$$CH_3CCH_2CH_2CH_2CO_2H$$

Solution: Addition occurs β to the keto group in a 1,4-addition.

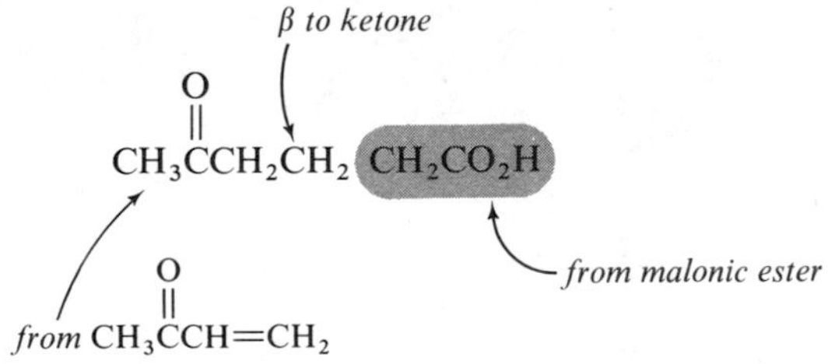

β to ketone

$$CH_3CCH_2CH_2\,\boxed{CH_2CO_2H}$$

from malonic ester

from $CH_3CCH=CH_2$

(1) $CH_2(CO_2C_2H_5)_2 \underset{\longleftarrow}{\overset{NaOC_2H_5}{\longrightarrow}} \ ^-CH(CO_2C_2H_5)_2$

(2) $CH_3C-CH=CH_2 + \ ^-CH(CO_2C_2H_5)_2 \rightleftharpoons CH_3C=CHCH_2CH(CO_2C_2H_5)_2$

$\xrightarrow{H^+} CH_3CCH_2CH_2CH(CO_2C_2H_5)_2$

(3) $\xrightarrow[\text{heat}]{H_2O, H^+} CH_3CCH_2CH_2CH_2CO_2H$

Sample Problem

A chemist decided to try the sequence of reactions in the preceding sample problem. After Step 2, he discovered that he had a *cyclic* product, along with the keto diester that he had predicted. What happened?

Solution: The initial product of Step 2 underwent a Dieckmann ring closure. (Note that this intermediate has a nucleophilic carbon that can attack a carbonyl group to yield a six-membered ring.)

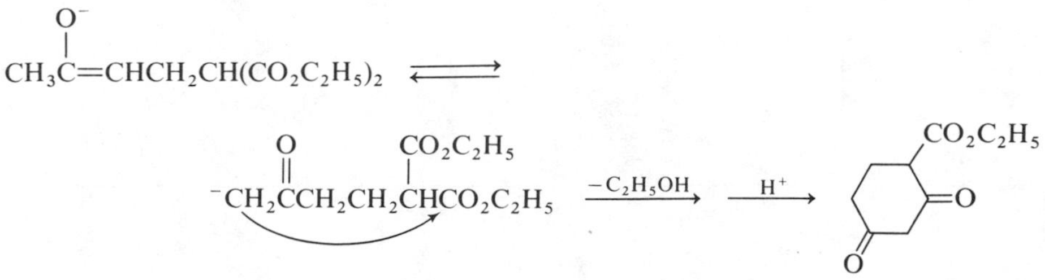

$$CH_3\overset{\overset{\displaystyle O^-}{|}}{C}=CHCH_2CH(CO_2C_2H_5)_2 \;\rightleftharpoons$$

$$^-CH_2\overset{\overset{\displaystyle O}{\|}}{C}CH_2CH_2\overset{\overset{\displaystyle CO_2C_2H_5}{|}}{C}HCO_2C_2H_5 \xrightarrow{-C_2H_5OH} \xrightarrow{H^+}$$

STUDY PROBLEM

14.26 If the chemist had subjected the cyclic product in the preceding sample problem to acid hydrolysis and then distilled the organic material, what final product would he have observed?

Sample Problem

How would you prepare the following keto ester by a Michael addition?

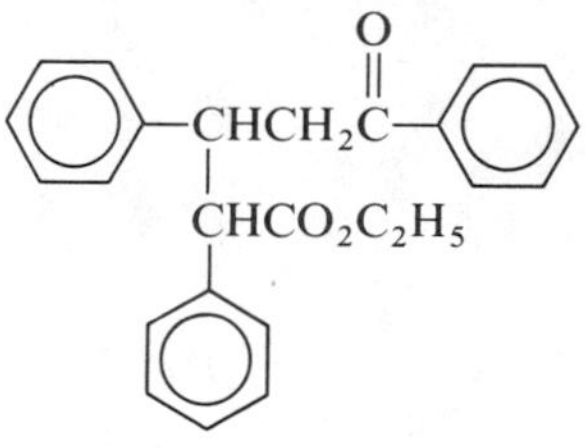

Solution: Addition occurs β to the ketone.

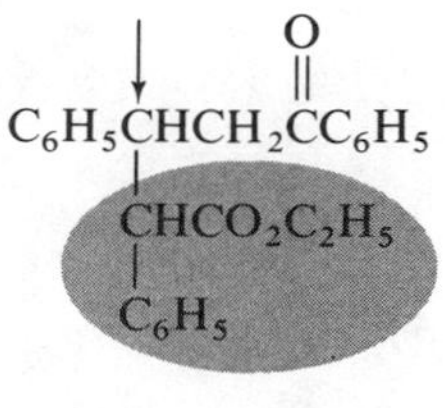

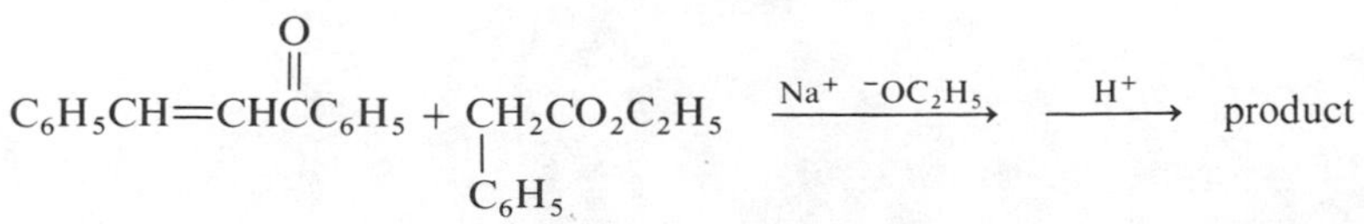

$$C_6H_5\overset{\downarrow}{C}HCH_2\overset{\overset{\displaystyle O}{\|}}{C}C_6H_5$$

$$\overset{\overset{\displaystyle CHCO_2C_2H_5}{|}}{\underset{\displaystyle C_6H_5}{}}$$

$$C_6H_5CH=CH\overset{\overset{\displaystyle O}{\|}}{C}C_6H_5 + \underset{\overset{\displaystyle |}{C_6H_5}}{CH_2CO_2C_2H_5} \xrightarrow{Na^+ \; ^-OC_2H_5} \xrightarrow{H^+} \text{product}$$

STUDY PROBLEM

14.27 Show by equations how you would prepare the following carboxylic acids by Michael additions:

(a) 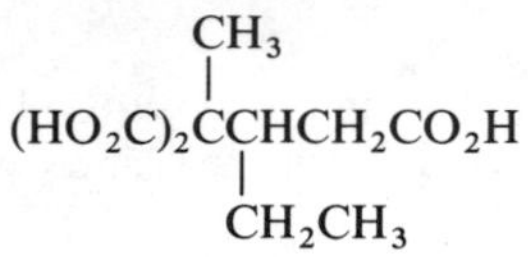 $(HO_2C)_2\overset{\displaystyle CH_3}{\underset{\displaystyle CH_2CH_3}{C}}CHCH_2CO_2H$ (b) $HO_2CCH_2\overset{}{\underset{\displaystyle CH_3}{C}}HCH_2CO_2H$

(c)

$$\overset{\displaystyle CO_2H}{\underset{\displaystyle C(CH_3)_3}{\bigcirc}}\!\!-CH_2CO_2H$$

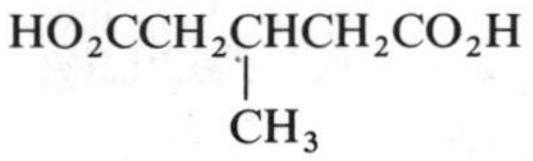

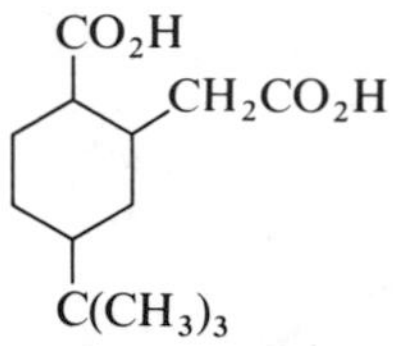

SUMMARY

In this chapter, we have looked at a variety of ways to synthesize compounds with complex carbon skeletons. Each of these reactions is caused by a species with carbanion character.

Alkylations: $\diagdown CH^- + RX \longrightarrow \diagdown CHR + X^-$

Condensations: $\diagdown CH^- + R-\overset{\displaystyle O}{\overset{\|}{C}}-R \longrightarrow R-\overset{\displaystyle OH}{\underset{\displaystyle -CH-}{\overset{|}{\underset{|}{C}}}}-R$

1,4-Additions: $\diagdown CH^- + CH_2=CH\overset{\displaystyle O}{\overset{\|}{C}}- \longrightarrow CH_2-CH_2\overset{\displaystyle O}{\overset{\|}{C}}-$

Table 14.2 gives an overview of the more important products available from these reactions.

Table 14.2. **Major Synthetic Reactions**

Malonic ester:	$CH_2(CO_2C_2H_5)_2$	$\xrightarrow[\text{(3) R'X}]{\overset{\text{(1) }^-OC_2H_5}{\text{(2) RX}}}$ $\underset{R'}{\overset{R}{\diagup}}C(CO_2C_2H_5)_2$
Acetoacetic ester:	$CH_3\overset{\displaystyle O}{\overset{\|}{C}}CH_2CO_2C_2H_5$	$\xrightarrow[\text{(3) R'X}]{\overset{\text{(1) }^-OC_2H_5}{\text{(2) RX}}}$ $CH_3\overset{\displaystyle O}{\overset{\|}{C}}\underset{R\ \ R'}{\overset{}{C}}CO_2C_2H_5$
Aldol condensation:	$2\ RCH_2CHO$	$\overset{OH^-}{\rightleftharpoons}$ $RCH_2\overset{\displaystyle OH}{\overset{|}{C}}H\underset{R}{\overset{}{C}}HCHO$
Crossed aldol:	$RCHO + R'CH_2CHO$	$\overset{OH^-}{\rightleftharpoons}$ $R\overset{\displaystyle OH}{\overset{|}{C}}H\underset{R'}{\overset{}{C}}HCHO$
Claisen condensation:	$2\ RCH_2CO_2C_2H_5$	$\xrightarrow[\text{(2) H}^+]{\text{(1) }^-OC_2H_5}$ $RCH_2\overset{\displaystyle O}{\overset{\|}{C}}\underset{R}{\overset{}{C}}HCO_2C_2H_5$
Crossed Claisen:	$R\overset{\displaystyle O}{\overset{\|}{C}}OC_2H_5 + R'CH_2CO_2C_2H_5$	$\xrightarrow[\text{(2) H}^+]{\text{(1) }^-OC_2H_5}$ $R\overset{\displaystyle O}{\overset{\|}{C}}\underset{R'}{\overset{}{C}}HCO_2C_2H_5$

Michael addition:

$$RCH{=}CHCO_2C_2H_5 + R'CH(CO_2C_2H_5)_2 \xrightarrow[\text{(2) H}^+]{\text{(1) }^-OC_2H_5} \underset{R'C(CO_2C_2H_5)_2}{RCH{-}CH_2CO_2C_2H_5}$$

STUDY PROBLEMS

14.28 In each structure, indicate the most acidic hydrogen:

(a) $C_6H_5CHCO_2C_2H_5$
          |
         CH_3

(b) $CH_3\overset{\displaystyle O}{\overset{\|}{C}}CH_2CN$

(c) $H\overset{\displaystyle O}{\overset{\|}{C}}CHCH=CH\overset{\displaystyle O}{\overset{\|}{C}}H$
            |
           CH_3

(d) $(CH_3)_3CCH_2CO_2H$

(e) $CH_3CH_2NO_2$

(f) $CH_3CCl_2CHCl_2$

14.29 Write an equation for the reversible acid–base reaction of each of the following compounds with sodium ethoxide in ethanol:

(a) $C_2H_5\overset{\displaystyle O}{\overset{\|}{O}C}CH_2CN$

(b) $C_6H_5CH_2CN$

(c)

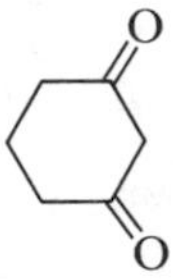

(d) $CH_3CH_2\overset{\displaystyle O}{\overset{\|}{C}}CH\overset{\displaystyle O}{\overset{\|}{C}}CH_2CH_3$
                |
                CH_3

(e) 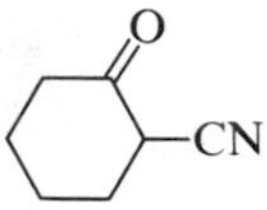 —CN

14.30 Write resonance structures for each of the following anions:

(a) $C_6H_5CH_2{}^-$

(b) $C_6H_5\overset{-}{C}H\overset{\displaystyle O}{\overset{\|}{C}}CH_3$

(c) $C_6H_5CH_2\overset{\displaystyle O}{\overset{\|}{C}}CH_2{}^-$

(d) $^-CH_2CH=CHCO_2C_2H_5$

(e) $CH_3CH_2CH_2\overset{\displaystyle O}{\overset{\|}{C}}CH_2{}^-$

(f) $CH_3\overset{\displaystyle O}{\overset{\|}{C}}\overset{-}{C}HCN$

14.31 Rank the following compounds in order of increasing acid strength (weakest acid first):

(a) 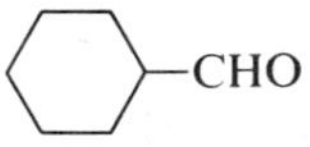 —CHO

(b) 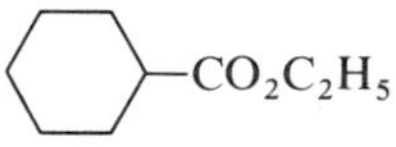 —$CO_2C_2H_5$

(c) 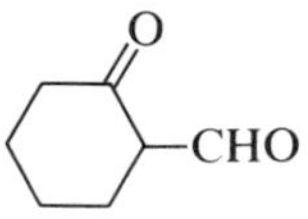 —CHO

(d) 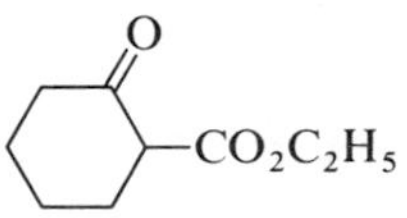 —$CO_2C_2H_5$

(e) C_2H_5OH

(f) 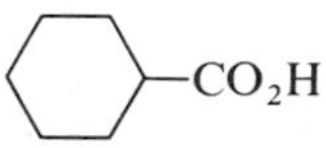 —CO_2H

14.32 Complete the following equations for *acid–base reactions*, and indicate by arrow size if each equilibrium is to the right or to the left:

(a) $^-CH_2CO_2C_2H_5 + CH_3\overset{\displaystyle O}{\overset{\|}{C}}CH_2CO_2C_2H_5 \;\rightleftharpoons$

(b) $CH_3\overset{\displaystyle O}{\overset{\|}{C}}CH_2NO_2 + OH^- \;\rightleftharpoons$

(c) 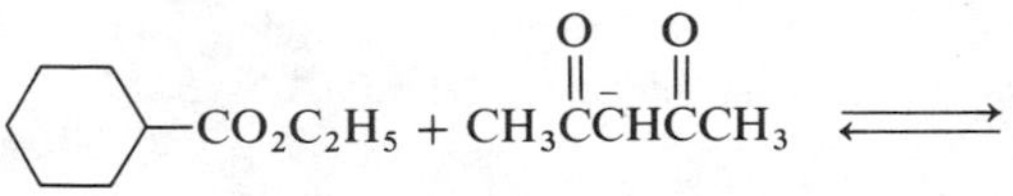 —CO$_2$C$_2$H$_5$ + CH$_3$CCHCCH$_3$ $\rightleftharpoons$

(with O, O double bonds and negative charge)

(d) CH$_3$CO$_2$C$_2$H$_5$ + $^-$CH$_2$CCH$_3$ $\rightleftharpoons$

(with O double bond)

14.33 Predict the major organic product:

(a) 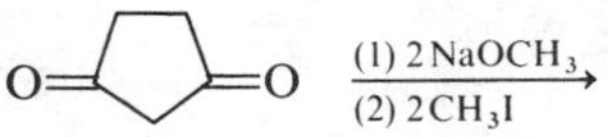 O==O $\xrightarrow[\text{(2) 2 CH}_3\text{I}]{\text{(1) 2 NaOCH}_3}$

(b) 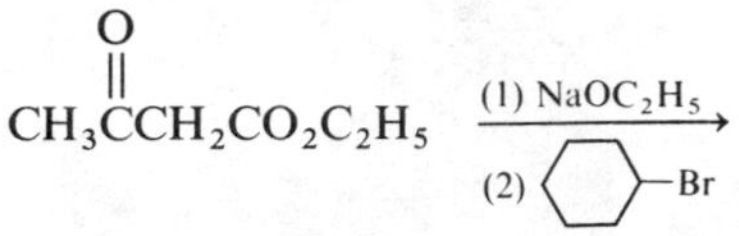 CH$_3$CCH$_2$CO$_2$C$_2$H$_5$ $\xrightarrow[\text{(2)}]{\text{(1) NaOC}_2\text{H}_5}$ —Br

(with O double bond)

(c) [the product from (b)] $\xrightarrow[\text{heat}]{\text{H}_2\text{O, H}^+}$

(d) 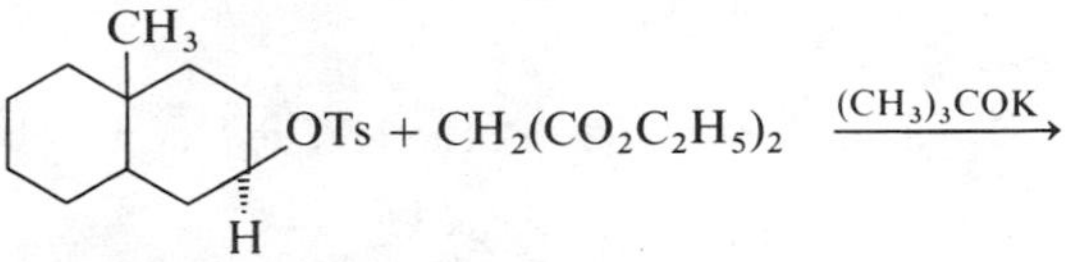 —OTs + CH$_2$(CO$_2$C$_2$H$_5$)$_2$ $\xrightarrow{\text{(CH}_3)_3\text{COK}}$

(*Hint*: See Section 7.16C.)

(e) 2 CH$_2$(CO$_2$C$_2$H$_5$)$_2$ $\xrightarrow[\text{(2) CH}_2\text{I}_2]{\text{(1) NaOC}_2\text{H}_5}$

(f) [the product from (e)] $\xrightarrow[\text{heat}]{\text{H}_2\text{O, H}^+}$

(g) CH$_3$CCH$_2$CO$_2$C$_2$H$_5$ $\xrightarrow[\text{(2) BrCH}_2\text{CCH}_3]{\text{(1) NaOC}_2\text{H}_5}$

(with O double bonds)

(h) [the product from (g)] $\xrightarrow[\text{heat}]{\text{H}_2\text{O, H}^+}$

14.34 How would you prepare each of the following compounds from diethyl malonate or ethyl acetoacetate?

(a) 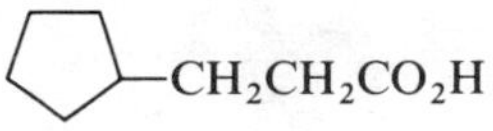 —CH$_2$CH$_2$CO$_2$H   (b) HO$_2$CCH$_2$CHCO$_2$H
                                                              |
                                                              CH$_3$

(c) C$_6$H$_5$CH$_2$CH$_2$CCH$_3$ (d) 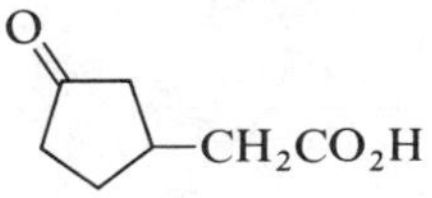 —CH$_2$CO$_2$H

(with O double bond)

14.35 What solvent, base, and alkyl halide would you use in the following conversion?

CH$_2$(CO$_2$CH$_3$)$_2$ $\longrightarrow$ (CH$_3$)$_2$CHCH(CO$_2$CH$_3$)$_2$

14.36 In the preparation of diethyl methylpentylmalonate, why would it be better to treat diethyl malonate first with *n*-pentyl bromide and second with methyl iodide (rather than with methyl iodide first)?

14.37 Show the mechanism for the formation of the enamine of cyclopentanone and piperidine, followed by reaction with benzoyl chloride (C_6H_5COCl).

14.38 Show with equations how you could synthesize the following ketones from cyclohexanone:

(a) 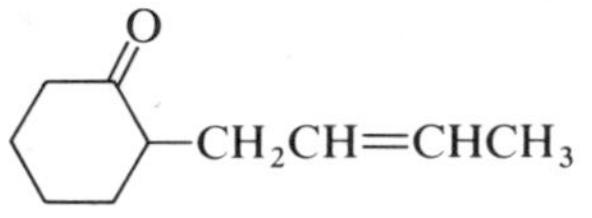 [cyclohexanone ring]—$CH_2CH{=}CHCH_3$ (b) 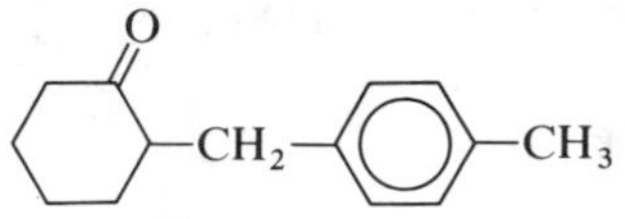 [cyclohexanone ring]—CH_2—[benzene ring]—CH_3

(c) 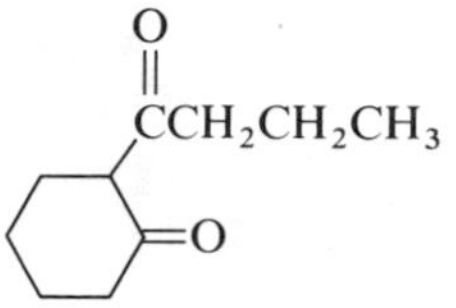 [cyclohexanone ring with substituent]
$$\overset{O}{\overset{\|}{C}}CH_2CH_2CH_3$$
[ring]$=O$

14.39 An aqueous NaOH solution is added to a mixture of acetone and formaldehyde.

(a)   What is the structure of the organic anion formed?

(b)   Would this anion undergo reaction with acetone or with formaldehyde at the faster rate?

(c)   Show each step in the mechanism for the crossed aldol condensation that would occur.

14.40 Predict the major organic product:

(a) $\overset{O}{\overset{\|}{H}C}(CH_2)_4\overset{O}{\overset{\|}{C}}H \xrightarrow[\text{(2) H}^+\text{, heat}]{\text{(1) OH}^-\text{, H}_2\text{O}}$

(b) $C_6H_5CHO + $ [cyclopentanone ring]$=O \xrightarrow{\text{OH}^-}$

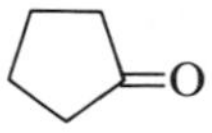

(c) $C_6H_5CHO + CH_3\overset{O}{\overset{\|}{C}}CH_2CO_2C_2H_5 \xrightarrow{\text{OH}^-}$

(d) 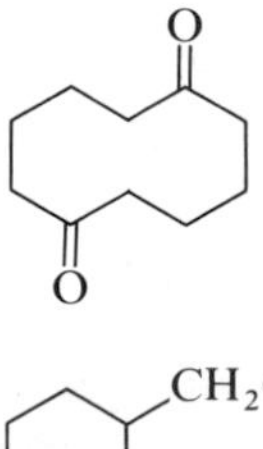   [bicyclic diketone] $\xrightarrow[\text{(2) H}^+\text{, heat}]{\text{(1) OH}^-\text{, H}_2\text{O}}$

(e) 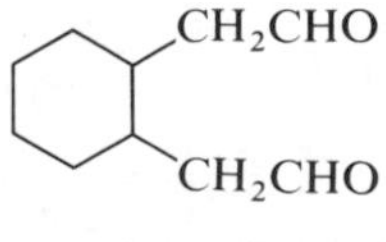   [cyclohexane ring with two CH_2CHO substituents] $\xrightarrow[\text{(2) H}^+\text{, heat}]{\text{(1) OH}^-\text{, H}_2\text{O}}$

(f) $C_6H_5CHO + NCCH_2CN \xrightarrow{\text{CH}_3\text{CO}_2^-}$

14.41 How would you make the following conversions?

(a) cyclopentanone to ⬠=CC₆H₅
CO₂C₂H₅

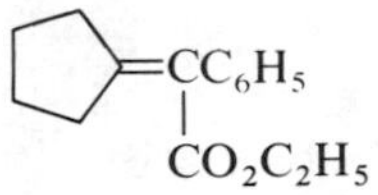

(b) benzaldehyde to C₆H₅CH=CHCC₆H₅ (with O double-bonded above the C)

(c) furan-CHO to furan-CH=CHNO₂

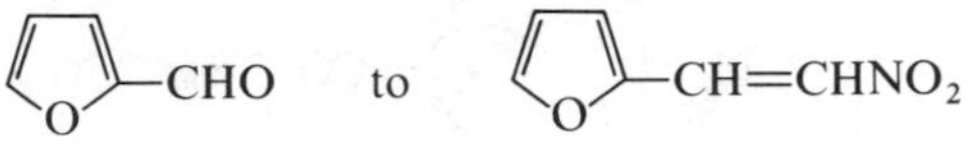

(d) benzaldehyde to ethyl 2,3-diphenylpropenoate

(e) phenylacetic acid to ethyl 2-phenyl-3-methyl-2-butenoate

14.42 Predict the major organic products:

(a) 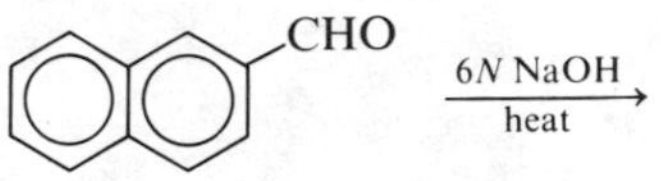 naphthalene-CHO $\xrightarrow[\text{heat}]{6N\ NaOH}$

(b) (CH₃)₃CCHO $\xrightarrow[\text{heat}]{6N\ NaOH}$

14.43 Predict the organic products:

(a) 2 CH₃(CH₂)₃CO₂C₂H₅ $\xrightarrow[\text{(2) H}_2\text{O, H}^+\text{, heat}]{\text{(1) NaOC}_2\text{H}_5}$

(b) 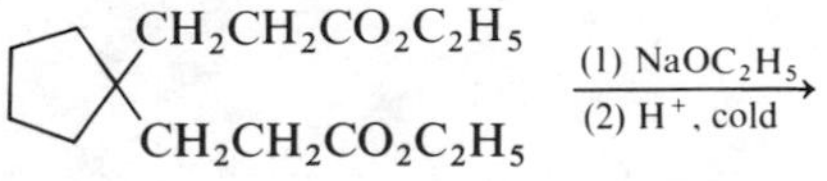 cyclopentane with CH₂CH₂CO₂C₂H₅ and CH₂CH₂CO₂C₂H₅ $\xrightarrow[\text{(2) H}^+\text{, cold}]{\text{(1) NaOC}_2\text{H}_5}$

(c) C₆H₅CH₂CO₂C₂H₅ + C₂H₅OCOC₂H₅ (with O double-bonded above central C) $\xrightarrow[\text{(2) H}^+\text{, cold}]{\text{(1) NaOC}_2\text{H}_5}$
diethyl carbonate

(d) cyclohexanone =O + HCO₂C₂H₅ $\xrightarrow[\text{(2) H}^+\text{, cold}]{\text{(1) NaOC}_2\text{H}_5}$

(e) cyclohexane with CH₂CCH₃ (O double-bonded) and CH₂CO₂C₂H₅ $\xrightarrow[\text{(2) H}^+\text{, cold}]{\text{(1) NaOC}_2\text{H}_5}$

(f) CH₃C(CH₂)₄CO₂C₂H₅ (with O double-bonded above C) $\xrightarrow[\text{(2) H}^+\text{, cold}]{\text{(1) NaOC}_2\text{H}_5}$

(g) 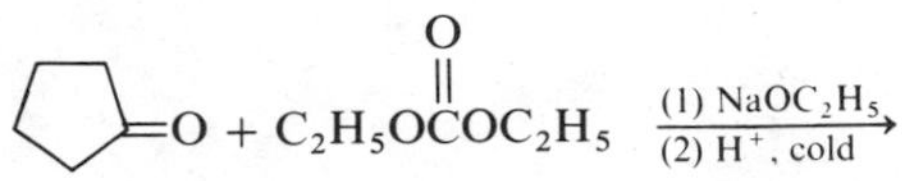 cyclopentanone =O + C₂H₅OCOC₂H₅ (with O double-bonded above central C) $\xrightarrow[\text{(2) H}^+\text{, cold}]{\text{(1) NaOC}_2\text{H}_5}$

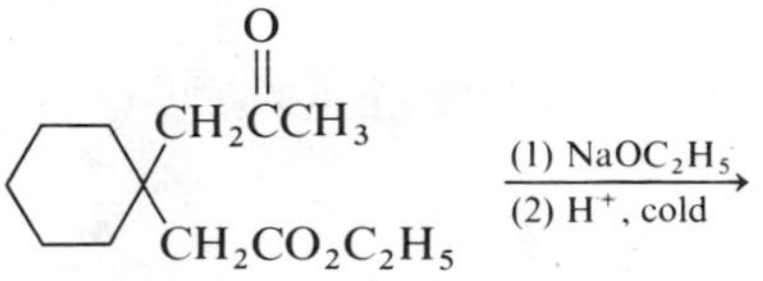

14.44 Suggest synthetic paths leading to the following compounds:

(a) 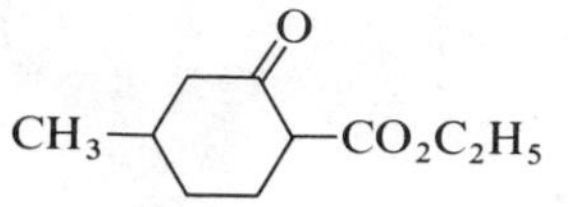 CH$_3$—⬡—CO$_2$C$_2$H$_5$

(b) $\underset{\underset{CN}{|}}{C_6H_5\overset{\overset{O}{\|}}{C}CHCO_2C_2H_5}$

(c) 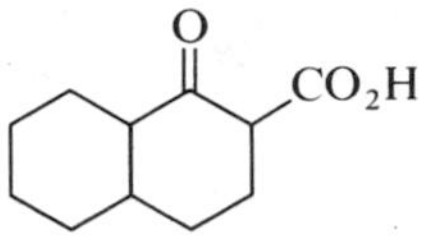 [decalin system with =O and CO$_2$H]

(d) 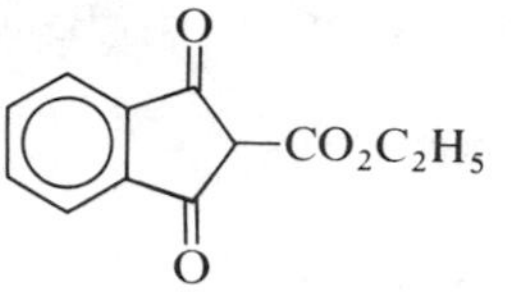 [indanone system with =O, =O and CO$_2$C$_2$H$_5$]

(e) $\underset{\underset{CH_3}{|}}{(CH_3)_3C\overset{\overset{O}{\|}}{C}CHCO_2C_2H_5}$

(f) $\underset{\underset{C_6H_5}{|}}{C_6H_5\overset{\overset{O}{\|}}{C}CHCO_2CH_3}$

(g) $\underset{\underset{CH_2CH_3}{|}}{C_2H_5O_2C\overset{\overset{O}{\|}}{C}CHCO_2C_2H_5}$

14.45 Predict the major organic product of each of the following Michael addition reactions:

(a) 1 CH$_2$=CH$\overset{\overset{O}{\|}}{C}CH_2CH_3$ + CH$_2$(CO$_2$C$_2$H$_5$)$_2$ $\xrightarrow{\text{NaOC}_2\text{H}_5}$

(b) 2 CH$_2$=CH$\overset{\overset{O}{\|}}{C}CH_2CH_3$ + CH$_2$(CO$_2$C$_2$H$_5$)$_2$ $\xrightarrow{\text{NaOC}_2\text{H}_5}$

(c) 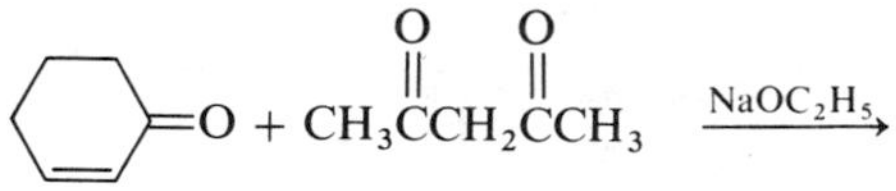 ⬡=O + CH$_3\overset{\overset{O}{\|}}{C}CH_2\overset{\overset{O}{\|}}{C}CH_3$ $\xrightarrow{\text{NaOC}_2\text{H}_5}$

(d) CH$_3$CH=CHCO$_2$C$_2$H$_5$ + C$_6$H$_5$CH$_2$CO$_2$C$_2$H$_5$ $\xrightarrow{\text{NaOC}_2\text{H}_5}$

14.46 How would you prepare the following compounds by Michael additions?

(a) 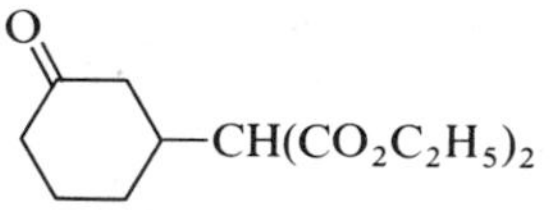 [cyclohexanone]—CH(CO$_2$C$_2$H$_5$)$_2$

(b) 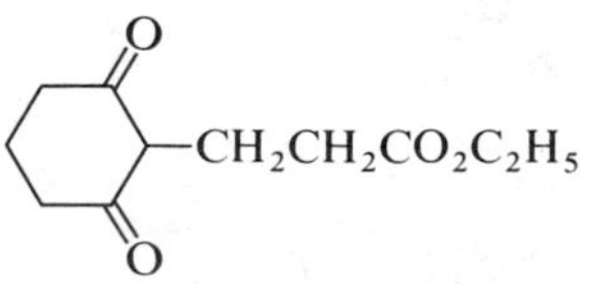 [1,3-cyclohexanedione]—CH$_2$CH$_2$CO$_2$C$_2$H$_5$

(c) CH$_3\overset{\overset{O}{\|}}{C}$CHCH$_2CH_2$CN
         |
        CO$_2$C$_2$H$_5$

14.47 (a)   How would you prepare the following compound from 2-methylcyclohexanone?

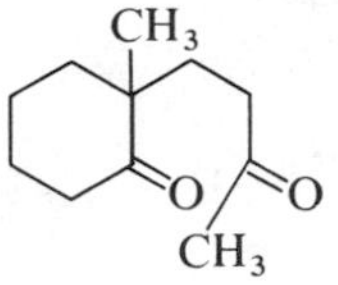

(b)   From the dione in (a), show how you could prepare:

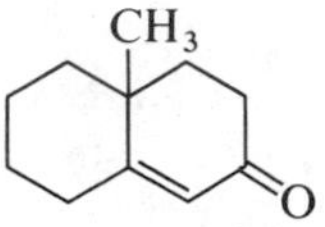

14.48 Suggest a reaction sequence for the following conversion:

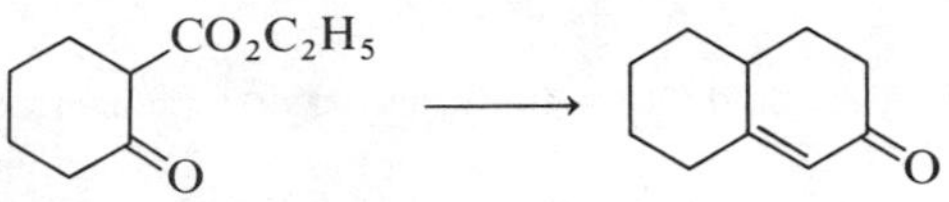

14.49 A chemist has on his shelf: dilute HCl, dilute NaOH, sodium metal, magnesium metal, anhydrous ethanol, anhydrous ether, bromine, diethyl malonate, a tank of anhydrous HCl, glacial acetic acid, PBr_3, and acetone. (He also has water, heat sources, and solvents for working up his products.) Suggest ways that he could synthesize the following compounds: (a) ethyl acetate; (b) ethyl acetoacetate; (c) 2-pentanone; (d) 2-ethylbutanoic acid; (e) ethyl α-bromoacetate.

14.50 It is observed that $(R)\text{-}C_6H_5\overset{\displaystyle OH}{\underset{\displaystyle |}{C}}HCO_2C_2H_5$ undergoes racemization in alkaline solution. Explain.

14.51 Propose a mechanism for the following reaction:

$$\text{excess HCHO} + CH_3CHO \xrightarrow{CO_3^{2-}} HOCH_2\overset{\displaystyle CH_2OH}{\underset{\displaystyle CH_2OH}{C}}CHO$$

14.52 Show how the following cyclic compounds could be synthesized by Robinson annelations:

(a) 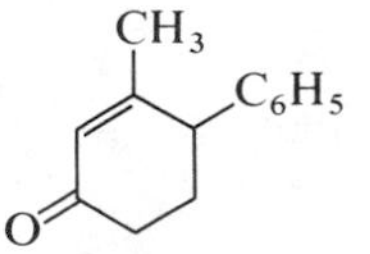   (b) 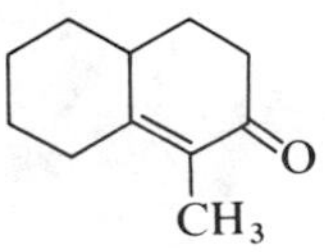   (c)

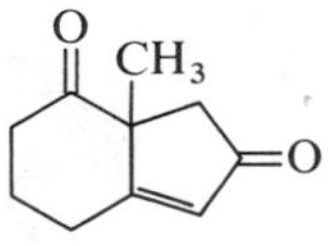

14.53 Suggest a mechanism for the following reaction:

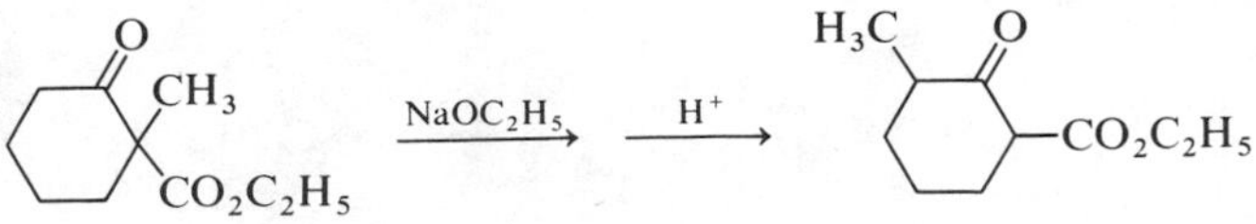

14.54 *Dimedone* can be obtained from *mesityl oxide* by a combination of a Michael condensation and a Dieckmann ring closure. Outline the synthesis.

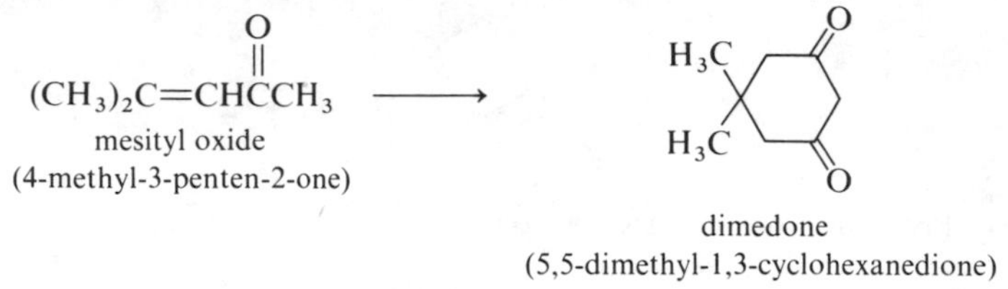

$$(CH_3)_2C{=}CHCCH_3 \longrightarrow$$
$$\overset{O}{\overset{\|}{}}$$

mesityl oxide
(4-methyl-3-penten-2-one)

dimedone
(5,5-dimethyl-1,3-cyclohexanedione)

14.55 Outline a general synthetic method for the preparation of cycloalkanecarboxylic acids, based upon the alkylation of malonic ester.

14.56 Cyclohexanone is treated with a strong base followed by methyl iodide. Predict the monoalkylation and the dialkylation products. Which dialkylated product predominates?

14.57 Devise a general method for the synthesis of γ-keto acids from ethyl α-chloroacetate.

14.58 How would you prepare the following carboxylic acids from the *same starting materials*?

(a) 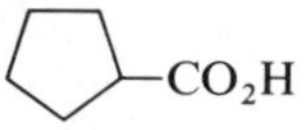 $\bigcirc$—CO$_2$H   (b) HO$_2$CCH$_2$(CH$_2$)$_4$CH$_2$CO$_2$H

14.59 Give the structures of compounds **I** and **II**:

$$CH_3CH_2CH_2CO_2C_2H_5 + (CO_2C_2H_5)_2 \xrightarrow{NaOC_2H_5} \underset{\textbf{I}}{C_{10}H_{16}O_5} \xrightarrow[\text{heat}]{H_2O, H^+} \underset{\textbf{II}}{C_5H_8O_3}$$

14.60 Write each step in the mechanism of the following reaction sequence:

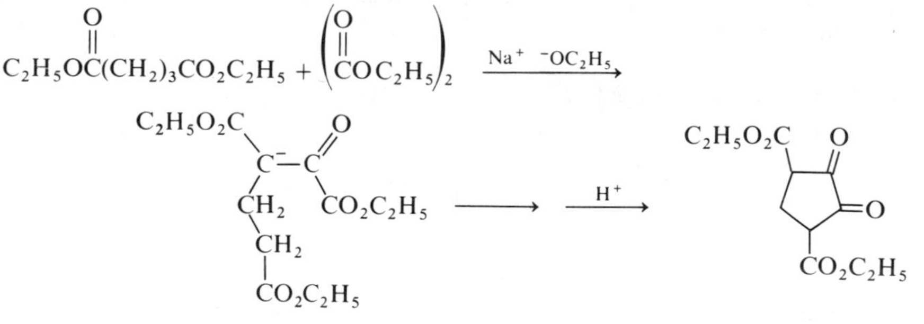

$$C_2H_5OC(CH_2)_3CO_2C_2H_5 + \left(COC_2H_5\right)_2 \xrightarrow{Na^+ \ ^-OC_2H_5}$$

$$\xrightarrow{H^+}$$

14.61 Suggest a synthesis for the following keto ester from acetoacetic ester:

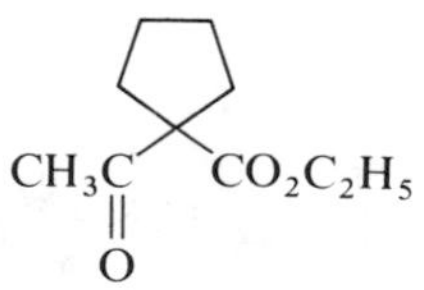

$$CH_3C \qquad CO_2C_2H_5$$
$$\overset{\|}{O}$$

14.62 Give the structure of each indicated product:

excess malonic ester $\xrightarrow[\text{BrCH}_2\text{CH}_2\text{Br}]{Na^+ \ ^-OC_2H_5} \xrightarrow{H^+}$

$$\underset{\textbf{I}}{C_{16}H_{26}O_8} \xrightarrow[\text{BrCH}_2\text{CH}_2\text{Br}]{Na^+ \ ^-OC_2H_5} \xrightarrow{H^+} \underset{\textbf{II}}{C_{18}H_{28}O_8} \xrightarrow[\text{heat}]{H_2O, H^+} \underset{\textbf{III}}{C_8H_{12}O_4}$$

Chapter 15

Amines

Carbon, hydrogen, and oxygen are the three most common elements in living systems. Nitrogen is fourth. Nitrogen is found in proteins and nucleic acids, as well as in many other naturally occurring compounds of both plant and animal origin. We have already discussed the nitrogen-containing amides and nitriles (Chapter 13) and later we will discuss some nitrogen-containing aromatic hetero-cycles, including nucleic acids (Chapter 16), and proteins (Chapter 18). In this chapter, we will discuss the **amines**, organic compounds containing trivalent nitrogen atoms bonded to one or more carbon atoms.

$$CH_3NH_2 \qquad\qquad \bigcirc\!\!-\!NH_2 \qquad\qquad (CH_3)_3N$$

an alkylamine:	*an arylamine:*	*a trialkylamine:*
N attached to alkyl group	*N attached to aromatic ring*	*N attached to three alkyl groups*

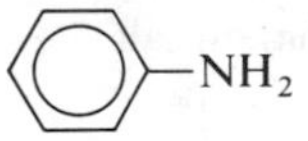

Classification of Amines

Amines may be classed as **primary**, **secondary**, or **tertiary**, according to the number of alkyl or aryl substituents attached to the nitrogen.

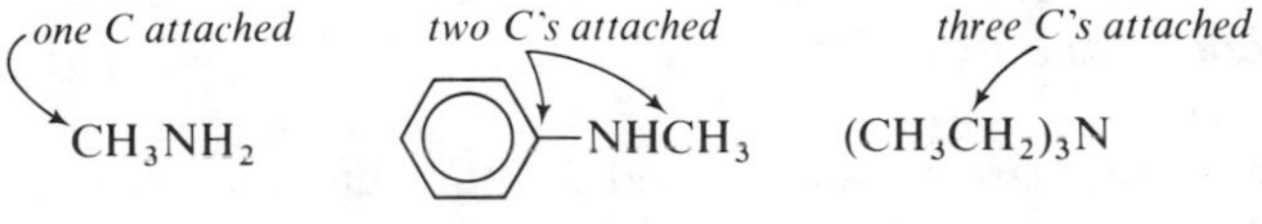

one C attached	*two C's attached*	*three C's attached*
CH_3NH_2	$\bigcirc\!\!-\!NHCH_3$	$(CH_3CH_2)_3N$
a 1° amine	*a 2° amine*	*a 3° amine*

Note that this classification is different from that for alkyl halides or alcohols. The classification of the latter is based upon the number of alkyl groups attached to the carbon that has the halide or hydroxyl group.

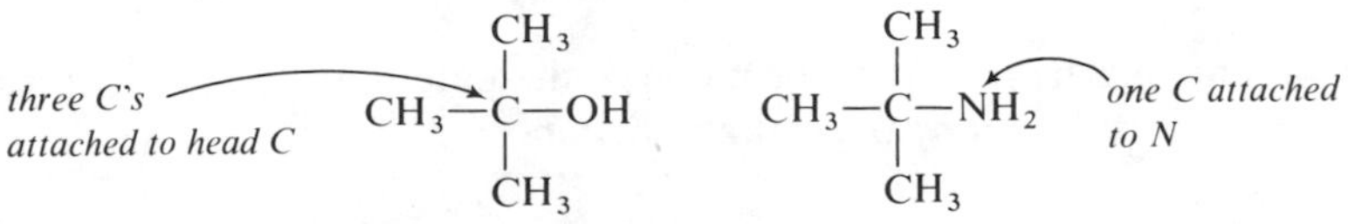

three C's attached to head C

$$CH_3\!-\!\underset{\underset{\textstyle CH_3}{|}}{\overset{\overset{\textstyle CH_3}{|}}{C}}\!-\!OH \qquad\qquad CH_3\!-\!\underset{\underset{\textstyle CH_3}{|}}{\overset{\overset{\textstyle CH_3}{|}}{C}}\!-\!NH_2$$

one C attached to N

t-butyl alcohol	*t-butylamine*
a 3° alcohol	*a 1° amine*

An amine nitrogen can have *four* groups or atoms bonded to it, in which case the nitrogen is part of a positive ion. These ionic compounds fall into two categories. If one or more of the attachments is H, the compound is an **amine salt**. If all four groups are alkyl or aryl (no H's on the N), the compound is a **quaternary ammonium salt**.

Amine salts:

$$(CH_3)_2NH_2^+ \ Cl^-$$

dimethylammonium chloride
salt of a 2° amine

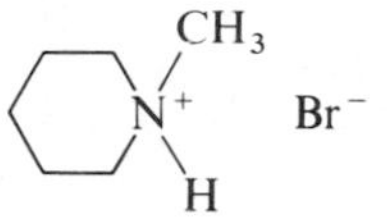

N-methylpiperidinium bromide
salt of a 3° amine

Quaternary ammonium salts:

$$(CH_3)_4N^+ \ Cl^-$$

tetramethylammonium
chloride

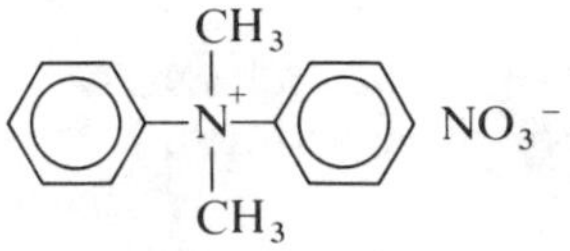

dimethyldiphenylammonium
nitrate

STUDY PROBLEM

15.1 Classify each of the following compounds as a 1°, 2°, or 3° amine; as a salt of a 1°, 2°, or 3° amine; or as a quaternary ammonium salt:

(a) $CH_3CH_2\overset{\overset{\displaystyle CH_3}{|}}{C}HNH_2$ (b)  ⬡NH (c) $(CH_3)_3NH^+ \ NO_3^-$

(d) $(CH_3CH_2)_3CNH_2$ (e)  ⬡$\overset{+}{N}(CH_3)_2 \ Cl^-$ (f)  ⬡NCH_3

(g) $C_6H_5NHC_6H_5$

Section 15.2

Nomenclature of Amines

Simple amines are usually named by the functional-group system. The alkyl or aryl group is named, then the ending **-amine** is added.

$$CH_3CH_2CH_2NH_2 \qquad \text{⬡}-NH_2 \qquad (CH_3CH_2)_2NH$$

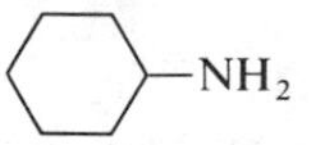

propylamine   cyclohexylamine   diethylamine

Diamines are named from the name of the parent alkane (with appropriate prefix numbers) followed by the ending **-diamine**.

$$H_2NCH_2CH_2CH_2NH_2$$

1,3-propanediamine

If more than one type of alkyl group is attached to the nitrogen, the largest alkyl group is considered the parent. A subsidiary alkyl group is designated by an **N-alkyl-** prefix.

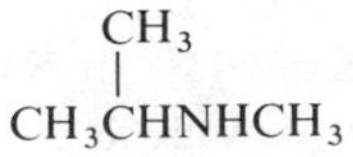

$$\overset{\overset{\displaystyle CH_3}{|}}{CH_3CHNHCH_3}$$

N-methyl-2-propylamine

$$\overset{\overset{\displaystyle CH_3}{|}}{CH_3CHN(CH_3)_2}$$

N,N-dimethyl-2-propylamine

If functionality of higher nomenclature priority is present, an **amino-** prefix is used.

$$H_2NCH_2CH_2OH$$

2-amino-1-ethanol

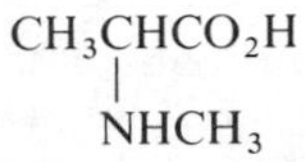

$$\overset{\displaystyle CH_3CHCO_2H}{\underset{\displaystyle NHCH_3}{|}}$$

2-(*N*-methylamino)propanoic acid

STUDY PROBLEM

15.2 Give each of the following compounds an acceptable name:

(a) $H_2NCH_2CH_2CH_2CH_2NH_2$ (commonly called *putrescine*, an odoriferous compound found in decaying flesh)

(b) $H_2NCH_2(CH_2)_4CH_2NH_2$ (*cadaverine*, origin similar to that of putrescine)

(c) $(CH_3)_2CHCH_2NH_2$

(d) $CH_3CH_2N(CH_3)_2$

(e) 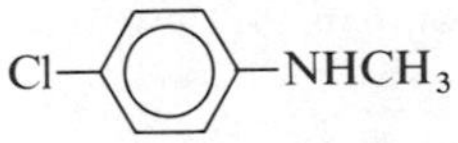 Cl—⟨○⟩—NHCH$_3$ (Name as a derivative of aniline.)

The chemistry of the **nonaromatic heterocyclic amines** is similar to that of their open-chain counterparts. Although we will not discuss the aromatic heterocycles until the next chapter, the chemistry of the nonaromatic nitrogen heterocycles will be included in this chapter. The commonly encountered compounds of this class generally have individual names.

pyrrolidine 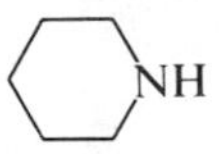   piperidine    piperazine    morpholine

In the numbering of heterocyclic rings, the heteroatom is considered position 1.

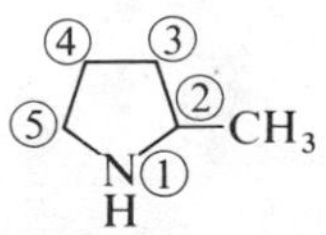

2-methylpyrrolidine

Section 15.3

Bonding in Amines

The bonding in an amine is directly analogous to that in ammonia: an sp^3 nitrogen atom bonded to three other atoms or groups (H or R) and with a pair of unshared electrons in the remaining sp^3 orbital (see Figure 2.19, page 59).

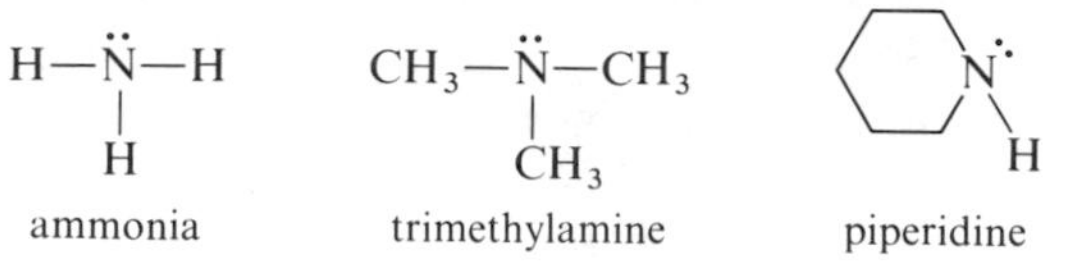

| ammonia | trimethylamine | piperidine |

In an amine salt or a quaternary ammonium salt, the unshared pair of electrons forms the fourth sigma bond. The cations are analogous to the ammonium ion.

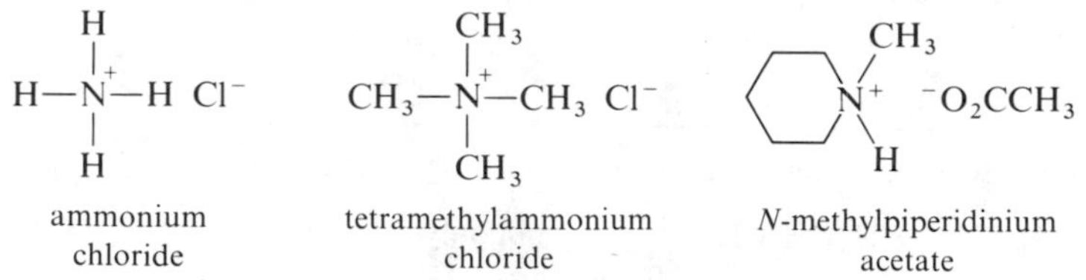

| ammonium chloride | tetramethylammonium chloride | N-methylpiperidinium acetate |

An amine molecule with three different groups attached to the nitrogen is chiral; however, enantiomers of most amines cannot be isolated because rapid inversion between mirror images occurs at room temperature. The inversion proceeds by way of a planar transition state (sp^2 nitrogen). The result is that the nitrogen pyramid flips inside out, much as an umbrella in a strong wind. The energy required for this inversion is about 6 kcal/mole, about twice the energy required for rotation around a carbon–carbon sigma bond.

The mirror images are interconvertible:

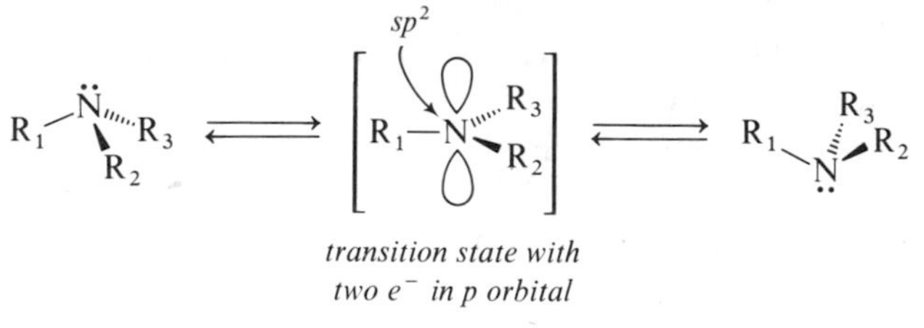

*transition state with
two e⁻ in p orbital*

If an amine nitrogen has three different substituents and interconversion between the two mirror-image structures is restricted, then a pair of enantiomers may be isolated. **Tröger's base** is an example of such a molecule. The methylene bridge between the two nitrogens prevents interconversion between the mirror images, and Tröger's base can be separated into a pair of enantiomers.

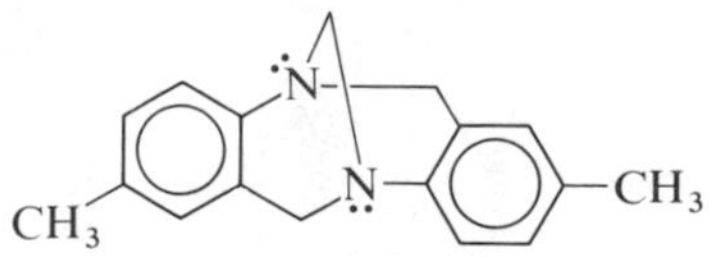

Tröger's base

Another case in which the existence of isolable enantiomers is possible is that of the quaternary ammonium salts. These compounds are structurally similar to compounds containing sp^3 carbon atoms. If four different groups are attached to the nitrogen, the ion is chiral and the salt can be separated into enantiomers.

A pair of enantiomers:

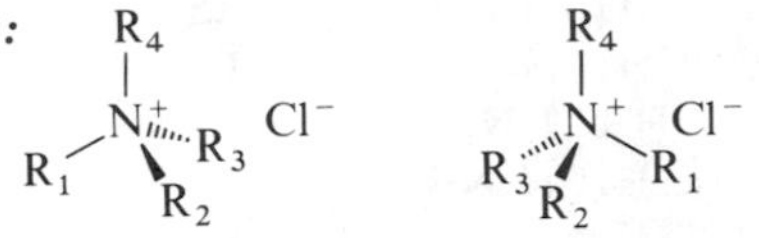

$$\underset{R_2}{\overset{R_4}{\underset{|}{R_1-\overset{+}{N}\text{''''}R_3}}} \;Cl^- \qquad\qquad \underset{R_2}{\overset{R_4}{\underset{|}{R_3\text{'''}\overset{+}{N}R_1}}} \;Cl^-$$

STUDY PROBLEM

15.3 Which of the following structures could exist as isolable enantiomers?

(a) 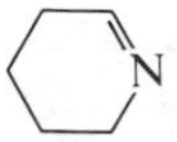 [cyclic structure with N]

(b) $CH_3NHCH_2CH_2Cl$

(c) $[(CH_3)_2CH]_2\overset{+}{N}(CH_2CH_2Cl)_2 \;Cl^-$

(d) 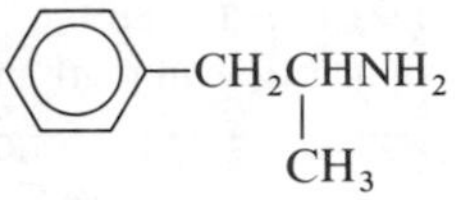 [benzene ring]—$CH_2\underset{\underset{CH_3}{|}}{CHNH_2}$

Section 15.4

Physical Properties of Amines

As we mentioned in Chapter 1, amines undergo hydrogen bonding. The $N---H-N$ hydrogen bond is weaker than the $O---H-O$ hydrogen bond because N is less electronegative than O and therefore the NH bond is less polar. This weak hydrogen bonding between amine molecules results in boiling points that fall between those for nonhydrogen-bonded compounds (like alkanes or ethers) and those for strongly hydrogen-bonded compounds (like alcohols) of comparable molecular weight. (See Table 15.1, page 706.)

$$CH_3CH_2OCH_2CH_3 \qquad (CH_3CH_2)_2NH \qquad CH_3CH_2CH_2CH_2OH$$

$$\text{bp } 34.5° \qquad\qquad \text{bp } 56° \qquad\qquad \text{bp } 117°$$

Because they do not have an $N-H$ bond, tertiary amines in the pure liquid state cannot undergo hydrogen bonding. The boiling points of tertiary amines are lower than those for comparable primary or secondary amines, and are closer to the boiling points of alkanes of similar molecular weight.

no hydrogen bonding   *hydrogen bonding*

$$(CH_3)_3N \qquad (CH_3)_3CH \qquad CH_3CH_2CH_2NH_2$$

$$\text{bp } 3° \qquad\quad \text{bp } -10° \qquad\quad \text{bp } 48°$$

Amines of low molecular weight are soluble in water because they can undergo hydrogen bonding with water. Tertiary amines, as well as primary and secondary amines, can undergo this type of hydrogen bonding because they have unshared pairs of electrons that can be used to form hydrogen bonds with water.

A 3° amine: $$CH_3\underset{\underset{CH_3}{|}}{\overset{\overset{CH_3}{|}}{N}}:---H-\overset{\overset{H}{|}}{O}$$

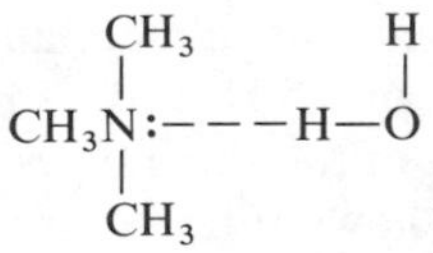

Table 15.1. Physical Properties of Some Amines

Name	Structure	Bp, °C	Solubility in water
methylamine	CH_3NH_2	−7.5	∞
dimethylamine	$(CH_3)_2NH$	7.5	∞
trimethylamine	$(CH_3)_3N$	3	∞
ethylamine	$CH_2CH_2NH_2$	17	∞
benzylamine	$C_6H_5CH_2NH_2$	185	∞
aniline	$C_6H_5NH_2$	184	3.7 g/100 g

STUDY PROBLEM

15.4   Show all types of hydrogen bonding that could exist in   (a) pure dimethylamine; (b) aqueous dimethylamine; (c) pure *N*-methylpiperidine; and   (d) a solution of *N*-methylpiperidine in methanol.

Volatile amines have very distinctive odors. Methylamine has an odor similar to that of ammonia; trimethylamine smells like dead salt-water salmon; and piperidine smells like dead fresh-water fish. Arylamines are not as unpleasant smelling as alkylamines; however, arylamines such as aniline are toxic and are especially insidious because they can be absorbed through the skin. *β*-Naphthylamine is carcinogenic.

β-naphthylamine
a carcinogenic arylamine

Amine salts and quaternary ammonium salts behave physically like inorganic salts—high-melting, water-soluble, and odorless.

Section 15.5

Spectral Properties of Amines

A. Infrared Spectra

The bonds that give rise to infrared absorption characteristic of amines are the C—N and N—H bonds (Table 15.2). All aliphatic amines show C—N stretching in the fingerprint region. However, only primary and secondary amines show the distinctive NH stretching absorption, which is observed to the left of CH absorption in the spectrum. This is the same region where OH absorption is observed; however, the two can often be differentiated because the OH absorption is usually broader and stronger than NH absorption. The stronger absorption by an OH bond is due to the greater polarity and hydrogen bonding of this group.

In Chapter 8, we mentioned that primary amines show two NH absorption peaks, secondary amines show one NH peak, and tertiary amines show no absorption in this region. Spectra of the three types of amines are shown in Figure 8.11 (page 324). Figure 15.1 shows infrared spectra of an alkylamine and an arylamine. Both of these amines are primary; both exhibit double NH peaks.

Table 15.2.   Characteristic Infrared Absorption for Amines

Type of absorption	Position of absorption	
	cm^{-1}	μm
1° amines:		
N—H stretching (pure liquid)	3250–3400 (2 peaks)	2.9–3.1
C—N stretching	1020–1250	8.0–9.8
2° amines:		
N—H stretching (pure liquid)	3330	3.0
C—N stretching	1020–1250	8.0–9.8
3° amines:		
C—N stretching	1020–1250	8.0–9.8

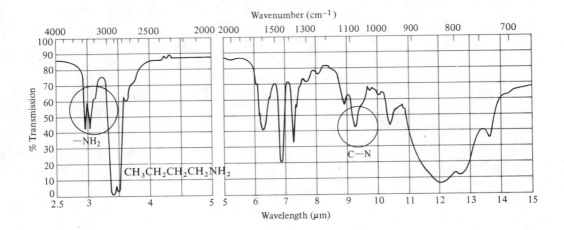

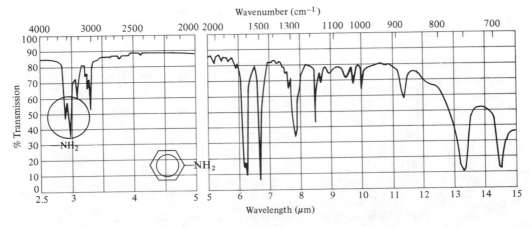

Figure 15.1.   Infrared spectra of *n*-butylamine and aniline.

B. Nmr Spectra

The NH absorption in the nmr spectrum is generally a sharp singlet, not split by adjacent protons. In this respect, N—H absorption is similar to O—H absorption (Section 8.11E). Aliphatic amines show NH absorption at about 1.0–2.8 ppm, while arylamines absorb at around 2.6–4.7 ppm. (The exact position depends upon the solvent used.) The α protons are somewhat deshielded by the electronegative nitrogen; the chemical shift for these protons is from 2.2–2.8 ppm (see Figure 15.2).

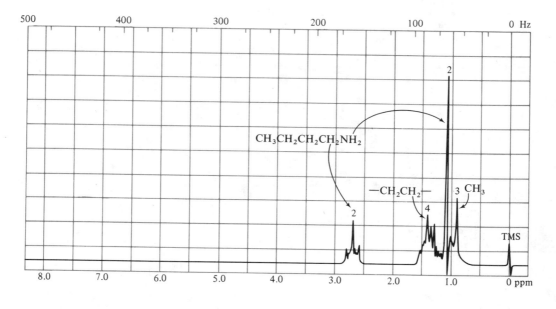

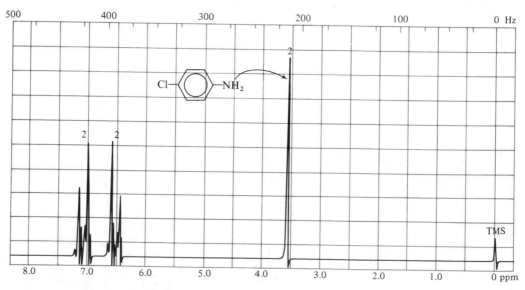

Figure 15.2. Nmr spectra of *n*-butylamine and *p*-chloroaniline.

Section 15.6

Preparation of Amines

Techniques for the preparation of amines fall into three general categories. We will discuss each category in turn.

Nucleophilic substitution:

$$RX \quad + NH_3 \xrightarrow{\ S_N2\ } RNH_3{}^+ X^- \xrightarrow{\ OH^-\ } RNH_2$$

an alkyl halide

Reduction:
$$\overset{\overset{\displaystyle O}{\|}}{R C}NH_2 \quad or \quad RCN \xrightarrow{\ [H]\ } RCH_2NH_2$$

an amide or nitrile

Amide rearrangement:
$$\overset{\overset{\displaystyle O}{\|}}{R C}NH_2 \xrightarrow{\ Br_2,\ OH^-\ } RNH_2$$

an amide

A. Synthesis by Substitution Reactions

Reaction of Amines and Alkyl Halides Ammonia or an amine carries an unshared pair of electrons and can act as a nucleophile in a substitution reaction with an alkyl halide. The reaction of a nitrogen nucleophile is similar to the reaction of any other nucleophile with RX. The product of the reaction with ammonia or an amine is an amine salt. The free amine can be obtained by the treatment of this amine salt with a base such as NaOH.

S_N2 Reaction:

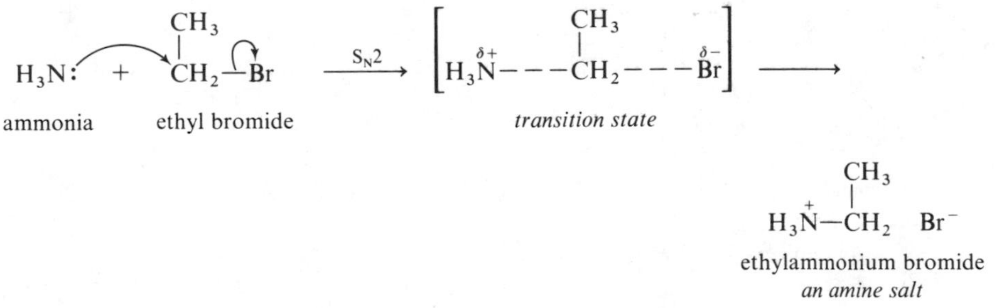

$$H_3N\colon \quad + \quad \overset{\overset{\displaystyle CH_3}{|}}{CH_2}{-}Br \xrightarrow{\ S_N2\ } \left[H_3\overset{\delta+}{N}{-}{-}{-}\overset{\overset{\displaystyle CH_3}{|}}{CH_2}{-}{-}{-}\overset{\delta-}{Br} \right] \longrightarrow$$

ammonia   ethyl bromide   *transition state*

$$H_3\overset{+}{N}{-}\overset{\overset{\displaystyle CH_3}{|}}{CH_2} \quad Br^-$$

ethylammonium bromide
an amine salt

Treatment with base:

$$CH_3CH_2NH_3{}^+ \ Br^- + OH^- \longrightarrow CH_3CH_2NH_2 + H_2O + Br^-$$

ethylamine

The order of reactivity of alkyl halides is typical for S_N2 reactions: $CH_3X >$ $1° > 2°$. Tertiary alkyl halides do not undergo S_N2 reactions with ammonia or amines; elimination products are obtained.

The principal disadvantage of this route to amines is that the product amine salt can exchange a proton with the starting ammonia or amine.

$$CH_3CH_2NH_3{}^+ \ Br^- + NH_3 \ \rightleftharpoons \ CH_3CH_2NH_2 + NH_4{}^+ \ Br^-$$
also a nucleophile

This proton exchange results in two nucleophiles competing in the reaction with the alkyl halide. For this reason, a mixture of mono-, di-, and trialkylamines and the quaternary ammonium salt is frequently obtained from the reaction of ammonia with an alkyl halide.

$$NH_3 \ \xrightarrow{RX} \ RNH_2 \ \xrightarrow{RX} \ R_2NH \ \xrightarrow{RX} \ R_3N \ \xrightarrow{RX} \ R_4N^+ \ X^-$$

Because all these products are formed, the S_N2 reaction of ammonia or an amine with an alkyl halide is not generally considered a useful synthetic reaction. If the amine is very inexpensive or if ammonia is used, a large excess can be used to favor monoalkylation. In this case, RX is more likely to collide with the molecules of the desired reactant and less likely to collide with those of the alkylated product. In the following example, an excess of ammonia favors the primary amine product.

$$CH_3CH_2CH_2CH_2Br + \text{excess } NH_3 \ \longrightarrow \ \xrightarrow{OH^-} \ CH_3CH_2CH_2CH_2NH_2 + Br^-$$
n-butyl bromide   n-butylamine
45%

If the quaternary ammonium salt is desired, the S_N2 reaction might also be useful. In this case, an excess of the alkyl halide would be used.

$$(CH_3CH_2)_2NH + \text{excess } CH_3CH_2I \ \longrightarrow \ (CH_3CH_2)_4N^+ \ I^-$$

Gabriel Phthalimide Synthesis   A synthesis that gives primary amines without secondary and tertiary amines is the **Gabriel phthalimide synthesis**. The reaction is an S_N2 substitution using the phthalimide anion as the nucleophile. The amine is then obtained by a hydrolysis reaction of the substituted phthalimide.

potassium
phthalimide   N-ethylphthalimide

$+ \ H_2NCH_2CH_3$
 ethylamine
free of 2° and 3°
amines

Phthalimide is prepared by heating phthalic anhydride with ammonia. The potassium salt is made by treating phthalimide with KOH. Normally, a proton cannot be removed from an amide nitrogen so easily. However, like other β-dicarbonyl compounds, imides are acidic because the anion is resonance-stabilized. Phthalimide has a pK_a of 9; it is ten times a stronger acid than phenol!

Preparation of phthalimide anion:

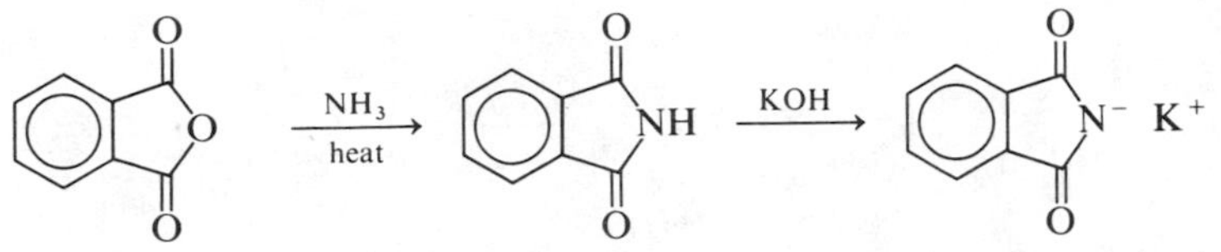

phthalic anhydride   phthalimide   *resonance-stabilized*

STUDY PROBLEM

15.5 Write the resonance structures for the phthalimide anion.

After the potassium phthalimide is prepared, it is treated with an alkyl halide. It is the nitrogen, not the oxygen, that attacks the carbon of the alkyl halide because the nitrogen is more nucleophilic than the oxygen.

Attack on RX:

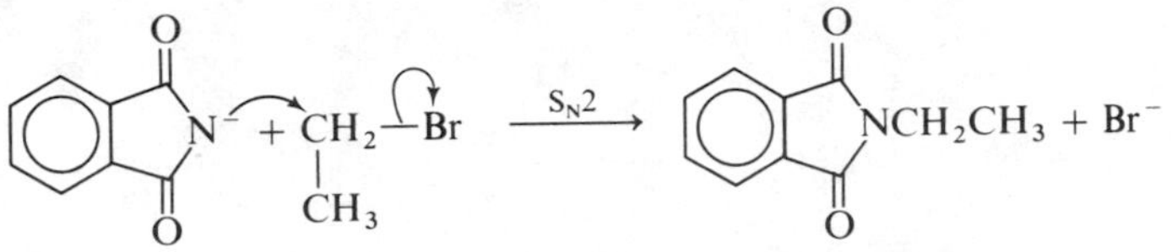

an N-alkylphthalimide

Finally, the alkylphthalimide is hydrolyzed. This reaction is simply the hydrolysis of an amide (Section 13.9C).

Hydrolysis:

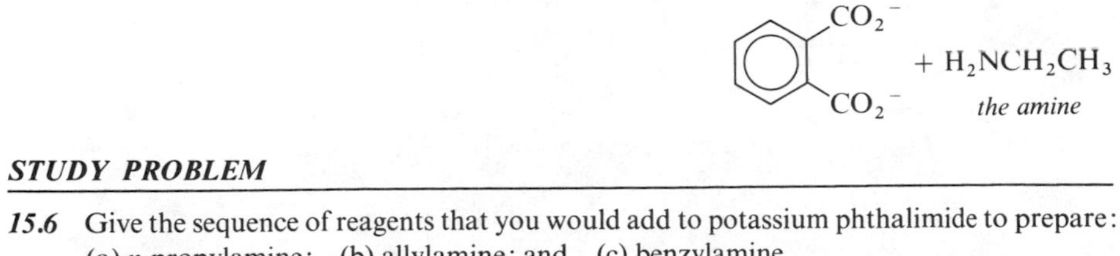

half-hydrolyzed

$+ H_2NCH_2CH_3$

the amine

STUDY PROBLEM

15.6 Give the sequence of reagents that you would add to potassium phthalimide to prepare:
(a) *n*-propylamine; (b) allylamine; and   (c) benzylamine.

An ingenious variation of the Gabriel phthalimide synthesis is used to prepare α-amino acids, the building blocks of proteins. This sequence is: (1) treatment of potassium phthalimide with diethyl bromomalonate; (2) treatment of the imide–malonate with base to remove the α hydrogen; and (3) treatment with RX, which gives a typical malonic ester alkylation reaction.

(1) Reaction with bromomalonic ester:

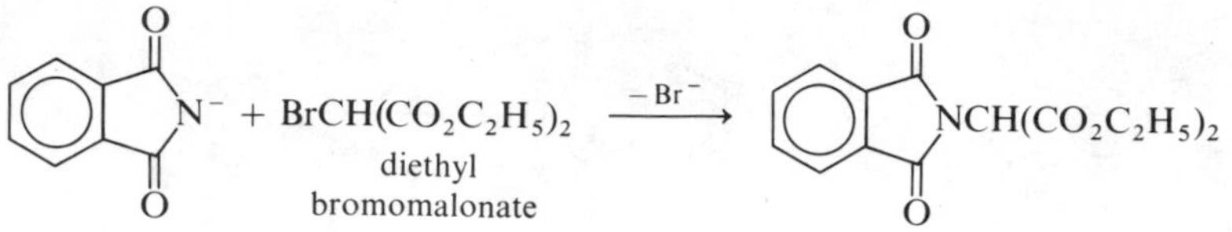

$$\text{phthalimide anion} + BrCH(CO_2C_2H_5)_2 \xrightarrow{-Br^-} \text{the imide–malonate}$$

diethyl
bromomalonate

the imide–malonate

(2) Treatment with base:

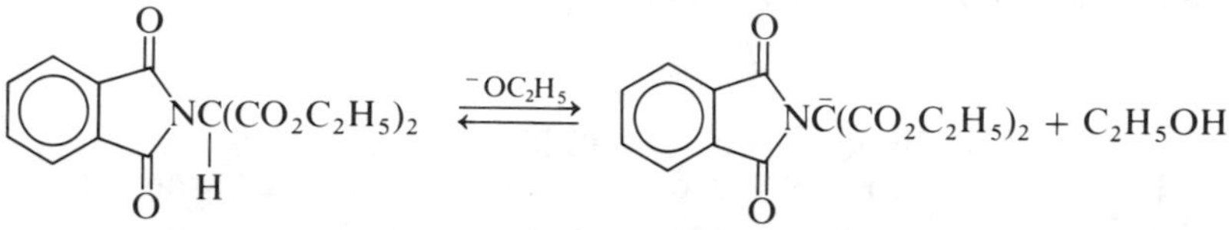

$$\xrightarrow[\text{}]{^-OC_2H_5} \quad \text{NC}(CO_2C_2H_5)_2 + C_2H_5OH$$

an enolate ion

(3) Reaction with RX:

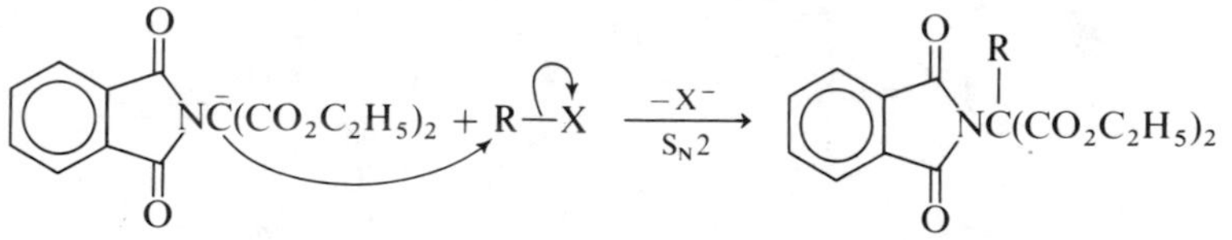

$$\text{N\bar{C}}(CO_2C_2H_5)_2 + R{-}X \xrightarrow[S_N2]{-X^-} \text{NC}(CO_2C_2H_5)_2$$

Acid hydrolysis results in hydrolysis of both imide and diester and yields the amino acid:

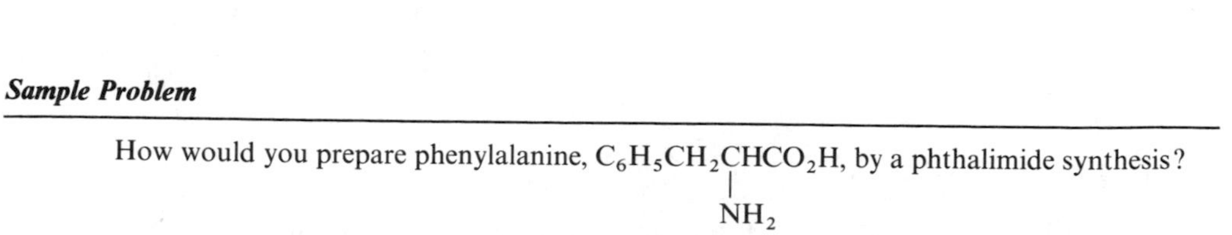

hydrolyzed

hydrolyzed and decarboxylated

$$\text{N}{-}\text{C}(CO_2C_2H_5)_2 \xrightarrow[\text{heat}]{H_2O,\ H^+} H_3\overset{+}{N}CHCO_2H + C_2H_5OH + \text{(benzene ring with } CO_2H, CO_2H) + CO_2$$

an amino acid

Sample Problem

How would you prepare phenylalanine, $C_6H_5CH_2CHCO_2H$, by a phthalimide synthesis?

$$\underset{NH_2}{\overset{}{C_6H_5CH_2CHCO_2H}}$$

Solution:

(1) *Determination of reagents needed:*

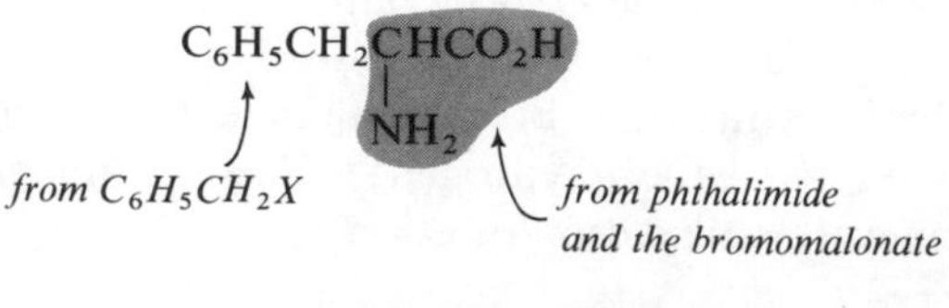

$$C_6H_5CH_2\underset{NH_2}{CHCO_2H}$$

from $C_6H_5CH_2X$

from phthalimide
and the bromomalonate

(2) *Steps in the synthesis*:

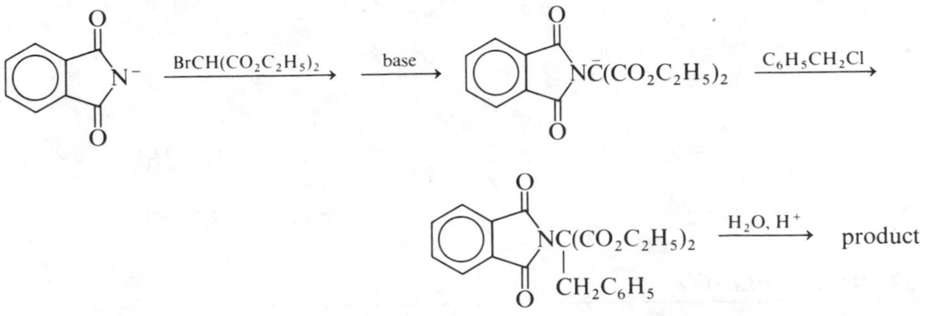

STUDY PROBLEM

15.7 How would you prepare the following amino acid by a phthalimide synthesis?

$$(CH_3)_2CHCH_2CHCO_2H$$
$$|$$
$$NH_2$$

leucine

B. Synthesis by Reduction

Reduction reactions often provide convenient routes to amines. **Nitriles** undergo catalytic hydrogenation or reduction with $LiAlH_4$ to yield primary amines of the type RCH_2NH_2 in yields of approximately 70%. Nitriles are available from alkyl halides; therefore, a nitrile synthesis is a technique for lengthening a carbon chain as well as for preparing an amine.

$$(CH_3)_2CHCH_2Br \xrightarrow[-Br^-]{CN^-} (CH_3)_2CHCH_2CN \xrightarrow[(2) H_2O]{(1) LiAlH_4} (CH_3)_2CHCH_2CH_2NH_2$$

1-bromo-2-methylpropane   3-methylbutanenitrile   (3-methyl-1-butyl)amine
a 1° alkyl halide

Amides also yield amines when treated with reducing agents.

$$\overset{\displaystyle O}{\overset{\displaystyle \|}{CH_3CNH_2}} \xrightarrow[(2) H_2O]{(1) LiAlH_4} CH_3CH_2NH_2$$

acetamide   ethylamine
an amide

Reductive amination, a reaction that converts ketones or aldehydes to primary amines, was discussed in Section 11.14D. This reaction is much better for synthesizing an amine of the type R_2CHNH_2 than is the reaction of R_2CHBr and NH_3 because the latter reaction may lead to elimination products. Secondary and tertiary amines may also be synthesized by reductive amination if a primary or secondary amine is used instead of ammonia.

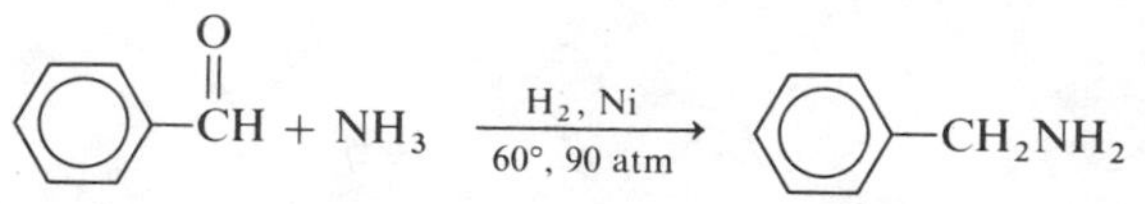

$$\underset{\text{benzaldehyde}}{\boxed{}} \overset{\text{O}}{\overset{\|}{-\text{CH}}} + \text{NH}_3 \xrightarrow[60°,\ 90\ \text{atm}]{\text{H}_2,\ \text{Ni}} \underset{\substack{\text{benzylamine} \\ 85\%}}{\boxed{}} -\text{CH}_2\text{NH}_2$$

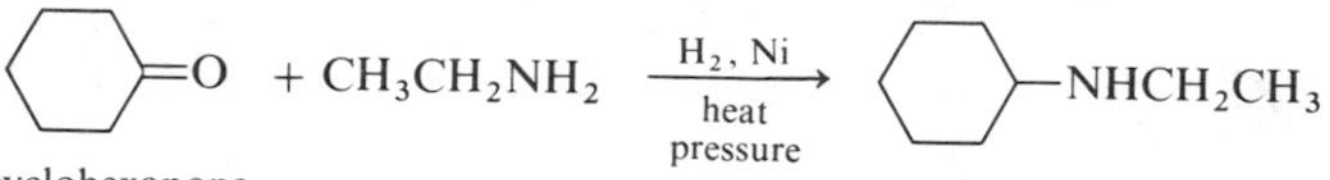

$$\underset{\text{cyclohexanone}}{\boxed{}}=\text{O} + \text{CH}_3\text{CH}_2\text{NH}_2 \xrightarrow[\substack{\text{heat} \\ \text{pressure}}]{\text{H}_2,\ \text{Ni}} \underset{N\text{-ethylcyclohexylamine}}{\boxed{}}-\text{NHCH}_2\text{CH}_3$$

STUDY PROBLEMS

15.8 Show how you would carry out each of the following syntheses:

(a) cyclohexylamine from cyclohexanone
(b) $\text{CH}_2{=}\text{CHCH}_2\text{CH}_2\text{CH}_2\text{NH}_2$ from 4-bromo-1-butene
(c) N,N-dimethylbenzylamine from an amide

15.9 Suggest two techniques for preparing *sec*-butylamine free of higher alkylation products.

C. Amide Rearrangement

When an unsubstituted amide (RCONH_2) is treated with an alkaline, aqueous solution of bromine, it undergoes rearrangement to yield an amine. This reaction is called the **Hofmann rearrangement**. Note that the carbonyl group is lost as $\text{CO}_3{}^{2-}$; therefore, the amine contains one less carbon than the starting amide.

$$\underset{\text{hexanamide}}{\text{CH}_3(\text{CH}_2)_4\overset{\overset{\text{O}}{\|}}{\text{C}}\text{NH}_2} + 4\,\text{OH}^- + \text{Br}_2 \xrightarrow{\text{H}_2\text{O}} \underset{\substack{n\text{-pentylamine} \\ 85\%}}{\text{CH}_3(\text{CH}_2)_4\text{NH}_2} + \text{CO}_3{}^{2-} + 2\,\text{H}_2\text{O} + 2\,\text{Br}^-$$

Because the carbonyl group appears to be abstracted from the interior of the molecule, it is of interest to look at the mechanism of the Hofmann rearrangement. The reaction proceeds by a series of discrete steps. *Step 1* is bromination at the nitrogen. *Step 2* is loss of a proton from the nitrogen and results in an unstable anion. The rearrangement step is *Step 3* of the sequence. Note that this rearrangement is a *1,2-shift* very similar to those we have encountered in carbocation rearrangements (Section 5.7E). The product of the rearrangement is an isocyanate, stable under some conditions, but not in aqueous base. In aqueous base, the isocyanate undergoes hydrolysis (*Step 4*) to an amine and the carbonate ion.

Step 1 (bromination of N):

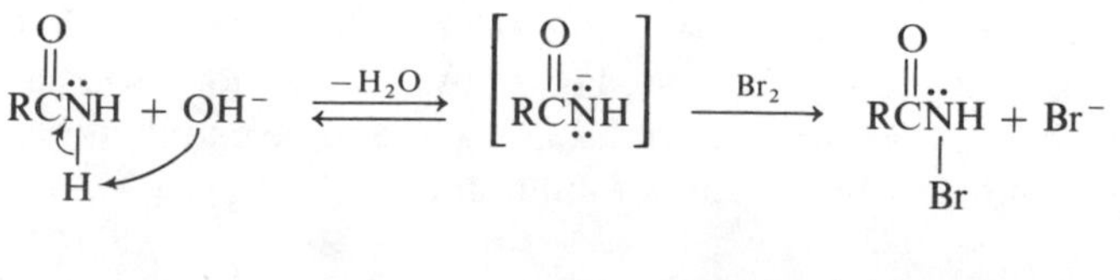

$$\underset{\underset{\text{H}}{\overset{\curvearrowleft}{|}}}{\text{RC}\overset{\overset{\text{O}}{\|}}{\ddot{\text{N}}}\text{H}} + \text{OH}^- \underset{}{\overset{-\text{H}_2\text{O}}{\rightleftharpoons}} \left[\overset{\overset{\text{O}}{\|}}{\text{RC}\ddot{\underset{..}{\text{N}}}\text{H}} \right] \xrightarrow{\text{Br}_2} \underset{\underset{\text{Br}}{|}}{\text{RC}\overset{\overset{\text{O}}{\|}}{\ddot{\text{N}}}\text{H}} + \text{Br}^-$$

Step 2 *(extraction of H$^+$ by OH$^-$):*

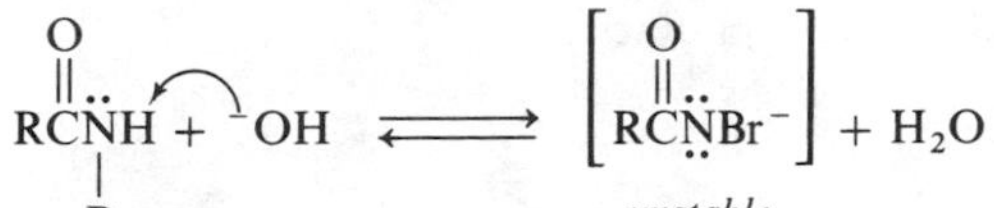

$$\underset{\underset{\displaystyle Br}{|}}{\overset{\overset{\displaystyle O}{\|}}{RC\ddot{N}H}} + \,^-OH \;\rightleftharpoons\; \left[\overset{\overset{\displaystyle O}{\|}}{RC\ddot{N}Br^-} \right] + H_2O$$

$$\qquad\qquad\qquad\qquad\qquad\quad \textit{unstable}$$

Step 3 *(displacement of Br$^-$ by R—, a 1,2-shift):*

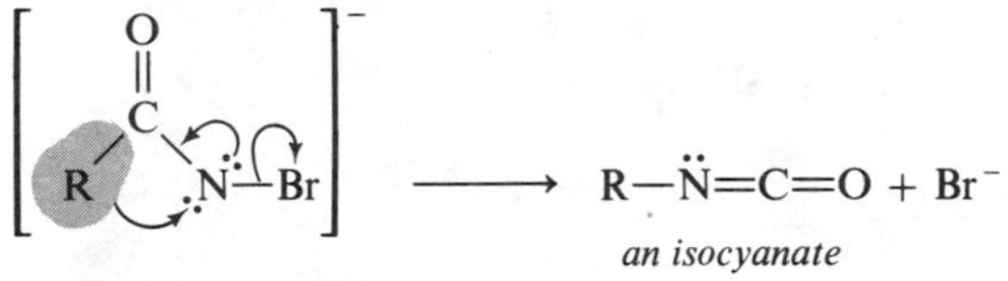

$$\left[\begin{array}{c} \overset{\overset{\displaystyle O}{\|}}{C} \\ R \diagup \quad \diagdown \ddot{N}\!\!-\!\!Br \end{array} \right]^{-} \;\longrightarrow\; R\!-\!\ddot{N}\!=\!C\!=\!O \,+\, Br^-$$

$$\qquad\qquad\qquad\qquad\qquad \textit{an isocyanate}$$

Step 4 *(hydrolysis of the isocyanate):*

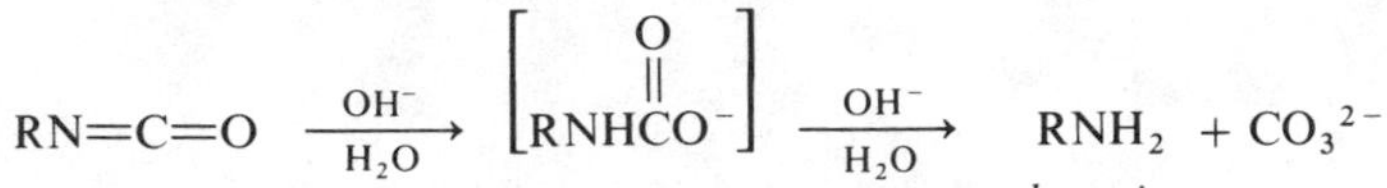

$$RN\!=\!C\!=\!O \;\xrightarrow[H_2O]{OH^-}\; \left[R\overset{\overset{\displaystyle O}{\|}}{NHCO^-} \right] \;\xrightarrow[H_2O]{OH^-}\; RNH_2 \,+\, CO_3{}^{2-}$$

$$\qquad\qquad\qquad\qquad\qquad\qquad\qquad \textit{the amine}$$

It has been found that the Hofmann rearrangement proceeds with *retention of configuration* at the α carbon of the amide. This evidence leads us to believe that the rearrangement step (Step 3) has a bridged transition state.

$$\xrightarrow{Br_2,\,OH^-}$$

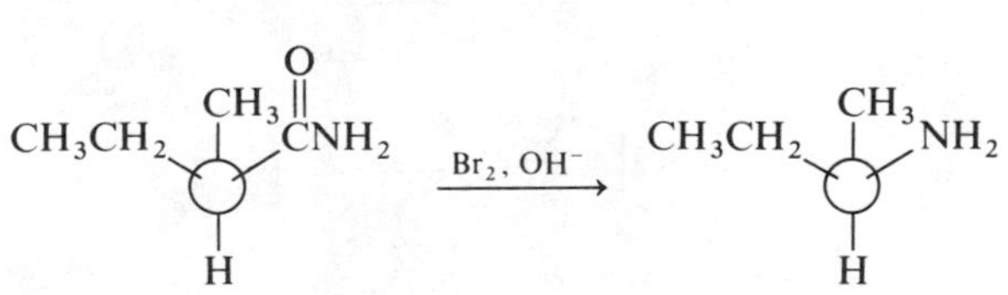

(R)-2-methylbutanamide   (R)-2-butylamine

A bridged transition state in Step 3:

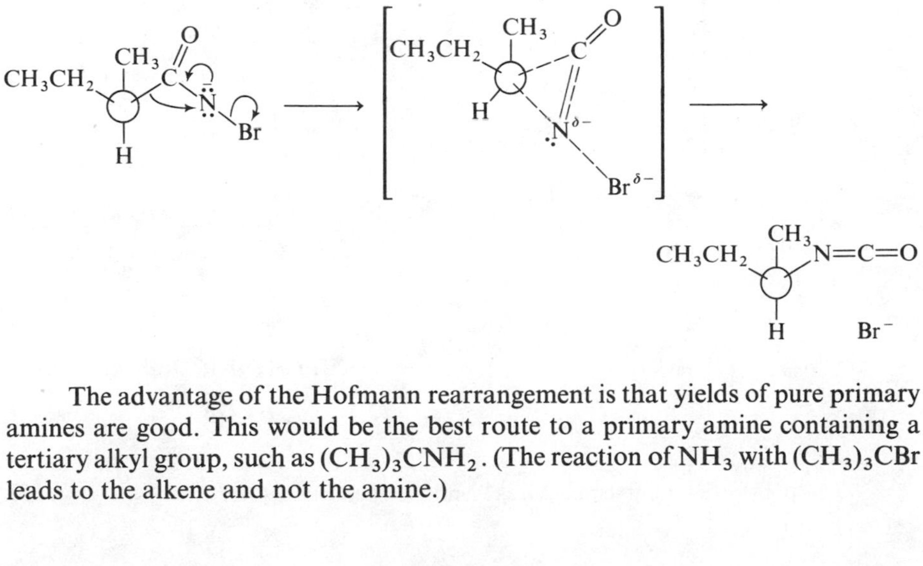

The advantage of the Hofmann rearrangement is that yields of pure primary amines are good. This would be the best route to a primary amine containing a tertiary alkyl group, such as $(CH_3)_3CNH_2$. (The reaction of NH_3 with $(CH_3)_3CBr$ leads to the alkene and not the amine.)

STUDY PROBLEM

15.10 Predict the major organic products:

(a) 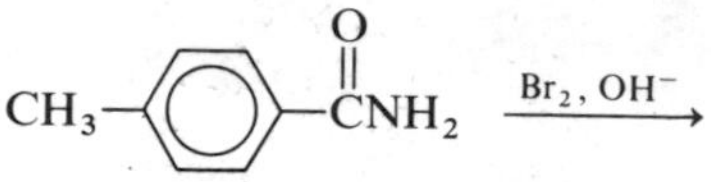 CH_3—⟨benzene ring⟩—$\overset{\overset{\text{O}}{\|}}{C}NH_2$ $\xrightarrow{\text{Br}_2,\ \text{OH}^-}$

(b) 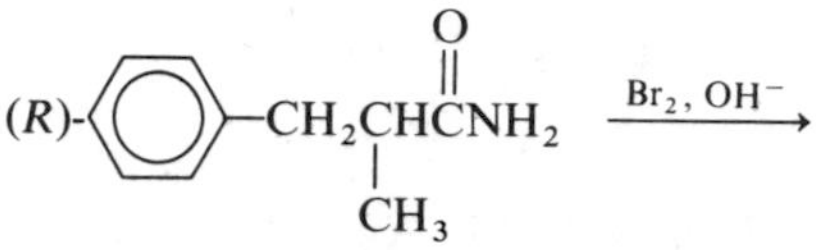 (R)-⟨benzene ring⟩—$CH_2\underset{\underset{CH_3}{|}}{CH}\overset{\overset{\text{O}}{\|}}{C}NH_2$ $\xrightarrow{\text{Br}_2,\ \text{OH}^-}$

(c) $H_2N\overset{\overset{\text{O}}{\|}}{C}CH_2CH_2CH_2\overset{\overset{\text{O}}{\|}}{C}NH_2$ $\xrightarrow{\text{Br}_2,\ \text{OH}^-}$

Table 15.3.   Preparations of Amines

Primary amines:

Substitution
$\begin{cases} 1° \text{RX} + \text{excess NH}_3 \longrightarrow \text{RNH}_2 \\ \\ \text{RX} + \text{⟨phthalimide anion⟩ N}^- \longrightarrow \text{RNH}_2 \end{cases}$

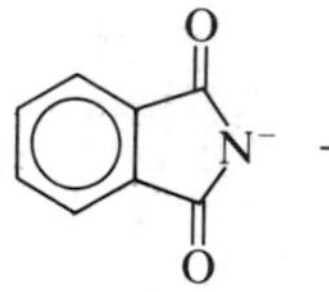

Reduction
$\begin{cases} \text{ArNO}_2 \xrightarrow{\text{Fe, HCl}} \text{ArNH}_2{}^a \\ \\ \text{RCN} \ \text{or} \ \text{R}\overset{\overset{\text{O}}{\|}}{C}NH_2 \xrightarrow{\text{LAH}} \text{RCH}_2NH_2 \\ \\ \text{R}_2\text{C=O} \xrightarrow{\text{NH}_3,\ \text{H}_2,\ \text{Ni}} \text{R}_2\text{CHNH}_2 \end{cases}$

Rearrangement
$\begin{cases} \text{R}\overset{\overset{\text{O}}{\|}}{C}NH_2 \xrightarrow{\text{X}_2,\ \text{OH}^-} \text{RNH}_2 \end{cases}$

Secondary and tertiary amines:

Reduction
$\begin{cases} \text{R}\overset{\overset{\text{O}}{\|}}{C}NHR' \ \text{or} \ \text{R}\overset{\overset{\text{O}}{\|}}{C}NR'_2 \xrightarrow{\text{LAH}} \text{RCH}_2NHR' \ \text{or} \ \text{RCH}_2NR'_2 \\ \\ \text{R}_2\text{C=O} + \text{R'NH}_2 \xrightarrow{\text{H}_2,\ \text{Ni}} \text{R}_2\text{CHNHR'} \end{cases}$

---

^{a} This preparation of arylamines was mentioned in Section 10.12.

D. *Summary of Amine Syntheses*

We have shown several routes to amines. By one or another of these routes, a chemist may synthesize:

(1) an amine with the same number of carbons as the starting material;

(2) an amine with one additional carbon; or

(3) an amine with one less carbon.

The specific reactions are summarized in Table 15.3.

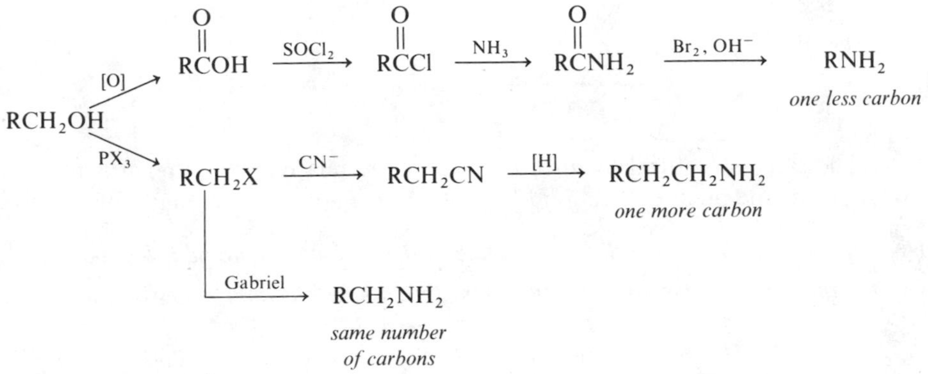

Section 15.7

Basicity of Amines

The pair of electrons in the filled, nonbonded orbital of ammonia or an amine may be donated to an electron-deficient atom, ion, or molecule. In water solution, an amine is a *weak base* and accepts a proton from water in a reversible acid–base reaction.

dimethylamine

N,N-dimethylaniline

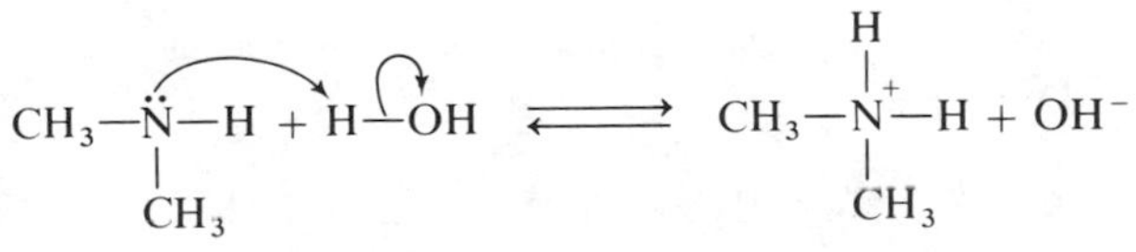

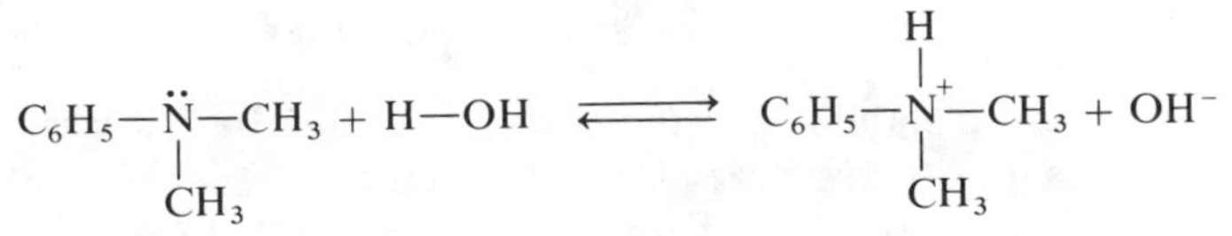

The calculation of basicity constants and pK_b values for weak bases was discussed in Section 1.10. Table 15.4 lists a few amines along with their pK_b values. (Recall that decreasing values for pK_b indicate increasing base strength.)

Table 15.4. pK_b *Values for Some Amines*

Structure	pK_b
NH_3	4.75
CH_3NH_2	3.34
$(CH_3)_2NH$	3.27
$(CH_3)_3N$	4.19
(cyclohexyl)NH	2.88
(phenyl)—NH_2	9.37

The same structural features that affect the relative acid strengths of carboxylic acids and phenols (Section 12.7) affect the relative base strengths of amines.

(1)   *If the free amine is stabilized relative to the cation, the amine is less basic.*

(2)   *If the cation is stabilized relative to the free amine, the amine is a stronger base.*

if the free amine
is stabilized, R_3N
is a weaker base

if the cation is
stabilized, R_3N is
a stronger base

$$R_3N: + H_2O \rightleftharpoons R_3NH^+ + OH^-$$

An *electron-releasing group*, such as an alkyl group, on the nitrogen increases basicity by dispersing the positive charge in the cation. (This dispersal of positive charge is analogous to that in carbocations, Section 5.7D.) By dispersal of the positive charge, the cation is stabilized relative to the free amine. Therefore, base strength increases in the series NH_3, CH_3NH_2, and $(CH_3)_2NH$.

NH_3 $\qquad$ CH_3NH_2 $\qquad$ CH_3NHCH_3

ammonia $\qquad$ methylamine $\qquad$ dimethylamine
$pK_b = 4.75$ $\qquad$ $pK_b = 3.34$ $\qquad$ $pK_b = 3.27$

$$CH_3 \rightarrow \ddot{N}H_2 + H_2O \rightleftharpoons CH_3 \rightarrow NH_3^+ + OH^-$$

stabilized by
dispersal of
positive charge

The cation is also stabilized by *increasing solvation*. In this case, the solvent helps disperse the positive charge. Dimethylamine ($pK_b = 3.27$) is a slightly stronger base than methylamine; however, trimethylamine ($pK_b = 4.19$) is a *weaker base* than dimethylamine. The reason is that trimethylamine is more hindered, and the cation is less stabilized by solvation. These arguments explain why the nonaromatic heterocyclic amines (with their alkyl groups "tied back" away from the unshared electrons of the nitrogen) are more basic than comparable open-chain secondary amines.

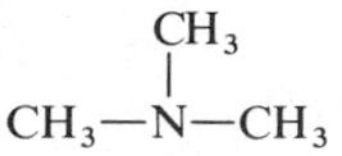

$$\underset{\substack{\text{trimethylamine}\\ \text{p}K_b = 4.19}}{\text{CH}_3-\overset{\overset{\displaystyle\text{CH}_3}{|}}{\text{N}}-\text{CH}_3}\quad \text{is a weaker base than}\quad \underset{\substack{\text{dimethylamine}\\ \text{p}K_b = 3.27}}{\text{CH}_3-\overset{\overset{\displaystyle\text{CH}_3}{|}}{\text{N}}-\text{H}}$$

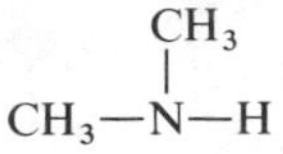

$$\underset{\substack{\text{diethylamine}\\ \text{p}K_b = 3.01}}{\text{CH}_3\text{CH}_2\text{NHCH}_2\text{CH}_3}\quad \text{is a weaker base than}\quad \underset{\substack{\text{pyrrolidine}\\ \text{p}K_b = 2.73}}{}$$

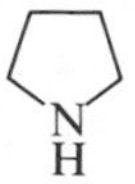

Hybridization of the nitrogen atom in a nitrogen compound also affects the base strength. An sp^2 orbital contains more s character than an sp^3 orbital; therefore, an sp^2 nitrogen holds its electrons more tightly than does an sp^3 nitrogen. A molecule with an sp^2 nitrogen is less basic because the unshared electrons are more tightly held, and the free nitrogen compound is stabilized (rather than the cation).

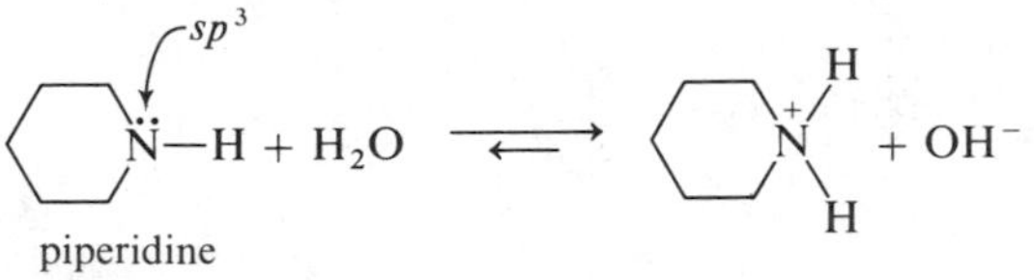

piperidine
pK_b = 2.88

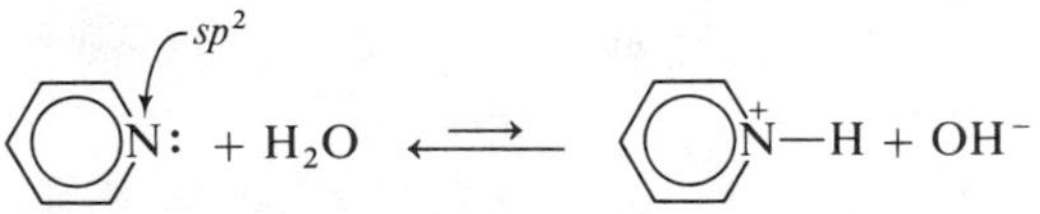

pyridine
pK_b = 8.75

Resonance also affects the base strength of an amine. Cyclohexylamine is a far stronger base than is aniline.

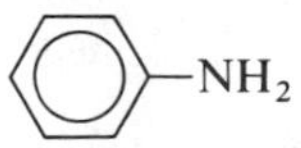

aniline
pK_b = 9.37

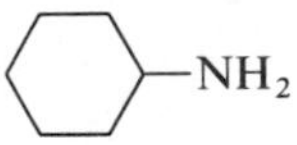

cyclohexylamine
pK_b = 3.3

The reason for the low basicity of aniline is that the positive charge of the anilinium ion cannot be delocalized by the aromatic pi cloud. However, the pair of electrons of the free amine are delocalized by the ring. The result is that the free amine is stabilized in comparison to the conjugate acid (the cation).

aniline:

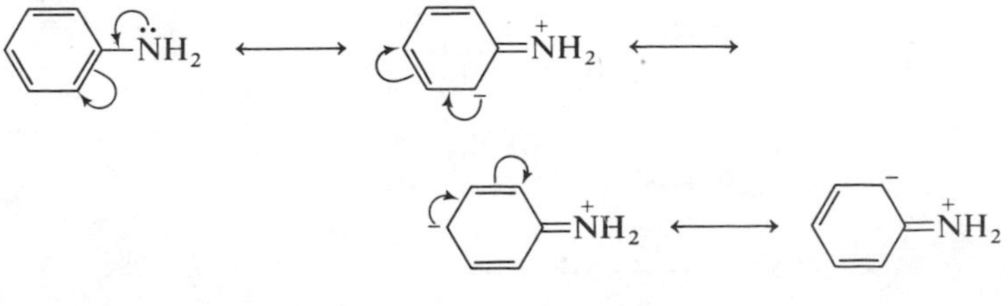

anilinium ion :   ⟨benzene⟩—ṄH₃   *no resonance-*
stabilization of
positive charge

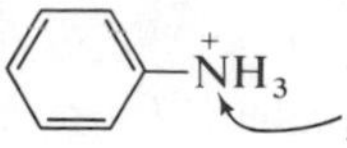

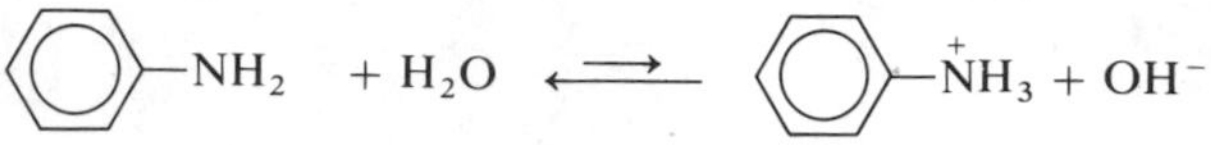

⟨benzene⟩—NH₂ + H₂O ⇌ ⟨benzene⟩—ṄH₃ + OH⁻

resonance-stabilized
and favored

Sample Problem

Explain why piperidine is a stronger base than morpholine.

⟨ring⟩NH   O⟨ring⟩NH

piperidine   morpholine
pK$_b$ = 2.88   pK$_b$ = 5.67

Solution: The oxygen atom in morpholine is *electron-withdrawing*, making the nitrogen more positive. The cation is not stabilized relative to the free morpholine, but is *destabilized*:

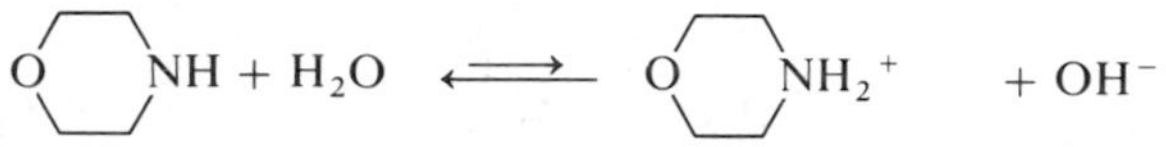

O⟨ring⟩NH + H₂O ⇌ O⟨ring⟩NH₂⁺   + OH⁻

less stable
because of less
dispersal of + charge

Piperidine has no such destabilizing effect. Its cation is stabilized by electron release of the attached CH₂ groups:

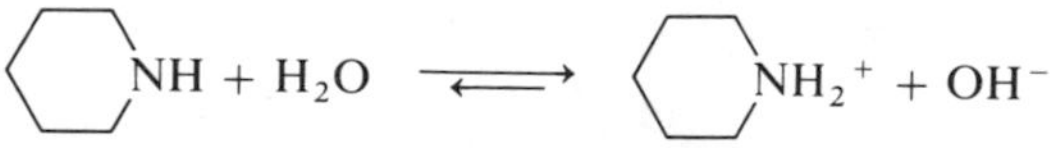

⟨ring⟩NH + H₂O ⇌ ⟨ring⟩NH₂⁺ + OH⁻

stabilized

STUDY PROBLEMS

15.11 Which would you expect to be more basic: (a) methylamine or (chloromethyl)amine?
(b) piperazine (page 703) or piperidine?   (c) piperazine or hexamethylenetetramine?

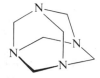

hexamethylenetetramine

15.12 Benzylamine (C₆H₅CH₂NH₂) has about the same base strength as an alkylamine, not that of an arylamine. How do you explain this fact?

15.13 Explain the following trend in pK$_b$ values:

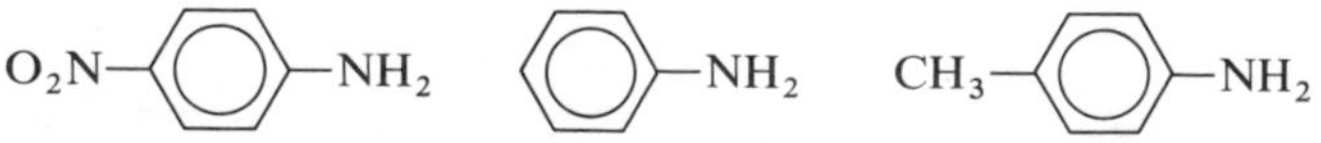

O₂N—⟨benzene⟩—NH₂   ⟨benzene⟩—NH₂   CH₃—⟨benzene⟩—NH₂

pK$_b$ = 13.0   pK$_b$ = 9.37   pK$_b$ = 8.9

Section 15.8

Amine Salts

The reaction of an amine with a mineral acid (such as HCl) or a carboxylic acid (such as acetic acid) yields an **amine salt**. The salts are commonly named in one of two ways: as **substituted ammonium salts** or as **amine–acid complexes**.

$$(CH_3)_3N \ + HCl \ \rightleftharpoons \ (CH_3)_3NH^+ \ Cl^-$$

trimethylamine   trimethylammonium chloride
or
trimethylamine hydrochloride

$$CH_3CH_2NH_2 + HBr \ \rightleftharpoons \ CH_3CH_2NH_3^+ \ Br^-$$

ethylamine   ethylammonium bromide
or
ethylamine hydrobromide

Because of its ability to form salts, an amine that is insoluble in water may be made soluble by treatment with dilute acid. In this fashion, compounds containing amino groups may be separated from water- and acid-insoluble materials. Naturally occurring amines in plants, called **alkaloids**, may be extracted from their sources, such as leaves or bark, by aqueous acid. Many compounds containing amino groups are used as drugs. These drugs are often administered as their water-soluble salts rather than as water-insoluble amines.

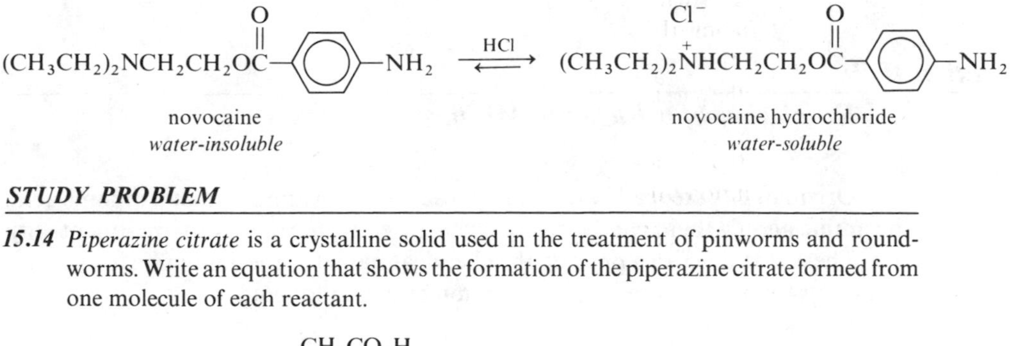

novocaine   novocaine hydrochloride
water-insoluble   *water-soluble*

STUDY PROBLEM

15.14 *Piperazine citrate* is a crystalline solid used in the treatment of pinworms and roundworms. Write an equation that shows the formation of the piperazine citrate formed from one molecule of each reactant.

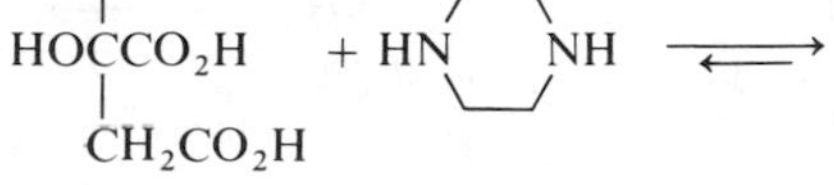

citric acid   piperazine

A free amine may be regenerated from one of its salts by treatment with a strong base, usually NaOH. Quaternary ammonium salts, which have no acidic protons, do not undergo this reaction.

$$RNH_3^+ \ Cl^- + OH^- \ \longrightarrow \ RNH_2 \ + H_2O$$

an amine salt   *an amine*

$$R_4N^+ \ Cl^- \ + OH^- \ \longrightarrow \ \text{no reaction}$$

a quaternary
ammonium salt

Because of the ionic charge of a quaternary ammonium ion, quaternary ammonium salts have some interesting applications. Quaternary ammonium salts with long hydrocarbon chains are used as detergents. Phospholipids, some of which are quaternary ammonium salts, are naturally occurring emulsifying agents. In either case, the combination of a long, hydrophobic, hydrocarbon tail with an ionic, hydrophilic head results in two types of interaction with other substances. Part of the molecule is soluble in nonpolar organic solvents, fats, and oils, while part is soluble in water. Soaps (Section 19.2) exhibit similar behavior.

hydrocarbon chains

$$CH_2OC(CH_2)_{14}CH_3$$

$$CH_3(CH_2)_{14}CO—C—H$$

ionic end

$$CH_2OPOCH_2CH_2\overset{+}{N}(CH_3)_3$$

$$O^-$$

a phosphatidylcholine
(a phospholipid)

Section 15.9

Resolution of a Racemic Mixture

Organic salts are readily formed by reaction of an amine with an organic acid. The amine and the acid can be easily regenerated from the salt by treatment with base. These two reactions provide the chemical basis for the **resolution**, or separation, of a racemic mixture into its enantiomeric components.

$$RCO_2H + R'NH_2 \longrightarrow RCO_2^- \ R'NH_3^+ \xrightarrow{NaOH} RCO_2^- + R'NH_2$$

a carboxylic   *an amine*   *a salt*   *a carboxylate* *an amine*
acid

A racemic mixture is a 50:50 mixture of a pair of enantiomers. Enantiomers cannot be separated from each other by standard laboratory procedures because they have identical chemical and physical properties (melting points, solubilities, etc.). However, *diastereomers* (stereoisomers that are not mirror images) have different properties and may be separated by such techniques as fractional crystallization, which depends on solubility-differences for success.

Let us illustrate a general procedure for the resolution of $(R)(S)$-RCO_2H, a racemic mixture of a carboxylic acid, where (R)-RCO_2H and (S)-RCO_2H represent the two enantiomers. Reaction of this racemic acid with an amine yields a mixture of salts. If the amine is chosen such that it is chiral and is a single enantiomer, then the resulting salt mixture is a mixture of separable diastereomers.

$$
\begin{array}{c}
\text{(R)-RCO}_2\text{H} \\
\text{and} \\
\text{(S)-RCO}_2\text{H}
\end{array}
\quad + \quad
\text{(S)-R'NH}_2
\quad \longrightarrow \quad
\left\{
\begin{array}{c}
\text{(R)-RCO}_2^- \; \text{(S)-R'NH}_3^+ \\
\text{and} \\
\text{(S)-RCO}_2^- \; \text{(S)-R'NH}_3^+
\end{array}
\right\}
$$

racemic mixture   *an enantiomeric*   *the (R,S)-salt and the (S,S)-salt are*
                amine   *diastereomers and may be separated*

In this reaction, the only possible products are the (R,S)-salt and the (S,S)-salt, which are diastereomers. The enantiomers of these two salts are the (S,R)-salt and the (R,R)-salt. Neither of these enantiomers can be formed in this reaction because only the (S)-amine was used as a reactant.

After separation, each diastereomeric salt is treated with a strong base to regenerate the amine and the carboxylate ion. The amine and the carboxylate ion may be separated by extraction with a solvent such as diethyl ether (in which the amine is soluble, but the carboxylate salt is not). Acidification of the aqueous phase yields the free enantiomeric carboxylic acid.

$$
\text{(R)-RCO}_2^- \; \text{(S)-RNH}_3^+ \quad \xrightarrow{\text{OH}^-} \quad \text{(R)-RCO}_2^- \; + \; \text{(S)-RNH}_2
$$

one of the pure
diastereomeric salts

$$
\xrightarrow{\text{HCl}} \text{(R)-RCO}_2\text{H}
$$

as a pure enantiomer

This resolution of a racemic acid depends on salt formation with a single enantiomer of a chiral amine. Commonly used amines are the naturally occurring brucine and strychnine and the synthetic amphetamine, which is commercially available as pure enantiomers.

strychnine   brucine   amphetamine
a toxic stimulant of the
central nervous system

STUDY PROBLEM

15.15 Write equations that show how racemic *sec*-butylamine can be resolved with (2R,3S)-tartaric acid, $\text{HO}_2\text{CCHCHCO}_2\text{H}$.
$$
\underset{\text{HO} \quad \text{OH}}{| \quad |}
$$

Conversion of racemic mixtures to diastereomeric amine salts is the most general procedure for resolution; however, it is not the only one. The first laboratory resolution was carried out in 1848 by Louis Pasteur, who used tweezers to separate right- and left-handed crystals of sodium ammonium tartrate (see Section 4.7). This type of separation is not general because racemic mixtures that crystallize in this manner are very rare.

Living systems are capable of resolving racemic mixtures. For example, when an organism ingests a racemic mixture of alanine, only the (*S*)-alanine becomes incorporated into protein structures. The (*R*)-alanine is not used in proteins; rather, it is oxidized to a keto acid and, as such, enters other metabolic schemes.

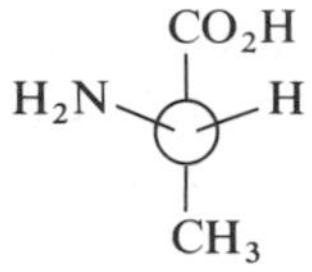

(*S*)-alanine

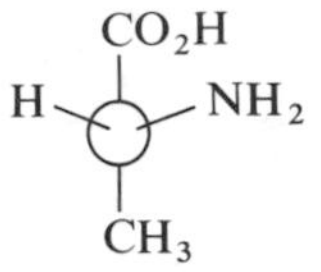

(*R*)-alanine

An organism is capable of resolving racemic mixtures and of synthesizing particular stereoisomers because the enzymes of the organism are stereoisomers themselves. The result is that the nucleic acids, proteins, carbohydrates, steroids, and most other biomolecules are chiral. As to what initiated the stereospecificity (the first enzyme or the first nucleic acid), we do not know.

Resolution by enzymes has found practical laboratory application. For example, the enzyme **deacylase** catalyzes the hydrolysis of (*S*)-*N*-acylamino acids, but not hydrolysis of the (*R*)-enantiomers. Treatment of a racemic mixture of an *N*-acetylamino acid with this enzyme thus results in a mixture that is easily separated.

a racemic N-acetylamino acid

an easily separated mixture

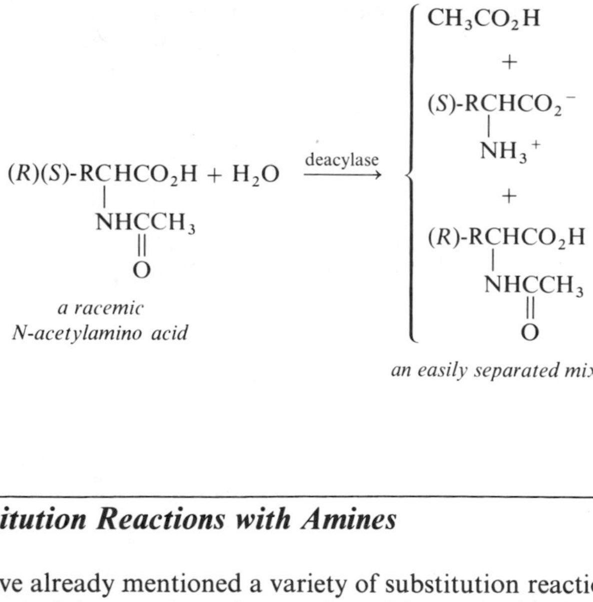

Section 15.10
Substitution Reactions with Amines

We have already mentioned a variety of substitution reactions with amines. The problems of the reaction of an amine with an alkyl halide were discussed earlier in this chapter (Section 15.6).

$$RNH_2 + R'Cl \xrightarrow{S_N2} R\overset{+}{N}H_2(R')\ Cl^- \quad \text{and also} \quad R\overset{+}{N}HR'_2\ Cl^- \quad \text{and} \quad R\overset{+}{N}R'_3\ Cl^-$$

In Section 13.3C, we discussed the acylation of amines as a technique for the synthesis of amides.

$$CH_3\overset{\displaystyle O}{\overset{\|}{C}}Cl + CH_3NH_2 \longrightarrow \left[CH_3\overset{\displaystyle O^-}{\underset{\underset{H}{\overset{\|}{\underset{+NHCH_3}{C}}}}{\overset{\curvearrowright}{C}}Cl} \right] \longrightarrow CH_3\overset{\displaystyle O}{\overset{\|}{\underset{NHCH_3}{C}}} + HCl$$

acetyl   methylamine   *N*-methylacetamide
chloride

The utility of this reaction is that amines can be used to synthesize other amines by conversion to the amide, followed by reduction.

$$RCCl + R'_2NH \longrightarrow R\overset{\displaystyle O}{\overset{\|}{C}}NR'_2 \xrightarrow[\text{(2) } H_2O]{\text{(1) LiAlH}_4} RCH_2NR'_2$$

an acid chloride   an amine   an amide   a new amine

Amines also undergo reactions with aldehydes and ketones to yield imines and enamines. Although the result of these reactions is substitution, the mechanism is one of addition to the carbonyl group followed by elimination of water. (For the mechanisms, see Section 11.10.)

cyclohexanone

$$\xrightarrow[H^+]{H_2NR(1°)} \bigcirc\!\!=NR + H_2O$$

an imine

$$\xrightarrow[H^+]{HNR_2(2°)} \bigcirc\!\!-NR_2 + H_2O$$

an enamine

Section 15.11

Reactions of Amines with Nitrous Acid

Nitrous acid (HNO_2, or HONO) is an unstable reagent that is generated in a reaction mixture by the action of aqueous HCl or other strong acid on sodium nitrite ($NaNO_2$). Nitrous acid undergoes reaction with all types of amines by electrophilic attack of ^+NO, but the products are not all the same. A **primary alkylamine** yields a **diazonium salt** ($RN_2^+\ X^-$) that is unstable and decomposes to nitrogen and a mixture of alcohols and alkenes. The decomposition proceeds by way of a carbocation.

Formation of diazonium salt:

$$H^+ + HONO \rightleftharpoons H_2O + NO^+$$

$$(CH_3)_2CHNH_2 + NO^+ + Cl^- \xrightarrow[-H_2O]{\text{a series of steps}} (CH_3)_2CH{-}\overset{+}{N}{\equiv}N\ Cl^-$$

isopropylamine   isopropyldiazonium
a 1° alkylamine   chloride

Decomposition of diazonium salt:

$$(CH_3)_2CH{-}\overset{+}{N}{\equiv}N \xrightarrow{-N_2} [(CH_3)_2CH^+] \xrightarrow{H_2O} CH_3CH{=}CH_2 + CH_3\overset{\overset{\displaystyle OH}{|}}{C}HCH_3$$

A **primary arylamine** yields a diazonium salt that is stable at 0°C and that undergoes reaction with a variety of reagents. We will discuss some of these reactions shortly.

$$\langle \bigcirc \rangle - NH_2 + HONO + HCl \xrightarrow{\ 0°\ } \langle \bigcirc \rangle - \overset{+}{N}\equiv N \ Cl^- + H_2O$$

aniline
a 1° arylamine

benzenediazonium
chloride
stable at 0°

Secondary amines (alkyl or aryl) yield **N-nitrosoamines**, compounds containing the N—N=O group. Many *N*-nitrosoamines are carcinogenic.

nitroso group

$$\langle \bigcirc \rangle - NHCH_3 + HONO \longrightarrow \langle \bigcirc \rangle - \underset{\underset{CH_3}{|}}{N} - \widetilde{NO} + H_2O$$

N-methylaniline
a 2° amine

an N-nitrosoamine

Tertiary amines are not entirely predictable in their reactions with nitrous acid. A tertiary arylamine usually undergoes ring substitution because of the ring activation by the —NR$_2$ group.

$$\langle \bigcirc \rangle - N(CH_3)_2 + HONO \longrightarrow ON - \langle \bigcirc \rangle - N(CH_3)_2 + H_2O$$

N,N-dimethylaniline
a 3° arylamine

p-nitroso-*N,N*-
dimethylaniline

A tertiary alkylamine (and sometimes tertiary arylamines, too) may lose an R group and form an *N*-nitroso derivative of a secondary amine.

STUDY PROBLEMS

15.16 When *n*-butylamine is treated with a cold aqueous solution of HCl and NaNO$_2$, the following products are obtained: 1-chlorobutane, 2-chlorobutane, 2-butanol, 1-butene, 2-butene, and nitrogen gas. Suggest a mechanism (or mechanisms) that accounts for each of these products.

15.17 Suggest a reason that benzenediazonium chloride is more stable than ethyldiazonium chloride.

Section 15.12

Benzenediazonium Salts

Aryldiazonium salts are valuable in the synthesis of substituted aromatic compounds. The usefulness of aryldiazonium salts lies in their reactivity. The

$-\overset{+}{N}\equiv N$ group is easily displaced as nitrogen gas by a variety of nucleophiles, including such weak nucleophiles as halide ions. The treatment of an aryldiazonium salt with a copper(I) halide results in an aryl halide in yields of about 70%. This reaction is called the **Sandmeyer reaction**.

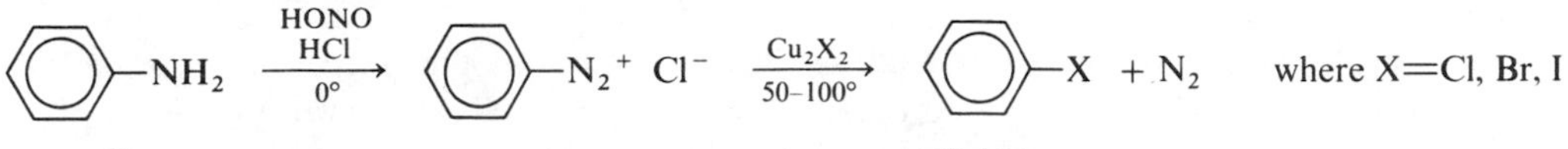

aniline   *a halobenzene*

A similar reaction may be used to prepare an arylnitrile, which is easily hydrolyzed to a carboxylic acid. The usual route to an aromatic carboxylic acid is the oxidation of an alkylbenzene. However, the following toluic acid could not have been prepared by oxidation of a xylene (dimethylbenzene) because *both* methyl groups would have been oxidized.

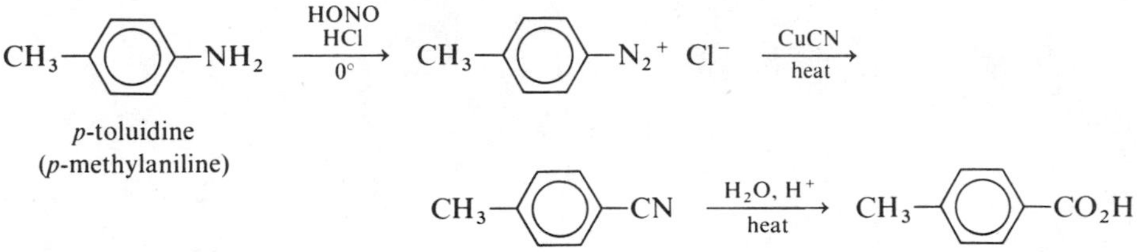

p-toluidine
(*p*-methylaniline)

p-toluic acid
(*p*-methylbenzoic acid)

Phenols may be prepared from diazonium salts by reaction with hot water.

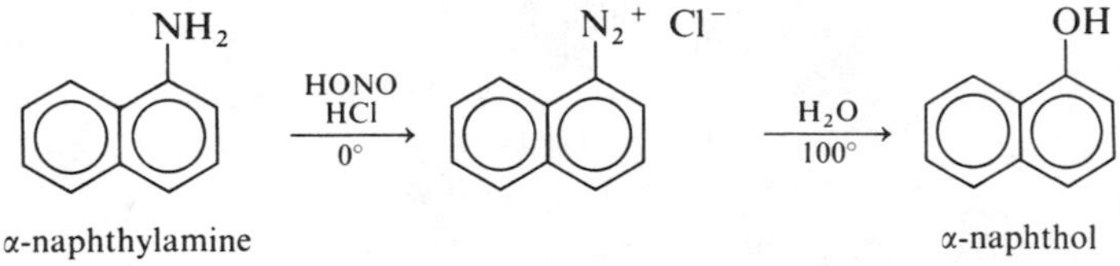

α-naphthylamine   α-naphthol

The $-N_2^+$ group may be converted to $-H$ by reduction with hypophosphorous acid, H_3PO_2. This reaction provides a method for the removal of an $-NH_2$ group (or a nitro group after reduction) from a benzene ring.

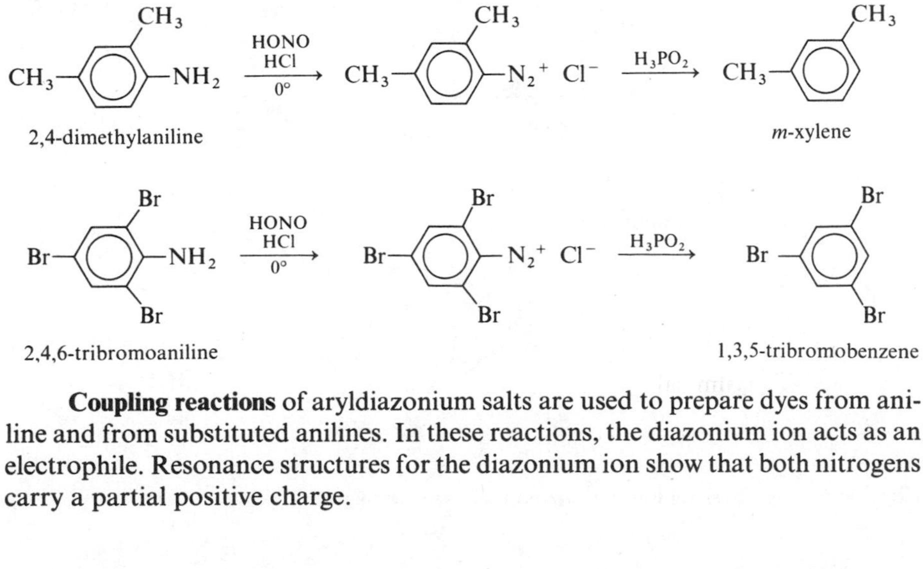

2,4-dimethylaniline   *m*-xylene

2,4,6-tribromoaniline   1,3,5-tribromobenzene

Coupling reactions of aryldiazonium salts are used to prepare dyes from aniline and from substituted anilines. In these reactions, the diazonium ion acts as an electrophile. Resonance structures for the diazonium ion show that both nitrogens carry a partial positive charge.

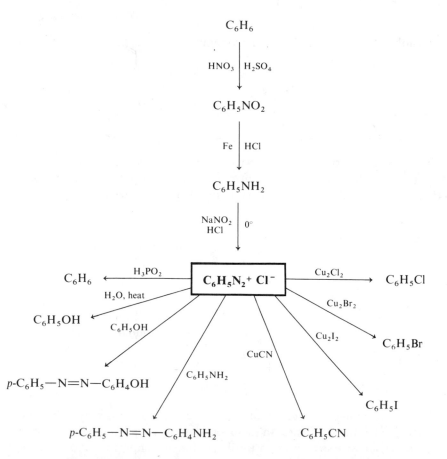

The terminal nitrogen attacks the *para*-position of an activated benzene ring (one substituted with an electron-releasing group like NH_2 or OH). The coupling product contains an **azo group** ($-N=N-$) and is generally referred to as an **azo compound**.

p-aminoazobenzene

p-hydroxyazobenzene

Figure 15.3. Preparation and reactions of a benzenediazonium salt.

Two azo dyes:

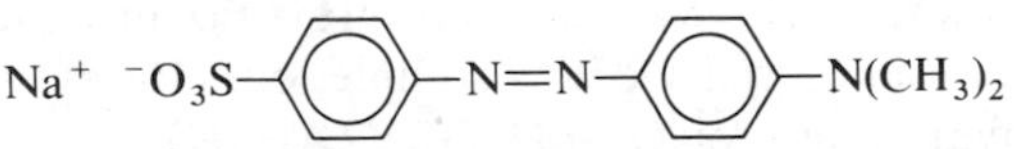

$Na^+ \ \ ^-O_3S-$⟨benzene⟩$-N{=}N-$⟨benzene⟩$-N(CH_3)_2$

methyl orange
an indicator

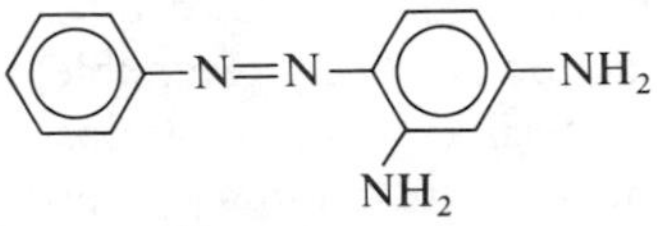

⟨benzene⟩$-N{=}N-$⟨benzene⟩$-NH_2$
NH_2

Basic Orange 2
used to dye leather and paper

The preparation of benzenediazonium chloride from benzene and the reactions that this compound can undergo are summarized in Figure 15.3.

STUDY PROBLEM

15.18 How would you make the following conversions?

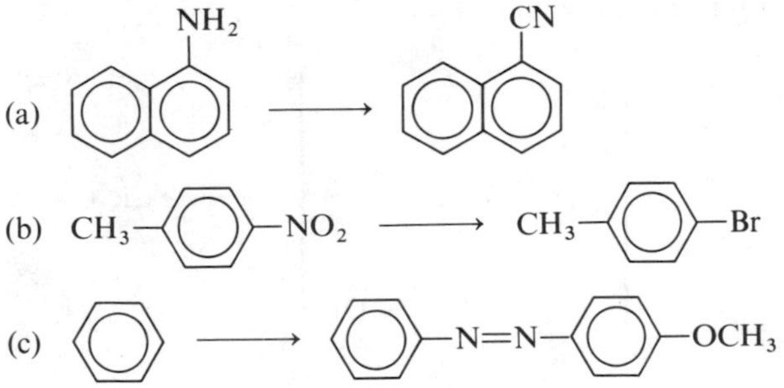

(a) ⟨naphthalene with NH_2⟩ $\longrightarrow$ ⟨naphthalene with CN⟩

(b) CH_3-⟨benzene⟩$-NO_2 \longrightarrow CH_3-$⟨benzene⟩$-Br$

(c) ⟨benzene⟩ $\longrightarrow$ ⟨benzene⟩$-N{=}N-$⟨benzene⟩$-OCH_3$

Section 15.13

Hofmann Elimination

Quaternary ammonium hydroxides ($R_4N^+ \ OH^-$) are amine derivatives that are used in structure-determination studies because they undergo elimination reactions to yield alkenes and amines. We will look briefly at how these compounds are prepared, then at their elimination reactions, and finally at their utility in structure studies.

A. Formation of Quaternary Ammonium Hydroxides

When a quaternary ammonium halide is treated with silver oxide, the quaternary ammonium hydroxide is obtained:

$$2\,R_4N^+ \ X^- \ + Ag_2O + H_2O \longrightarrow 2\,R_4N^+ \ OH^- \ + 2\,AgX{\downarrow}$$

a quaternary
ammonium halide

a quaternary
ammonium hydroxide

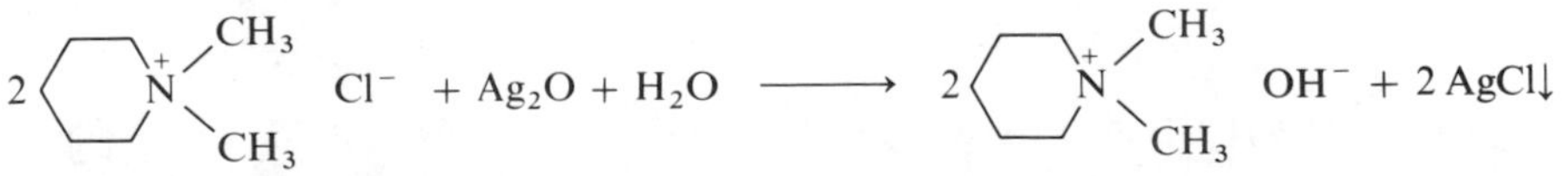

2 ⟨piperidinium with CH_3, N^+, CH_3⟩ $Cl^- \ + Ag_2O + H_2O \longrightarrow 2$ ⟨piperidinium with CH_3, N^+, CH_3⟩ $OH^- + 2\,AgCl{\downarrow}$

N,N-dimethylpiperidinium
chloride

N,N-dimethylpiperidinium
hydroxide

A quaternary ammonium hydroxide is a strong base, and therefore cannot be obtained by the direct treatment of R_4N^+ X^- with aqueous OH^-. Because the reaction is readily reversible, there is nothing to drive it to completion. However, moist silver oxide contains silver hydroxide ($Ag_2O + H_2O \rightleftarrows 2\,AgOH$), which undergoes reaction with the quaternary ammonium halide to form the quaternary ammonium hydroxide and the insoluble silver halide. The precipitation of the silver halide drives the reaction to completion.

B.   The Elimination

When a quaternary ammonium hydroxide (as a solid) is heated, an elimination reaction called a **Hofmann elimination** occurs. This reaction is an E2 reaction in which the leaving group is an amine.

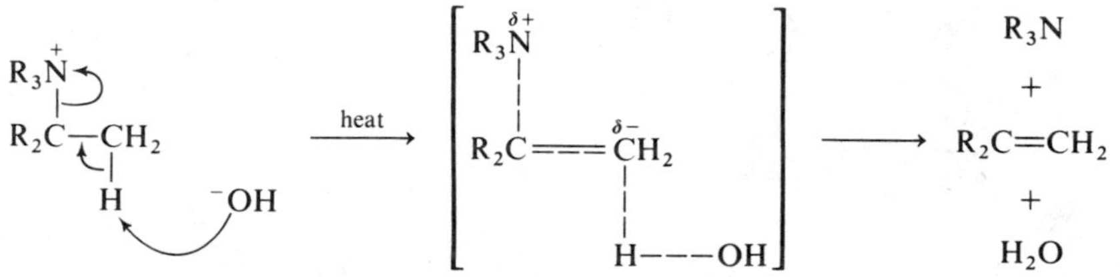

E2 transition state

This elimination generally yields the *Hofmann product*, the alkene with *fewer alkyl groups* on the pi-bonded carbons. The formation of the less substituted, less stable alkene may be attributed to steric hindrance in the transition state (Section 5.10D).

$$(CH_3)_3\overset{+}{N}\!-\!\overset{\displaystyle CH_3}{\overset{|}{C}H}CH_2CH_3 \;\; OH^- \xrightarrow{\;heat\;}$$

sec-butyltrimethylammonium hydroxide

$$(CH_3)_3N + CH_2{=}CHCH_2CH_3 + H_2O \qquad \text{and very little} \quad CH_3CH{=}CHCH_3$$

1-butene
less substituted

STUDY PROBLEM

15.19 Predict the major organic products:

(a) $(CH_3)_2CHN\overset{+}{\underset{\displaystyle CH_3}{\overset{\displaystyle CH_3}{|}}}\!-\!CH_2CH_3 \;\; OH^- \xrightarrow{\;heat\;}$

(b) $C_6H_5CH_2CH_2\overset{+}{\underset{\displaystyle CH_3}{\overset{\displaystyle CH_3}{|}}}\!-\!CH_2CH_3 \;\; OH^- \xrightarrow{\;heat\;}$

C. Exhaustive Methylation

Many compounds in nature contain heterocyclic nitrogen rings. A quaternary ammonium hydroxide of a heterocyclic ring undergoes elimination in the same fashion as an open-chain amine. When the nitrogen atom is part of a ring, fragmentation does not occur. Instead, the product amino group and alkenyl group both remain in the same molecule.

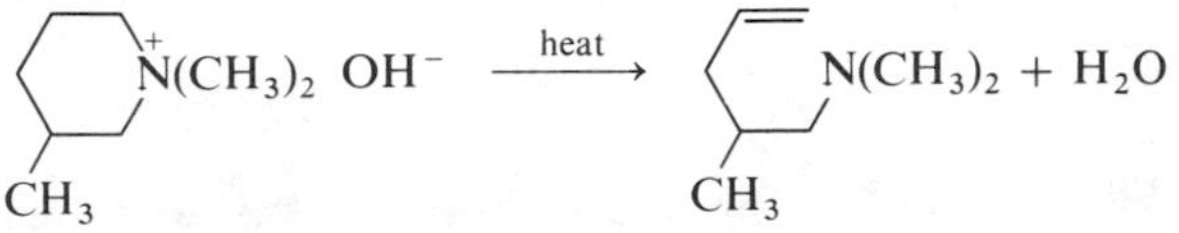

The mechanism for Hofmann elimination of a nitrogen heterocycle is the same as that for an open-chain compound. The hydroxide ion abstracts a hydrogen from the least hindered β position. The product is the least substituted alkene.

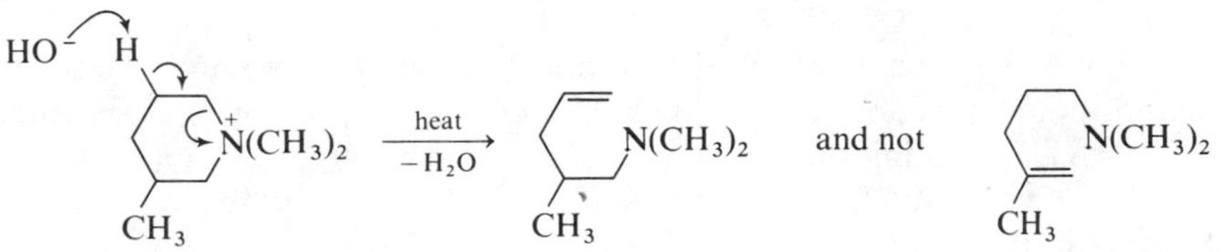

Sample Problem

Predict the major organic elimination products when each of the following compounds is heated:

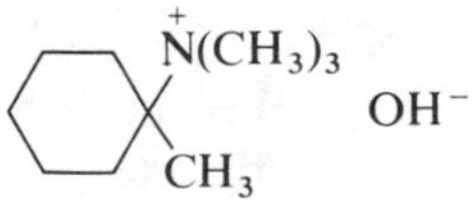

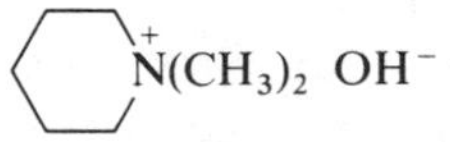

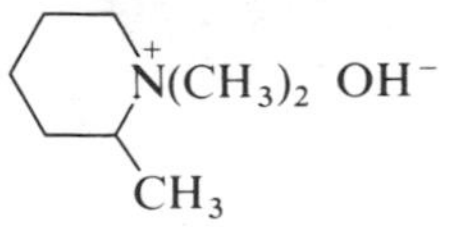

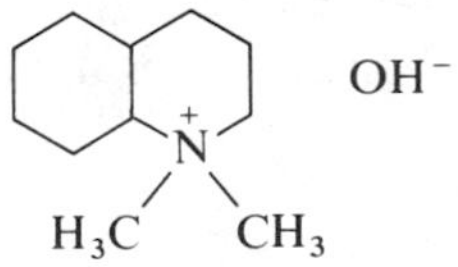

Solution:

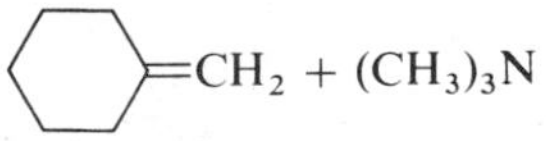

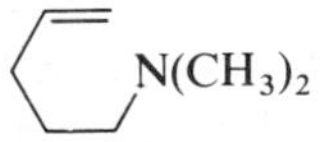

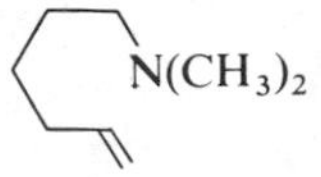

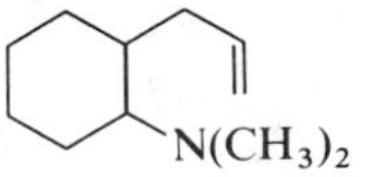

To see how the Hofmann elimination can be applied toward structure elucidation, let us take a simple heterocycle, 3-ethylpiperidine, as an example. First, a quaternary ammonium hydroxide is prepared by treatment with methyl iodide (S_N2) followed by reaction with Ag_2O. A primary amine takes up *three* CH_3 groups; a secondary amine takes up *two* CH_3 groups; and a tertiary amine takes up only *one*. (This information alone tells us something about the nitrogen in the unknown compound.) In the case at hand, 3-ethylpiperidine is a secondary amine and takes up two CH_3 groups.

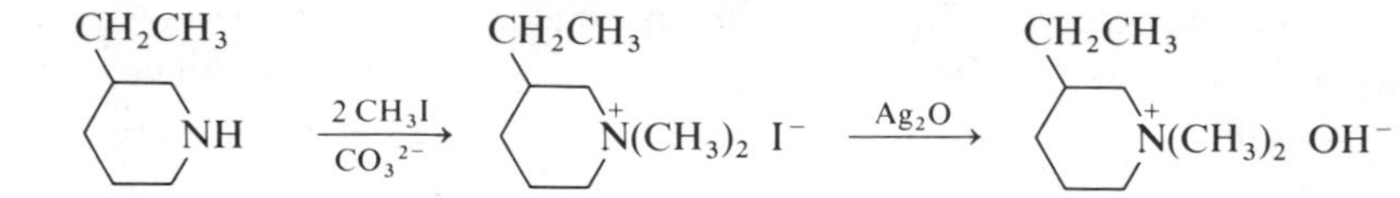

3-ethylpiperidine
a 2° amine

Heating the quaternary ammonium hydroxide results in an amine and the least substituted alkene:

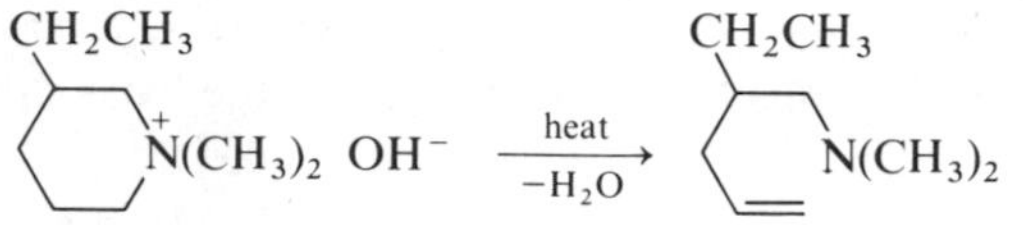

Because the product of this elimination still contains an amino group, it can undergo another reaction with CH_3I and Ag_2O to yield a new quaternary ammonium hydroxide. Heating this product results in a new alkene. The nitrogen is expelled, or "exhausted," as trimethylamine. This series of reactions is called **exhaustive methylation**.

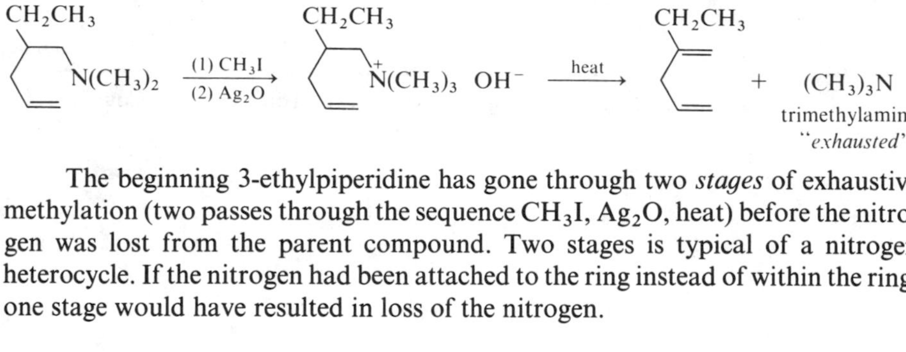

trimethylamine
"exhausted"

The beginning 3-ethylpiperidine has gone through two *stages* of exhaustive methylation (two passes through the sequence CH_3I, Ag_2O, heat) before the nitrogen was lost from the parent compound. Two stages is typical of a nitrogen heterocycle. If the nitrogen had been attached to the ring instead of within the ring, one stage would have resulted in loss of the nitrogen.

STUDY PROBLEMS

15.20 Fill in the blanks:

(a)

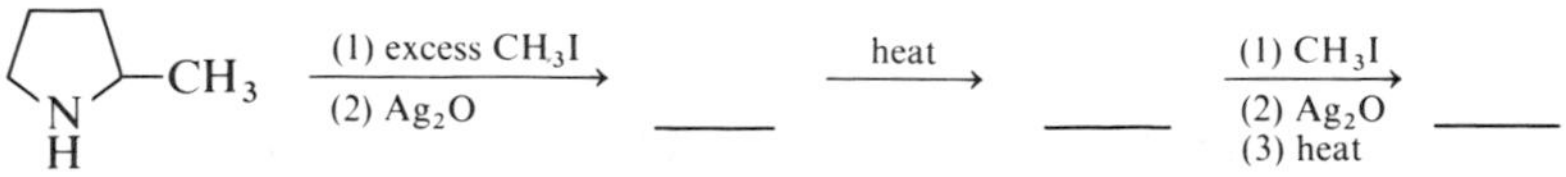

(b)

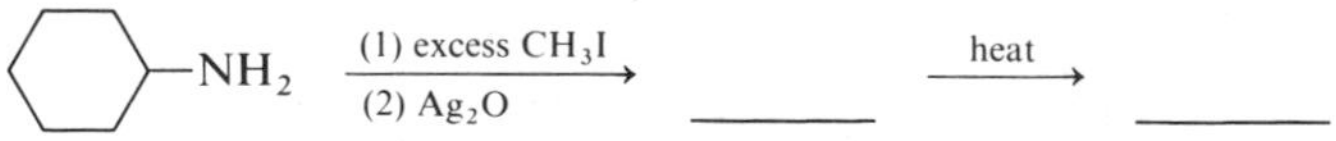

15.21 *Coniine*, $C_8H_{17}N$, is a toxic constituent of poison hemlock (*Conium maculatum*), the extract of which is believed to have killed Socrates. The nmr spectrum of coniine shows no doublets. Coniine undergoes reaction with two moles of methyl iodide. Reaction with Ag_2O followed by pyrolysis yields an intermediate ($C_{10}H_{21}N$) which, upon further methylation followed by conversion to the hydroxide and pyrolysis, yields trimethylamine, 1,5-octadiene, and 1,4-octadiene. What are the structures of coniine and the intermediate compound?

Section 15.14

Some Amines of Biological Importance

Amines are widely distributed in plants and animals. Rather than trying to outline the various types of amines in nature, we will devote this section to only one important class, the **sympathomimetic amines**. (Other amines of biological importance will be encountered in coming chapters.)

In higher animals, the autonomic nervous system is composed of two types of subsystem: the **sympathetic** and the **parasympathetic** (see Figure 15.4). The *parasympathetic system* has been called the "housekeeping" system; it stimulates the digestive processes, for example. Discharge of the *sympathetic system* prepares an animal for "fight or flight"—the rate of the heartbeat increases, the blood pressure rises, and the bronchial tissues shrink (so as to dilate the bronchi and increase oxygen uptake).

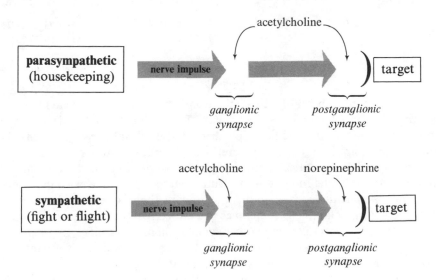

Figure 15.4. Diagrams of the sympathetic and parasympathetic nervous systems.

Nerve impulses are transmitted across gaps between nerve cells (**ganglionic synapses**) and across gaps between nerve cells and receptors in the target organs (**postganglionic synapses**) by compounds called **chemical mediators**. The chemical mediator in the parasympathetic system is *acetylcholine*:

$$CH_3CO_2CH_2CH_2N(CH_3)_3{}^+$$

In the sympathetic system, the mediator in the ganglionic synapses is also acetylcholine, while the mediator in the postganglionic synapses is *norepinephrine*. Discharge of the sympathetic nervous system allows norepinephrine to trigger the receptors that bring about the physiological effects noted. In times of stress, the adrenal glands secrete *epinephrine* (adrenaline), which can also trigger the sympathetic receptors.

$$HO{-}\text{(ring)}{-}\underset{\underset{OH}{|}}{C}HCH_2NH_2 \qquad HO{-}\text{(ring)}{-}\underset{\underset{OH}{|}}{C}HCH_2NHCH_3$$

norepinephrine   epinephrine
(adrenaline)

Both norepinephrine and epinephrine are β-phenylethylamines. A number of other β-phenylethylamines act upon the sympathetic receptors. These compounds are referred to as *sympathomimetic amines* because they "mimic," to an extent, the pharmacological action of norepinephrine and epinephrine.

$$\text{(ring)}{-}CH_2CH_2NH_2$$

β-phenylethylamine

$$\text{(ring)}{-}\underset{\underset{CH_3}{|}}{C}H\underset{\underset{OH}{|}}{C}HNHCH_3 \qquad CH_3O{-}\text{(ring)}{-}CH_2CH_2NH_2 \qquad \text{(ring)}{-}CH_2\underset{\underset{CH_3}{|}}{C}HNH_2$$

ephedrine   mescaline   amphetamine
a decongestant   *a hallucinogen*   *a stimulant*

Well before the birth of Christ, the drug *ephedrine* was extracted from the *ma-huang* plant in China and used as a drug. Today, it is the active decongestant in nose drops and cold remedies. Ephedrine causes shrinkage of swollen nasal membranes and inhibition of nasal secretions. (Overdoses cause nervousness and sleeplessness.) *Mescaline*, a hallucinogen isolated from the peyote cactus, has been used for centuries by the Indians of the southwestern U.S. and Mexico in religious ceremonies. *Amphetamine* is a synthetic stimulant that causes sleeplessness and nervousness. Amphetamine is sometimes prescribed for obesity, because it is also an appetite depressant. Like many other sympathomimetic amines, amphetamine contains a chiral center and has a pair of enantiomers. The more active enantiomer of amphetamine (the dextrorotatory one) is called *dexedrine*.

Norepinephrine and epinephrine are both biosynthesized from tyrosine (an amino acid from proteins). The precursers *dopa*, used in treatment of Parkinson's disease, and *dopamine* are stimulants of the sympathetic system, just as are norepinephrine and epinephrine.

Biosynthetic route to norepinephrine and epinephrine:

$$HO{-}\text{(ring)}{-}CH_2\underset{\underset{NH_2}{|}}{C}H{-}CO_2H \longrightarrow HO{-}\text{(ring,}HO){-}CH_2\underset{\underset{NH_2}{|}}{C}H{-}CO_2H \longrightarrow$$

tyrosine   dopa

$$HO{-}\text{(ring,}HO){-}CH_2CH_2NH_2 \nearrow \text{norepinephrine}$$

dopamine

$$\searrow HO{-}\text{(ring,}HO){-}CH_2CH_2NHCH_3 \longrightarrow \text{epinephrine}$$

epinine

SUMMARY

An **amine** is a compound that contains a trivalent nitrogen that has one to three alkyl or aryl groups attached: RNH_2, R_2NH, or R_3N. A compound with four groups attached to the nitrogen is an **amine salt** $(R_3NH^+ \ X^-)$ or a **quaternary ammonium salt** $(R_4N^+ \ X^-)$.

Amines may be prepared by S_N2 *reactions*, by *reduction reactions*, or by *rearrangement*. These synthetic reactions are summarized in Table 15.3 (page 716).

Because the nitrogen of an amine has a pair of unshared electrons, amines are *weak bases*. The base strength is affected by *hybridization* ($sp^3 > sp^2 > sp$), by *electron-withdrawing groups* (base-weakening), by *electron-releasing groups* (base-strengthening), and by *conjugation* (base-weakening).

$$\langle\!\!\!\!\!\!\!\!\rangle NH > \langle\!\!\!\!\!\!\!\!\rangle N \qquad\qquad CH_3 \rightarrow NH_2 > NH_3$$
hybridization   *electron-release*

$$CH_3NH_2 > Cl \leftarrow CH_2NH_2 \qquad \langle\!\!\!\!\!\!\!\!\rangle\!\!-NH_2 > \langle\!\!\!\!\!\!\!\!\rangle\!\!-NH_2$$
electron-withdrawal   *conjugation*

Amines undergo reaction with acids to yield amine salts:

$$R_3N \underset{OH^-}{\overset{HX}{\rightleftharpoons}} R_3NH^+ \ X^-$$
$$an\ amine\ salt$$

Amines are nucleophiles and can displace good leaving groups or can attack carbonyl groups.

$$\overset{O}{\overset{\|}{RC}}-Cl \ + 2\,R_2NH \longrightarrow \overset{O}{\overset{\|}{RC}}-NR_2 + R_2NH_2^+ \ Cl^-$$
an acid chloride   *an amide*

$$R_2C{=}O + RNH_2 \ (1°) \longrightarrow R_2C{=}NR + H_2O$$
a ketone   *an imine*

$$RCH_2\overset{|}{\underset{R}{C}}{=}O + R_2NH \ (2°) \longrightarrow RCH{=}\overset{|}{\underset{R}{C}}NR_2 + H_2O$$
a ketone   *an enamine*

When primary amines are treated with cold nitrous acid, **diazonium salts** are formed. Alkyldiazonium salts are unstable, but aryldiazonium salts may be used to prepare a variety of substituted aromatic compounds. Figure 15.3 (page 728) outlines the synthesis and reactions of a benzenediazonium halide.

Quaternary ammonium hydroxides, when heated, undergo elimination of water and an amine. The least substituted alkene is usually formed.

$$CH_3CH_2\overset{+}{\underset{\overset{|}{CH_2CH_2CH_3}}{N}}(CH_3)_2 \ OH^- \xrightarrow{\ heat\ } CH_2{=}CH_2 + \underset{\overset{|}{CH_2CH_2CH_3}}{N}(CH_3)_2 + H_2O$$

STUDY PROBLEMS

15.22 Write structures for the following compounds: (a) cyclopentylamine; (b) (2-methylcyclohexyl)amine; (c) p-nitro-N,N-diethylaniline; (d) 2-(N,N-dimethylamino)-hexanoic acid.

15.23 Name the following amines:

(a)
$$\overset{\displaystyle \text{NHCH}_2\text{CH}_2\text{CH}_3}{\underset{\displaystyle}{\text{CH}_3\text{CHCH}_2\text{CH}_2\text{CH}_3}}$$

(b) 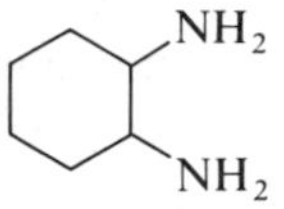 [cyclohexane ring with two NH$_2$ groups on adjacent carbons]

(c) [piperidine ring with NCH$_2$CH$_3$]

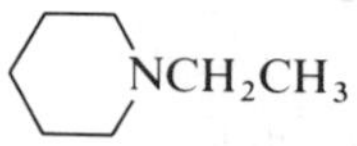

(d) $$\text{CH}_3\overset{\displaystyle \text{NH}_2}{\underset{\displaystyle}{\text{CH}}}\text{CH}_2\text{CH}_2\overset{\displaystyle \text{O}}{\overset{\displaystyle \|}{\text{CH}}}$$

15.24 Name the following compounds:

(a) $C_6H_5NHCH_2CH{=}CH_2$

(b) 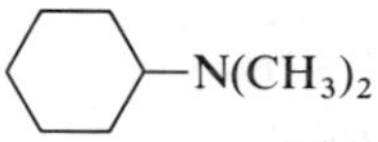 [cyclohexyl]$-N(CH_3)_2$

(c) $ClCH_2CH_2CH_2NH_2$

(d) $$C_6H_5CH_2\overset{\displaystyle}{\underset{\displaystyle \text{CH}_2\text{CH}_3}{\text{NCH}_3}}$$

(e) $(CH_3CH_2)_4N^+ \ Cl^-$

(f) 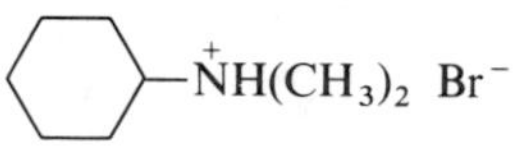 [cyclohexyl]$-\overset{+}{N}H(CH_3)_2 \ Br^-$

15.25 Classify each of the following compounds as a primary, secondary, or tertiary amine; as an amine salt of one of these; or as a quaternary ammonium salt:

(a)  [pyrrolidine ring with N–CH$_3$]

(b) 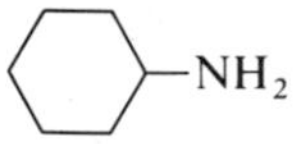 [cyclohexyl]$-NH_2$

(c) 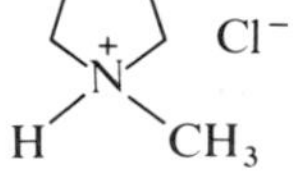 [pyrrolidinium ring with $\overset{+}{N}$, H and CH$_3$] Cl^-

(d) $(CH_3)_3CNH_3^+ \ HSO_4^-$

(e) $(CH_3)_2CH\overset{+}{N}(CH_3)_3 \ Br^-$

(f) 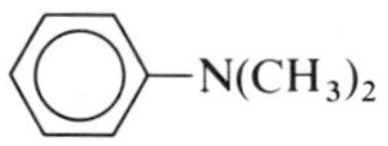 [benzene ring]$-N(CH_3)_2$

(g) 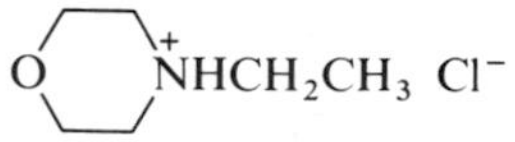 O[morpholine ring]$\overset{+}{N}HCH_2CH_3 \ Cl^-$

15.26 Which of the following structures has enantiomers, geometric isomers, both, or neither? [*Hint*: In (g), (h), and (i), consider the hybridization of the N and the resultant geometry.]

(a) $$\text{C}_6\text{H}_5\overset{\displaystyle}{\underset{\displaystyle \text{CH}_2\text{CH}_3}{\text{CHNH}_2}}$$

(b) $(CH_3)_2NCH_2CH_3$

(c) $$\text{CH}_3\overset{\displaystyle}{\underset{\displaystyle \text{C}_6\text{H}_5}{\text{NCH}_2\text{CH}_3}}$$

(d) 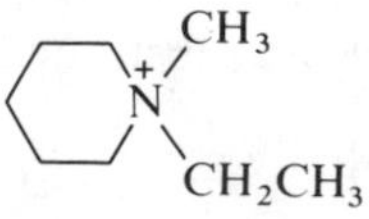 [piperidine ring with $\overset{+}{N}$, CH$_3$ and CH$_2$CH$_3$] Cl^-

(e) 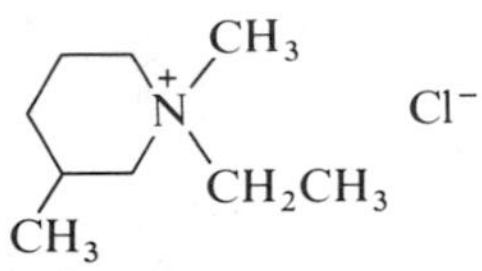 [structure: cyclohexane ring with N+ bearing CH₃, CH₂CH₃, and CH₃ substituents] Cl⁻ (f) 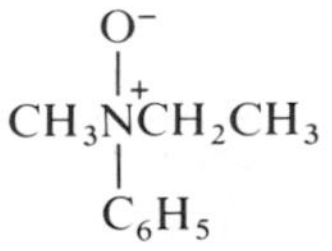 CH₃ṄCH₂CH₃ with O⁻ above N and C₆H₅ below

(g) C₆H₅N=NCH₃ (h) C₆H₅CH=NOH

(i) (C₆H₅)₂C=NOH (j) 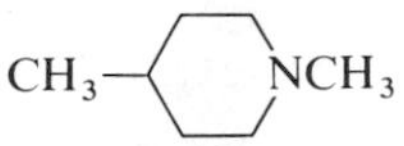 CH₃—⟨ring⟩—NCH₃

15.27 Which of the following species can act as a nucleophile?

(a) (CH₃)₂NH (b) (CH₃)₃N (c) H₂N—NH₂

(d)  ⟨pyridine⟩N (e) 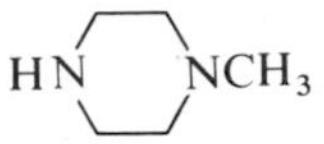 HN⟨ring⟩NCH₃ (f) 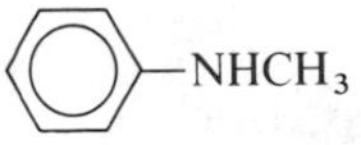 ⟨benzene⟩—NHCH₃

(g) 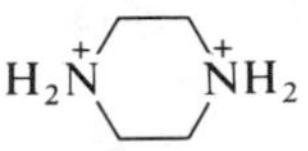 H₂Ṅ⟨ring⟩ṄH₂ (h) (C₂H₅)₄N⁺ (i) 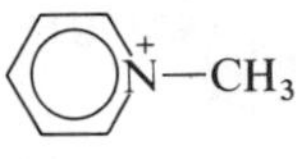 ⟨benzene⟩Ṅ—CH₃

15.28 Explain the following observations:

(a) Cyclohexylamine is more water-soluble than cyclohexanol.
(b) Trimethylamine has a lower boiling point than dimethylamine.
(c) Ethylamine is higher boiling than dimethylamine.

15.29 Suggest syntheses for the following compounds from organohalogen compounds or alcohols:

(a) 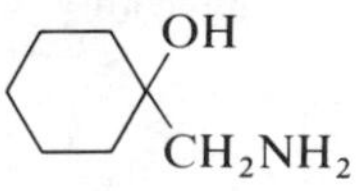 [cyclohexane with OH and CH₂NH₂]

(b) 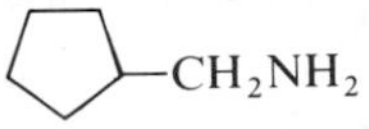 [cyclopentane]—CH₂NH₂

(c) 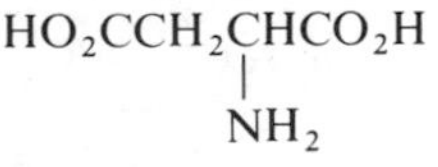 HO₂CCH₂CHCO₂H with NH₂ below

(d) (CH₃)₂CHNH₂

(e)  [cyclohexane]—NHCH₂CH₂CH₃

15.30 How would you convert 1-pentanol to: (a) *n*-pentylamine (free of higher alkylated amines)? (b) *n*-hexylamine? (c) *n*-butylamine?

15.31 Suggest a way to make each of the following conversions: (a) benzene to aniline; (b) benzamide to aniline; (c) aniline to acetanilide (C₆H₅NHCOCH₃): (d) glutaric anhydride to 4-aminobutanoic acid; (e) (*R*)-2-butanol to (*S*)-2-butylamine; (f) toluene to benzylamine; (g) acetic acid to acetamide.

15.32 Which is more basic? (a) aniline or benzylamine; (b) aniline or *p*-bromoaniline; (c) aniline or cyclohexylamine; (d) trimethylamine or tetramethylammonium hydroxide; (e) *p*-nitroaniline or 2,4-dinitroaniline; (f) ethylamine or ethanolamine (HOCH₂CH₂NH₂); (g) *p*-toluidine (*p*-methylaniline) or *p*-(trichloromethyl)aniline.

15.33 Complete the following equations:

(a) 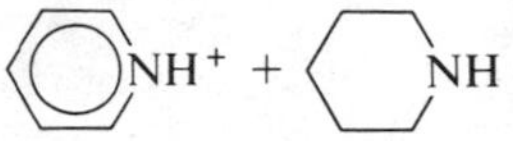 $\text{C}_5\text{H}_5\text{NH}^+$ + NH $\longrightarrow$

(b)  NH$^+$ + OH$^-$ $\longrightarrow$

(c) 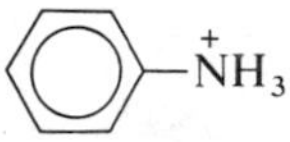 —$\overset{+}{\text{N}}\text{H}_3$ Cl$^-$ + (CH$_3$)$_3$N $\longrightarrow$

(d) (CH$_3$)$_3$NH$^+$ + —NH$_2$ $\longrightarrow$

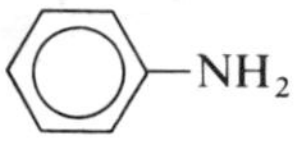

15.34 Complete the following equations:

(a) (CH$_3$)$_4$N$^+$ Cl$^-$ + OH$^-$ $\longrightarrow$

(b) (CH$_3$)$_4$N$^+$ OH$^-$ + CH$_3$CO$_2$H $\longrightarrow$

(c)  NH + CH$_3$CO$_2$H $\longrightarrow$

(d) 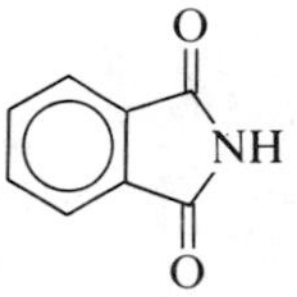 NH + $^-$OCH$_3$ $\longrightarrow$

15.35 List each of the following groups of cations in order of increasing acidity (weakest acid first):

(a) 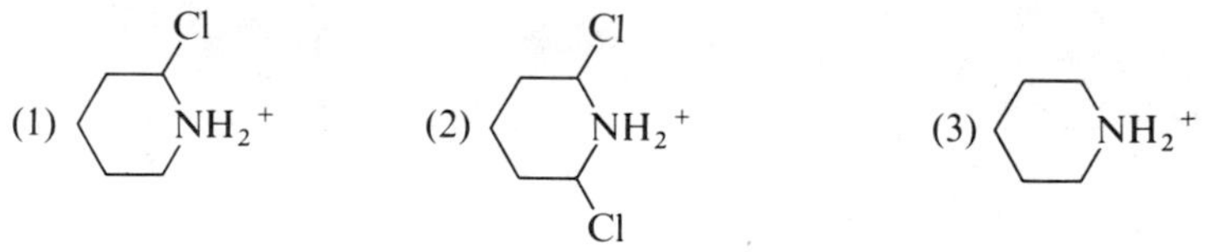 (1)   (2)   (3)

(b) 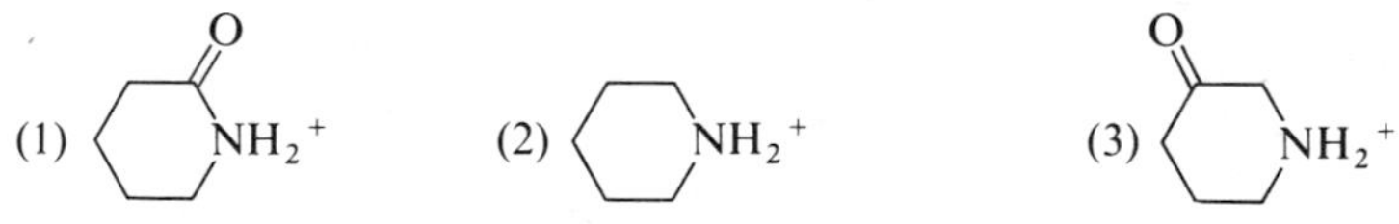 (1)   (2)   (3)

(c) (1)   (2)

(d) 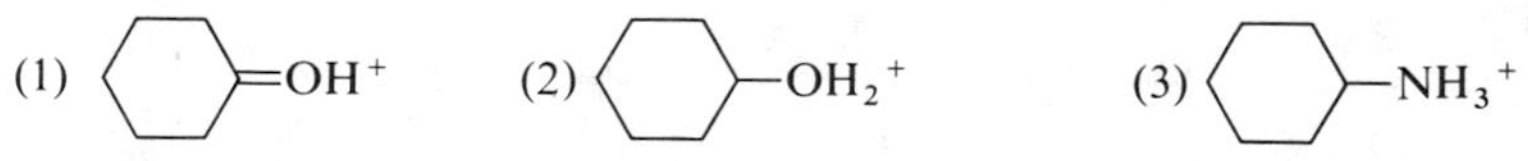 (1) =OH$^+$ (2) —OH$_2{}^+$ (3) —NH$_3{}^+$

(e) 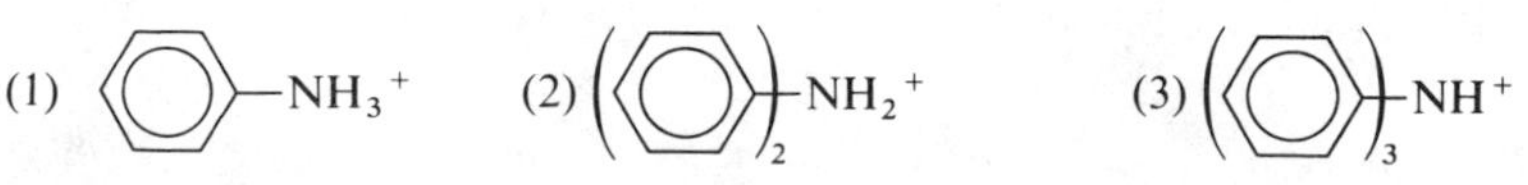 (1) —NH$_3{}^+$ (2) $_2$—NH$_2{}^+$ (3) $_3$—NH$^+$

(f) (1) H$_3$O$^+$ (2)

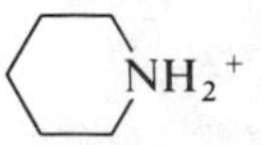

15.36 A chemist mixes a solution that is 0.0100 *M* in NaOH and 0.00100 *M* in methylamine ($pK_b = 3.34$).

(a) What concentration of methylammonium ion is present in the solution?
(b) At what pH would the concentrations of methylamine and methylammonium ion be equal?

15.37 Suggest techniques for separating the following mixtures:

(a) cyclohexanol, cyclohexylamine, and cyclohexanecarboxylic acid
(b) hexanamide and *n*-hexylamine

15.38 Which nitrogen in LSD is the most basic?

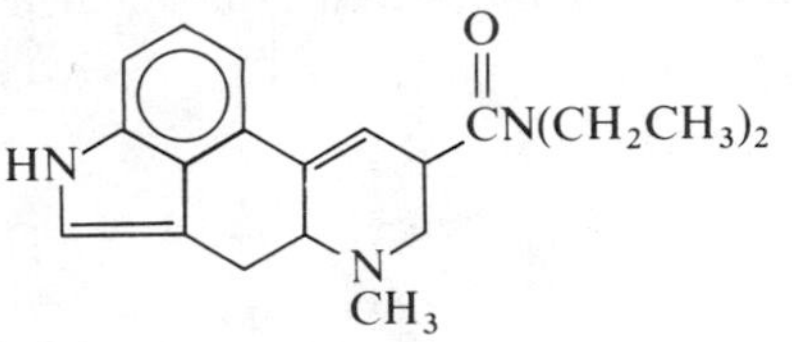

LSD

15.39 Predict the organic products when the local anesthetic novocaine (page 721) is treated with: (a) 1 equivalent cold dilute H_2SO_4; (b) excess dilute HCl and heat; and (c) excess dilute NaOH and heat.

15.40 Predict the products when xylocaine (another local anesthetic) is treated with the reagents in Problem 15.39.

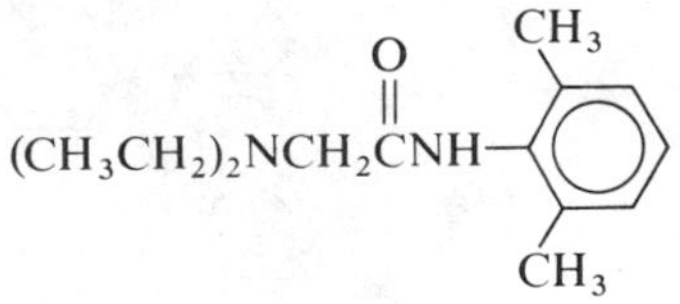

xylocaine

15.41 What would be an appropriate technique for resolving each of the following compounds?

(a) $C_6H_5CH(NH_2)CH_3$ (b) 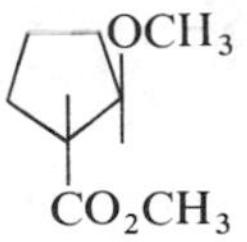

15.42 Predict the major organic products:

(a) $CH_3I + NH_3$ (excess) $\longrightarrow$ (b) CH_3I (excess) $+ NH_3$ $\longrightarrow$

(c) 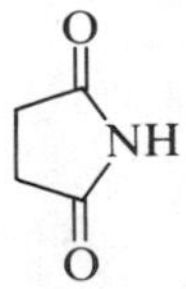 $\xrightarrow[\text{heat}]{OH^-,\ H_2O}$ (d) 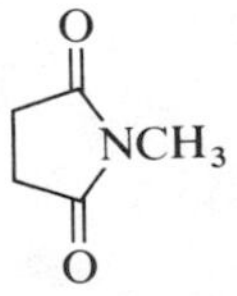 $\xrightarrow[\text{heat}]{OH^-,\ H_2O}$

15.43 Predict the major product of the reaction of pyrrolidine (page 703) with   (a) benzoyl chloride;   (b) acetic anhydride;   (c) methyl iodide (excess);   (d) phthalic anhydride; (e) benzenesulfonyl chloride ($C_6H_5SO_2Cl$);   (f) acetyl chloride, followed by $LiAlH_4$ (then hydrolysis);   (g) nitrous acid;   (h) dilute HCl;   (i) acetone.

15.44 Predict the major product of the reaction of *N*-methylpyrrolidine with each of the reagents [except (g)] in Problem 15.43.

15.45 How would you distinguish (chemically) between:

(a)   aniline and *n*-hexylamine?
(b)   *n*-octylamine and octanamide?
(c)   triethylammonium chloride and tetraethylammonium chloride?

15.46 Predict the major organic products:

(a)   *p*-ethylaniline + HONO + HCl $\xrightarrow{0°}$

(b)   *β*-naphthylamine (page 706) + HONO + HCl $\xrightarrow{0°}$

(c)   [the product from (a)] + CuCN $\xrightarrow{100°}$

(d)   [the product from (b)] + phenol $\xrightarrow{100°}$

15.47 How would you carry out the following conversions?

(a)   nitrobenzene $\longrightarrow$

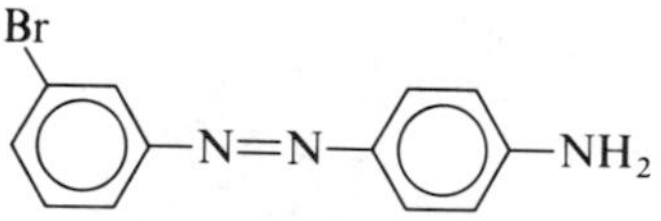

(b)   *p*-nitrotoluene $\longrightarrow$

15.48 Predict the major organic products when each of the following compounds is heated:

(a) $CH_3CH_2CH_2CH_2\overset{+}{\underset{\underset{CH_3}{|}}{\overset{\overset{CH_3}{|}}{N}}}CH_2CH(CH_3)_2$ OH^-
(b) 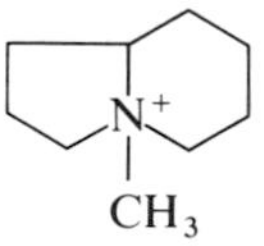 OH^-

(c) 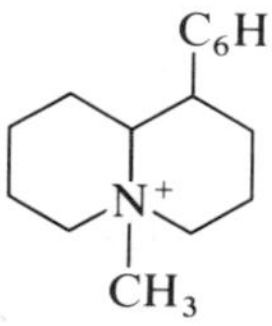 OH^-
(d) 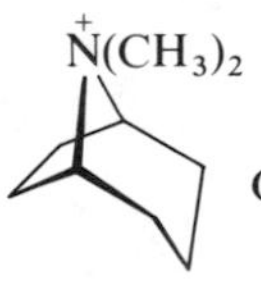 OH^-

15.49 Predict the products of exhaustive methylation of the following heterocycle:

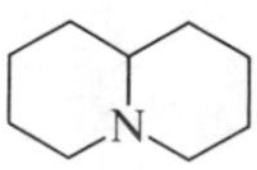

15.50 An amine (C$_8$H$_{15}$N) is subjected to two stages of exhaustive methylation. The final products are trimethylamine and the following diene:

What is a likely structure for the original amine?

15.51 The treatment of (cyclopentylmethyl)amine with nitrous acid resulted in a 76% yield of cyclohexanol. Another alcohol and three alkenes were also present in the product mixture.

    (a)   Give a plausible mechanism for the formation of cyclohexanol.
    (b)   What are the likely structures of the other products?

15.52 A chemist attempted to carry out a Hofmann rearrangement of butanamide with bromine and potassium hydroxide in methanol, rather than in water. Instead of propylamine, the chemist obtained CH$_3$CH$_2$CH$_2$NHCO$_2$CH$_3$. Explain how this carbamate was formed.

15.53 When the following compound is subjected to catalytic hydrogenation, a compound with the formula C$_9$H$_{17}$N is produced. What is the structure of this product?

CH$_2$CH$_2$CN

=O

15.54 A tertiary amine is oxidized by peroxides such as H$_2$O$_2$ to an **amine oxide**, a compound containing the —NO group. An amine oxide with a β hydrogen undergoes elimination when heated. (This reaction is called a **Cope elimination**.) Suggest a mechanism for the following elimination reaction of an amine oxide.

$$\underset{(S)\qquad\qquad\qquad (R)}{\underset{CH_3\ \ CH_3}{C_6H_5CH-CH\overset{+}{N}(CH_3)_2}} \longrightarrow \underset{\underset{major\ alkene}{(E)}}{\underset{H_3C\qquad CH_3}{\overset{C_6H_5\qquad H}{C=C}}} + (CH_3)_2NOH$$

15.55 Suggest a method for the resolution of (R)(S)-2-butanol using glutaric anhydride (page 588) and (+)-amphetamine.

15.56 A chemist treated ethyl bromide with ammonia and isolated products A and B. When A was treated with acetic anhydride, C was obtained. When B was treated with acetic anhydride, D was obtained. The infrared spectra of C and D are shown in Figure 15.5 (page 742). Identify A, B, C, and D.

15.57 The infrared spectrum for Compound A (C$_8$H$_{11}$N) is given in Figure 15.6 (page 742). A is soluble in dilute acid. Oxidation of A with hot KMnO$_4$ yields benzoic acid. What are the two possible structures for A? How could you distinguish these two possibilities by nmr spectroscopy?

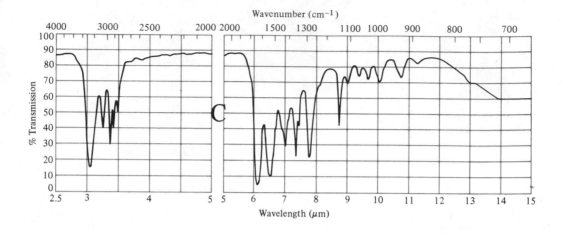

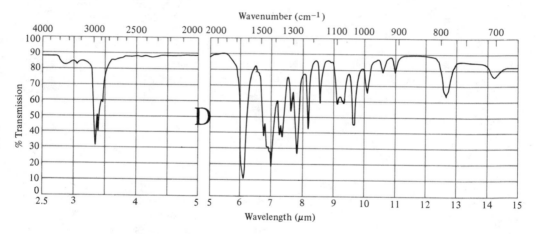

Figure 15.5.   Infrared spectra for Problem 15.56.

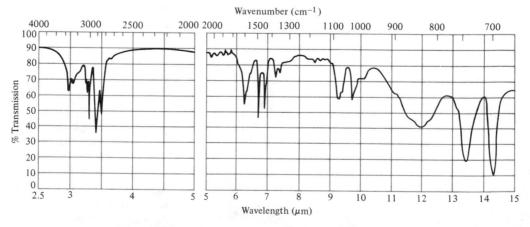

Figure 15.6.   Infrared spectrum for A in Problem 15.57.

15.58 A compound $C_{10}H_{13}NO$ (A) has the nmr spectrum shown in Figure 15.7. A is insoluble in dilute aqueous acid. Heating A with aqueous NaOH, followed by acidification, results in two compounds: acetic acid and an amine salt. The free amine (B) from this salt has the formula $C_8H_{11}N$.

   B was subjected to high-pressure hydrogenation to yield C ($C_8H_{17}N$). C was subjected to one stage of exhaustive methylation (in which it took up 2 moles of CH_3I) and yielded trimethylamine and 3-methyl-1-cyclohexene. What are the structures of A, B, and C?

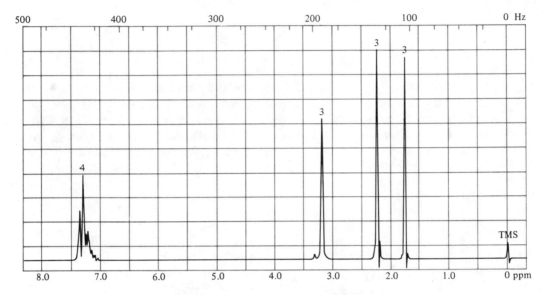

Figure 15.7. Nmr spectrum of A in Problem 15.58.

Chapter 16

Polycyclic and Heterocyclic Aromatic Compounds

In Chapter 10, we discussed benzene and substituted benzenes. However, benzene is but one member of a large number of aromatic compounds. Many other aromatic compounds may be grouped into two classes: **polycyclic and heterocyclic compounds**. The polycyclic aromatic compounds are also referred to as *polynuclear*, *fused-ring*, or *condensed-ring*, aromatic compounds. These aromatic compounds are characterized by rings that jointly share carbon atoms and by a common aromatic pi cloud.

Some polycyclic aromatic compounds:

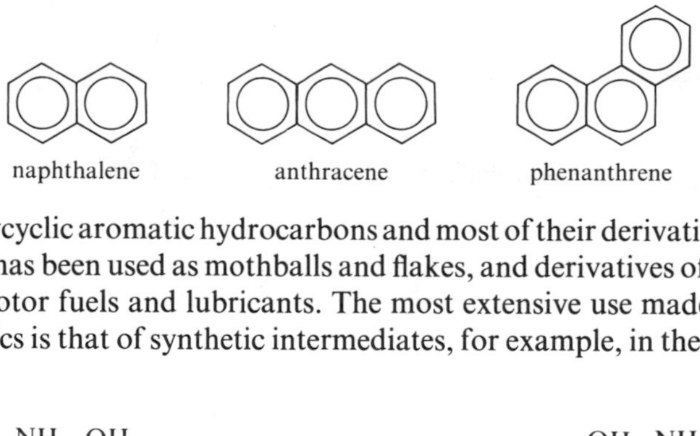

naphthalene   anthracene   phenanthrene

The polycyclic aromatic hydrocarbons and most of their derivatives are solids. Naphthalene has been used as mothballs and flakes, and derivatives of naphthalene are used in motor fuels and lubricants. The most extensive use made of the polycyclic aromatics is that of synthetic intermediates, for example, in the manufacture of dyes.

Direct Blue 2B
a dye

Graphite is one of the more interesting polycyclic compounds. The structure of graphite consists of planes of fused benzene rings (Figure 16.1). The distance (3.5 Å) between any pair of planes is believed to be the width of the pi system of benzene. The "slipperiness" of graphite is due to the ability of these planes to slide across each other. Because of this property, graphite is a valuable lubricant that can be used even in outer space where ordinary oils and greases would solidify. Because of its mobile pi electrons, graphite can conduct electricity and finds use where an inert electrode is needed. Dry cells used in flashlights, for example, contain graphite electrodes.

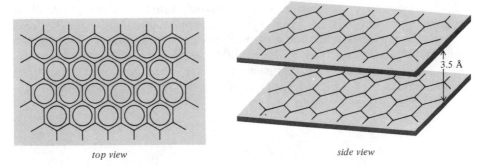

Figure 16.1. The structure of graphite.

A **heterocyclic compound** is a cyclic compound in which the ring atoms are of carbon and some other element. The atom of the other element (for example, N, S, or O) is called the **heteroatom**. Heterocyclic rings can be aromatic, just as carbon rings can. Approximately a third of the organic chemical literature deals with heterocyclic compounds. The importance of these compounds will become clear as we approach the end of the chapter and discuss some naturally occurring heterocycles—the **alkaloids**, such as morphine; the **nucleic acids**, the carriers of the genetic code; and a few other compounds of biological importance.

Some aromatic heterocyclic compounds:

pyridine   pyrrole*   furan*

Section 16.1

Nomenclature of Polycyclic Aromatic Compounds

The ring systems of common polycyclic aromatic compounds have individual names. Unlike the numbering of benzene or a cycloalkane ring, which starts at the position of a substituent, the numbering of a polycyclic ring is fixed by convention and does not change with the position of a substituent.

naphthalene   anthracene   phenanthrene

*A circle in the ring is not a proper representation of an aromatic pi cloud in a five-membered heterocycle. How the aromatic pi cloud is formed in these compounds will be discussed in Section 16.9.

The position of a substituent in a monosubstituted naphthalene is often designated by a Greek letter. The positions adjacent to the ring-junction carbons are called α positions, while the next positions are β positions. By this system, 1-nitronaphthalene is called α-nitronaphthalene, while 2-nitronaphthalene is called β-nitronaphthalene. Naphthalene itself has four equivalent α positions and four equivalent β positions. (Only number designations are used in the anthracene and phenanthrene systems.)

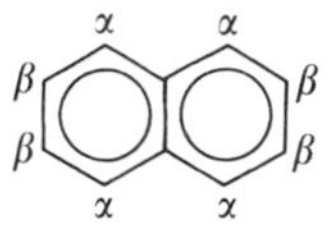

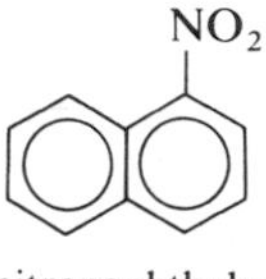

1-nitronaphthalene
(α-nitronaphthalene)

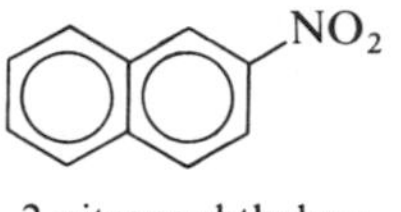

2-nitronaphthalene
(β-nitronaphthalene)

Section 16.2

Bonding in Polycyclic Aromatic Compounds

For a ring system to be aromatic, it must meet three criteria:

(1)   Each atom in the ring system must be in the sp^2-hybrid state.
(2)   The ring system must be planar.
(3)   There must be $4n + 2$ pi electrons in the ring system (Hückel rule).

These criteria were discussed in Section 10.7. The Hückel rule, which was devised for monocyclic systems, also is applicable to polycyclic systems in which the sp^2 carbons are peripheral, or on the outside edge of the ring system. In the polycyclic compounds, the number of pi electrons is easily counted when Kekulé formulas are used. (Figure 2.25, page 67, shows the aromatic pi cloud in naphthalene.)

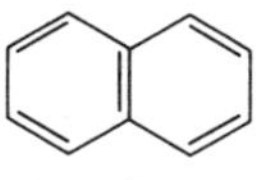

10 pi electrons
($n = 2$)

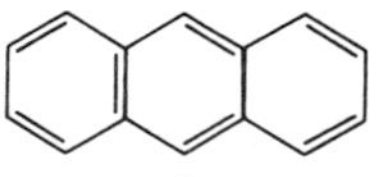

14 pi electrons
($n = 3$)

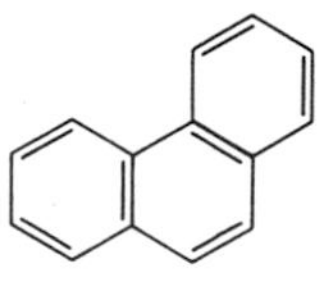

14 pi electrons
($n = 3$)

Like benzene, the polycyclic aromatic systems are more stable than the corresponding hypothetical polyenes with localized pi bonds. The energy differences between the hypothetical polyenes and the real compounds (that is, the *resonance energies*) have been calculated from heats of combustion and hydrogenation data.

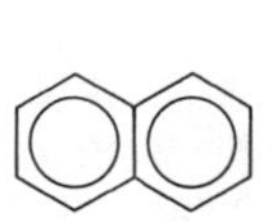

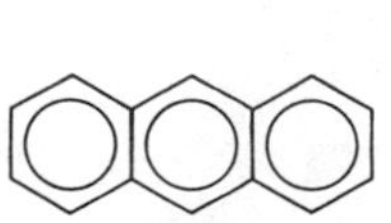

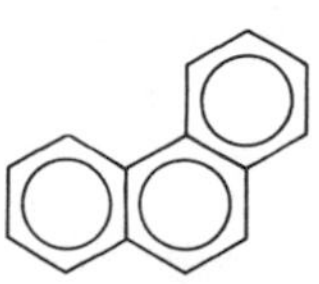

resonance energy
(*kcal/mole*):   36   61   84   92

Note that the resonance energy for a polycyclic aromatic compound is less than the sum of the resonance energies for a comparable number of benzene rings. Although the resonance energy for benzene is 36 kcal/mole, that for naphthalene is only 61 kcal/mole (about 30 kcal/mole for each ring).

In benzene, all carbon–carbon bond distances are the same. This fact leads us to believe that there is an equal distribution of pi electrons around the benzene ring. In the polycyclic aromatic compounds, the carbon–carbon bond distances are *not* all the same. For example, the bond distance between carbons 1 and 2 (1.36 Å) in naphthalene is smaller than the distance between carbons 2 and 3 (1.40 Å).

C—C in ethane: 1.54 Å

C=C in ethene: 1.34 Å

C—C in benzene: 1.40 Å

From these measurements, we conclude that there is *not* an equal distribution of pi electrons around the naphthalene ring. From a comparison of bond distances, we would say that the carbon 1–carbon 2 bond of naphthalene has more double-bond character than the carbon 2–carbon 3 bond.

The resonance structures for naphthalene also indicate that the carbon 1–carbon 2 bond has more double-bond character.

two out of three resonance structures show a carbon 1–carbon 2 double bond

Because all the carbon–carbon bonds in naphthalene are not the same, many chemists prefer to use Kekulé-type formulas for this compound instead of using circles to represent the pi cloud. We will use Kekulé-type formulas in our discussion of the reactions of naphthalene.

Phenanthrene shows similar differences between its bonds. The double-bond character of the 9,10-bond of phenanthrene is particularly evident in its chemical reactions. These positions of the phenanthrene ring system undergo addition reactions that are typical of alkenes but are not typical for benzene.

double-bond character

STUDY PROBLEM

16.1   Write the Kekulé resonance structures for phenanthrene. On the basis of these structures, explain why the 9,10-bond has double-bond character.

Section 16.3

Oxidation of Polycyclic Aromatic Compounds

The polycyclic aromatic compounds are more reactive toward oxidation, reduction, and electrophilic substitution than is benzene. The reason for the greater reactivity is that the polycyclic compounds can undergo reaction at one ring and still have one or more intact benzenoid rings in the intermediate and in the product. Less energy is required to overcome the aromatic character of a single ring of the polycyclic compounds than is required for benzene.

Benzene is not easily oxidized; however, naphthalene can be oxidized to products in which much of the aromaticity is retained. Phthalic anhydride is prepared commercially by the oxidation of naphthalene; this reaction probably proceeds by way of *o*-phthalic acid.

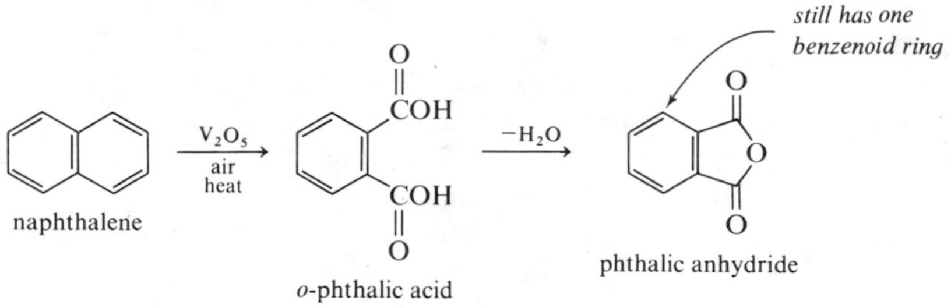

Under controlled conditions, 1,4-naphthoquinone may be isolated from an oxidation of naphthalene (although yields are usually low).

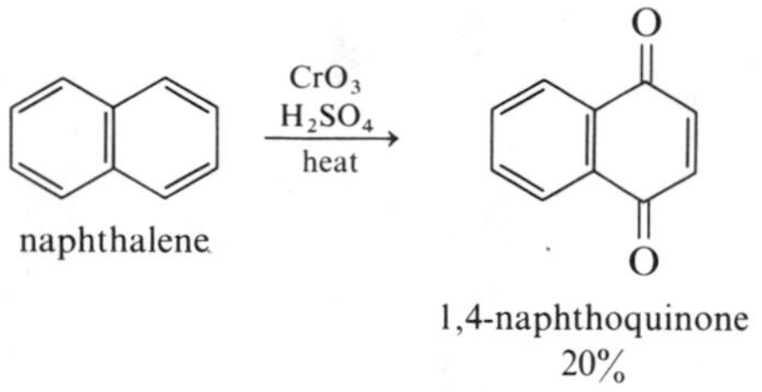

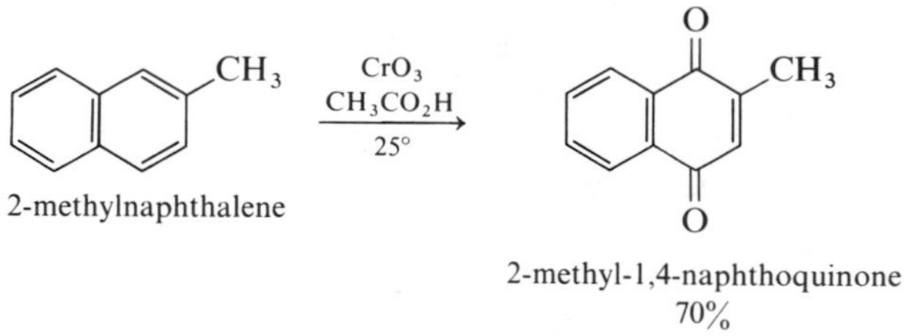

Anthracene and phenanthrene can also undergo oxidation to quinones:

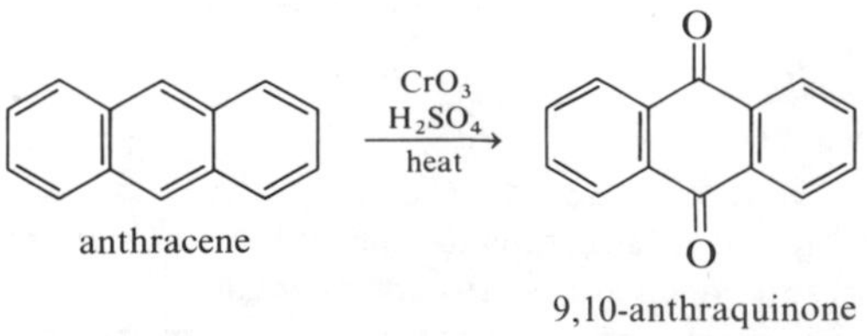

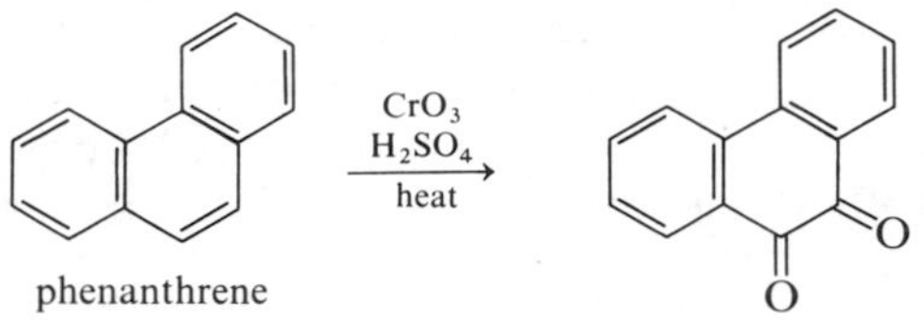
CrO_3
H_2SO_4
heat
O
O

phenanthrene

9,10-phenanthraquinone
50%

STUDY PROBLEM

16.2 From the following observations, tell whether chromate oxidation of naphthalene derivatives involves an initial *electrophilic attack* or *nucleophilic attack.*

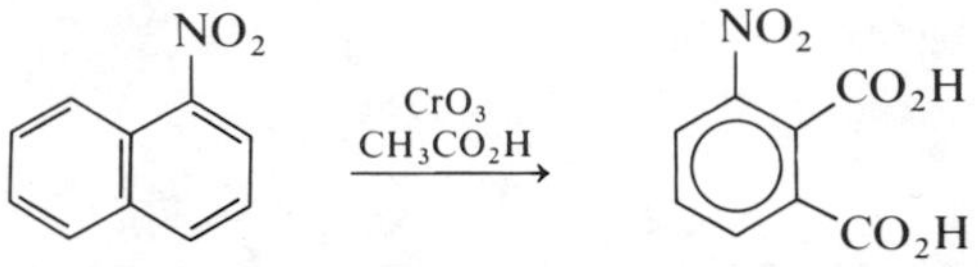
NO_2
CrO_3
CH_3CO_2H
NO_2
CO_2H
CO_2H

1-nitronaphthalene

3-nitro-1,2-phthalic acid

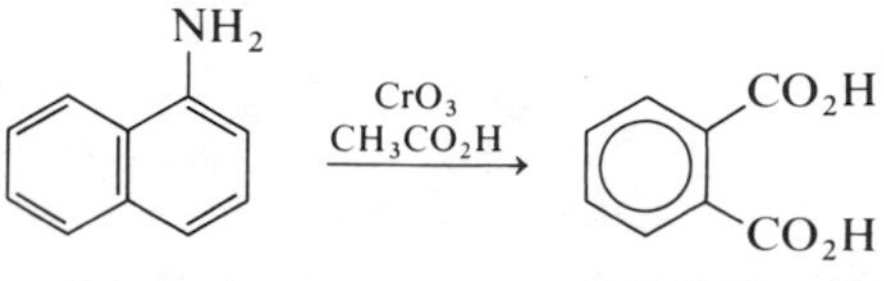
NH_2
CrO_3
CH_3CO_2H
CO_2H
CO_2H

1-naphthylamine

o-phthalic acid

Section 16.4

Reduction of Polycyclic Aromatic Compounds

Unlike benzene, the polycyclic compounds may be partially hydrogenated without heat and pressure, or they may be reduced with sodium and ethanol.

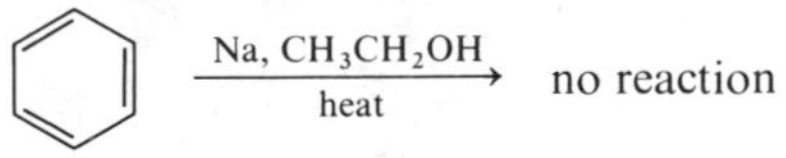
Na, CH_3CH_2OH
heat
no reaction

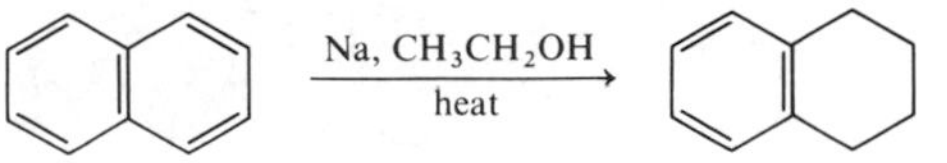
Na, CH_3CH_2OH
heat

tetralin

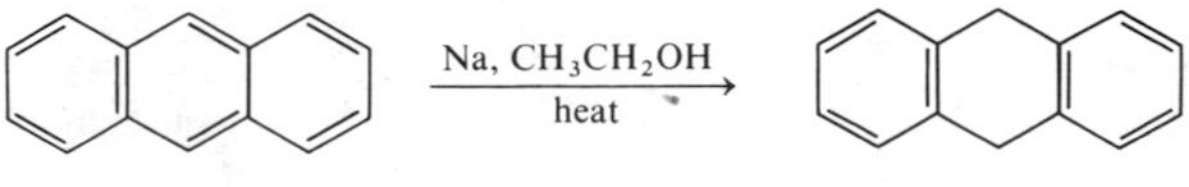
Na, CH_3CH_2OH
heat

9,10-dihydroanthracene

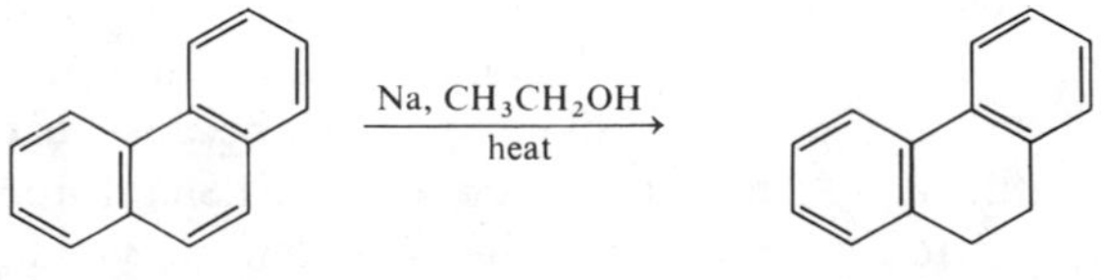
Na, CH_3CH_2OH
heat

9,10-dihydrophenanthrene

Note that the partially reduced ring systems still contain one or more benzenoid rings. Most of the aromatic character of the original ring systems has been retained in these partially reduced products. To hydrogenate the polycyclic aromatics completely would, of course, require heat and pressure, just as it does for benzene.

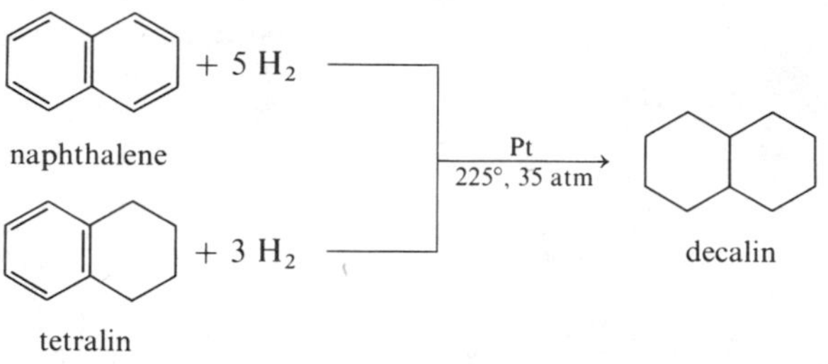

naphthalene

tetralin

decalin

Section 16.5

Electrophilic Substitution Reactions of Polycyclic Aromatic Compounds

The polycyclic aromatic ring systems are more reactive toward electrophilic attack than is benzene. Naphthalene undergoes electrophilic aromatic substitution reactions predominantly at the 1-position. The reasons for the enhanced reactivity and for this position of substitution will be discussed shortly.

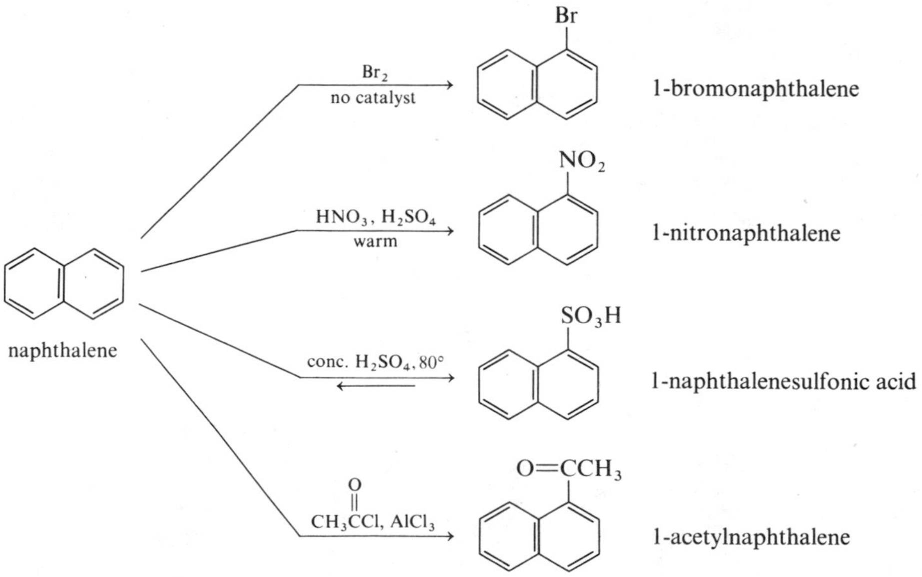

1-bromonaphthalene

1-nitronaphthalene

1-naphthalenesulfonic acid

1-acetylnaphthalene

Anthracene, phenanthrene, and larger fused-ring compounds are even more reactive than naphthalene toward electrophilic substitution. However, these reactions are not as important as those of naphthalene because mixtures of isomers (which are often difficult to separate) are obtained. Phenanthrene, for example, undergoes mononitration at each available position to yield five nitrophenanthrenes.

A.   *Position of Substitution of Naphthalene*

The mechanism for naphthalene substitution is similar to that for benzene substitution. Let us look at the stepwise bromination reaction to see why substitution at the 1-position is favored and why this reaction occurs more readily than the bromination of benzene.

1-Substitution (favored):

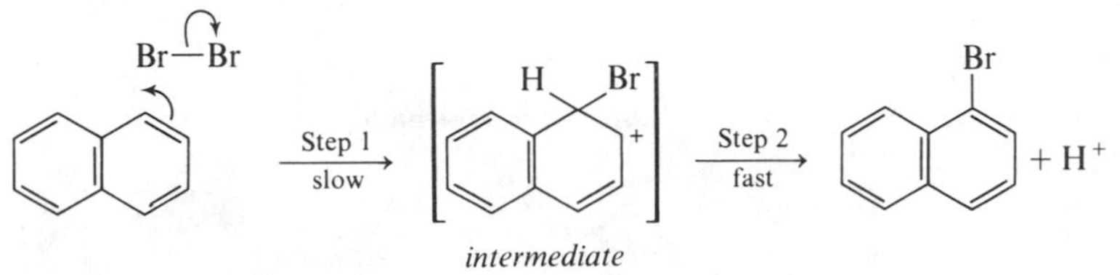

Resonance structures for the 1-substitution intermediate:

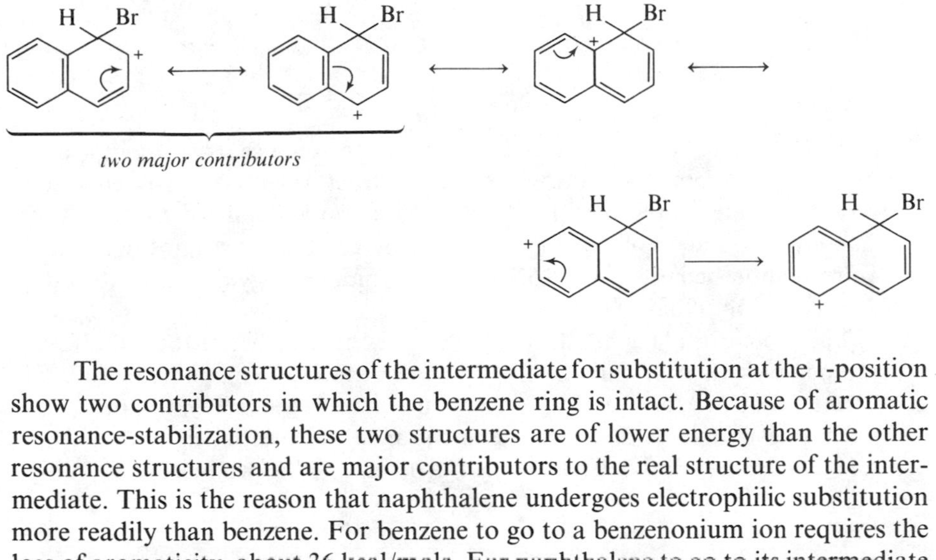

two major contributors

The resonance structures of the intermediate for substitution at the 1-position show two contributors in which the benzene ring is intact. Because of aromatic resonance-stabilization, these two structures are of lower energy than the other resonance structures and are major contributors to the real structure of the intermediate. This is the reason that naphthalene undergoes electrophilic substitution more readily than benzene. For benzene to go to a benzenonium ion requires the loss of aromaticity, about 36 kcal/mole. For naphthalene to go to its intermediate requires only partial loss of aromaticity, about 25 kcal/mole (the difference in resonance energy between naphthalene and benzene). Because of the lower E_{act} leading to the intermediate, the rate of bromination of naphthalene is faster than that of benzene.

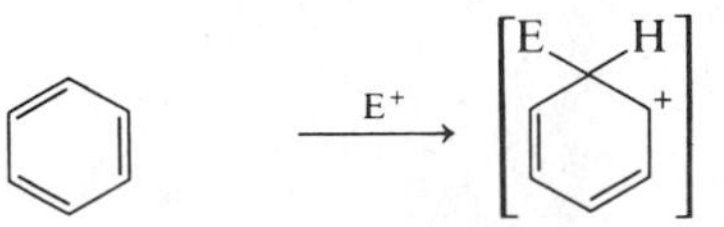

requires 36 kcal/mole to destroy aromaticity

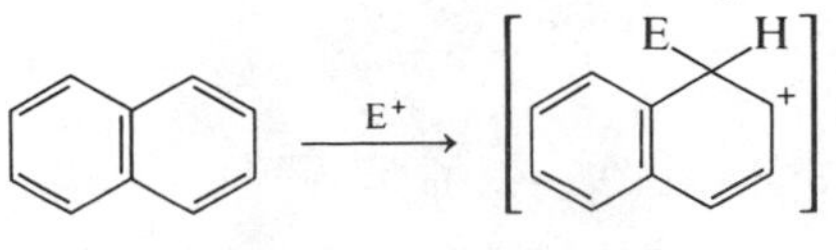

requires only 25 kcal/mole

Now let us consider the reasons why 1-substitution is favored over 2-substitution for naphthalene. Inspect the resonance structures for the intermediate leading to 2-substitution:

2-Substitution (*not favored*):

$$\text{Step 1, slow} \quad [\text{intermediate}] \quad \text{Step 2, fast} \quad + \text{H}^+$$

intermediate

Resonance structures for the 2-substitution intermediate:

only one major contributor

The 2-intermediate has only one contributing resonance structure in which a benzenoid ring is intact, while the resonance structures for the 1-intermediate show two such structures. The 1-intermediate is more stabilized by resonance, and its transition state is of lower energy. For this reason, the E_{act} is lower and its rate of formation higher. Figure 16.2 shows potential-energy diagrams for the 1- and 2-substitution of naphthalene.

The sulfonation of naphthalene, which is a reversible reaction (Section 10.9F), is more complex than bromination. At 80°, the expected 1-naphthalenesulfonic acid is the product. However, at higher temperatures (160–180°), the product is 2-naphthalenesulfonic acid. At low temperatures, the reaction is under **kinetic control**—that is, the relative rates of reaction determine the product ratio. At high

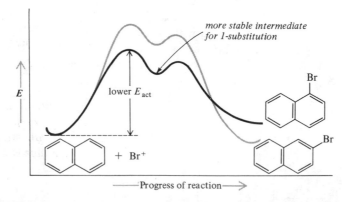

Figure 16.2. Energy diagrams for bromination of naphthalene in the 1- and 2-positions.

temperatures, the reaction is under **thermodynamic**, or **equilibrium, control**—the relative stabilities of the products determine the product ratio. In this respect, the sulfonation of naphthalene is similar to 1,4-additions to conjugated dienes (Section 9.15).

We have already seen why the rate of 1-substitution of naphthalene is higher than that of 2-substitution. At less than 80°, the rate of formation of either naphthalenesulfonic acid is relatively slow; the reaction proceeds through the lower-energy 1-intermediate just as it does for bromination.

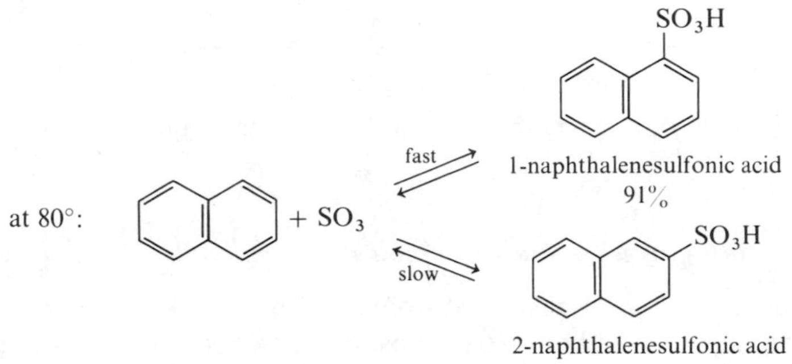

at 80°:

1-naphthalenesulfonic acid
91%

2-naphthalenesulfonic acid

Even though 1-naphthalenesulfonic acid is formed at low temperatures, this isomer is less stable than the 2-isomer because of repulsions between the —SO_3H group and the hydrogen at position 8.

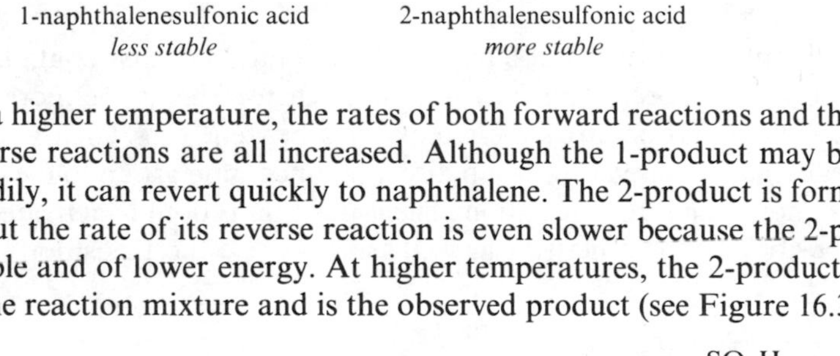

1-naphthalenesulfonic acid
less stable

2-naphthalenesulfonic acid
more stable

At a higher temperature, the rates of both forward reactions and the rates of both reverse reactions are all increased. Although the 1-product may be formed more readily, it can revert quickly to naphthalene. The 2-product is formed more slowly, but the rate of its reverse reaction is even slower because the 2-product is more stable and of lower energy. At higher temperatures, the 2-product accumulates in the reaction mixture and is the observed product (see Figure 16.3).

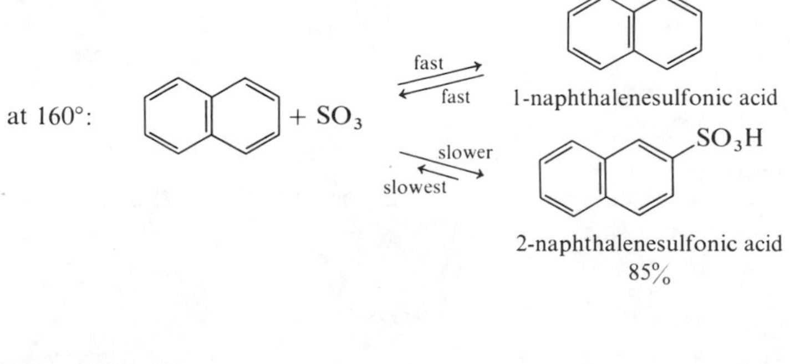

at 160°:

1-naphthalenesulfonic acid

2-naphthalenesulfonic acid
85%

Polycyclic and Heterocyclic Aromatic Compounds

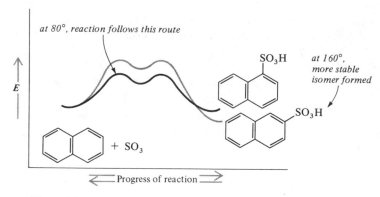

Figure 16.3.   Energy diagram for the sulfonation of naphthalene.

B.   Substitution of a Second Group on Naphthalene

There can be ten disubstituted isomers of naphthalene when the two substituents are the same, and fourteen disubstituted isomers when the two groups are
different. Disubstitution reactions of naphthalene are generally useful only when
they lead to predominantly one isomer.

The pattern of reactivity of substituted naphthalenes is similar to that of
substituted benzenes. *An electron-releasing group, such as OH or R, activates its
ring toward electrophilic substitution.* (See Section 10.10 for a list of activating
groups and why they are activating.)

$$CH_3 \longleftarrow electron\text{-}releasing$$

*this ring
activated toward E^+*

The second substitution of a naphthalene compound that contains an electron-releasing group occurs on the same ring because this is the more activated
ring. All activating groups are *o,p*-directors on a benzene ring. On a 1-substituted
naphthalene ring, an activating group directs an incoming group to the 4-position
and, to a minor extent, the 2-position. The 4-position is doubly activated because
it is an α position to the other ring as well as "*para*" to the 1-position.

α and p

1-methylnaphthalene

$\xrightarrow{HNO_3}$

1-methyl-4-nitronaphthalene

+ some

An electron-releasing group in the 2-position directs the incoming group to
the 1-position of the same ring, which is an α position and also is an "*ortho*"
position.

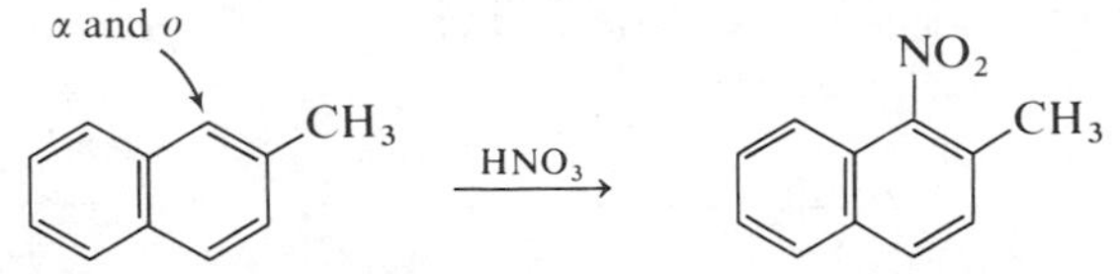

α and *o*

2-methylnaphthalene

HNO₃ →

2-methyl-1-nitronaphthalene
75%

An electron-withdrawing group such as —NO_2 decreases the reactivity of the ring to which it is attached, and the incoming electrophile attacks the *other* ring. Which position is attacked? As in the first substitution, the α position is favored. Because the ring system already has a substituent on one ring, there are two non-equivalent α positions on the other ring. Attack occurs at both.

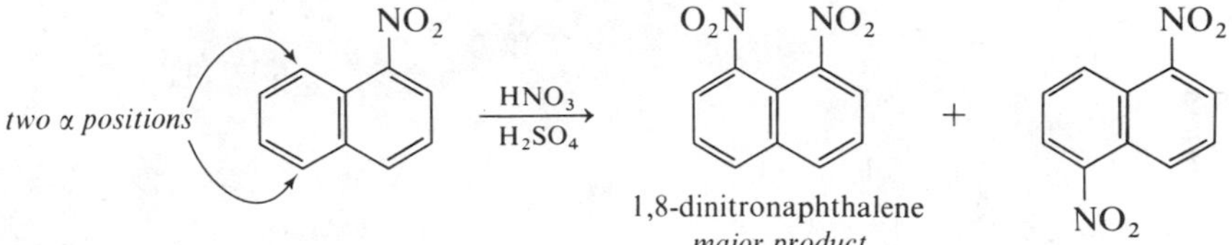

two α positions

$\xrightarrow[\text{H}_2\text{SO}_4]{\text{HNO}_3}$

1,8-dinitronaphthalene
major product

+

1,5-dinitronaphthalene

STUDY PROBLEM

16.3 Predict the major organic products:

(a)

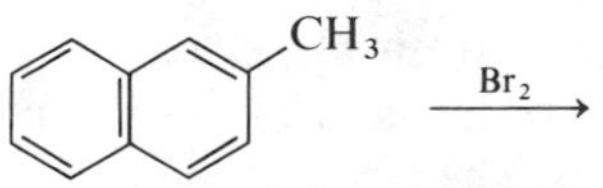

$\xrightarrow{\text{Br}_2}$

(b)

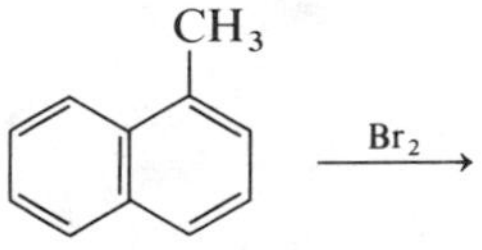

$\xrightarrow{\text{Br}_2}$

(c)

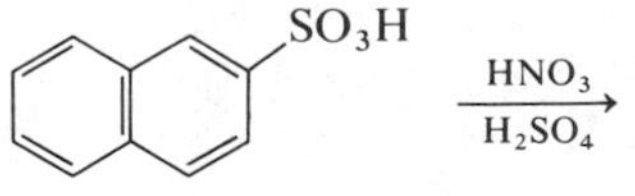

$\xrightarrow[\text{H}_2\text{SO}_4]{\text{HNO}_3}$

(d)

$\xrightarrow[\text{H}_2\text{SO}_4]{\text{HNO}_3}$

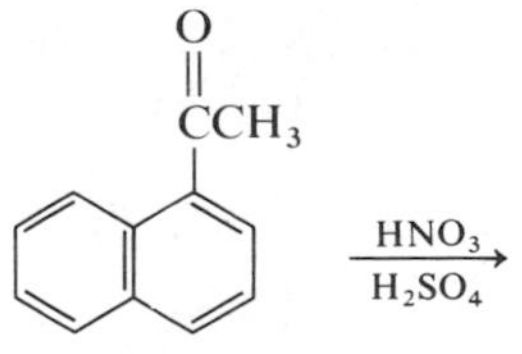

Section 16.6

Nomenclature of Aromatic Heterocyclic Compounds

Because of their widespread occurrence in nature, the aromatic heterocycles are of more general interest to chemists than are the polycyclic compounds containing only carbon atoms in their rings. Like the polycyclic aromatic compounds, the aromatic heterocycles generally have individual names. The names and structures of some of the more important members of this class of compound are listed in Table 16.1.

The numbering of three representative heterocycles follows:

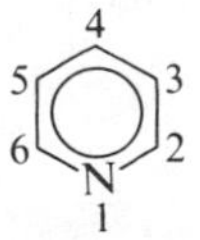

pyridine 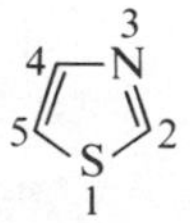   thiazole 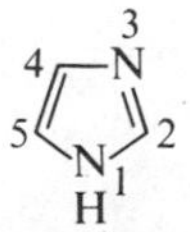   imidazole

Polycyclic and Heterocyclic Aromatic Compounds

Table 16.1.   *Some Important Aromatic Heterocyclic Compounds*

Structure	Name	Structure	Name
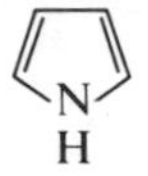	pyrrole	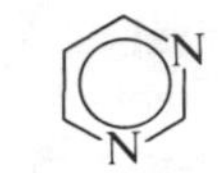	pyrimidine
	furan	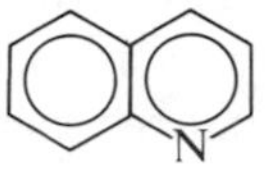	quinoline
	thiophene	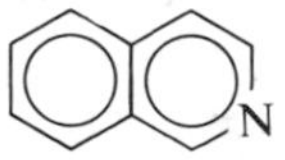	isoquinoline
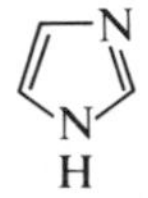	imidazole	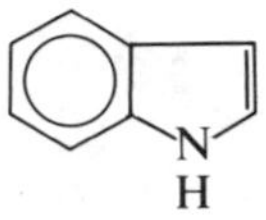	indole
	thiazole	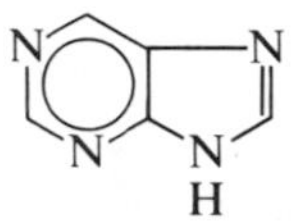	purine
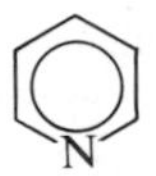	pyridine		

When a heterocycle contains only one heteroatom, Greek letters may also be used to designate ring position. The carbon atom adjacent to the heteroatom is the α carbon. The next carbon is the β carbon. The next carbon in line, if any, is γ. Pyridine has two α positions, two β positions, and one γ position. Pyrrole has two α and two β positions.

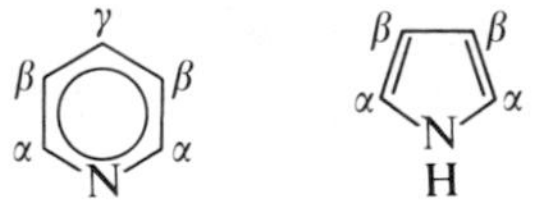

pyridine   pyrrole

Section 16.7

Pyridine, a Six-Membered Aromatic Heterocycle

Of the common six-membered heterocycles, only the nitrogen heterocycle can form a stable aromatic compound.

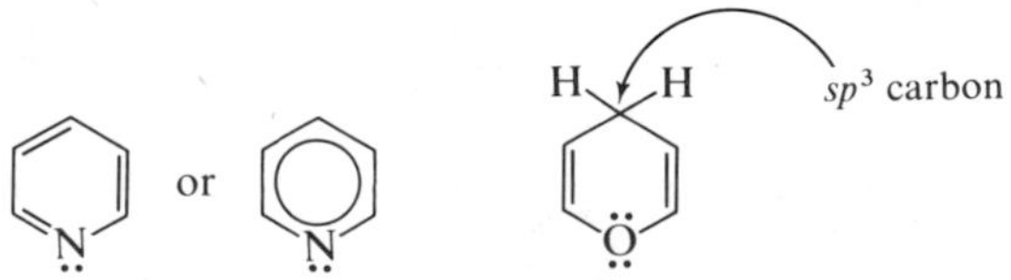

or

pyridine   pyran
aromatic   *not aromatic*

sp^3 carbon

Pyridine has a structure similar to that of benzene. Pyridine contains a planar, six-membered ring consisting of five carbons and one nitrogen. Each of these ring atoms is sp^2-hybridized and has one electron in a p orbital that contributes to the aromatic pi cloud (six pi electrons). Figure 2.24 (page 67) shows the lowest-energy bonding molecular orbital of pyridine.

Note the differences between benzene and pyridine. First, benzene is symmetrical and nonpolar, but pyridine contains an electronegative nitrogen and therefore is *polar*. (The crossed arrow shows the direction of the dipole moment.)

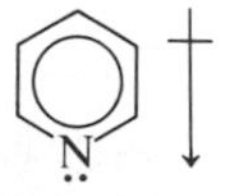

dipole moment $\mu = 2.26$ D

Because the nitrogen is more electronegative than carbon, the rest of the pyridine ring is electron-deficient. An electron-deficient ring means that the carbon atoms in the ring carry a *partial positive charge*. A pyridine ring therefore has a low reactivity toward electrophilic substitution.

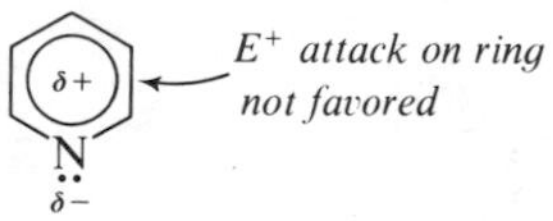

E$^+$ attack on ring not favored

Another major difference between pyridine and benzene is that the nitrogen in pyridine contains an unshared pair of electrons in an sp^2 orbital. This pair of electrons can be donated to a hydrogen ion. Like amines, pyridine is basic.

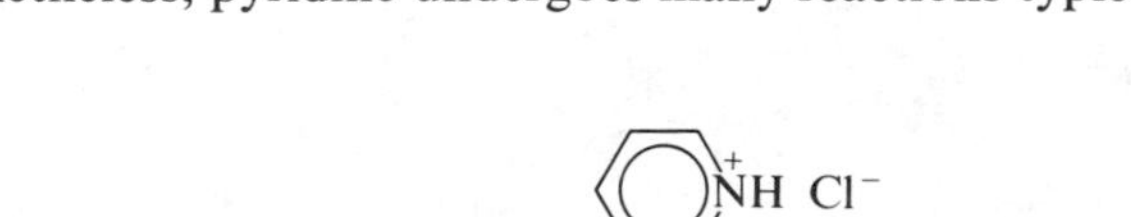

pyridinium ion

The basicity of pyridine ($pK_b = 8.75$) is less than that of aliphatic amines ($pK_b = \sim 4$) because the unshared electrons are in an sp^2 orbital instead of an sp^3 orbital. Nonetheless, pyridine undergoes many reactions typical of amines.

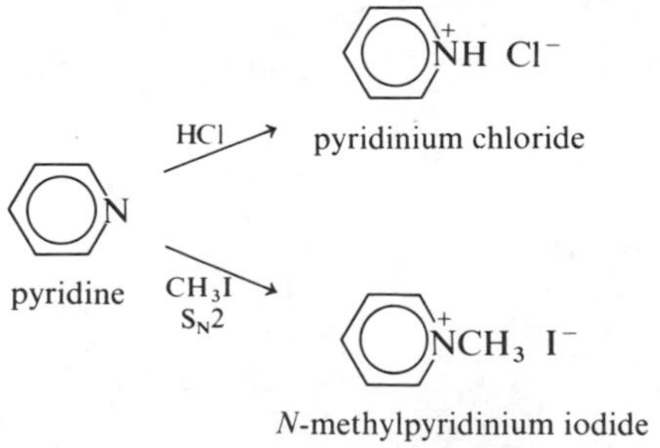

pyridinium chloride

pyridine

N-methylpyridinium iodide

Like that of benzene, the aromatic ring of pyridine is resistant to oxidation. Side chains can be oxidized to carboxyl groups under conditions that leave the ring intact.

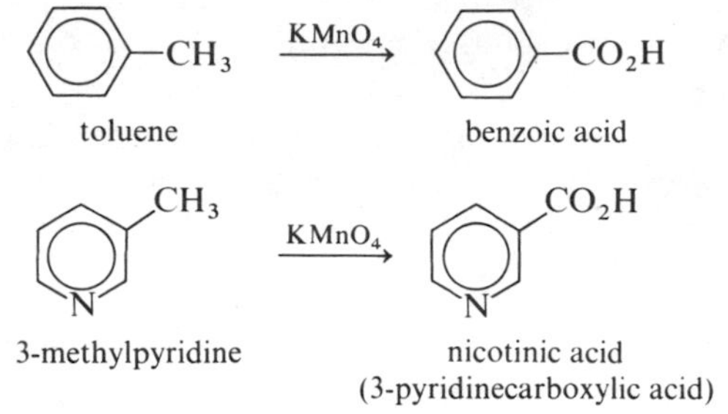
CH_3
$KMnO_4$
CO_2H
toluene
benzoic acid
CH_3
$KMnO_4$
CO_2H
N
N
3-methylpyridine
nicotinic acid
(3-pyridinecarboxylic acid)

A. *Electrophilic Substitution*

Pyridine can undergo aromatic electrophilic substitution, but the ring is deactivated compared to benzene. Besides the electronegative nitrogen rendering the ring partially positive, pyridine forms a cation with many Lewis acids. Cation formation renders the ring even more electron-deficient.

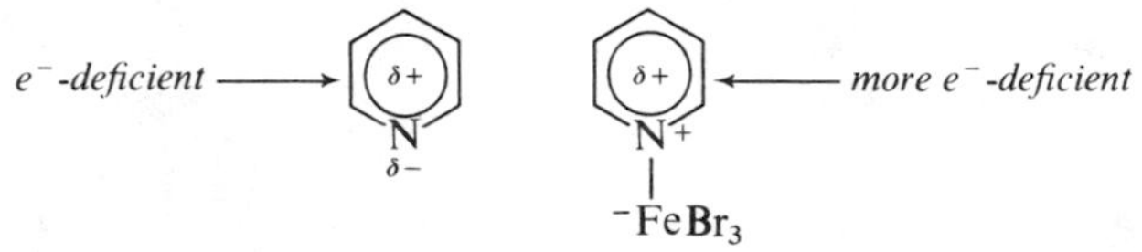
e^--deficient
$\delta+$
N
$\delta-$
$\delta+$
N^+
$^-FeBr_3$
more e^--deficient

Pyridine does not undergo Friedel–Crafts alkylations or acylations, nor does it undergo coupling with diazonium salts. Bromination proceeds only at high temperatures in the vapor phase and probably proceeds by a free-radical path. When substitution does occur, it occurs at the 3-position.

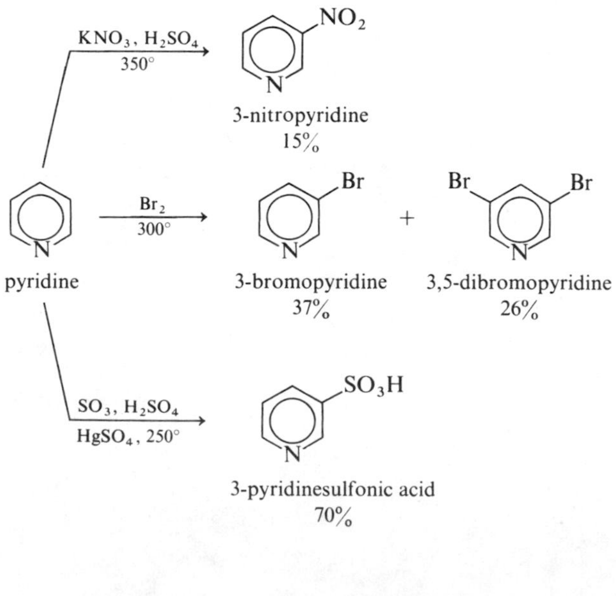
KNO_3, H_2SO_4
350°
NO_2
N
3-nitropyridine
15%
Br_2
300°
Br
N
+
Br
Br
N
pyridine
3-bromopyridine
37%
3,5-dibromopyridine
26%
SO_3, H_2SO_4
$HgSO_4$, 250°
SO_3H
N
3-pyridinesulfonic acid
70%

B. *Nucleophilic Substitution*

When a benzene ring is substituted with electron-withdrawing groups such as $-NO_2$, *aromatic nucleophilic substitutions* can take place (see Section 10.14).

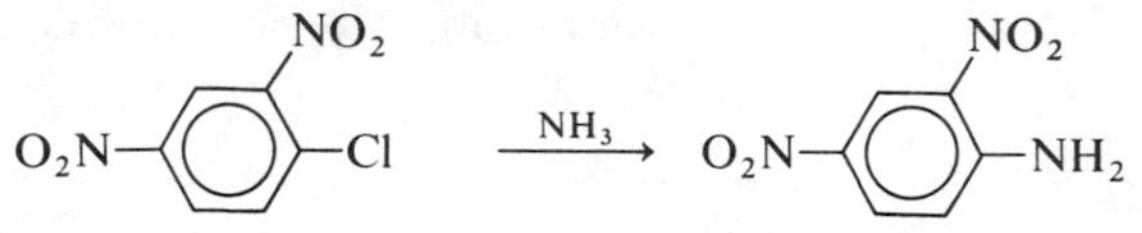

1-chloro-2,4-dinitrobenzene 2,4-dinitroaniline

The nitrogen in pyridine withdraws electrons from the rest of the ring. It is not surprising, then, that nucleophilic substitution also occurs with pyridine. Substitution proceeds most readily at the 2-position, followed by the 4-position, but not at the 3-position.

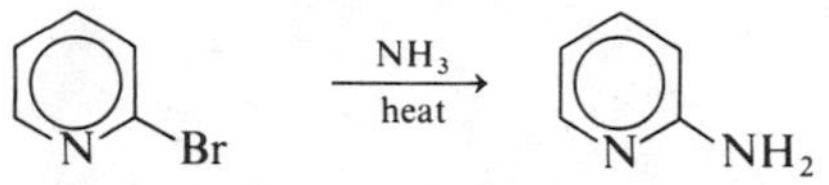

2-bromopyridine 2-aminopyridine

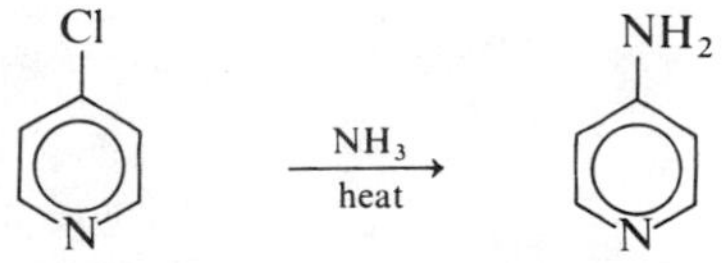

4-chloropyridine 4-aminopyridine

Let us look at the mechanisms for substitution at the 2- and 3-positions to see why the former reaction proceeds more readily.

2-Substitution (favored):

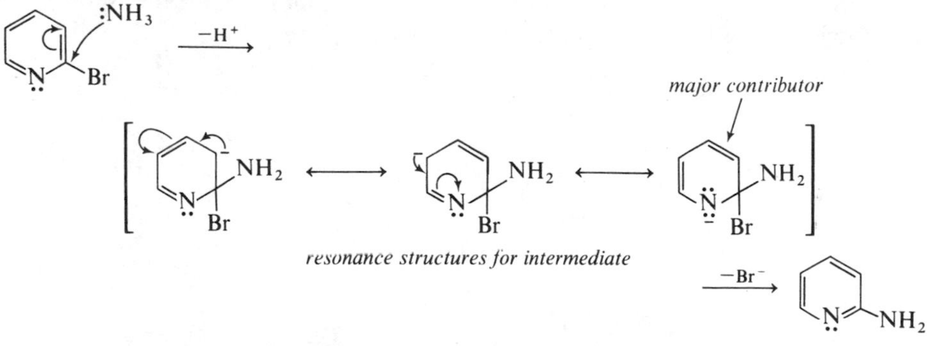
:NH3
−H+
Br
major contributor
NH2
Br
resonance structures for intermediate
−Br−
NH2

3-Substitution (not favored):

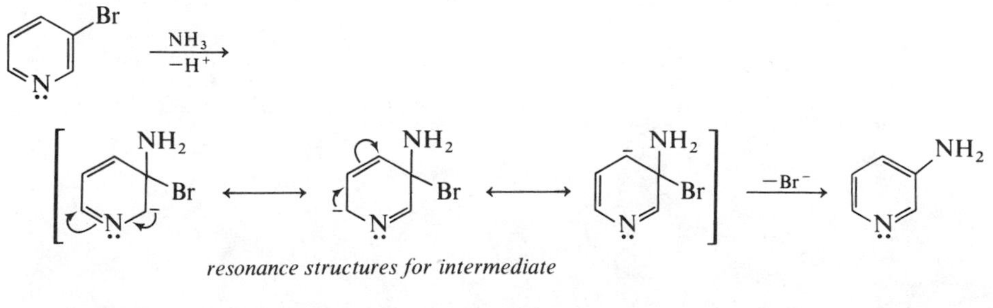
Br
NH3
−H+
NH2
Br
−Br−
NH2
resonance structures for intermediate

Polycyclic and Heterocyclic Aromatic Compounds

The intermediate for 2-substitution is especially stabilized by the contribution of the resonance structure in which nitrogen carries the negative charge. Substitution at the 3-position goes through an intermediate in which the nitrogen cannot help stabilize the negative charge. The intermediate for 3-substitution is of higher energy; the rate of reaction going through this intermediate is less.

STUDY PROBLEM

16.4   Give the resonance structures for the intermediate in the reaction of 4-chloropyridine with ammonia.

Benzene itself (with no substituents) does not undergo nucleophilic substitution. This reaction does occur with pyridine if a very strong base such as a lithium reagent or amide ion ($NH_2{}^-$) is used.

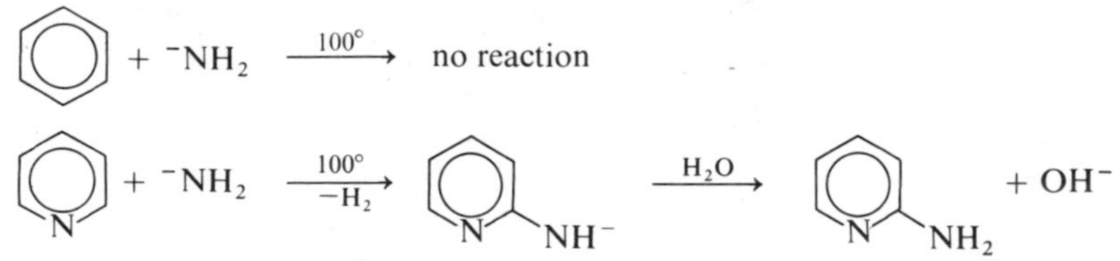

2-aminopyridine
70%

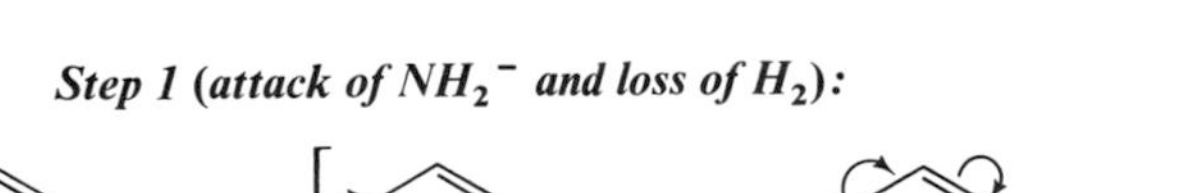

2-phenylpyridine
50%

In the reaction of pyridine with $NH_2{}^-$, the initial product is the anion of 2-aminopyridine. The free amine is obtained by hydrolysis.

Step 1 (attack of $NH_2{}^-$ and loss of H_2):

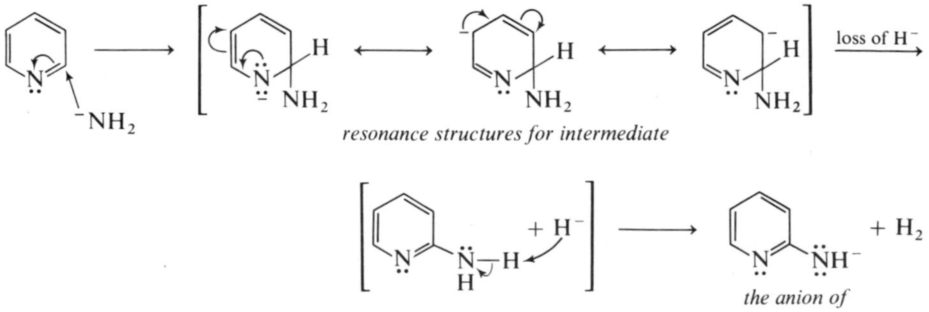

resonance structures for intermediate

the anion of 2-aminopyridine

Step 2 (hydrolysis):

2-aminopyridine

Section 16.8

Quinoline and Isoquinoline

Quinoline is a fused-ring heterocycle that is similar in structure to naphthalene, but with a nitrogen at position 1. Isoquinoline is the 2-isomer. (Note that the numbering of isoquinoline starts at a carbon, not at the nitrogen.)

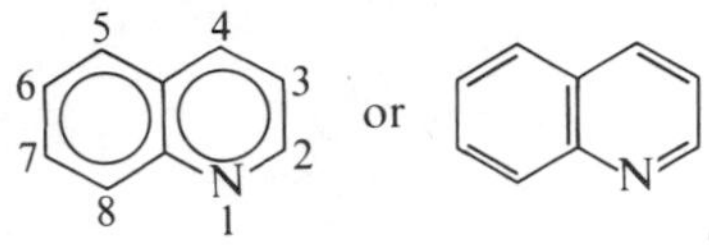

quinoline 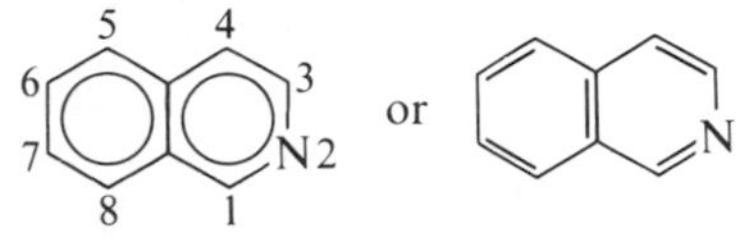   isoquinoline

Both quinoline and isoquinoline contain a pyridine ring fused to a benzene ring. The nitrogen ring in each of these two compounds behaves somewhat like the pyridine ring. Both quinoline and isoquinoline are weak bases ($pK_b = 9.1$ and 8.6, respectively). Both compounds undergo *electrophilic substitution* more easily than pyridine, but in positions 5 and 8 (on the benzenoid ring, not on the deactivated nitrogen ring). The positions of substitution are determined by intermediates similar to those in naphthalene substitution reactions.

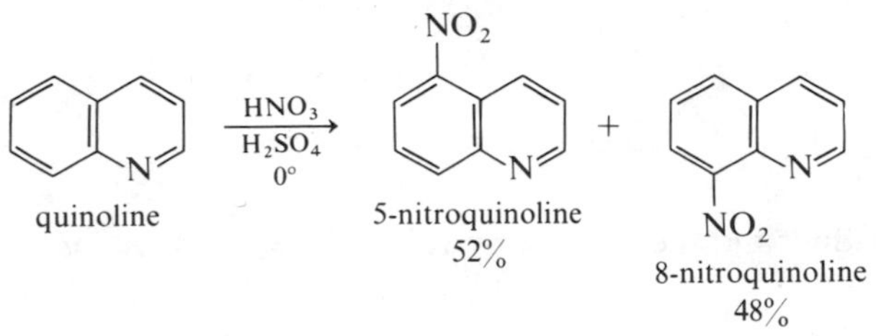

quinoline $\xrightarrow[\substack{H_2SO_4 \\ 0°}]{HNO_3}$ 5-nitroquinoline 52%   +   8-nitroquinoline 48%

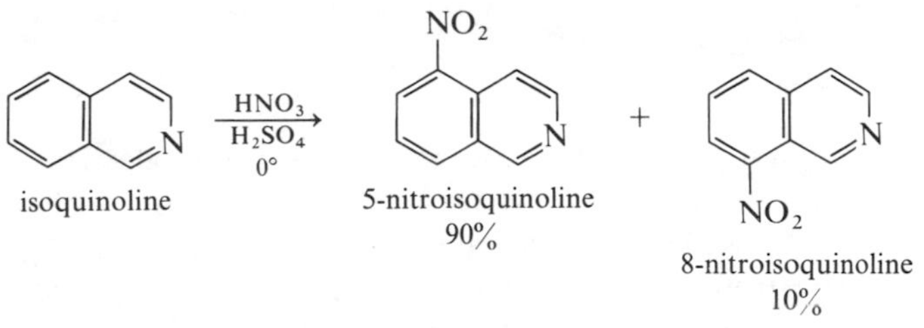

isoquinoline $\xrightarrow[\substack{H_2SO_4 \\ 0°}]{HNO_3}$ 5-nitroisoquinoline 90%   +   8-nitroisoquinoline 10%

STUDY PROBLEM

16.5   Draw resonance structures for the intermediates for nitration at the 5- and 6-positions of quinoline to show why 5-nitroquinoline is formed preferentially.

Like pyridine, the nitrogen-containing ring of either quinoline or isoquinoline can undergo **nucleophilic substitution**. The position of attack is α to the nitrogen in either ring system, just as it is in pyridine.

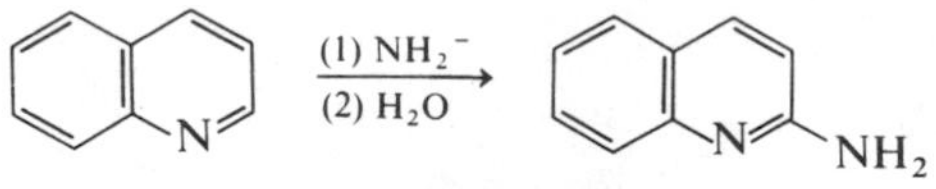

quinoline

2-aminoquinoline

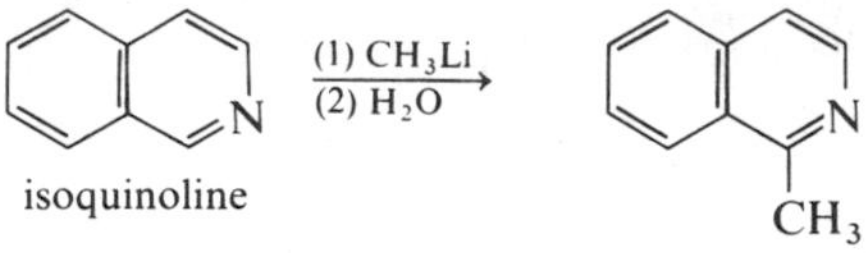

isoquinoline

1-methylisoquinoline

Section 16.9

Pyrrole, a Five-Membered Aromatic Heterocycle

For a five-membered ring heterocycle to be aromatic, the heteroatom must have two electrons to donate to the aromatic pi cloud. Pyrrole, furan, and thiophene all meet this criterion and therefore are aromatic. We will emphasize pyrrole in our discussion of five-membered aromatic heterocycles because it is typical in terms of both bonding and chemical reactivity.

pyrrole   furan   thiophene

Unlike pyridine and the amines, pyrrole ($pK_b = \sim 14$) is *not basic*.

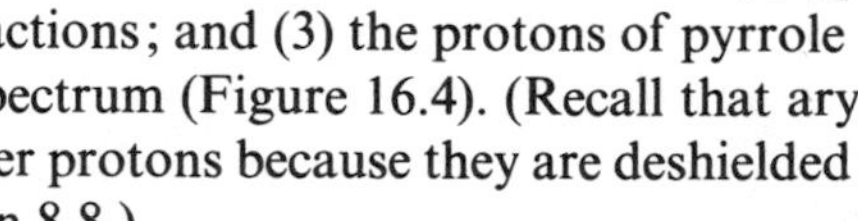

To see why pyrrole is not basic, we must consider the electronic structure of pyrrole. We know that pyrrole is aromatic because (1) its heat of combustion is about 25 kcal/mole less than that calculated for a diene structure; (2) pyrrole undergoes aromatic substitution reactions; and (3) the protons of pyrrole absorb in the aromatic region of the nmr spectrum (Figure 16.4). (Recall that aryl protons absorb downfield from most other protons because they are deshielded by the effects of the ring current; see Section 8.8.)

In a five-membered ring, the minimum number of pi electrons needed for aromaticity is six ($4n + 2$, where $n = 1$). The four carbons of pyrrole each contribute one electron; therefore, the nitrogen atom of pyrrole must contribute *two* electrons (not just one as it does in pyridine). In addition to contributing two electrons to the pi molecular orbitals, the nitrogen in pyrrole shares three electrons in sigma bonds to two ring carbons and to a hydrogen. Consequently, all five bonding electrons of the nitrogen are used in bonding. The pyrrole nitrogen does not have unshared bonding electrons and is not nucleophilic. Figure 16.5 shows the *p*-orbital picture.

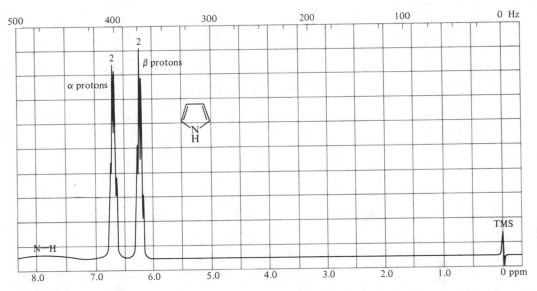

Figure 16.4. Nmr spectrum of pyrrole, C_4H_5N. (The NH absorption is a low, broad band near 8 ppm.)

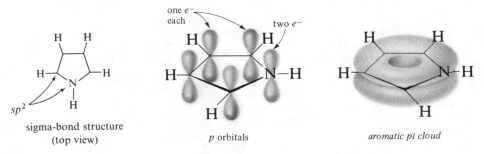

Figure 16.5. The bonding in pyrrole, C_4H_5N.

STUDY PROBLEM

16.6 If pyrrole did form a cation when treated with HCl, what would its structure be? (Show the orbitals.) Would the pyrrole cation be aromatic or not?

Because the nitrogen atom in pyrrole contributes two electrons to the aromatic pi cloud, the nitrogen atom is electron-deficient and therefore not basic. The pyrrole ring, however, has six pi electrons for only five ring atoms. The ring is electron-rich and therefore partially negative. The dipole moments reflect this: nitrogen is usually the negative end of a dipole, but the nitrogen in pyrrole is the positive end of the molecule.

μ: 2.26 D   1.81 D

Polycyclic and Heterocyclic Aromatic Compounds

Because the ring carbons are the negative part of the pyrrole molecule, these carbons are *activated toward electrophilic attack*, but *deactivated to nucleophilic attack*. (This reactivity is opposite to that of pyridine.)

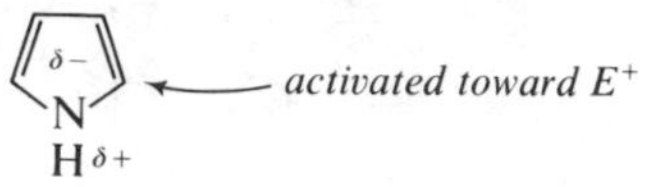

A.   Electrophilic Substitution

The principal chemical characteristic of pyrrole and the other five-membered aromatic heterocycles is the ease with which they undergo electrophilic substitution.

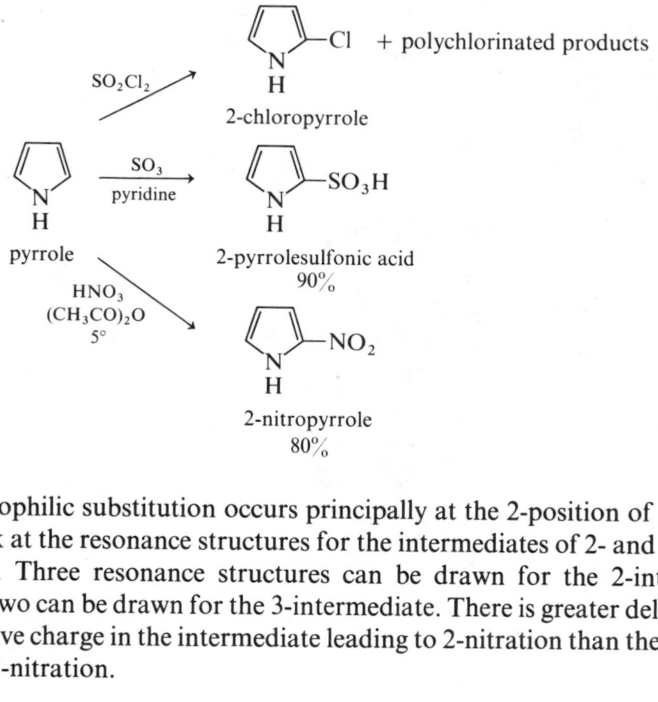

Electrophilic substitution occurs principally at the 2-position of the pyrrole ring. A look at the resonance structures for the intermediates of 2- and 3-nitration shows why. Three resonance structures can be drawn for the 2-intermediate, while only two can be drawn for the 3-intermediate. There is greater delocalization of the positive charge in the intermediate leading to 2-nitration than there is in that leading to 3-nitration.

2-Nitration (favored):

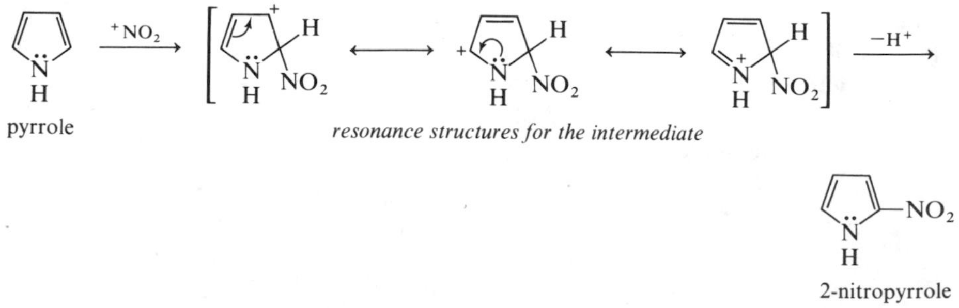

3-Nitration (*not favored*):

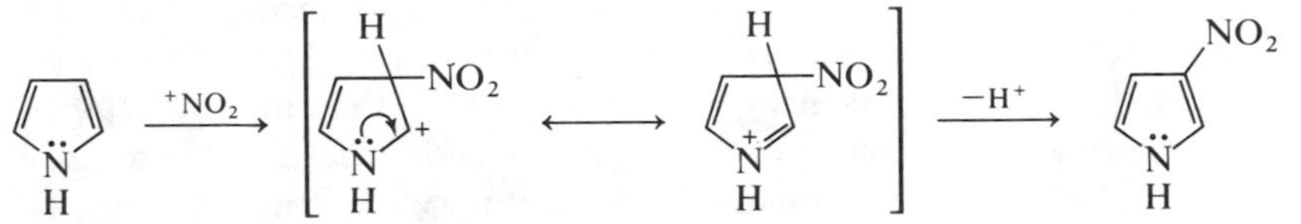

resonance structures for the intermediate   3-nitropyrrole

STUDY PROBLEM

16.7 Predict the major organic monosubstitution products:

(a) furan + $(CH_3CO)_2O$ $\xrightarrow[\text{(a mild Lewis acid)}]{BF_3}$

(b) thiophene + H_2SO_4 $\xrightarrow{25°}$

(c) pyrrole + $C_6H_5N_2{}^+ \ Cl^-$ $\xrightarrow{25°}$

(d) furan + Br_2 $\xrightarrow[25°]{\text{dioxane}}$

Section 16.10

Alkaloids

Primitive people have often used extracts of roots, bark, leaves, flowers, berries, and seeds as drugs. This use of plants for medicinal purposes was not necessarily based on superstition or wishful thinking. Many plants contain compounds that have profound physiological impact. The active agents in many of these plant substances have been isolated and have been found to be heterocyclic nitrogen compounds.

Many of the nitrogen compounds in plants contain basic nitrogen atoms and thus can be extracted from the bulk of the plant material by dilute acid. These compounds are called **alkaloids**, which means "like an alkali." After extraction, the free alkaloids can be regenerated by subsequent treatment with aqueous base.

Extraction: $R_3N: + HCl \ \xrightarrow{H_2O} \ R_3NH^+ \ Cl^-$

Regeneration:

$$R_3NH^+ \ Cl^- + OH^- \longrightarrow R_3N: + H_2O + Cl^-$$

Alkaloids vary from simple to complex in their structures. One of the simplest in structure, but not in its physiological effects, is *nicotine*.

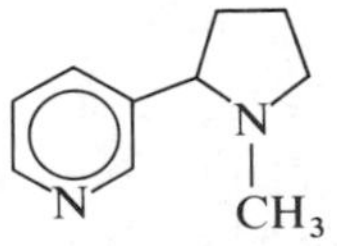

nicotine

Polycyclic and Heterocyclic Aromatic Compounds

In large doses, nicotine is toxic; nicotine sulfate is used as an insecticide. In small doses (such as a smoker obtains from cigarettes), nicotine acts by stimulating the autonomic (involuntary) nervous system. If small doses are continued, nicotine can depress this same nervous system into less than normal activity.

The vigorous oxidation of nicotine yields *nicotinic acid*, a B vitamin. Nicotinic acid is a precursor of nicotinamide, the working end of the coenzyme NAD$^+$ (Section 16.13).

The first isolation of an alkaloid in the pure state was reported in 1805. This alkaloid was *morphine* (from the Greek *Morpheus*, the god of dreams), one of many alkaloids to come from the gum and seeds of the opium poppy, *Papaver somniferum.*

morphine   codeine   heroin

Codeine is the methoxy derivative of morphine (at the phenolic group), while *heroin* is the diacetyl derivative. Codeine, like morphine, is a powerful analgesic and occurs naturally in the seeds of the opium poppy. Codeine is also an excellent cough suppressant that is sometimes used in prescription cough medicines. In recent years, it has been largely replaced by *dextromethorphan*, a nonaddictive, synthetic drug that is an equally effective cough suppressant.

dextromethorphan

Heroin does not occur naturally, but may be synthesized from morphine in the laboratory. Heroin, like morphine and codeine, is a powerful analgesic. In some parts of the world, heroin is used to relieve pain in terminal cancer patients. Because it is even more addictive than morphine, its medicinal use is prohibited in the United States.

A large number of physiologically active alkaloids contain the **tropane ring system**:

tropane

One of the tropane alkaloids is *atropine*, found in *Atropa belladonna* and other members of the nightshade plant family. Atropine is used in eye drops to dilate the pupils. *Scopolamine* (a so-called "truth" serum) is used as a preoperative sedative; chemically, it is the epoxide of atropine. *Cocaine*, a habituating stimulant and pain reliever, also contains the tropane ring system.

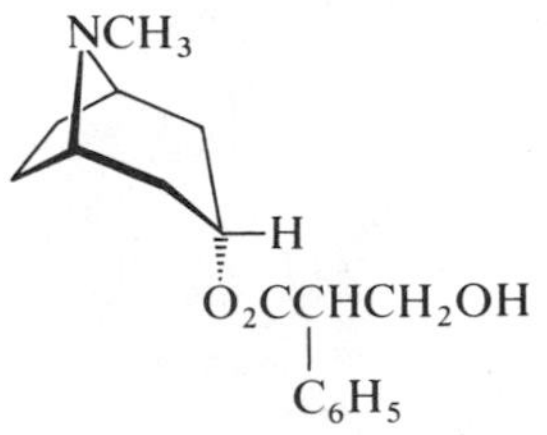

atropine 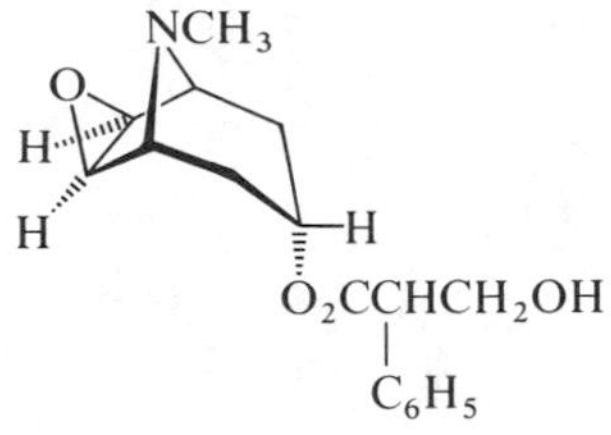   scopolamine 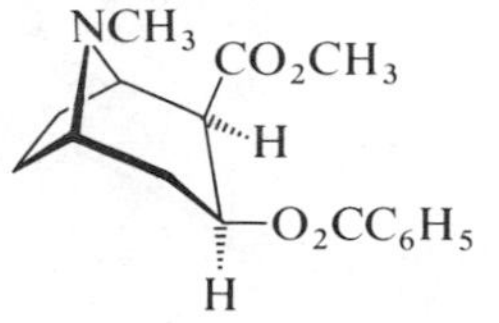   cocaine

STUDY PROBLEMS

16.8 When atropine is subjected to acid hydrolysis, two products are obtained: *tropine*, which is not optically active, and *tropic acid*, which is obtained as a racemic mixture. What are the structures of these two compounds?

16.9 What are the products of acid hydrolysis of cocaine?

Quinine is an alkaloid occurring in the bark of the cinchona tree, which is native to the Andes. Quinine was an important early export from the New World because of its antimalarial activity. Although synthetic antimalarials have been developed, quinine is still used.

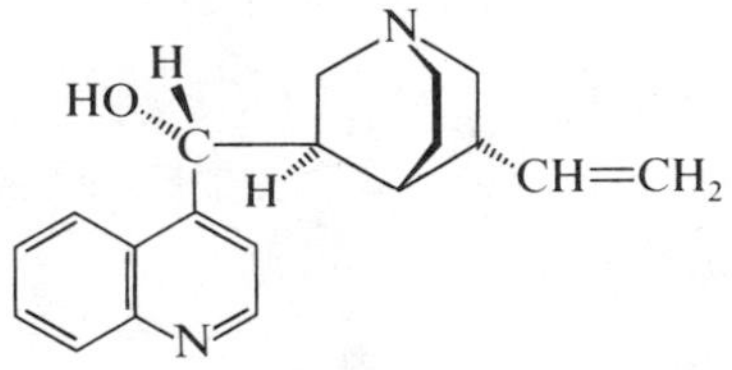

quinine

STUDY PROBLEM

16.10 Which nitrogen in quinine is the more basic?

Section 16.11

Porphyrins

The **porphyrin ring system** is a biologically important unit found in *heme*, the oxygen-carrying component of hemoglobin; in *chlorophyll*, a plant pigment; and in the *cytochromes*, compounds involved in utilization of O_2 by animals. Structures of these compounds are shown in Figure 16.6.

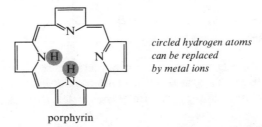

circled hydrogen atoms can be replaced by metal ions

porphyrin

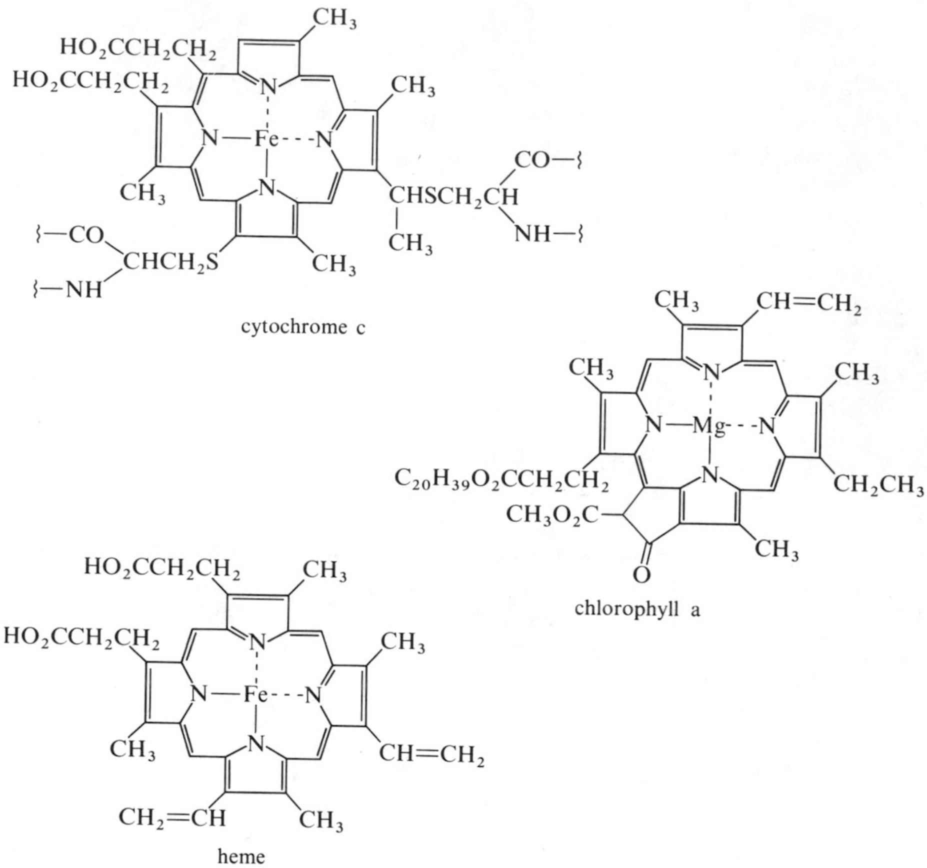

cytochrome c

chlorophyll a

heme

Figure 16.6.   Some biologically important porphyrins.

The pyrrole hydrogens in the porphyrin ring system can be replaced by a variety of metal ions. The chelate product is planar around the metal ion, and resonance results in four equivalent bonds from the nitrogen atoms to the metal.

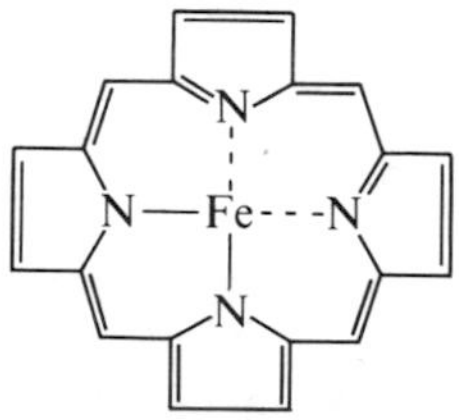

planar and resonance-stabilized

Section 16.12

Nucleic Acids

One of the most fascinating areas of modern research has been that of the **nucleic acids**, which are the carriers of the genetic codes in living systems. Because of information contained in the structure of the nucleic acids, an organism is able to biosynthesize different types of protein (hair, skin, muscles, enzymes, and so forth) and to reproduce more organisms of its own kind.

There are two principal types of nucleic acid: the **deoxyribonucleic acids (DNA)** and the **ribonucleic acids (RNA)**. DNA is found only in the cell nucleus; it is the carrier of the genetic code and can reproduce, or *replicate*, itself for purposes of forming new cells or for reproduction of the organism. In most organisms, the DNA of a cell directs the synthesis of **messenger RNA molecules**. It is the messenger RNA that leaves the cell nucleus and directs the biosynthesis of the different types of protein in the organism.

A. The Structure of DNA

DNA is a polymer. The backbone of this polymer is a long chain composed of the sugar *deoxyribose* (which will be discussed in Chapter 17) linked together by phosphate groups. (Note that the sugar–phosphate links form inorganic esters of alcohols; see Section 7.16.)

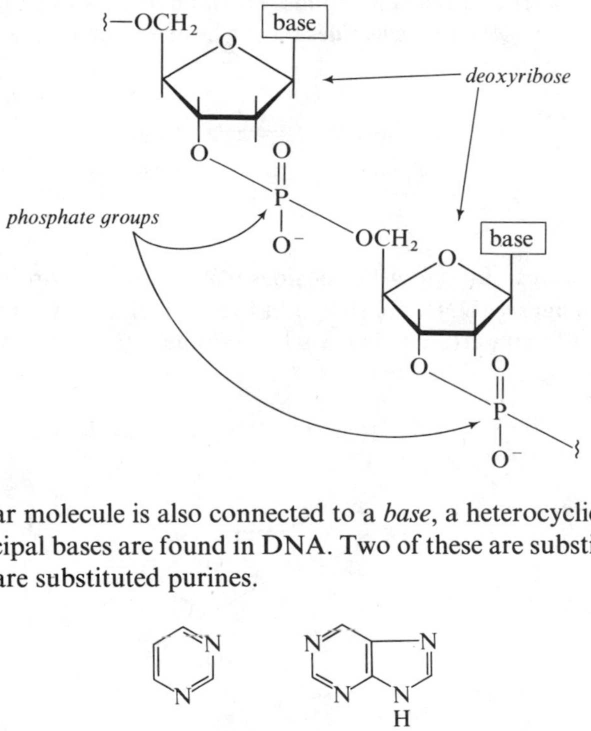

Each sugar molecule is also connected to a *base*, a heterocyclic ring system. Only four principal bases are found in DNA. Two of these are substituted pyrimidines and two are substituted purines.

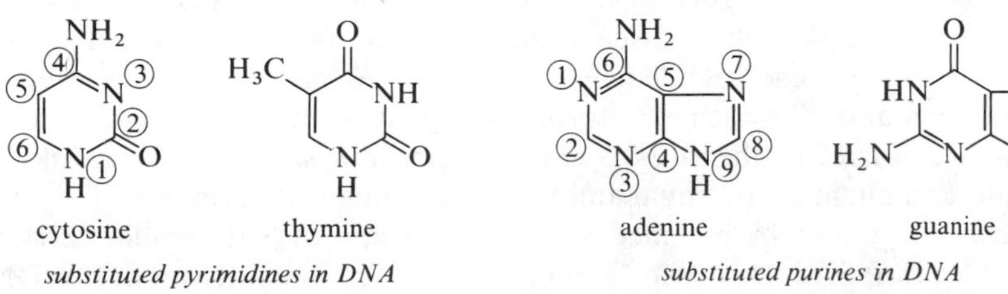

pyrimidine   purine

cytosine   thymine   adenine   guanine

substituted pyrimidines in DNA   *substituted purines in DNA*

STUDY PROBLEM

16.11 Cytosine is shown in its *lactam* (cyclic amide) form. This structure is one tautomer for cytosine. Show the tautomeric enol form of cytosine.

In DNA, the bases are attached to the deoxyribose at position 1 of the pyrimidines or position 9 of the purines.

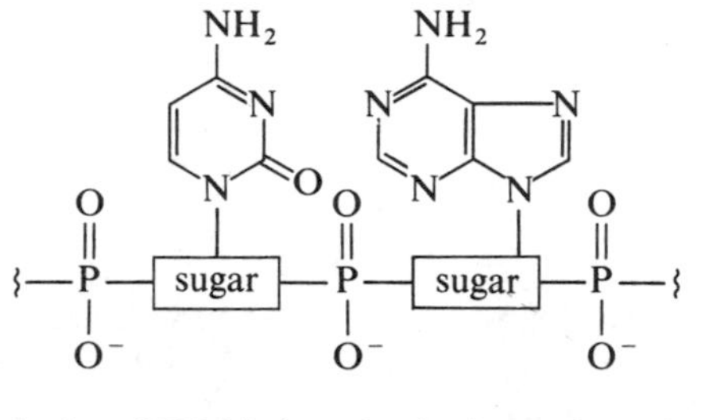

Complete hydrolysis of DNA breaks it down into its smallest fragments: the sugar, the bases, and phosphate ions. Partial hydrolysis results in **nucleosides** (sugar bonded to base) and **nucleotides** (sugar bonded to base and phosphate).

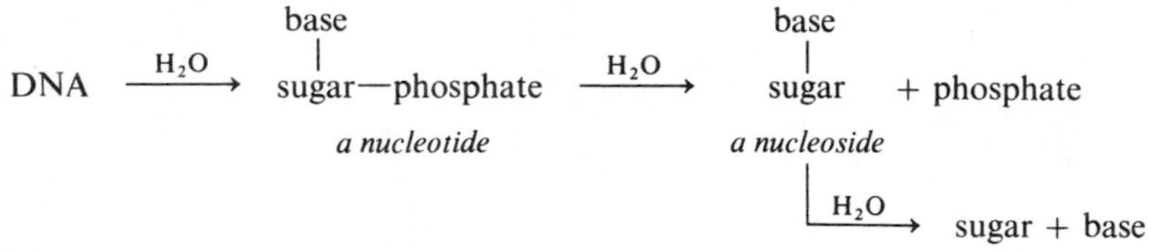

The structures of the four nucleosides isolated after hydrolysis of the phosphate ester linkages of DNA are shown in Figure 16.7. The four nucleotides that can be isolated from partial hydrolysis have similar structures, but with a phosphate group attached to the sugar.

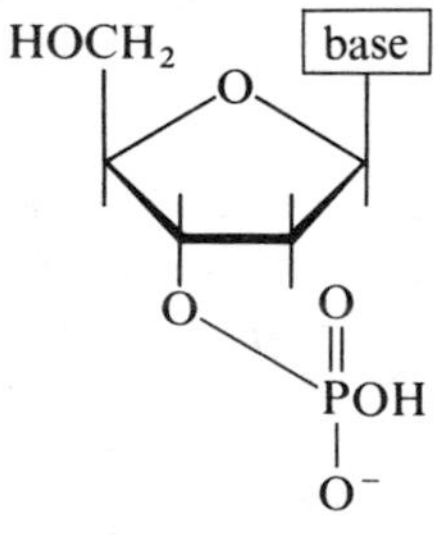

a nucleotide

DNA isolated from different tissues of the same organism contains approximately the same proportions of bases; however, these proportions vary from species to species. For example, human tissue contains approximately 20% each of cytosine and guanine and 30% each of adenine and thymine. *Escherichia coli* (an intestinal bacterium) contains 37% each of cytosine and guanine and 13% each of adenine and thymine. Notice that the bases from DNA appear in *pairs*, with equal amounts of cytosine and guanine and equal amounts of adenine and thymine.

How does the DNA polymer with its succession of heterocycles carry the genetic code? In 1953, J. D. Watson and F. H. C. Crick proposed a model for DNA

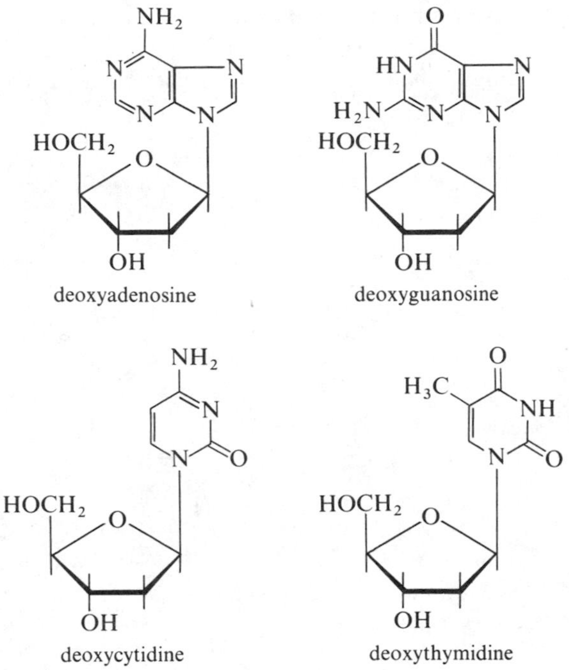

deoxyadenosine

deoxyguanosine

deoxycytidine

deoxythymidine

Figure 16.7.   The nucleosides obtained from the hydrolysis of DNA.

that accounts for its behavior. In 1962, these two men, along with Maurice Wilkins, who verified the structure of the model by x-ray analysis, were awarded the Nobel prize for their work. The Watson–Crick model of DNA is that of a *double helix of two long DNA molecules held together by hydrogen bonds* (see Figure 16.8).

The hydrogen bonds between DNA strands are not random, but are *specific between pairs of bases*: guanine is hydrogen-bonded to cytosine, and adenine to thymine. Why are these hydrogen bonds specific? Thymine and adenine can be

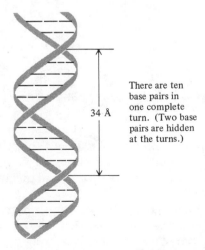

34 Å

There are ten base pairs in one complete turn. (Two base pairs are hidden at the turns.)

Figure 16.8.   A pair of complementary DNA molecules form a double-stranded helix held together by hydrogen bonds.

Polycyclic and Heterocyclic Aromatic Compounds

joined by *two* hydrogen bonds (approximate strength, 10 kcal/mole). Cytosine and guanine can be joined by *three* hydrogen bonds (approximate strength, 17 kcal/mole). No other pairing of the four bases leads to such strong hydrogen bonding.

Thymine and adenine:

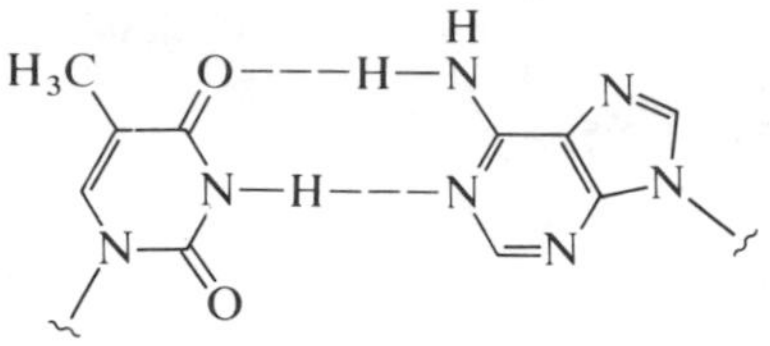

Cytosine and guanine:

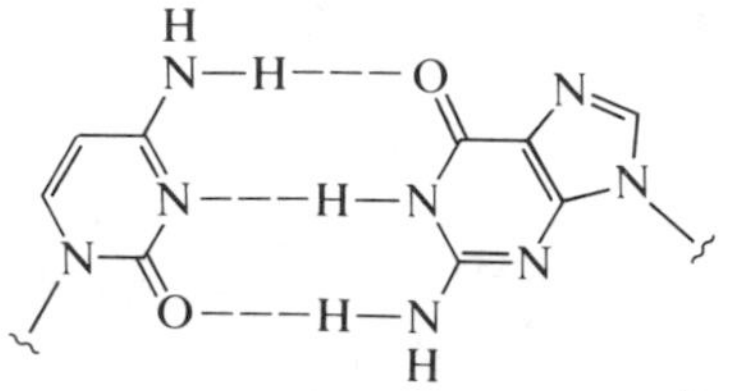

Not between thymine and guanine:

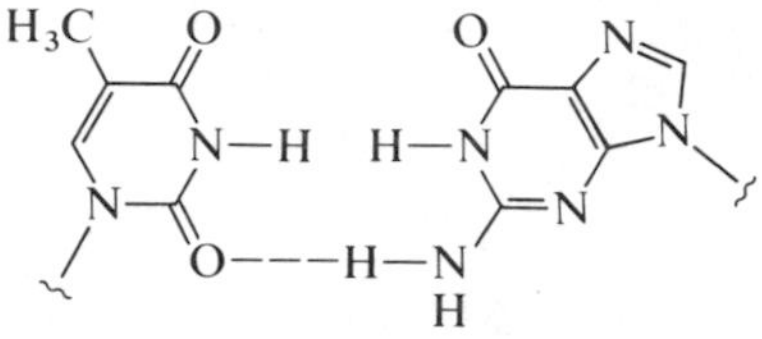

Now let us picture the double helix of DNA held together by series of particular hydrogen-bonded pairs. We will use initials for the bases: **A** for adenine, **T** for thymine, **G** for guanine, and **C** for cytosine.

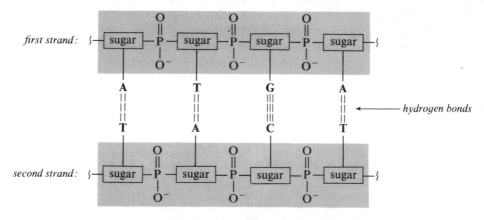

Wherever an **A** appears in one strand, a **T** must appear opposite it in the other strand. The two strands are completely complementary in this respect. The pairing of bases explains why equal amounts of adenine and thymine and equal amounts of cytosine and guanine are found in DNA.

It is the *sequence of bases* that determines the genetic code; therefore, it is not surprising that different species contain differing amounts of the four bases. It is estimated that a single gene contains 1500 base pairs (a figure that is variable, depending on the gene). With this size gene, there can be 4^{1500} different possible base-pair combinations!

B.   *Replication of DNA*

The process of replication of DNA in a typical cell begins with an enzyme-catalyzed unwinding of the double strand (see Figure 16.9). As the double strand unwinds, new nucleotides become aligned along each strand. The nucleotides line up in an exactly complementary fashion: thymine to adenine and cytosine to guanine.

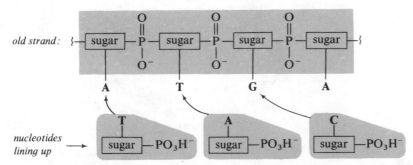

The polymerization of these nucleotides, catalyzed by the enzyme *DNA polymerase*, results in a pair of new strands. Each new strand is the complement of one of the old strands. The result is a pair of identical DNA helices where only one helix existed before.

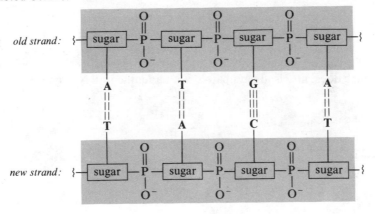

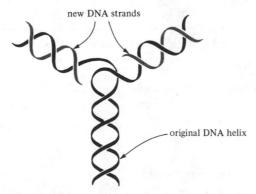

Figure 16.9.   Replication of DNA involves the unwinding of the helix and the formation of new complementary strands.

Polycyclic and Heterocyclic Aromatic Compounds

C.   The Structure of RNA

The structure of RNA is similar to that of DNA: a series of sugar units (*ribose*, in this case) joined together by phosphate links, each sugar linked to a base.

The RNA polymer:

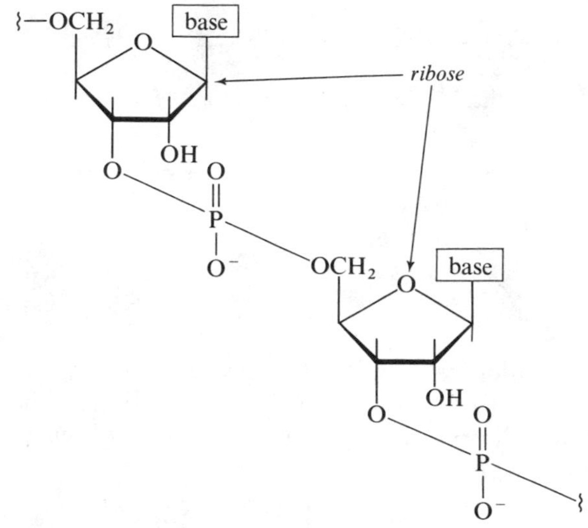

The principal bases in RNA are *adenine, guanine, cytosine,* and *uracil* (instead of thymine). Uracil forms the same favorable hydrogen bonds with adenine that thymine does, and is always paired with adenine in RNA synthesis.

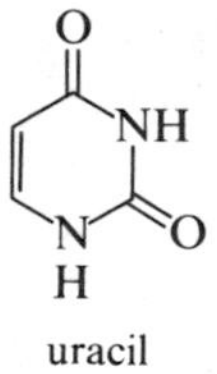

uracil

STUDY PROBLEM

16.12 Give the structures and show the hydrogen bonding between uracil and adenine.

Hydrolysis of RNA results in nucleotides, nucleosides, phosphate ions, and, finally, ribose and the bases. The structures of the nucleosides are shown in Figure 16.10.

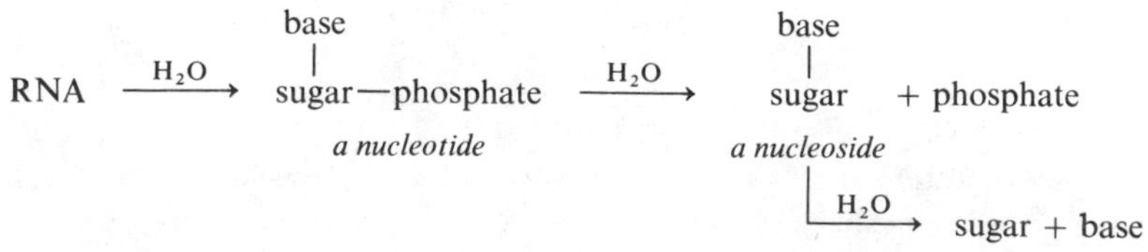

adenosine

guanosine

cytidine

uridine

Figure 16.10. The nucleosides obtained from the hydrolysis of RNA.

Messenger RNA (mRNA) is synthesized under the direction of DNA. The mRNA molecules are smaller than DNA molecules. In the synthesis of an mRNA molecule, only a portion of the DNA helix unwinds; then complementary ribonucleotides line up and are polymerized.

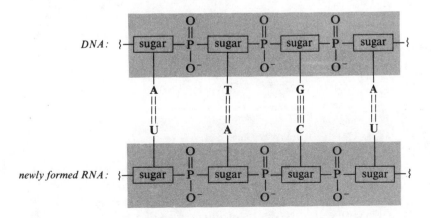

After polymerization, an mRNA molecule does not form a helix with the DNA molecule, but leaves the nucleus to aid in protein biosynthesis, a topic we will discuss in Section 18.9.

Section 16.13

Compounds Related to Nucleotides

Nucleotides and closely related compounds perform a variety of functions in living systems besides that of being monomers for DNA and RNA polymers. **Adenosine triphosphate (ATP)** is the storehouse of biological energy. In this case, it is the *triphosphate group* that is the important part of the molecule. ATP has a pair of anhydride bonds in this group.

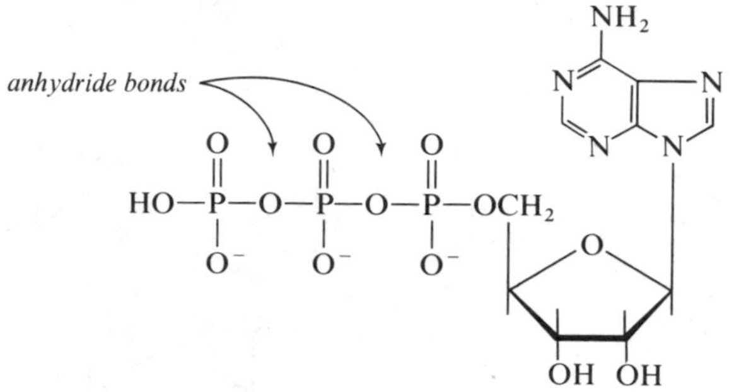

ATP

Hydrolysis of one phosphate group from ATP yields **adenosine diphosphate (ADP)** and energy. When an organism requires energy, enzymes catalyze the hydrolysis of the higher-energy ATP to the lower-energy ADP. In the following equation, R represents the sugar and base portion of the ATP molecule.

When an organism uses energy:

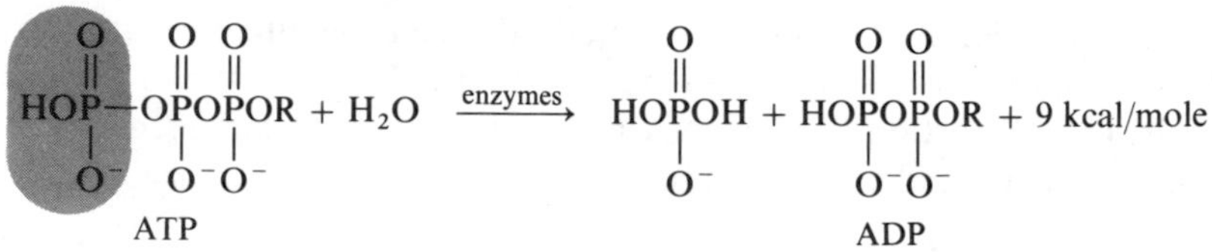

An organism gains energy from the food it eats. When food is metabolized, some of the energy is used to convert ADP back to the higher-energy ATP, ready to be used again when necessary.

When an organism stores energy:

$$\text{ADP} + \text{H}_2\text{PO}_4^- + 9\,\text{kcal/mole} \longrightarrow \text{ATP} + \text{H}_2\text{O}$$

Two of the principal biological oxidizing agents contain two nucleotide units each. These two compounds are **nicotinamide adenine dinucleotide (NAD$^+$)** and **flavin adenine dinucleotide (FAD)**. Their structures are shown in Figure 16.11.

The working end of NAD$^+$ is *nicotinamide* (also called *niacinamide*), which is one of the B vitamins. Lack of nicotinamide in the diet leads to *pellagra*, a condition that was recognized as early as 1735 by Gaspar Casal, physician to Philip V of Spain. Pellagra is characterized by dermatitis, an atrophic tongue, and

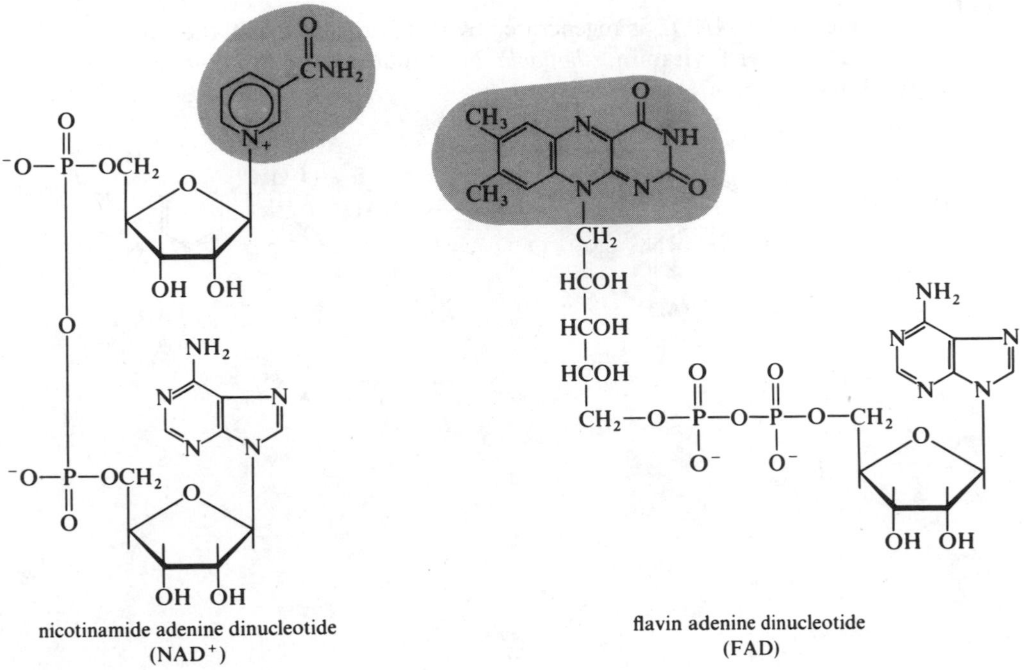

Figure 16.11.   The structures of NAD$^+$ and FAD. (The functional units are circled.)

disturbances of the digestive tract and nervous system. Both nicotinic acid and the amino acid tryptophan can be converted to nicotinamide in the body and are effective substitutes for this vitamin.

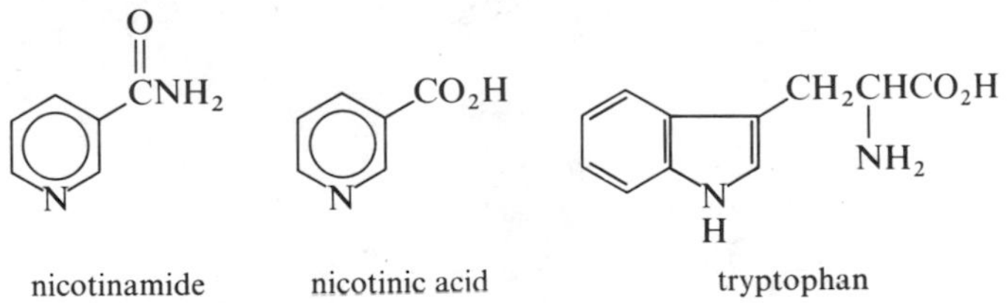

The function of NAD$^+$ is that of an oxidizing agent:

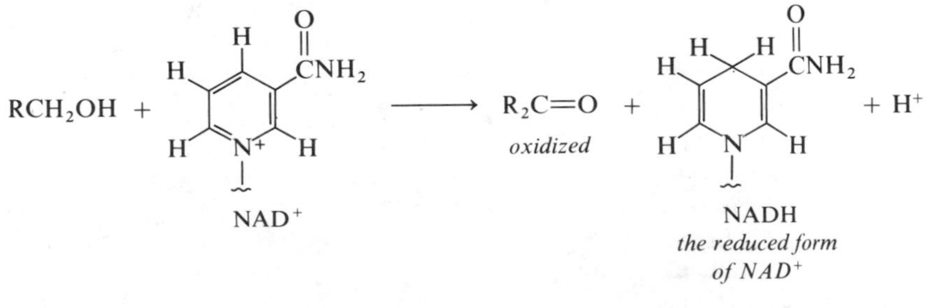

Polycyclic and Heterocyclic Aromatic Compounds

Generally, NAD$^+$ is regenerated by reaction with FAD, the working end of which is another B vitamin, *riboflavin*. Note that this oxidation–reduction results in a 1,4-addition of H$_2$ to FAD.

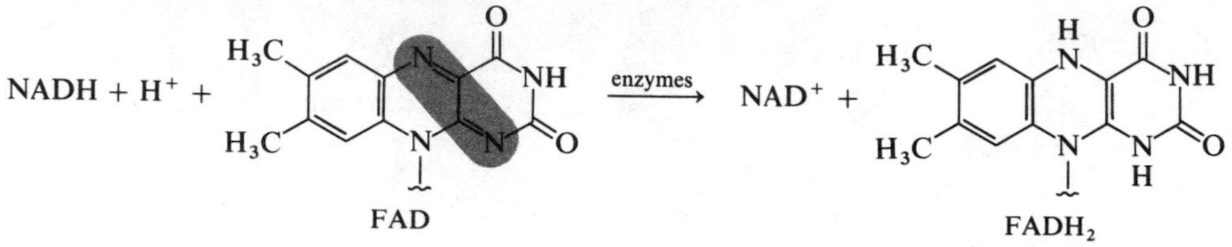

NADH + H$^+$ +   FAD $\xrightarrow{\text{enzymes}}$ NAD$^+$ +   FADH$_2$
*the reduced form
of FAD*

SUMMARY

Three common **polycyclic aromatic compounds** are **naphthalene, anthracene**, and **phenanthrene**. These compounds exhibit less resonance energy per ring than benzene, and certain C—C bonds have more double-bond character than others. These compounds may be oxidized to quinones or may be partially hydrogenated.

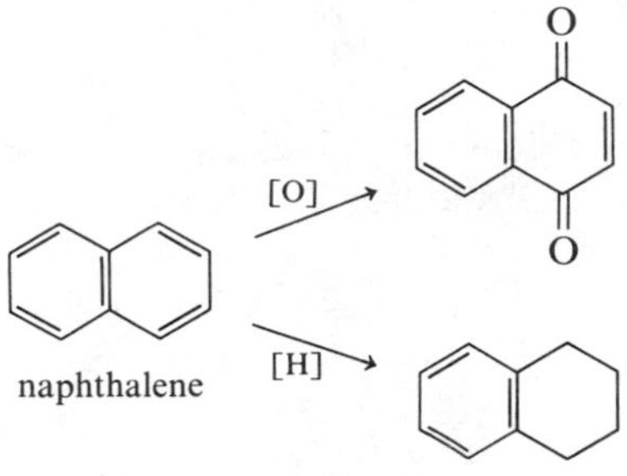

Naphthalene undergoes electrophilic substitution at the 1-position. If the first substituent is *electron-releasing*, the second substitution occurs at an α position on the same ring. If the first substituent is *electron-withdrawing*, the second substitution occurs in an α position of the other ring.

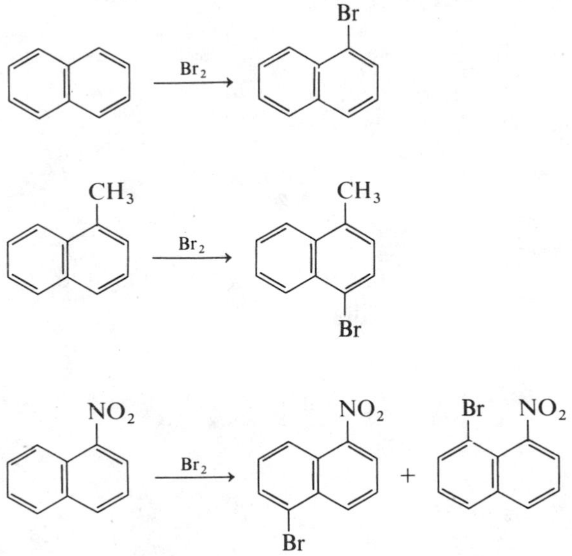

The six-membered aromatic heterocycle **pyridine** is a weak base and has a partially positive ring. Compared to benzene, pyridine is deactivated toward electrophilic substitution, but activated toward nucleophilic substitution.

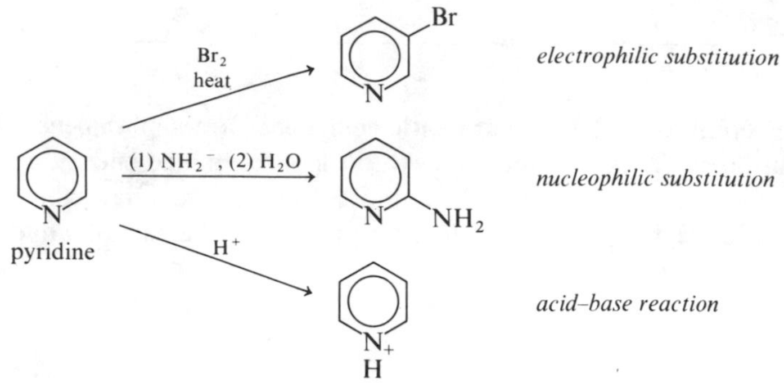

Polycyclic and Heterocyclic Aromatic Compounds

electrophilic substitution

nucleophilic substitution

acid–base reaction

Quinoline and **isoquinoline** undergo electrophilic substitution on the benzenoid ring, but nucleophilic substitution on the nitrogen ring.

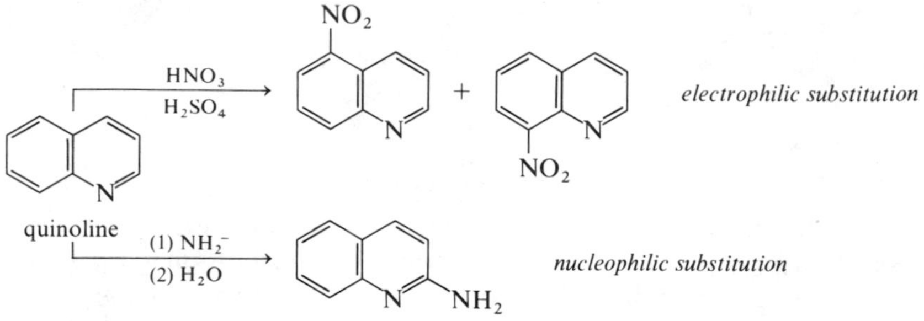

electrophilic substitution

nucleophilic substitution

Pyrrole is an aromatic five-membered nitrogen heterocycle. It is not basic. Its ring is partially negative and is activated toward electrophilic substitution, but deactivated toward nucleophilic substitution.

electrophilic substitution

no nucleophilic substitution

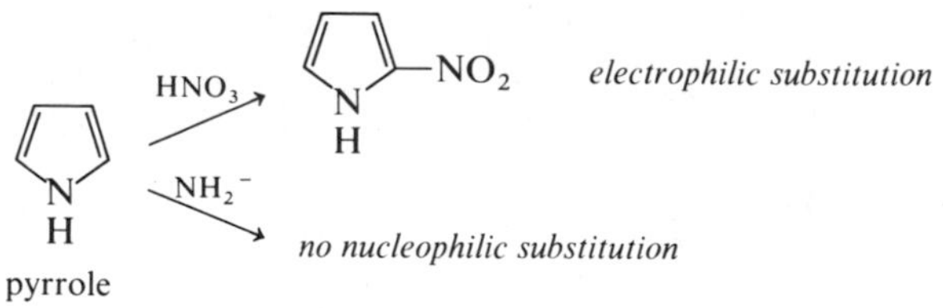

The order of reactivity of the heterocycles and benzene toward electrophilic and nucleophilic substitution follows:

Electrophilic substitution:

Nucleophilic substitution:

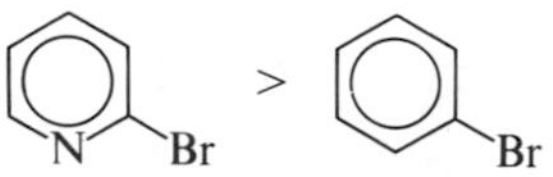

Alkaloids are acid-soluble, nitrogen-containing plant materials. Typical alkaloids are nicotine, morphine, codeine, atropine, and quinine.

The **porphyrin ring system** is found in heme, chlorophyll, and the cytochromes. In each of these, a metal ion is chelated by the ring system.

The **nucleic acids** are polymers. The backbone consists of sugar molecules (deoxyribose in DNA and ribose in RNA) linked together by phosphate units. Each sugar unit is also bonded to a heterocycle. Hydrogen bonding between specific heterocycles is one of the principal factors responsible for the genetic code. Nucleic acids may be hydrolyzed to **nucleotides** (phosphate–sugar–base) and to **nucleosides** (sugar–base). Nucleotide structural units are also found in ATP, ADP, NAD^+, and FAD.

STUDY PROBLEMS

16.13 Name the following compounds:

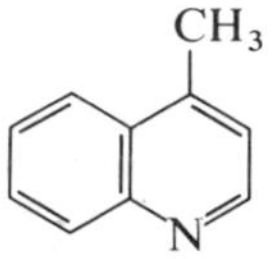

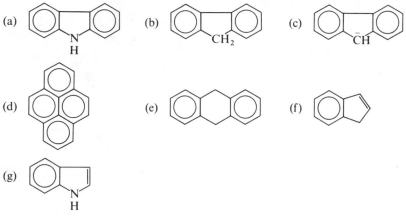

16.14 Give structures for each of the following names: (a) 2-acetylnaphthalene; (b) 1-chloronaphthalene; (c) 2-butylpyrrole; (d) 2,4-dinitrothiophene; (e) *N*-phenyl-pyrrole.

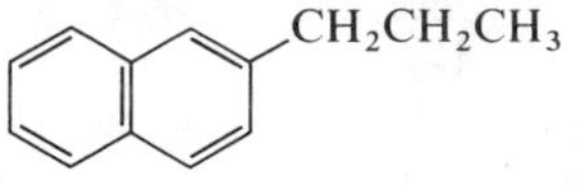

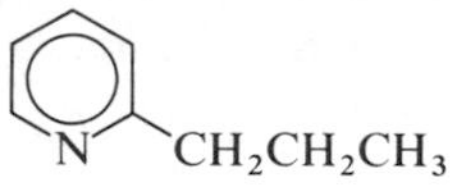

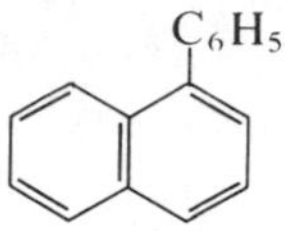

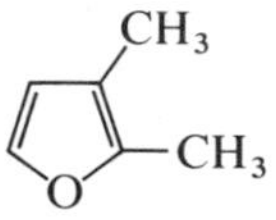

16.15 How many pi electrons does each of the following structures have? Which structures are *fully aromatic*, the aromatic pi cloud involving the entire ring system?

16.16 Draw *p*-orbital pictures for the following compounds. Indicate the number of electrons in each *p* orbital and whether or not the compound is aromatic. Also show any unshared bonding electrons and indicate the type of orbital in which they are found.

(a) thiazole   (b) pyrimidine   (c) purine   (d) thiophene   (e) pyran

16.17 Show the direction of the dipole in   (a) 2-methylpyridine,   (b) 2-ethylpyrrole, and (c) isoquinoline.

16.18 Predict the major organic products. (If no reaction occurs, write *no reaction*.)

(a) 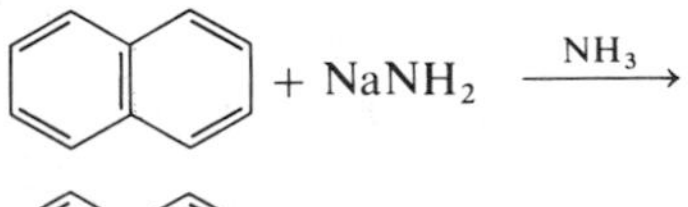 [naphthalene] + NaNH$_2$ $\xrightarrow{\text{NH}_3}$

(b) 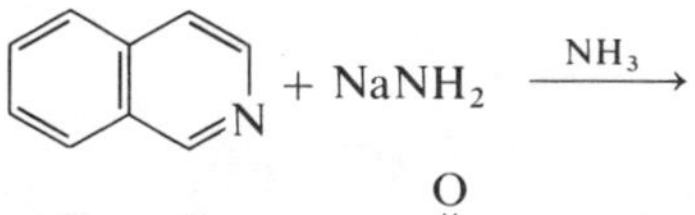 [isoquinoline] + NaNH$_2$ $\xrightarrow{\text{NH}_3}$

(c) 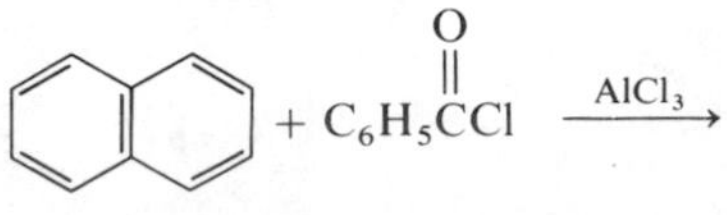 [naphthalene] + C$_6$H$_5$CCl (ketone, O double bond) $\xrightarrow{\text{AlCl}_3}$

(d) 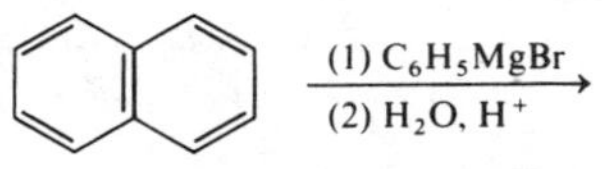 $\xrightarrow[\text{(2) H}_2\text{O, H}^+]{\text{(1) C}_6\text{H}_5\text{MgBr}}$

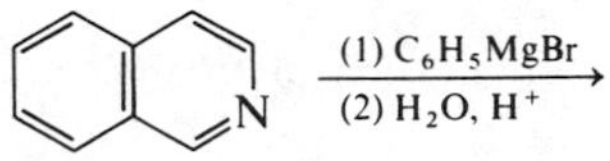

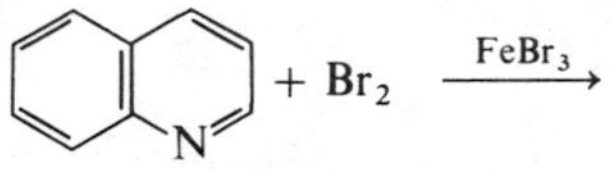

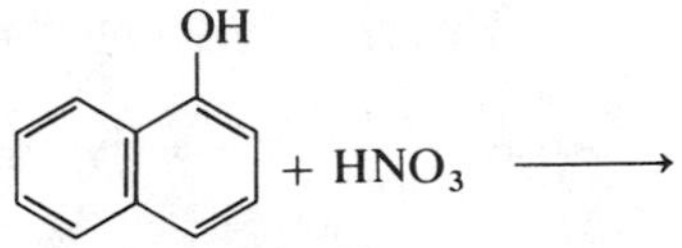

(e) $\xrightarrow[\text{(2) H}_2\text{O, H}^+]{\text{(1) C}_6\text{H}_5\text{MgBr}}$

(f) $+ \text{Br}_2 \xrightarrow{\text{FeBr}_3}$

(g) $+ \text{HNO}_3 \longrightarrow$

(h) $+ \text{HNO}_3 \xrightarrow{\text{H}_2\text{SO}_4}$

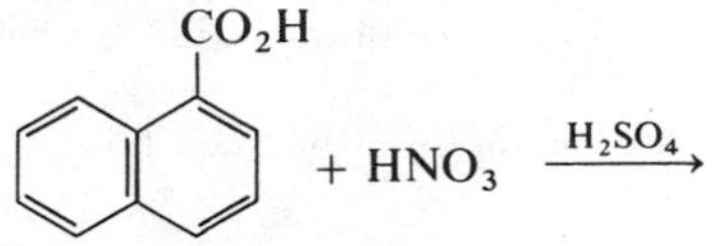

16.19 Complete the following equations:

(a) 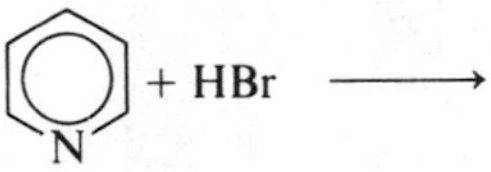 $+ \text{HBr} \longrightarrow$

(b) 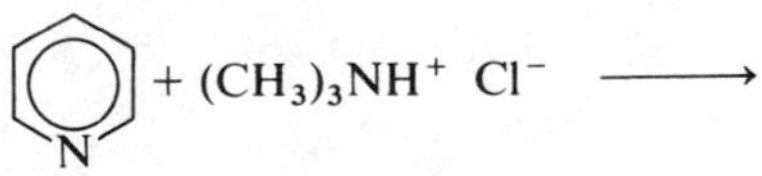 $+ (\text{CH}_3)_3\text{NH}^+ \ \text{Cl}^- \longrightarrow$

(c) 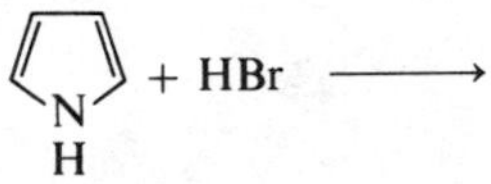 $+ \text{HBr} \longrightarrow$

(d) 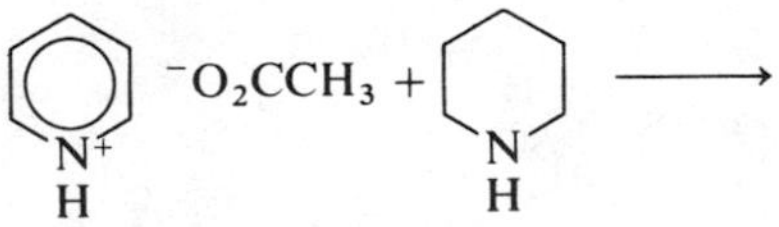 $^-\text{O}_2\text{CCH}_3 +$ $\longrightarrow$

(e) 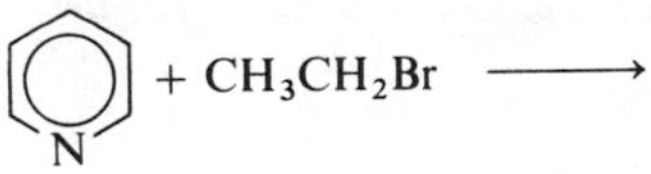 $+ \text{CH}_3\text{CH}_2\text{Br} \longrightarrow$

(f) 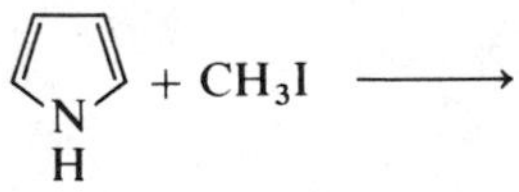 $+ \text{CH}_3\text{I} \longrightarrow$

(g) $-\text{CH}_2\text{CH}_2\text{C}_6\text{H}_5 \xrightarrow[\text{heat}]{\text{KMnO}_4}$

(h) $\xrightarrow[\text{(2) H}_2\text{O}]{\text{(1) NaNH}_2}$

(i) $+ \text{KOH} \longrightarrow$

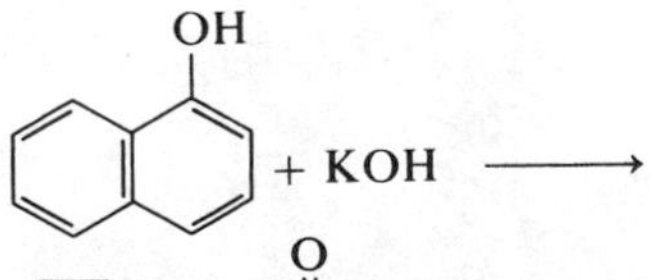

(j) 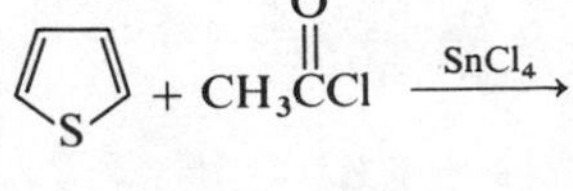 $+ \text{CH}_3\overset{\overset{\displaystyle O}{\|}}{\text{C}}\text{Cl} \xrightarrow{\text{SnCl}_4}$

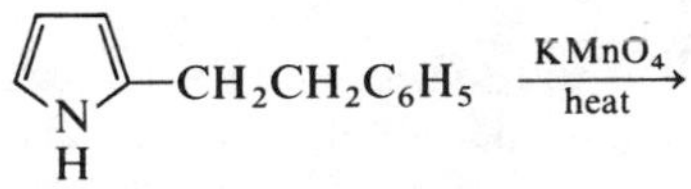

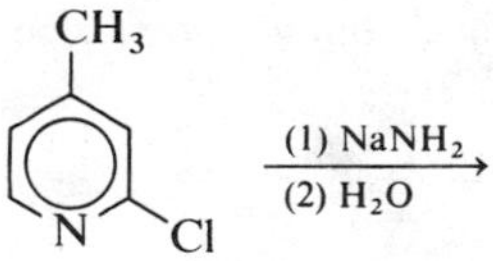

16.20 Which reaction would you expect to have the faster rate and why: (a) the reaction of pyridine and sodamide ($NaNH_2$) or (b) the reaction of 2-chloropyridine and sodamide?

16.21 Suggest a reason that the rate of aromatic bromination of furan-2-carboxylic acid (2-furoic acid) is less than that of furan.

16.22 Although pyrrole is not basic, thiazole is. Explain.

16.23 Pyrrole ($pK_a = \sim 15$) is a weak acid: it can lose a proton and form an anion. Suggest a reason for the stability of this anion compared to that of $(CH_3CH_2)_2N^-$.

16.24 List the following compounds in order of increasing rates of reaction (slowest first) toward acetic anhydride with $AlCl_3$ catalyst:

(a) 3-nitrofuran   (b) 2,5-dinitrofuran   (c) 3,4-dinitrofuran   (d) 3-methylfuran

16.25 Suggest a reaction sequence for preparation of the following compound from naphthalene and furan:

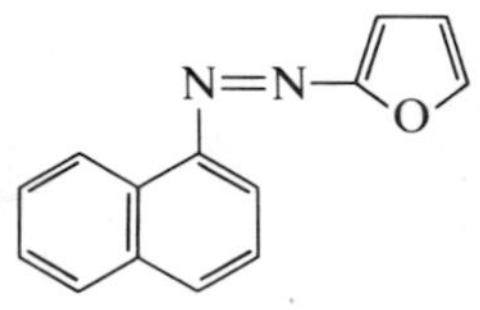

16.26 The structure of the toxic alkaloid *strychnine* follows. Tell which nitrogen is the more basic.

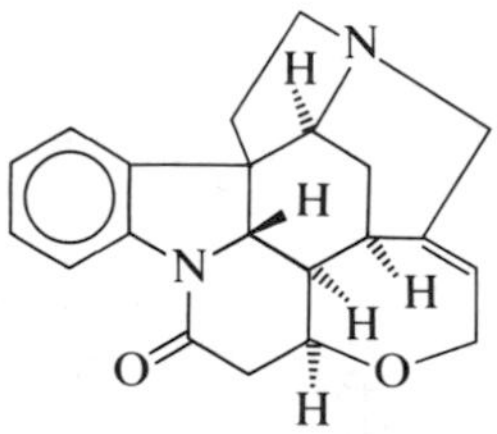

strychnine

16.27 Give the structures of the products:
(a) dextromethorphan + cold, dilute HCl $\longrightarrow$
(b) morphine + cold, dilute HCl $\longrightarrow$
(c) morphine + cold, dilute NaOH $\longrightarrow$
(d) codeine + cold, dilute NaOH $\longrightarrow$

16.28 Using an unsubstituted porphyrin ring system with a chelated magnesium ion, show four resonance structures (there are more) that illustrate four equivalent bonds to the Mg.

16.29 Why are guanine and cytosine paired in the DNA helix, but not adenine and cytosine? (Use structures to show the hydrogen bonding.)

16.30 Show a stepwise mechanism for each of the following reactions. (Show resonance structures of the intermediates.)

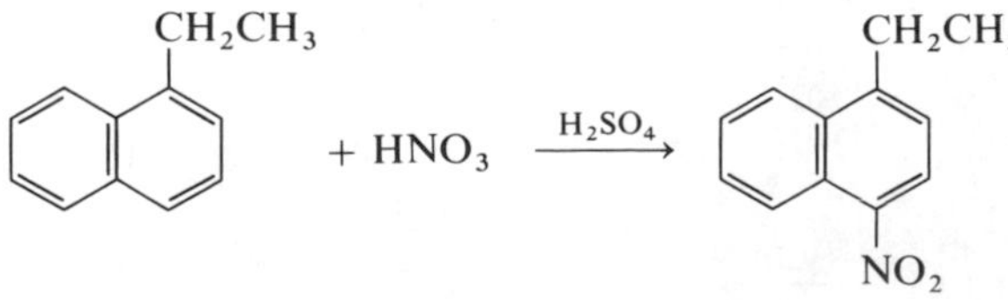

(b) 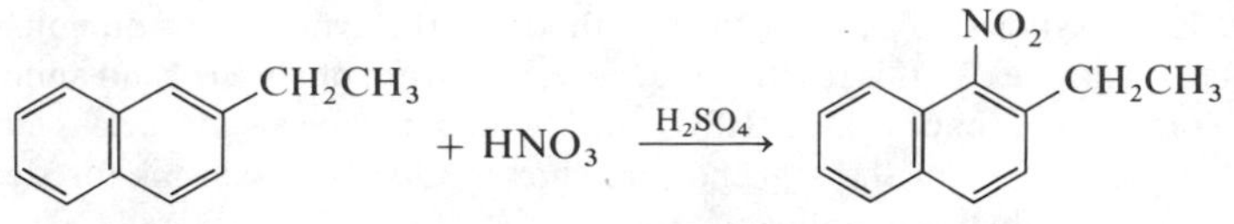 + HNO$_3$ $\xrightarrow{H_2SO_4}$

(c) 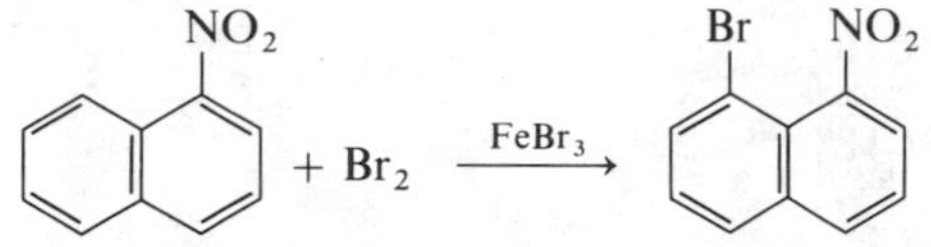 + Br$_2$ $\xrightarrow{FeBr_3}$

16.31 *Isoniazid* is used in the treatment of tuberculosis. Show how this compound may be prepared from 4-methylpyridine.

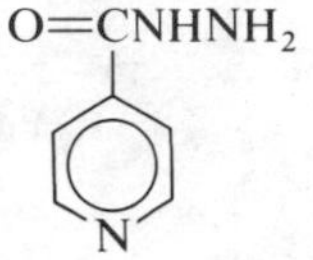

isoniazid

16.32 When pyrrole is treated with strong acid, a polymer called *pyrrole red* is formed. Suggest a mechanism for the first step in the polymerization.

16.33 What is the most likely position of substitution by Br$_2$ on the indole ring system? Explain your answer by showing the mechanism.

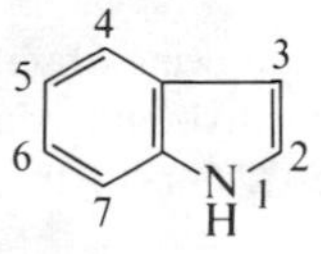

indole

16.34 Predict the position of electrophilic and nucleophilic substitution of pyrimidine. Would you expect pyrimidine to be more or less reactive than pyridine toward electrophilic substitution? Toward nucleophilic substitution?

16.35 *Imidazole* (Table 16.1) is found in proteins. The equilibrium between imidazole (pK_b = 7) and the imidazolium ion (imidazole + H$^+$) helps buffer proteins in biological systems. Use *p*-orbital pictures to explain why imidazole and the imidazolium ion are both aromatic.

16.36 Substituted naphthalene compounds may be prepared by Friedel–Crafts acylations of substituted benzenes with succinic anhydride. Tell what intermediate and final products would be obtained in the following sequence. [*Hints:* HF catalyzes aromatic acylation with a carboxylic acid, and Pd/heat causes catalytic dehydrogenation (loss of H$_2$) leading to aromatization of nonaromatic rings.]

toluene + succinic anhydride $\xrightarrow{AlCl_3}$ (a) $\xrightarrow{Zn(Hg)}$ (b) $\xrightarrow{HF}$ (c) $\xrightarrow[heat]{Pd}$ (d)

16.37 The **Skraup synthesis** is the classical method for the synthesis of quinoline and substituted quinolines. In this reaction sequence, a mixture of glycerol and aniline is heated in the presence of concentrated H_2SO_4 and a mild oxidizing agent, such as nitrobenzene. The principal steps in the sequence are shown. Give mechanisms for steps 1 and 2 leading to 1,2-dihydroquinoline.

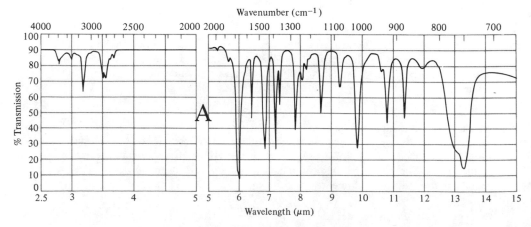

(1)
$$
\begin{array}{c}
CH_2OH \\
| \\
CHOH \\
| \\
CH_2OH
\end{array}
\xrightarrow[\text{heat}]{H_2SO_4}
\begin{array}{c}
CHO \\
| \\
CH \\
\| \\
CH_2
\end{array}
+ \ 2\ H_2O
$$

glycerol   *not isolated*

(2) aniline $+ \ \begin{array}{c} CHO \\ | \\ CH \\ \| \\ CH_2 \end{array} \xrightarrow{H^+}$ 1,2-dihydroquinoline $+ \ 3\ H_2O$

aniline   *not isolated*

(3) 3 (quinoline structure) $+$ nitrobenzene—NO_2 $\xrightarrow{H^+}$ 3 quinoline $+$ —$NH_2 + 2\ H_2O$

quinoline
85%

16.38 Predict the product of the reaction of aniline and 3-buten-2-one in the presence of a Lewis-acid catalyst.

16.39 How would you explain the following observations? Aromatic nitration of 2-methylnaphthalene yields 75% 2-methyl-1-nitronaphthalene, but aromatic sulfonation of 2-methylnaphthalene yields 80% 6-methylnaphthalene-2-sulfonic acid.

16.40 Acid hydrolysis of the carbohydrates in oat hulls or corncobs gives Compound A, $C_5H_4O_2$, in almost 100% yield. Catalytic hydrogenation of A with $CuO—Cr_2O_3$ catalyst at 175° and 100 atm gives Compound B, $C_5H_6O_2$. The infrared and nmr spectra of A and B are shown in Figure 16.12. What are the structures of A and B?

Figure 16.12. Spectra for Problem 16.40.

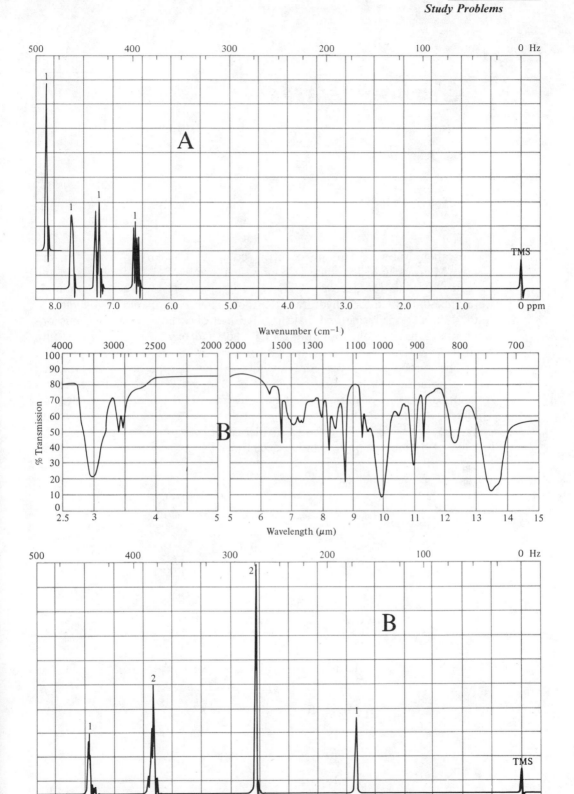

Figure 16.12 (continued). Spectra for Problem 16.40.

Chapter 17

Carbohydrates

Carbohydrates are naturally occurring compounds of carbon, hydrogen, and oxygen. Many carbohydrates have the empirical formula CH_2O; for example, the molecular formula for glucose is $C_6H_{12}O_6$ (six times CH_2O). These compounds were once thought to be "hydrates of carbon," hence the name carbohydrates. In the 1880's, it was recognized that the "hydrates of carbon" idea was a misconception and that carbohydrates are actually polyhydroxy aldehydes and ketones or their derivatives.

The carbohydrates vary dramatically in their properties. For example, *sucrose* (table sugar) and *cotton* are both carbohydrates. One of the principal differences between various types of carbohydrates is the size of the molecules. The **monosaccharides** (often called *simple sugars*) are the simplest carbohydrate units; they cannot be hydrolyzed to smaller carbohydrate molecules. Table 17.1 lists five of the most important monosaccharides.

Table 17.1.   Some Important Monosaccharides

CHO	CH$_2$OH	CHO
HCOH	C=O	HCOH
HOCH	HOCH	HOCH
HCOH	HCOH	HOCH
HCOH	HCOH	HCOH
CH$_2$OH	CH$_2$OH	CH$_2$OH
D-glucose	D-fructose	D-galactose

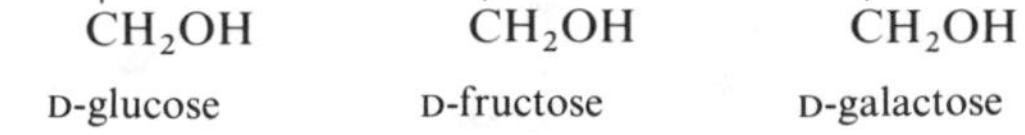

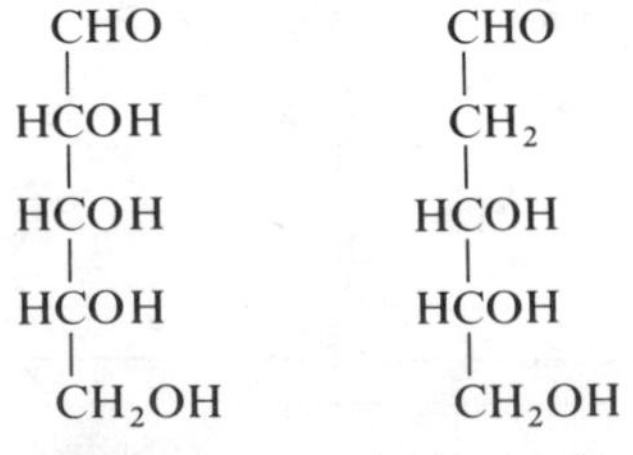

CHO	CHO
HCOH	CH$_2$
HCOH	HCOH
HCOH	HCOH
CH$_2$OH	CH$_2$OH
D-ribose	2-deoxy-D-ribose

Monosaccharides can be joined together into dimers, trimers, and, ultimately, polymers. A carbohydrate that contains molecules composed of two monosaccharide units is called a **disaccharide**. Sucrose is a disaccharide that can be hydrolyzed to one unit of glucose plus one unit of fructose. The monosaccharides and disaccharides are soluble in water and are generally sweet-tasting.

$$1 \text{ sucrose} \xrightarrow[\text{heat}]{H_2O, H^+} 1 \text{ glucose} + 1 \text{ fructose}$$
a disaccharide

Carbohydrates composed of two to eight units of monosaccharide are referred to as **oligosaccharides** (Greek *oligo-*, "a few"). If more than eight units of monosaccharide result from hydrolysis, the carbohydrate is a **polysaccharide**. Examples of polysaccharides are *starch*, found in flour and cornstarch, and *cellulose*, a fibrous constituent of plants and the principal component of cotton.

$$\text{starch or cellulose} \xrightarrow[\text{heat}]{H_2O, H^+} \text{many units of glucose}$$
polysaccharides

In this chapter, we will consider first the monosaccharides and the conventions used by carbohydrate chemists. Then we will discuss some disaccharides, and finally, some polysaccharides.

Section 17.1

Some Common Monosaccharides

Glucose, the most important of the monosaccharides, is sometimes called *blood sugar* (because it is found in the blood), *grape sugar* (because it is found in grapes), or *dextrose* (because it is dextrorotatory). Mammals can convert sucrose, lactose (milk sugar), maltose, and starch to glucose, which is then used by the organism for energy or stored as *glycogen* (a polysaccharide). When the organism needs energy, the glycogen is again converted to glucose. Excess carbohydrates can be converted to fat; therefore a person can become obese on a fat-free diet. Carbohydrates can also be converted to steroids (such as cholesterol) and, to a limited extent, to protein. (A source of nitrogen is also needed in protein synthesis.) Conversely, an organism can convert proteins and fats to carbohydrates.

fats

$$CO_2 + H_2O + \text{energy} \longleftarrow \boxed{\text{glucose}} \rightleftharpoons \overset{\overset{\textstyle O}{\|}}{CH_3C-} \rightleftharpoons \text{(proteins)}$$

acetyl groups
in acetylcoenzyme A

cholesterol
and other steroids

Fructose, also called *levulose* because it is levorotatory, is the sweetest-tasting of all the sugars. It occurs in fruit and honey, as well as in sucrose. **Galactose** is found, bonded to glucose, in the disaccharide lactose. **Ribose** and **deoxyribose** form part of the polymeric backbones of nucleic acids. The prefix *deoxy*-means "minus an oxygen"; the structures of ribose and deoxyribose (Table 17.1) are the same except that deoxyribose lacks an oxygen at carbon 2.

Section 17.2

Classification of the Monosaccharides

The suffix **-ose** is used in systematic carbohydrate nomenclature to designate a **reducing sugar**, a sugar that contains an aldehyde group or an α-hydroxyketone grouping. Reducing sugars will be discussed in Section 17.6. Many of the oligo-saccharides and polysaccharides that are not reducing sugars have trivial names ending in *-ose* (for example, sucrose and cellulose). In this chapter, we will use both systematic and trivial nomenclature for carbohydrates; our emphasis will be on those names that are in common usage.

Monosaccharides that contain aldehyde groups are referred to as **aldoses** (*ald*ehyde plus *-ose*). Glucose, galactose, ribose, and deoxyribose are all aldoses. Monosaccharides, such as fructose, with ketone groups are called **ketoses** (*ket*one plus *-ose*).

The number of carbon atoms in a monosaccharide (usually three to seven) may be designated by tri-, tetr-, etc. For example, a **triose** is a three-carbon mono-saccharide, while a **hexose** is a six-carbon monosaccharide. Glucose is an example of a hexose. These terms may be combined. Glucose is an **aldohexose** (six-carbon aldose), while ribose is an **aldopentose** (five-carbon aldose). Ketoses are often given the ending **-ulose**. Fructose is an example of a **hexulose** (six-carbon ketose).

$$
\begin{array}{cc}
 & CH_2OH \\
 & | \\
CHO & C{=}O \\
| & | \\
CH_2 & HOCH \\
| & | \\
HCOH & HCOH \\
| & | \\
HCOH & HCOH \\
| & | \\
CH_2OH & CH_2OH \\
\text{2-deoxyribose} & \text{fructose} \\
\textit{an aldopentose} & \textit{a hexulose}
\end{array}
$$

STUDY PROBLEM

17.1 Classify each of the following monosaccharides by the preceding system:

$$
\begin{array}{lll}
 & & CH_2OH \\
 & & | \\
 & CHO & C{=}O \\
 & | & | \\
\text{(a)} \quad HCOH & \text{(b)} \quad HCOH & \text{(c)} \quad \text{galactose (Table 17.1)} \\
 & | & | \\
 & HCOH & HCOH \\
 & | & | \\
 & CH_2OH & CH_2OH \\
 & \text{erythrose} & \text{ribulose}
\end{array}
$$

Section 17.3

Configurations of the Monosaccharides

A.   *Fischer Projections*

The monosaccharides all have one or more chiral carbon atoms. Glyceraldehyde (the simplest sugar) has one chiral carbon, while glucose has four. In the late 1800's, Emil Fischer, sometimes called "the father of carbohydrate chemistry," introduced projectional formulas for representing the configurations around the chiral carbons in carbohydrates. Examples of the type of Fischer projection used today follow:

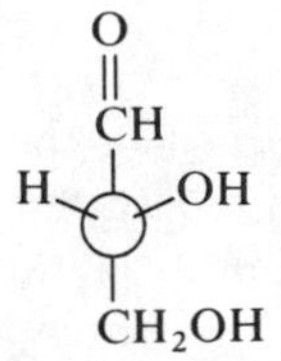

(*R*)-glyceraldehyde
one chiral carbon

becomes

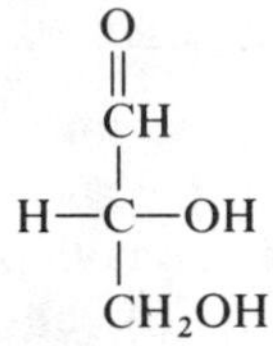

Fischer projection

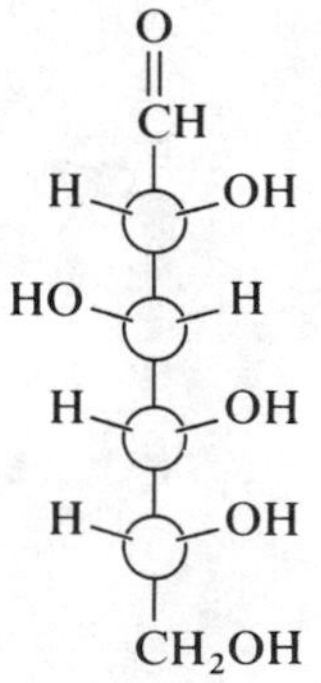

glucose
four chiral carbons

becomes

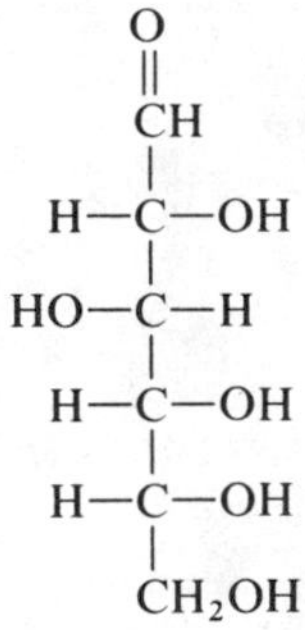

Fischer projection

Note that these Fischer projections are practically identical to the ball-and-stick formulas we have used previously to represent chiral molecules. By convention, the carbonyl group is placed at or near the top in the Fischer projection; thus, the top carbon atom is carbon 1. The configuration at each chiral carbon is indicated by the projection of the attached groups on each carbon to the right or to the left. Groups to the right and left represent groups toward the viewer in a stretched-out molecule, while groups attached by vertical bonds represent groups away from the viewer. (These projections are evident in the ball-and-stick formulas.)

away from viewer

toward viewer

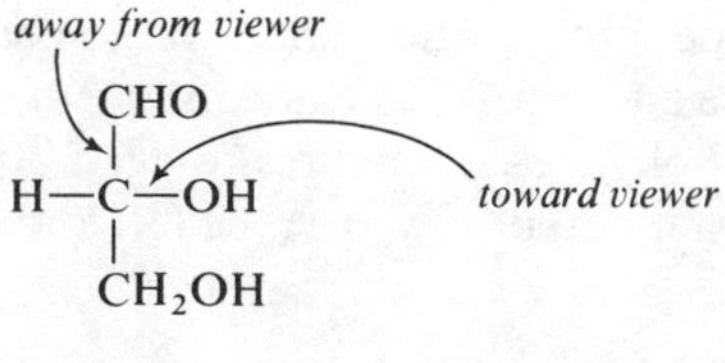

A Fischer projection may be rotated 180° on paper, but may not be rotated only 90° or flipped over. (Either of these last two operations would take the formula out of the Fischer projection.)

$$
\begin{array}{c}
\text{CHO} \\
|\\
\text{H}-\text{C}-\text{OH} \\
|\\
\text{CH}_2\text{OH}
\end{array}
\quad \xrightarrow{\text{rotate } 180°} \quad
\begin{array}{c}
\text{CH}_2\text{OH} \\
|\\
\text{HO}-\text{C}-\text{H} \\
|\\
\text{CHO}
\end{array}
$$

(R)-glyceraldehyde   (R)-glyceraldehyde
*same as left-hand
structure*

B. The D and L System

In the late 19th century, it was noted that each of the naturally occurring monosaccharides has the same configuration at the last chiral carbon as that of (+)-glyceraldehyde. Today, we call that configuration the (R)-configuration; however, the (R) and (S) conventions for denoting configuration had not been developed at that time. Instead, chemists devised the D and L system for designating configuration around the last chiral carbon. A carbohydrate is a member of the **D-series** if the hydroxyl group on the chiral carbon farthest from carbon 1 is *on the right* in the Fischer projection. Almost all naturally occurring carbohydrates are members of the D-series.

$$
\begin{array}{ccc}
& \text{CHO} & \text{CHO} \\
& | & | \\
& \text{HOCH} & \text{HCOH} \\
\text{CHO} & | & | \\
| & \text{HOCH} & \text{HCOH} \\
\text{HC(OH)} & | & | \\
| & \text{HC(OH)} & \text{HC(OH)} \\
\text{CH}_2\text{OH} & | & | \\
& \text{CH}_2\text{OH} & \text{CH}_2\text{OH}
\end{array}
$$

D-(+)-glyceraldehyde   D-lyxose   D-ribose

If that same OH is projected to the *left*, then the compound is a member of the **L-series**.

$$
\begin{array}{cc}
\text{CHO} & \text{CHO} \\
| & | \\
\text{HCOH} & \text{HOCH} \\
| & | \\
\text{HCOH} & \text{HOCH} \\
| & | \\
\text{(HO)CH} & \text{(HO)CH} \\
| & | \\
\text{CH}_2\text{OH} & \text{CH}_2\text{OH}
\end{array}
$$

L-lyxose   L-ribose

The limitations of the D and L system should be apparent. The D and L system does not specify the configurations at the other chiral carbons: for example, carbons 2 and 3 in lyxose and ribose. The advantage of the D and L system is that it allows us to relate carbohydrate structures to each other quickly; the relationship is not always readily apparent if we use the (R) and (S) system.

STUDY PROBLEM

17.2 The following structures are shown in Fischer projections. Assign each chiral carbon atom an (R) or (S) designation and tell whether each compound is D or L.

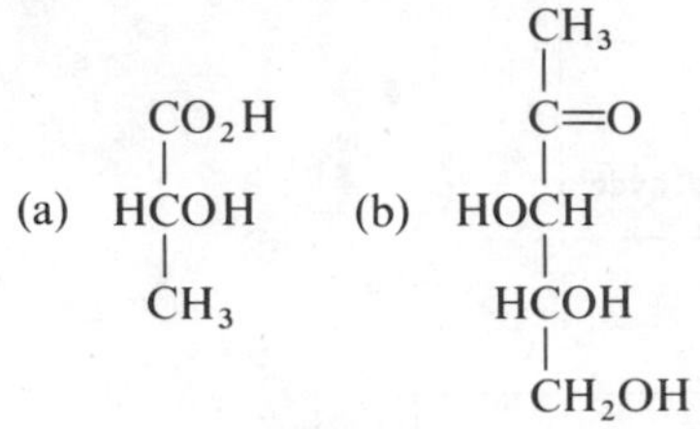

(a)
$$
\begin{array}{c}
\text{CO}_2\text{H} \\
| \\
\text{HCOH} \\
| \\
\text{CH}_3
\end{array}
$$

(b)
$$
\begin{array}{c}
\text{CH}_3 \\
| \\
\text{C}{=}\text{O} \\
| \\
\text{HOCH} \\
| \\
\text{HCOH} \\
| \\
\text{CH}_2\text{OH}
\end{array}
$$

C. *Relating Configurations*

In Section 4.8, we mentioned that early chemists could not determine the absolute configurations of chiral centers. Instead, configurations relative to that of (+)-glyceraldehyde were determined. How are other compounds related to glyceraldehyde? One example of determining a relative configuration follows. If the aldehyde group of D-glyceraldehyde is oxidized to a carboxylic acid, the product, glyceric acid, necessarily has the same configuration around the chiral carbon as that in D-glyceraldehyde. The product, even though levorotatory, is still a member of the D-series.

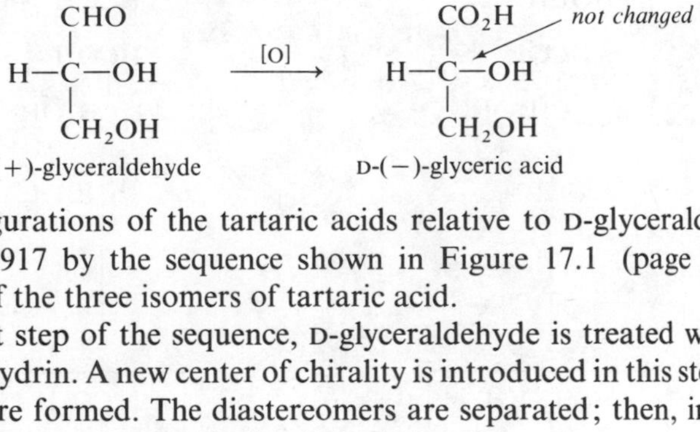

$$
\begin{array}{c}
\text{CHO} \\
| \\
\text{H}{-}\text{C}{-}\text{OH} \\
| \\
\text{CH}_2\text{OH}
\end{array}
\quad \xrightarrow{\ [\text{O}]\ } \quad
\begin{array}{c}
\text{CO}_2\text{H} \quad \text{\textit{not changed}} \\
| \\
\text{H}{-}\text{C}{-}\text{OH} \\
| \\
\text{CH}_2\text{OH}
\end{array}
$$

D-(+)-glyceraldehyde   D-(−)-glyceric acid

The configurations of the tartaric acids relative to D-glyceraldehyde were established in 1917 by the sequence shown in Figure 17.1 (page 794), which produced two of the three isomers of tartaric acid.

In the first step of the sequence, D-glyceraldehyde is treated with HCN to yield the cyanohydrin. A new center of chirality is introduced in this step; and both diastereomers are formed. The diastereomers are separated; then, in the second step, each diastereomeric cyanohydrin is hydrolyzed.

In the third step, the terminal CH_2OH group is oxidized to yield two tartaric acids. Carbon 3 of each of these tartaric acids has the same configuration as carbon 2 of D-glyceraldehyde because the series of reactions did not affect the configuration around that carbon. The configurations around carbon 2 in the tartaric acids are different, however. One of the tartaric acids produced does not rotate plane-polarized light. This is the *meso* isomer, the one with the internal plane of symmetry. The other diastereomer rotates plane-polarized light to the left; it must have the second structure.

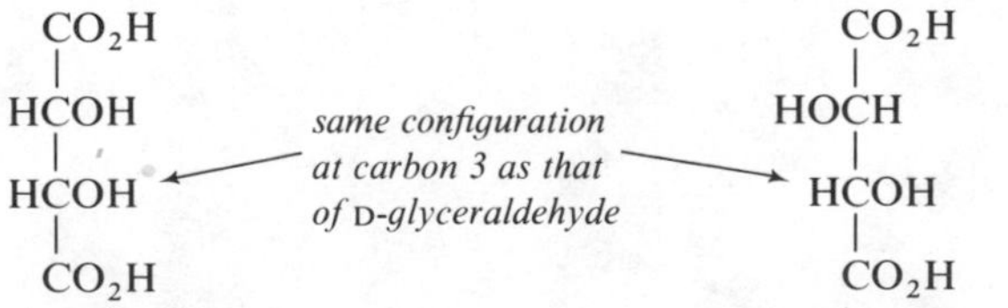

$$
\begin{array}{c}
\text{CO}_2\text{H} \\
| \\
\text{HCOH} \\
| \\
\text{HCOH} \\
| \\
\text{CO}_2\text{H}
\end{array}
\quad
\underset{\substack{\textit{same configuration} \\ \textit{at carbon 3 as that} \\ \textit{of D-glyceraldehyde}}}{\longleftarrow \quad \longrightarrow}
\quad
\begin{array}{c}
\text{CO}_2\text{H} \\
| \\
\text{HOCH} \\
| \\
\text{HCOH} \\
| \\
\text{CO}_2\text{H}
\end{array}
$$

meso-tartaric acid   D-(−)-tartaric acid

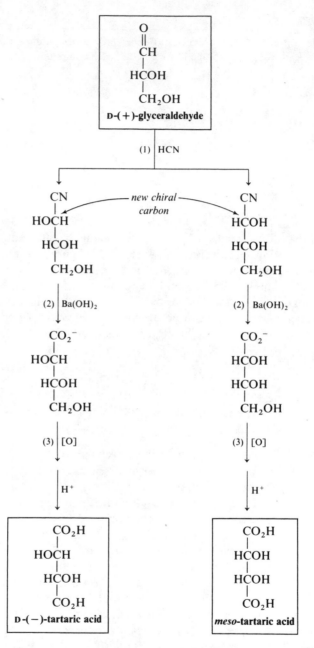

Figure 17.1.   Determining the relative configurations of tartaric acids.

STUDY PROBLEM

17.3 Starting with L-(−)-glyceraldehyde, what tartaric acid(s) would be produced in the preceding sequence?

D. *Configurations of the Aldohexoses*

Glucose has six carbon atoms. Four of the six carbons in glucose are chiral (carbons 2, 3, 4, and 5). Because the terminal carbons of the glucose molecule have different functionality, there can be no internal plane of symmetry; therefore, this compound has 2^4, or sixteen, stereoisomers. Only half of these stereoisomers belong to the D-series, and of these, only D-glucose, D-galactose, and D-mannose are found in nature in any quantity. Interest is rising in the other D-aldohexoses,

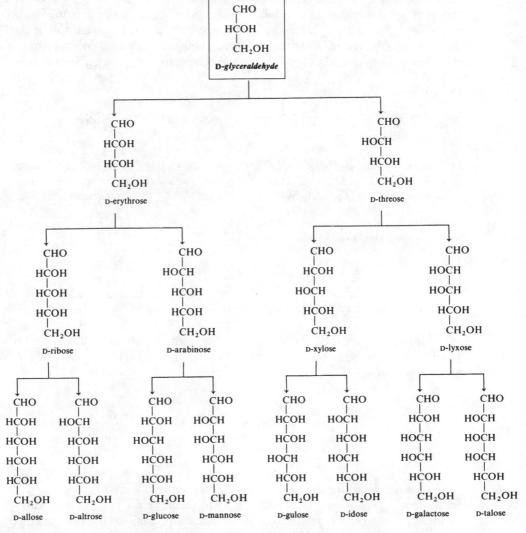

Figure 17.2. The D-aldoses.

however, because these have been isolated from the hydrolysis of naturally occurring antibiotics.

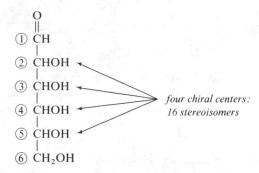

The Fischer projections of all the D-aldoses, from D-glyceraldehyde through the D-aldohexoses, are shown in Figure 17.2. Going from the triose, D-glyceraldehyde, to the tetroses, one carbon is added to the "top" of the molecule in the Fischer projection. The addition of one more carbon creates a new chiral carbon in each step down in the figure. Therefore, D-glyceraldehyde leads to a pair of tetroses, each tetrose leads to a pair of pentoses, and each pentose leads to a pair of hexoses.

STUDY PROBLEMS

17.4 How many chiral carbon atoms does each of the following aldoses have?

(a) D-talose   (b) L-allose   (c) D-arabinose

17.5 There are eight D-aldohexoses and also eight L-aldohexoses. Each of the eight L-stereoisomers is an enantiomer of one of the D-stereoisomers and is named accordingly. Write the Fischer projections of   (a) L-glucose,   and   (b) L-mannose.

17.6 What is the name of the aldohexose in which only the OH at carbon 5 has the opposite configuration from that of D-glucose?

Section 17.4

Cyclization of the Monosaccharides

Glucose has an aldehyde group at carbon 1 and hydroxyl groups at carbons 4 and 5 (as well as at carbons 2, 3, and 6). A general reaction of alcohols and aldehydes is that of *hemiacetal formation* (see Section 11.8).

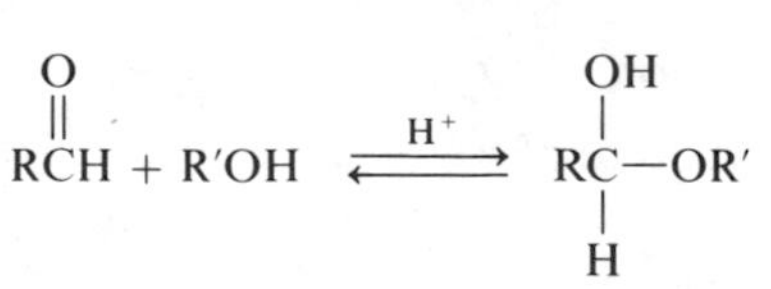

$$\underset{\text{RCH}}{\overset{\text{O}}{\overset{\|}{}}} + \text{R'OH} \xrightleftharpoons{\text{H}^+} \underset{\underset{\text{H}}{|}}{\overset{\overset{\text{OH}}{|}}{\text{RC}-\text{OR'}}}$$

a hemiacetal

In water solution, glucose can undergo an intramolecular reaction to yield *cyclic hemiacetals.* Either five-membered ring hemiacetals (using the hydroxyl group at carbon 4) or six-membered ring hemiacetals (using the hydroxyl group at carbon 5) can be formed.

CHO
|
HCOH
|
carbon 4   HOCH
|
HCOH
|
HCOH
|
CH₂OH

D-glucose

⇌

HCOH
|
HCOH   O
|
HOCH
|
HC—
|
HCOH
|
CH₂OH

+

HOCH
|
HCOH   O
|
HOCH
|
HC—
|
HCOH
|
CH₂OH

Fischer projections of the hemiacetal five-membered rings

CHO
|
HCOH
|
HOCH
|
carbon 5   HCOH
|
HCOH
|
CH₂OH

D-glucose

⇌

HCOH
|
HCOH
|
HOCH   O
|
HCOH
|
HC—
|
CH₂OH

+

HOCH
|
HCOH
|
HOCH   O
|
HCOH
|
HC—
|
CH₂OH

Fischer projections of the hemiacetal six-membered rings

In the Fischer projections for the cyclic hemiacetals, note that carbon 1 (the aldehyde carbon), which is not chiral in the open-chain structure, becomes chiral in the cyclization. Therefore, a pair of diastereomers results from the cyclization.

Because all the hemiacetal structures are in equilibrium with the aldehyde in water solution, they are also in equilibrium with each other.

5-membered cyclic hemiacetal   ⇌   glucose   ⇌   6-membered cyclic hemiacetal

(*two diastereomers*)   (open-chain)   (*two diastereomers*)

STUDY PROBLEM

17.7   Write equations for the cyclization of 2-deoxy-D-ribose. Use Fischer projections, and show the formation of both the five- and six-membered cyclic hemiacetals.

A.   Furanose and Pyranose Rings

A monosaccharide in the form of a five-membered ring hemiacetal is called a **furanose**. *Furan-* is from the name of the five-membered oxygen heterocycle *furan*. Similarly, the six-membered ring form is called a **pyranose** after *pyran*. The terms furanose and pyranose are often combined with the name of the mono-saccharide—for example, D-**glucopyranose** for the six-membered ring of D-glucose, or D-**fructofuranose** for the five-membered ring of fructose.

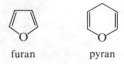

furan   pyran

Of the two ring systems for glucose, the six-membered cyclic hemiacetal, or glucopyranose, is favored; we will emphasize this ring size in our discussion. Part of the reason that glucose preferentially forms the six-membered ring in solution is that the bond angles and staggering of attached groups are favorable in the chair form of this ring. Even though the pyranose ring of a monosaccharide may predominate in equilibrium in water, it may be the furanose ring that is incorporated enzymatically into natural products. For example, in ribonucleic acids, ribose is found as a furanose, and not as a pyranose.

B.   Anomers

To yield a pyranose, the hydroxyl group at carbon 5 of glucose attacks the aldehyde carbon, carbon 1. A hemiacetal group is formed. Two of the most important consequences of this cyclization reaction are that a new chiral center is formed at carbon 1, and that a pair of diastereomers results. These diastereomers, monosaccharides that differ only in the configuration at carbon 1, are called **anomers** of each other. The carbonyl carbon in any monosaccharide is the **anomeric carbon**. This is the carbon that becomes chiral in the cyclization reaction.

In the Fischer projection for one anomer of D-glucopyranose, the hydroxyl group at carbon 1 is projected to the *left*; this anomer is called β-D-**glucopyranose**, or simply β-D-**glucose**. The anomer in which the hydroxyl group at carbon 1 is projected to the right is called α-D-**glucopyranose**, or α-D-**glucose**.

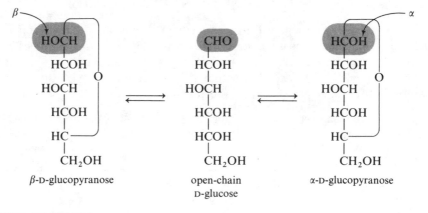

β-D-glucopyranose   open-chain   α-D-glucopyranose
                           D-glucose

17.8   Write Fischer projections for the two D-ribofuranoses and label each as α or β.

C.   Haworth and Conformational Formulas

In solution, only about 0.02% of glucose exists in the open-chain aldehyde form; the rest exists as cyclic hemiacetals. While the Fischer projection is adequate to show the configurations of the chiral centers of a carbohydrate in its open-chain form, it is a rather poor representation of the actual cyclic structures of a carbohydrate in solution. To better represent the cyclic structures of the sugars, **Haworth perspective formulas** were developed. With a Haworth formula, it is clear that the hydroxyl groups (or other groups) at the chiral centers are actually *cis* and *trans* to one another on the ring. Also, the Haworth formula eliminates the artificial, curved bonds to the ring oxygen that are necessary in a Fischer projection.

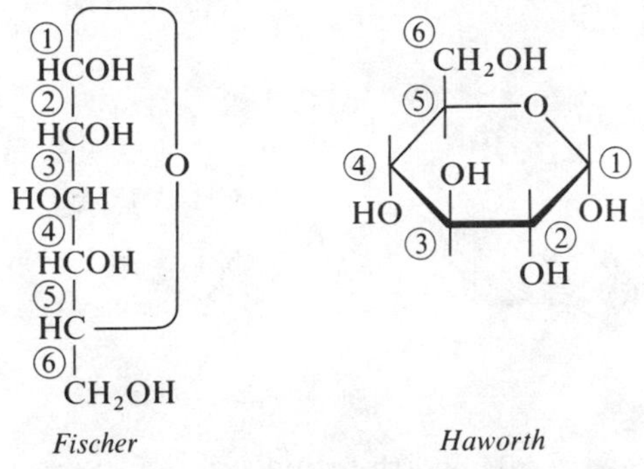

Fischer   *Haworth*

α-D-glucopyranose

In a Haworth formula, the terminal CH_2OH is *up* in the D-series, but *down* in the L-series.

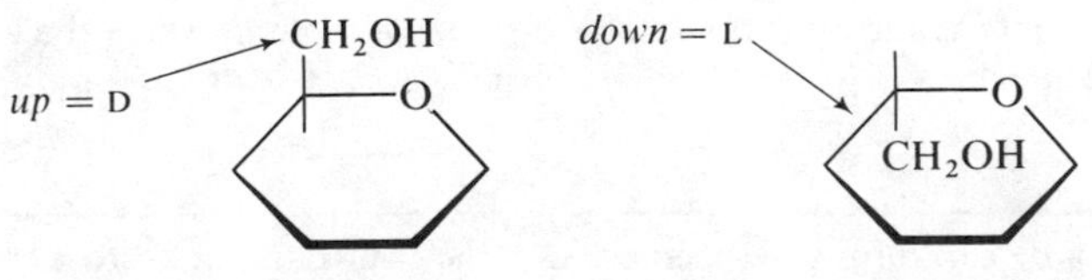

In a Haworth formula of a D-sugar, the structure in which the anomeric OH is projected *down* (*trans* to the terminal CH_2OH) is the α-anomer; the structure in which the anomeric OH is projected *up* is the β-anomer.

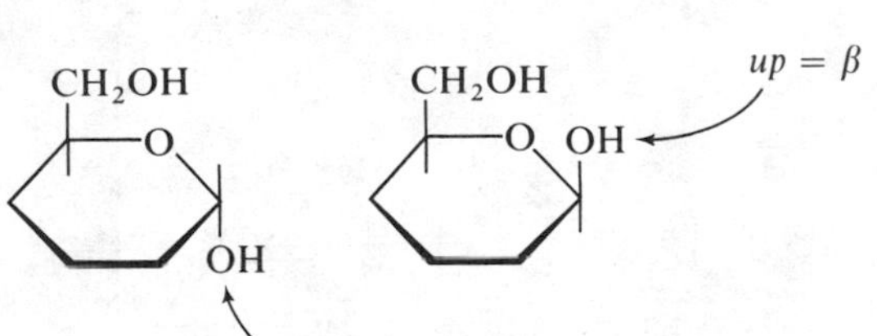

Note that *any group that is to the right in the Fischer projection is down in the Haworth projection*. Of course, any group that is to the *left* in the Fischer projection is *up* in the Haworth formula.

The Haworth formula is not an entirely correct representation of a pyranose ring (although it is fairly correct for the more planar furanose ring). A pyranose, like cyclohexane, exists primarily in the chair form, as the following conformational formulas show. In this chapter, we will use both Haworth formulas and conformational formulas.

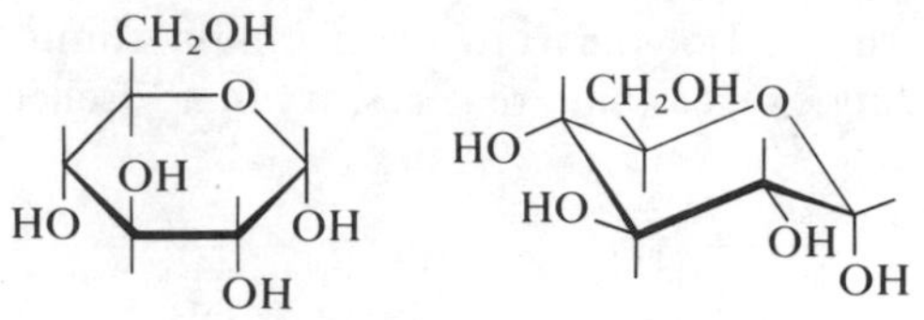

α-D-glucopyranose

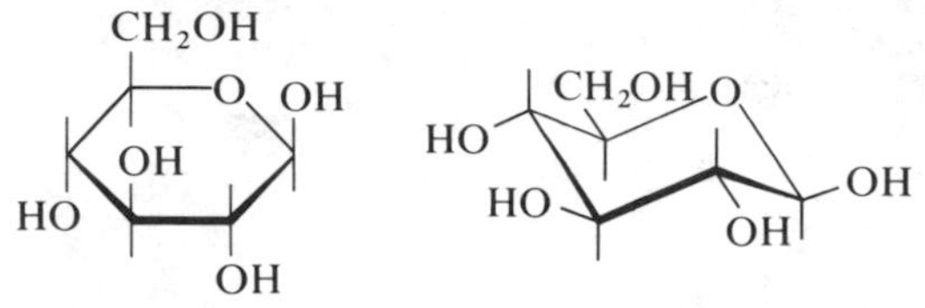

β-D-glucopyranose

If an OH is down in a Haworth formula, it is also down (below the plane of the ring) in the conformational formula. Similarly, if an OH is up in the Haworth formula, it is also up in the conformational formula. As for any substituted six-membered ring, the ring assumes the conformation in which the majority of the groups are equatorial.

STUDY PROBLEM

17.9 Draw a conformational formula of α-D-glucopyranose in which the CH_2OH is in an axial position.

Sample Problem

Although fructose can form a six-membered cyclic hemiketal, in sucrose it is found in the furanose form. Give Fischer projections and Haworth formulas for α- and β-D-fructofuranose. (*Note:* The CH_2OH group on the keto carbon of a sugar is treated in the formula just like the H on an aldehyde carbon.)

Solution:

Fischer:

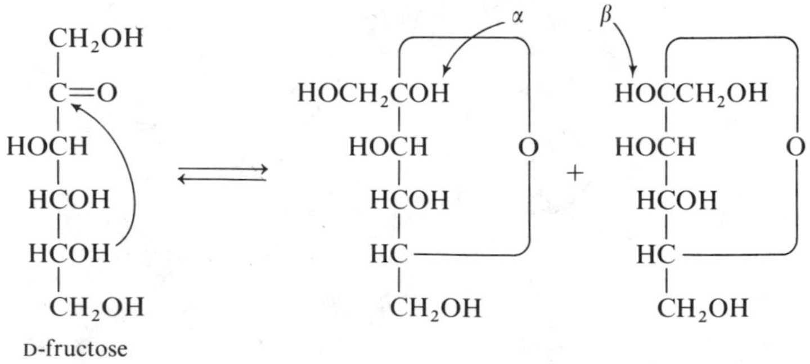

D-fructose

Haworth:

D-fructose ⇌

up = β

down = α

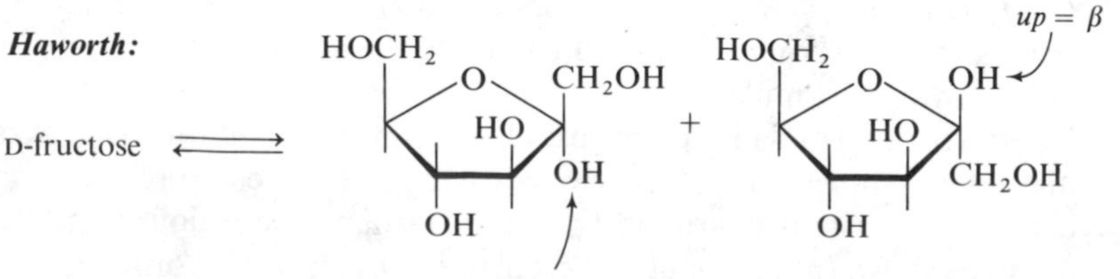

Give the Haworth formula and the Fischer projection for 2-deoxy-β-D-ribofuranose.

Solution:

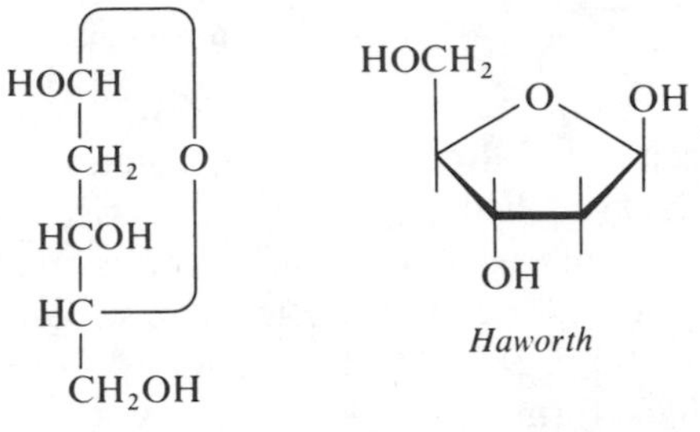

Fischer

Haworth

STUDY PROBLEM

17.10 Give the Fischer, Haworth, and conformational formulas for the anomers of D-galacto-pyranose.

D. Mutarotation

Pure glucose exists in two crystalline forms: α-D-glucose and β-D-glucose. Pure α-D-glucose has a melting point of 146°C. The specific rotation of a freshly prepared solution is $+112°$. Pure β-D-glucose has a melting point of 150°C and a specific rotation of $+18.7°$. The specific rotation of a solution of either α- or β-D-glucose changes slowly until it reaches an equilibrium value of $+52.6°$. This slow spontaneous change in optical rotation was first observed in 1846 and is called **mutarotation**.

Mutarotation occurs because, in solution, either α- or β-D-glucose undergoes a slow equilibration with the open-chain form and with the other anomer. Regardless of which anomer is dissolved, the result is an equilibrium mixture of 64% β-D-glucose, 36% α-D-glucose, and 0.02% of the aldehyde form of D-glucose. The final specific rotation is that of the equilibrium mixture.

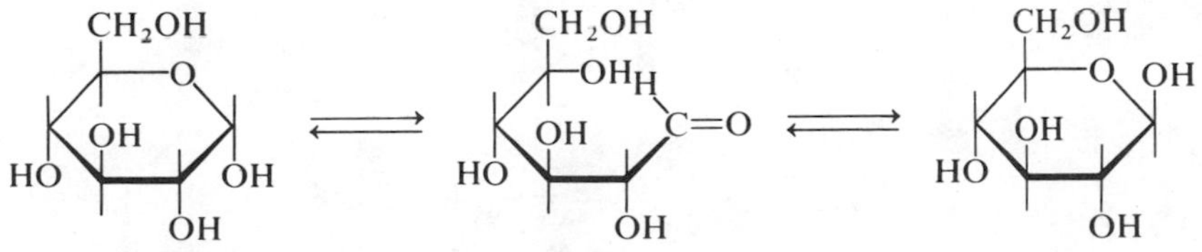

α-D-glucose	D-glucose	β-D-glucose
36%	0.02%	64%

Note that the equilibrium mixture of the anomers of D-glucose contains a greater percentage of the β-anomer than of the α-anomer. The reason is that the β-anomer is the more stable of the two. From our discussion of conformational analysis in Chapter 4, this is the expected result. The hydroxyl group at carbon 1 is *equatorial* in the β-anomer, but *axial* in the α-anomer.

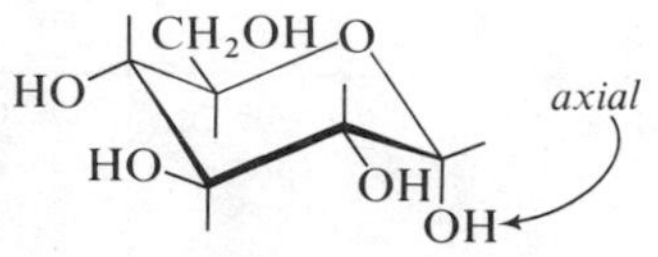

α-D-glucose 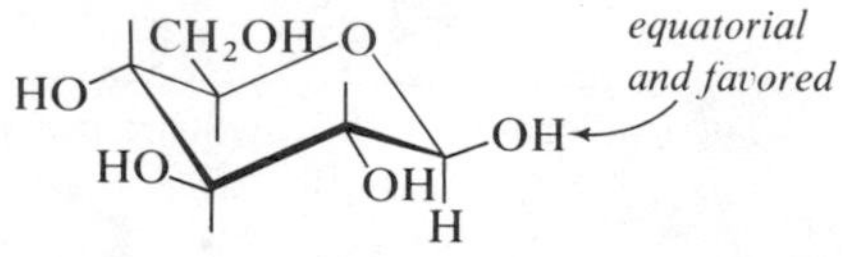   β-D-glucose

Other monosaccharides also exhibit mutarotation. In water solution, the other aldoses (if they have a 5-hydroxyl group) also exist primarily in the pyranose forms. However, the percentages of the various species involved in the equilibrium may vary. For example, the equilibrium mixture of D-ribose in water is 56% β-pyranose, 20% α-pyranose, 18% β-furanose, and 6% α-furanose (plus a trace of the open-chain, aldehyde form).

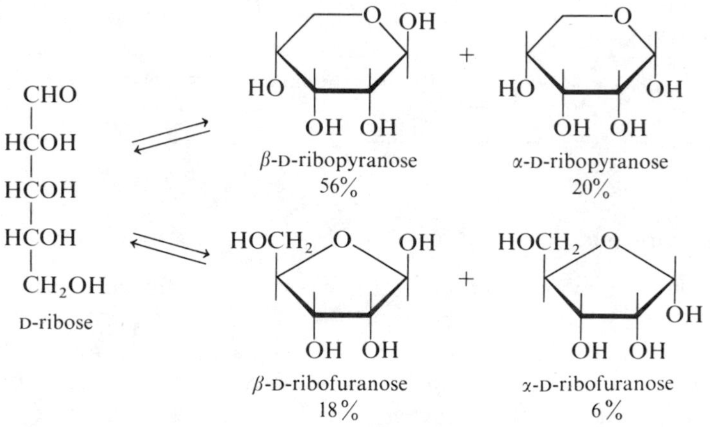

β-D-ribopyranose 56%   α-D-ribopyranose 20%

β-D-ribofuranose 18%   α-D-ribofuranose 6%

Because of the facile conversion in water of the hemiacetal OH group between α and β, it often is not possible to specify the configuration at this carbon. For this reason, we will sometimes represent the hemiacetal OH bond with a squiggle, which means the structure may be α or β or a mixture.

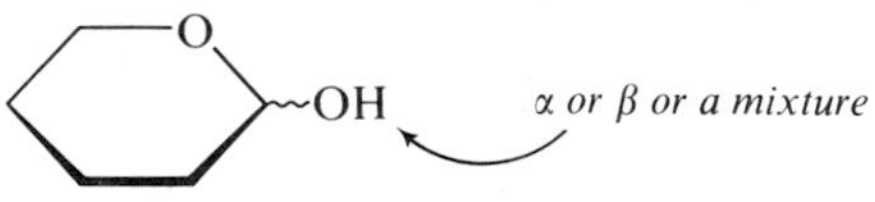

α or β or a mixture

Section 17.5

Glycosides

When a hemiacetal is treated with an alcohol, an acetal is formed (Section 11.8). The acetals of monosaccharides are called **glycosides** and have names ending in **-oside**.

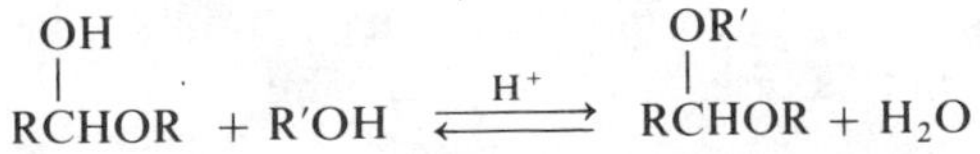

$$\underset{\text{a hemiacetal}}{\overset{\displaystyle \overset{\text{OH}}{|}}{\text{RCHOR}}} + \text{R'OH} \; \underset{}{\overset{\text{H}^+}{\rightleftharpoons}} \; \underset{\text{an acetal}}{\overset{\displaystyle \overset{\text{OR'}}{|}}{\text{RCHOR}}} + \text{H}_2\text{O}$$

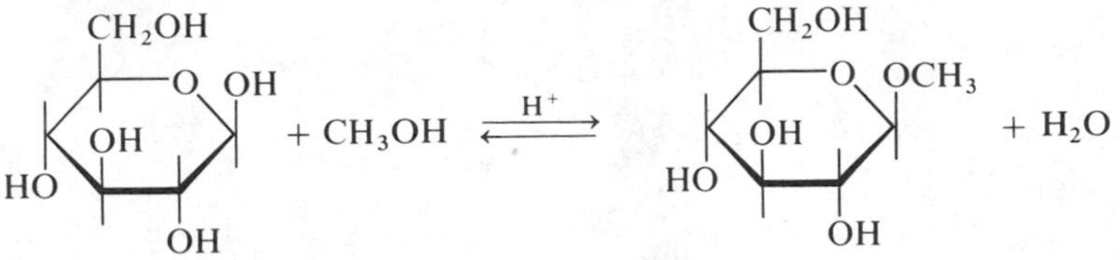

β-D-glucopyranose + CH$_3$OH $\overset{\text{H}^+}{\rightleftharpoons}$ methyl β-D-glucopyranoside (a glycoside) + H$_2$O

The glycoside carbon (carbon 1 in an aldose) is easy to recognize because it has two —OR groups attached.

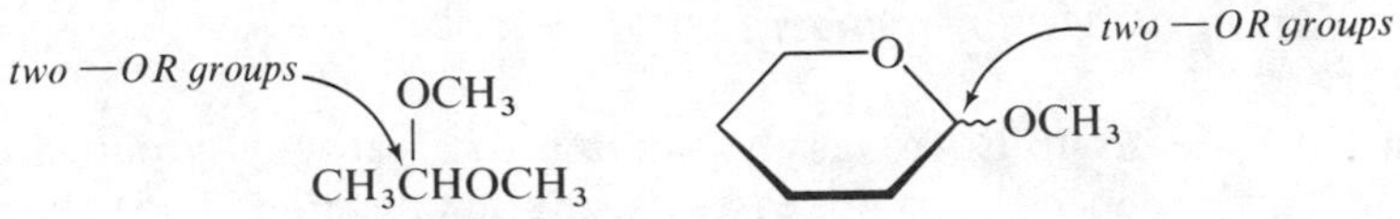

an acetal   a glycoside

Although a hemiacetal of a monosaccharide is in equilibrium with the open-chain form and with its anomer in water solution, an acetal is stable in neutral or alkaline solution. Therefore, a glycoside is not in equilibrium with the aldehyde or with its anomer in water solution. However, glycosides may be hydrolyzed to the hemiacetal (and aldehyde) forms by treatment with aqueous acid. This reaction is simply the reverse of glycoside formation.

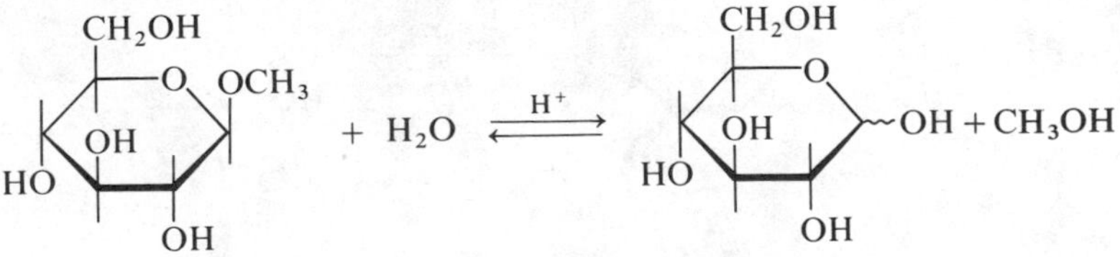

methyl β-D-glucopyranoside + H$_2$O $\overset{\text{H}^+}{\rightleftharpoons}$ D-glucopyranose + CH$_3$OH

Disaccharides and polysaccharides are glycosides; we will discuss these compounds later in this chapter. Other types of glycosides are also common in plants and animals. *Amygdalin* and *Laetrile* (Section 11.9) are glycosides found in the kernels of apricot pits and bitter almonds. The *digitalis drugs* (used as cardiac stimulants) are glycosides in which the nonsugar portions are steroidal (Section 19.8). The circled OH groups in the following steroid structures are those used to form the glycoside link with a sugar (often a di- or trisaccharide).

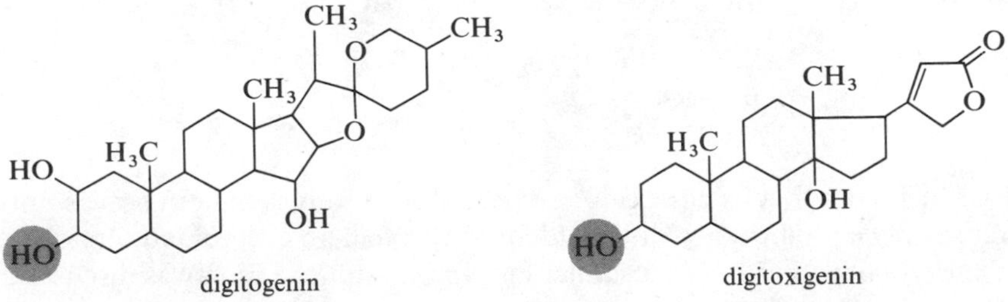

digitogenin   digitoxigenin

Vanillin (used as vanilla flavoring) is another example of a structure found in nature as a glycoside, in this case, as a β-D-glucoside.

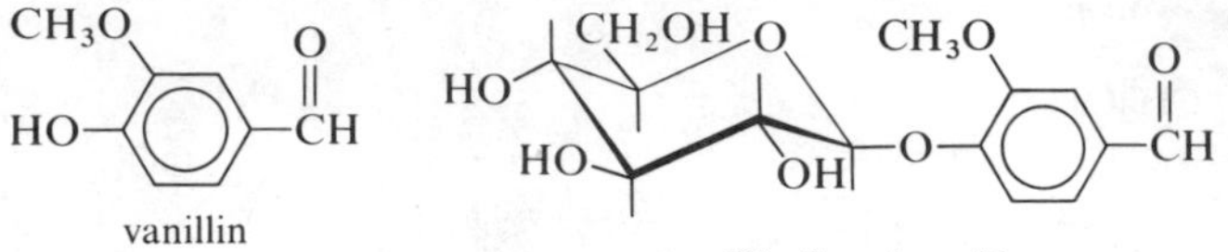

vanillin

vanillin β-D-glucoside
(glucovanillin)

Section 17.6

Oxidation of Monosaccharides

An aldehyde group is very easily oxidized to a carboxyl group. Chemical tests for aldehydes depend upon this ease of oxidation (Section 11.15). Sugars that can be oxidized by such mild oxidizing agents as Tollens reagent, an alkaline solution of $Ag(NH_3)_2{}^+$, are called **reducing sugars** (because the inorganic oxidizing agent is *reduced* in the reaction). The cyclic hemiacetal forms of all aldoses are readily oxidized because they are in equilibrium with the open-chain aldehyde form.

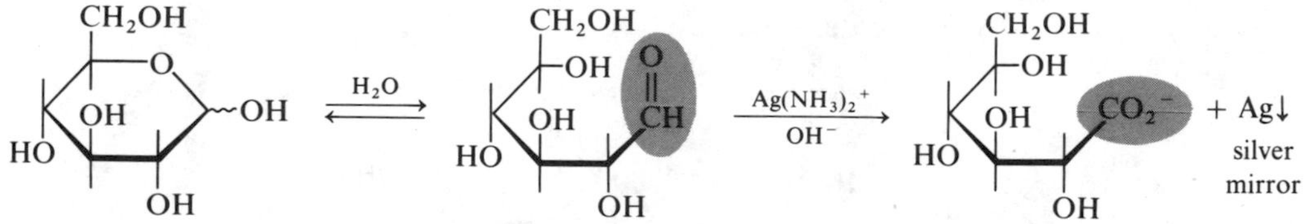

D-glucopyranose
a reducing sugar

Although fructose is a ketone, it is also a reducing sugar.

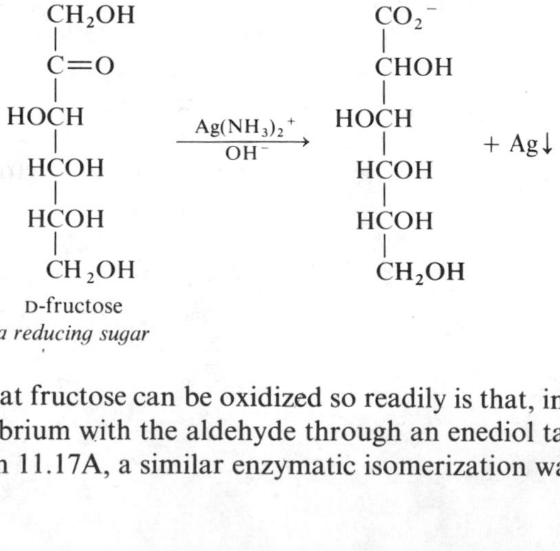

D-fructose
a reducing sugar

The reason that fructose can be oxidized so readily is that, in basic solution, fructose is in equilibrium with the aldehyde through an enediol tautomeric intermediate. (In Section 11.17A, a similar enzymatic isomerization was discussed.)

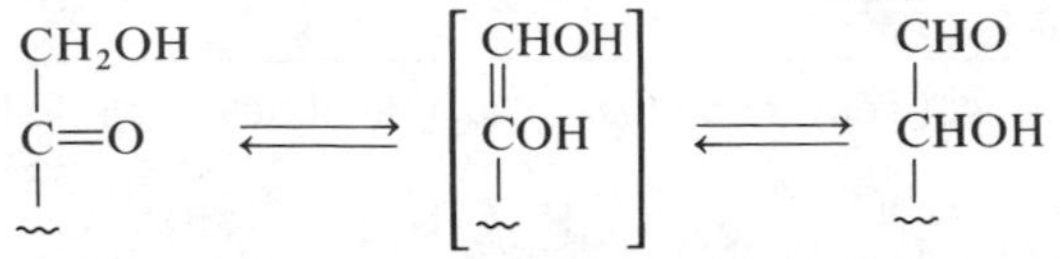

a ketose   *an enediol intermediate*   *an aldose*

In glycosides, the carbonyl group is blocked. Glycosides are **nonreducing sugars**.

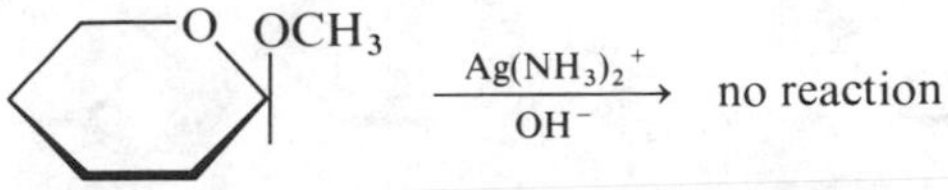

a glycoside

A. Aldonic Acids

The product of oxidation of the aldehyde group of an aldose is a polyhydroxy carboxylic acid called an **aldonic acid**. Although Tollens reagent can effect the conversion, a more convenient and less expensive reagent for the synthetic reaction is a buffered solution of bromine.

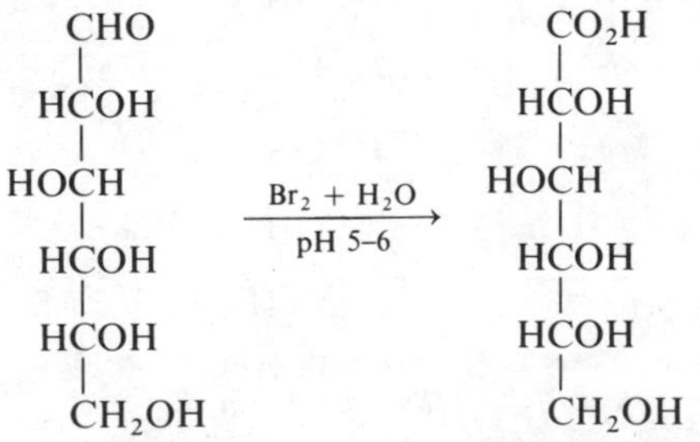

D-glucose   D-gluconic acid *an aldonic acid*

In alkaline solution, the aldonic acids exist as open-chain carboxylate ions. Upon acidification, they quickly form lactones (cyclic esters) just as any γ- or δ-hydroxy acid would (Section 13.6). Most aldonic acids have both γ and δ hydroxyl groups, and either a five- or a six-membered ring could be formed. The five-membered rings (γ-lactones) are favored in these cases.

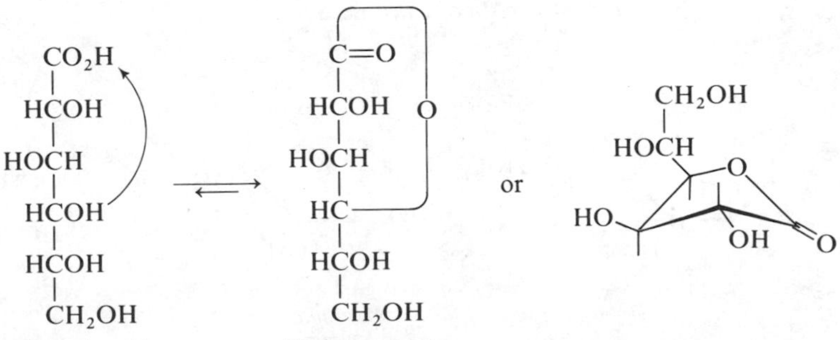

D-gluconic acid   *Fischer projection of lactone*   or

STUDY PROBLEM

17.11 Predict the product (if any) of bromine oxidation of each of the following compounds:

(a)
```
    CHO
     |
   HCOH
     |
   CH₂OH
```

(b) [cyclic structure with HOCH₂, O, OH at top and OH OH at bottom]

(c) [cyclic structure with HOCH₂, O at top, OCH₃ on right, OH OH at bottom]

(d) [disaccharide structure with two rings joined by O, with OH on right]

B.   Aldaric Acids

Vigorous oxidizing agents oxidize the aldehyde group and also the terminal hydroxyl group (a primary alcohol) of a monosaccharide. The product is a polyhydroxy dicarboxylic acid called an **aldaric acid**.

```
    CHO                    CO₂H
     |                      |
   HCOH                   HCOH
     |                      |
   HOCH      HNO₃         HOCH
     |      ───────→        |          oxidized
   HCOH      heat         HCOH
     |                      |
   HCOH                   HCOH
     |                      |
   CH₂OH                  CO₂H
   D-glucose            D-glucaric acid
                         an aldaric acid
```

STUDY PROBLEM

17.12 Which of the aldohexoses form *meso*-aldaric acids upon oxidation with hot nitric acid?

C.   Uronic Acids

Although it is not easy to do in the laboratory, in biological systems the terminal CH_2OH group may be oxidized enzymatically without oxidation of the aldehyde group. The product is called a **uronic acid**.

```
oxidized    CH₂OH                      CO₂H                          CHOH
               O                          O                           |
          OH      OH    ─────[O]────→  OH      OH      or           HCOH
       HO                   enzymes   HO                              |
            OH                             OH                       HOCH      O
       D-glucose                      D-glucuronic acid               |
                                      a uronic acid                 HCOH
                                                                      |
                                                                    HC───┘
                                                                     |
                                                                    CO₂H
                                                            Fischer projection
```

Glucuronic acid is important in animal systems because many toxic substances are excreted in the urine as **glucuronides**, derivatives of this acid. Also, in plant and animal systems, D-glucuronic acid may be converted to L-gulonic acid, which is used to biosynthesize L-ascorbic acid (vitamin C). (This last conversion does not take place in primates or guinea pigs, which require an outside source of vitamin C.) The fact that a compound of the D-series becomes a compound of the L-series is not due to a biochemical change in configuration; rather, the change arises from the change in the numbering of the carbons, as may be seen in the following equation.

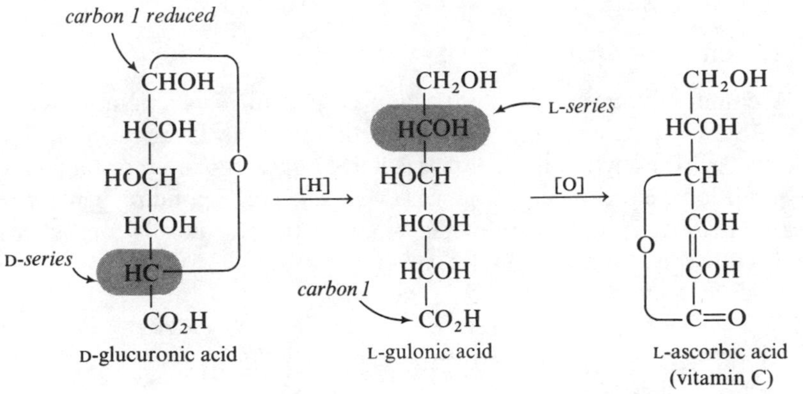

D-glucuronic acid   L-gulonic acid   L-ascorbic acid (vitamin C)

Section 17.7

Reduction of Monosaccharides

Both aldoses and ketoses can be reduced by carbonyl reducing agents, such as hydrogen and catalyst or a metal hydride, to polyalcohols called **alditols**. The suffix for the name of one of these polyalcohols is **-itol**. The product of reduction of D-glucose is called D-*glucitol*, or *sorbitol*.

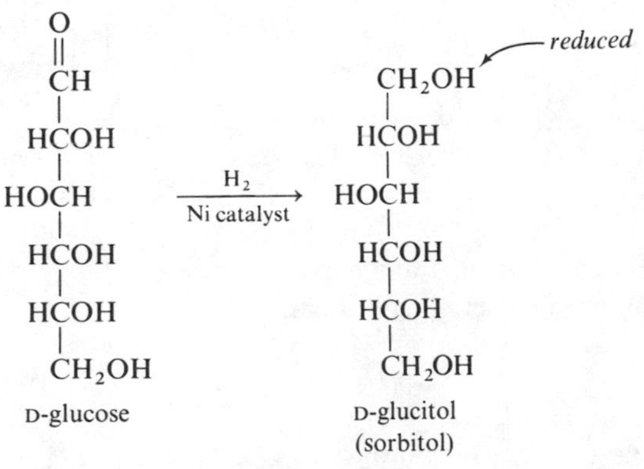

D-glucose   D-glucitol (sorbitol)

Natural D-glucitol has been isolated from many fruits (for example, cherries, plums, apples, pears, and mountain ash berries) and from algae and seaweed. Synthetic D-glucitol is used as an artificial sweetener.

Section 17.8

Reactions at the Hydroxyl Groups

The hydroxyl groups in carbohydrates behave in a manner similar to that of other alcohol groups. They may be esterified by either carboxylic acids or inorganic acids, and they may be subjected to ether formation. These reactions were discussed in Chapter 7.

A. Acetate Formation

A common reagent for esterification of alcohols is acetic anhydride, with either sodium acetate or pyridine as an alkaline catalyst. If the reaction is carried out below 0°C, the acylation reaction is faster than the α–β interconversion. Under these conditions, either α- or β-D-glucose yields its corresponding pentacetate. At higher temperatures, a mixture of the α- and β-pentacetates is formed with the β-pentacetate predominating. (Why?)

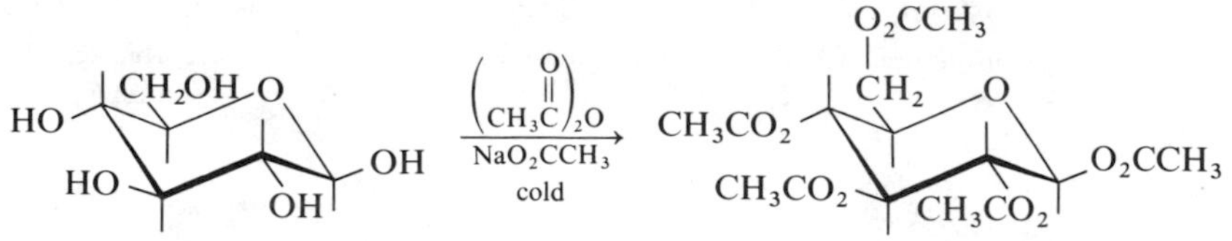

β-D-glucopyranose   penta-*O*-acetyl-β-D-glucopyranose

B. Ether Formation

Treatment of an aldose, such as glucose, with methyl alcohol yields a methyl glycoside.

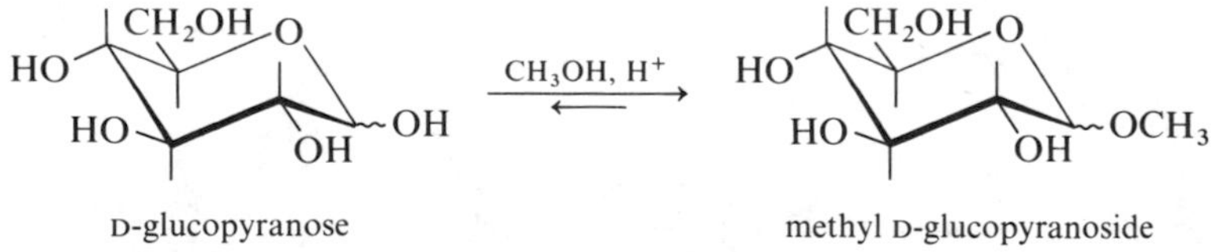

D-glucopyranose   methyl D-glucopyranoside

The other hydroxyl groups in a carbohydrate can be converted to methoxyl groups by reaction with dimethyl sulfate and NaOH.

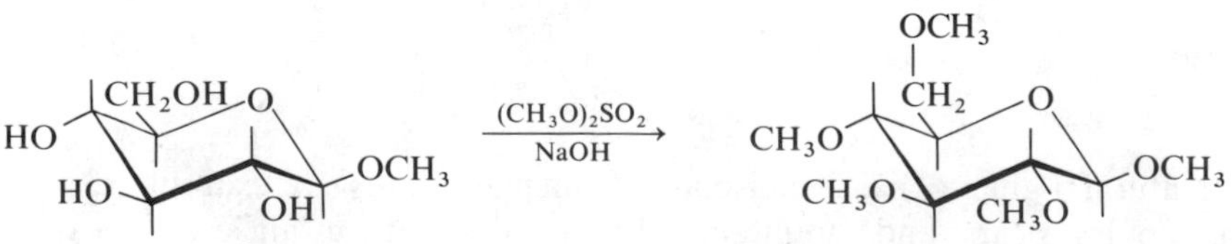

methyl β-D-glucopyranoside   methyl tetra-*O*-methyl-β-D-glucopyranoside

In a usual Williamson ether synthesis $(RO^- + RX \rightarrow ROR + X^-$; Section 7.5B), the alkoxide must be prepared with a stronger base than NaOH. In the case of the carbohydrates, NaOH is a sufficiently strong base to yield alkoxide ions. (The inductive effect of the electronegative oxygens on adjacent carbons renders each hydroxyl group more acidic than a hydroxyl group in an ordinary alcohol.) Because the acetal bond is stable in base, the configuration at the anomeric carbon of a glycoside is not changed in this methylation reaction.

STUDY PROBLEM

17.13 Give the structure of the product of the treatment of methyl 2-deoxy-α-D-ribofuranoside with: (a) acetic anhydride, and (b) an alkaline solution of dimethyl sulfate.

Section 17.9

The Structure Determination of Glucose

In 1888, it was known that glucose is an aldohexose. The question was, "Which of the 16 possible stereoisomeric aldohexoses is it?" In 1891, the German chemist Emil Fischer reported the structure of the open-chain aldehyde form of D-glucose; for this work, he received the Nobel prize in 1902.

The determination of configuration of a compound with four chiral centers might seem an overwhelming task, but Fischer accomplished this task in a series of simple reactions. From his data, it was possible to determine only the *relative configuration* of glucose, not the absolute configuration, which had to wait another 50 years for x-ray diffraction. Therefore, Fischer made the assumption that the OH on carbon 5 in D-(+)-glucose is projected to the right. (It turned out later that his assumption was correct; see Section 4.8.) This assumption reduced the number of unknown chiral centers in glucose from four to three.

$$
\begin{array}{c}
\text{CHO} \\
| \\
-\text{C}- \\
| \\
-\text{C}- \\
| \\
-\text{C}- \qquad \textit{assumed to be on the right} \\
| \\
\text{HCOH} \longleftarrow \\
| \\
\text{CH}_2\text{OH}
\end{array}
$$

D-(+)-glucose

Fact 1: It was known that the aldopentose (−)-arabinose could be converted to the aldohexoses (+)-glucose and (+)-mannose. Heinrich Kiliani discovered the chain-lengthening step in 1886, and Fischer accomplished the reduction of the lactone to the aldohexoses in 1890. The following sequence is consequently known as the **Kiliani–Fischer synthesis**.

$$
\begin{array}{ccc}
\text{CHO} & & \overset{\text{CN}}{|} \quad \overset{new\ chiral}{center} \quad \overset{\text{CN}}{|} \\
| & & \text{HCOH} \qquad\qquad \text{HOCH} \\
-\text{C}- & \xrightarrow{\text{HCN}} & -\text{C}- \qquad and \qquad -\text{C}- \qquad \xrightarrow{\cdot\text{H}_2\text{O, H}^+} \\
| & & | \qquad\qquad\qquad | \\
-\text{C}- & & -\text{C}- \qquad\qquad -\text{C}- \\
| & & | \qquad\qquad\qquad | \\
\text{HCOH} & & \text{HCOH} \qquad\qquad \text{HCOH} \\
| & & | \qquad\qquad\qquad | \\
\text{CH}_2\text{OH} & & \text{CH}_2\text{OH} \qquad\qquad \text{CH}_2\text{OH}
\end{array}
$$

D-(−)-arabinose   *two cyanohydrins*

from −CN → two lactones:

C=O / HCOH / −C− / −C− / HC— (with O bridge) / CH₂OH   **and**   C=O / HOCH / −C− / −C− / HC— (with O bridge) / CH₂OH

$\xrightarrow[\text{CO}_2]{\text{Na(Hg)}}$

CHO / HCOH / −C− / −C− / HCOH / CH₂OH   **+**   CHO / HOCH / −C− / −C− / HCOH / CH₂OH

two lactones   D-(+)-glucose and D-(+)-mannose

Because (−)-arabinose yields both (+)-glucose and (+)-mannose, all three of these sugars have *the same configuration at the last three chiral carbons* (carbons 3, 4, and 5 of glucose and mannose). (+)-Glucose and (+)-mannose must differ *only* by the configuration at carbon 2. These conclusions are pictured in Figure 17.3 with the now-known structures.

Fact 2: Fischer found that the oxidation of both end groups of (−)-arabinose yielded an optically active diacid, and not the *meso*-diacid.

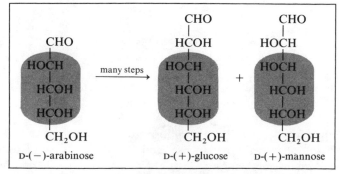

Figure 17.3.   D-(+)-Glucose and D-(+)-mannose have the same configuration at the last three chiral carbons.

```
         CHO                           CO₂H
          |                             |
         —C—                           —C—
          |                             |
         —C—         HNO₃              —C—
          |          ────→              |
        HCOH          heat            HCOH
          |                             |
        CH₂OH                          CO₂H
     (−)-arabinose                   not meso
```

Therefore, Fischer concluded that carbon 2 in (−)-arabinose must have OH on the *left*. If it were on the right, the *meso*-diacid would result.

```
                CO₂H              CO₂H
                 |                 |
  left     HO CH               HCOH          this diacid would be
   ───→       |                 |            meso, regardless
             —C—               —C—           of configuration
              |                 |            at carbon 3
            HCOH              HCOH
              |                 |
             CO₂H              CO₂H

        only possibility      not this
```

From the data presented so far, it is possible to write almost-complete structures for (−)-arabinose, (+)-glucose, and (+)-mannose. Figure 17.4 shows these data with the known structures.

```
                              CHO            CHO
          CHO                HCOH           HOCH
         HOCH                HOCH           HOCH
         —C—                 —C—            —C—
         HCOH                HCOH           HCOH
         CH₂OH               CH₂OH          CH₂OH

    D-(−)-arabinose          ‾‾‾‾‾‾‾‾‾‾‾‾‾‾‾‾‾‾‾
                             one is D-(+)-glucose;
                             one is D-(+)-mannose
```

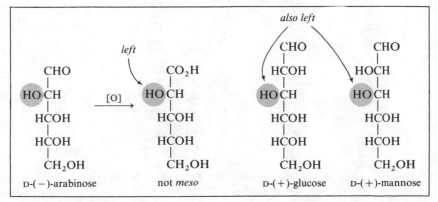

Figure 17.4. Because D-(−)-arabinose yields an optically active aldaric acid, the —OH at C2 must be projected on the left.

Fact 3: Fischer observed that both (+)-glucose and (+)-mannose are oxidized to optically active diacids. This means that the OH at carbon 4 of both of these monosaccharides is *on the right*. (If it were on the left, one of the two sugars would yield a *meso*-diacid.) Figure 17.5 shows these reactions with the known structures.

```
        CHO                              CO₂H
         |                                |
        CHOH                             CHOH
         |              right             |          not meso,
       HOCH           ─────────▶        HOCH         regardless of
         |             HNO₃              |           configuration
       HCOH  ◀──────   heat            HCOH   ◀────  at carbon 2
         |                               |
       HCOH                             HCOH
         |                                |
       CH₂OH                            CO₂H
```

D-(+)-glucose
or
D-(+)-mannose

If OH at carbon 4 were on the left:

```
        CHO                              CO₂H
         |                                |
       HCOH                             HCOH
         |                                |
       HOCH            HNO₃             HOCH
         |           ─────────▶    - - - - | - - - - -    plane of
       HOCH            heat             HOCH             symmetry
         |                                |
       HCOH                             HCOH
         |                                |
       CH₂OH                            CO₂H
```

meso

Now a complete structure for (−)-arabinose may be written—all that is needed is to differentiate between (+)-glucose and (+)-mannose.

```
                            CHO              CHO
          CHO             HCOH             HOCH
           |                |                |
         HOCH             HOCH             HOCH
           |                |                |
         HCOH             HCOH             HCOH
           |                |                |
         HCOH             HCOH             HCOH
           |                |                |
         CH₂OH            CH₂OH            CH₂OH
```

D-(−)-arabinose

> one is D-(+)-glucose;
> one is D-(+)-mannose

Fact 4: The sugar (+)-gulose (another aldohexose) and (+)-glucose both give the *same diacid* when oxidized. Of the possible diacids that can be obtained from the two structures that are (+)-glucose and (+)-mannose, *only one* can come from two *different* sugars.

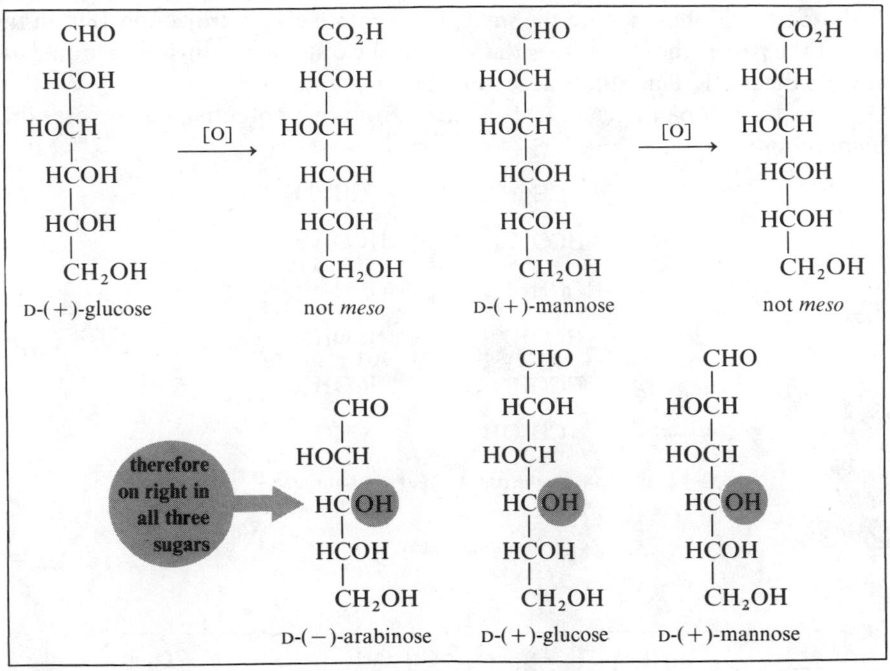

Figure 17.5. Because both D-(+)-glucose and D-(+)-mannose yield optically active aldaric acids, the 4-hydroxyl must be on the right.

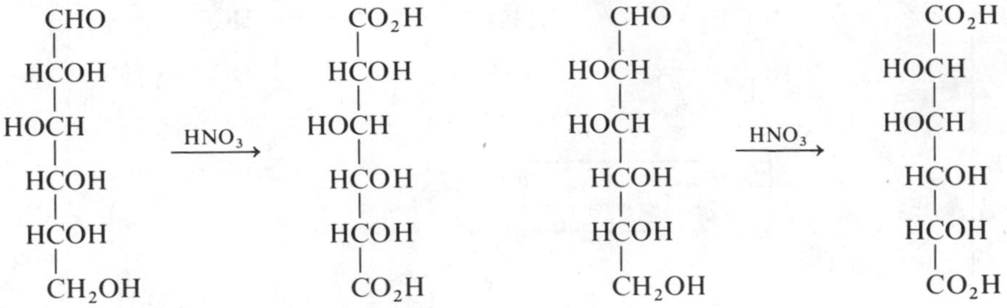

I — *can arise from two aldohexoses*

II — *can arise from only one aldohexose*

Let us look at diacid II first. The two potential aldohexoses that can lead to diacid II follow:

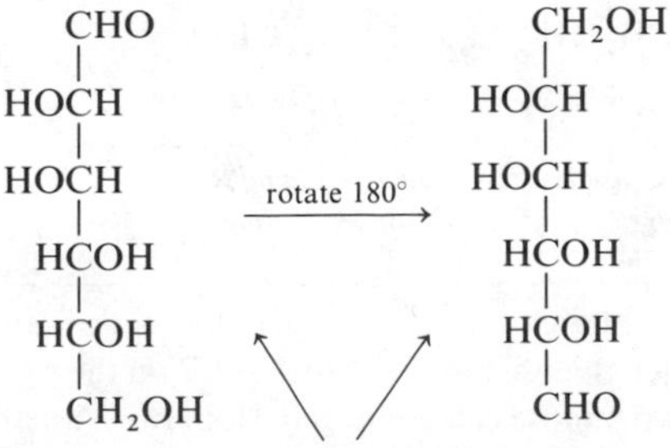

both are D-(+)-*mannose*

But these two aldohexoses are the *same*. If we rotate either projection 180° in the plane of the paper, the structure is the same as the other. Only this one aldohexose can yield diacid II. This aldohexose must be (+)-mannose.

Now let us look at diacid I. It can arise from two potential aldohexoses that are *not the same*.

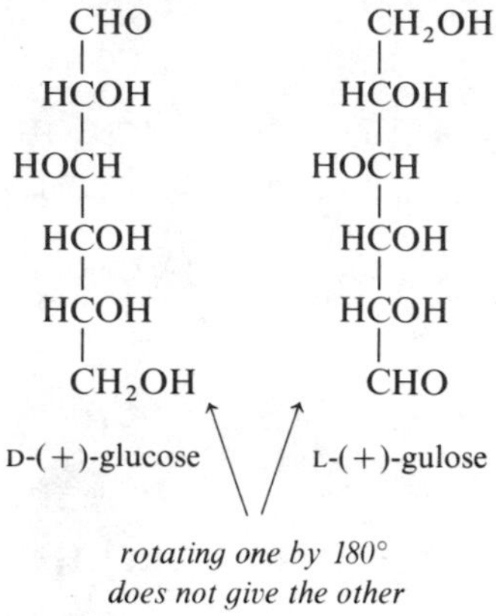

D-(+)-glucose   L-(+)-gulose

rotating one by 180°
does not give the other

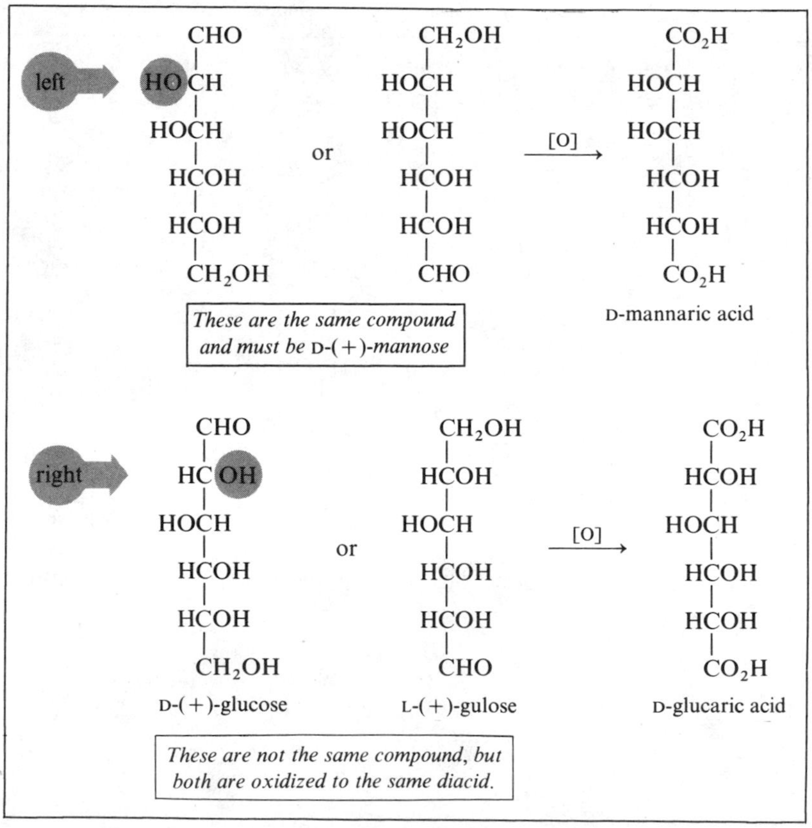

These are the same compound and must be D-(+)-mannose

D-mannaric acid

D-(+)-glucose   L-(+)-gulose   D-glucaric acid

These are not the same compound, but both are oxidized to the same diacid.

Figure 17.6.   Because the aldaric acid from D-(+)-glucose can also be formed from L-(+)-gulose, D-(+)-glucose has the —OH at C2 on the right. Because the aldaric acid from D-(+)-mannose can come *only* from D-(+)-mannose, this sugar is the one with the —OH at C2 on the left.

If these two sugars give the same diacid (that is, diacid I), then the left-hand structure is (+)-glucose, the right-hand structure is (+)-gulose, and the aldohexose that leads to diacid II is (+)-mannose. See Figure 17.6 for these reactions with known structures.

A. Determination of Ring Size

The cyclic structures for glucose were postulated in 1895, but it was not shown until 1926 that glucose forms six-membered cyclic hemiacetals and glycosides. The reactions that were used to determine the ring size were, again, not complex.

A methyl glycoside undergoes reaction with methyl sulfate to yield a completely methylated structure. In acidic solution, the methylated methyl glycoside can be hydrolyzed and the ring opened. The methoxyl groups, which are ethers, are not affected by this reaction. The hydrolyzed acetal therefore has only one hydroxyl group. Determination of the position of this hydroxyl group is the information needed to know the ring size of the original acetal.

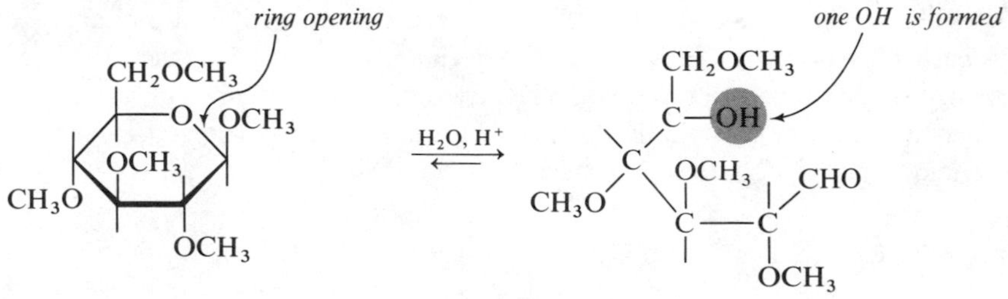

ring opening   *one OH is formed*

$$\xrightarrow[\text{H}_2\text{O, H}^+]{\quad\quad}$$

The position of the —OH group was determined by vigorous oxidation in which the —CHO group is oxidized to —CO_2H and the single —OH group is oxidized to a ketone. Under these oxidizing conditions, cleavage of the molecule occurs adjacent to the ketone group (on either side) to yield two dicarboxylic acids. (See Section 11.17 for a discussion of this type of oxidation.)

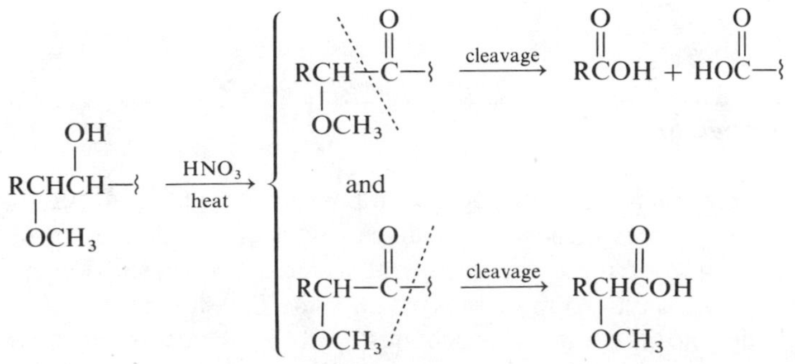

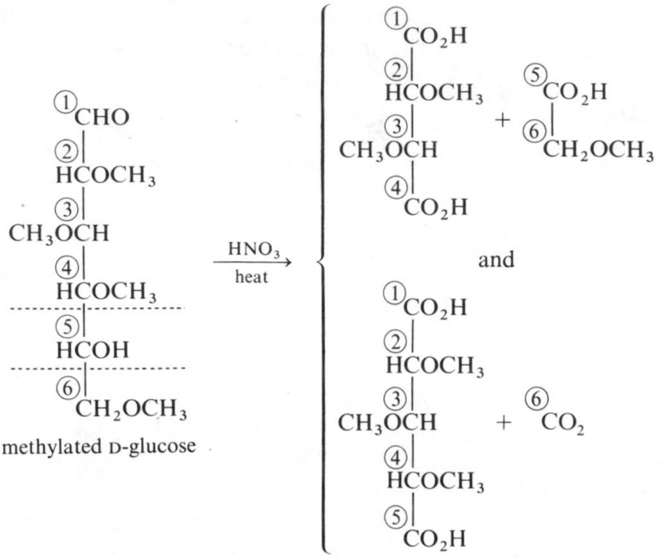

①CHO
②|
HCOCH₃
③|
CH₃OCH
④|
HCOCH₃
⑤|
HCOH
⑥|
CH₂OCH₃

methylated D-glucose

$\xrightarrow[\text{heat}]{\text{HNO}_3}$

①CO₂H
②|
HCOCH₃
③|
CH₃OCH
④|
CO₂H
+
⑤CO₂H
⑥|
CH₂OCH₃

and

①CO₂H
②|
HCOCH₃
③|
CH₃OCH
④|
HCOCH₃
⑤|
CO₂H
+ ⑥CO₂

From methylated glucose, the two methoxy diacids shown in the preceding equation were observed as principal products (along with methoxyacetic acid and CO_2). The structures of the two diacids were determined by comparing their physical properties with those of methoxy diacids of known structure. Because these product diacids are methoxy derivatives of *four-* and *five-carbon* diacids, it was concluded that carbon 5 holds the OH group in the hydrolyzed glycoside and that the original glycoside ring is a six-membered ring.

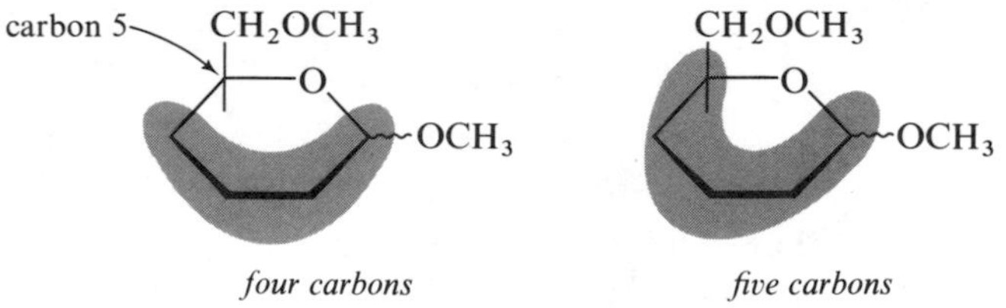

four carbons   *five carbons*

STUDY PROBLEM

17.14 What products would be observed from methylation, hydrolysis, and oxidation of a methyl D-glucofuranoside?

Section 17.10

Disaccharides

A **disaccharide** is a carbohydrate composed of two units of monosaccharide joined together by a glycoside link from carbon 1 of one unit of an —OH of the other unit. A common mode of attachment is an α or β glycoside link from the first unit to the 4-hydroxyl group of the second unit. This link is called a 1,4′-α or a 1,4′-β link, depending on the stereochemistry at the glycoside carbon.

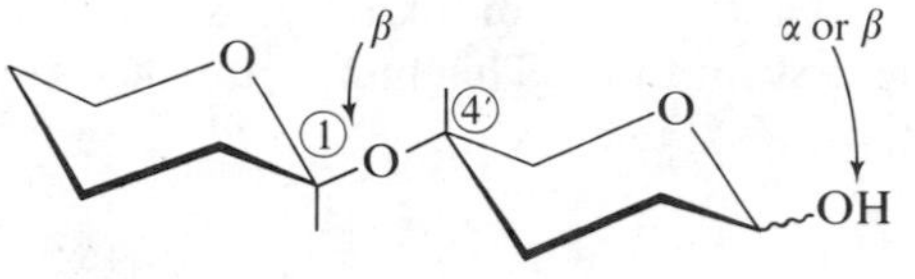

a 1,4′-β link
(*conformational*)

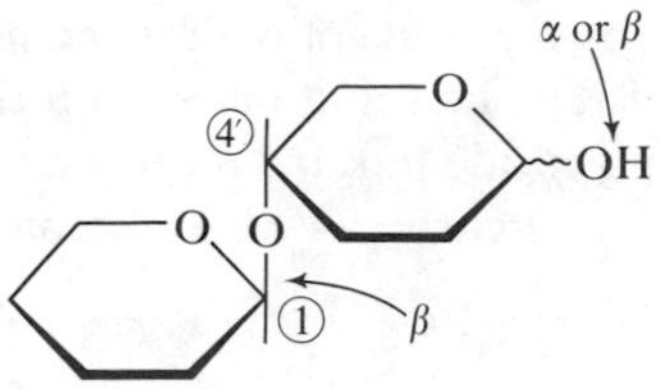

a 1,4′-β link
(*Haworth*)

Let us look at the preceding structures more closely. Unit 1 (the left-hand unit in each structure) has a β-glycoside link to unit 2. In aqueous solution, this glycoside link is fixed. It is not in equilibrium with the anomer. However, unit 2 (the right-hand unit in each structure) contains a hemiacetal group. In aqueous solution, this particular group is in equilibrium with the open-chain aldehyde form and with the other anomer.

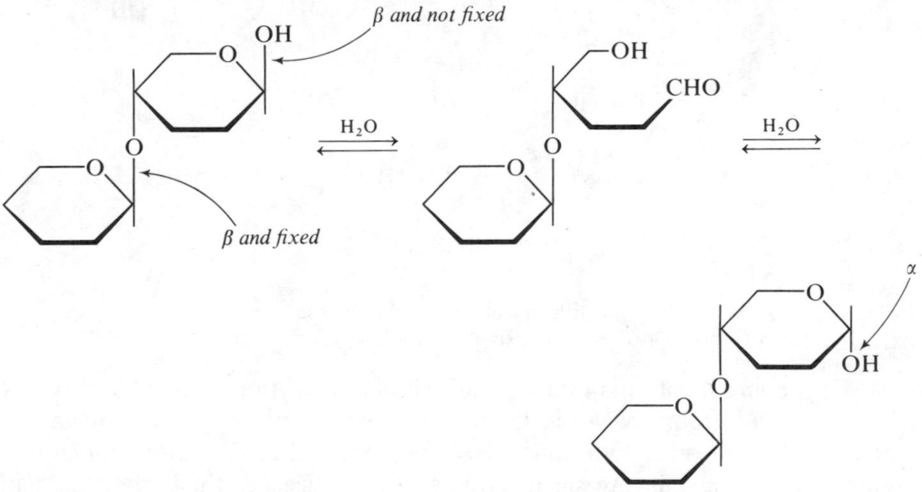

A. Maltose

The disaccharide **maltose** is used in baby foods and malted milk. It is the principal disaccharide obtained from the hydrolysis of starch. Starch is broken down into maltose in an apparently random fashion by an enzyme in saliva called α-*1,4-glucan 4-glucanohydrolase*. The enzyme α-*1,4-glucan maltohydrolase*, found in sprouted barley (*malt*), converts starch specifically into maltose units. In beer-making, malt is used for the conversion of starches from corn or other sources into maltose. An enzyme in yeast (α-*glucosidase*) catalyzes the hydrolysis of the maltose into D-glucose, which is acted upon by other enzymes from the yeast to yield ethanol. One molecule of maltose yields two molecules of D-glucose, regardless of whether the hydrolysis takes place in a laboratory flask, in an organism, or in a fermentation vat.

$$\text{starch} \xrightarrow[\text{H}^+ \text{ or enzymes}]{\text{H}_2\text{O}} \text{maltose} \xrightarrow[\text{H}^+ \text{ or enzymes}]{\text{H}_2\text{O}} \text{D-glucose} \xrightarrow[\text{enzymes}]{} \underset{\text{ethanol}}{\text{CH}_3\text{CH}_2\text{OH}}$$

A molecule of maltose contains two units of D-glucose, both in the pyranose form. The first unit (shown on the left) is in the form of an α-glycoside—that is, the glycoside link from carbon 1 of the first unit is α. This link is attached to the oxygen at carbon 4′ in the second unit.

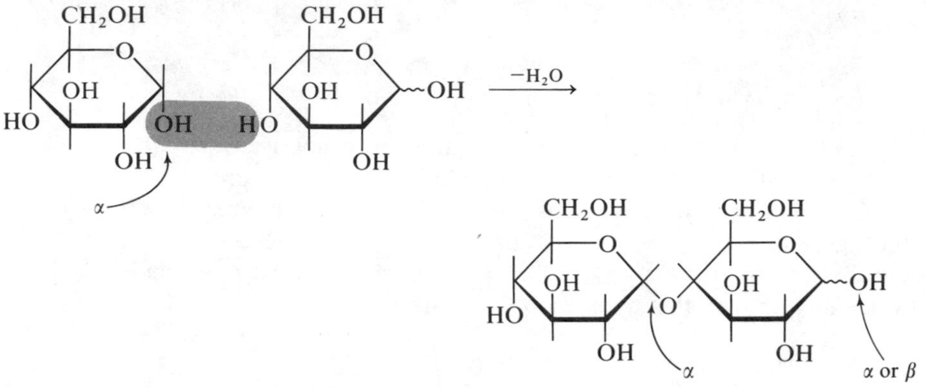

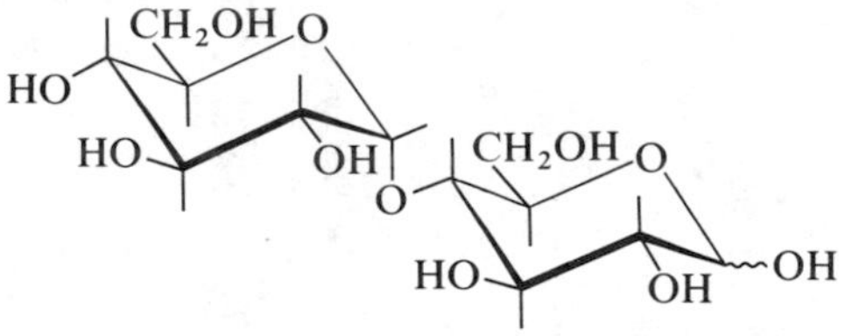

conformational formula for maltose
4-*O*-(α-D-glucopyranosyl)-D-glucopyranose

The anomeric carbon of the second unit of glucopyranose in maltose is part of a hemiacetal group. As a result, there are two forms of maltose (α- and β-maltose), which are in equilibrium with each other in solution. Maltose undergoes mutarotation, is a reducing sugar, and can be oxidized to the carboxylic acid **maltobionic acid** by a bromine–water solution.

STUDY PROBLEMS

17.15 Give the conformational structures for α-maltose and β-maltose.

17.16 Give the structures of the products:

(a) α-maltose $\xrightarrow{\text{H}_2\text{O, H}^+}$

(b) β-maltose $\xrightarrow{\text{Br}_2, \text{H}_2\text{O}}$

B. Cellobiose

The disaccharide obtained from the partial hydrolysis of cellulose is called **cellobiose**. Like maltose, cellobiose is composed of two glucopyranose units joined together by a 1,4′-link. Cellobiose differs from maltose in that the 1,4-linkage is β rather than α.

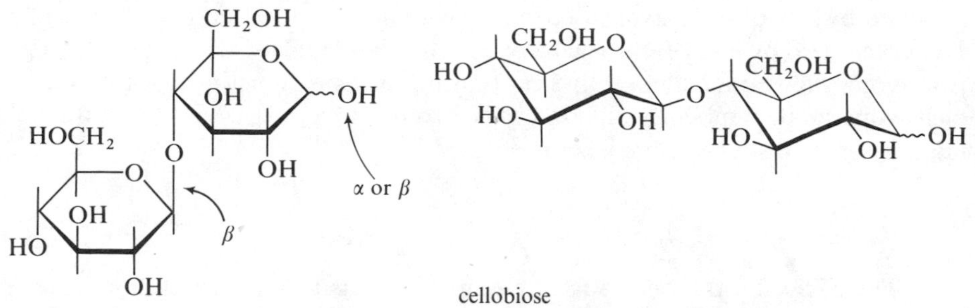

cellobiose
4-*O*-(β-D-glucopyranosyl)-D-glucopyranose

Chemical hydrolysis of cellobiose with aqueous acid yields a mixture of α- and β-D-glucose, the same products that are obtained from maltose. Cellobiose can also be hydrolyzed with the enzyme β-*glucosidase* (also called *emulsin*), but not by α-*glucosidase*, which is specific for the α link (that is, maltose).

STUDY PROBLEMS

17.17 Give the structures of the products:

(a) α-cellobiose $\xrightarrow{\text{H}_2\text{O, H}^+}$ (b) β-cellobiose $\xrightarrow{\text{H}_2\text{O, H}^+}$

(c) α-cellobiose $\xrightarrow{\text{Br}_2,\ \text{H}_2\text{O}}$ (d) α-cellobiose $\xrightarrow{\text{Tollens reagent}}$

(e) α-cellobiose $\xrightarrow{\text{β-glucosidase}}$

17.18 Which would you expect to be more stable, β-maltose or β-cellobiose? Why?

C. Lactose

The disaccharide **lactose** (milk sugar) is different from maltose or cellobiose in that it is composed of two different monosaccharides, D-glucose and D-galactose. In lactose, β-D-galactose is connected by a glycoside link to carbon 4 of D-glucose.

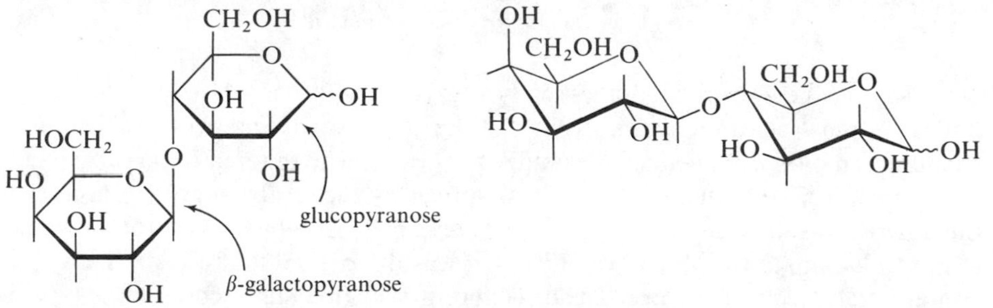

lactose
4-*O*-(β-D-galactopyranosyl)-D-glucopyranose

Lactose is a naturally occurring disaccharide found only in mammals; it comprises about 5% of cow's milk or human milk. Lactose is obtained commercially as a by-product in the manufacture of cheese.

In normal human metabolism, lactose is hydrolyzed enzymatically to D-galactose and D-glucose; then the galactose is converted to glucose, which can undergo metabolism. A condition called **galactosemia** that affects some infants is caused by lack of the enzyme used to convert galactose to glucose. Galactosemia is characterized by high levels of galactose in the blood and urine. Symptoms range from vomiting to mental and physical retardation and sometimes death. Treatment consists of removing milk and milk products from the diet. (An artificial milk made from soybeans may be substituted.)

D.   *Sucrose*

The disaccharide **sucrose** is common table sugar. Whether it comes from beets or sugar cane, the chemical composition is the same, one unit of fructose joined to one unit of glucose. The glycoside link joins carbon 1 of each monosaccharide and is β from fructose and α from glucose. Note the difference between sucrose and the other disaccharides we have discussed: in sucrose, *both* anomeric carbon atoms (not just one) are used in the glycoside link. In sucrose, neither fructose nor glucose has a hemiacetal group; therefore, sucrose in water is not in equilibrium with an aldehyde form. Sucrose does not exhibit mutarotation and is not a reducing sugar.

sucrose
β-D-fructofuranosyl α-D-glucopyranoside

Sugar cane was grown domestically as early as 6000 B.C. in India. (The words "sugar" and "sucrose" come from the Sanskrit word *sarkara*.) Sucrose was encountered by the soldiers of Alexander the Great, who entered India in 325 B.C. In later centuries, the use of sucrose was spread by the Arabs and the Crusaders. Sugar cane was introduced into the New World by Columbus, who brought some to Santo Domingo in 1493. In the 1700's, it was discovered that certain beets also contain high levels of sucrose. The discovery meant that sugar could be obtained from plants grown in temperate climates as well as from sugar cane grown in the tropics. Today, more sucrose is produced than any other pure organic compound.

Invert sugar is a mixture of D-glucose and D-fructose obtained by the acidic or enzymatic hydrolysis of sucrose. The enzymes that catalyze the hydrolysis of sucrose, called *invertases*, are specific for the β-D-fructofuranoside link and are found in yeast and in bees. (Honey is primarily invert sugar.) Because of the presence of free fructose (the sweetest sugar), invert sugar is sweeter than sucrose. A synthetic invert sugar called *Isomerose* is prepared by the enzymatic isomerization of glucose in corn syrup. It has commercial use in the preparation of ice cream, soft drinks, and candy.

The name "invert sugar" is derived from inversion in the sign of the specific rotation when sucrose is hydrolyzed. Sucrose has a specific rotation of $+66.5°$, a *positive* rotation. The mixture of products (glucose, $[\alpha] = +52.7°$, and fructose, $[\alpha] = -92.4°$) has a net *negative* rotation.

Section 17.11

Polysaccharides

A **polysaccharide** is a compound in which the molecules contain many units of monosaccharide joined together by glycoside links. Upon complete hydrolysis, a polysaccharide yields monosaccharides.

Polysaccharides serve three purposes in living systems: architectural, nutritional, and as specific agents. Typical architectural polysaccharides are *cellulose*, which gives strength to the stems and branches of plants, and *chitin*, the structural component of the exoskeletons of insects. Typical nutritional polysaccharides are *starch* (as is found in wheat and potatoes) and *glycogen*, an animal's internal store of readily available carbohydrate. *Heparin*, an example of a specific agent, is a polysaccharide that prevents blood coagulation.

heparin

Polysaccharides may also be bonded to other types of molecules, as in *glycoproteins* (polysaccharide–protein complexes; see Chapter 18), and *glycolipids* (polysaccharide–lipid complexes; see Chapter 19).

A. Cellulose

Cellulose is the most abundant organic compound on earth. It has been estimated that about 10^{11} tons of cellulose are biosynthesized each year, and that cellulose accounts for about 50% of the bound carbon on earth! Dry leaves contain 10–20% cellulose; wood, 50%; and cotton, 90%. The most convenient laboratory source of pure cellulose is filter paper.

Cellulose forms the fibrous component of plant cell walls. The rigidity of cellulose arises from its overall structure. Cellulose molecules are chains, or microfibrils, of up to 14,000 units of D-glucose that occur in twisted rope-like bundles held together by hydrogen bonding.

A single molecule of cellulose is a linear polymer of $1,4'$-β-D-glucose. Complete hydrolysis in 40% aqueous HCl yields only D-glucose. The disaccharide isolated from partially hydrolyzed cellulose is cellobiose, which can be further hydrolyzed to D-glucose with an acidic catalyst or with the enzyme emulsin.

Cellulose itself has no hemiacetal carbon—it cannot undergo mutarotation or be oxidized by such test reagents as Tollens reagent. (There may be a hemiacetal at one end of each cellulose molecule; however, this is but a small portion of the whole and does not lead to observable reaction.)

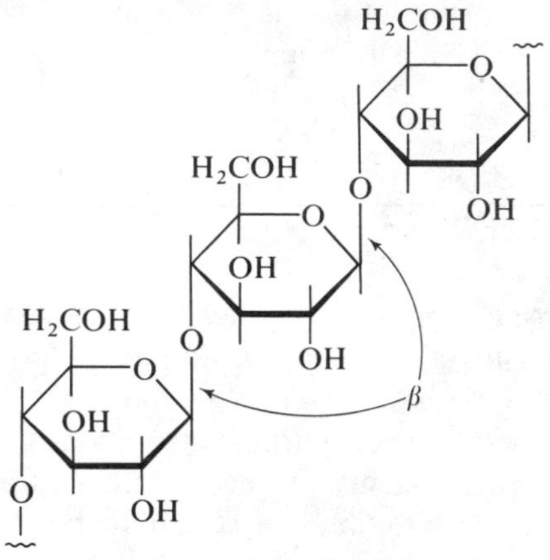

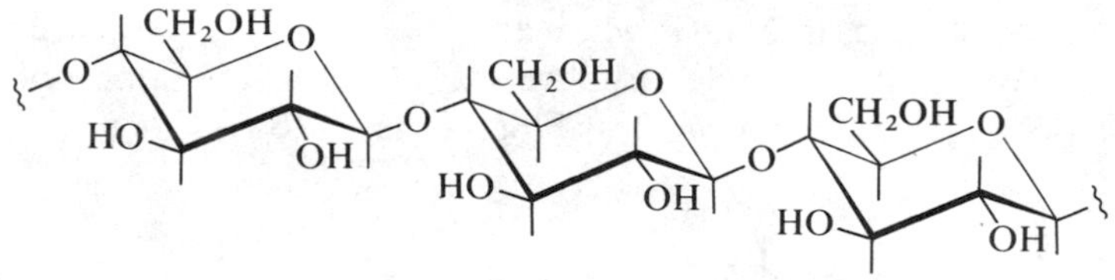

cellulose

STUDY PROBLEM

17.19 Predict the major product (and give a structure or partial structure) when cellulose is treated with: (a) an excess of hot aqueous H_2SO_4, then water; (b) hot water; (c) hot aqueous NaOH solution; (d) an excess of NaOH and dimethyl sulfate.

Although mammals do not produce the proper enzymes for breaking down cellulose into glucose, certain bacteria and protozoa do have these enzymes. Grazing animals are capable of using cellulose as food only indirectly. Their stomachs and intestines support colonies of microorganisms that live and reproduce on cellulose; the animal uses these microorganisms and their by-products as food.

Rayon There are two types of rayon, **acetate rayon** and **viscose rayon**, both made from cellulose. The synthesis of acetate rayon is carried out by way of cellulose acetate, which is prepared by esterification of cellulose with acetic anhydride.

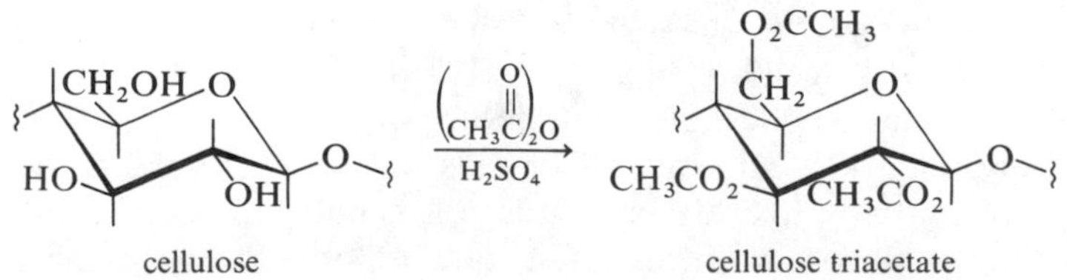

There are three free hydroxyl groups in one glucose unit of cellulose. Complete esterification leads to cellulose triacetate, in which almost all hydroxyl groups are converted to ester groups. Acetate rayon is the partially hydrolyzed product in which some acetate groups are cleaved and the chains of cellulose are shortened (by hydrolysis of some of the glucoside links).

When cellulose is treated with carbon disulfide (S=C=S) in aqueous NaOH, the hydroxyl groups undergo reaction to form *xanthate groups*, which are carbonate groups with two oxygens replaced by sulfur. **Viscose** is a viscous colloidal suspension of cellulose xanthate that can be used to make threads or sheets.

a cellulose monoxanthate
"viscose"

In preparation of viscose rayon filaments, viscose is forced through narrow orifices into a dilute acid bath. In the bath, the xanthate groups are hydrolyzed back to hydroxyl groups and the cellulose chains are cleaved into shorter chains. **Cellophane** is made by the same process except that the viscose is forced through slits to form sheets instead of through holes to form fibers.

Cellulose Nitrate An alcohol undergoes reaction with nitric acid to yield a nitrate ester ($RONO_2$). When cellulose is almost completely nitrated, the product is **cellulose trinitrate**, or **guncotton**; it is an explosive. A less highly nitrated product has been used to make a type of celluloid.

cellulose trinitrate

B. Starch

Starch is the second most abundant polysaccharide. Starch can be separated into two principal fractions based upon solubility when triturated (pulverized) with hot water: about 20% of starch is **amylose** (soluble) and the remaining 80% is **amylopectin** (insoluble).

Amylose Complete hydrolysis of amylose yields only D-glucose; partial hydrolysis yields maltose as the only disaccharide. We conclude that amylose is a linear polymer of 1,4'-linked α-D-glucose. The difference between amylose and cellulose is the glycoside link: β in cellulose, α in amylose. This difference is responsible for the different properties of these two polysaccharides.

amylose

There are 250 or more glucose units per amylose molecule; the exact number depends upon the species of animal or plant. (Measurement of chain length is complicated by the fact that natural amylose degrades into smaller chains upon separation and purification.)

Amylose molecules form helices around I_2 molecules (Figure 17.7); a deep blue color arises from electronic interactions between the two. This color is the basis of the **iodine test for starch**, in which a solution of iodine is added to an unknown as a test for the presence of starch.

coiled amylose molecule

Figure 17.7. The I_2 molecule is trapped in an amylose helix.

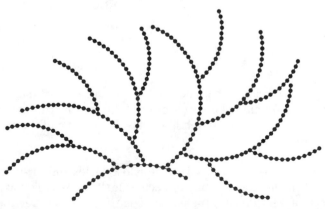

Figure 17.8. A representation of the branched structure of amylopectin. Each ●–● represents a glucose molecule.

Amylopectin, a much larger polysaccharide than amylose, contains 1000 or more glucose units per molecule. Like the chain in amylose, the main chain of amylopectin contains 1,4'-α-D-glucose. Unlike amylose, amylopectin is *branched* so that there is a terminal glucose about every 25 glucose units (Figure 17.8). The bonding at the branch point is a 1,6'-α-glycosidic bond.

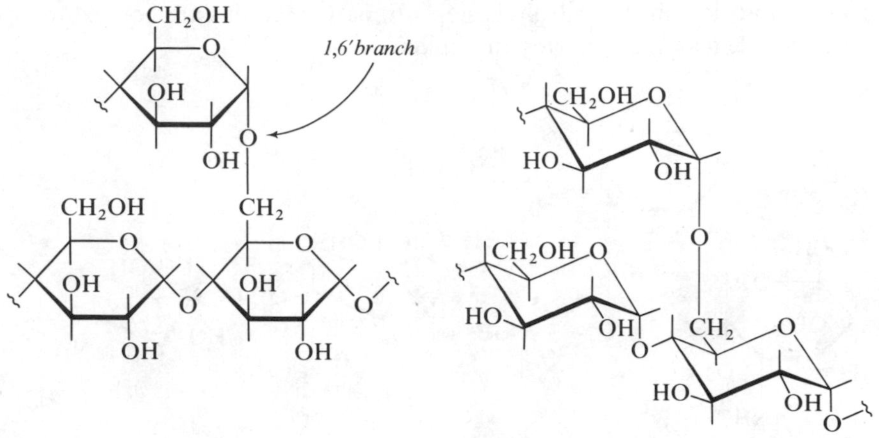

amylopectin

Complete hydrolysis of amylopectin yields only D-glucose. However, incomplete hydrolysis yields a mixture of the disaccharides maltose and isomaltose, the latter arising from the 1,6'-branching. The oligosaccharide mixture obtained from the partial hydrolysis of amylopectin, which is referred to as **dextrins**, is used to make glue, paste, and fabric sizing.

$$\text{amylopectin} \xrightarrow{\text{H}_2\text{O}} \text{dextrins} \xrightarrow{\text{H}_2\text{O}} \text{maltose} + \text{isomaltose} \xrightarrow{\text{H}_2\text{O}} \text{D-glucose}$$

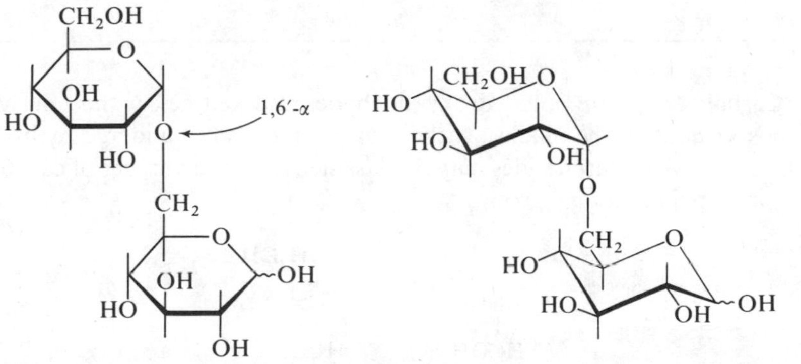

isomaltose
6-*O*-(α-D-glucopyranosyl)-D-glucopyranose

C. Glycogen

Glycogen is a polysaccharide that is used as a storehouse (primarily in the liver and muscles) for glucose in an animal system. Structurally, glycogen is related to amylopectin. It contains chains of 1,4'-α-linked glucose with branches (1,6'-α). The difference between glycogen and amylopectin is that glycogen is more branched than amylopectin.

D.   Chitin

The principal structural polysaccharide of the arthropods (for example, crabs and insects) is **chitin**. It has been estimated that 10^9 tons of chitin are biosynthesized each year! Chitin is a linear polysaccharide consisting of β-linked *N*-acetyl-D-glucosamine. Upon hydrolysis, chitin yields 2-amino-2-deoxy-D-glucose. (The acetyl group is lost in the hydrolysis step.) In nature, chitins are bonded to non-polysaccharide material (proteins and lipids).

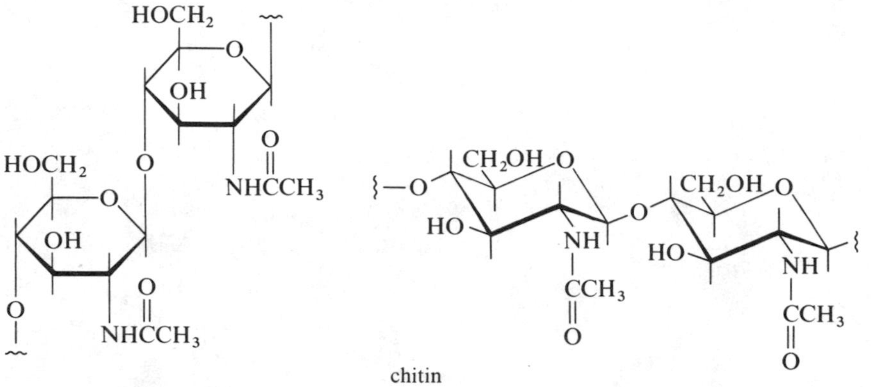

chitin

STUDY PROBLEM

17.20 Give the structures for the major organic products when chitin is treated with: (a) hot dilute aqueous HCl,   and   (b) hot dilute aqueous NaOH.

SUMMARY

Carbohydrates are polyhydroxy aldehydes and ketones or their derivatives. A **monosaccharide** is the smallest carbohydrate; it does not undergo hydrolysis to smaller units. Monosaccharides may be classified as to the number of carbons and to the principal functional group:

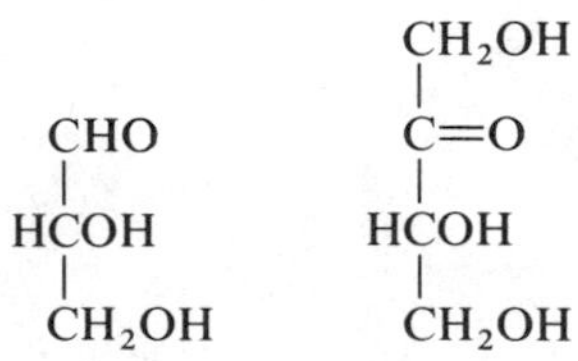

an aldotriose   *a tetrulose*

Natural monosaccharides generally belong to the D-**series**. Because of the presence of both hydroxyl and carbonyl groups, monosaccharides that can form **furanose** or **pyranose** hemiacetal or hemiketal rings undergo cyclization. The cyclization creates a new chiral center and therefore gives rise to a pair of diastereomers called α **and** β **anomers**. In solution, the anomers are in equilibrium with each other.

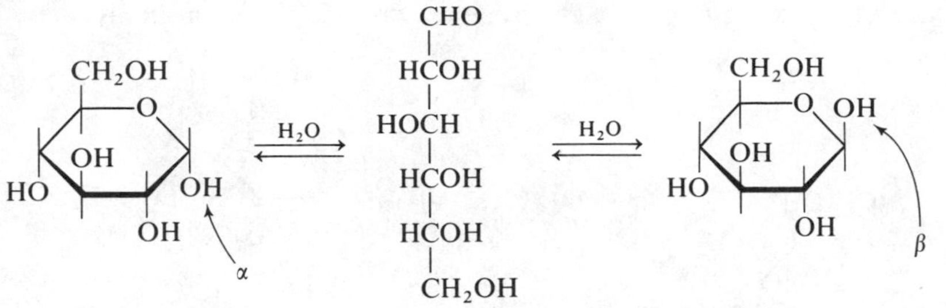

Because of the equilibrium, a monosaccharide undergoes reactions typical of aldehydes.

a glycoside

an aldonic acid

an alditol

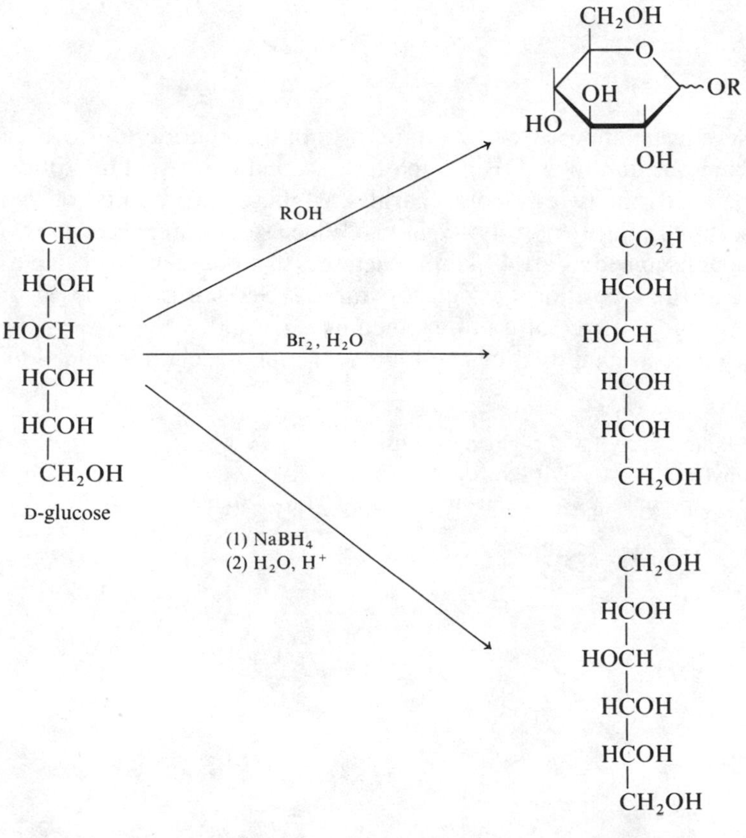

Vigorous oxidation of an aldose gives an **aldaric acid**.

D-glucose *an aldaric acid*

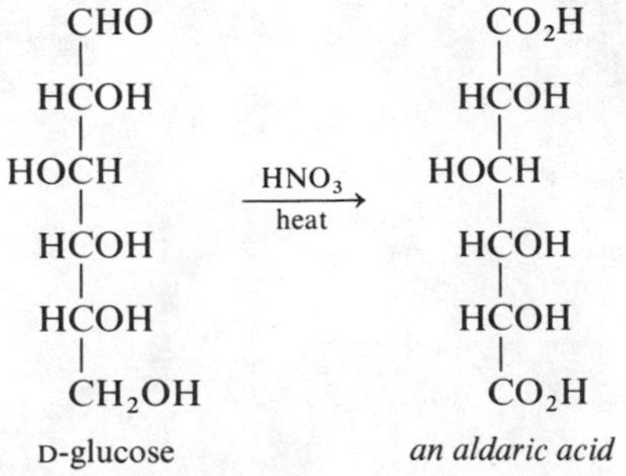

The hydroxyl groups of a glycoside may be acetylated or methylated:

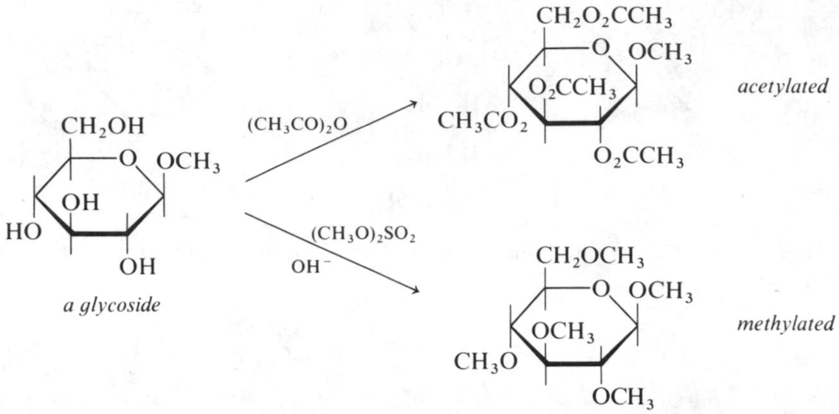

a glycoside

acetylated

methylated

Disaccharides are composed of two units of monosaccharide joined by a glycoside link from one unit to an OH group of the second unit. Acid hydrolysis of a disaccharide yields the two monosaccharides. **Maltose** is composed of two D-glucopyranose units joined by a 1,4'-α link. **Cellobiose** is composed of two D-glucopyranose units joined by a 1,4'-β link. **Lactose** is composed of β-D-galacto-pyranose joined to the 4-position of D-glucopyranose. **Sucrose** is composed of α-D-glucopyranose and β-D-fructofuranose joined by a 1,1' link.

A **polysaccharide** is composed of many units of monosaccharide joined by glycosidic links:

cellulose:	1,4'-β-D-glucopyranose
amylose:	1,4'-α-D-glucopyranose
amylopectin:	1,4'-α-D-glucopyranose with 1,6'-α-branching

STUDY PROBLEMS

17.21 Match each of the following classes of compound with a structure on the right:

(a)   a hexulose   (1)

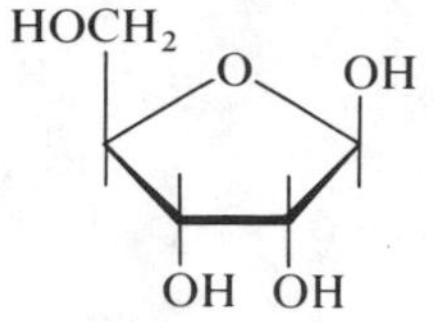

(b)   a pentopyranose   (2)

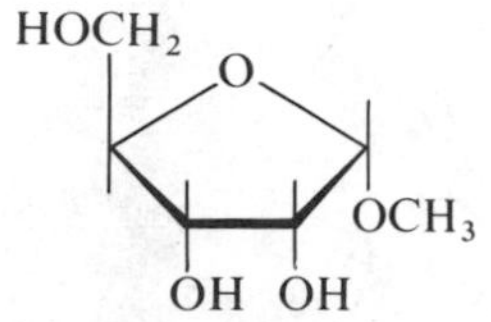

(c)   a pentofuranose   (3)

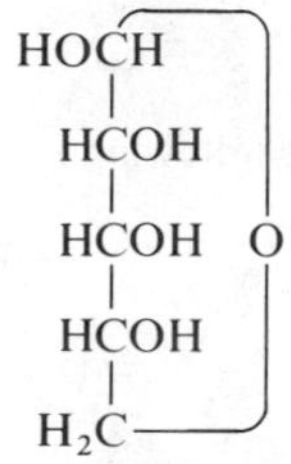

(d)   a pentofuranoside   (4)

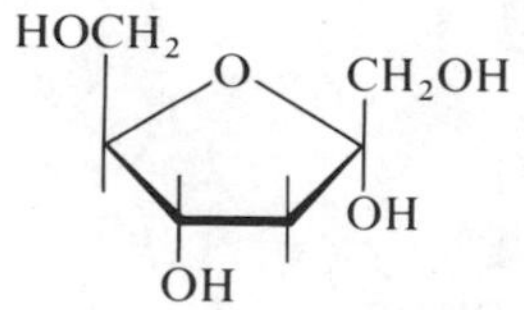

17.22 Label each of the structures in Problem 17.21 as D or L.

17.23 Give the structure for (and label as α or β) the anomer of each structure in Problem 17.21.

17.24 Give the Fischer projections for the open-chain forms of all the isomeric D-hexuloses and indicate the chiral carbons in each.

17.25 Assign (R) or (S) configuration to (a) L-glyceraldehyde; (b) D-erythrose; and (c) D-lactic acid (2-hydroxypropanoic acid).

17.26 Give Fischer projections (all possibilities) for: (a) *meso*-2,3,4-trichloropentane; (b) D-2,3,4,5-tetrahydroxypentanoic acid; (c) (R)-glyceraldehyde; (d) (2R,3R)-2,3,4-trihydroxybutanal; (e) 1,3-dibromo-2-propanol.

17.27 (a)   When (R)-2-hydroxypropanal is treated with HCN, what products are obtained?
(b)   Are those products optically active? Explain.

17.28 A chemist has a single stereoisomer of 1,2,3,4-butanetetraol of unknown configuration. He also has a flask of D-glyceraldehyde. Suggest a reaction sequence that could be used to relate the configuration of the tetraol to that of D-glyceraldehyde.

17.29 Give Haworth projections for the following monosaccharides:

(a)

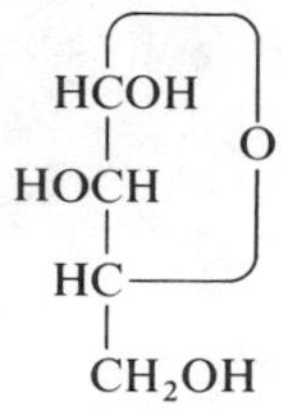

HCOH
|
HOCH   O
|
HC————
|
CH₂OH

(b)

HOCH
|
HOCH
|
HCOH   O
|
HOCH
|
HC————
|
CH₂OH

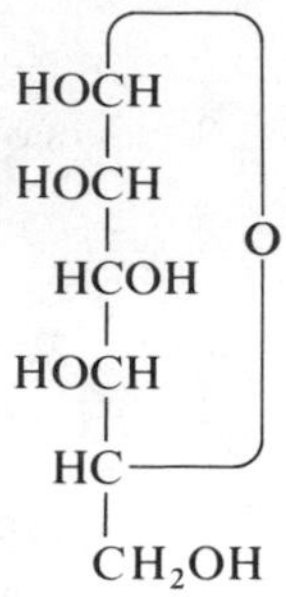

(c)

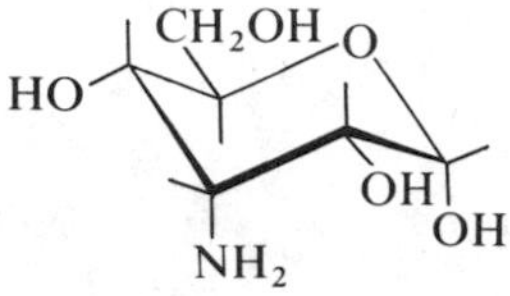

(d) β-D-altropyranose

17.30 Give Fischer projections for the following monosaccharides:

(a)

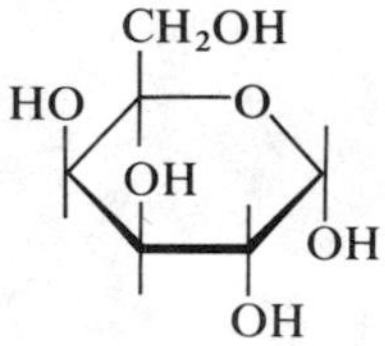

(b)

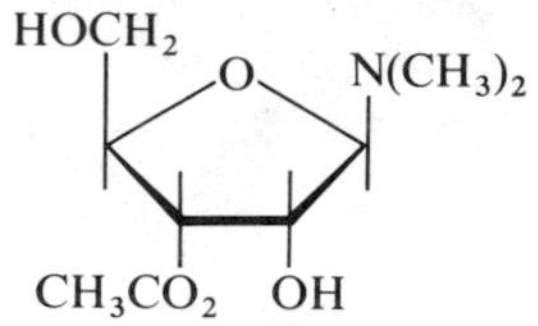

(c)

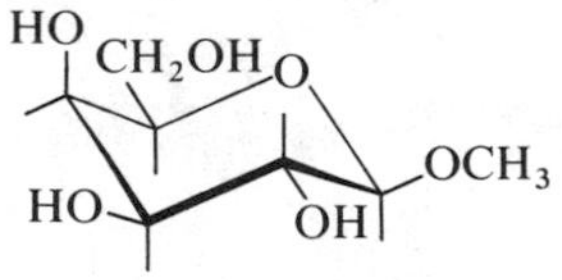

(d) α-D-lyxofuranose

17.31 Write equations (using Haworth formulas) that illustrate:

(a)   the mutarotation of pure α-D-mannopyranose in water
(b)   the reversible formation of α- and β-D-arabinofuranose from the aldehyde form in water
(c)   the conversion of β-D-fructofuranose to β-D-fructopyranose
(d)   the mutarotation of β-maltose.

17.32 Which of the following compounds would *not* undergo mutarotation?

(a)

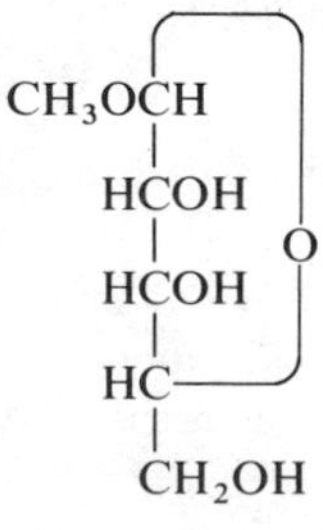

CH₃OCH
|
HCOH
| O
HCOH
|
HC————
|
CH₂OH

(b)

HOCH
|
CH₃OCH
| O
CH₃OCH
|
HC————
|
CH₂OCH₃

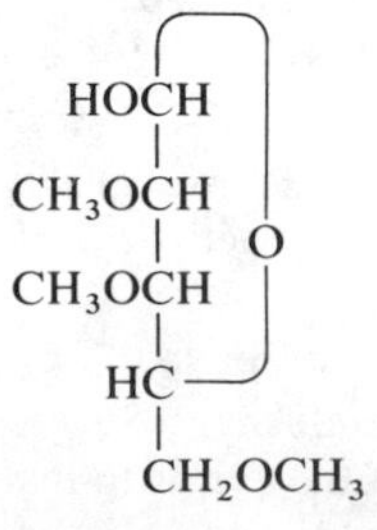

(c)

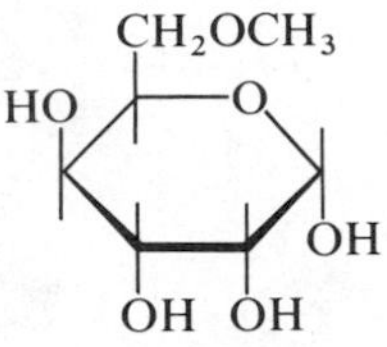

(d)

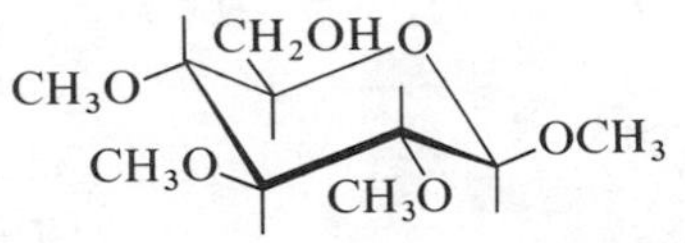

(e)

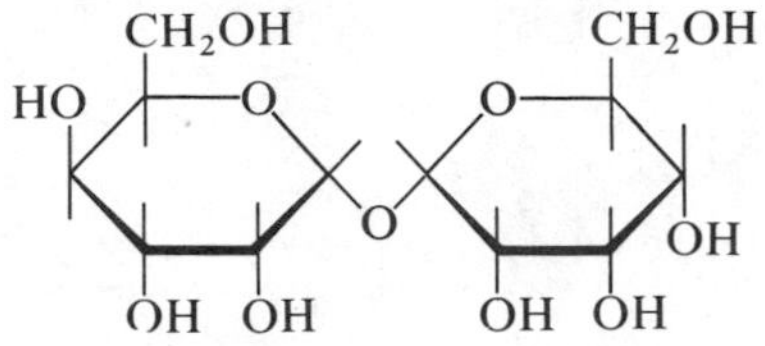

(f)

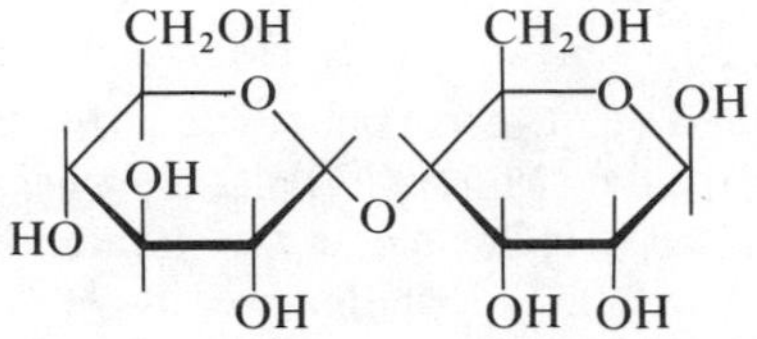

(g) 6-*O*-(α-D-galactopyranosyl)-β-D-glucopyranose
(h) α-D-glucopyranosyl α-D-glucopyranoside

17.33 Which of the structures in Problem 17.32 are nonreducing sugars?

17.34 What would you expect to be the most stable conformation for: (a) β-D-manno-pyranose; (b) β-D-galactopyranose; and (c) α-D-idopyranose? Give structures and reasons for your answers.

17.35 Which would be the more stable, β-D-galactopyranose or β-D-glucopyranose? Why?

17.36 Give the structures of the major organic products:

(a) D-glucose + $(CH_3)_2CHOH$ $\xrightarrow{H^+}$

(b) D-galactose + CH_3CH_2OH $\xrightarrow{H^+}$

(c) methyl α-D-ribofuranoside $\xrightarrow[\text{heat}]{H_2O,\ H^+}$

17.37 The oxidation of D-fructose with Tollens reagent yields a mixture of anions of D-mannonic acid and D-gluconic acid. Explain.

17.38 *Algin* is a polysaccharide obtained from seaweed. It is hydrolyzed to D-mannuronic acid. What is the structure of this acid?

17.39 Give the structure and the name of the organic product obtained when D-galactose is treated with: (a) aqueous Br_2; (b) hot HNO_3; and (c) Tollens reagent.

17.40 Fill in the blanks (give *all* possibilities):

(a) _____ $\xrightarrow{\text{hot HNO}_3}$ *meso*-tartaric acid
     (a D-tetrose)

(b) _____ $\xrightarrow{\text{hot HNO}_3}$ a *meso*-aldaric acid
     (a D-hexose)

(c) _____ $\xrightarrow[\text{cold}]{\text{dil. HCl}}$

(d) _____ $\xrightarrow[\text{(2) H}_2\text{O, H}^+]{\text{(1) NaBH}_4}$ a *meso*-alditol
     (a D-aldohexose)

17.41 Predict the major organic product for the reaction of D-mannose with; (a) $Br_2 + H_2O$; (b) HNO_3; (c) ethanol $+ H^+$; (d) [the product from (c)] plus dimethyl sulfate and NaOH; (e) [the product from (c)] plus methyl iodide and Ag_2O; (f) acetic anhydride; (g) acetyl chloride $+$ pyridine; (h) $NaBH_4$; (i) HCN followed by H_2O and HCl; (j) $LiAlH_4$ followed by water; (k) H_2 and Ni catalyst; (l) [the product from (c)] plus H_2O, HCl.

17.42 Predict the major organic product of the treatment of amylose with dimethyl sulfate and NaOH, followed by hydrolysis in dilute HCl.

17.43 Methyl β-D-gulopyranoside is treated with (1) dimethyl sulfate plus NaOH; (2) H_2O, H^+; and then (3) hot HNO_3. Write the equations that illustrate the steps in this reaction sequence.

17.44 How would you distinguish chemically between (a) maltose and sucrose? (b) D-lyxose and D-xylose?

17.45 How many possible disaccharides could be formed from just D-glucopyranose? (The α and β links form *different* disaccharides.)

17.46 If a polysaccharide were composed of 1,4′-α-linked D-glucopyranose with 1,3′-α-linked branches, what are the possible disaccharides that would be obtained upon partial hydrolysis?

17.47 *Trehalose* is a nonreducing sugar with the formula $C_{12}H_{22}O_{11}$. Upon hydrolysis, only D-glucose is obtained. What are the possible structures of trehalose?

17.48 A carbohydrate A ($C_{12}H_{22}O_{11}$) was treated with (1) CH_3OH, H^+, and (2) excess methyl iodide and Ag_2O. The product B was hydrolyzed to 2,3,4,6-tetra-*O*-methyl-D-galactose and 2,3,6-tri-*O*-methyl-D-glucose. When A was treated with aqueous acid, the products were D-galactose and D-glucose in equal amounts. When A was treated with aqueous Br_2, a carboxylic acid C was isolated. Hydrolysis of C with aqueous HCl resulted in D-gluconic acid as the only acid. What are the structures of A, B, and C?

Chapter 18

Amino Acids and Proteins

Proteins are among the most important compounds in an animal organism. Appropriately, the word protein is derived from the Greek *proteios*, which means "first." Proteins are *polyamides*, and hydrolysis of a protein yields *amino acids*.

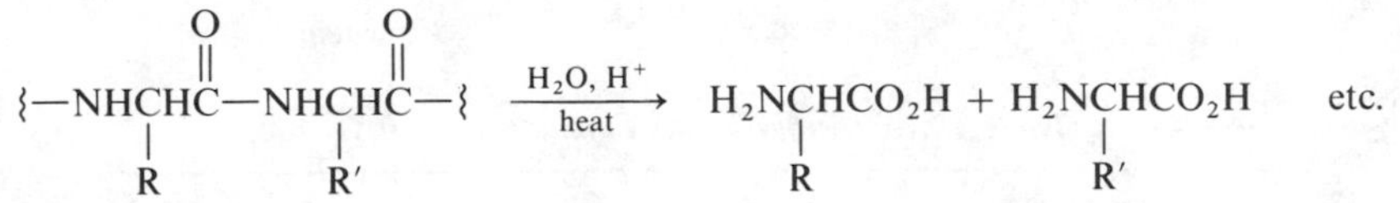

$$\{-NHCHC-NHCHC-\} \xrightarrow[\text{heat}]{H_2O, H^+} H_2NCHCO_2H + H_2NCHCO_2H \quad \text{etc.}$$

a protein   *amino acids*

Only twenty amino acids are commonly found in plant and animal proteins, yet these twenty amino acids can be combined in a variety of ways to form muscles, tendons, skin, fingernails, feathers, silk, hemoglobin, enzymes, antibodies, and many hormones. We will first consider the amino acids and then discuss how their combinations can lead to such diverse products.

The Structures of Amino Acids

The amino acids found in proteins are **α-aminocarboxylic acids**. Variation in the structures of these monomers occurs in the side chain.

α amino group $H_2N-\overset{\displaystyle CO_2H}{\underset{\displaystyle R}{C}}-H$ *variation in structure occurs in the side chain*

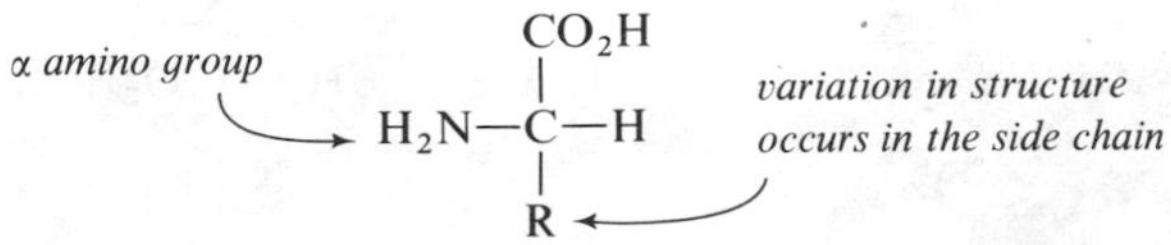

The simplest amino acid is aminoacetic acid ($H_2NCH_2CO_2H$), called *glycine*, which has no side chain and consequently does not contain a chiral center. All other amino acids have side chains, and therefore their α carbons are chiral. Naturally occurring amino acids have an (S)-configuration at the α carbon and are said to belong to the L-series—that is, the groups around the α carbon have the same configuration as in L-glyceraldehyde.

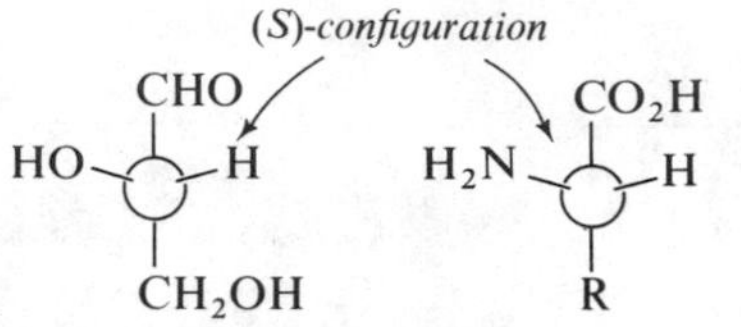

$$(S)\text{-configuration}$$

L-glyceraldehyde   an L-*amino acid*

Three examples of amino acids follow. Table 18.1 contains a complete list of the twenty amino acids commonly found in proteins. Also included in this table are abbreviations for the amino acid names. The use of these abbreviations will be discussed later in this chapter.

Fischer projections for three amino acids:

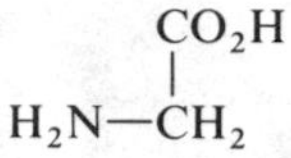

glycine
achiral

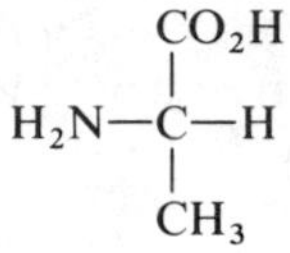

(S)-alanine 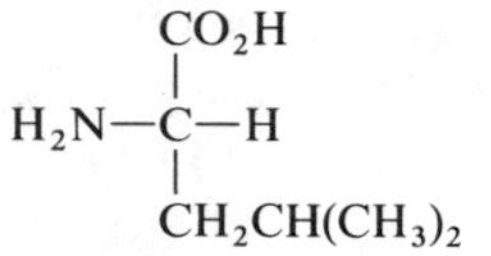   (S)-leucine

Table 18.1.   Amino Acids Found in Proteins

Name	Abbreviation	Structure
alanine	ala	CH_3CHCO_2H $\qquad$ | $\qquad NH_2$
arginine*	arg	$H_2NCNHCH_2CH_2CH_2CHCO_2H$ $\quad$ || $\qquad\qquad\qquad$ | $\quad NH \qquad\qquad\qquad\quad NH_2$
asparagine	asn	$\qquad\quad O$ $\qquad\quad$ || $H_2NCCH_2CHCO_2H$ $\qquad\qquad\quad$ | $\qquad\qquad\quad NH_2$
aspartic acid	asp	$HO_2CCH_2CHCO_2H$ $\qquad\qquad\quad$ | $\qquad\qquad\quad NH_2$
cysteine	cyS	$HSCH_2CHCO_2H$ $\qquad\quad$ | $\qquad\quad NH_2$
glutamic acid	glu	$HO_2CCH_2CH_2CHCO_2H$ $\qquad\qquad\qquad$ | $\qquad\qquad\qquad NH_2$
glutamine	gln	$\qquad\quad O$ $\qquad\quad$ || $H_2NCCH_2CH_2CHCO_2H$ $\qquad\qquad\qquad$ | $\qquad\qquad\qquad NH_2$
glycine	gly	CH_2CO_2H $\quad$ | $\quad NH_2$

Table 18.1 (*continued*)

Name	Abbreviation	Structure
histidine*	his	imidazole—CH_2CHCO_2H, with NH_2
isoleucine*	ile	$CH_3CH_2CHCHCO_2H$, with CH_3 and NH_2
leucine*	leu	$(CH_3)_2CHCH_2CHCO_2H$, with NH_2
lysine*	lys	$H_2NCH_2CH_2CH_2CH_2CHCO_2H$, with NH_2
methionine*	met	$CH_3SCH_2CH_2CHCO_2H$, with NH_2
phenylalanine*	phe	phenyl—CH_2CHCO_2H, with NH_2
proline	pro	pyrrolidine—CO_2H
serine	ser	$HOCH_2CHCO_2H$, with NH_2
threonine*	thr	$CH_3CHCHCO_2H$, with OH and NH_2
tryptophan*	try	indole—CH_2CHCO_2H, with NH_2
tyrosine	tyr	HO—phenyl—CH_2CHCO_2H, with NH_2
valine*	val	$(CH_3)_2CHCHCO_2H$, with NH_2

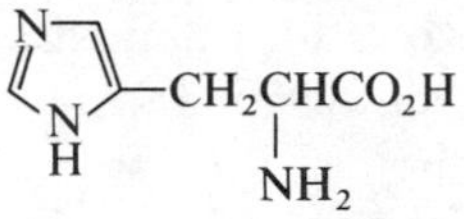

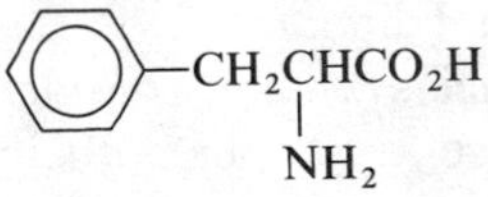

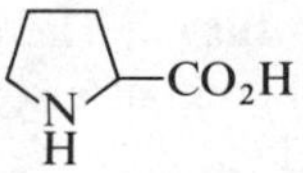

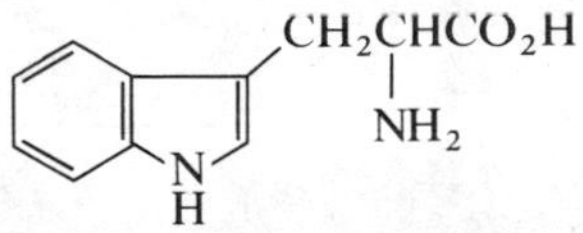

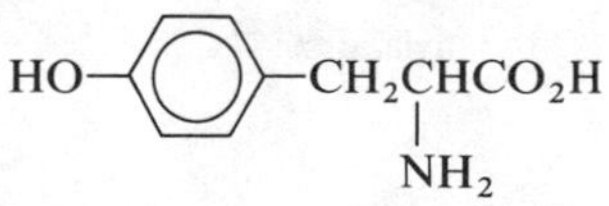

* Essential amino acid

A. Essential Amino Acids

Most amino acids can be synthesized by an organism from its "pool" of organic compounds. One such mode of synthesis is the conversion of an amino acid that is present in excess to a desired amino acid by a **transamination reaction**. The mechanism for this reaction was presented in Section 11.10.

Circled groups exchanged:

old amino acid	*old keto acid*	*new keto acid* *new amino acid*

Not all amino acids can be obtained by interconversions from other amino acids or by synthesis from other compounds in the animal system. Amino acids that are required for protein synthesis and cannot be synthesized by the organism must be present in the diet. Such compounds are referred to as **essential amino acids**. Which amino acids are essential depends upon the species of animal and even upon individual differences.

The amino acids usually considered essential for humans are starred in Table 18.1. Of these, tryptophan, phenylalanine, methionine, and histidine can be enzymatically converted from (R) to (S); thus, a racemic mixture of these amino acids can be totally utilized. The other essential amino acids must be provided in the diet in their (S)-configurations to be used in protein biosynthesis.

As an example of individual differences in requirements for amino acids, let us look at *tyrosine*. This amino acid is not considered an essential amino acid because, in most people, tyrosine can be synthesized from phenylalanine. A small percent of individuals who have inherited a condition known as **phenylketonuria** (PKU) do not have the enzyme necessary for this conversion. The diet of a person with PKU must contain some tyrosine and must be limited in its quantity of phenylalanine.

Note that *lysine* is one of the essential amino acids. Animal protein contains abundant lysine, but the protein in most grains contains an insufficient supply of lysine for human needs. Development of high-lysine corn in recent years has helped alleviate malnutrition due to lysine deficiency in parts of the world where meat is scarce.

B. *Importance of Side-Chain Structure*

How can polymers composed of twenty similar amino acids have such a wide variety of properties? Part of the answer lies in the nature of the side chains in the amino acids. Note in Table 18.1 that some amino acids have side chains that contain carboxyl groups; these are classified as **acidic amino acids**. Amino acids containing side chains with amino groups are classified as **basic amino acids**. These acidic and basic side chains help determine the structure and reactivity of the proteins in which they are found. The rest of the amino acids are classified as **neutral amino acids**. The side chains of neutral amino acids are also important. For example, some of these side chains contain —OH, —SH, or other polar groups that can undergo hydrogen bonding, which we will find is an important feature in overall protein structure.

$$CO_2H$$
$$H_2NCH$$
$$\boxed{CH_2CH_2CO_2H}$$

glutamic acid
an acidic amino acid

$$CO_2H$$
$$H_2NCH$$
$$\boxed{(CH_2)_4NH_2}$$

lysine
a basic amino acid

$$CO_2H$$
$$H_2NCH$$
$$\boxed{CH(CH_3)_2}$$

valine
a neutral amino acid
with a nonpolar side chain

$$CO_2H$$
$$H_2NCH$$
$$\boxed{CH_2OH}$$

serine
a neutral amino acid
with a polar side chain

The characteristics of a protein are changed if a carboxylic acid group in a side chain is converted to an amide. Note the difference in the side chains of glutamine and glutamic acid.

$$CO_2H$$
$$H_2NCH$$
$$CH_2CH_2CO_2H$$

acidic

glutamic acid

$$CO_2H$$
$$H_2NCH \quad\quad O$$
$$\quad\quad\quad\quad\quad \|$$
$$CH_2CH_2CNH_2$$

neutral

glutamine

The thiol side chain in cysteine plays a unique role in protein structure. Thiols can undergo oxidative coupling to yield disulfides (Section 7.20). This coupling between two units of cysteine yields a new amino acid called cystine and provides a means of cross-linking protein chains. Giving hair a "permanent wave" involves breaking some existing S—S cross-links by reduction and then reforming new S—S links in other positions of the protein chains.

$$
\text{first protein chain:}\quad \{-\text{NHCHC}-\}\atop{\underset{\text{CH}_2\text{SH}}{|}}
$$

first protein chain: }—NHCHC—{
                               |
                              CH₂SH

second protein chain: }—NHCHC—{
                               ||
                               O

$\xrightarrow[\text{[H]}]{\text{[O]}}$

}—NHCHC—{
      |
     CH₂
      |
      S   ← cross-link
      | between chains
      S
      |
     CH₂
      |
}—NHCHC—{
      ||
      O

The order in which amino acids are found in a protein molecule determines the relationship of the side chains to one another and consequently determines how the protein interacts with itself and with its environment. For example, a hormone or other water-soluble protein contains many amino acids with polar side chains, while an insoluble muscle protein contains a greater proportion of amino acids with nonpolar side chains.

The importance of the side chains of amino acids is illustrated by the condition known as **sickle-cell anemia**. The difference between normal hemoglobin and sickle-cell hemoglobin is that, in a protein molecule of 146 amino acid units, one single unit has been changed from glutamic acid (with an acidic side chain) to valine (with a nonpolar side chain). This one small error in the protein renders the affected hemoglobin less soluble and thus less able to perform its prescribed task of carrying oxygen to the cells of the body.

Section 18.2

Amino Acids as Dipolar Ions

Amino acids do not always behave like organic compounds. For example, they have melting points of over 200°, whereas most organic compounds of similar molecular weight are liquids at room temperature. Amino acids are soluble in water and other polar solvents, but insoluble in nonpolar solvents such as diethyl ether or benzene. Amino acids have large dipole moments. Also, they are less acidic than most carboxylic acids and less basic than most amines.

$$
\begin{array}{ccc}
\text{RCO}_2\text{H} & \text{RNH}_2 & \underset{\displaystyle R}{\overset{\displaystyle \text{CO}_2\text{H}}{\underset{|}{\overset{|}{\text{H}_2\text{NCH}}}}} \\
pK_a = \sim 5 & pK_b = \sim 4 & \\
& & pK_a = \sim 10 \\
& & pK_b = \sim 12
\end{array}
$$

Why do amino acids exhibit such unusual properties? The reason is that an amino acid contains a basic amino group and an acidic carboxyl group in the same molecule. An amino acid undergoes an internal acid–base reaction to yield a **dipolar ion**, also called a **zwitterion** (from German zwitter, "hybrid"). Because of the resultant ionic charges, an amino acid has many properties of a salt. Furthermore, the pK_a of an amino acid is not the pK_a of a —CO_2H group, but that of an

—NH_3^+ group. The pK_b is not that of a basic amino group, but that of the very weakly basic —CO_2^- group.

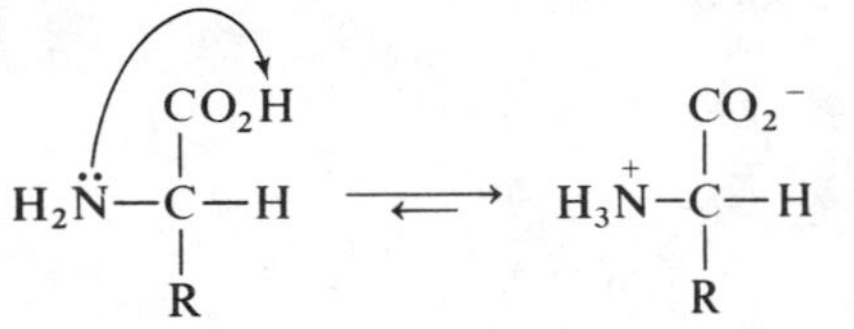

a dipolar ion

STUDY PROBLEMS

18.1 When each of the following amino acids is dissolved in water, would the solution be acidic, basic, or near-neutral? (Refer to Table 18.1 for the structures.)

(a) glutamic acid; (b) glutamine; (c) leucine; (d) lysine; (e) serine.

18.2 Monosodium glutamate (MSG) is widely used as a condiment. What is the most likely structure for this compound? (*Hint:* Which carboxyl group in glutamic acid is more acidic?)

Section 18.3

Amphoterism of Amino Acids

An amino acid contains both a carboxylate ion (—CO_2^-) and an ammonium ion (—NH_3^+) in the same molecule. Therefore, an amino acid is **amphoteric**: it can undergo reaction with either acid or base to yield a cation or an anion, respectively.

In acid:

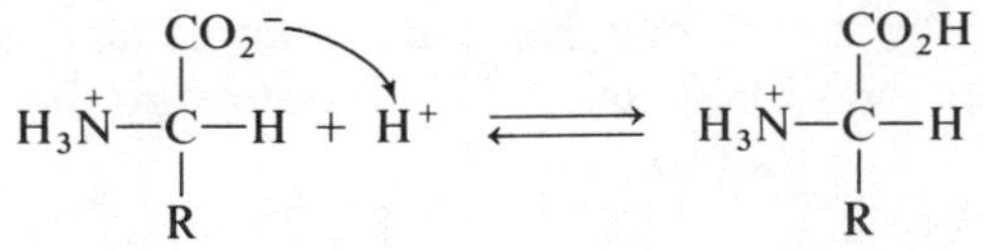

a cation

In base:

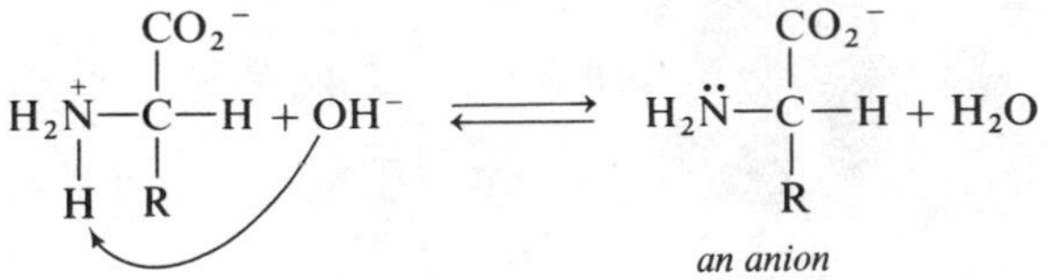

an anion

STUDY PROBLEM

18.3 Predict the product of reaction of each of the following amino acids with an excess of aqueous HCl and with an excess of aqueous NaOH:

(a) proline; (b) tyrosine; (c) serine; (d) aspartic acid.

You might think that an aqueous solution of a so-called neutral amino acid would be neutral. However, aqueous solutions of neutral amino acids are slightly *acidic* because the —NH_3^+ group is a stronger acid than —CO_2^- is a base. The result of the difference in acidity and basicity is that an aqueous solution of alanine contains more amino acid anions than cations. We can say that alanine carries a *net negative charge* in aqueous solution.

At pH 7, alanine carries a net negative charge:

$$
\underset{\substack{\text{weaker base}}}{}
$$

weaker base →

$$
\begin{array}{c}
CO_2^- \\
| \\
H_3\overset{+}{N}-C-H + H_2O \\
| \\
CH_3
\end{array}
\rightleftharpoons
\begin{array}{c}
CO_2^- \\
| \\
H_2N-C-H + H_3O^+ \\
| \\
CH_3
\end{array}
$$

stronger acid ↗

no net charge   *net negative charge*

If a small amount of HCl or other acid is added to an alanine solution, the acid–base equilibrium is shifted so that the net charge on the alanine ions becomes zero. The pH at which an amino acid carries no net ionic charge is defined as the **isoelectric point** of that amino acid. The isoelectric point of alanine is 6.0.

At pH 6, alanine carries no net charge:

$$
\begin{array}{c}
CO_2^- \\
| \\
H_2N-C-H + H_3O^+ \\
| \\
CH_3
\end{array}
\rightleftharpoons
\begin{array}{c}
CO_2^- \\
| \\
H_3\overset{+}{N}-C-H \\
| \\
CH_3
\end{array}
$$

Isoelectric points are determined by **electrophoresis**, a process of measuring the migration of ions in an electric field. This is accomplished by placing a pair of electrodes in an aqueous solution of an amino acid. In this cell, anions migrate toward the anode (positive electrode), and cations migrate toward the cathode (negative electrode). If alanine or other neutral amino acid is dissolved in plain water, there is a net migration of amino acid ions toward the cathode.

At its isoelectric point, an amino acid does not migrate toward either electrode in an electrophoresis cell. The isoelectric point of a given amino acid is a physical constant. The value varies from amino acid to amino acid, but falls into one of three general ranges.

For a *neutral amino acid*, the isoelectric point, which depends primarily on the relative pK_a and pK_b of the $-NH_3^+$ and $-CO_2^-$ groups, is around 5.5–6.0.

The second carboxyl group in an *acidic amino acid* means that there is another group that can interact with water. A water solution of an acidic amino acid is definitely acidic, and the amino acid ion carries a net negative charge.

$$
\underset{\underset{\displaystyle CH_2CH_2CO_2\;\text{H}}{\overset{\displaystyle \overset{+}{H_3N}-\overset{\displaystyle |}{\underset{|}{C}}-H}{\overset{\displaystyle CO_2^-}{|}}}}{}
\quad + H_2O \;\rightleftharpoons\;
\underset{\underset{\displaystyle CH_2CH_2CO_2{}^-}{\overset{\displaystyle \overset{+}{H_3N}-\overset{\displaystyle |}{\underset{|}{C}}-H}{\overset{\displaystyle CO_2^-}{|}}}}{}
\quad + H_3O^+
$$

acidic   *net negative charge*

A *greater concentration of H⁺* is required to bring an acidic amino acid to the iso-electric point than is needed for a neutral amino acid. The isoelectric points for acidic amino acids are near pH 3.

A *basic amino acid* has a second amino group that undergoes reaction with water to form a positive ion. Hydroxide ions are needed to neutralize a basic amino acid and bring it to its isoelectric point. For basic amino acids, we would expect the isoelectric points to be above pH 7, and that indeed is the case. These isoelectric points are in the range of 9–10. Isoelectric points of some representative amino acids are found in Table 18.2.

$$
\underset{\underset{\displaystyle (CH_2)_4\;NH_2}{\overset{\displaystyle \overset{+}{H_3N}-\overset{\displaystyle |}{\underset{|}{C}}-H}{\overset{\displaystyle CO_2^-}{|}}}}{}
\quad + H_2O \;\rightleftharpoons\;
\underset{\underset{\displaystyle (CH_2)_4\overset{+}{N}H_3}{\overset{\displaystyle \overset{+}{H_3N}-\overset{\displaystyle |}{\underset{|}{C}}-H}{\overset{\displaystyle CO_2^-}{|}}}}{}
\quad + OH^-
$$

basic   *net positive charge*

Table 18.2. *Isoelectric Points for Some Amino Acids*

Name	Structure	Isoelectric point
Neutral:		
alanine	CH_3CHCO_2H $\quad\;\;|$ $\quad\; NH_2$	6.00
glutamine	$\quad\quad O$ $\quad\quad\|\|$ $H_2NCCH_2CH_2CHCO_2H$ $\quad\quad\quad\quad\quad\;\; |$ $\quad\quad\quad\quad\quad\; NH_2$	5.65
Acidic:		
glutamic acid	$HO_2CCH_2CH_2CHCO_2H$ $\quad\quad\quad\quad\quad |$ $\quad\quad\quad\quad\; NH_2$	3.22
aspartic acid	$HO_2CCH_2CHCO_2H$ $\quad\quad\quad\quad |$ $\quad\quad\quad NH_2$	2.77
Basic:		
lysine	$H_2N(CH_2)_4CHCO_2H$ $\quad\quad\quad\quad\; |$ $\quad\quad\quad\; NH_2$	9.74
arginine	$H_2NCNH(CH_2)_3CHCO_2H$ $\quad\quad\|\|\quad\quad\quad\; |$ $\quad\quad NH\quad\quad\; NH_2$	10.76

STUDY PROBLEMS

18.4 Suggest a reason for the fact that the isoelectric point of lysine is 9.74, but that for tryptophan (Table 18.1) is only 5.89. (*Hint:* Think of a reason why the heterocyclic N in tryptophan is not basic.)

18.5 An amino acid undergoes reaction with two equivalents of the hydrate *ninhydrin* to yield *Ruhemann's purple*, a blue-violet product. This reaction is used as a test for the presence of amino acids in a sample of unknown composition. Draw the principal resonance structures for Ruehmann's purple.

ninhydrin

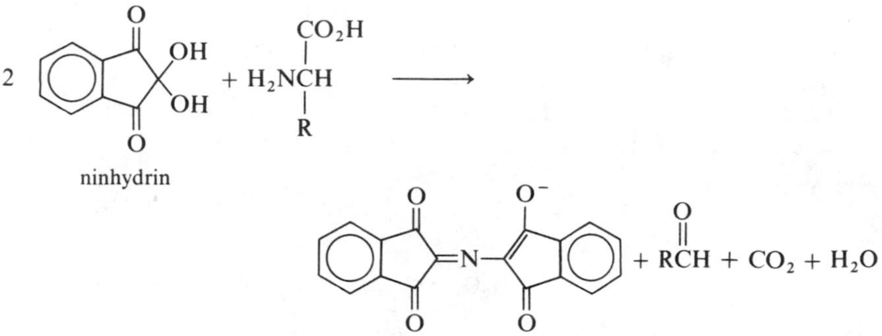

Ruhemann's purple
(*blue-violet*)

Section 18.4

Synthesis of Amino Acids

The common amino acids are relatively simple compounds, and the synthesis of racemic mixtures of most of these amino acids may be accomplished by standard techniques. The racemic mixtures may then be resolved to yield the pure enantiomeric amino acids.

The **Strecker synthesis** of amino acids, developed in 1850, is a two-step sequence. The first step is the reaction of an aldehyde with a mixture of ammonia and HCN to yield an aminonitrile. Hydrolysis of the aminonitrile results in the amino acid.

Step 1:

acetaldehyde

2-amino-
propanenitrile

Step 2:

(R)(S)-alanine

Another synthetic route to amino acids is by the **amination of an α-halo acid** with an excess of ammonia. (An excess of NH_3 must be used to neutralize the acid and to minimize overalkylation. See Section 15.6A.)

Formation of an α-halo acid (Section 13.3C):

$$(CH_3)_2CHCH_2CH_2CO_2H \xrightarrow[PBr_3]{Br_2} (CH_3)_2CHCH_2\overset{\overset{\displaystyle Br}{|}}{C}HCO_2H$$

4-methylpentanoic acid   2-bromo-4-methyl-
                                    pentanoic acid

Amination:

$$(CH_3)_2CHCH_2\overset{\overset{\displaystyle}{|}}{C}HCO_2H \xrightarrow{\ddot{N}H_3} (CH_3)_2CHCH_2\overset{\overset{\displaystyle NH_2}{|}}{C}HCO_2{}^- \; NH_4{}^+ \xrightarrow{H^+}$$

$$(CH_3)_2CHCH_2\overset{\overset{\displaystyle NH_2}{|}}{C}HCO_2H$$

(*R*)(*S*)-leucine

A more elegant route to amino acids is the **Gabriel phthalimide synthesis**, which was presented in Section 15.6A. The advantage of this synthesis over direct amination is that overalkylation cannot occur.

Reductive amination of an α-keto acid is another procedure used to obtain racemic amino acids.

$$CH_3\overset{\overset{\displaystyle O}{\|}}{C}CO_2H \xrightarrow{H_2, NH_3, Pd} CH_3\overset{\overset{\displaystyle NH_2}{|}}{C}HCO_2H$$

an α-keto acid   (*R*)(*S*)-alanine

Section 18.5

Peptides

A **peptide** is an amide formed from two or more amino acids. The amide link between an α-amino group of one amino acid and the carboxyl group of another amino acid is called a **peptide bond**. The following example of a peptide formed from alanine and glycine, called *alanylglycine*, illustrates the formation of a peptide bond.

$$H_2N\overset{\overset{\displaystyle O}{\|}}{C}HCOH + H_2N\overset{\overset{\displaystyle O}{\|}}{C}H_2COH \xrightarrow{-H_2O} H_2N\overset{\overset{\displaystyle O}{\|}}{C}HC\overset{peptide\ bond}{-}NHCH_2\overset{\overset{\displaystyle O}{\|}}{C}OH$$

          | |
         CH_3   CH_3

alanine   glycine   alanylglycine
                                              a dipeptide

Each amino acid in a peptide molecule is called a **unit**, or a **residue**. Depending upon the number of amino acid units in the molecule, a peptide may be referred to as a **dipeptide** (two units), a **tripeptide** (three units), and so forth. A **polypeptide** is a peptide with a large number of amino acid residues. What is the difference between a polypeptide and a protein? None, really. Both are polyamides constructed from amino acids. By convention, a polyamide with fewer than 50 amino acid residues is classified as a peptide, while a larger polyamide is considered to be a protein.

In the dipeptide alanylglycine, the alanine residue has a free amino group and the glycine unit has a free carboxyl group. However, alanine and glycine could be joined another way to form *glycylalanine*, in which glycine has the free amino group and alanine has the free carboxyl group.

Two different dipeptides from alanine and glycine:

$$\underset{\text{alanylglycine}}{\underset{\underset{CH_3}{|}}{H_2NCHC}\overset{\overset{O}{\|}}{}-NHCH_2\overset{\overset{O}{\|}}{C}OH} \qquad \underset{\text{glycylalanine}}{H_2NCH_2\overset{\overset{O}{\|}}{C}-\underset{\underset{CH_3}{|}}{NHCH}\overset{\overset{O}{\|}}{C}OH}$$

The greater the number of amino acid residues in a peptide, the greater the number of structural possibilities. Glycine and alanine can be bonded together in two ways. In a tripeptide, three amino acids can be joined in six different ways. Ten different amino acids could lead to over four trillion decapeptides!

For purposes of discussion, it is necessary to represent peptides in a systematic manner. The amino acid with the free amino group is usually placed at the left end of the structure. This amino acid is called the **N-terminal amino acid**. The amino acid with the free carboxyl group is placed at the right and is called the **C-terminal amino acid**. The name of the peptide is constructed from the names of the amino acids as they appear left-to-right, starting with the N-terminal amino acid.

N-terminal on left → ... ← *C-terminal on right*

$$H_2NCHC\overset{\overset{O}{\|}}{}-NHCHC\overset{\overset{O}{\|}}{}-NHCH_2\overset{\overset{O}{\|}}{C}OH$$

alanyltyrosylglycine
a tripeptide

For the sake of convenience and clarity, the names of the amino acids are often abbreviated. We have shown the abbreviations of the twenty common amino acids in Table 18.1. Using the abbreviated names, alanyltyrosylglycine becomes *ala–tyr–gly*.

Sample Problem

What is the structure of leu–lys–met?

Solution:

$$\underset{\underset{\text{leu}}{(CH_3)_2CHCH_2}}{H_2NCHC}\overset{\overset{O}{\|}}{}-\underset{\underset{\text{lys}}{(CH_2)_4NH_2}}{NHCHC}\overset{\overset{O}{\|}}{}-\underset{\underset{\text{met}}{CH_2CH_2SCH_3}}{NHCHCO_2H}$$

STUDY PROBLEM

18.6   Give all possibilities for the structure of a tripeptide consisting of ala, gly, and phe. (Use abbreviated names rather than structural formulas.)

Section 18.6

Bonding in Peptides

As was mentioned in Section 13.9C, an amide bond has some double-bond character due to partial overlap of the pi orbital of the carbonyl group with the unshared electrons of the nitrogen. The resonance structures show this overlap:

Evidence for the double-bond character of a peptide bond is found in bond lengths. The bond length of the peptide bond is shorter than that of the usual C—N single bond: 1.32 Å in the peptide bond versus 1.47 Å for a typical C—N single bond in an amine.

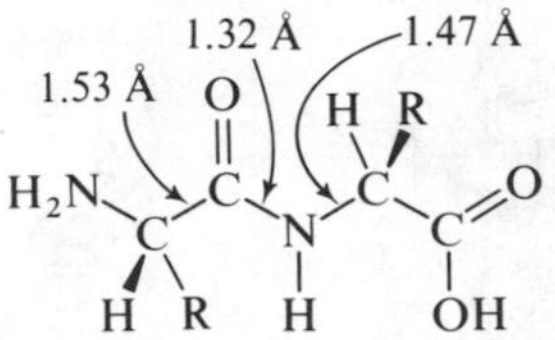

Because of the double-bond character of the peptide bond, rotation of groups around this bond is somewhat restricted, and the atoms attached to the carbonyl group and to the N all lie in the same plane.

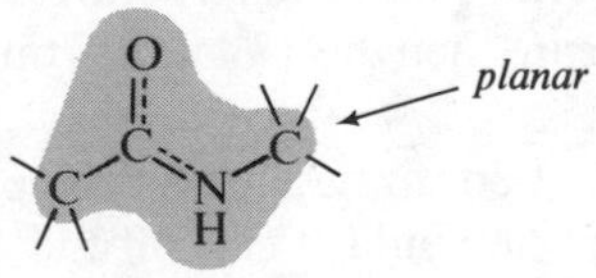

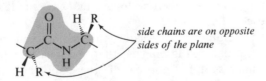

X-ray analysis shows that the amino acid side chains around the plane of the peptide bond are in a *trans* type of relationship. This stereochemistry minimizes steric hindrance between side chains.

side chains are on opposite sides of the plane

Section 18.7

Determination of Peptide Structure

The determination of a peptide structure is not an easy task. Complete hydrolysis in acidic solution yields the individual amino acids. These may be separated and identified by such techniques as chromatography or electrophoresis. The molecular weight of the peptide may be determined by physical–chemical methods. With this information, the chemist can determine the number of amino acid residues, the identity of the amino acid residues, and the number of residues of each amino acid in the original peptide. But this information reveals nothing about the order of attachment of the amino acids in the peptide.

Several techniques have been developed to determine the sequential order of amino acids in a peptide. The first is **terminal-residue analysis**. There are many ways of determining the *N*-terminal and *C*-terminal amino acid residues; we will mention just one technique for each.

Analysis for the *N*-terminal residue can be accomplished by treating the peptide with phenyl isothiocyanate.

phenyl isothiocyanate   *N-terminal*

a phenylthiohydantoin

The isothiocyanate undergoes reaction with the free amino group to form a thiourea derivative. Careful hydrolysis cleaves the *N*-terminal residue from the rest of the peptide and generates a cyclic structure called a *phenylthiohydantoin*. This modified end group can then be isolated from the reaction mixture and identified.

Why cannot the chemist continue to treat the peptide stepwise with phenyl isothiocyanate? In each step he could break off the *N*-terminal residue until the entire peptide was degraded and its order of amino acids determined. To a certain extent, this can be done; however, each cycle of thiourea formation and hydrolysis results in some hydrolysis of the remaining peptide. After about 40 cycles, the hydrolysis of the peptide is sufficient to produce many *N*-terminals in solution; the product phenylthiohydantoin is then no longer that of a single end group, but a mixture from a variety of end groups.

The *C*-terminal amino acid residue can be determined enzymatically. *Carboxypeptidase* is a pancreatic enzyme that specifically catalyzes hydrolysis of the *C*-terminal amino acid, but not that of other peptide bonds.

Partial hydrolysis of a peptide to dipeptides, tripeptides, tetrapeptides, and other fragments is one technique for determining the order of interior residues. The hydrolysis mixture is separated and the order of amino acid residues in each fragment determined (by end-group analysis, for example). The structures of the fragments are then pieced together like a jigsaw puzzle to give the structure of the entire peptide.

What is the structure of a pentapeptide that yields the following tripeptides when partially hydrolyzed?

gly–glu–arg, glu–arg–gly, arg–gly–phe

Solution: Fit the pieces together:

gly–glu–arg

glu–arg–gly

arg–gly–phe

The pentapeptide is gly–glu–arg–gly–phe.

Section 18.8

Synthesis of Peptides

As a check on a proposed structure for a peptide, a chemist may synthesize the peptide from the individual amino acids. The first peptide was synthesized by Emil Fischer, who in 1902 also put forth the idea that proteins were polyamides.

The synthesis of ordinary amides from acid chlorides and amines is a straight-forward reaction (Section 13.3C):

$$RCOCl + R'NH_2 \longrightarrow RCONHR'$$

However, the synthesis of peptides or proteins by this route is not straightforward. The principal problem is that there is more than one way in which the amino acids may join.

gly + ala $\longrightarrow$ gly–ala or ala–gly or gly–gly or ala–ala

gly–ala + phe $\longrightarrow$ phe–gly–ala or gly–ala–phe or

gly–ala–gly–ala or phe–phe

To prevent unwanted reactions, every other reactive group, including reactive groups in side chains, must be blocked. By leaving only the desired amino group and carboxyl group free, the chemist can control the positions of reaction.

$$\underset{\substack{\text{all other reactive} \\ \text{groups blocked}}}{\overset{O}{\underset{\|}{RCOH}}} \xrightarrow{SOCl_2} \left. \begin{array}{c} \overset{O}{\underset{\|}{RCCl}} \\ R'NH_2 \end{array} \right\} \xrightarrow{-HCl} \overset{O}{\underset{\|}{RCNHR'}}$$

The criteria for a good blocking group are (1) that it be inert to the reaction conditions needed for forming the desired amide link, and (2) that it be readily removable when the synthesis is complete. One such blocking group is a *carbamate group*—inert to the amide-formation reaction, but easily removed in a later step without disturbing the rest of the molecule. This approach to peptide synthesis was developed in 1932.

Preparation of carbamate to protect an amino group:

$$\text{C}_6\text{H}_5\text{—CH}_2\text{OCCl} \quad + \text{ H}_2\text{NCH}_2\text{COH} \xrightarrow{-\text{HCl}} \text{C}_6\text{H}_5\text{—CH}_2\text{OC}\underbrace{\text{—NHCH}_2\text{COH}}$$

from $Cl_2C{=}O + C_6H_5CH_2OH$ glycine   *carbamate group*

The amino-blocked glycine could be treated with $SOCl_2$ to form the acid chloride and then treated with a new amino acid to form an amide. However, acid chlorides are highly reactive and unwanted side reactions may occur despite blocking. Instead, the amino-blocked glycine is usually treated with ethyl chloroformate to yield an **activated ester**.

$$\{\text{—NHCH}_2\text{COH} + \text{ ClCOC}_2\text{H}_5 \xrightarrow{-\text{HCl}} \{\text{—NHCH}_2\underbrace{\text{COCOC}_2\text{H}_5}$$

amino-blocked   ethyl   *activated ester group*
glycine   chloroformate

Like an acid chloride, this activated ester can undergo reaction with an amino group of another amino acid to give the desired dipeptide.

$$\text{C}_6\text{H}_5\text{—CH}_2\text{OC—NHCH}_2\text{COCOC}_2\text{H}_5 + \text{H}_2\text{NCHCO}_2\text{H} \xrightarrow[-\text{C}_2\text{H}_5\text{OH}]{-\text{CO}_2}$$

$$\text{CH}_2\text{C}_6\text{H}_5$$

phenylalanine
or its ethyl ester

$$\text{C}_6\text{H}_5\text{—CH}_2\text{OC—NHCH}_2\text{C—NHCHCO}_2\text{H}$$
$$\text{CH}_2\text{C}_6\text{H}_5$$

amino-blocked gly–phe

At this point, the sequence can be repeated to add a third amino acid. When the peptide synthesis is complete, the carbamate group is reduced to yield the free peptide.

Removal of carbamate blocking group:

$$\text{C}_6\text{H}_5\text{—CH}_2\text{-}\!\!\frac{}{}\text{OC}\text{-}\!\!\frac{}{}\text{NHCH}_2\text{C—NHCHCO}_2\text{H} \xrightarrow{\text{H}_2,\ \text{Pd}}$$
$$\text{CH}_2\text{C}_6\text{H}_5$$

$$\text{C}_6\text{H}_5\text{—CH}_3 + \text{CO}_2 + \text{H}_2\text{NCH}_2\text{C—NHCHCO}_2\text{H}$$
$$\text{CH}_2\text{C}_6\text{H}_5$$

gly–phe

STUDY PROBLEM

18.7 Write the equations illustrating the addition of alanine to the amino-blocked gly–phe.

New and better peptide syntheses are always under investigation. One recently developed technique is the **solid-phase peptide synthesis**, in which resins hold the *C*-terminal amino acid by the carboxyl group as the peptide is being synthesized.

$$\underset{\substack{|\\ R}}{H_2NCHCO^-} + Cl\!-\!CH_2\!-\!\bullet \underset{\substack{\longrightarrow\\ -Cl^-}}{} \underset{\substack{|\\ R}}{H_2NCHCO}\!-\!CH_2\!-\!\bullet$$

— used to form amide link

resin   resin

Biosynthesis of Peptides

The biosynthesis of peptides and proteins in a typical cell is accomplished by ribonucleic acids (RNA) and enzymes. The various types of RNA, such as messenger RNA (mRNA), are synthesized under the direction of DNA in the nucleus of the cell (Section 16.12); then these RNA molecules leave the cell nucleus to perform their functions.

When mRNA leaves the nucleus, it becomes attached to **ribosomes**, granular bodies in the cytoplasm of the cell that are the sites of protein synthesis. A ribosome consists of approximately 60% *ribosomal RNA* and 40% protein. Each amino acid is brought to the mRNA and its ribosomes as an ester of one ribose unit in a *transfer RNA* (tRNA) molecule.

$$\{-OCH_2$$

$$H_2N$$

$$\underset{\substack{\|\\ O}}{RCHCO} \quad OH \quad \textit{ester group}$$

a ribose unit of tRNA

The mRNA is the template for the protein that is to be synthesized. The series of bases on a mRNA molecule is the code that determines the order of incorporation of amino acids into a growing protein molecule. (These bases were discussed in Section 16.12C.) A series of *three bases in a row*, called a **codon**, directs the inclusion of one particular amino acid. For example, three uracil bases in a row (U–U–U) in a mRNA molecule is a codon for phenylalanine. The codon guanine–cytosine–cytosine (**G–C–C**) signals that alanine is to be incorporated.

The tRNA with the proper amino acid is able to recognize its proper site because tRNA carries an **anticodon**, a series of three bases that are complementary to the codon of mRNA.

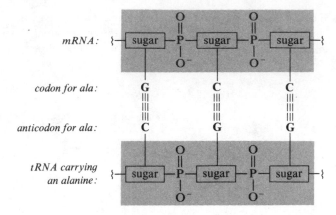

Protein biosynthesis can be likened to an assembly line. Figure 18.1 shows ribosomes moving along the mRNA chain (moving to the right in the figure). At each codon, a new amino acid is added to the growing protein molecule. When a completed protein molecule reaches the end of the mRNA chain, it leaves the site to carry out its own functions in the organism.

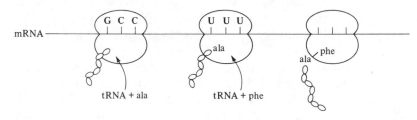

Figure 18.1.   The ribosomes move along the mRNA chain. For each codon, the proper amino acid is added to the protein molecule being formed.

Section 18.10

Some Interesting Peptides

Although most proteins are relatively large molecules, a peptide need not contain thousands of amino acid residues for biological activity. Consider the following tripeptide:

pyroglutamylhistidylprolinamide

This tripeptide is a **thyrotropic-hormone releasing factor** (TRF) that has been isolated from the hypothalamus glands of hogs and cattle. Administered to humans (intravenously or orally), it stimulates the secretion of thyrotropin, which in turn stimulates the secretion of thyroid hormones, the regulators of the body's metabolism.

The structure of TRF exemplifies some commonly encountered structural variations in peptides and proteins. The *N*-terminal amino acid is a derivative of glutamic acid: the side-chain carboxyl group has joined with the free amino group to form a lactam (a cyclic amide).

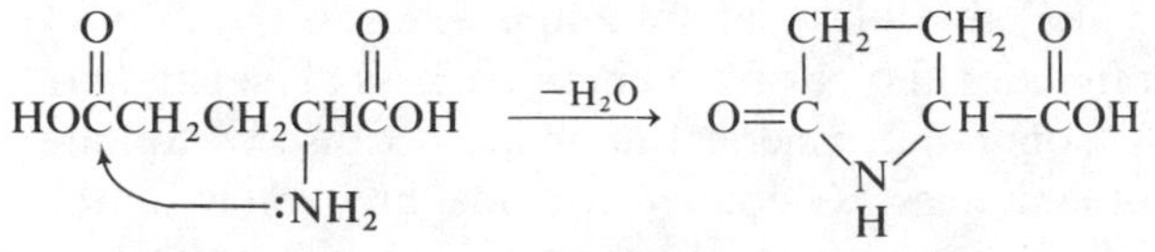

$$\text{HOCCH}_2\text{CH}_2\text{CHCOH} \xrightarrow{-H_2O} \text{pyroglutamic acid}$$

glutamic acid

pyroglutamic acid
a lactam

The *C*-terminal residue of TRF is an amide of proline. Amides of free carboxyl groups are not at all uncommon in natural protein structures. These are generally denoted in the abbreviated structures by adding NH_2 to the *C*-terminal: for example, *gly* means $-\text{NHCH}_2\text{CO}_2\text{H}$, but *gly*–$NH_2$ means $-\text{NHCH}_2\overset{\text{O}}{\underset{\|}{\text{C}}}\text{NH}_2$.

STUDY PROBLEM

18.8 Give the structural formula for pro–leu–ala–NH_2.

Oxytocin, a pituitary hormone that causes uterine contractions during parturition, is another important peptide. Note that oxytocin is a cyclic peptide joined by a S—S cystine link. Figure 18.2 shows the structural formula.

ile–tyr–cyS

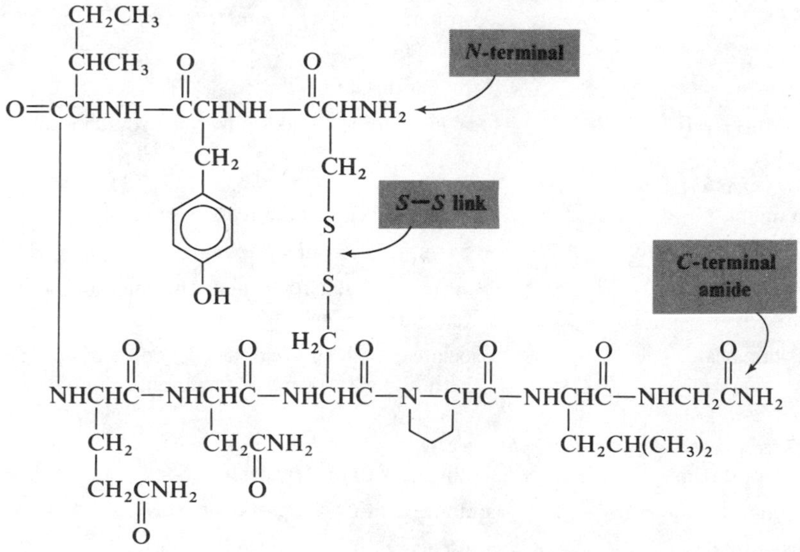

Figure 18.2. The structure of oxytocin, gln–asn–cyS–pro–leu–gly–NH_2.

Section 18.11

Classification of Proteins

Proteins may be roughly categorized by the type of function they perform. These classes are summarized in Table 18.3. **Fibrous proteins** (also called **structural proteins**), which form skin, muscles, the walls of arteries, and hair, are composed of long thread-like molecules that are tough and insoluble.

Another functional type of protein is the class of **globular proteins**. These are small proteins, somewhat spherical in shape because of folding of the protein chains upon themselves. Globular proteins are water-soluble and perform various functions in an organism. For example, *hemoglobin* transports oxygen to the cells; *insulin* aids in carbohydrate metabolism; *antibodies* render foreign protein inactive; *fibrinogen* (soluble) can form insoluble fibers that result in blood clots; and *hormones* carry messages throughout the body.

Conjugated proteins, proteins connected to a nonprotein moiety such as a sugar, perform various functions throughout the body. A common mode of linkage between the protein and nonprotein is by a functional side chain of the protein. For example, an acidic side chain of the protein can form an ester with an —OH group of a sugar molecule.

Table 18.3. Classes of Proteins

Class	Comments
Fibrous, or structural (insoluble):	
collagens	form connective tissue; comprise 30% of mammalian protein; lack cysteine and tryptophan; rich in hydroxyproline
elastins	form tendons and arteries
keratins	form hair, quills, hoofs, nails; rich in cysteine and cystine
Globular (soluble):	
albumins	examples are egg albumin and serum albumin
globulins	an example is serum globulin
histones	occur in glandular tissue and with nucleic acids; rich in lysine and arginine
protamines	associated with nucleic acids; contain no cysteine, methionine, tyrosine, or tryptophan; rich in arginine
Conjugated (combined with other substances):	
nucleoproteins	combined with nucleic acids
mucoproteins	combined with >4% carbohydrates
glycoproteins	combined with <4% carbohydrates
lipoproteins	combined with lipids, such as phosphoglycerides or cholesterol

Higher Structures of Proteins

The sequential order in which amino acids are joined together in a protein molecule is called the **primary structure** of the protein. However, there is much more to protein structure than just the primary structure. Many of the properties of a protein are due to the orientation of the molecule as a whole. The shape (such as a helix) into which a protein molecule arranges its backbone is called the **secondary structure**. Further interactions, such as folding of the backbone upon itself to form a sphere, are called the **tertiary structure**. The secondary and tertiary structures are collectively referred to as the **higher structure** of the protein.

One protein that has been well-studied in terms of its secondary structure is **keratin**, found in fur and feathers. Each protein molecule in keratin has the shape of a spiral, called a *right-handed α-helix* (Figure 18.3). "Right-handed" refers to the direction of the turns in the helix; the mirror image is a left-handed helix. In the mid-1930's, the term "α" was coined to differentiate the x-ray pattern of keratin from that of some other proteins.

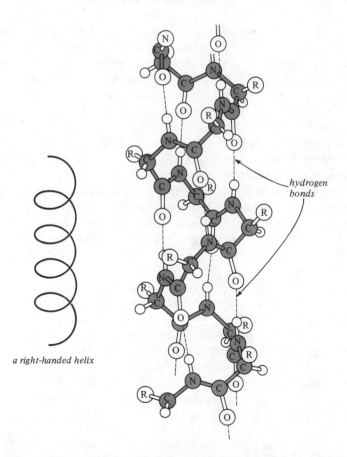

hydrogen bonds

a right-handed helix

Figure 18.3.   The protein chains in keratin form right-handed α-helices. From C. B. Anfinsen, *The Molecular Basis of Evolution* (John Wiley and Sons, Inc., New York, 1964).

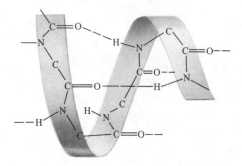

Figure 18.4.   The helix in keratin is held in its shape by hydrogen bonds. (Nonparticipating R's and H's have been omitted.) From R. J. Fessenden and J. S. Fessenden, *Chemical Principles for the Life Sciences* (Allyn and Bacon, Inc., Boston, 1976).

In keratin, each turn of the helix contains 3.6 amino acid residues. The distance from one coil to the next is 5.4 Å. The helix is held in its shape primarily by hydrogen bonds between one amide–carbonyl group and an NH group that is 3.6 amino acid units away (Figure 18.4). The helical shape gives a strong, fibrous, flexible product.

Hydrogen bonding between an α-amino group and a carbonyl group is one contributor to the shape of a protein molecule. Other inter- and intramolecular interactions also contribute to the higher structure. Some of these interactions are hydrogen bonding between side chains, S—S cross-links, and *salt bridges* (ionic bonds such as RCO_2^- ^+H_3NR between side chains). The most stable higher structure is the one with the greatest number of stabilizing interactions. (Each hydrogen bond lends ~ 5 kcal/mole of stability.) Given a particular primary structure, a protein naturally assumes its most stable higher structures.

Let us look at some other types of protein structure. **Collagen** is a general classification of a tough, strong protein that forms cartilage, tendons, ligaments, and skin. Collagen derives its strength from its higher structure of "super-helices": three right-handed, α-helical polypeptides entwined to form a triple, left-handed helical chain. The entwined molecules are collectively called a *tropocollagen molecule*. One of these tropocollagen molecules is about 15 Å in diameter and 2800 Å long. The tropocollagen triple helix, like a single helix, is held together by hydrogen bonding.

Gelatin is obtained by boiling collagen-containing animal material; however, gelatin is not the same type of protein as collagen. It has been found that the molecular weight of gelatin is only one-third that of collagen. Presumably, in gelatin-formation, the tropocollagen molecule is unraveled and the single strands form hydrogen bonds with water, resulting in the characteristic gel-formation.

Helical structures are not the only type of secondary structure of proteins. Another type of structure, referred to as a *β-sheet*, or *pleated sheet*, is found in silk fibroin. The pleated sheet is an arrangement in which single protein molecules are lined up side by side and held there by hydrogen bonds between the chains (Figure 18.5).

The protein chains in silk fibroin are not simply stretched-out zigzag chains. Analysis by x-ray diffraction shows repetitive units every 7.0 Å. This repetition probably arises from a puckering (or "pleating") in the chains that alleviates

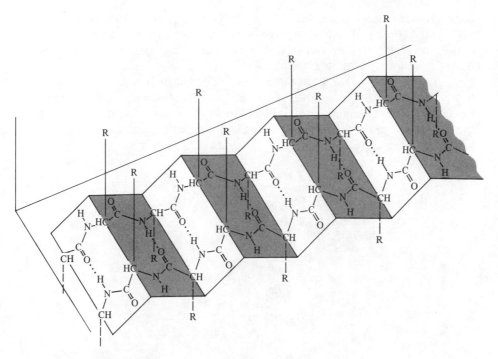

Figure 18.5. The pleated sheet structure of silk fibroin. From P. Karlson, *Introduction to Modern Biochemistry*, 3rd ed. (Georg Thieme Verlag, Stuttgart, 1968).

steric hindrance. It is interesting that silk fibroin contains 46% glycine (no side chain) and 38% of a mixture of alanine and serine (small side chains). The lack of bulky R groups in these amino acids allows the side-by-side arrangement of protein chains in the fibroin structure.

7.0 Å per pleat

A *globular protein* depends on a tertiary structure to maintain its intricately folded, globular shape, which is necessary to maintain solubility. In a globular protein, polar, hydrophilic side chains are situated on the outside of the sphere (to increase water-solubility) and nonpolar, hydrophobic side chains are arranged on the interior surface, where they may be used to catalyze nonaqueous reactions. The unique surface of each globular protein enables it to "recognize" certain complementary organic molecules. This recognition allows enzymes to catalyze reactions of particular molecules, but not others.

Hemoglobin, the portion of erythrocytes (red blood cells) that is responsible for the transport of oxygen in the blood stream, is a good example of a globular protein. One unit of hemoglobin, which has a "molecular weight" of about 65,000, contains four protein molecules called *globins*. Each globin is folded in such a way that (1) it fits perfectly with the three other globins to maintain the hemoglobin entity, and (2) it forms a molecular crevice of just the right size and shape to hold a unit of heme along with its O_2 molecule.

Heme (page 768) is a **prosthetic group**, a nonprotein organic molecule held firmly by a protein. It is composed of a porphyrin ring system with a chelated ferrous ion in the center. Each heme unit is bound to its globin by a coordinate bond from the ferrous ion to the nitrogen in an imidazole ring of histidine, one of the amino acids that forms the globin. The ferrous ion also can form a coordinate bond with an O_2 molecule.

For heme to function as a transporter of oxygen to the cells, the Fe^{2+} ion must release the oxygen readily. Such a release could not occur if Fe^{2+} were oxidized to Fe^{3+} and oxygen were reduced. The nonpolar hydrophobic environment of the protein around the O_2 binding site assures that electron-transfer from Fe^{2+} to O_2 does not occur. (Remember that nonpolar solvents cannot support ions in solution.) A similar phenomenon is observed in the laboratory when Fe^{2+} ions are imbedded in polystyrene. Oxygen is attracted, but no oxidation–reduction reaction takes place as it would in an ionic medium.

Carbon monoxide poisoning is the result of CO molecules taking the place of O_2 molecules in hemoglobin. The CO molecules are firmly held by the iron and are not as readily released as oxygen molecules.

Section 18.13

Denaturation of Proteins

Denaturation of a protein is the loss of its higher structural features by disruption of hydrogen bonding and other secondary forces that hold it together. The result of denaturation is the loss of many of the biological properties of the protein.

One of the factors that can cause denaturation of a protein is a *change in temperature*. Cooking an egg white is an example of an irreversible denaturation. An egg white is a colorless liquid containing albumins, which are soluble globular proteins. Heating the egg whites causes the albumins to unfold and precipitate; the result is a white solid.

A change in pH can also cause denaturation. When milk sours, the change in pH arising from lactic acid formation causes *curdling*, or precipitation of soluble proteins. Other factors that can cause denaturation are detergents, radiation, oxidizing or reducing agents (which can alter S—S links), and changes in the type of solvent.

Some proteins (skin and the lining of the gastrointestinal tract, for example) are quite resistant to denaturation, while other proteins are more susceptible. Denaturation may be reversible if a protein has been subjected to only mild denaturing conditions, such as a slight change in pH. When this protein is replaced in its natural environment, it may resume its natural higher structure in a process called **renaturation**. Unfortunately, renaturation may be very slow or may not occur at all. One of the problems in protein research is how to study proteins without disrupting the higher structures.

Section 18.14

Enzymes

The word **enzyme** means "in yeast." Even without any knowledge of their structures or functions, man has used enzymes since prehistoric times in the production of wine, vinegar, and cheese. Pasteur thought that living yeast cells were necessary for fermentation processes. We now know that a living cell is not necessary; the proper enzymes, plus reaction conditions that do not cause denaturation, are all that are needed for enzymatic reactions.

An enzyme is a *biological catalyst*. A higher animal contains thousands of enzymes. Virtually every biochemical reaction is catalyzed by an enzyme. Even the equilibrium $CO_2 + H_2O \rightleftarrows H_2CO_3$ is enzyme-catalyzed because the rate of the uncatalyzed equilibrium does not produce carbonic acid fast enough for an animal's needs.

Enzymes are more efficient catalysts than most laboratory or industrial catalysts (such as Pd in a hydrogenation reaction). Biological reactions in humans occur at 37°C and in aqueous media. High temperature, high pressure, or very reactive reagents (such as NaOH or $LiAlH_4$) are not available to an organism. Enzymes also allow a selectivity of reactants and a control over reaction rate that can be obtained with no other class of catalyst.

All enzymes are proteins. Some are relatively simple in structure; however, most are complex. The structures of many enzymes are still unknown. For biological activity, some enzymes require prosthetic groups, or **cofactors**. These cofactors are nonprotein portions of the enzyme. A cofactor may be a simple *metal ion*; for example, copper ion is the cofactor for the enzyme *ascorbic acid oxidase*. Other enzymes contain *nonprotein organic molecules* as cofactors. An organic prosthetic group is frequently referred to as a **coenzyme**. We have already encountered some examples of coenzymes: coenzyme A (Section 13.8), NAD^+, and FAD (Section 16.13).

If an organism cannot synthesize a necessary cofactor, it must be present in small amounts in the diet. The active units of many cofactors are vitamins. For example, the working end of NAD^+ is nicotinamide and that of FAD is riboflavin. Both are B vitamins. Table 18.4 shows a few cofactors and the corresponding vitamins.

Table 18.4.   Some Cofactors that Contain Vitamins

Name of cofactor	Vitamin needed	Structure of vitamin
vitamin C (ascorbic acid)	vitamin C	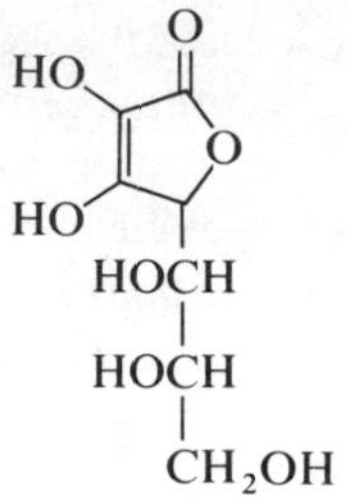
biotin	biotin	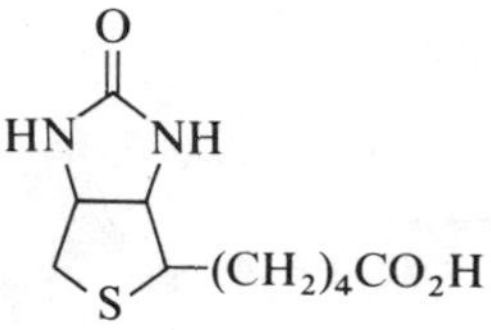
coenzyme A	pantothenic acid	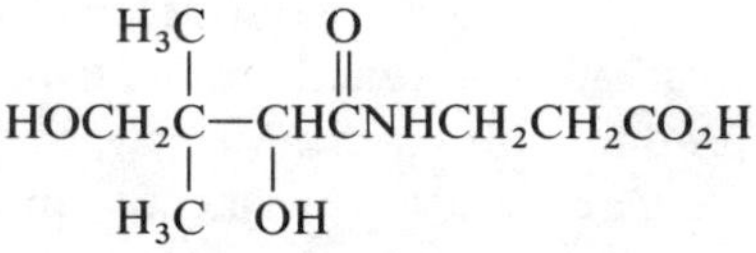
FAD	riboflavin	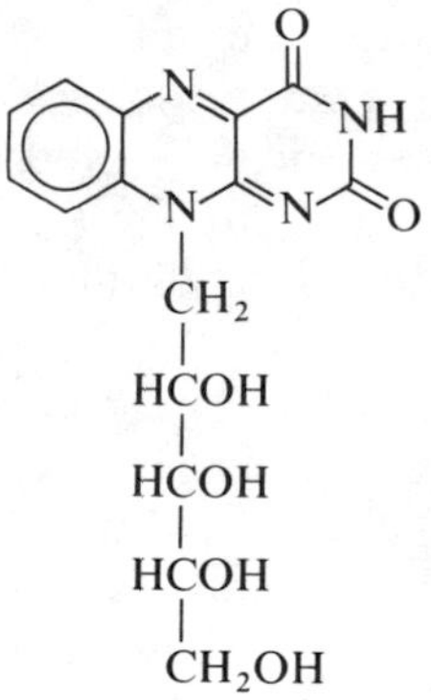
NAD$^+$	nicotinic acid (niacin) or nicotinamide (niacinamide)	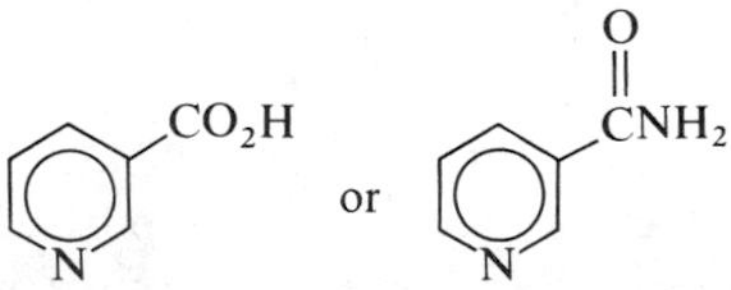
pyridoxyl phosphate	pyridoxine	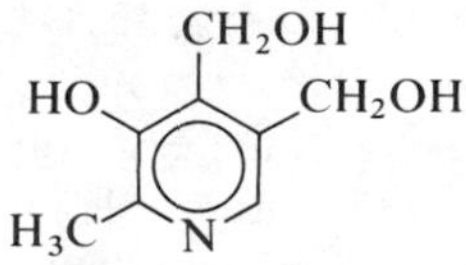

A. Naming Enzymes

Most enzymes are named after the reactions that they catalyze. The ending for an enzyme name is usually **-ase**. The name may be *general* and refer to a class of enzymes that catalyze a general type of reaction. For example, a **polymerase** is any enzyme that catalyzes a polymerization reaction, and a **reductase** is any enzyme that catalyzes a reduction reaction. An enzyme name may also refer to a *specific* enzyme: **ascorbic acid oxidase** is the enzyme that catalyzes the oxidation of ascorbic acid, while **phosphoglucoisomerase** catalyzes the isomerization of glucose 6-phosphate to fructose 6-phosphate.

STUDY PROBLEM

18.9 Suggest the function of each of the following enzymes: (a) an acetyltransferase; (b) phenylalanine hydroxylase; (c) pyruvate dehydrogenase.

B. How Enzymes Work

Some enzymes have been studied in detail, yet there is still much to learn about even the well-known enzymes. It is believed that an enzyme fits itself around the substrate (the molecule to be acted upon) to form an *enzyme–substrate complex*. The bonds of the substrate may be strained by attractions between itself and the enzyme. Strained bonds are of higher energy and are more easily broken; therefore, the desired reaction proceeds easily and yields an *enzyme–product complex*.

In many cases, the product is not the same shape as the reacting substrate; thus the fit between the product and the enzyme is no longer perfect. The altered shape of the product causes a dissociation of the complex, and the enzyme surface is ready to accept another molecule of substrate. This theory of enzyme activity is called the **induced-fit theory**.

$$E \; + \; S \; \longrightarrow \; E\!-\!S \; \longrightarrow$$

enzyme   substrate   enzyme–substrate
                              complex

$$E\!-\!P \; \longrightarrow \; E \; + \; P$$

enzyme–product   enzyme   product
complex

Enzymes have molecular weights of 12,000–120,000 and higher. Most substrates (for example, an amino acid or a unit of glucose) are much smaller molecules. Therefore, chemists believe that an enzyme contains an **active site**, a specific location in its structure where reaction occurs. The active site is where the prosthetic group (if any) is located. In NAD^+, the active site is the nicotinamide end of the cofactor. NAD^+ readily accepts hydrogen atoms and therefore catalyzes oxidation reactions (Section 16.13). Metallic prosthetic groups are thought to serve as electrophilic agents and, in this way, catalyze the desired reactions.

The rest of the enzyme molecule is not simply excess molecular weight! It is believed that this portion of the enzyme recognizes its substrate and holds it in place. It was suggested in the 1890's by Emil Fischer that enzymes are chiral molecules and that reactants must complement this chirality in order to undergo

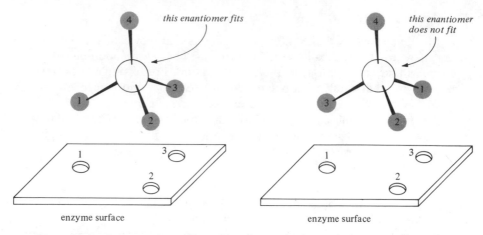

Figure 18.6. One enantiomer fits on the enzyme surface; its mirror image does not.

reaction. Fischer compared the fitting together of the substrate structure and the enzyme structure to a key fitting into a lock (see Figure 18.6).

Recognition may occur by a series of dipole–dipole interactions, by hydrogen bonding, or by covalent bonding, in which the stereochemistry must be just right. In some cases, the rest of the enzyme molecule is folded to form a hydrophobic pocket that holds a nonpolar portion of the substrate in place. (We mentioned this type of structure for hemoglobin.) If the nonpolar end of a potential substrate does not fit in the pocket correctly, enzyme catalysis diminishes or is nonexistent. Therefore, the functional group to be acted upon must fit the active site on the enzyme, and the rest of the substrate molecule must fit together with other portions of the enzyme molecule for reaction to proceed. This dual type of recognition is the basis of the unique specificity of most enzymes.

C.   How the Active Site May Be Blocked

Both the active site and the rest of an enzyme are important in enzyme activity. Let us look at one reaction in which the active site seems to be the more important factor in substrate recognition.

The enzyme *succinate dehydrogenase* catalyzes the dehydrogenation of succinic acid to the *trans*-diacid fumaric acid. (The *cis*-isomer, maleic acid, is not produced in this reaction.)

$$\underset{\text{succinic acid}}{HO_2CCH_2CH_2CO_2H} + FAD \underset{\longleftarrow}{\overset{\text{succinate}}{\underset{\text{dehydrogenase}}{\longrightarrow}}} \underset{\text{fumaric acid}}{\overset{HO_2C}{\underset{H}{\diagdown}}C=C\overset{H}{\underset{CO_2H}{\diagup}}} + FADH_2$$

Other diacids, such as oxalic acid, malonic acid, and glutaric acid, inhibit the dehydrogenation of succinic acid.

Inhibitors of succinate dehydrogenase:

$$\underset{\text{oxalic acid}}{HO_2C-CO_2H} \qquad \underset{\text{malonic acid}}{HO_2CCH_2CO_2H} \qquad \underset{\text{glutaric acid}}{HO_2CCH_2CH_2CH_2CO_2H}$$

Of these diacids, malonic acid has the greatest inhibiting effect. Malonic acid is very similar in structure to succinic acid, but is structurally incapable of undergoing dehydrogenation. If succinic acid contains only 2% malonic acid, the rate of enzymatic dehydrogenation of the succinic acid is halved! The probability is excellent that malonic acid competes with succinic acid for a position on the active site and that malonic acid is attracted and held there preferentially. The presence of malonic acid on the active site thus blocks the approach of succinic acid.

SUMMARY

A **protein** is a polyamide. Hydrolysis yields α-amino acids of (S)-configuration at the α carbon. Amino acids undergo an internal acid–base reaction to yield **dipolar ions**.

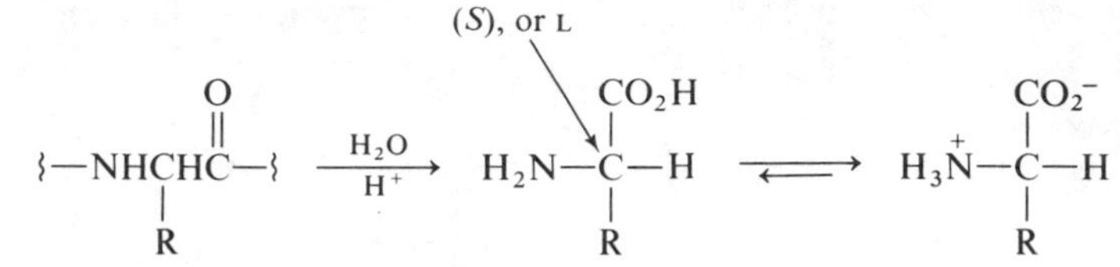

$$\{-NHCHC-\} \xrightarrow[H^+]{H_2O} \overset{(S), \text{ or } L}{H_2N-\underset{R}{\overset{CO_2H}{C}}-H} \rightleftharpoons H_3\overset{+}{N}-\underset{R}{\overset{CO_2^-}{C}}-H$$

an α-amino acid   *a dipolar ion*

Essential amino acids are those that cannot be synthesized by an organism and must be present in the diet. **Acidic amino acids** are those with a carboxyl group in the side chain (R in the preceding equation). **Basic amino acids** contain an amino group in the side chain. **Neutral amino acids** contain neither $-CO_2H$ nor $-NH_2$ in the side chain, but may contain OH, SH, or other polar group. **Cross-linking** in proteins may be provided by the SH group in cysteine, which can link with another SH in an oxidation reaction: $2\,RSH \rightarrow RSSR + 2\,H$.

The **isoelectric point** of an amino acid is the pH at which the dipolar ion is electrically neutral and does not migrate toward an anode or cathode. The isoelectric point depends on the acidity or basicity of the side chain.

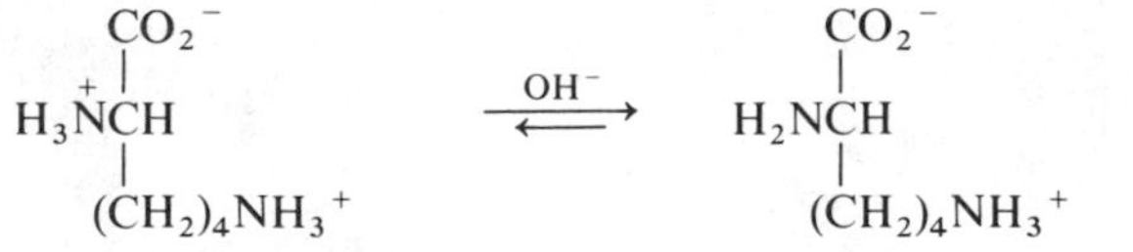

$$H_3\overset{+}{N}\underset{(CH_2)_4NH_3^+}{\overset{CO_2^-}{CH}} \underset{\longleftarrow}{\overset{OH^-}{\longrightarrow}} H_2N\underset{(CH_2)_4NH_3^+}{\overset{CO_2^-}{CH}}$$

in H_2O, a net positive charge   *at pH 9.74, no net charge*

Racemic amino acids may be synthesized by a variety of routes:

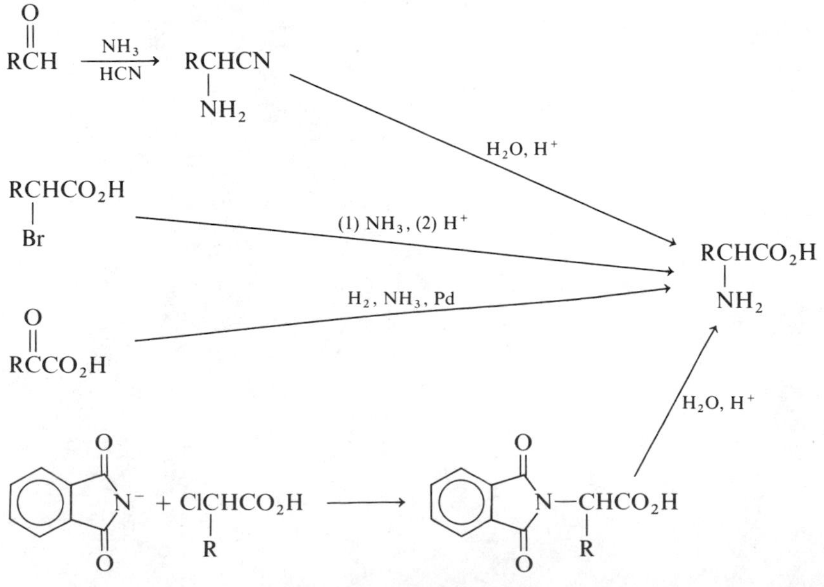

A **peptide** is a polyamide of fewer than 50 amino acid residues. The *N*-**terminal amino acid** is the amino acid with a free α-amino group, while the *C*-**terminal amino acid** has a free carboxyl group at carbon 1. **End-group analysis** to determine the *C*- and *N*-terminals and **partial hydrolysis** to smaller peptides are two techniques for peptide structure-determination.

In the synthesis of a peptide, reactive groups (except for the groups desired to undergo reaction) must be blocked. A **carbamate group** may be used to protect an amino group. A **solid-phase peptide synthesis** provides a blocking group for the *C*-terminal carboxyl group. The biosynthesis of proteins is accomplished by RNA. The order of incorporation of amino acids is determined by the order of attachment of the bases (*N*-heterocycles) in mRNA.

Proteins are polyamides of more than 50 amino acid residues. The order of side chains in a protein determines its **secondary** and **tertiary structures**, which arise from internal and external hydrogen bonding, van der Waals forces, and other interactions between side chains. The higher structures of proteins give them a variety of physical and chemical properties so that they may perform a variety of functions. **Denaturation** is the disruption of hydrogen bonds and thus the disruption of the higher structure of the protein.

Enzymes are proteins that catalyze biochemical reactions. Enzymes are efficient and specific in their catalytic action. The specificity is provided for by the unique shape and by the polar (or nonpolar) groups contained within the enzyme structure. Some enzymes work in conjunction with a nonprotein **cofactor**, which may be organic or inorganic.

STUDY PROBLEMS

18.10 Give Fischer projections for: (a) (S)-arginine;   (b) (S)-aspartic acid;   (c) L-proline;   (d) L-tryptophan.

18.11 Label each of the following amino acids as *acidic*, *basic*, or *neutral*:   (a) isoleucine;   (b) aspartic acid;   (c) asparagine;   (d) serine;   (e) histidine;   (f) glutamine.

18.12 Show the possible oxidative coupling products between 1.0 equivalent each of cysteine and the following compound:

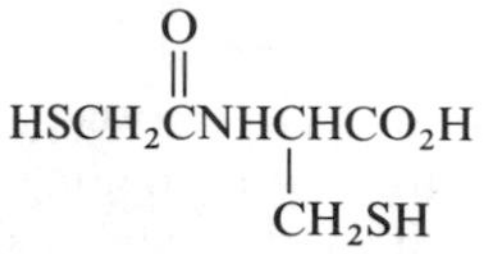

$$\underset{\underset{CH_2SH}{|}}{HSCH_2\overset{\overset{O}{\|}}{C}NHCHCO_2H}$$

18.13 Predict the products of the reaction of alanine with: (a) dilute aqueous HCl;   (b) dilute aqueous KOH;   (c) methanol + H_2SO_4 with heat;   (d) one equivalent of acetic anhydride.

18.14 Suggest a synthesis for valine from 3-methylbutanoic acid. Give the stereochemistry of the product.

18.15 Suggest a route to alanine from (R)-lactic acid (2-hydroxypropanoic acid) using a reductive amination. What is the stereochemistry of the product?

18.16 Explain the following observations:

(a) Although saturated carboxylic acids absorb at about 1720 cm^{-1} (5.81 μm) in the infrared region, amino acids do not absorb at this position.

(b) If a neutral solution of an amino acid is acidified, the infrared spectrum then shows absorption at 1720 cm^{-1}.

18.17 Outline a Strecker synthesis for: (a) phenylalanine,   and   (b) valine.
    (c) What would be the configuration of the chiral carbons in the products?

18.18 Predict the major organic products:

(a) $CH_3CH_2CO_2H$ $\xrightarrow[\text{(2) excess NH}_3]{\text{(1) Br}_2,\ PBr_3}$

(b) 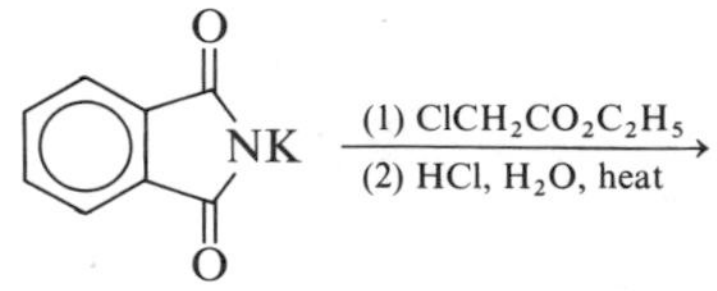   [phthalimide-NK structure] $\xrightarrow[\text{(2) HCl, H}_2O,\ heat]{\text{(1) ClCH}_2CO_2C_2H_5}$

(c) 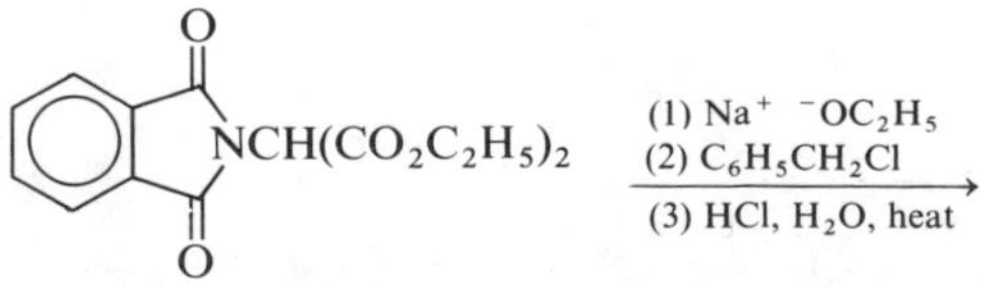   [phthalimide-NCH(CO$_2$C$_2$H$_5$)$_2$ structure] $\xrightarrow[\substack{\text{(2) C}_6H_5CH_2Cl \\ \text{(3) HCl, H}_2O,\ heat}]{\text{(1) Na}^+\ ^-OC_2H_5}$

(d) $(CH_3)_2CHCH_2\overset{\overset{\displaystyle O}{\|}}{C}H + NH_3 + HCN \longrightarrow$

(e) $C_6H_5CH_2\underset{\underset{\displaystyle NH_2}{|}}{C}HCO_2H + CH_3OH + HCl \xrightarrow{\text{heat}}$

18.19 Without referring to the text, match the amino acid with its isoelectric point.

(a) cysteine   (1) 10.76
(b) aspartic acid   (2) 6.30
(c) proline   (3) 5.07
(d) arginine   (4) 2.77

18.20 Without referring to the text, predict the approximate isoelectric point of each of the following amino acids: (a) serine; (b) histidine; (c) glutamic acid; (d) glutamine; (e) lysine.

18.21 Predict the major products:

(a) $H_2N\underset{\underset{\displaystyle CH(CH_3)_2}{|}}{C}HCO_2^- + 1.0$ equivalent HCl $\longrightarrow$

(b) $H_2N\underset{\underset{\displaystyle (CH_2)_4NH_2}{|}}{C}HCO_2^- + 1.0$ equivalent HCl $\longrightarrow$

(c) $^+H_3N\underset{\underset{\displaystyle CH(CH_3)_2}{|}}{C}HCO_2H + 1.0$ equivalent NaOH $\longrightarrow$

(d) $^+H_3N\underset{\underset{\displaystyle (CH_2)_4NH_3^+}{|}}{C}HCO_2H + 1.0$ equivalent NaOH $\longrightarrow$

18.22 Write equations to represent: (a) dipolar-ion formation of histidine; (b) the equilibria between histidine and water; (c) the reaction of histidine with dilute aqueous HCl; (d) the reaction of histidine with dilute aqueous NaOH.

18.23 In the following structure, label: (a) the peptide bond(s); (b) the *N*-terminal amino acid; and (c) the *C*-terminal amino acid.
(d) Is this structure a dipeptide, tripeptide, or tetrapeptide?
(e) Would this peptide be considered acidic, basic, or neutral?

$$(CH_3)_2CHCH_2\underset{\underset{\displaystyle NH_2}{|}}{C}H\overset{\overset{\displaystyle O}{\|}}{C}NH\underset{\underset{\displaystyle CH_2CH_2SCH_3}{|}}{C}H\overset{\overset{\displaystyle O}{\|}}{C}NHCH_2CO_2H$$

18.24 Label each of the following peptides as a dipeptide, a tripeptide, etc.:

(a) phe–gly   (b) ala–ala–ala   (c) $H_2NCH_2\overset{\overset{\displaystyle O}{\|}}{C}NHCH_2\overset{\overset{\displaystyle O}{\|}}{C}NH\underset{\underset{\displaystyle CO_2H}{|}}{C}HCH_3$

(d) $H_3\overset{+}{N}CH_2\overset{\overset{\displaystyle O}{\|}}{C}\left(\text{NHCH}_2\overset{\overset{\displaystyle O}{\|}}{C}\right)_8 NHCH_2CO_2^-$

18.25 Write the structures for   (a) glycylglycine, and   (b) alanylleucylmethionine.

18.26 Give the full name and the abbreviated name for each of the following peptides:

(a) 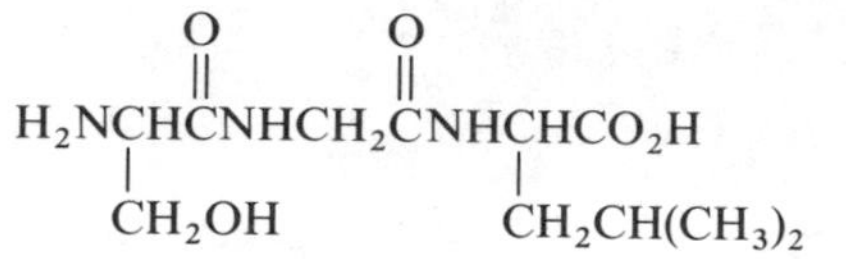 $\underset{}{H_2NCHCNHCH_2CNHCHCO_2H}$

with substituents CH_2OH and $CH_2CH(CH_3)_2$, and two $\overset{O}{\overset{\|}{C}}$ groups

(b) 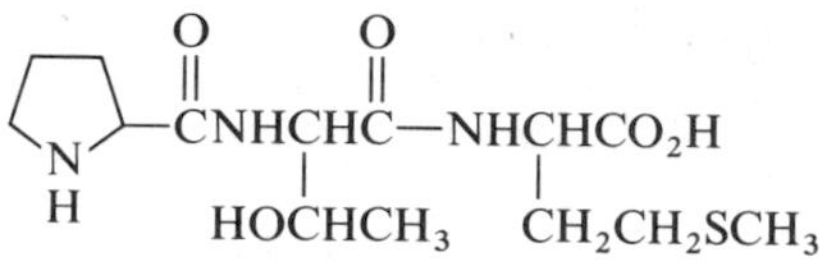   pyrrolidine ring (N–H)$-\overset{O}{\overset{\|}{C}}NHCHC-NHCHCO_2H$

with substituents $HOCHCH_3$ and $CH_2CH_2SCH_3$, and $\overset{O}{\overset{\|}{C}}$ group

18.27 Give the structures of the principal organic ionic species in each of the following solutions:

(a)   glycyllysine in dilute aqueous HCl
(b)   glycylglutamic acid in dilute aqueous NaOH
(c)   glycyltyrosine in dilute aqueous NaOH

18.28 A globular protein is hydrolyzed by aqueous acid. When the reaction mixture is neutralized, ammonia is given off. What can you deduce about the structure of the protein from this observation?

18.29 Each of the following peptides is subjected to reaction with an alkaline solution of phenyl isothiocyanate, followed by acid hydrolysis. Give the structures of the products.

(a)   gly–ala   (b)   ala–gly   (c)   ser–phe–met

18.30 Each of the peptides in Problem 18.29 is treated with the enzyme carboxypeptidase. What products are formed?

18.31 *Bradykinin* is a pain-causing nonapeptide that is released by globulins in blood plasma as a response to toxins in wasp stings. Partial hydrolysis of bradykinin results in the following tripeptides:

ser–pro–phe   gly–phe–ser   pro–phe–arg   arg–pro–pro

pro–gly–phe   pro–pro–gly   phe–ser–pro

What is the amino acid sequence in bradykinin?

18.32 A chemist decided to prepare the dipeptide val–ala by the following sequence of reactions. Using structural formulas, rewrite each set of reactants and tell what possible products were obtained in each case.

(a)   val + $SOCl_2$ (b)   [product(s) from (a)] + ala

18.33 Using a benzyl carbamate blocking group, show how you would convert ala–ala to ala–ala–gly.

18.34 Which of the following structural features would contribute to water-solubility of a protein?

(a)   rich in glutamic acid
(b)   rich in valine
(c)   formation of bundles of helices

(d) formation of a helix folded into a sphere

(e) combination with glucose

(f) combination with cholesterol (page 889)

18.35 A chemist adds ethanol to an aqueous solution of a globular protein. What would you expect to happen?

18.36 Meat may be tenderized by soaking it overnight in a marinade of vinegar, spices, and sugar.

(a) Why is the meat tenderized in this process?

(b) Would a water solution of sucrose alone have the same tenderizing effect?

18.37 Match each of the following enzymes (or class of enzymes) with a reaction on the right that it might catalyze:

(a) a phosphatase

(b) a glycosidase

(c) α-1,4-glucan 4-glucanohydrolase

(d) an aminopeptidase

(e) an oxidase

(f) phosphohexose isomerase

(1) $Fe^{2+} \longrightarrow Fe^{3+}$

(2) cleavage of the *N*-terminal amino acid from a protein

(3) sucrose $\longrightarrow$ fructose + glucose

(4) glucose 6-phosphate $\longrightarrow$ glucose

(5) cellulose $\longrightarrow$ glucose

(6) amylose $\longrightarrow$ glucose

(7) glucose 6-phosphate $\longrightarrow$
fructose 6-phosphate

18.38 Which of the following compounds would be most likely to inhibit the enzymatic incorporation of nicotinic acid (3-pyridinecarboxylic acid) into NAD^+?

(a) pyridine

(b) 3-pyridinesulfonic acid

(c) 3-methylpyridine

(d) adenine

(e) acetic acid

(f) malonic acid

18.39 The tripeptide pyroglutamylhistidylprolinamide (page 850) is subjected to complete hydrolysis with HCl and H_2O. What is the structure of each product?

18.40 A peptide containing one equivalent each of tyr, ile, gly, arg, and cyS had no *C*-terminal amino acid and no *N*-terminal amino acid. Explain.

18.41 Suggest a reason for the differences in the isoelectric points of lysine (9.74) and histidine (7.59). (*Hint:* Consider the hybridization of the side-chain nitrogens.)

18.42 An amino acid with an (*R*), or D, configuration at the α carbon cannot be enzymatically incorporated into proteins. Many D-amino acids are oxidized in a reaction catalyzed by **D-amino acid oxidase**.

$$\begin{array}{c} CO_2H \\ | \\ HCNH_2 \\ | \\ R \end{array} + \tfrac{1}{2}O_2 \longrightarrow \begin{array}{c} CO_2H \\ | \\ C{=}O \\ | \\ R \end{array}$$

This enzyme-catalyzed reaction is very slow for L-amino acids, D-glutamic acid, D-lysine, and D-aspartic acid. The reaction is fast for D-proline, D-alanine, D-methionine, and D-tyrosine.

(a) Would you say that the differences in reaction rate are due to steric hindrance or to electronic effects?

(b) Would you predict that the binding site on the enzyme is polar or nonpolar?

(c) Which would be likely to undergo this enzymatic oxidation at a faster rate, D-cysteine or D-arginine?

18.43 Suggest a reason for the difference in the isoelectric points of lysine and arginine.

18.44 *Vasopressin* is a pituitary hormone that can cause fluid retention and a rise in blood pressure. What tripeptides would be obtained in the partial hydrolysis of vasopressin?

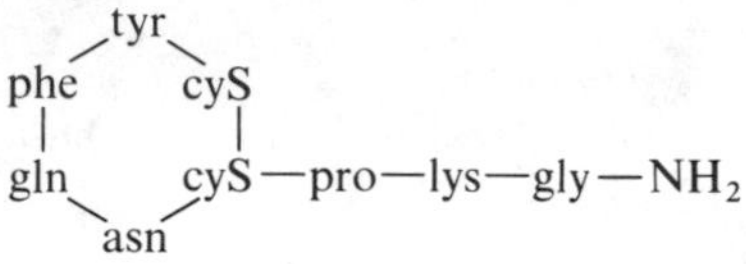

$$
\begin{array}{c}
\text{tyr} \\
\text{phe} \qquad \text{cyS} \\
| \qquad\quad | \\
\text{gln} \qquad \text{cyS}\!-\!\text{pro}\!-\!\text{lys}\!-\!\text{gly}\!-\!NH_2 \\
\text{asn}
\end{array}
$$

vasopressin

18.45 In mammals, arginine undergoes enzymatic hydrolysis to urea $(H_2N)_2C\!=\!O$, which is excreted in the urine, and a basic amino acid called *ornithine*. What is the structure of ornithine?

18.46 Treatment of ornithine (see Problem 18.45) with an alkaline solution of $H_2N\!-\!CN$ yields arginine. Suggest a mechanism for this reaction. (*Hint:* Your first step should be to assign $\delta+$ and $\delta-$ charges to the atoms.)

18.47 *Glutathione* is a tripeptide found in most living cells. Partial hydrolysis yields cyS, glu, gly, glu–cyS, and cyS–gly.

(a)   What is the amino acid sequence in glutathione?

(b)   It has been discovered that glutamic acid forms a peptide link in glutathione with the *side chain* carboxyl group, rather than the carboxyl group adjacent to the amino group. What is the structural formula of glutathione?

Chapter 19

Lipids and Related
Natural Products

A **lipid** is defined as a naturally occurring organic compound that is insoluble in water, but soluble in nonpolar organic solvents such as a hydrocarbon or an ether. This definition sounds as if it might include many types of compounds, and indeed it does. The various classes of lipid are related to each other by this shared physical property, but their chemical, functional, and structural relationships are often remote. We will discuss here the classes usually thought of as lipids: fats and oils, terpenes, steroids, and a few other compounds of interest. (Line formulas are generally used for terpenes and steroids, as the following examples show. These formulas were introduced in Section 9.16.)

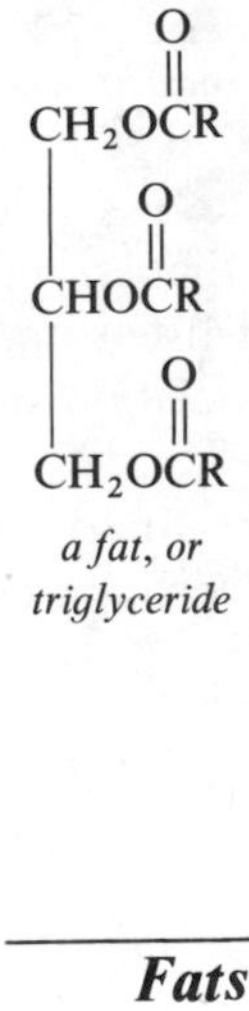

a fat, or triglyceride 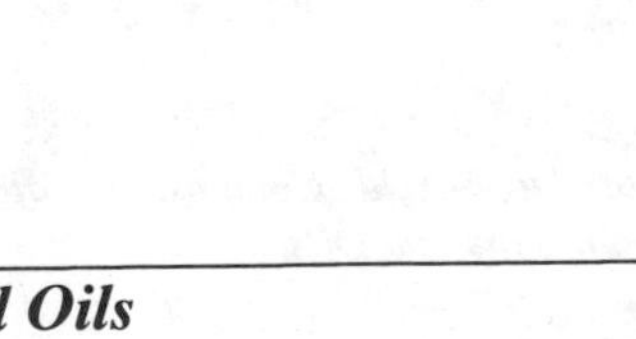   menthol a terpene   cholesterol a steroid

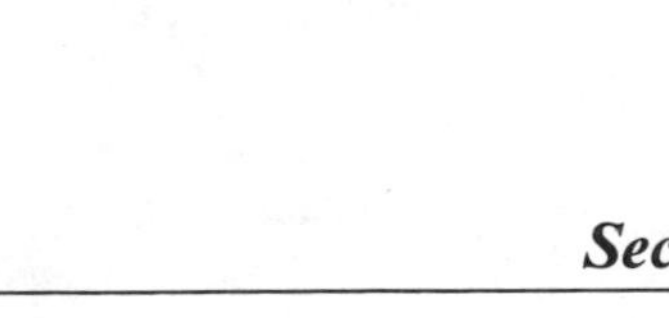

Fats and Oils

Fats and oils are **triglycerides**, or **triacylglycerols**, both terms meaning "triesters of glycerol." The distinction between a fat and an oil is arbitrary: at room temperature a fat is solid and an oil is liquid. Most glycerides in animals are fats, while those in plants tend to be oils; hence the terms *animal fats* (bacon fat, beef fat) and *vegetable oils* (corn oil, safflower oil).

The carboxylic acid obtained from the hydrolysis of a fat or oil, called a **fatty acid**, generally has a long, unbranched hydrocarbon chain. Fats and oils are often named as derivatives of these fatty acids. For example, the tristearate of glycerol is named tristearin, and the tripalmitate of glycerol is named tripalmitin.

Lipids and Related Natural Products

Table 19.1.   Selected Fatty Acids and Their Sources

Name of acid	Structure	Source
Saturated:		
butyric	$CH_3(CH_2)_2CO_2H$	milk fat
palmitic	$CH_3(CH_2)_{14}CO_2H$	animal and plant fat
stearic	$CH_3(CH_2)_{16}CO_2H$	animal and plant fat
Unsaturated:		
palmitoleic	$CH_3(CH_2)_5CH{=}CH(CH_2)_7CO_2H$	animal and plant fat
oleic	$CH_3(CH_2)_7CH{=}CH(CH_2)_7CO_2H$	animal and plant fat
linoleic	$CH_3(CH_2)_4CH{=}CHCH_2CH{=}CH(CH_2)_7CO_2H$	plant oils
linolenic	$CH_3CH_2CH{=}CHCH_2CH{=}CHCH_2CH{=}CH(CH_2)_7CO_2H$	linseed oil

$$
\begin{array}{l}
CH_2O_2C(CH_2)_{16}CH_3 \\
|\\
CHO_2C(CH_2)_{16}CH_3 \quad + 3\,H_2O \quad \xrightarrow{\;H^+\;} \\
|\\
CH_2O_2C(CH_2)_{16}CH_3
\end{array}
\qquad
\begin{array}{l}
CH_2OH \\
|\\
CHOH \qquad + 3\,CH_3(CH_2)_{16}CO_2H \\
|\\
CH_2OH
\end{array}
$$

tristearin   glycerol   stearic acid

(glyceryl tristearate)   (1,2,3-propanetriol)   *a fatty acid*

a typical fat

Most naturally occurring fats and oils are *mixed* triglycerides—that is, the three fatty-acid portions of the glyceride are not the same. Table 19.1 lists some representative fatty acids, and Table 19.2 shows the fatty-acid composition of some plant and animal triglycerides.

Almost all naturally occurring fatty acids have an *even* number of carbon atoms because they are biosynthesized from the two-carbon acetyl groups in acetylcoenzyme A.

Table 19.2.   Approximate Fatty-Acid Composition of Some Common Fats and Oils

Source	Composition (%)[a]			
	palmitic	stearic	oleic	linoleic
corn oil	10	5	45	38
soybean oil	10	—	25	55
lard	30	15	45	5
butter	25	10	35	—
human fat	25	8	46	10

[a] Other fatty acids are also found in lesser amounts.

two carbons

an even number of carbons

$$8\ CH_3C\overset{\displaystyle O}{\overset{\displaystyle \|}{}}\!-\!SCoA \xrightarrow{\text{many steps}} CH_3(CH_2)_{14}CO_2H$$

acetylcoenzyme A   palmitic acid

The hydrocarbon chain in a fatty acid may be saturated or it may contain double bonds. The most widely distributed fatty acid in nature, oleic acid, contains one double bond. Fatty acids with more than one double bond are not uncommon, particularly in vegetable oils; these oils are the so-called *polyunsaturates*.

The configuration around any double bond in a naturally occurring fatty acid is *cis*, a configuration that results in the low melting points of oils. A saturated fatty acid forms zigzag chains that can fit compactly together, resulting in high van der Waals attractions; therefore, saturated fats are solids. If a few *cis* double bonds are present in the chains, the molecules cannot form neat, compact lattices, but tend to coil; polyunsaturated triglycerides tend to be oils.

CH_2O_2C
$|$
CHO_2C
$|$
CH_2O_2C

can fit into a solid lattice

CH_2O_2C
$|$
CHO_2C
$|$
CH_2O_2C

cannot fit as well into a lattice

Triglycerides are one of the three principal foodstuffs, carbohydrates and proteins being the other two. As an energy source, triglycerides are the most efficient: they provide 9.5 kcal/gram, while the proteins provide 4.4 kcal/gram and the carbohydrates provide 4.2 kcal/gram.

In an organism, ingested fats are hydrolyzed into monoglycerides, diglycerides, fatty acids, and glycerol, all of which can be absorbed through the intestinal wall. The organism (1) uses these hydrolyzed or partially hydrolyzed fats as raw materials to synthesize its own fats; (2) converts the fatty acids to other compounds such as carbohydrates or cholesterol; or (3) converts the fatty acids to energy.

CH_2O_2CR CH_2O_2CR CH_2O_2CR CH_2OH
$|$ $\xrightarrow[\text{enzymes}]{H_2O}$ $|$ $|$ $|$
CHO_2CR CHO_2CR $+$ $CHOH$ $+$ $CHOH$ $+$ RCO_2H
$|$ $|$ $|$ $|$
CH_2O_2CR CH_2OH CH_2OH CH_2OH

                    a diglyceride   *a monoglyceride*   glycerol   *a fatty acid*

Section 19.2

Soaps and Detergents

The word *saponify* means "make soap." Saponification of an ester with NaOH yields the sodium salt of a carboxylic acid (Section 13.5C). Saponification of a triglyceride yields a salt of a long-chain fatty acid, which is a **soap**. Pioneers used beef or pork fat and wood ashes (which contain alkaline salts, such as K_2CO_3) to make soap. (It was reported by Julius Caesar that Teutonic tribes of his era also made soap this way.)

Saponification:

$$
\begin{array}{l}
CH_2O_2C(CH_2)_{16}CH_3 \\
| \\
CHO_2C(CH_2)_{16}CH_3 \quad + \; 3\,NaOH \quad \xrightarrow{\text{heat}} \\
| \\
CH_2O_2C(CH_2)_{16}CH_3
\end{array}
\qquad
\begin{array}{l}
CH_2OH \\
| \\
CHOH \quad + \; 3\,CH_3(CH_2)_{16}CO_2^-\;Na^+ \\
| \\
CH_2OH
\end{array}
$$

tristearin   glycerol   sodium stearate *a soap*

A molecule of a soap contains a long hydrocarbon chain plus an ionic end. The hydrocarbon portion of the molecule is hydrophobic and soluble in nonpolar substances, while the ionic end is hydrophilic and water-soluble. Because of the hydrocarbon chain, a soap molecule as a whole is not truly soluble in water. However, soap is readily suspended in water because it forms **micelles**, clusters of hydrocarbon chains with their ionic ends facing the water (see Figure 19.1).

The value of a soap is that it can emulsify oily dirt so that it can be rinsed away. The ability to act as an emulsifying agent arises from two properties of the soap. First, the hydrocarbon chain of a soap molecule dissolves in nonpolar substances, such as droplets of oil. Second, the anionic end of the soap molecule, which is attracted to water, is repelled by the anionic ends of soap molecules protruding from other drops of oil. Because of these repulsions between the soap–oil droplets, the oil cannot coalesce, but remains suspended. Figure 19.2 shows a diagram of the emulsification of an oil by a soap.

water
and Na$^+$ ions

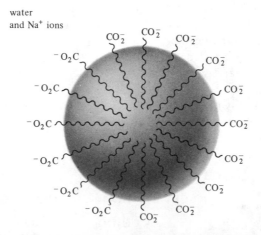

Figure 19.1. A micelle of the alkylcarboxylate ions of a soap.

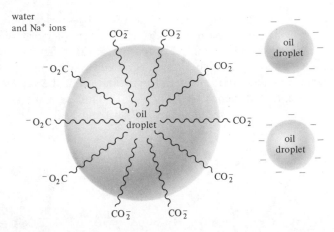

Figure 19.2. Emulsification of an oil by a soap: the droplets of oil and soap repel each other, but are attracted to water.

A disadvantage of soaps is that they form insoluble salts (bathtub ring) with Ca^{2+}, Mg^{2+}, and other ions found in hard water. ("Softening" water involves exchanging these ions for Na^+.)

$$2 CH_3(CH_2)_{16}CO_2Na + Ca^{2+} \longrightarrow [CH_3(CH_2)_{16}CO_2]_2Ca + 2 Na^+$$

sodium stearate   calcium stearate
                                                                insoluble

Most laundry products and many toilet "soaps" and shampoos are not soaps, but **detergents**. A detergent is a compound with a hydrophobic hydrocarbon end plus a sulfonate or sulfate ionic end. Because of this structure, a detergent has the same emulsifying properties as a soap. The advantage of a detergent is that most metal alkylsulfonates and sulfates are water-soluble; detergents do not precipitate with the metal ions found in hard water.

One of the first detergents in common use was a highly branched alkylbenzenesulfonate. The alkyl portion of this compound is synthesized by the polymerization of propylene and is attached to the benzene ring by a Friedel–Crafts alkylation reaction. Sulfonation, followed by treatment with base, yields the detergent.

Although the microorganisms in septic tanks or sewage-treatment plants can break down continuous-chain alkyl groups into smaller organic molecules, they cannot degrade branched chains. The reason for this difference in biodegradability is that long-chain hydrocarbons are degraded two carbons at a time by way of a keto ester. Branching interferes with the formation of the ketone group, and thus blocks the entire sequence. (FAD, NAD$^+$, and HSCoA, shown in the following equation, are discussed in Sections 16.13 and 13.8.)

$$RCH_2CH_2\overset{\overset{\displaystyle O}{\|}}{C}SCoA \xrightarrow[-2\,H]{FAD} RCH{=}CH\overset{\overset{\displaystyle O}{\|}}{C}SCoA \xrightarrow{H_2O}$$

$$R\overset{\overset{\displaystyle OH}{|}}{C}HCH_2\overset{\overset{\displaystyle O}{\|}}{C}SCoA \xrightarrow[-2\,H]{NAD^+} R\overset{\overset{\displaystyle O}{\|}}{C}CH_2\overset{\overset{\displaystyle O}{\|}}{C}SCoA \xrightarrow{HSCoA} R\overset{\overset{\displaystyle O}{\|}}{C}SCoA + CH_3\overset{\overset{\displaystyle O}{\|}}{C}SCoA$$

keto group   *two carbons removed*

To prevent the build-up of detergents in rivers and lakes, present-day detergents are designed with biodegradability in mind. One type of biodegradable detergent is an alkylbenzenesulfonate with a continuous-chain, rather than a branched-chain, alkyl group. Another type of biodegradable detergent is a continuous-chain alkylsulfate.

$$CH_3(CH_2)_{16}CH_2OSO_3^- \ Na^+$$

an alkylsulfate detergent

STUDY PROBLEM

19.1 Write equations for a reaction sequence that would convert triolein into a sodium alkylsulfate detergent.

Section 19.3

Waxes

Although the principal lipid of higher animals is the triglyceride, the principal lipid of many marine plankton organisms (a primary food source in the ocean) is a **wax**. A wax is a monoester of a long-chain fatty acid and a long-chain alcohol. Let us mention a few important waxes.

Beeswax, from which bees make their honeycombs, is a mixture of esters of C_{24} to C_{26} fatty acids and C_{28} to C_{30} alcohols. *Carnauba wax*, used in automobile polishes, occurs in the coating of the leaves of a Brazilian palm tree and is collected by shredding and beating the leaves. It is composed primarily of esters of C_{16} to C_{28} acids and C_{30} to C_{32} alcohols. *Spermaceti* is a wax obtained from the heads of sperm whales (*Cetaceae*) and used in cosmetics and candles. It is largely cetyl palmitate (*cetyl* referring to the C_{16} alcohol).

$$C_{25}H_{51}CO_2C_{28}H_{57} \qquad C_{27}H_{55}CO_2C_{32}H_{65} \qquad C_{15}H_{31}CO_2C_{16}H_{33}$$

in beeswax   *in carnauba wax*   cetyl palmitate
                                                      in spermaceti

Phospholipids

Phospholipids are lipids that contain phosphate ester groups. **Phosphoglycerides**, one type of phospholipid, are closely related to the fats and oils. These compounds usually contain fatty-acid esters at two positions of glycerol with a phosphate ester at the third position. Naturally occurring phosphoglycerides, like amino acids, are related to L-glyceraldehyde in the configuration of the chiral center.

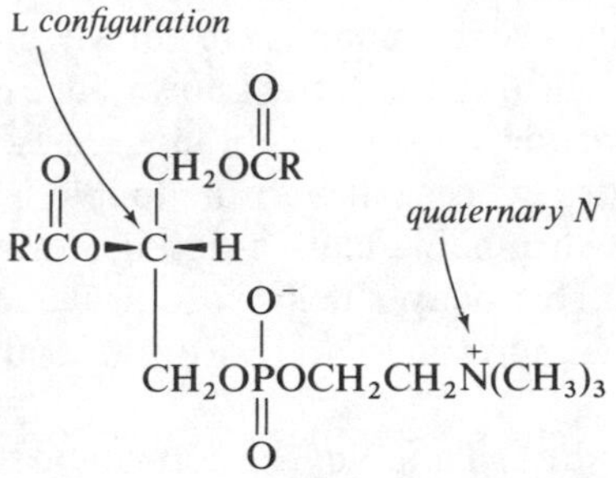

a lecithin,
or phosphatidylcholine

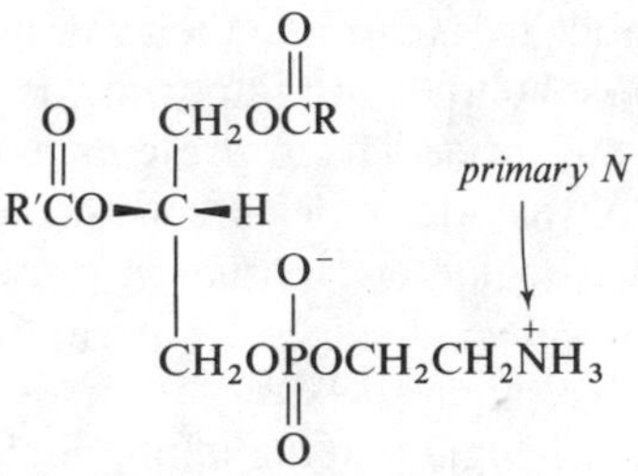

a cephalin,
or phosphatidylethanolamine

Lecithins and **cephalins** are two types of phosphoglyceride that are found principally in the brain, nerve cells, and liver of animals and are also found in egg yolks, wheat germ, yeast, soybeans, and other foods. These two types of compound are similar to each other in structure. Lecithins are derivatives of choline chloride, $HOCH_2CH_2N(CH_3)_3{}^+$ Cl^-, which is involved in the transmission of nerve impulses (Section 15.14). Cephalins are derivatives of ethanolamine, $HOCH_2CH_2NH_2$.

Other classes of phospholipid are represented by **plasmalogens**, which have vinyl ether groups instead of ester groups at carbon 1 of glycerol, and **sphingolipids**, of which sphingomyelin is an example. Sphingomyelin is a phosphate ester, not of glycerol, but of a long-chain allyl alcohol with an amide side chain.

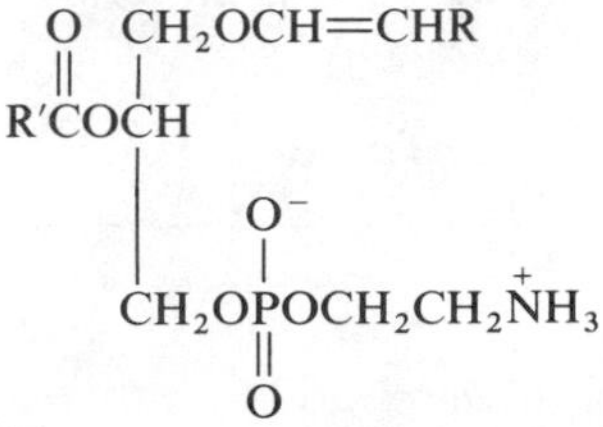

a plasmalogen

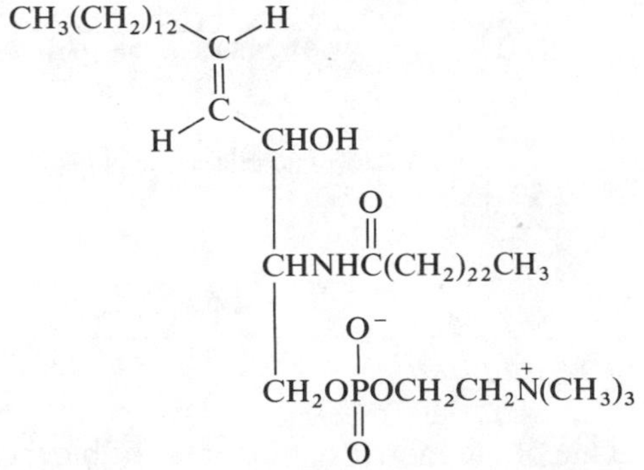

sphingomyelin
a sphingolipid

STUDY PROBLEM

19.2 Hydrolysis of sphingomyelin yields phosphoric acid, choline, a 24-carbon fatty acid, and *sphingosine*. What is the structure of sphingosine?

Like soaps and detergents, phospholipids contain long-chain, hydrophobic hydrocarbon groups. The phosphate–amine end of a phospholipid is hydrophilic. Because of these structural features, the phospholipids are excellent emulsifying agents. In mayonnaise, it is the phosphoglycerides of the egg yolk that keep the vegetable oil emulsified in the vinegar.

Interest in phospholipids is high because of their occurrence in nerve cells and the brain. Some biological functions of these compounds are known, but there is still much to learn about their role in biological systems. It is known, for example, that phospholipids are important in the action of cell membranes. These membranes are formed from proteins associated with a bilayer, or double layer, of phosphoglyceride molecules with their hydrophobic ends pointing inward and their hydrophilic ends pointing outward. This bilayer helps form a barrier that allows selective passage of water, nutrients, hormones, and wastes in and out of the cell (see Figure 19.3).

It is thought that the sphingolipids such as sphingomyelin contribute strength to the myelin (nerve cell) sheath by the intertwining of their hydrocarbon chains. Phospholipids are also thought to act as electrical insulation for the nerve cells. The myelin sheaths of people with multiple sclerosis (and some other diseases that affect this membrane) are deficient in the long hydrocarbon chains.

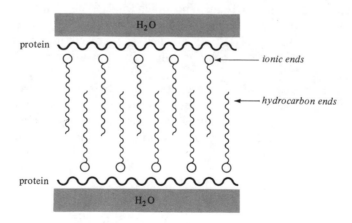

Figure 19.3. The bilayer of phospholipids in a cell membrane.

Section 19.5

Prostaglandins

One of the more exciting areas of biochemical research today is that of the **prostaglandins**. These compounds were first discovered in semen, and it was recognized that they were synthesized in the prostate gland (hence the name). We now know that prostaglandins are found throughout the body and are also synthesized in the lungs, liver, uterus, and other organs and tissues.

Just how the prostaglandins act is still unknown. It is thought that they are moderators of hormone activity in the body, a theory that explains their far-reaching biological effects. For example, administration of remarkably small doses of some prostaglandins stimulates uterine contractions and can cause abortion. Imbalances in prostaglandins can lead to nausea, diarrhea, inflammation, pain, fever, menstrual disorders, asthma, ulcers, hypertension, drowsiness, or blood clots.

Although the structures of the prostaglandins are not particularly complex, their structures were not determined until 1962. The prostaglandins are 20-carbon carboxylic acids that contain cyclopentane rings. They are biosynthesized from the 20-carbon unsaturated fatty acids (one reason unsaturated fats are necessary in a good diet).

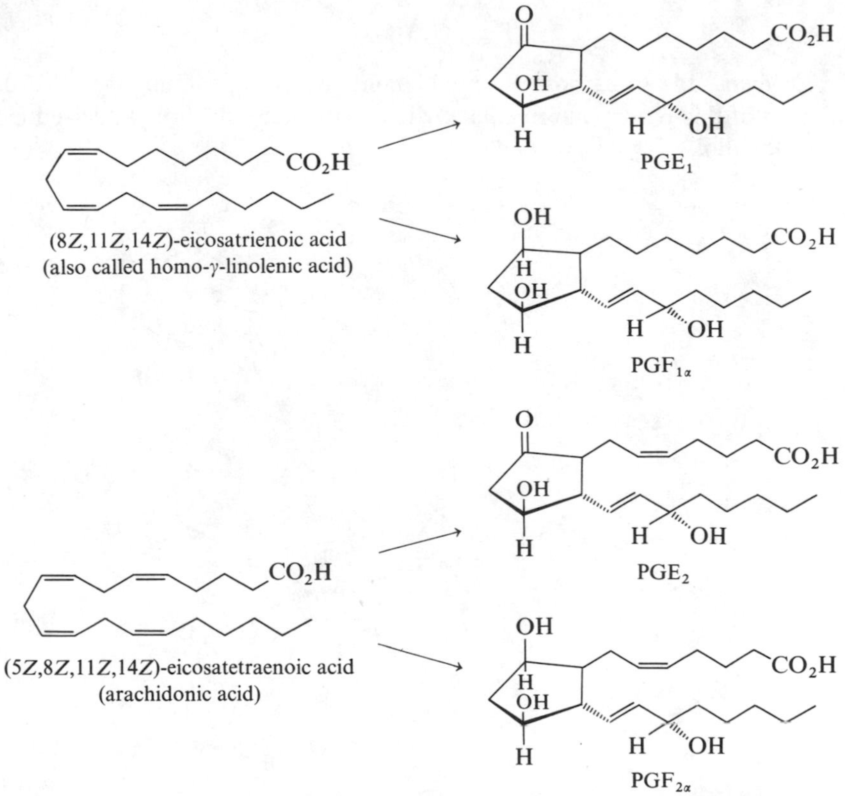

(8Z,11Z,14Z)-eicosatrienoic acid
(also called homo-γ-linolenic acid)

PGE$_1$

PGF$_{1\alpha}$

(5Z,8Z,11Z,14Z)-eicosatetraenoic acid
(arachidonic acid)

PGE$_2$

PGF$_{2\alpha}$

There are several known prostaglandins, but the four shown as products in the preceding equations are the most common ones. Although similar to each other in structure, the prostaglandins differ in (1) the number of double bonds, and (2) whether the cyclopentane portion is a diol or a keto alcohol. The terms PGE$_1$, PGF$_{1\alpha}$, PGE$_2$, and PGF$_{2\alpha}$ are symbols for these compounds. PG means *prostaglandin*, E means the *keto alcohol*, and F means the *diol*. The subscript numbers refer to the number of double bonds. (For example, the subscript 1 means *one* double bond.) The subscript α refers to the configuration of the —OH at carbon 9 (*cis* to the carboxyl side chain).

The biosynthesis of the prostaglandins probably proceeds by a free-radical mechanism. Abstraction of a doubly allylic hydrogen, followed by an allylic rearrangement of one double bond, leads to attack by a hydroxyl radical at carbon 15 of the fatty acid.

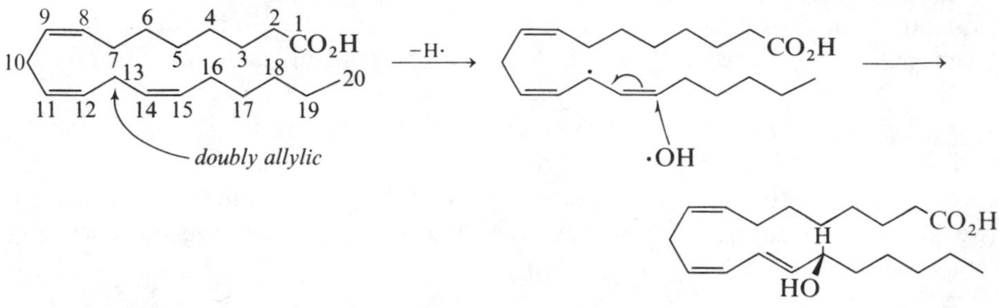

Oxygen adds to carbons 9 and 11, and the cyclopentane ring is formed. Oxidation of this peroxy intermediate leads to the keto alcohol, while reduction leads to the diol.

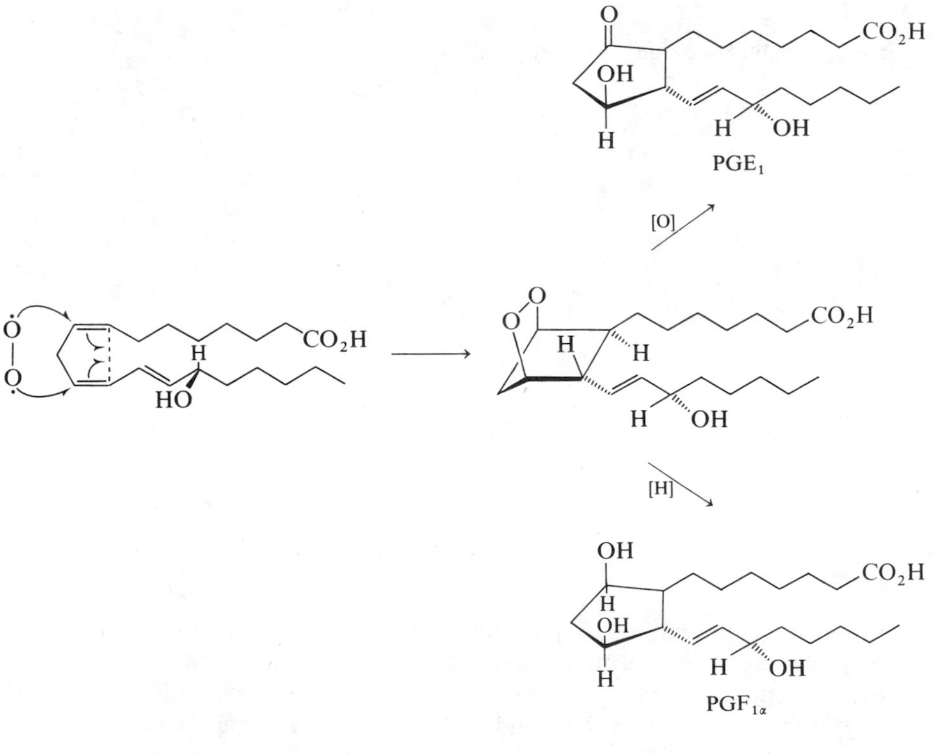

STUDY PROBLEM

19.3   What products would you expect from the oxidation of   (a) PGE_1, and   (b) $PGF_{1\alpha}$ with hot aqueous $KMnO_4$?

Terpenes

The odorous components of plants that can be separated from other plant materials by steam distillation are called **essential oils**. Many essential oils, such as those from flowers, are used in perfumes. Most essential oils are mixtures of **terpenes**, a class of natural products found in both plants and animals. The name comes from *turpentine*, which is rich in terpenes.

All terpenes appear to have been constructed by the *head-to-tail joining of isoprene units*. (The *head* is the end closer to the methyl branch; the *tail* is the end farther from the methyl branch.) Terpenes may contain two, three, or more isoprene units. Their molecules may be open-chain or cyclic. They may contain double bonds, hydroxyl groups, carbonyl groups, or other functional groups.

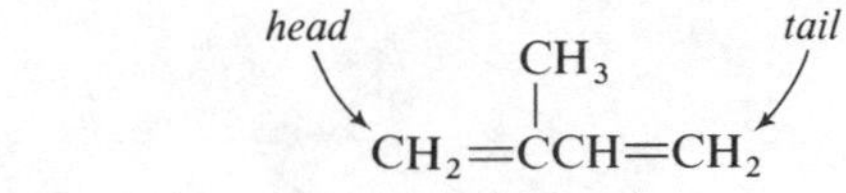

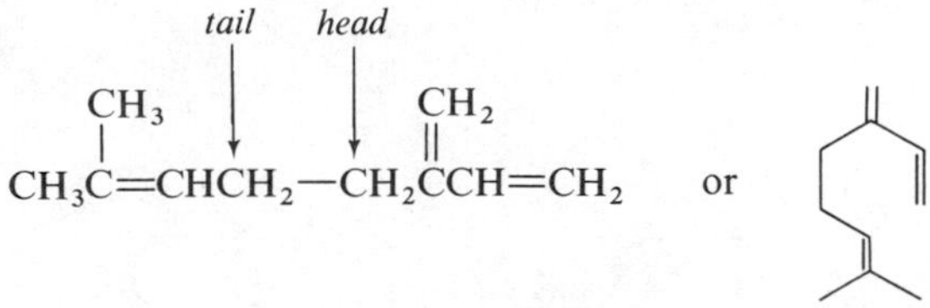

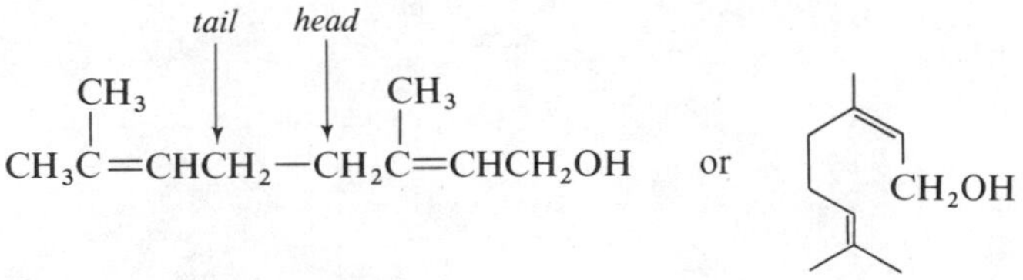

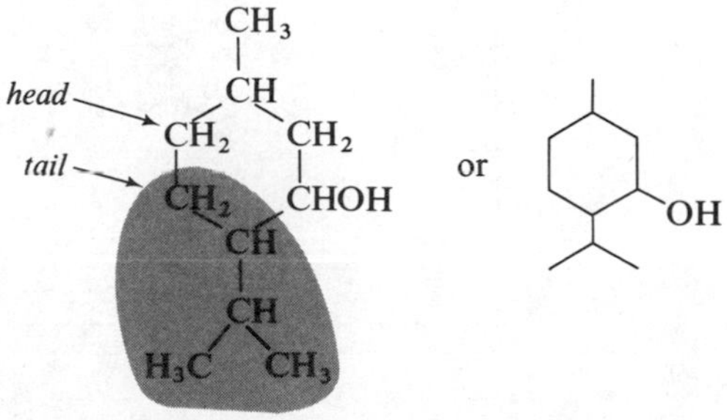

Although the idea is appealing, terpenes do not arise from polymerization of isoprene; rather, they arise from an enzymatic ester condensation of the acetyl portions of acetylcoenzyme A. Intermediates in the formation of terpenes are the pyrophosphates (diphosphates) of mevalonic acid and a pair of isopentenyl alcohols. An abbreviated biosynthetic route to terpenes and cholesterol is found in Figure 19.4. (The phosphate groups are not shown in the figure.)

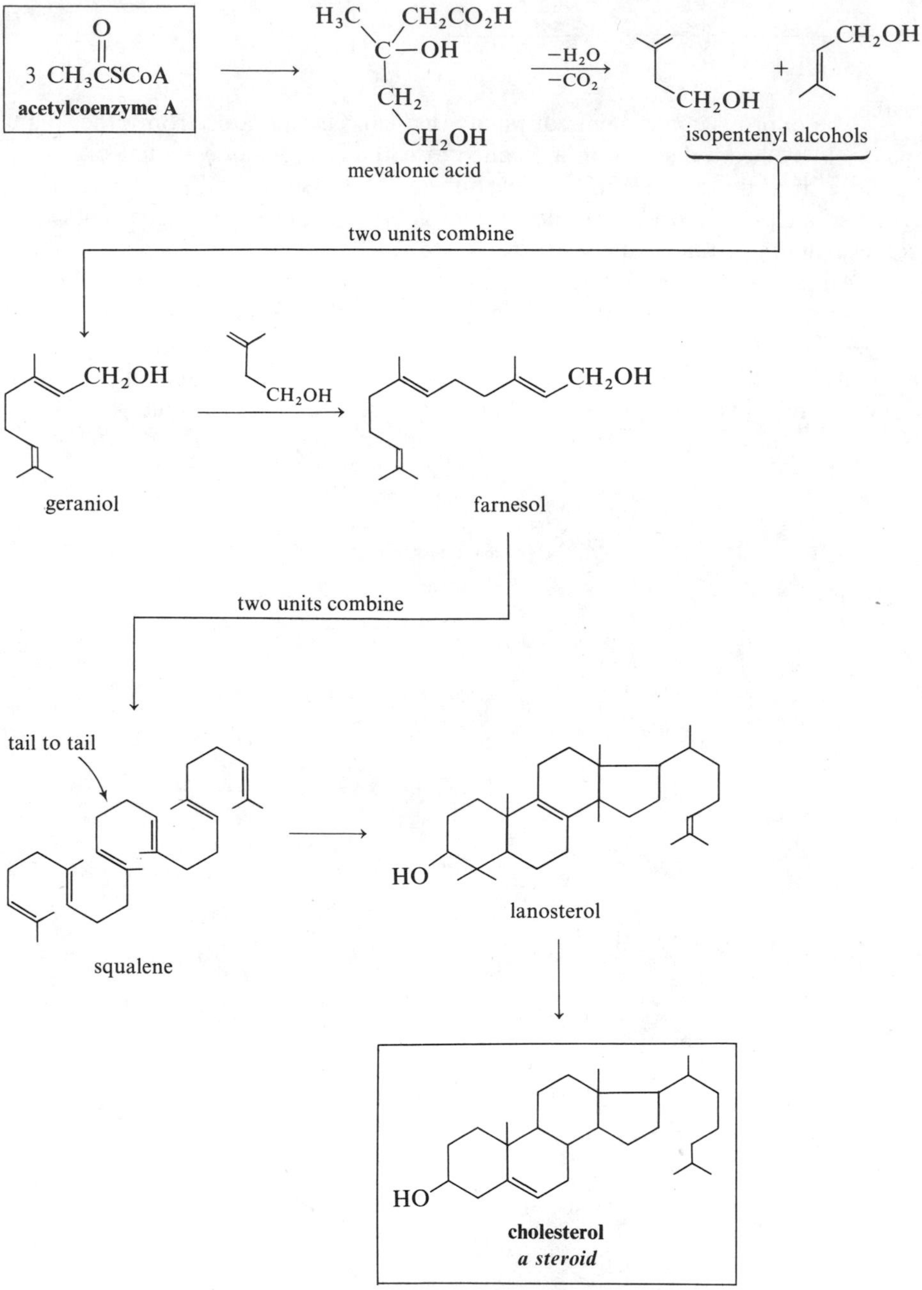

Lipids and Related Natural Products

Figure 19.4. Abbreviated biosynthetic path from acetylcoenzyme A to cholesterol. (The conversion of squalene to lanosterol, including stereochemistry, is shown in Figure 19.5.)

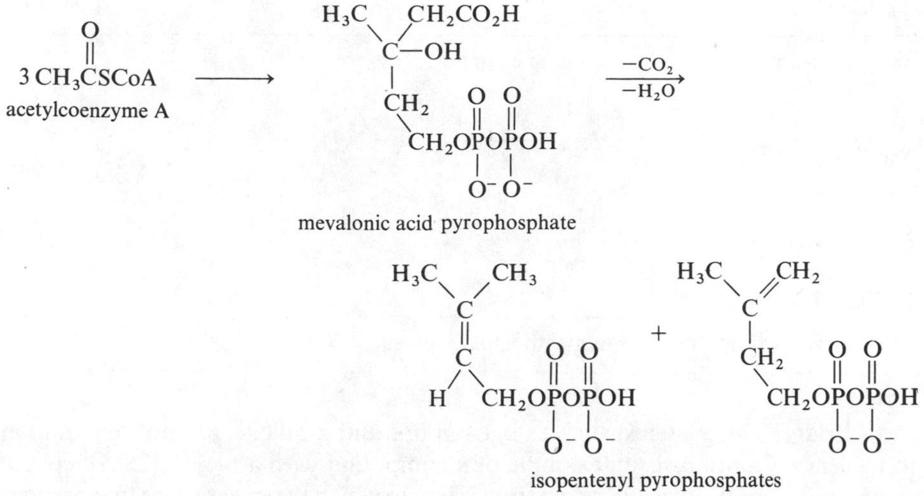

$$3 \underset{\text{acetylcoenzyme A}}{CH_3\overset{\overset{\displaystyle O}{\|}}{C}SCoA} \longrightarrow$$

(structure: mevalonic acid pyrophosphate)

$$\overset{-CO_2}{\underset{-H_2O}{\longrightarrow}}$$

mevalonic acid pyrophosphate

(structures: isopentenyl pyrophosphates) +

isopentenyl pyrophosphates

Terpenes are categorized by the *number of pairs of isoprene units* they contain:

monoterpenes: two isoprene units
sesquiterpenes: three isoprene units
diterpenes: four isoprene units
triterpenes: six isoprene units
tetraterpenes: eight isoprene units

A.   Monoterpenes

Monoterpenes, with skeletons that contain only two isoprene units, are the simplest of the terpenes. Yet, even monoterpenes exhibit a variety of structures.

Acyclic monoterpenes:

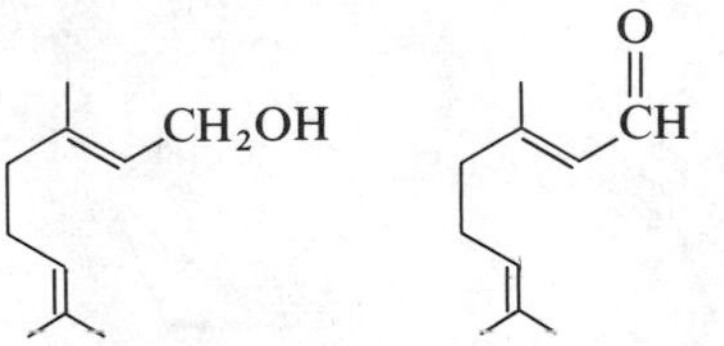

geraniol
in roses

citral (geranial)
in lemongrass

Cyclic monoterpenes:

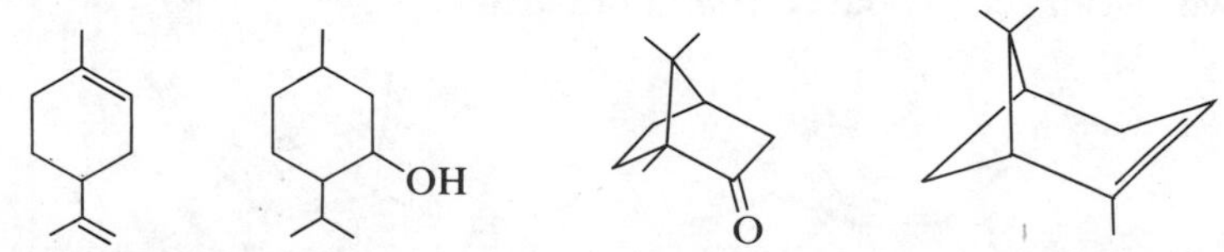

limonene
in citrus fruits

menthol
in mint

camphor
from camphor trees

α-pinene
in turpentine

Sample Problem

Show the isoprene units in citral and in camphor.

Solution:

STUDY PROBLEM

19.4   Show the isoprene units in menthol and α-pinene.

Bridged ring systems, such as in camphor and α-pinene, are not uncommon in terpenes. Camphor is an example of a compound with a bicyclo[2.2.1]heptane skeleton. The prefix **bicyclo-** refers to a system in which two rings share two or more carbon atoms between them (that is, fused rings). The numbers [2.2.1] represent the number of carbon atoms in each "arm" of the ring system. (An arm constitutes the carbon atoms between bridgehead carbons.)

one C

bridgehead
carbons   *two C's* { } *two C's*

bicyclo[2.2.1]heptane
(norbornane)

Bridged systems are invaluable for mechanistic studies because the rings are frozen into one conformation. For example, the six-membered ring in camphor is frozen into a boat form, rather than the usual chair form.

Unless the ring size is quite large, bridged rings must have *cis*-ring junctures. Overlap of orbitals to form a *trans*-ring juncture would be sterically impossible.

cis

CH$_2$

H   H   CH$_2$

H   H   *trans is too*
strained to exist

Another restriction of bridged rings, called **Bredt's rule**, is that the bridgehead carbon cannot be doubly bonded. A model of a bridged system such as in camphor or pinene will demonstrate that the geometry is wrong for *p*-orbital overlap. Bredt's rule does not apply to fused rings that share only two carbons or to large rings, which can accomodate a *trans* double bond.

H   H

stable   *no double bond here*

B. Higher Terpenes

We have shown several examples of monoterpenes, which are common in plants. Some higher terpenes of interest are *squalene* (found in yeast, wheat germ, and shark liver oil) and *lanosterol* (a component of lanolin, which is obtained from wool fat). Both these compounds are intermediates in the biosynthesis of steroids. The conversion of squalene to lanosterol is an important one that will be discussed shortly. (See Figure 19.4 or 19.5 for the structures of these two compounds.) Natural rubber (Section 9.18B) is a polyterpene that we have already discussed.

Carrots contain an orange-colored tetraterpene called *carotene*. (If a person eats too many carrots, the deposition of carotene will color his skin orange. However, time is a cure for this condition.) Carotene can be cleaved enzymatically into two units of vitamin A. (The role of vitamin A in vision will be discussed in Chapter 20.)

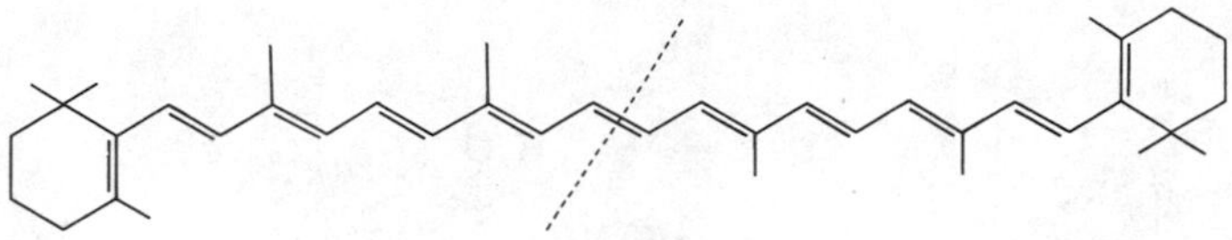

β-carotene
an orange tetraterpene

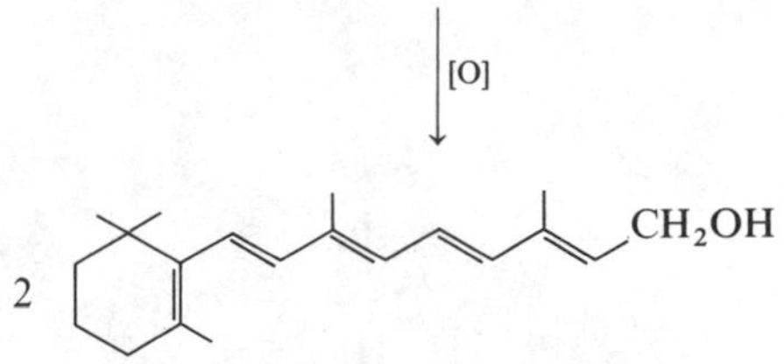

[O]

CH₂OH

2

all-*trans*-vitamin A

C. Reactions of Terpenes

Terpenes undergo reactions typical of their functional groups. For example, addition to alkene double bonds can occur.

Sample Problem

Predict the product of addition of HCl to limonene. (Remember Markovnikov's rule.)

Solution:

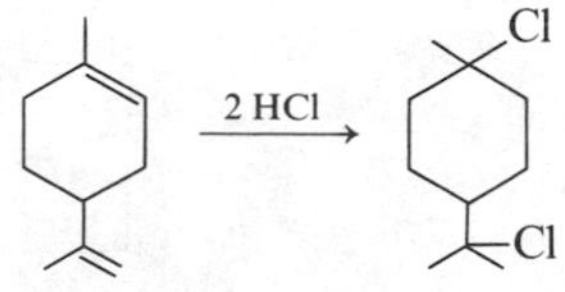

2 HCl →

Cl

Cl

Terpene structures contain secondary and tertiary carbon atoms and often contain double bonds. Addition of H^+ to a double bond can lead to a carbocation, which then can undergo rearrangement to a more stable carbocation (Section 5.7E). Rearrangements of terpene skeletons are very common. For example,

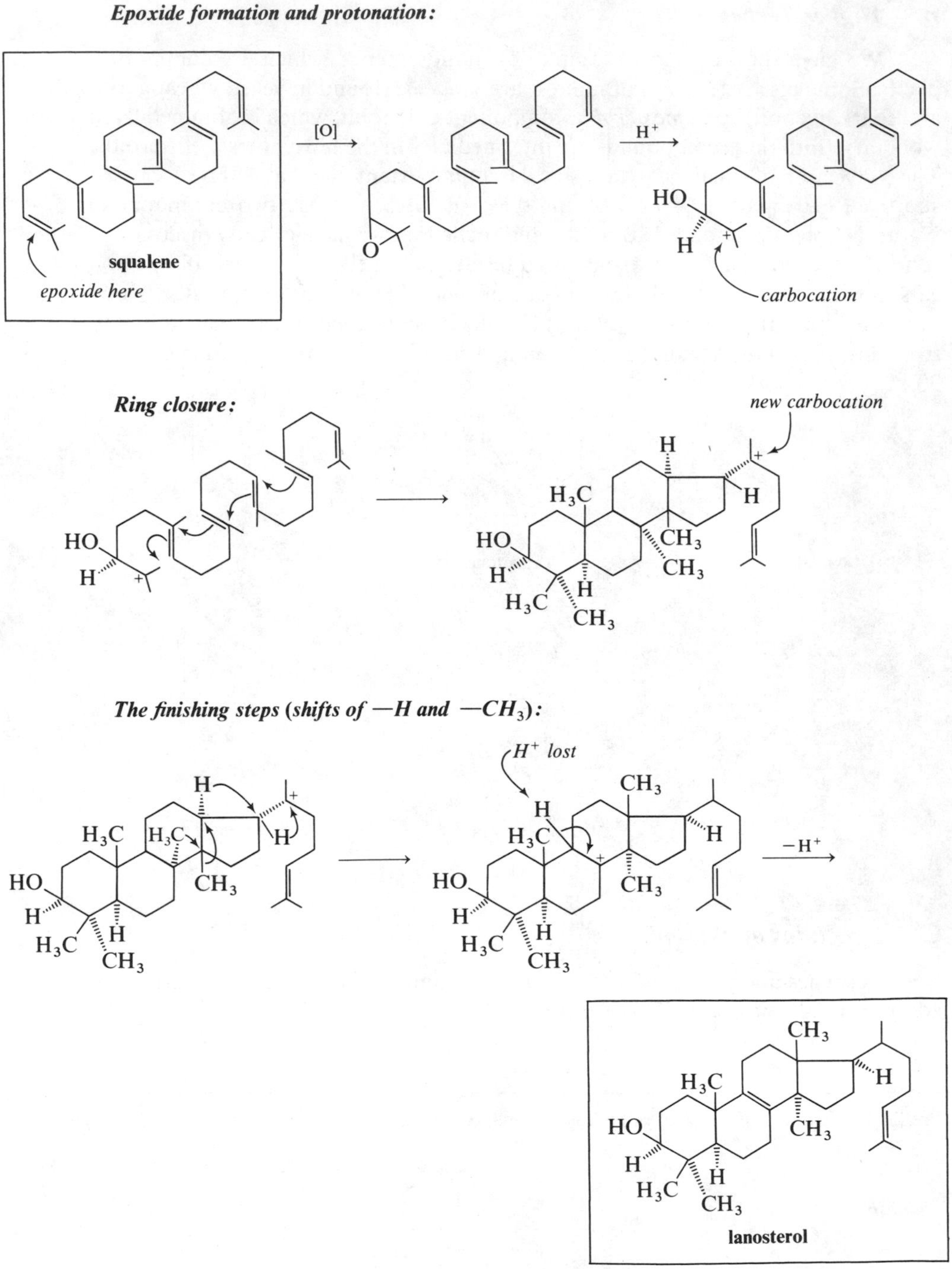

Lipids and Related Natural Products

Epoxide formation and protonation:

Ring closure:

The finishing steps (shifts of —H and —CH₃):

Figure 19.5. The conversion of squalene to lanosterol.

the addition of HCl to α-pinene does not yield a product with the α-pinene ring system intact. Instead, bornyl chloride, with a bornane ring system, is obtained.

α-pinene   bornyl chloride

The sequence of reactions leading from squalene to lanosterol, which occurs in the biosynthesis of steroids, shows many of the features of terpene reactions. This sequence is shown in Figure 19.5. The first step is an enzymatic epoxide formation. Next, the epoxide oxygen is protonated and the epoxide ring is opened, leaving a carbocation. The formation of this carbocation sets in motion a concerted series of electron shifts that results in the ring closures of *four rings* and yields the steroid ring system. The ring closures are followed by hydride and methyl shifts to yield lanosterol. It is amazing that this whole sequence is catalyzed by only one enzyme, squalene oxide cyclase!

Section 19.7

Pheromones

Humans communicate by talking, using the telephone, painting pictures, or writing letters (or books). But insects and some animals communicate chemically. A chemical secreted by one individual of a species that brings forth a response in another individual of the same species is called a **pheromone** (from the Greek *phero*, "carrier"). Insect pheromones called alarm pheromones signify danger. Pheromones are also used to recruit others; for example, a pheromone secreted by one bee helps alert other bees to the location of a food source. Some pheromones that act as sex attractants have been used for insect control. (Male insects may be lured by a sex attractant pheromone, trapped, and then sterilized or killed.)

Pheromones are usually not complex in structure. Geraniol and citral, both terpenes, are recruiting pheromones for honeybees, while isoamyl acetate (not a terpene) is a bee alarm pheromone.

$$CH_3COCH_2CH_2CH(CH_3)_2$$

geraniol   citral   isoamyl acetate
                                                 (3-methylbutyl ethanoate)

The following compounds are sex attractants for a few different species of insects:

cis-$(CH_3)_2CH(CH_2)_4CHCH(CH_2)_9CH_3$

gypsy moth

cis-$CH_3(CH_2)_3CH{=}CH(CH_2)_6OCCH_3$

cabbage looper

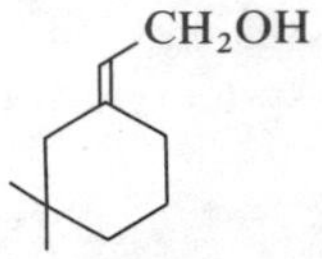

boll weevil

$$cis\text{-}CH_3(CH_2)_{12}CH=CH(CH_2)_7CH_3$$

house fly

Extremely small quantities of a pheromone can elicit the desired response. A typical female insect may carry only 10^{-8} gram of sex attractant, yet that is enough to attract over a billion males! (Imagine the work involved in extracting enough pheromone from a species of insect to determine the structure!)

STUDY PROBLEM

19.5 The formula for the alarm pheromone for one species of ant is $C_7H_{14}O$. When treated with I_2 and NaOH, this pheromone yields iodoform and *n*-hexanoic acid. What is the structure of the pheromone?

Section 19.8

Steroids

We have mentioned steroids several times. Now let us take a more detailed look at these compounds. A **steroid** is a compound that contains the following ring system. The four rings are designated *A*, *B*, *C*, and *D*. The carbons are numbered as shown, starting with ring *A*, progressing to ring *D*, then to the angular (bridgehead) methyl groups, and finally to a side chain if it is present.

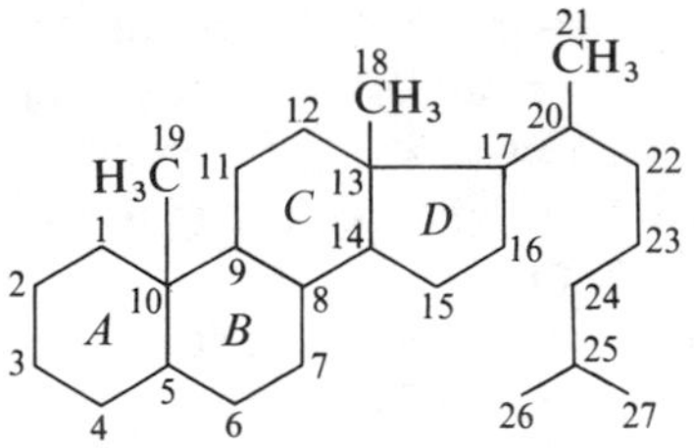

cholestane

Many steroids may be named as derivatives of this structure, which is called **cholestane**. (Steroid nuclei with different side chains also have names; however, we will not present them here.)

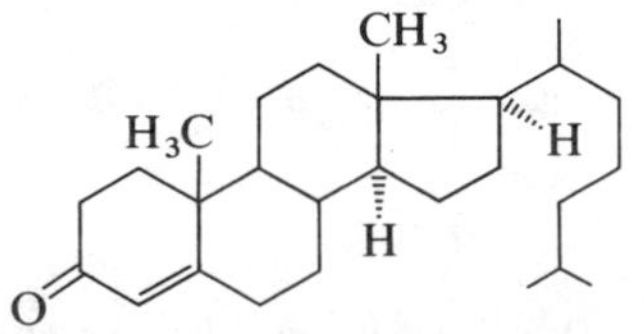

4-cholesten-3-one
a steroid with a cholestane skeleton

A. *Conformation of Steroids*

Recall from Section 4.5B that the more stable isomer of a 1,2-dialkylcyclo-hexane is the one with both substituents *equatorial*.

trans:

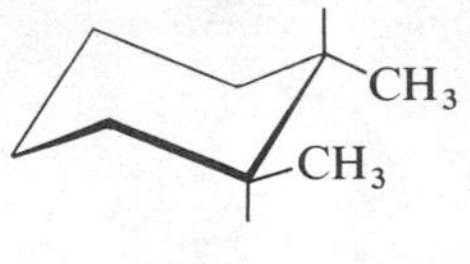

more stable than

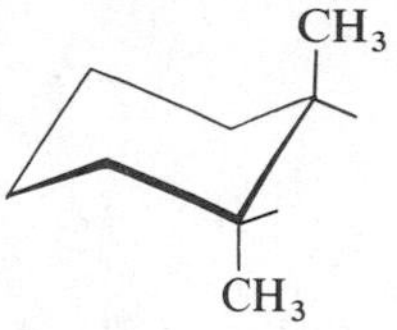

CH₃

CH₃

e,e

CH₃

CH₃

a,a

cis:

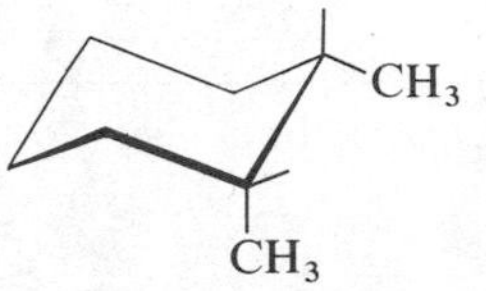

CH₃

same stability as

CH₃

CH₃

CH₃

a,e

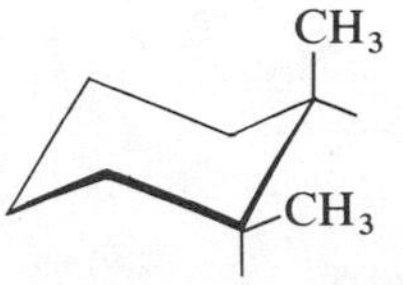

e,a

A *trans*-1,2-disubstituted cyclohexane can exist in a preferred conformation in which both substituents are equatorial, while the *cis*-isomer must have one axial substituent and one equatorial substituent. The *trans*-isomer is therefore the more stable one.

One ring fused to another in the 1,2-positions can be *cis* or *trans*. The following structures represent *cis*- and *trans*-decalin.

cis-decalin:

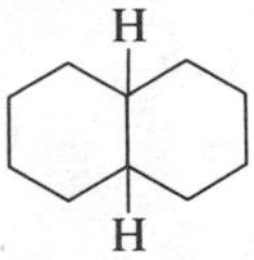

H

H

or

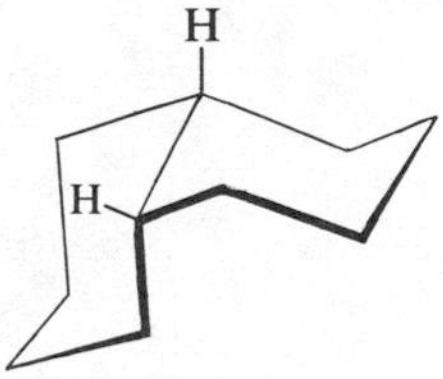

H

H

trans-decalin:

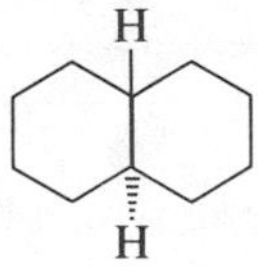

H

H

or

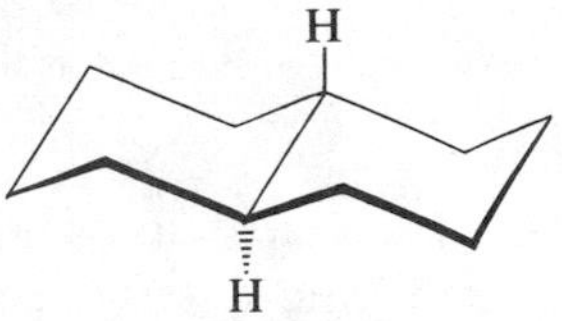

H

H

To verify that these two formulas represent *cis* and *trans* ring junctures, make the models. Alternatively, check the hydrogens on the ring-juncture carbons. They, too, must be *cis* at a *cis* ring juncture or *trans* at a *trans* ring juncture.

Note that when ring *B* is *trans* on ring *A*, ring *A* is also *trans* on ring *B*.

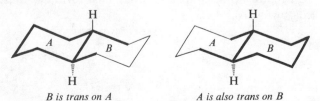

B is trans on A   *A is also trans on B*

As may be seen in the formulas for *trans*- and *cis*-decalin, the *trans* ring junc-ture is *e,e*, while the *cis* ring juncture is *a,e*. The *trans*-isomer is more stable than the *cis*-isomer by about 3 kcal/mole. The steroid nucleus contains three ring junctures (*A*/*B*, *B*/*C*, and *C*/*D*). In nature, these are usually the more stable *trans* ring junctures (but we will encounter an exception later in this chapter).

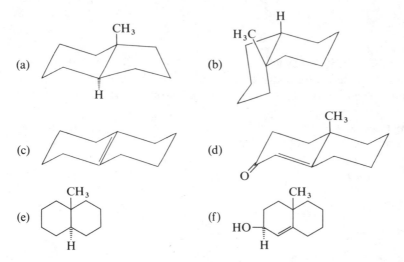

trans ring junctures

Sample Problem

Tell whether each of the following ring junctures is *cis*, *trans*, or neither:

(a)

(b)

(c)

(d)

(e)

(f)

Solution: (a) *trans*;   (b) *cis*;   (c) neither;   (d) neither;   (e) *trans*;   (f) neither.

Groups substituted on a steroid ring system may be *below* or *above* the plane of the ring as the ring system is generally drawn. A group that is below the plane (*trans* to the angular methyl groups) is called an α group, while one that is above the plane (*cis* to the angular methyl groups) is called a β group. (Do not confuse this use of α and β with their use in carbohydrate chemistry, where they refer to groups only at the anomeric carbon. In both classes of compound, however, β denotes a group projected upward in the usual conformational formula, while α denotes a group projected downward.)

angular methyl groups

CH₃   R

CH₃

HO

H

β: up (cis to angular methyl groups)

The terms α and β may be used in the names of steroids to designate the stereo-chemistry of substituents. In the name, α or β immediately follows the position number for the substituent.

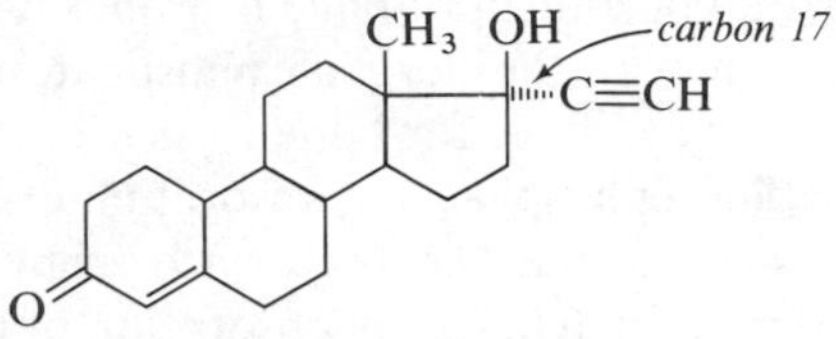

17α-ethynyl-17β-hydroxy-4-estren-3-one
an oral contraceptive, usually called norethinodrone

STUDY PROBLEMS

19.6 Give conformational formulas for:
(a) cholestane   (b) 3α-cholestanol   (c) norethinodrone.

19.7 Which is the more stable isomer, 3α-cholestanol or 3β-cholestanol? Why?

B. Cholesterol

Cholesterol is the most widespread animal steroid and is found in almost all animal tissues. Human gallstones and egg yolks are especially rich sources of this compound. Cholesterol is a necessary intermediate in the biosynthesis of the steroid hormones; however, since it can be synthesized from acetylcoenzyme A, it is not a dietary necessity. High levels of blood cholesterol are associated with arteriosclerosis (hardening of the arteries), a condition in which cholesterol and other lipids coat the insides of the arteries. Whether or not the level of cholesterol in the blood can be controlled by diet is still a topic of controversy.

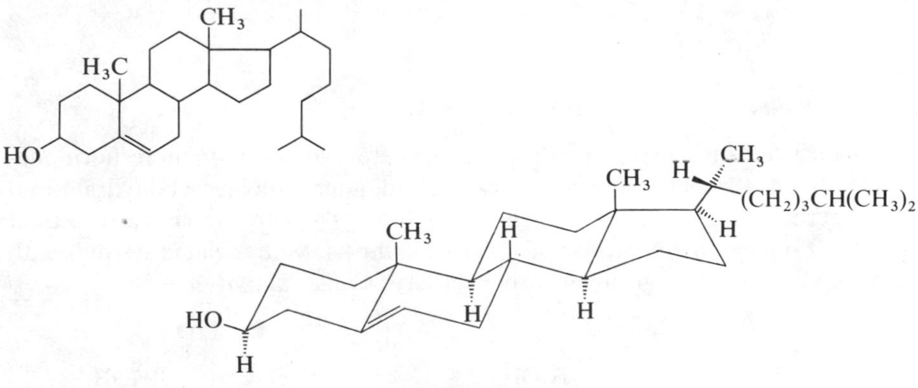

cholesterol
(5-cholesten-3β-ol)

STUDY PROBLEM

19.8 What is the configuration (*cis* or *trans*) of each ring juncture in cholesterol?

C. *Vitamin D*

If the proper ratios of calcium, phosphorus, and vitamin D are not available to a growing child (or other vertebrate), the bones do not develop properly and rickets results. The inorganic constituent of bone is primarily calcium phosphate. The action of vitamin D is to increase the inorganic phosphate level in the blood and thus to make more phosphate available for bone formation. (Too much vitamin D, however, increases the blood phosphates by resorption of bone phosphate.)

Vitamin D is not a steroid, but can be formed from some steroids. For example, a photochemical reaction (caused by absorption of ultraviolet radiation from sunlight) of 7-dehydrocholesterol in the skin gives rise to vitamin D. The results of absorption of light by the conjugated diene are the opening of ring *B* and the formation of a conjugated triene.

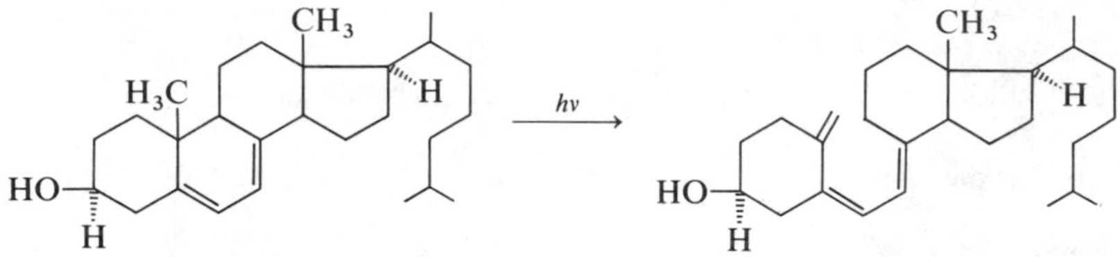

7-dehydrocholesterol
in the skin
                        vitamin D_3

Fish-liver oils are another source of vitamin D. Today, adequate vitamin D consumption is assured by the addition of irradiated ergosterol to milk. (The subscripts in vitamin D_2 and D_3 in the equations refer to the slightly different structures of these two compounds. Both have the same physiological activity.)

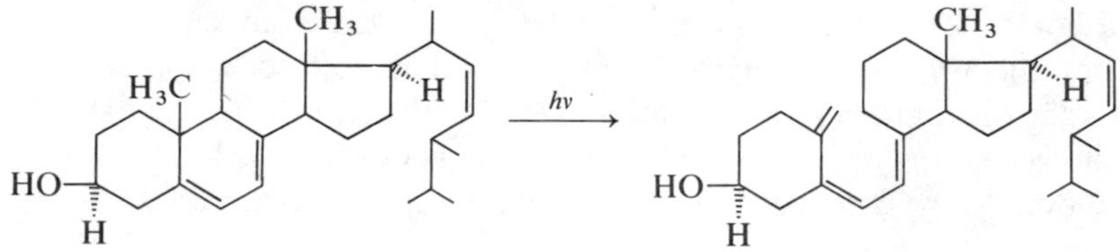

ergosterol
in yeast, soybean oil,
and ergot (a fungus)
                        vitamin D_2
                        (calciferol)

D. *Cortisone*

Cortisone and cortisol (hydrocortisone) are two of 28 or more hormones secreted by the adrenal cortex. Both these steroids alter protein, carbohydrate, and lipid metabolism in ways not entirely understood. They are widely used to treat inflammation due to allergies or rheumatoid arthritis. Many related steroids with a carbonyl or hydroxyl group at carbon 11 have similar activity.

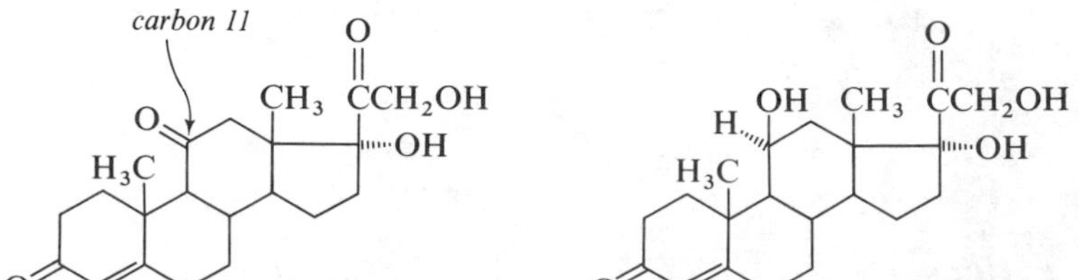

cortisone   cortisol

E.   Sex Hormones

The sex hormones are produced primarily in the testes or the ovaries; their production is regulated by pituitary hormones. The sex hormones impart secondary sex characteristics and regulate the sexual and reproductive functions. Male hormones are collectively called **androgens**; female hormones, **estrogens**; and pregnancy hormones, **progestins**.

In pregnant females, the presence of progesterone suppresses ovulation and menstruation. Synthetic progestins, such as norethynodrel (Enovid), are used to suppress ovulation as a method of birth control.

Androgens:

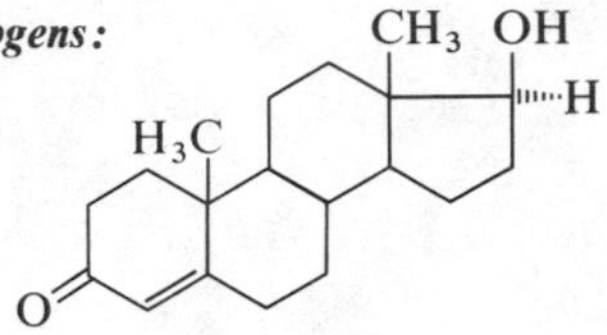

testosterone
the principal male hormone

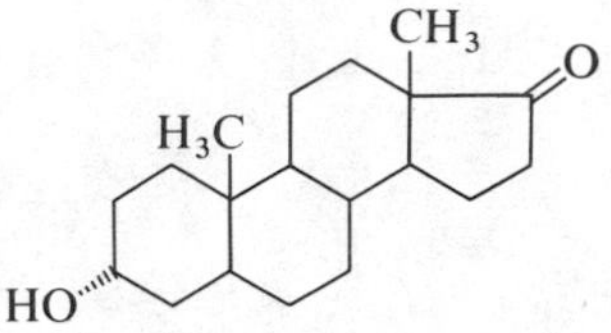

androsterone
a metabolized form of testosterone

Estrogens:

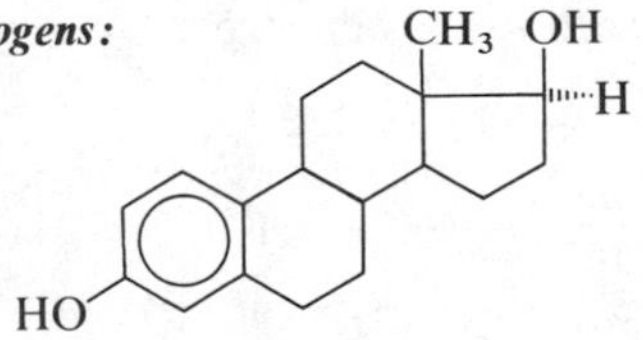

estradiol

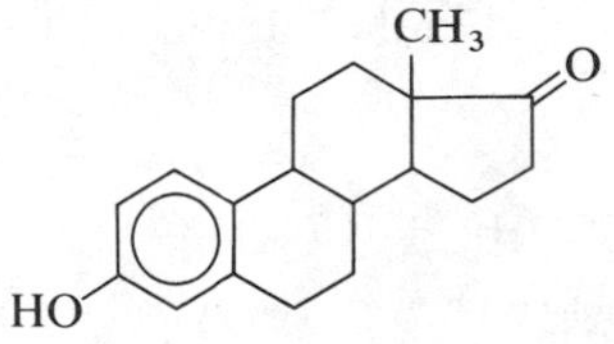

estrone

Progestins:

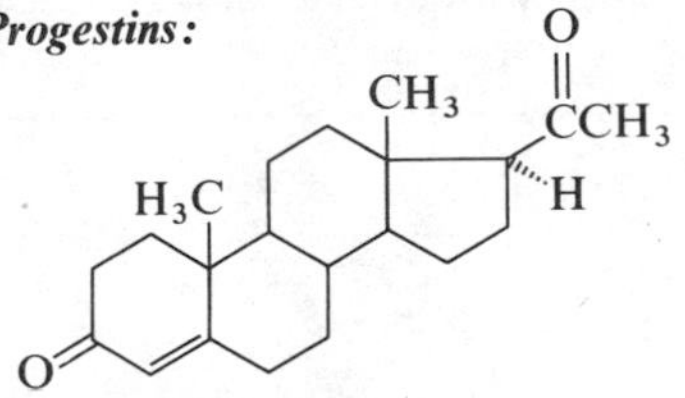

progesterone
suppresses ovulation

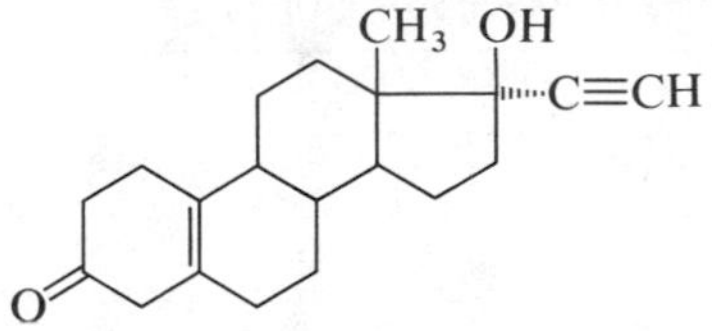

norethynodrel
a synthetic progestin

F.   Bile Acids

The bile acids are found in bile, which is produced in the liver and stored in the gall bladder. The structure of cholic acid, the most abundant bile acid, follows. Cholic acid, as well as other bile acids, has a *cis A/B* ring juncture instead of the usual *trans A/B* ring juncture.

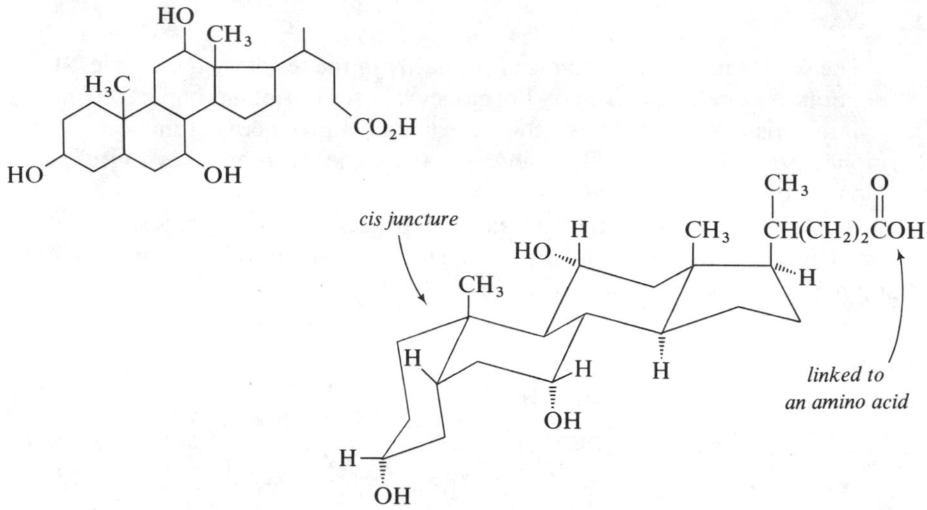

Lipids and Related Natural Products

cholic acid

Bile acids are secreted into the intestines in combination with sodium salts of either glycine or taurine ($H_2NCH_2CH_2SO_3H$). The bile acid–amino acid link is an amide link between the carboxyl group of the bile acid and the amino group of the amino acid. In this combined form, the bile acid–amino acid acts to keep lipids emulsified in the intestines, thereby promoting their digestion.

$$RCO_2H \ + \ H_2NCH_2CO_2^- \ Na^+ \ \xrightarrow[-H_2O]{\text{enzymes}} \ \overset{\overset{\displaystyle O}{\displaystyle \|}}{R}CNHCH_2CO_2^- \ Na^+$$

cholic acid   sodium salt of   *an emulsifying agent*
                      glycine

STUDY PROBLEM

19.9 What structural features of cholic acid combined with glycine allow it to act as an emulsifying agent?

SUMMARY

Fats and **oils** are triglycerides: triesters of glycerol and long-chain fatty acids. Generally, oils (liquid) contain more unsaturation than fats (solid). Fatty acids contain even numbers of carbon atoms and *cis* double bonds.

A **soap** is the alkali-metal salt of a fatty acid. A **detergent** is a salt of a sulfonate or sulfate that contains a long hydrocarbon chain. Naturally occurring **waxes** are esters of fatty acids and long-chain alcohols.

Phosphoglycerides, such as lecithins and cephalins, generally contain glycerol esterified with two fatty acids and a phosphatidylamine. Other phospholipids may differ in structure, but all contain long hydrocarbon chains plus a phosphate group and an amino group.

Prostaglandins, thought to be moderators of hormone activity, are 20-carbon carboxylic acids containing a cyclopentane ring plus hydroxyl groups, one or more double bonds, and sometimes a keto group. They are biosynthesized from unsaturated, 20-carbon fatty acids.

Terpenes, found in both plants and animals, have the structures of diisoprene, triisoprene, etc. They are not synthesized from isoprene, but from acetylcoenzyme A, and are the precursors of steroids. Functional groups may also be present in terpene structures.

A **pheromone** is a chemical secreted by one individual of a species (notably insects) that elicits a response in another individual of the same species. Generally of simple structure, pheromones are used to signify danger or food, or to act as sex attractants.

Steroids are compounds that contain the following ring system:

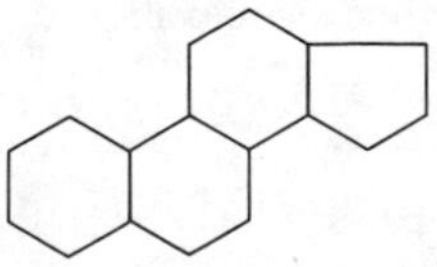

Derivatives of the steroid cholesterol are precursors for vitamin D and some hormones. Cortisone, the sex hormones, and the bile acids are all steroids.

STUDY PROBLEMS

19.10 Write an equation for the conversion of trilinolein to a solid fat.

19.11 A mixed triglyceride contains two units of stearic acid and one unit of palmitoleic acid. What are the major organic products when this triglyceride is treated with:

(a)   an excess of dilute aqueous NaOH and heat?
(b) H_2, copper chromite catalyst, heat, and pressure?
(c)   bromine in CCl_4?

19.12 What are the major organic products of ozonolysis, followed by oxidative work-up, of each of the following fatty acids?   (a) palmitic acid;   (b) palmitoleic acid;   (c) linoleic acid;   (d) linolenic acid.

19.13 How would you distinguish chemically between: (a) tripalmitin and tripalmitolein;   (b) beeswax and beef fat;   (c) beeswax and paraffin wax;   (d) linoleic acid and linseed oil;   (e) sodium palmitate and sodium *p*-decylbenzenesulfonate;   (f) a vegetable oil and a motor oil?

19.14 Hydrolysis of *trimyristin*, a fat obtained from nutmeg, yields only one fatty acid, myristic acid. This same acid can be obtained from dodecyl bromide (the 12-carbon, continuous-chain alkyl bromide) and diethyl malonate in a malonic ester synthesis. What are the structures of myristic acid and trimyristin?

19.15 Show by an equation how you would prepare cetyl palmitate from an appropriate acid and alcohol.

19.16 Which of the following compounds would show detergent activity?

(a) CH_3OSO_3Li

(b) $CH_3(CH_2)_4\overset{\displaystyle CH_3}{\overset{|}{CH}}(CH_2)_2OSO_3K$

(c) $(CH_3)_2CHCH_2SO_3Na$

(d) $CH_3(CH_2)_{16}CH_2OH$

(e) 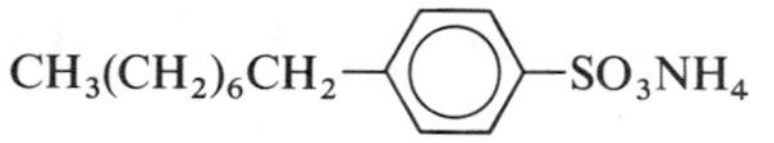 $CH_3(CH_2)_6CH_2$—⟨◯⟩—SO_3NH_4

19.17 A fat of unknown structure is found to be optically active. Saponification, followed by acidification, yields two equivalents of palmitic acid and one equivalent of oleic acid. What is the structure of the fat?

19.18 Starting with tristearin as the only organic reagent, show by equations how you would prepare a wax.

19.19 Write the structures of the products of complete hydrolysis of each of the following phosphoglycerides with dilute aqueous NaOH:

(a) 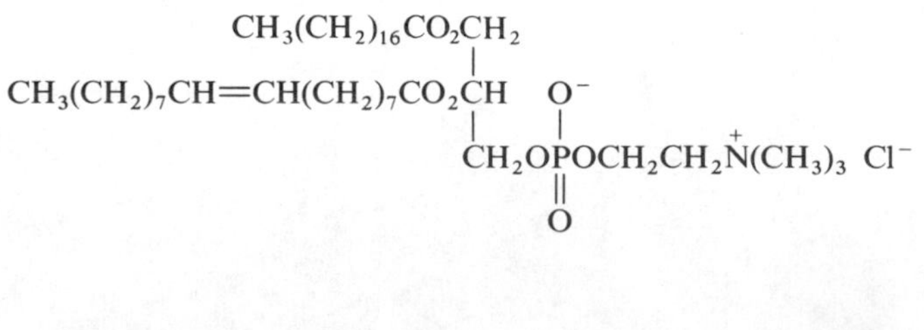 $CH_3(CH_2)_7CH{=}CH(CH_2)_7CO_2\overset{\displaystyle CH_3(CH_2)_{16}CO_2CH_2}{\overset{|}{\underset{\underset{\displaystyle O}{\overset{\displaystyle |}{\underset{\displaystyle \|}{CH_2OPOCH_2CH_2\overset{+}{N}(CH_3)_3}}} \ \ Cl^-}{CH}}}$ $\overset{\displaystyle O^-}{\overset{|}{}}$

$$CH_3(CH_2)_{16}CO_2CH_2$$

(b) 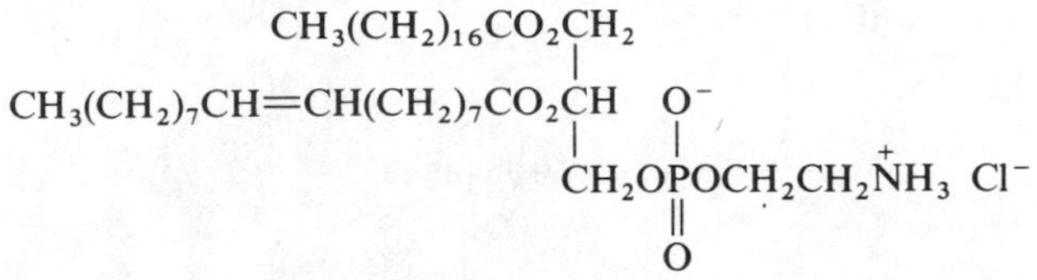 $CH_3(CH_2)_7CH{=}CH(CH_2)_7CO_2CH \quad O^-$

$$CH_2OPOCH_2CH_2\overset{+}{N}H_3 \quad Cl^-$$
$$\underset{\displaystyle O}{\|}$$

19.20 *Cerebrosides* are glycosphingolipids that are found primarily in the sheaths of nerve cells. What fatty acid and sugar would be isolated from hydrolysis of the following cerebroside in acidic solution?

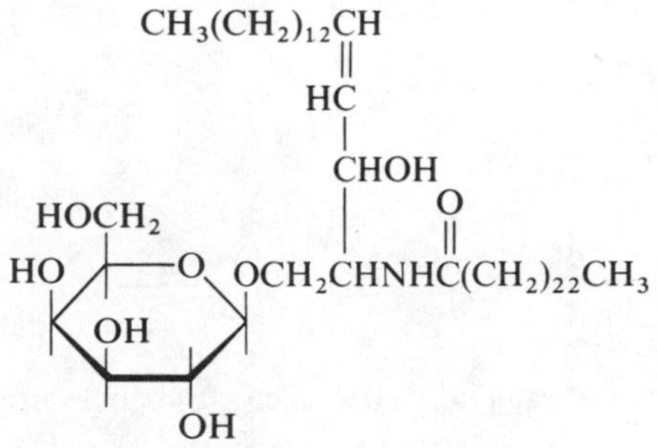

$$CH_3(CH_2)_{12}CH$$
$$HC$$
$$CHOH \qquad O$$
$$HOCH_2 \qquad \qquad \|$$
$$HO{-}\!\!\!-\!\!\!-O \quad OCH_2CHNHC(CH_2)_{22}CH_3$$
$$OH$$
$$OH$$

19.21 Convert each of the following condensed structural formulas to a terpene line formula:

(a)

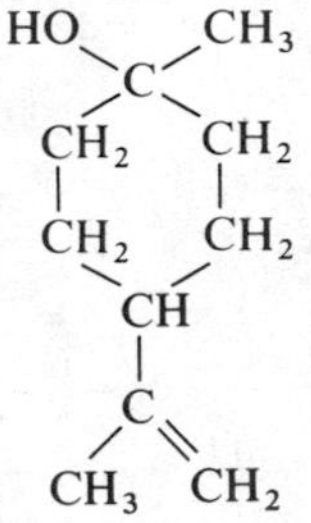

$$HO \quad CH_3$$
$$C$$
$$CH_2 \quad CH_2$$
$$CH_2 \quad CH_2$$
$$CH$$
$$C$$
$$CH_3 \quad CH_2$$

(b)

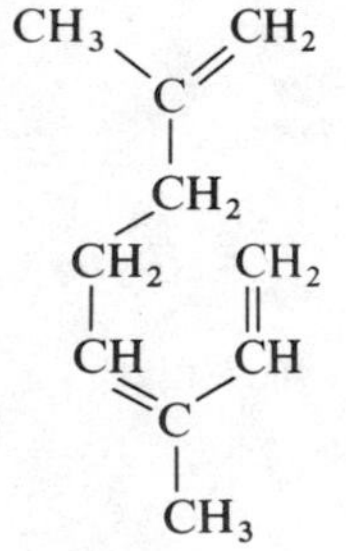

$$CH_3 \quad CH_2$$
$$C$$
$$CH_2$$
$$CH_2 \quad CH_2$$
$$CH \quad CH$$
$$C$$
$$CH_3$$

19.22 Classify each structure as a monoterpene, sesquiterpene, or diterpene:

(a)

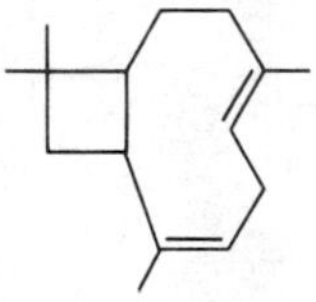

caryophyllene
(oil of cloves)

(b)

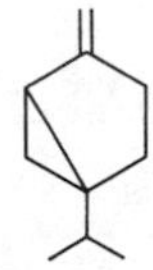

sabinene
(oil of savin)

(c) 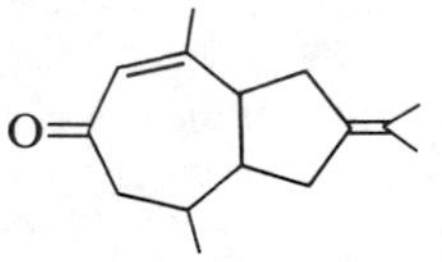 O=

vetivone

19.23 Indicate the isoprene units in the following structure, which is the major constituent of *oil of balsam*. Is this compound a mono-, sesqui-, or diterpene?

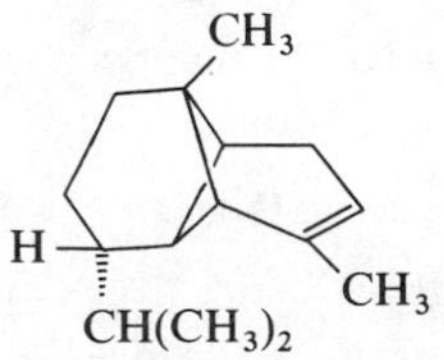

$$CH_3$$

$$H{-}$$
$$CH(CH_3)_2 \qquad CH_3$$

in oil of balsam

Lipids and Related Natural Products

19.24 Match the structure with its name:

(a)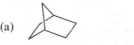

(1) bicyclo[3.2.0]heptane

(b)

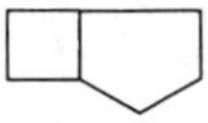

(2) bicyclo[3.1.1]heptane

(c)

(3) bicyclo[2.2.1]heptane

19.25 Name the following ring systems:

(a)    (b) 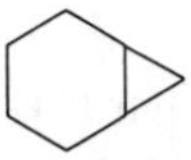   (c)

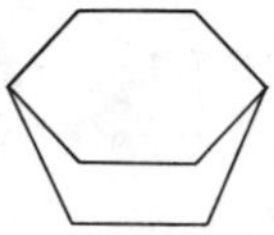

19.26 Draw the structures of camphor and α-pinene, and circle any chiral carbon atoms.

19.27 Predict the possible products of E2 elimination of the following alkyl chlorides:

(a) *cis*-1-chloro-2-methylcyclohexane   (b)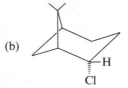

19.28 Draw conformational formulas for the following terpenes:

(a) 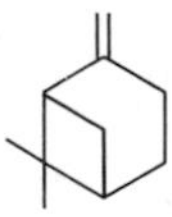   (b)

β-pinene   1,8-cineole

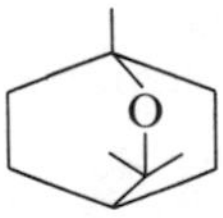

19.29 The structure of the aggregating pheromone of the bark beetle follows:

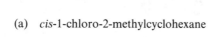

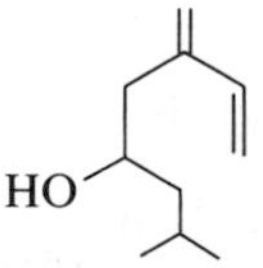

What are the organic products of its reaction with: (a) excess Br_2 in CCl_4; (b) excess gaseous HBr; and (c) hot $KMnO_4$ solution?

19.30 Tell whether the substituents or the ring junctures in the following compounds are *cis* or *trans*:

(a) 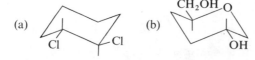   (b) CH_2OH O

OH

(c)

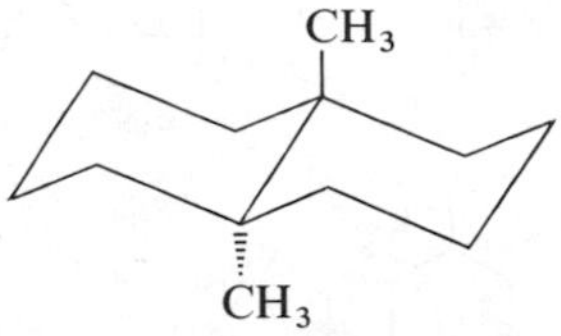

(d)

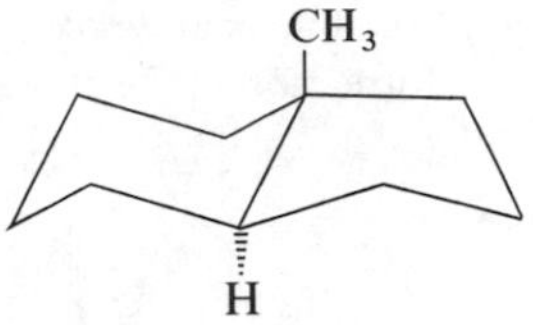

(e)

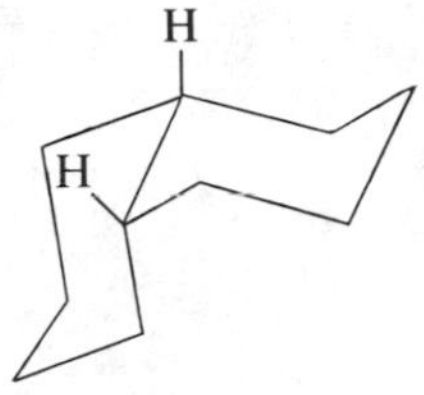

(f)

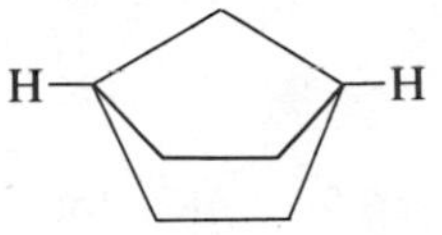

(g)

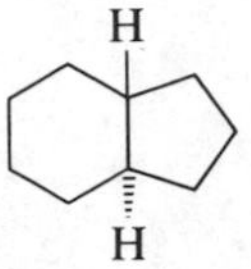

(h)

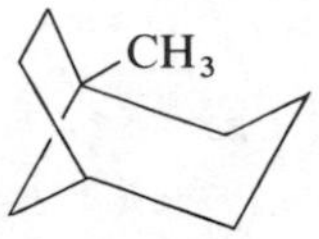

19.31 Which structure of each of the following pairs is more stable?

(a)

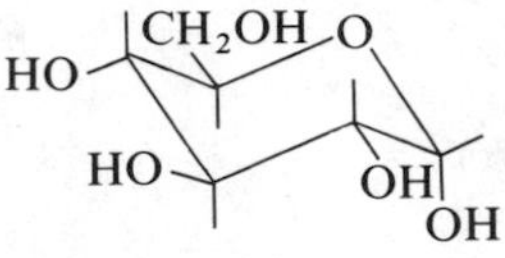

(1)

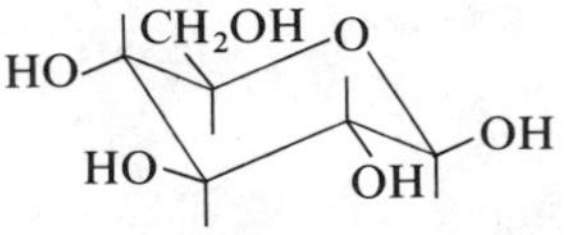

(2)

(b)

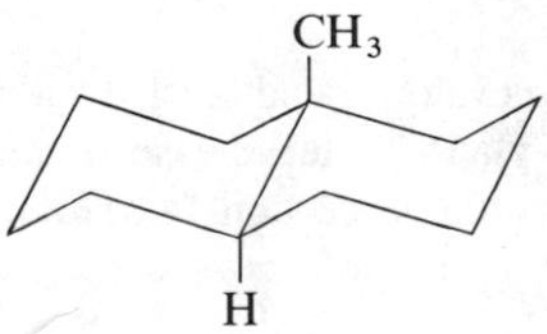

(1)

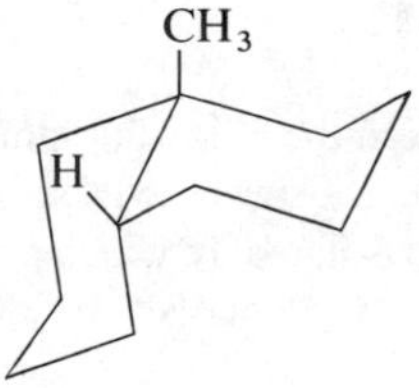

(2)

(c)

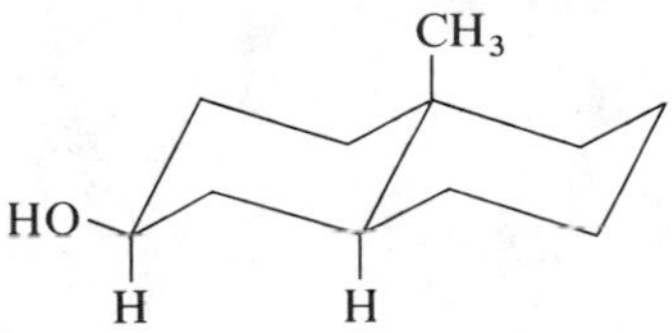

(1)

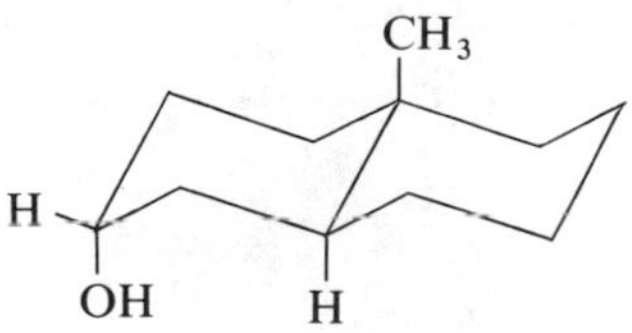

(2)

19.32 Draw the structure of each of the following steroids. (*Acetoxy-* means CH_3CO_2—.)

(a) 5-cholesten-3α-ol
(b) 1-cholesten-3-one
(c) 4,6-cholestadien-3β-ol
(d) 3β-acetoxy-6α,7β-dibromocholestane

19.33 How would you separate a mixture of estradiol and testosterone?

19.34 The structure of the bile acid *desoxycholic acid* is shown below. Redraw the structure showing the conformation of the ring system.

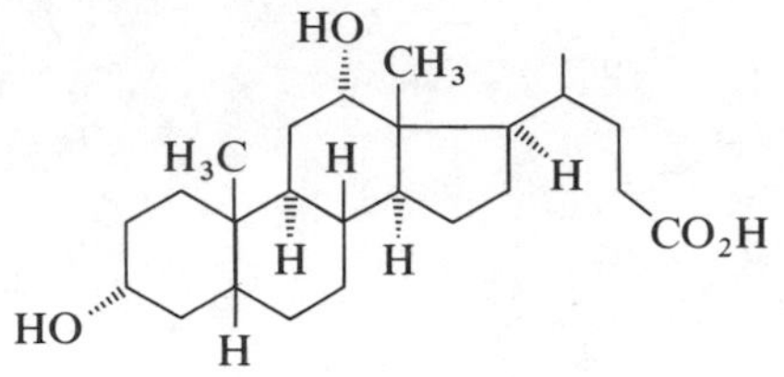

19.35 Suggest mechanisms for the following terpene rearrangements:

(a)

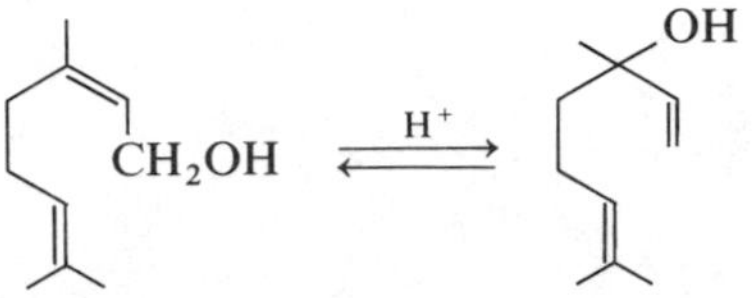

(b)

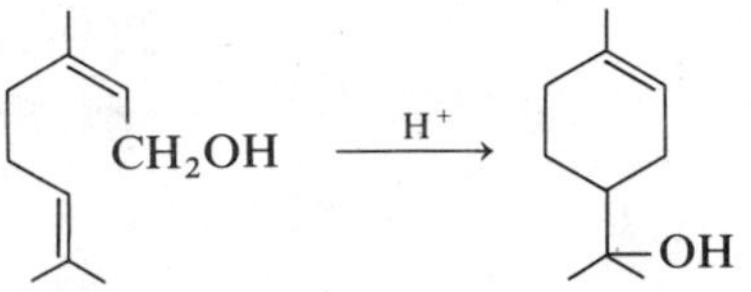

(c)

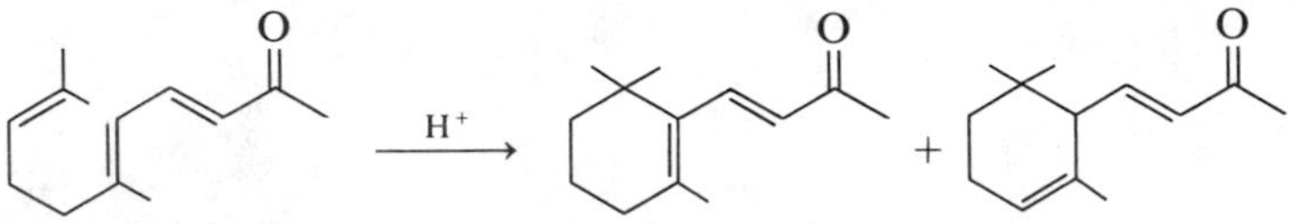

19.36 A biochemist prepared the following samples of mevalonic acid labeled with carbon-14. The three mevalonic acids were fed to a series of plants. Later, the isopentenyl alcohols from the plants were isolated. In which position would the carbon-14 be found in each of the product isopentenyl alcohols?

(a)
$$\begin{array}{l} \quad\quad OH \\ \quad\quad | \\ CH_3CCH_2{-}^{14}CO_2H \\ \quad\quad | \\ \quad\quad CH_2CH_2OH \end{array}$$

(b)
$$\begin{array}{l} \quad\quad OH \\ \quad\quad | \\ CH_3CCH_2CO_2H \\ \quad\quad | \\ \quad\quad CH_2{-}^{14}CH_2OH \end{array}$$

(c)
$$\begin{array}{l} \quad\quad OH \\ \quad\quad | \\ CH_3C{-}^{14}CH_2CO_2H \\ \quad\quad | \\ \quad\quad CH_2CH_2OH \end{array}$$

19.37 In a plant, two isopentenyl alcohol molecules combine to yield geraniol (see Figure 19.4). Identify the position of carbon-14 in geraniol arising from the labeled mevalonic acid in Problem 19.36(b).

19.38 *Citronellal* ($C_{10}H_{18}O$) is a terpene that undergoes reaction with Tollens reagent to yield citronellic acid ($C_{10}H_{18}O_2$). Chromate oxidation of citronellal yields acetone and $HO_2CCH_2CH(CH_3)CH_2CH_2CO_2H$. What is the structure of citronellal?

19.39 When cholesterol is treated with Br_2, a dibromide **I** is formed. When **I** is heated, another dibromide **II** is formed. **I** and **II** are isomers that differ only in the ring juncture between rings *A* and *B* (one dibromide has a *trans A/B* ring juncture; the other has a *cis A/B* ring juncture).

(a) Give the conformational structures of **I** and **II**.
(b) Show the mechanism for the formation of **I**.
(c) Explain why heating causes the ring juncture to change.

Chapter 20

Spectroscopy II:
Ultraviolet Spectra, Color and Vision, Mass Spectra

In Chapter 8, we studied the absorption of infrared and radiofrequency radiation by organic compounds and saw how the absorption can be used in structure identification. In this chapter, we will consider the absorption of **ultraviolet (uv) and visible light** by organic compounds. Ultraviolet and visible spectra are also used in structure determination. More important, the absorption of visible light results in vision; we will also discuss this topic, along with colors and dyes. Last, we will introduce **mass spectra**, which arise from fragmentation of molecules when they are bombarded with high-energy electrons.

Section 20.1

Ultraviolet and Visible Spectra

The wavelengths of uv and visible light are substantially shorter than the wavelengths of infrared radiation (see Figure 8.2). The unit we will use to describe these wavelengths is the *nanometer* (1 nm $= 10^{-7}$ cm). The visible spectrum spans from about 400 nm (violet) to 750 nm (red), while the ultraviolet spectrum ranges from 100 to 400 nm.

The quantity of energy absorbed by a compound is inversely proportional to the wavelength of the radiation:

$$\Delta E = h\nu = \frac{hc}{\lambda}$$

where ΔE = energy absorbed, in ergs
h = Planck's constant, 6.6×10^{-27} erg-sec
ν = frequency, in Hz
c = speed of light, 3×10^{10} cm/sec
λ = wavelength, in cm

Infrared radiation is relatively low-energy radiation. Absorption of infrared radiation by a molecule leads to increased vibrations of covalent bonds. Molecular transitions from the ground state to an excited vibrational state require about 2–15 kcal/mole.

Both uv and visible radiation are of higher energy than infrared radiation. Absorption of ultraviolet or visible light results in **electronic transitions**, promotion of electrons from low-energy, ground-state orbitals to higher-energy excited-state orbitals. These transitions require about 40–300 kcal/mole. The energy absorbed is subsequently dissipated as heat, as light (see Section 20.9), or in chemical reactions (such as isomerization or free-radical reactions).

The wavelength of uv or visible light absorbed depends on the ease of electron promotion. Molecules that require *more energy* for electron-promotion absorb at *shorter wavelengths*. Molecules that require *less energy* absorb at *longer wavelengths*. Compounds that absorb light in the visible region (that is, colored compounds) have more-easily promoted electrons than compounds that absorb at shorter uv wavelengths.

absorption at 100 nm (uv) ⟶ 750 nm (visible)

increasing ease of electronic transition

STUDY PROBLEM

20.1 Which would have the more-easily promoted electrons, benzene (colorless) or quinone (yellow)?

quinone

A uv or visible spectrometer has the same basic design as an infrared spectrometer (see Figure 8.5). Absorption of radiation by a sample is measured at various wavelengths and plotted by a recorder to give the spectrum. (Figure 20.1 shows a typical uv spectrum.)

Since energy absorption by a molecule is quantized, we might expect that the absorption for electronic transitions would be observed at discrete wavelengths as a spectrum of lines or sharp peaks. This is not the case. Rather, a uv or visible spectrum consists of broad absorption bands over a wide range of wavelengths. The reason for the broad absorption is that the energy levels of both the ground

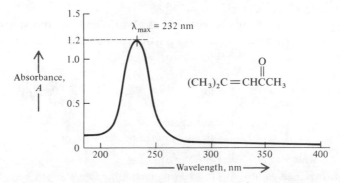

Figure 20.1. Ultraviolet spectrum of mesityl oxide, 9.2×10^{-5} M, 1.0-cm cell.

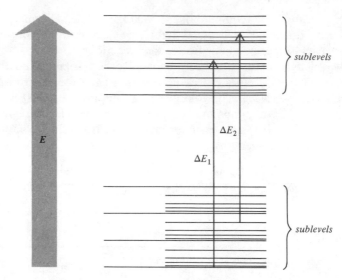

Figure 20.2.   Schematic representation of electronic transitions from a low energy level to a high energy level.

state and the excited state of a molecule are subdivided into *rotational and vibrational sublevels.* Electronic transitions may occur from any one of the sublevels of the ground state to any one of the sublevels of an excited state (Figure 20.2). Since these various transitions differ slightly in energy, their wavelengths of absorption also differ slightly and give rise to the broad band observed in the spectrum.

Section 20.2

Expressions Used in Ultraviolet Spectroscopy

Figure 20.1 shows the uv spectrum of a dilute solution of mesityl oxide (4-methyl-3-penten-2-one). The spectrum shows the scan from 200–400 nm. (Because absorption by atmospheric carbon dioxide becomes significant below 200 nm, the 100–200 nm region is usually not scanned.) The wavelength of absorption is usually reported as λ_{max}, the wavelength of the highest point of the curve. The λ_{max} for mesityl oxide is 232 nm.

The absorption of energy is recorded as **absorbance** (not transmittance as in infrared spectra). The absorbance at a particular wavelength is defined by the equation:

$$A = \log \frac{I_0}{I}$$

where A = absorbance
I_0 = intensity of the reference beam
I = intensity of the sample beam

The absorbance of a compound at a particular wavelength arises from the number of electrons undergoing transition. Therefore, the absorbance depends on the electronic structure of the compound and also upon the concentration of the sample and the length of the sample cell. (The greater the number of absorbing molecules in the path of the light, the greater is the absorbance.) For this reason, chemists report the energy absorption as **molar absorptivity** ε rather than as the actual absorbance. Some uv spectra are replotted to show ε or log ε instead of A as the ordinate. The log ε value is especially useful when values for ε are very large.

$$\varepsilon = \frac{A}{cl}$$

where ε = molar absorptivity
A = absorbance
c = concentration, in M
l = cell length, in cm

The molar absorptivity, usually reported at the λ_{max}, is a reproducible value that takes into account concentration and cell length. Although ε has the units $M^{-1}\,cm^{-1}$, it is usually shown as a unitless quantity. For mesityl oxide, the ε_{max} is $1.2 \div (9.2 \times 10^{-5} \times 1.0)$, or 13,000 (values taken from Figure 20.1).

Sample Problem

A flask of cyclohexane is known to be contaminated with benzene. At 260 nm, benzene has a molar absorptivity of 230, and cyclohexane has a molar absorptivity of zero. A uv spectrum of the contaminated cyclohexane (1.0-cm cell length) shows an absorbance of 0.030. What is the concentration of benzene?

Solution: $c = \dfrac{0.030}{230 \times 1.0} = 0.00013\ M$

Section 20.3

Types of Electron Transition

Let us consider the different types of electron transition that give rise to ultraviolet or visible spectra. The ground state of an organic molecule contains valence electrons in three principal types of molecular orbital: **sigma (σ) orbitals**; **pi (π) orbitals**; and **filled, but nonbonded, orbitals (n)**.

Both σ and π orbitals are formed from the overlap of two atomic or hybrid orbitals. Each of these molecular orbitals therefore has an antibonding σ^* or π^* orbital associated with it. An orbital containing n electrons does not have an antibonding orbital (because it was not formed from two orbitals). Electron transitions involve the promotion of an electron from one of the three ground states (σ, π, or n) to one of the two excited states (σ^* or π^*). There are six possible transitions; the four important transitions and their relative energies are shown in Figure 20.3.

The most useful region of the uv spectrum is at wavelengths higher than 200 nm. The following transitions give rise to absorption in the nonuseful 100–200 nm range: $\sigma \rightarrow \sigma^*$, and $\pi \rightarrow \pi^*$ for an isolated double bond. The useful transitions (200–400 nm) are $\pi \rightarrow \pi^*$ for compounds with conjugated double bonds, and some $n \rightarrow \sigma^*$ and $n \rightarrow \pi^*$ transitions.

Ultraviolet Spectra, Color and Vision, Mass Spectra

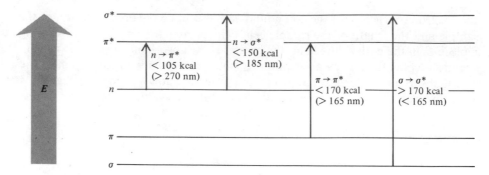

Figure 20.3. Energy requirements for important electronic transitions. (The corresponding wavelengths are in parentheses.)

A. *Absorption by Polyenes*

Less energy is required to promote a π electron of 1,3-butadiene than is needed to promote a π electron of ethylene. The reason is that the energy difference between the HOMO (Highest Occupied Molecular Orbital) and the LUMO (Lowest Unoccupied Molecular Orbital) for conjugated double bonds is less than the energy difference for an isolated double bond. Resonance-stabilization of the excited state of a conjugated diene is one factor that decreases the energy of the excited state.

For $CH_2{=}CH_2$:

For $CH_2{=}CHCH{=}CH_2$:

Because less energy is needed for a $\pi \rightarrow \pi^*$ transition of 1,3-butadiene, this diene absorbs uv radiation of longer wavelengths than does ethylene. As more conjugated double bonds are added to a molecule, the energy required to reach the first excited state decreases. Sufficient conjugation shifts the absorption to wavelengths that reach into the visible region of the spectrum; a compound with sufficient conjugation is colored. For example, lycopene, the compound responsible for the red color of tomatoes, has eleven conjugated double bonds.

lycopene
$\lambda_{max} = 505$ nm

Table 20.1. *Ultraviolet Absorption for Some Unsaturated Aldehydes*

Structure	λ_{max}, nm
$CH_3CH{=}CHCHO$	217
$CH_3(CH{=}CH)_2CHO$	270
$CH_3(CH{=}CH)_3CHO$	312
$CH_3(CH{=}CH)_4CHO$	343
$CH_3(CH{=}CH)_5CHO$	370

Table 20.1 lists the λ_{max} values for $\pi \rightarrow \pi^*$ transitions of a series of aldehydes with increasing conjugation. Inspection of the table reveals that the position of absorption is shifted to longer wavelengths as the extent of the conjugation increases. Generally, this increase is about 30 nm per conjugated double bond in a series of polyenes.

STUDY PROBLEMS

20.2 List the following polyenes in order of increasing λ_{max}:

(a) all-*trans*-$CH_3(CH{=}CH)_{10}CH_3$ (b) all-*trans*-$CH_3(CH{=}CH)_9CH_3$
(c) all-*trans*-$CH_3(CH{=}CH)_8CH_3$

20.3 The λ_{max} for Compound (a) in Problem 20.2 is 476 nm. Predict the λ_{max} values for Compounds (b) and (c).

B. Absorption by Aromatic Systems

Benzene and other aromatic compounds exhibit more-complex spectra than can be explained by simple $\pi \rightarrow \pi^*$ transitions. The complexity arises from the existence of *several* low-lying excited states. Benzene absorbs strongly at 184 nm ($\varepsilon = 47,000$) and at 202 nm ($\varepsilon = 7,000$) and has a series of absorption bands between 230–270 nm. A value of 260 nm is often reported as the λ_{max} for benzene because this is the position of strongest absorption above 200 nm. Solvents and substituents on the ring alter the uv spectra of benzene compounds.

The absorption of uv radiation by aromatic compounds composed of fused benzene rings is shifted to longer wavelengths as the number of rings is increased. This fact is not surprising; more rings mean greater conjugation and greater resonance-stabilization of the excited state.

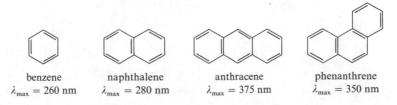

benzene	naphthalene	anthracene	phenanthrene
$\lambda_{max} = 260$ nm	$\lambda_{max} = 280$ nm	$\lambda_{max} = 375$ nm	$\lambda_{max} = 350$ nm

naphthacene
$\lambda_{max} = 450$ nm
(yellow)

pentacene
$\lambda_{max} = 575$ nm
(blue)

coronene
$\lambda_{max} = 400$ nm
(yellow)

STUDY PROBLEM

20.4 Suggest a reason that coronene absorbs a *shorter* wavelength than does naphthacene. (*Hint:* see Section 16.2.)

C.   Absorption Arising from Transitions of n Electrons

Compounds that contain nitrogen, oxygen, sulfur, phosphorus, or one of the halogens all have unshared n electrons. If the structure contains no π bonds, these n electrons can undergo only $n \rightarrow \sigma^*$ transitions. Because the n electrons are of higher energy than either the σ or π electrons, less energy is required to promote an n electron, and transitions occur at longer wavelengths than $\sigma \rightarrow \sigma^*$ transitions. Note that some of these values are within the usual uv spectral range of 200–400 nm (Table 20.2). The π^* orbital is of lower energy than the σ^* orbital; consequently, $n \rightarrow \pi^*$ transitions require less energy than $n \rightarrow \sigma^*$ transitions and often are in the range of a normal instrument scan.

The n electrons are in a different region of space from σ^* and π^* orbitals, and the probability of an n transition is low. Since molar absorptivity depends on the number of electrons undergoing transition, ε values for n transitions are low, in the 10–100 range (compared to about 10,000 for a $\pi \rightarrow \pi^*$ transition).

A compound such as acetone that contains both a π bond and n electrons exhibits both $\pi \rightarrow \pi^*$ and $n \rightarrow \pi^*$ transitions. Acetone shows absorption at 187 nm ($\pi \rightarrow \pi^*$) and 270 nm ($n \rightarrow \pi^*$).

Table 20.2. *Ultraviolet Absorption Arising from* $n \rightarrow \sigma^*$ *Transitions*

Structure	λ_{max}, nm	ε
$CH_3\overset{..}{\underset{..}{O}}H$	177	200
$(CH_3)_3\overset{..}{N}$	199	3950
$CH_3\overset{..}{\underset{..}{C}l}:$	173	200
$CH_3CH_2CH_2\overset{..}{\underset{..}{B}r}:$	208	300
$CH_3\overset{..}{\underset{..}{I}}:$	259	400

Electron transitions of acetone, $CH_3\overset{\overset{\displaystyle \cdot\ddot{O}\cdot}{\|}}{C}CH_3$:

$$\pi^* \quad \underline{\downarrow} \qquad\qquad\qquad \underline{\downarrow}\ \pi^*$$

$$n \quad \underline{\uparrow\downarrow\ \uparrow} \qquad\qquad \underline{\uparrow\downarrow\ \uparrow\downarrow}\ n$$

$$\pi \quad \underline{\uparrow\downarrow} \qquad\qquad\qquad \underline{\quad}\ \pi$$

excited state $\qquad n \rightarrow \pi^* \qquad\qquad \pi \rightarrow \pi^* \qquad$ *excited state*

$$\pi^* \quad \underline{\quad\quad}$$

$$n \quad \underline{\uparrow\downarrow\ \uparrow\downarrow}$$

$$\pi \quad \underline{\uparrow\downarrow}$$

ground state

Section 20.4

Color and Vision

Color has played a significant role in human society ever since man first learned to color his clothes and other articles. Color is the result of a complex set of physiological and psychological responses to wavelengths of light of 400–750 nm striking the retina of the eye. If all wavelengths of visible light strike the retina, we perceive white; if none of them do, we perceive black or darkness. If a small range of wavelengths hits the eye, then we observe individual colors. Table 20.3 lists the wavelengths of the visible spectrum with their corresponding colors and complementary colors, which we will discuss shortly.

Our perception of color arises from a variety of physical processes. A few examples of how light of a particular wavelength may be directed to the eye follow: (1) The yellow-orange color of a sodium flame results from the **emission of light** with a wavelength of 589 nm; the emission is caused by excited electrons returning to the ground state. (2) A prism causes a **diffraction of light** that varies with the wavelength; we observe the separated wavelengths as a rainbow pattern. (3) **Interference** results from light being reflected from two surfaces of a very thin film (e.g., soap bubbles or bird feathers). The light wave reflected from the farther surface is reflected out of phase with the reflection from the nearer surface, resulting in wave interference and cancellation of some wavelengths; hence, we see color instead of white.

Table 20.3. *Colors in the Visible Spectrum*

Wavelength, nm	Color	Complementary (subtraction) color
400–424	violet	green-yellow
424–491	blue	yellow
491–570	green	red
570–585	yellow	blue
585–647	orange	green-blue
647–700	red	green

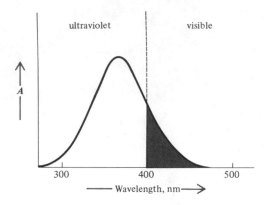

Figure 20.4.   A compound with a λ_{max} in the uv region may also absorb light in the visible region.

The most common manner by which color is generated is by a fourth process: **absorption of certain wavelengths**. Organic compounds with extensive conjugation absorb certain wavelengths of light because of $\pi \rightarrow \pi^*$ and $n \rightarrow \pi^*$ transitions. We do not observe the color absorbed, but we see its **complement**, which is reflected. A complementary color, sometimes called a **subtraction color**, is thus the result of subtraction of some of the visible wavelengths from the entire visual spectrum. For example, pentacene (page 906) has a λ_{max} at 575 nm, which is in the yellow portion of the visible spectrum. Pentacene absorbs the yellow light (and, to a lesser extent, that of the surrounding wavelengths) and reflects the other wavelengths. Pentacene has a blue color, which is the complement of yellow.

Some compounds appear yellow although their λ_{max} is in the ultraviolet range of the spectrum (for example, coronene, page 906). In such a case, the tail of absorption by that compound extends from the ultraviolet into the visible region and absorbs the violet to blue wavelengths. Figure 20.4 depicts the spectrum of such a compound.

A.   Mechanism of Vision

The human eye is an amazingly intricate organ that converts photons of light into nerve pulses that travel to the brain and result in vision. The mechanism of the eye is remarkably sensitive. About one quantum of light energy is all that is necessary to trigger the mechanism resulting in a visual nerve pulse. We can detect as few as five quanta of light. (For comparison, a typical flashlight bulb radiates about 2×10^{18} quanta per second.)

The eye contains two types of photoreceptor—the **rods** and the **cones**. The cones contain pigments and are responsible for color vision and for vision in bright light. Animals that lack cones are color-blind. The rods are responsible for black and white photoreception and for vision in very dim light. While more is known about rods than cones, much is still to be learned—for example, how the nerve impulse is generated.

In the rods, light is detected by a reddish-purple pigment called **rhodopsin**, or **visual purple** ($\lambda_{max} = 498$ nm). Rhodopsin is formed from an aldehyde called *11-cis-retinal* and a protein called *opsin*. These two components of rhodopsin are bonded together by an imine link between the aldehyde group of 11-*cis-*

retinal and an amino group in opsin. As is frequently the case with protein complexes, opsin has a shape that holds the 11-*cis*-retinal in a pocket. Compounds with other shapes do not fit into this pocket. In the combined form, the imine bond joining 11-*cis*-retinal and opsin is protected by the rest of the opsin molecule and is not readily hydrolyzed.

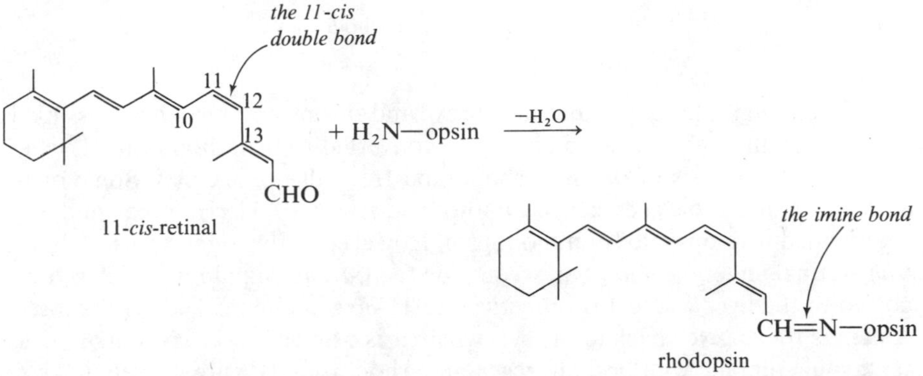

*the 11-cis
double bond*

11-*cis*-retinal $+ H_2N—opsin \xrightarrow{-H_2O}$

the imine bond

CH=N—opsin

rhodopsin

When a photon of light (*hv*) strikes rhodopsin, the rhodopsin undergoes a series of transformations to intermediates called **metarhodopsins**. In this process, the nerve impulse is generated and the 11-*cis*-retinal part of rhodopsin is converted to an all-*trans*-structure. (The double bond at carbon 11 is converted from *cis* to *trans*.) The all-*trans*-structure does not fit in the pocket of the opsin, so the imine group becomes exposed and is hydrolyzed. The result is all-*trans*-retinal plus opsin.

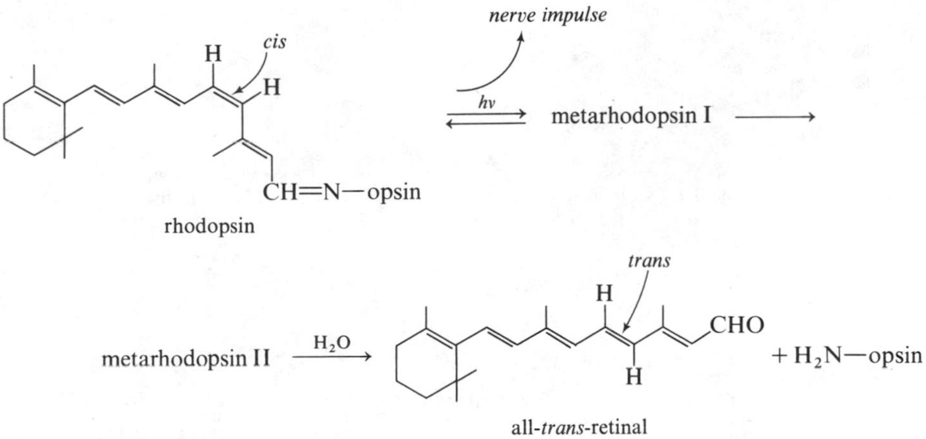

nerve impulse

cis

CH=N—opsin

rhodopsin

$\xrightarrow{hv}$ metarhodopsin I $\longrightarrow$

metarhodopsin II $\xrightarrow{H_2O}$ *trans*   CHO $+ H_2N—opsin$

all-*trans*-retinal

How does the isomerization of the *cis*-double bond at carbon 11 occur? The absorption of light causes the promotion of one pi electron from the bonding orbital to an antibonding orbital. In this excited state, there is no overlap between bonding *p* orbitals, the energy barrier for rotation is lower, and rotation can occur fairly easily.

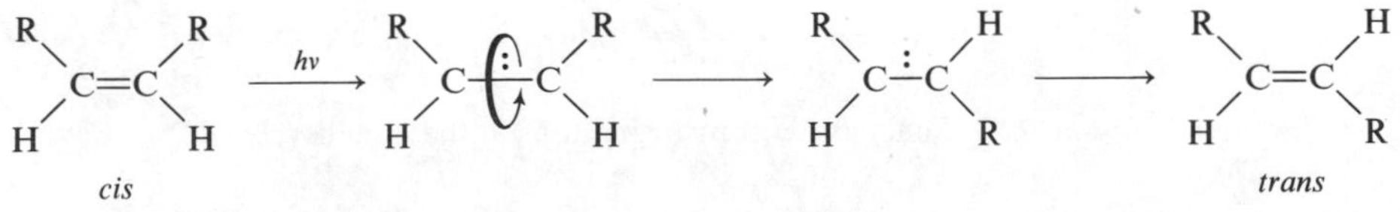

cis $\xrightarrow{hv}$ $\longrightarrow$ $\longrightarrow$ *trans*

Rhodopsin must be regenerated for sustained vision to occur. There are two principal processes by which rhodopsin may be regenerated: one is photo-induced and the other is chemical. The photo-induced process occurs prior to the hydrolysis of the imine bond: in bright light, metarhodopsin I can revert to rhodopsin so that an equilibrium is maintained and vision continues.

$$\text{rhodopsin} \underset{h\nu}{\overset{h\nu}{\rightleftharpoons}} \text{metarhodopsin I}$$
$$(cis) \qquad\qquad\qquad (trans)$$

In dim light, fewer photons hit the eye and this reverse reaction is less likely to occur. In this case, metarhodopsin I is converted to metarhodopsin II, which undergoes hydrolysis of the imine bond and frees all-*trans*-retinal. Some of the all-*trans*-retinal molecules can be photo-isomerized to 11-*cis*-retinal and then recombined with opsin to form rhodopsin. However, in dim light, some of the all-*trans*-retinal undergoes enzymatic reduction to all-*trans*-vitamin A, which is transported to the liver where it is isomerized to 11-*cis*-vitamin A. The 11-*cis*-vitamin A then is transported back to the eye, where it is oxidized to 11-*cis*-retinal, which can again combine with opsin to regenerate rhodopsin. (Figure 20.5 summarizes the chemistry of the visual cycle.)

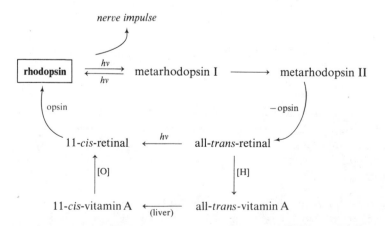

Figure 20.5. Summary of transformations in the visual cycle.

Types of Colored Compounds

The history of dyes goes back to prehistoric times. *Indigo* (from *India*) is the oldest known dye; it was used by the ancient Egyptians to dye mummy cloths. *Tyrian purple* was used by the Romans to dye the togas of the emperors. *Alizarin* (Turkey red), from the roots of the madder plant, was used in the 1700's and 1800's to dye the red coats of British soldiers.

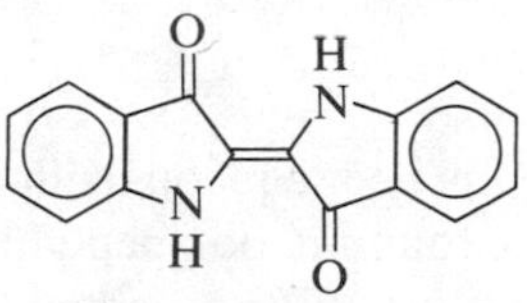

indigo
blue

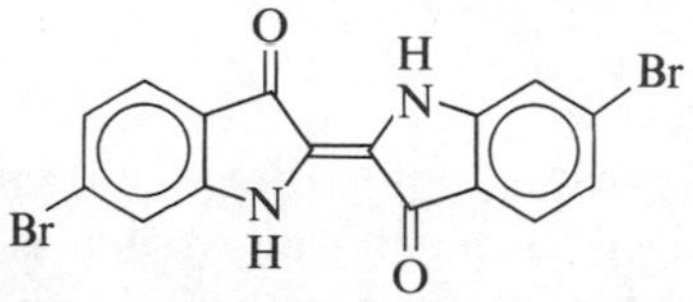

Tyrian purple

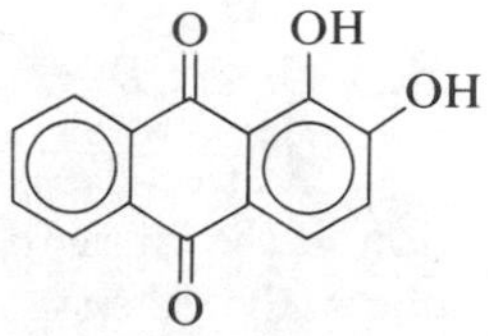

alizarin
red

Before the theories of electronic transition were developed, it was observed that some types of organic structure give rise to color, while others do not. The partial structures necessary for color (unsaturated groups that can undergo $\pi \rightarrow \pi^*$ transitions) were called **chromophores**, a term coined in 1876 (Greek *chroma*, "color," and *phoros*, "bearing").

Some chromophores:

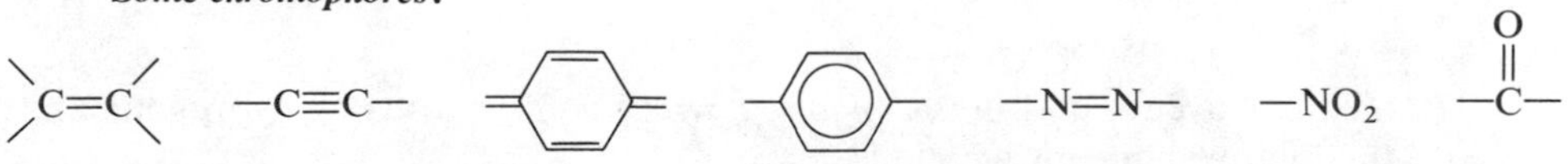

It was also observed that the presence of some other groups caused an intensification of color. These groups were called **auxochromes** (Greek *auxanein*, "to increase"). We now know that auxochromes are groups that cannot undergo $\pi \rightarrow \pi^*$ transitions, but can undergo transitions of *n* electrons.

Some auxochromes:

$$-OH \quad -OR \quad -NH_2 \quad -NHR \quad -NR_2 \quad -X$$

Dyes and Dyeing

A **dye** is a colored organic compound that is used to impart color to an object or a fabric. There are numerous colored organic compounds; however, only a few are suitable as dyes. To be useful as a dye, a compound must be *fast* (remain in the fabric during washing or cleaning). To be fast, a dye must, in one way or another, be bonded to the fabric.

A fabric composed of fibers of polypropylene or a similar hydrocarbon is difficult to dye because it has no functional groups to attract dye molecules. Successful dyeing of these fabrics can be accomplished, however, by the incorporation of a metal–dye complex into the polymer. Dyeing of cotton (cellulose) is easier because hydrogen bonding between hydroxyl groups of the glucose units and groups of the dye molecule hold the dye to the cloth. Polypeptide fibers, such as wool or silk, are the easiest fabrics to dye because they contain numerous polar groups that can interact with dye molecules.

A. Direct Dyes

A direct dye is a dye that is applied directly to cloth from a hot aqueous solution. If the fabric to be dyed has polar groups, such as those found in polypeptide fibers, then the incorporation of a dye with either an amino group or a strongly acidic group will render the dye fast. *Martius yellow* is a typical direct dye. The acidic phenol group in Martius yellow undergoes reaction with basic side chains in wool or silk.

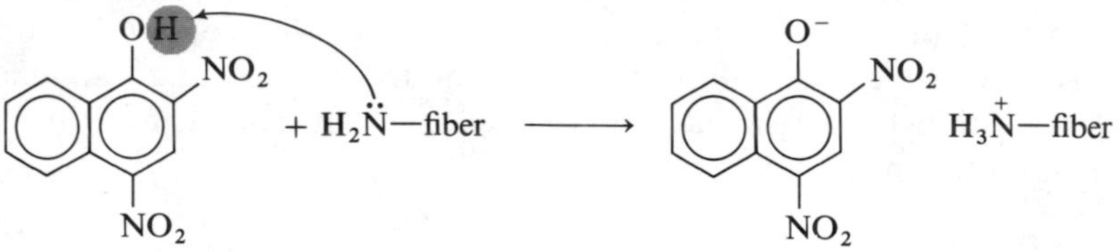

Martius yellow

A direct dye for cotton is *Congo red*, which can form strong hydrogen bonds with the hydroxyl groups of cellulose.

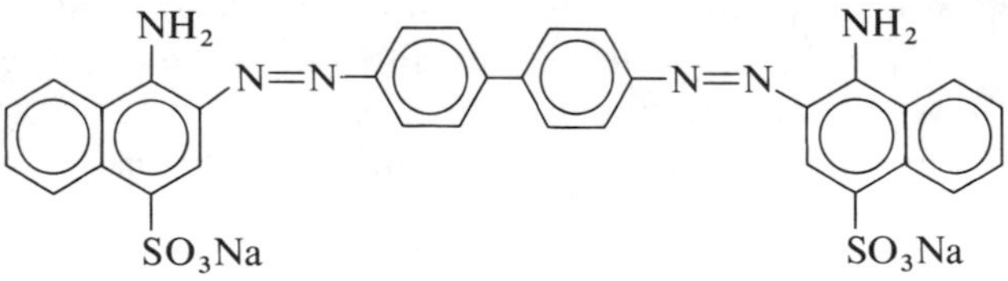

Congo red

STUDY PROBLEM

20.5 Which groups in Congo red would be *most* likely to form hydrogen bonds with the OH groups in cotton? Show a partial structure.

B. Vat Dyes

A vat dye is a dye that is applied to fabric (in a vat) in a soluble form and then is allowed to undergo reaction to an insoluble form. The blue coats supplied by the French to the Americans during the American Revolution were dyed with *indigo*, a typical vat dye. Indigo was obtained by a fermentation of the woad plant (*Isatis tinctoria*) of Western Europe or of plants of the *Indigofera* species, found in tropical countries. Both types of plant contain the glucoside *indican*, which on hydrolysis yields glucose and *indoxyl*, a colorless precursor of indigo. Air oxidation of indoxyl yields the blue, insoluble indigo. Fabrics were soaked in the fermentation mixture containing indoxyl, then were allowed to air dry. Indigo is deposited in the *cis*-form, which undergoes spontaneous isomerization to the *trans*-isomer. (Suggest a reason for this transformation.)

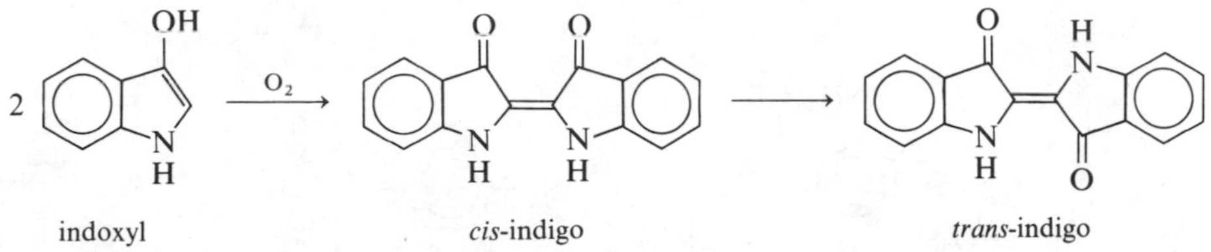

indoxyl   *cis*-indigo   *trans*-indigo

Indigo is now synthesized commercially from either phthalic anhydride or aniline. In dyeing, indigo is reduced to the base-soluble, yellow *leucoindigo* (also called *indigo white*). Cloth is impregnated with a solution of leucoindigo, then is subjected to oxidizing conditions such as air or perboric acid. The result is the blue, insoluble indigo.

indigo   leucoindigo
insoluble   *water-soluble*

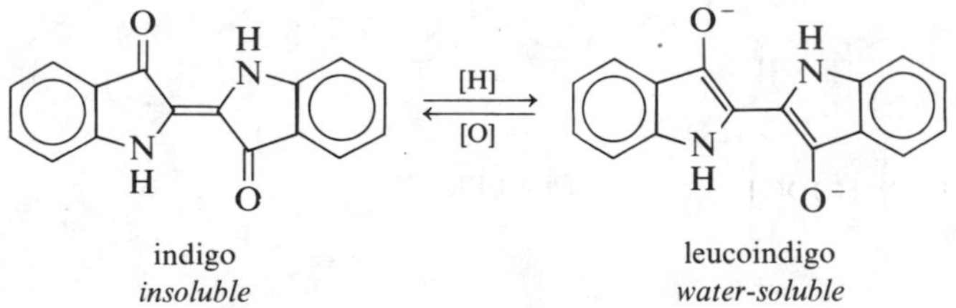

C.   Mordant Dyes

A mordant dye is one that is rendered insoluble on a fabric by complexing or chelation with a metal ion, called a **mordant** (Latin *mordere*, "to bite"). The fabric is first treated with the metal salt (such as one of Al, Cu, Co, or Cr), then treated with a soluble form of the dye. The chelation reaction on the surface of the fabric results in a fast dye.

One of the oldest mordant dyes is *alizarin*, which forms different colors depending upon the metal ion used. For example, with Al^{3+}, alizarin gives a rose-red color; with Ba^{2+}, a blue color.

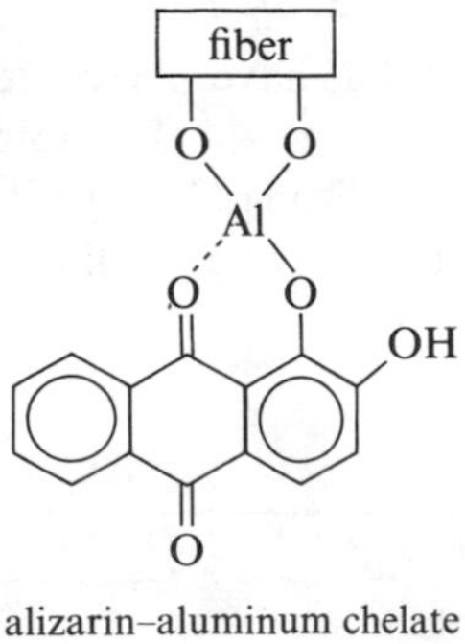

alizarin–aluminum chelate

D.   Azo Dyes

Azo dyes are the largest and most important class of dyestuffs, their numbers running into the thousands. An insoluble azo dye is formed on the surface of a fabric by a diazonium-coupling reaction. The fabric is first impregnated with a compound capable of undergoing diazonium coupling (an aromatic compound that is activated toward electrophilic substitution by electron-releasing substituents), then is treated with a diazonium salt.

Direct Blue 2B

Section 20.7

Acid–Base Indicators

An **acid–base indicator** is an organic compound that changes color with a change in pH. These compounds are most frequently encountered as titration endpoint indicators. Test papers, such as litmus paper, are impregnated with one or more of these substances.

Two typical indicators are *methyl orange* and *phenolphthalein*. Methyl orange is red in acidic solutions that have pH values less than 3.1. It is yellow in solutions with pH values greater than 4.4. Phenolphthalein, on the other hand, changes color on the alkaline side of the pH range. Up to pH 8.3, phenolphthalein is colorless. At pH 10, it is red. In strongly alkaline solutions, it again becomes colorless.

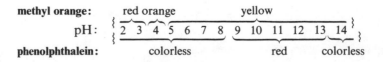

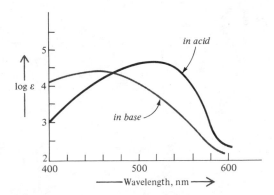

Figure 20.6. Visible spectra of methyl orange in acidic and alkaline solutions (pH 1 and 13, respectively).

Indicators change color because the chromophoric system is changed by an acid–base reaction. In acidic solution, methyl orange exists as a resonance hybrid of a protonated azo structure; this resonance hybrid is red. The azo nitrogen is not strongly basic, and the protonated azo group loses the hydrogen ion at about pH 4.4. The loss of the proton changes the electronic structure of the compound, resulting in a change of color from red to yellow. Figure 20.6 shows spectra of methyl orange at two different pH values.

$$\text{}^-O_3S-\bigcirc-N{=}N-\bigcirc-N(CH_3)_2$$

methyl orange
yellow in base

$$OH^- \Big\updownarrow H^+$$

$$\text{}^-O_3S-\bigcirc-\overset{+}{\underset{H}{N}}{=}N-\bigcirc-N(CH_3)_2 \quad\longleftrightarrow\quad \text{}^-O_3S-\bigcirc-\underset{H}{N}{-}N{=}\bigcirc{=}\overset{+}{N}(CH_3)_2$$

red in acid

The commercial value of phenolphthalein is that it serves as the active ingredient in "candy" and "gum" laxatives. However, phenolphthalein is also one of the best-known titration indicators. In acidic solution, phenolphthalein exists as a colorless lactone. In the lactone, the center carbon is in the sp^3-hybrid state; consequently, the three benzene rings are isolated, not conjugated.

At pH values greater than 8.3 (alkaline solution), a phenolic hydrogen is removed from phenolphthalein, the lactone ring opens, and the center carbon becomes sp^2 hybridized. Now the benzene rings are in conjugation, and the extensive pi system gives rise to the red color of phenolphthalein in mildly alkaline solution.

In strongly alkaline solution, the center carbon is hydroxylated and again is converted to the sp^3 state, isolating the three pi systems. At high pH values, phenolphthalein is again colorless.

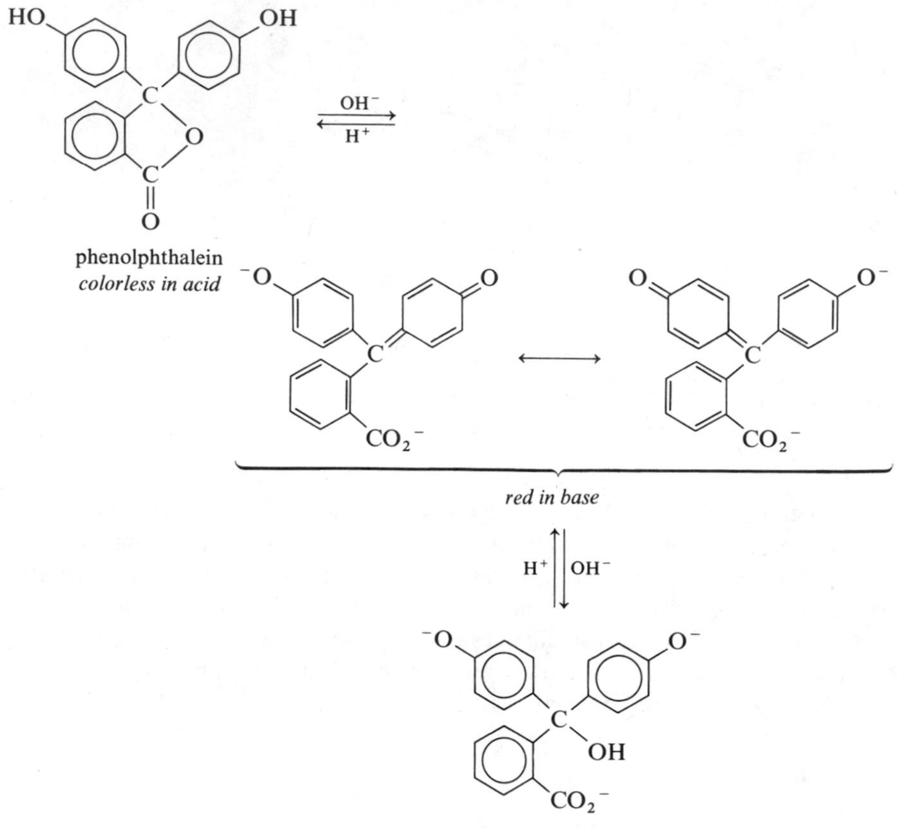

Ultraviolet Spectra, Color and Vision, Mass Spectra

phenolphthalein
colorless in acid

red in base

colorless in strong base

STUDY PROBLEMS

20.6 One of the following indicators is blue-green at pH 7; the other is violet. Which is which? Explain your answer.

(a)

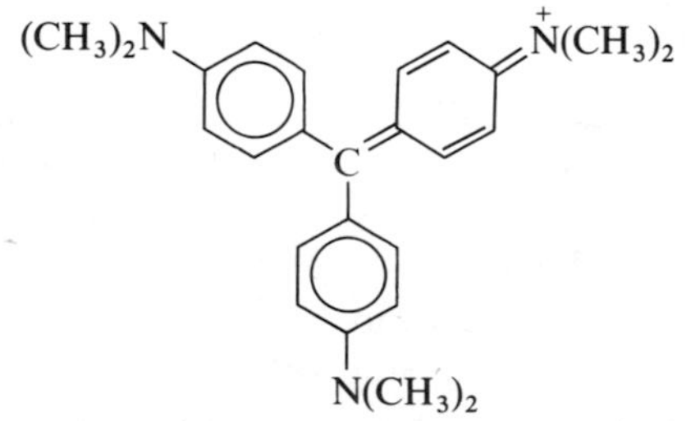

(b)

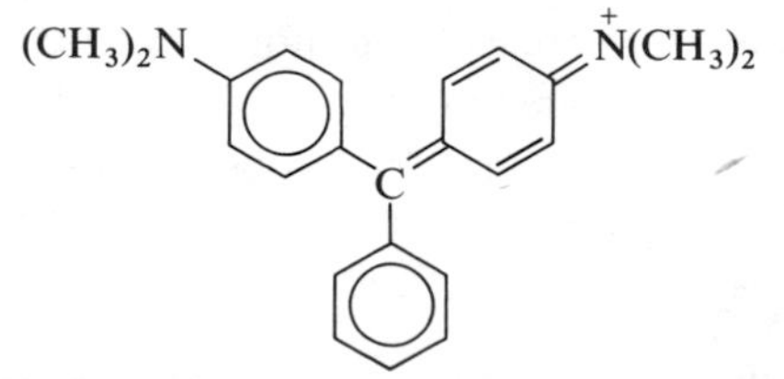

20.7 *p*-Nitrophenol is colorless at pH 5, but yellow at pH 8. Draw the resonance structures for each form of *p*-nitrophenol. Tell which structure is colorless and which is yellow.

Section 20.8

Natural Colors

Nature abounds with color. Some colors, such as those of hummingbird or peacock feathers, arise from light diffraction by the unique structure of the feathers. However, most of Nature's colors are due to the absorption of certain wavelengths of visible light by organic compounds.

Most red and blue flowers owe their coloring to glucosides called **anthocyanins**. The nonsugar portion of the glucoside is called an *anthocyanidin* and is a type of *flavylium salt* (see below). The particular color imparted by an anthocyanin depends, in part, on the pH of the flower. The blue of cornflowers and the red of roses are due to the same anthocyanin, *cyanin*. In a red rose, cyanin is in its phenol form. In a blue cornflower, cyanin is in its anionic form, with a proton removed from one of the phenolic groups.

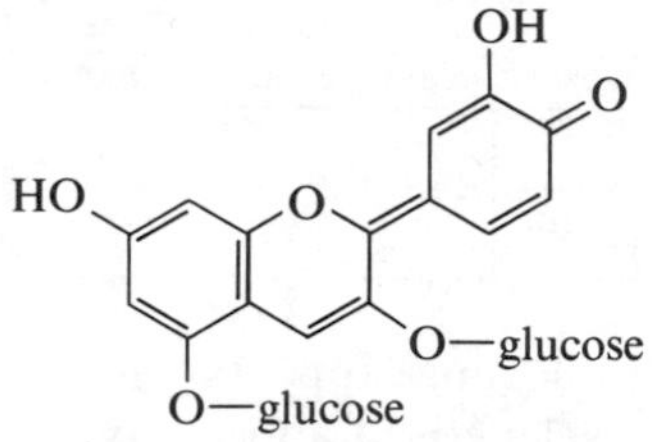

cyanin

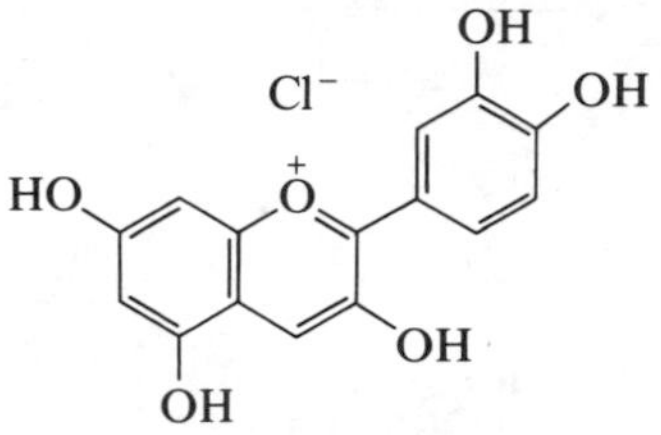

cyanidin choride
a flavylium salt

The term flavylium salt comes from the name for *flavone*, which itself is a colorless compound. The addition of a 3-hydroxyl group leads to flavonol, which is yellow (Latin, *flavus*, "yellow").

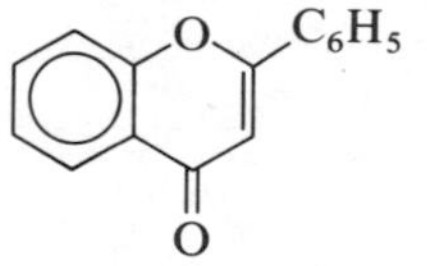

flavone
colorless

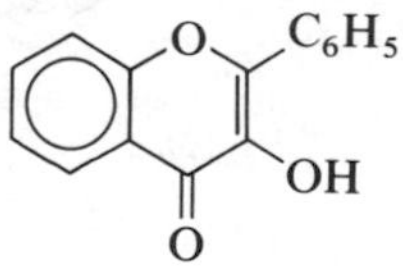

flavonol
yellow

Naphthoquinones and **anthraquinones** are also common natural coloring materials. *Juglone* is a naphthoquinone that is partly responsible for the coloring of walnut hulls. *Lawsone* is similar in structure to juglone; it is found in Indian henna, which is used as a red hair dye. A typical anthraquinone, carminic acid, is the principal red pigment of *cochineal*, a ground-up insect (*Coccus cacti L.*) that is used as a red dye in food and cosmetics. Alizarin, mentioned earlier, is another red dye of the anthraquinone class.

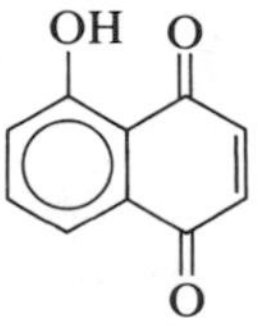

juglone

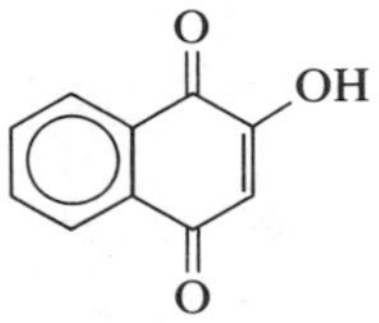

lawsone

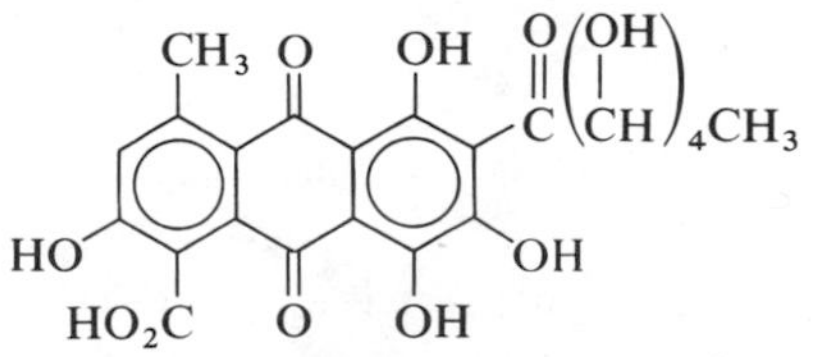

carminic acid

Section 20.9

Fluorescence and Chemiluminescence

When a molecule undergoes absorption of ultraviolet or visible light, an electron is promoted from the ground state to an **excited singlet state**. (*Singlet* refers to a state in which electrons are *paired*; see the footnote on page 405.) Immediately after promotion (on the order of 10^{-11} sec), the electron drops to the lowest-energy excited singlet state. One of the ways in which an excited molecule with electrons in this lowest-energy singlet state can return to the ground state is to lose its energy as light. This process is also fast (10^{-7} sec). The energy lost by this emission of light is slightly *less* than the energy that was initially absorbed. (The difference results in increased molecular motion.) Consequently, the wavelength of light emitted is slightly longer than that which was absorbed.

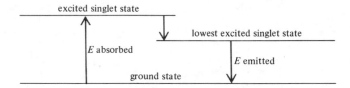

A compound that absorbs light in the visible range appears colored. When the same compound emits light of a different wavelength, it appears two-colored, or **fluorescent**. An example of a fluorescent compound is *fluorescein*, which has been used as a marker for airplanes downed at sea. In aqueous solution and in the presence of light, fluorescein appears red with an intense yellow-green fluorescence.

fluorescein

Some fluorescent compounds, called **optical bleaches**, are used as fabric whiteners. These are colorless compounds that absorb ultraviolet light just out of the visible range, then emit blue-violet light at the edge of the visible spectrum. This blue-violet color masks yellowing of the fabric.

Two optical bleaches:

Blankophor R

Calcofluor SD

Chemiluminescence is a phenomenon in which (1) a reaction leads to products that contain excited molecules, and (2) the return to the ground state is accompanied by emission of light. A familiar example of chemiluminescence is the light of the firefly, caused by the enzymatic oxidation of *luciferin* and the subsequent return of the excited products to the ground state.

luciferin

Mass Spectra

Most of the spectral techniques we have discussed arise from absorption of energy by molecules and the resultant change in their energy states. **Mass spectroscopy** is based on different principles. In a mass spectrometer, a sample in the gaseous state is bombarded with electrons of sufficient energy to exceed the first ionization potential of the compound. (The ionization potentials of most organic compounds are in the range of 185–300 kcal/mole.) Collision between an organic molecule and one of these high-energy electrons results in the loss of an electron from the molecule and the formation of an organic ion.

Most organic ions are unstable and break apart into fragments. In a mass spectrometer, the positively charged organic ions and fragments are detected and recorded to give a graph of the relative concentration, called *abundance*, of ions versus their *mass-to-charge ratio* (m/e). The graph is called a **mass spectrum**.

The ionic charge of most particles detected in a mass spectrometer is $+1$; the m/e value for such an ion is equal to its mass. Consequently, from a practical standpoint, the mass spectrum is a record of particle mass versus relative abundance. How a molecule breaks into fragments depends upon the carbon skeleton and functional groups. Therefore, the structure and mass of the fragments give clues about the structure of the molecule. Also, it is frequently possible to determine the molecular weight of a compound from its mass spectrum.

Let us introduce the concept of mass spectroscopy with methanol as an example. When methanol is bombarded with high-energy electrons, one of the valence electrons is lost. The result is an **ion radical**, a species with one unpaired electron and a charge of $+1$. An ion radical is symbolized by $\dagger$. The ion radical that results from abstraction of one electron of a molecule is called the **molecular ion** and is symbolized $M^{\dagger}$. The mass of the molecular ion is the molecular weight of the compound. The molecular ion of methanol has a mass of 32 and a charge of $+1$. Its mass-to-charge ratio (m/e) is 32. (In the following example, the half-headed arrow signifies the loss of one electron.)

$$CH_3\ddot{O}H \longrightarrow CH_3\ddot{O}H^+, \quad \text{usually written} \quad [CH_3OH]^{\dagger}$$

the molecular ion of methanol, $m/e = 32$

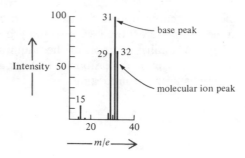

Figure 20.7. Mass spectrum of methanol, CH_3OH.

The $[CH_3OH]^{\ddagger}$ ion radical can lose a hydrogen atom and become a cation: $[CH_2=OH]^+$. This fragment has a m/e of 31. In the mass spectrum of methanol (Figure 20.7), peaks for the particles with m/e values of 31 and 32 are evident. (The fragments that give rise to the other peaks in this mass spectrum will be discussed in Section 20.13.)

$$\left[\begin{array}{c} \text{H} \\ \text{H:C:O:H} \\ \text{H} \end{array} \right]^{\ddagger} \longrightarrow \text{H}\cdot + \left[\begin{array}{c} \text{H} \\ \text{C::OH} \\ \text{H} \end{array} \right]^{+}$$

a cation, m/e = 31
(*not an ion radical because*
all electrons are paired)

As may be seen in Figure 20.7, a mass spectrum is presented as a bar graph. Each peak in the spectrum represents a fragment of the molecule. The fragments are scanned so that the peaks are arranged by increasing m/e from left to right in the spectrum. The intensities of the peaks are proportional to the relative abundance of the fragments, which depends on their relative stabilities. By convention, the largest peak in a spectrum, called the **base peak**, is given the intensity value of 100%; lesser peaks are reported as 20%, 30%, or whatever their value is relative to the base peak. The base peak sometimes arises from the molecular ion, but often arises from a smaller fragment.

STUDY PROBLEMS

20.8 Give the product and tell whether it is a cation, an ion-radical, or a free radical:

    (a) CH_4 minus one e^- (b) $[CH_4]^{\ddagger}$ minus H·
    (c) $[CH_3CH_2]^+$ minus H·   (d) $[CH_3CH_2]^{\ddagger}$ minus H·

20.9 Write the formulas for the molecular ions of   (a) CH_4 and   (b) $CH_3CH_2CH_3$.

20.10 Give the m/e value for each of the following particles:

    (a) $[CH_4]^{\ddagger}$ (b) $[(CH_3)_2CH]^+$ (c) $[O_2]^{\ddagger}$ (d) $[H_2O]^{\ddagger}$

Section 20.11

The Mass Spectrometer

The mass spectrometer (Figure 20.8) is composed of two principal parts. The first is the *ionization chamber*. The second is the *analyzer section*, which contains an *accelerator*, an *analyzer tube*, and an *ion collector*. The ion collector detects the intensity of the ion beam, amplifies the signal, and passes the information on to a recorder.

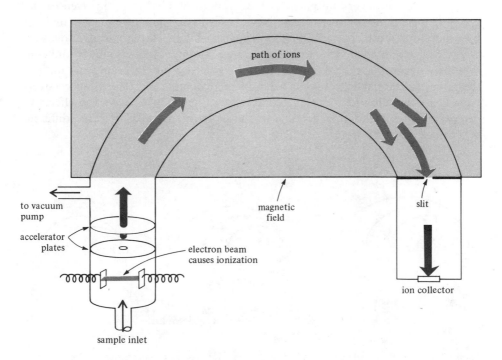

Figure 20.8.   Diagram of a mass spectrometer.

A.   The Ionization Chamber

The ionization chamber (as well as the rest of the mass spectrometer) is kept under a high vacuum (about 10^{-7} mm). The vacuum is necessary to minimize collisions (and subsequent reaction) between the high-energy electrons and molecules of air, between radicals, and so forth. The sample is introduced, vaporized, and allowed to feed in a continuous stream into the ionization chamber. As the sample enters the ionization chamber, it passes through a beam of high-energy electrons, which cause ionization of the molecules to their molecular ions. Excess sample is removed by the vacuum system.

After its formation, a molecular ion can undergo fragmentation and rearrangement. These processes are extremely rapid (10^{-10}–10^{-6} sec). The longer-lived particles can be detected by the ion collector, but a shorter-lived particle may not have a sufficient lifetime to reach the ion collector. In some cases, the molecular ion is too short-lived to be detected, and only its fragmentation products exhibit peaks.

B. Acceleration and Analysis

As the ion radicals and other particles are formed, they are fed past two electrodes, the *ion accelerator plates*, which attract and accelerate the positively charged particles. (The neutral and negatively charged particles are removed continuously by the vacuum pumps.) From the accelerator plates, the positively charged particles pass into the analyzer tube, where they are deflected into a circular path by a magnetic field.

In the magnetic field, the particles of higher m/e have a path with wider radius, while the lower-m/e particles have a path of smaller radius (see Figure 20.9). The continuous flow of positively charged particles through the analyzer tube therefore forms a pattern: higher-m/e particles with a larger radius and lower-m/e particles with a smaller radius. If the accelerating voltage is slowly and continuously decreased, the velocities of all the particles decrease, and the radii of the paths of all the particles also decrease. By this technique, particles of successively higher m/e are allowed to strike the detector. Figure 20.9 shows the effects of decreasing the accelerating voltage on the paths of particles of three different m/e values.

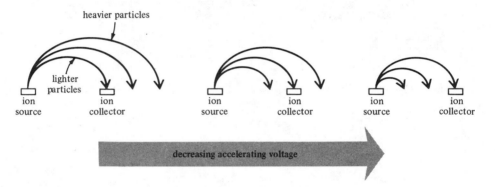

Figure 20.9. As the accelerating voltage is decreased, particles of successively higher m/e hit the ion collector.

Section 20.12

Isotopes in Mass Spectra

A mass spectrometer is so sensitive that particles differing by 1.0 mass unit give separate signals. The molecular weight of CH_3Br is 94.9 (15 atomic mass units for CH_3 and 79.9 for Br). However, the mass spectrum of this compound (Figure 20.10) does not show one molecular ion peak at $m/e = 94.9$; instead two peaks are observed, one at $m/e = 94$ and the other at $m/e = 96$. The reason for the two peaks is that naturally occurring Br exists in two isotopic forms, one with atomic mass 79 and the other with atomic mass 81. Usually, when we calculate the molecular weight of a bromine compound, we use a weighted average of these two isotopic masses (79.9). A mass spectrometer, however, detects particles containing each of these isotopes as individual species. Consequently, we cannot use average

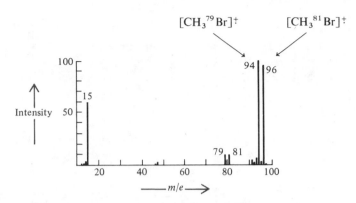

Figure 20.10. Mass spectrum of methyl bromide, CH_3Br.

atomic masses when dealing with mass spectra as we do when calculating the stoichiometry of a chemical reaction.

Table 20.4 lists the common natural isotopes and their relative abundance. Naturally occurring bromine exists as a 50.5%–49.5% mixture of bromine-79 and bromine-81, respectively. Particles of the same structure containing Br give a pair of peaks of approximately the same intensity that are 2.0 mass units apart. *The particle containing the lower-mass isotope is considered the molecular ion*; the peak for the other particle is called the **M + 2 peak** (molecular ion plus two mass units).

Naturally occurring chlorine is a mixture of 75.5% chlorine-35 and 24.5% chlorine-37. The particle containing chlorine-35 is considered the molecular ion, while the particle containing chlorine-37 gives rise to the M + 2 peak, which has an intensity approximately one-third that of the molecular ion peak.

Most elements common in organic compounds (except for Cl and Br) exist in nature as predominantly one isotope. For example, carbon is 98.89% carbon-12, and hydrogen is 99.985% hydrogen-1. For this reason, we generally assume for mass spectral purposes that all of C is carbon-12 and ignore the tiny proportion that is carbon-13. The presence of the isotopes of the common elements explains the multitude of small peaks surrounding a large peak in a mass spectrum (for example, the small peaks around the peaks at $m/e = 94$ and $m/e = 96$ in Figure 20.10).

Table 20.4. Natural Abundance of Some Isotopes

Isotope	Abundance, %	Isotope	Abundance, %	Isotope	Abundance, %
^1H	99.985	^2H	0.015		
^{12}C	98.89	^{13}C	1.11		
^{14}N	99.63	^{15}N	0.37		
^{16}O	99.76	^{17}O	0.04	^{18}O	0.20
^{32}S	95.0	^{33}S	0.76	^{34}S	4.2
^{19}F	100				
^{35}Cl	75.5			^{37}Cl	24.5
^{79}Br	50.5			^{81}Br	49.5
^{127}I	100				

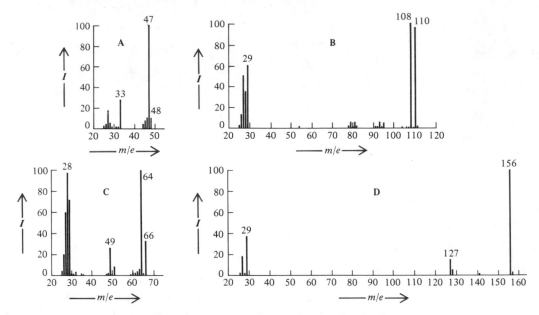

Figure 20.11. Mass spectra for Problem 20.12.

STUDY PROBLEMS

20.11 Calculate the *m/e* value for the molecular ion of each of the following compounds: (a) ethane; (b) chloroethane; (c) 1,2-dichloroethane; (d) ethanol; (e) *p*-bromophenol.

20.12 Figure 20.11 contains mass spectra of four compounds. Which of these compounds contains Br? Which contains Cl?

Section 20.13

Fragmentation Patterns in Mass Spectra

In a mass spectrometer, a molecule does not fragment in a random fashion, but tends to form the most-stable fragments possible. The first step in the fragmentation is the initial ionization—the abstraction of a single electron. The loss of an electron gives rise to the molecular ion. From the peak for this ion radical, which is usually the peak that is farthest to the right in the spectrum, the molecular weight of the compound may be determined. (Remember, it is the exact molecular weight for a molecule containing single isotopes and not an average molecular weight.)

The question arises, "Which electron of the molecule is removed?" This question cannot be answered with accuracy. It is believed that the electron with the highest-energy ground state (the "loosest" electron) is the first to be removed. If a molecule has *n* (unshared) electrons, one of these is removed. If there are no *n* electrons, then a pi electron is removed. If there are neither *n* electrons nor pi electrons, the molecular ion is formed by removal of a sigma electron.

$$CH_3\overset{..}{\underset{..}{O}}H \longrightarrow [CH_3OH]^{\ddagger} + n\ e^-$$

$$CH_3CH::CH_2 \longrightarrow [CH_3CH-CH_2]^{\ddagger} + \pi\ e^-$$

$$H:CH_3 \longrightarrow [CH_4]^{\ddagger} + \sigma\ e^-$$

Let us reconsider the mass spectrum of methyl alcohol in Figure 20.7. The spectrum consists of three principal peaks at $m/e = 29$, 31, and 32. The structures of the fragments may often be deduced from their masses. The M^+ peak (at 32) of methanol arises from loss of one electron. The peak at 31 must arise from loss of H (which has a mass of 1.0). The peak at 29 must arise from an ion that has lost two more H atoms. What about the minor peak at 15? This peak arises from the loss of $\cdot OH$ from the molecular ion.

$$[CH_2{=}OH]^+ \xrightarrow{-H_2} [CH{\equiv}O]^+$$
$$m/e = 31 \qquad\qquad m/e = 29$$

$$CH_3OH \xrightarrow{-e^-} [CH_3OH]^{\ddagger}$$
$$m/e = 32$$

$$\xrightarrow{-H\cdot} \qquad \searrow^{-\cdot OH}$$

$$[CH_3]^+$$
$$m/e = 15$$

Could other fragmentation patterns occur? For example, could the molecular ion lose H^+ to become $[CH_3O]^{\cdot}$? It possibly could, but we do not know, because only the positively charged particles are detected.

A. Effect of Branching

Branching in a hydrocarbon chain leads to fragmentation primarily at the branch because secondary ion radicals and secondary carbocations are more stable than primary ion radicals and primary carbocations. The mass spectrum of 3-methylpentane has the base peak at $m/e = 57$ and lesser peaks at 86 (M^+ peak), 42, and 29. Peaks at $m/e = 15$ and 71 are virtually nonexistent.

fission here

$$\left[CH_3CH_2\overset{\overset{\displaystyle CH_3}{|}}{CH}CH_2CH_3 \right]^{\ddagger} \longrightarrow \left[CH_3CH_2\overset{\overset{\displaystyle CH_3}{|}}{CH} \right]^+ \quad \text{and} \quad [CH_3CH_2]^+$$
$$m/e = 86 \qquad\qquad\qquad m/e = 57 \qquad\qquad\qquad m/e = 29$$

$$\text{but very little} \quad \left[CH_3CH_2\overset{\overset{\displaystyle CH_3}{|}}{CH}CH_2 \right]^+ \quad \text{or} \quad [CH_3]^+$$
$$m/e = 71 \qquad\qquad\qquad m/e = 15$$

STUDY PROBLEMS

20.13 To what particle would you attribute the peak at $m/e = 42$ in the mass spectrum of 3-methylpentane?

20.14 What would be the molecular ion and the principal positively charged fragments arising from ionization of: (a) 2-methylpentane, and (b) 2,2-dimethylpropane?

B.   *Effect of a Heteroatom*

Consider another spectrum, that of N-ethylpropylamine (Figure 20.12). The molecular ion has $m/e = 87$. Fragmentation of this molecular ion takes place alpha to the nitrogen atom and yields fragments with $m/e = 58$ (loss of an ethyl group) and 72 (loss of a methyl group). This type of fragmentation is called **α-fission.**

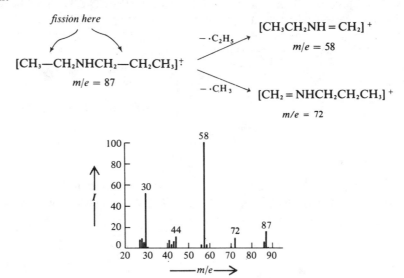

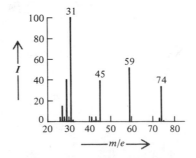

Figure 20.12.   Mass spectrum of *N*-ethylpropylamine, $CH_3CH_2NHCH_2CH_2CH_3$.

STUDY PROBLEM

20.15 The mass spectrum of an ether is shown in Figure 20.13. What is the structure of the ether?

Figure 20.13.   Mass spectrum for Problem 20.15.

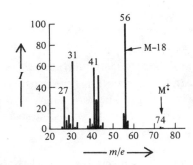

Figure 20.14. Mass spectrum of 1-butanol.

C. Loss of a Small Molecule

Small stable molecules, such as H_2O, CO_2, CO, and C_2H_4, can be lost from a molecular ion. An alcohol, for example, readily loses H_2O and shows a peak at 18 mass units less than the peak of the molecular ion. This peak is referred to as the **M — 18 peak**. In many alcohols, elimination of H_2O is so facile that the molecular-ion peak is not even observed in the spectrum. The spectrum of 1-butanol (Figure 20.14) is a typical mass spectrum of an alcohol.

$$[CH_3CH_2CH_2CH_2OH]^{\ddagger} \xrightarrow{\;-H_2O\;} [CH_3CH_2CH{=}CH_2]^{\ddagger}$$
$$M^{\ddagger},\, m/e = 74 \qquad\qquad M-18,\, m/e = 56$$

D. McLafferty Rearrangement

When there is a hydrogen atom γ to a carbonyl group in the molecular ion, a **McLafferty rearrangement** may occur. In this rearrangement, an alkene is lost from the molecular ion.

$$\overset{\gamma\ hydrogen}{\underset{}{}} $$

$$\underset{}{\overset{H}{\underset{|}{}}\quad \overset{O}{\underset{\|}{}}}$$
$$-\overset{}{\underset{|}{C}}H_2CH_2C-$$

Rearrangement:
$$\left[\begin{matrix} H_2C \\ H_2C \end{matrix} \overset{H}{\underset{CH_2}{\underset{}{\diagup}}} \overset{O}{\underset{CH}{\overset{\|}{}}}\right]^{\ddagger} \longrightarrow \begin{matrix} H_2C \\ \| \\ H_2C \end{matrix} + \left[\begin{matrix} HO \\ | \\ CH \\ \| \\ CH_2 \end{matrix}\right]^{\ddagger}$$
$$m/e = 72 \qquad\qquad m/e = 44$$

STUDY PROBLEM

20.16 Predict the *m/e* values for the products of the McLafferty rearrangement of the following compounds:

(a) $CH_3CH_2CH_2\overset{\overset{\displaystyle O}{\|}}{C}CH_3$

(b) $CH_3\overset{\overset{\displaystyle CH_3}{|}}{C}HCH_2\overset{\overset{\displaystyle O}{\|}}{C}H$

(c) $(CH_3)_2CHCH_2O\overset{\overset{\displaystyle O}{\|}}{C}CH_2CH_3$

SUMMARY

Absorption of ultraviolet (200–400 nm) or visible (400–750 nm) light results in **electronic transitions**, promotion of electrons from the ground-state orbitals to orbitals of higher energy. The wavelength λ of absorption is inversely proportional to the energy required. The uv or visible spectrum is a plot of **absorbance** A or **molar absorptivity** ε vs λ, where $\varepsilon = A/cl$. The position of maximum absorption is reported as $\lambda_{\max}$.

The important electronic transitions are $\pi \to \pi^*$ for conjugated systems and $n \to \pi^*$. Increasing amounts of conjugation result in shifts of $\lambda_{\max}$ toward longer wavelengths. Compounds that absorb at wavelengths longer than 400 nm are colored; the apparent color is the **complementary color** of the wavelength absorbed.

Vision is made possible by the conversion of 11-*cis*-retinal in rhodopsin to all-*trans*-retinal, which in turn is reduced to all-*trans*-vitamin A. The regeneration of 11-*cis*-retinal is accomplished by enzymatic conversion of all-*trans*-vitamin A to 11-*cis*-vitamin A and then to 11-*cis*-retinal.

Dyes are colored compounds that adhere to fabric or other substance. An **acid–base indicator** is a compound that undergoes a color change in a reaction with acid or base. The color change arises from a change in the conjugated system and thus in the wavelength of absorption.

Fluorescence and **chemiluminescence** are the results of emission of light as excited molecules return to the ground state.

A **mass spectrum** is a graph of **abundance** versus **mass-to-charge ratio** (m/e) of positively charged particles that result from bombardment of a compound with high-energy electrons. Removal of one electron from a molecule of the compound results in the **molecular ion**. The molecular ion can lose atoms, ions, radicals, and small molecules to yield a variety of fragmentation products.

STUDY PROBLEMS

20.17 A chemist prepared 1,3,5-hexatriene and 1,3,5,7-octatetraene, placed them in separate flasks, but neglected to label them. How could he differentiate the two by uv spectroscopy?

20.18 Which of the following pairs of compounds could probably be distinguished from each other by their uv spectra?

(a) HO—$\bigcirc$—CH=CH$_2$, $\bigcirc$—CH=CH$_2$

(b) CH$_3$CO$_2$CH$_2$CH$_3$,   CH$_3$CH$_2$CO$_2$CH$_3$

(c) CH$_3$—$\bigcirc$=O,   [structure with CH$_3$]=O

(d) [structures]

(e) CH$_3$CH=CHCH$_2$CCH$_3$,   CH$_3$CH$_2$CH=CHCCH$_3$ (each with O double bond)

(f) [structures]

20.19 The uv spectrum of acetone (0.50 M in cyclohexane, 1.0-cm cell) shows a λ_{max} at 270 nm with an absorbance of 7.4. (This absorption arises from the $n \rightarrow \pi^*$ transitions.) What is the molar absorptivity of acetone at 270 nm?

20.20 Cyclopentanone (0.038 M in a 1.0-cm cell) has a λ_{max} at 288 nm with an absorbance of 0.75. What is its molar absorptivity?

20.21 Methyl vinyl ketone shows uv absorption maxima at 219 nm and 324 nm. (a) Why are there two maxima? (b) Which has the greater ε_{max}?

20.22 What types of electronic transition would give rise to uv absorption in each of the following compounds?

(a) 2,4-octadiene   (b) 2-cyclohexenone   (c) aniline   (d) formaldehyde

20.23 Rank the following compounds in the order of increasing λ_{max}: (a) benzene; (b) biphenyl (C$_6$H$_5$—C$_6$H$_5$); (c) styrene (C$_6$H$_5$CH=CH$_2$); (d) stilbene (C$_6$H$_5$CH=CHC$_6$H$_5$).

20.24 A chemist has a liquid compound of unknown structure with the formula C$_5$H$_8$; the uv spectrum shows a λ_{max} at about 220 nm. What are the likely possible structures of this compound?

20.25 Suggest a reason that the λ_{max} for *trans*-stilbene (C$_6$H$_5$CH=CHC$_6$H$_5$) is 295 nm, while that for *cis*-stilbene is 280 nm.

20.26 Suggest a mechanism for the photochemical isomerization of *trans*-stilbene to *cis*-stilbene.

20.27 *Indophenol blue* is a vat dye that is oxidized to an insoluble blue dye after application to fabric. Give the structure of the oxidized form.

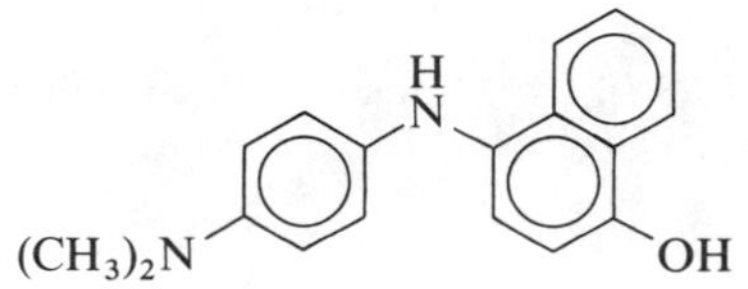

reduced form of indophenol blue

20.28 As a solution of *Crystal violet* is acidified, it turns from violet to blue, then to green, and finally to yellow. Write equations that could explain these color changes.

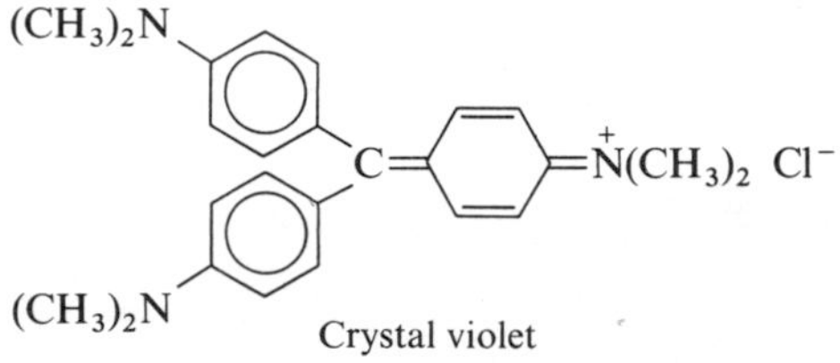

Crystal violet

20.29 *Phenol red* is an acid–base indicator that is yellow at pH 6 but red at pH 9. Give the structures (and resonance structures) for the two forms of this compound.

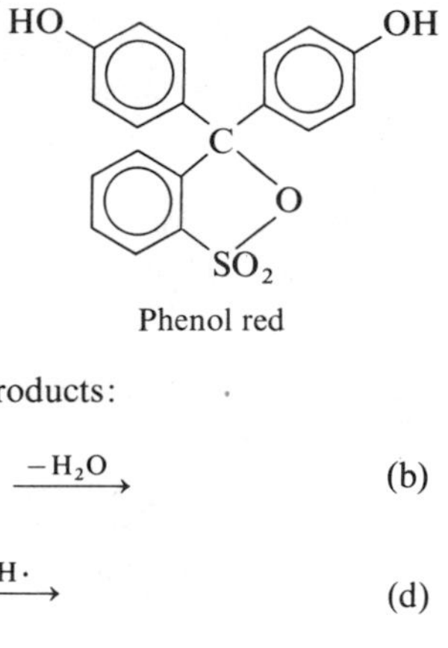

Phenol red

20.30 Give the structures of the products:

(a) $[CH_3CH_2CH_2OH]^{\ddagger}$ $\xrightarrow{-H_2O}$

(b)  $\xrightarrow{-e^-}$

(c) 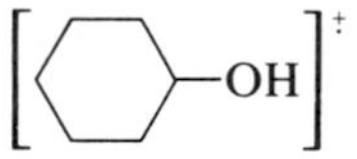 $\left[\langle \rangle\text{—OH} \right]^{\ddagger}$ $\xrightarrow{-H\cdot}$

(d) $[(CH_3)_2CHCl]^{\ddagger}$ $\xrightarrow{-Cl\cdot}$

20.31 For each of the following compounds, give the structures and m/e values for the molecular ion and likely positively charged fragmentation products: (a) ethyl isopropyl ether; (b) ethyl isobutyl ether; (c) isopropyl chloride; (d) 2,5-dimethylhexane; (e) isopropyl alcohol; (f) 4-cyclopentylbutanal (McLafferty fragment only).

20.32 Suggest structures and fragmentation patterns that account for the following observed peaks in the mass spectra:

(a) *n*-butane, $m/e = 58, 57, 43, 29, 15$
(b) benzamide, $m/e = 121, 105, 77$
(c) 1-bromopropane, $m/e = 124, 122, 43, 29, 15$

20.33 What reactants would you need to prepare the yellow azo dye *Crysamine G*?

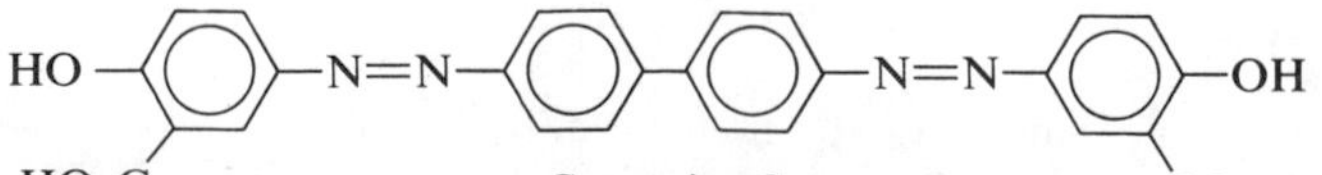

Crysamine G

20.34 Propose a synthetic route to *Orange II* from naphthalene and sulfanilic acid (*p*-amino-benzenesulfonic acid).

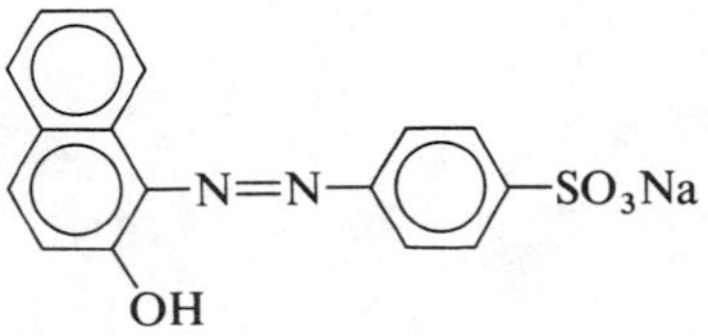

Orange II

20.35 In uv spectra, the presence of an additional double bond in conjugation adds about 30 nm to the λ_{max}. From the following observed values for λ_{max}, state how the degree of substitution on the sp^2 carbons of a polyene affects the position of the λ_{max}.

Structure	λ_{max}, nm
$CH_2=CHCH=CH_2$	217
$CH_3CH=CHCH=CH_2$	223
$CH_3CH=CHCH=CHCH_3$	227
$CH_2=CCH=CHCH_3$ $\quad\quad$ CH_3	227

20.36 From your answer in Problem 20.35, predict the λ_{max} values for the following polyenes:

(a)

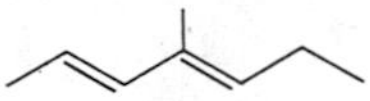

(b)

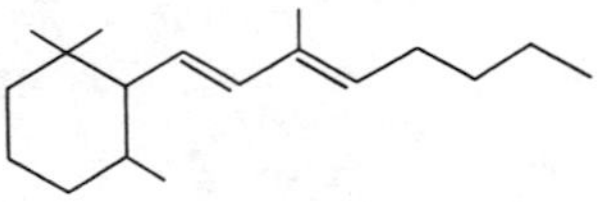

(c)

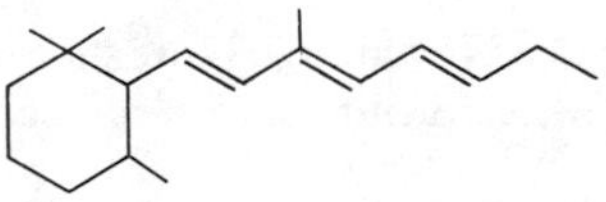

20.37 Predict the λ_{max} values where indicated:

Structure	λ_{max}, nm
$CH_2=CHCCH_3$ (with O double bond)	219
$CH_3CH=CHCCH_3$ (with O double bond)	224
$(CH_3)_2C=CHCCH_3$ (with O double bond)	(a)
$(CH_3)_2C=CCCH_3$ with CH_3 and O double bond	(b)
$CH_2=CHCH=CHCCH_3$ (with O double bond)	(c)

20.38 A ketone ($C_6H_{12}O$) gives a positive iodoform test and shows principal peaks in the mass spectrum at the following m/e values: 100, 85, 58, and 43. Which of the following compounds are compatible with these data?

(a) $CH_3CH_2\overset{\overset{\displaystyle O}{\|}}{C}CH_2CH_2CH_3$ (b) $CH_3\overset{\overset{\displaystyle O}{\|}}{C}CH_2CH_2CH_2CH_3$

(c) $CH_3\overset{\overset{\displaystyle O}{\|}}{C}\underset{\underset{\displaystyle CH_3}{|}}{C}HCH_2CH_3$ (d) $CH_3\overset{\overset{\displaystyle O}{\|}}{C}CH_2CH(CH_3)_2$

20.39 A compound contains only C, H, and O. The infrared spectrum shows strong absorption at 1724 cm^{-1} (5.8 μm), 1388 cm^{-1} (7.2 μm), and 1231 cm^{-1} (8.1 μm) (plus other minor absorption). The nmr spectrum shows only one singlet at 2.1 ppm. The mass spectrum has principal peaks at 58 m/e and 43 m/e. What is the structure of the compound?

20.40 Figure 20.15 shows a pair of uv spectra superimposed. One spectrum is of acetone and the other is of crotonaldehyde (propenal).

(a)   Which compound gives the spectrum represented by the light line?
(b)   The dark-line spectrum shows two maxima. Why?
(c)   Why does not the light-line spectrum show two peaks?

20.41 The infrared, nmr, and mass spectra for Compounds A through D are shown in Figures 20.16 through 20.19. From the spectra, deduce the structure of each compound.

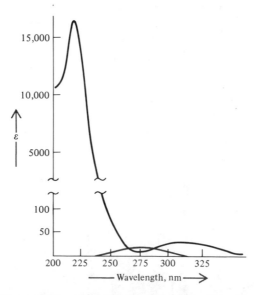

Figure 20.15.   Ultraviolet spectra for Problem 20.40.

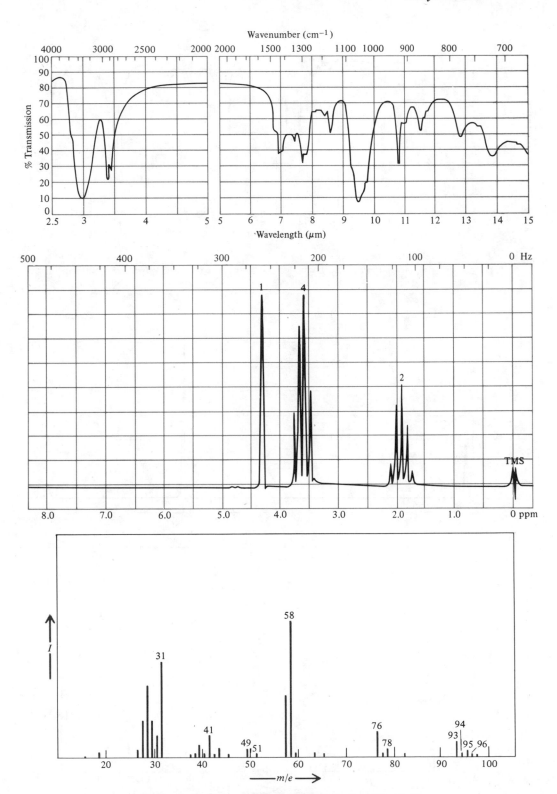

Figure 20.16. Spectra for Compound A, Problem 20.41.

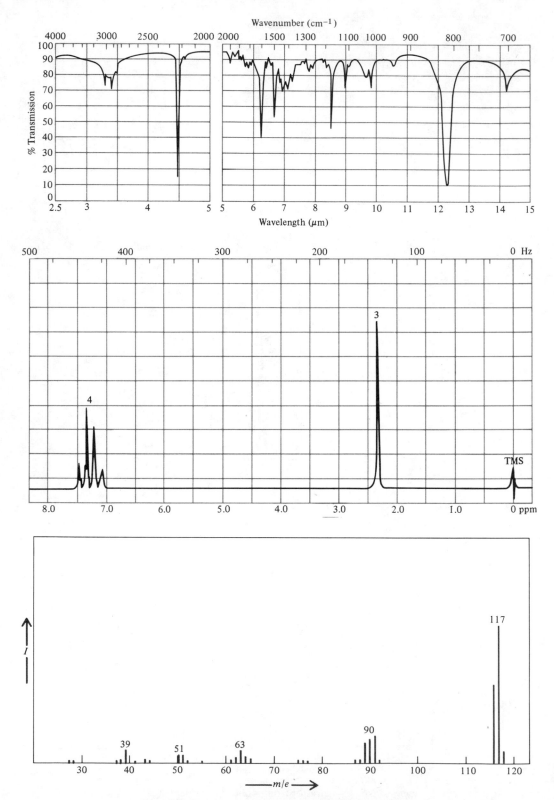

Figure 20.17. Spectra for Compound B, Problem 20.41.

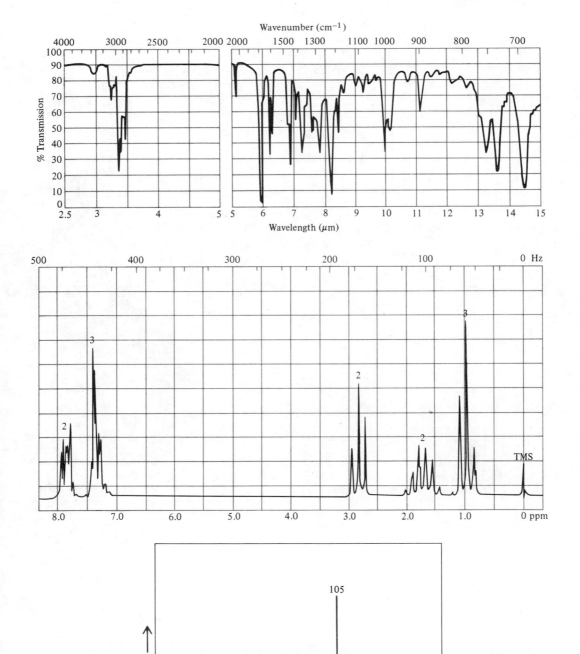

Figure 20.18. Spectra for Compound C, Problem 20.41.

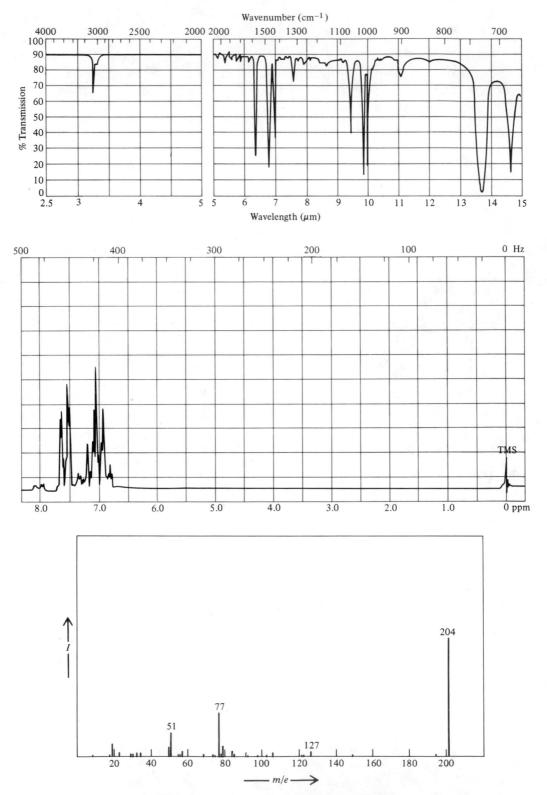

Figure 20.19. Spectra for Compound D, Problem 20.41.

Nomenclature of Organic Compounds

A complete discussion of definitive rules of organic nomenclature would require more space than can be allotted in this text. We will survey some of the more common nomenclature rules, both IUPAC and trivial. The following references contain more detail:

> *IUPAC Nomenclature of Organic Chemistry, Sections A, B, & C, 2nd Ed.*, Butterworths, London, 1971. Now available from Pergamon Press, Elmsford, New York. [Also may be found in *Pure Appl. Chem. II* (1–2) (1965).]

> Chemical Abstracts Service, *Naming and Indexing of Chemical Substances for* Chemical Abstracts *during the Ninth Collective Period (1972–1976)* (*January–June, 1972*), American Chemical Society, Columbus, Ohio, 1973.

> Chemical Abstracts Service, *Combined Introductions to the Indexes to Volume 66* (*January–June, 1967*), American Chemical Society, Columbus, Ohio, 1968.

> A. M. Patterson, L. T. Capell, and D. F. Walker, *The Ring Index, 2nd Ed.*, American Chemical Society, Washington D.C., 1960; *Supplement I (1957–1959)*, 1963; *Supplement II (1960–1961)*, 1964; *Supplement III (1962–1963)*, 1965.

> R. S. Cahn, *J. Chem. Ed.*, **41**, 116 (1964).

Alkanes

The names for the first thirty continuous-chain alkanes are listed in Table A1.

Branched Alkanes   In naming an alkane with alkyl substituents, the longest continuous chain is considered the parent. The parent is numbered from one end to the other, the direction being chosen to give the lowest numbers to the substituents. The entire name of the structure is then composed of (1) the numbers of the positions of the substituents; (2) the names of the substituents; and (3) the name of the parent.

Alkyl Substituents   The names of the alkyl substituents (also called *branches*, or *radicals*) are derived from the names of their corresponding alkanes with the ending changed from *-ane* to *-yl*. For example, CH_3CH_2— is ethyl (from ethane). Multiple substituents are placed in alphabetical order, each preceded by its respective number and like substituents grouped together. Some common branched alkyl substituents have trivial names (see Table A2).

Table A1.   Names of Continuous-Chain Alkanes

Molecular formula	Name	Molecular formula	Name
CH_4	methane	$C_{16}H_{34}$	hexadecane
C_2H_6	ethane	$C_{17}H_{36}$	heptadecane
C_3H_8	propane	$C_{18}H_{38}$	octadecane
C_4H_{10}	butane	$C_{19}H_{40}$	nonadecane
C_5H_{12}	pentane	$C_{20}H_{42}$	eicosane
C_6H_{14}	hexane	$C_{21}H_{44}$	heneicosane
C_7H_{16}	heptane	$C_{22}H_{46}$	docosane
C_8H_{18}	octane	$C_{23}H_{48}$	tricosane
C_9H_{20}	nonane	$C_{24}H_{50}$	tetracosane
$C_{10}H_{22}$	decane	$C_{25}H_{52}$	pentacosane
$C_{11}H_{24}$	undecane	$C_{26}H_{54}$	hexacosane
$C_{12}H_{26}$	dodecane	$C_{27}H_{56}$	heptacosane
$C_{13}H_{28}$	tridecane	$C_{28}H_{58}$	octacosane
$C_{14}H_{30}$	tetradecane	$C_{29}H_{60}$	nonacosane
$C_{15}H_{32}$	pentadecane	$C_{30}H_{62}$	triacontane

Table A2.   Trivial Names for Some Common Alkyl Groups

Structure	Name
$CH_3CH_2CH_2—$	*normal-*, or *n*-propyl[a]
$(CH_3)_2CH—$	isopropyl
$CH_3CH_2CH_2CH_2—$	*n*-butyl[a]
$(CH_3)_2CHCH_2—$	isobutyl
$CH_3CH_2CH(CH_3)—$	*secondary-*, or *sec*-butyl
$(CH_3)_3C—$	*tertiary-*, *tert-*, or *t*-butyl[b]
$CH_3CH_2CH_2CH_2CH_2—$	*n*-pentyl (or *n*-amyl)[a]
$(CH_3)_2CHCH_2CH_2—$	isopentyl (or isoamyl)
$(CH_3)_3CCH_2—$	neopentyl

[a] The use of *n-* (to denote a continuous chain) is optional.

[b] *tert-* is preferred.

$$CH_2CH_3$$
$$|$$
$$CH_3CH_2CHCH_2CH_2CH_3$$
$$①\ ②\ ③\ ④\ ⑤\ ⑥$$

3-ethylhexane

$$CH_3 \quad CH_2CH_3$$
$$| \qquad | \qquad ⑥\ ⑦\ ⑧$$
$$CH_3CHCH_2CHCH_2CHCH_2CH_3$$
$$①\ ②\ ③\ ④\ ⑤\ |$$
$$CH_3$$

4-ethyl-2,6-dimethyloctane

Alkenes and Alkynes

Unbranched hydrocarbons having one double bond are named in the IUPAC system by replacing the ending -*ane* of the alkane name with -*ene*. If there are two or more double bonds, the ending is -*adiene*, -*atriene*, etc. The chain is numbered to give the lowest possible numbers to the double bonds. (The *lower* number of the two carbons joined by the double bond is used to give the position.)

$$\overset{①\quad②\quad\quad③\,④\quad⑤}{CH_3CH{=}CHCH_2CH_3}$$

2-pentene

$$\overset{①\quad\quad②\,③\quad\quad④\,⑤}{CH_2{=}CHCH{=}CHCH_3}$$

1,3-pentadiene

Unbranched hydrocarbons having one triple bond are named by replacing the ending *-ane* of the alkane name with *-yne*. If there are two or more triple bonds, the ending is *-adiyne*, *-atriyne*, etc. The chain is numbered to give the lowest possible numbers to the triple bonds. Again, the lower number is used to give the position. For example, $CH_3CH_2C{\equiv}CH$ is 1-butyne.

Unbranched hydrocarbons with both double and triple bonds are named by replacing the ending *-ane* of the name of the alkane with the ending *-enyne*. When necessary, position numbers are inserted. The double bond is assigned the lowest number; for example, $CH_2{=}CHC{\equiv}CCH_3$ is 1-penten-3-yne. Trivial names for some alkenes and alkynes are found in Table A3.

Table A3. Trivial Names for Some Alkenes and Alkynes

Structure	Name
$CH_2{=}CH_2$	ethylene
$CH{\equiv}CH$	acetylene
$CH_2{=}C{=}CH_2$	allene
$CH_2{=}CHCH_3$	propylene
$CH_3C{\equiv}CH$	methylacetylene
$(CH_3)_2C{=}CH_2$	isobutylene
$CH_2{=}C(CH_3)CH{=}CH_2$	isoprene

Branched Alkenes and Alkynes In the IUPAC name of a branched alkene or alkyne, the parent chain is the longest chain that contains the maximum number of double or triple bonds. (This may or may not be the longest continuous chain in the structure.)

$$CH_3CH_2CH_2$$
$$|\quad\;④\quad\quad⑥\;⑦$$
$$\overset{①\quad\quad②\,③\quad\;|⑤}{CH_2{=}CHC{=}CCH{=}CHCH_3}$$
$$CH_2CH_2CH_3$$

3,4-dipropyl-1,3,5-heptatriene

Several unsaturated substituents have trivial names; some of these are listed in Table A4.

**Table A4.   IUPAC Names for Some Un-
saturated Groups**

Structure	Name
$CH_2=$	methylene
$CH_2=CH-$	ethenyl (vinyl)[a]
$CH_3CH=$	ethylidene
$CH\equiv C-$	ethynyl
$CH_2=CHCH_2-$	2-propenyl (allyl)[a]
$CH_3CH=CH-$	1-propenyl
$(CH_3)_2C=$	isopropylidene

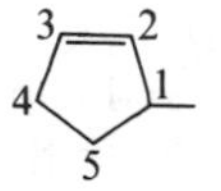

2-cyclopenten-1-yl

[a] Names in parentheses are trivial.

In complex compounds, the symbol Δ is sometimes used to denote double bonds.

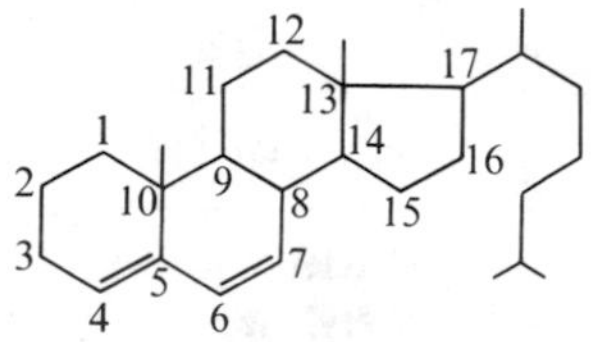

is $\Delta^{4,6}$-cholestadiene

Geometric Isomers   There are two methods for naming geometric isomers. One method employs the prefixes *cis-* (same side) or *trans-* (opposite sides) to designate the geometric isomers.

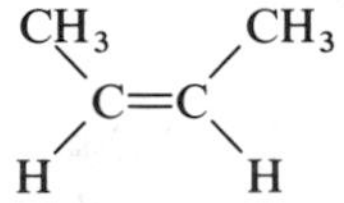

cis-2-butene 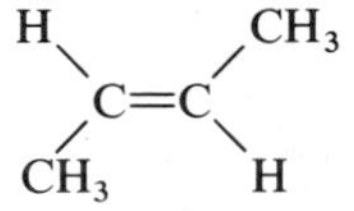   *trans*-2-butene

The other method employs (*E*) (groups with higher priority, according to the Cahn–Ingold–Prelog system, on opposite sides) or (*Z*) (groups with higher priority on the same side) for designation of the geometric isomers. The priority rules are found in Section 4.1B (page 115).

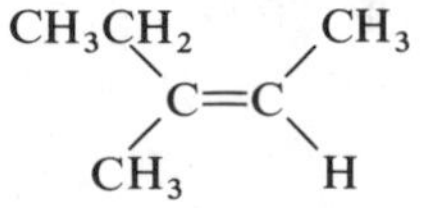

(*Z*)-3-methyl-2-pentene 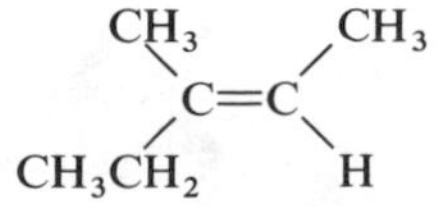   (*E*)-3-methyl-2-pentene

ethyl has priority over methyl; methyl has priority over H

Cyclic Hydrocarbons

Cycloalkanes and Cycloalkenes The names of saturated monocyclic hydrocarbons are formed by attaching the prefix *cyclo-* to the name of the alkane with the same number of carbon atoms.

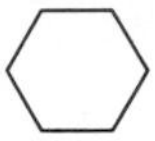

is cyclohexane

A ring is considered the parent unless there is a longer chain attached, in which case the longer chain is the parent.

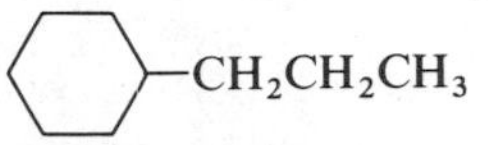

—$CH_2CH_2CH_3$ —$CH_2(CH_2)_5CH_3$

propylcyclohexane 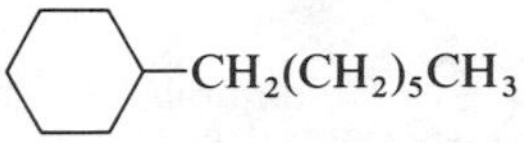   1-cyclohexylheptane

Alkyl substituents are named as prefixes and are given the lowest possible position numbers.

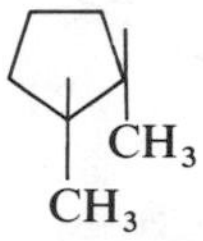

cis-1,2-dimethylcyclopentane

Unsaturated monocyclic hydrocarbons are named by changing the ending from *-ane* to *-ene* (*-adiene*, etc.). The ring is numbered to give the lowest numbers possible to the double bonds. With both alkyl substituents and double bonds, the ring is numbered so that the double bonds receive the lowest possible numbers.

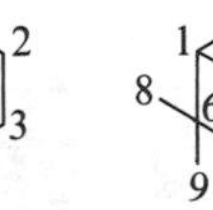

1,3-cyclohexadiene 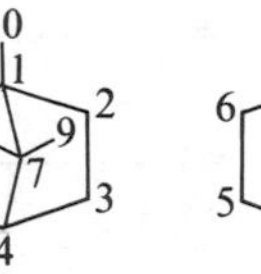   5-methyl-1,3-cyclohexadiene

Some common terpene ring structures have individual names.

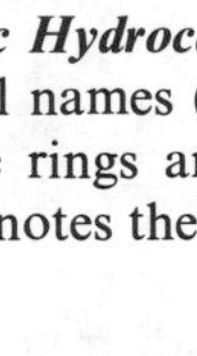

menthane 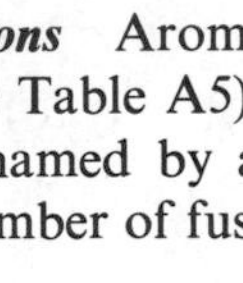   pinane 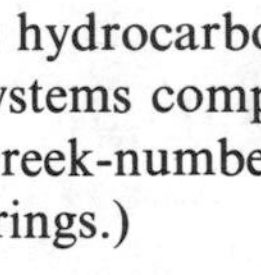   bornane 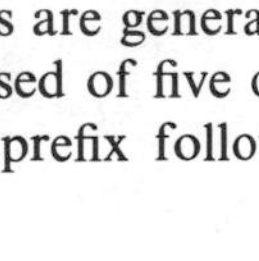   norbornane

Aromatic Hydrocarbons Aromatic hydrocarbons are generally referred to by their trivial names (see Table A5). Systems composed of five or more linear fused benzene rings are named by a Greek-number prefix followed by *-cene*. (The prefix denotes the number of fused rings.)

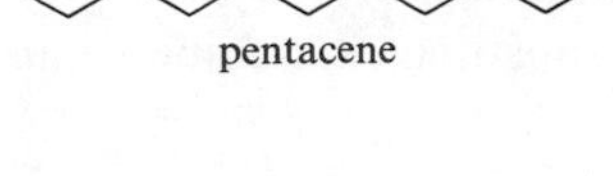

pentacene

Nomenclature of Organic Compounds

Table A5. Names for Some Arenes and Aryl Groups

Structure	Name	Structure	Name
Arenes:		**Aryl groups:**	
 (benzene ring)	benzene	C_6H_5-	phenyl-
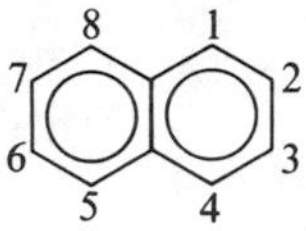 (naphthalene ring, positions 8,1 top; 7,2; 6,3; 5,4 bottom)	naphthalene	$C_6H_5CH_2-$	benzyl-
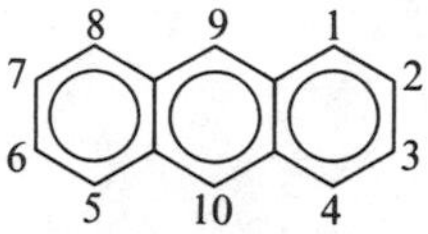 (anthracene ring, positions 8,9,1 top; 7,2; 6,3; 5,10,4 bottom)	anthracene	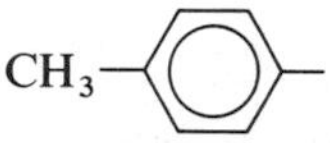 CH_3-(ring)$-$	*p*-tolyl-
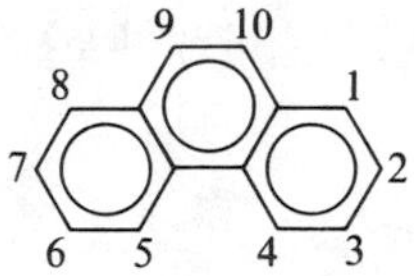 (phenanthrene ring, positions 9,10; 8,1; 7,2; 6,5,4,3)	phenanthrene	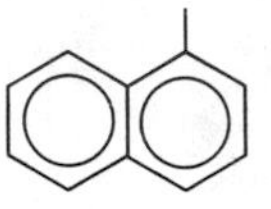 (1-naphthyl ring with substituent at position 1)	1-naphthyl- (α-naphthyl-)
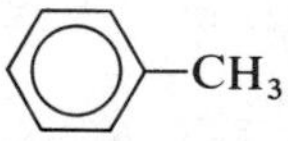 (benzene ring)$-CH_3$	toluene	$C_6H_5CH=CHCH_2-$	cinnamyl-
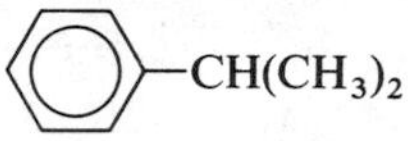 (benzene ring)$-CH(CH_3)_2$	cumene		
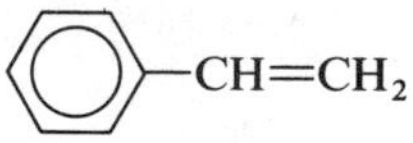 (benzene ring)$-CH=CH_2$	styrene		
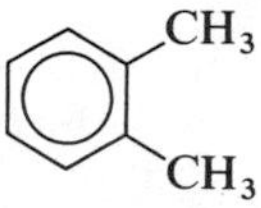 (benzene ring) $\begin{smallmatrix}CH_3\\CH_3\end{smallmatrix}$	*o*-xylene		
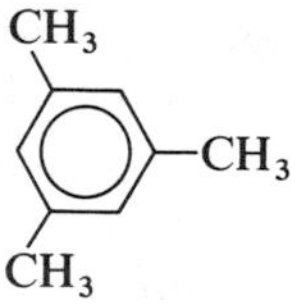 $\begin{smallmatrix}CH_3\\(ring)-CH_3\\CH_3\end{smallmatrix}$	mesitylene		

The aromatic system is considered the parent unless a longer chain is attached.

$$C_6H_5CH_2CH_2CH_3 \qquad C_6H_5CH_2(CH_2)_5CH_3$$

propylbenzene   1-phenylheptane

If there are only two substituents on a benzene ring, their positions may be designated either by prefix numbers or by *o*-, *m*-, or *p*- (*ortho*, *meta*-, or *para*-). If there are more than two substituents, numbers must be used.

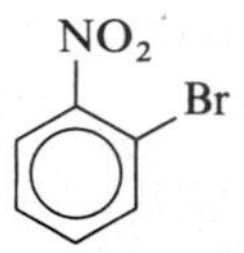

o-bromonitrobenzene 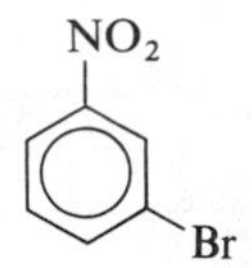 *m*-bromonitrobenzene  *p*-bromonitrobenzene

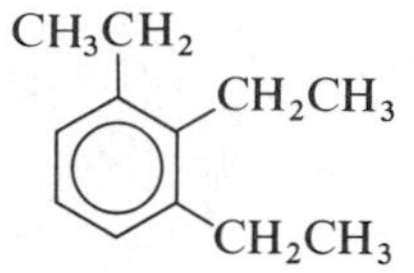

1,2,3-triethylbenzene

The principal group, or a group that is part of the parent (for example, the CH_3 in toluene), is always considered to be attached to position 1 on the ring. The numbers of substituents are chosen to be as low as possible.

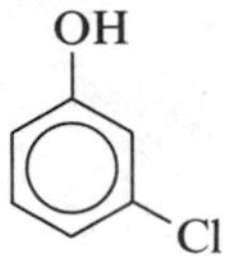

m-chlorophenol 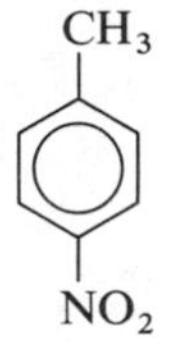 *p*-nitrotoluene 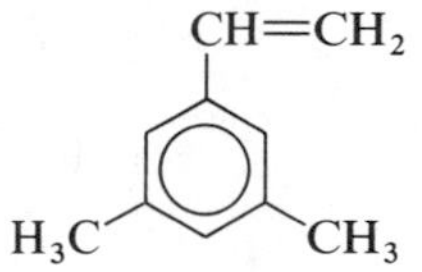 3,5-dimethylstyrene

Heterocycles

Some common heterocycles are listed in Table A6. In monocyclic heterocycles with only one heteroatom, that atom is considered position 1. Other ring systems are numbered by convention (see Table A6).

To name monocyclic compounds with one or more heteroatoms, prefixes may be used: *oxa-* (—O—), *aza-* (—NH—), *thia-* (—S—). For unsaturated rings, the ring size is designated by suffixes; *-ole* means five, and *-ine* means six (used only with rings that contain nitrogen). *Example:* An *oxazole* is a five-membered ring containing O and N.

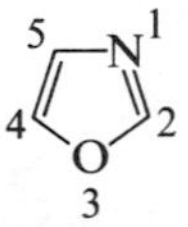

1,3-oxazole 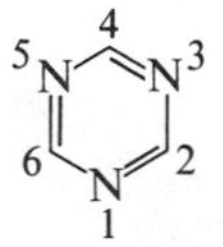 1,3,5-triazine

Heteroatoms in Chains

The *oxa-*, *aza-* system may also be used for naming aliphatic compounds. This method is called *replacement nomenclature*. All the atoms in the chain are numbered in such a way that the heteroatoms receive the lowest possible numbers.

Table A6.   *Names of Some Common Heterocycles*

Structure	Name	Structure	Name
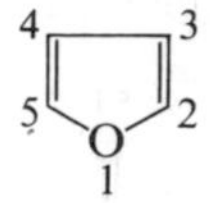	furan	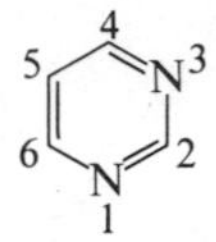	pyrimidine
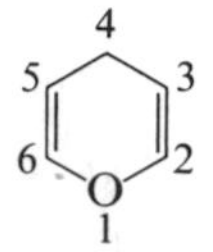	4*H*-pyran (γ-pyran)	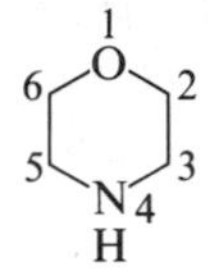	morpholine
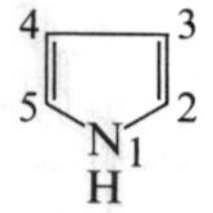	pyrrole	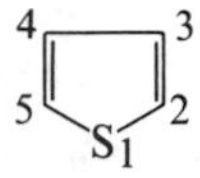	thiophene
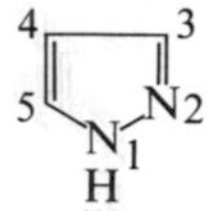	pyrazole	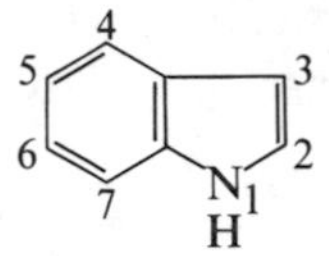	indole
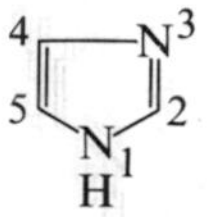	imidazole	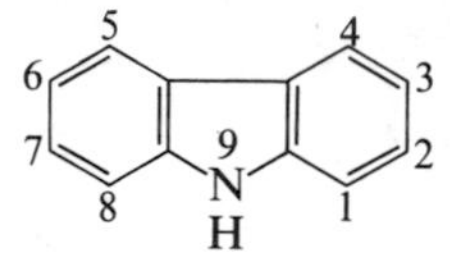	carbazole
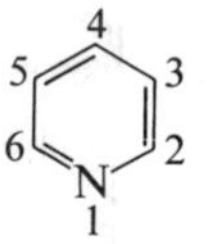	pyridine	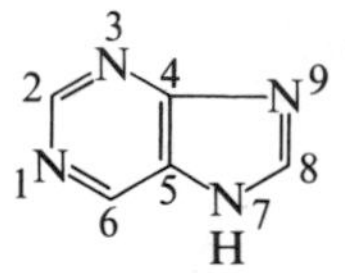	purine
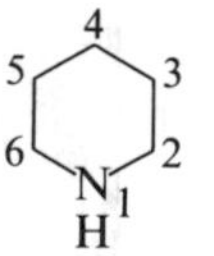	piperidine	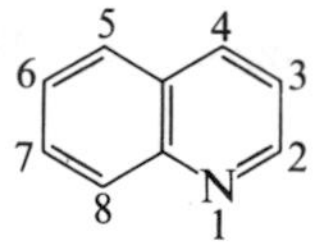	quinoline
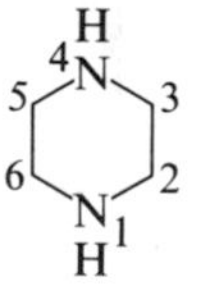	piperazine	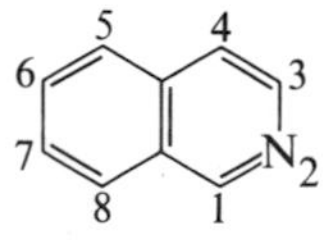	isoquinoline

The parent is considered to be the alkane that has the same number of carbon atoms as the total number of atoms in the continuous chain (heteroatoms, but not hydrogens, included).

$$①②③④⑤⑥⑦⑧⑨⑩$$
$$CH_3OCH_2CH_2OCH_2CH_2OCH_2CH_3$$

2,5,8-trioxadecane

Table A7. *Some Common Functional Groups Named*
as Prefixes

Structure	Name	Structure	Name
—OR	alkoxy-[a]	—F	fluoro-
—NH$_2$	amino-	—H	hydro-[b]
—N=N—	azo-	—I	iodo-
—Br	bromo-	—NO$_2$	nitro-
—Cl	chloro-	—NO	nitroso-

[a] *methoxy-*, *ethoxy-*, etc., depending upon the R group.

[b] *Hydro-* is a prefix used to designate a hydrogenated derivative of an unsaturated parent. *Perhydro-* means completely hydrogenated.

4a,8a-dihydronaphthalene   perhydrophenanthrene

Putting Names Together

The Prefixes   In the IUPAC system, alkyl and aryl substituents and many functional groups are named as prefixes on the parent (for example, iodomethane). Some common functional groups named as prefixes are listed in Table A7. Other prefix names are sometimes used for carbonyl groups, hydroxyl groups, etc. These are mentioned under their specific headings.

Like Treatment of Like Things   Names should be as simple as possible and as consistent as possible. Two identical substituents should be treated alike, even though a few other rules may be broken. Although $C_6H_5CH_3$ would be methylbenzene or toluene (rather than phenylmethane), $(C_6H_5)_2CH_2$ is called diphenylmethane.

Prefixes to Designate Like Things   In simple compounds, the prefixes *di-*, *tri-*, *tetra-*, *penta-*, *hexa-*, etc. (not italicized) are used to indicate the number of times a substituent is found in the structure: e.g., dimethylamine for $(CH_3)_2NH$ or dichloromethane for CH_2Cl_2.

In complex structures, the prefixes *bis-*, *tris-*, and *tetrakis-* (not italicized) are used: *bis-* means two of a kind; *tris-*, three of a kind; and *tetrakis-*, four of a kind.

   $[(CH_3)_2N]_2$ is bis(dimethylamino)- and not di(dimethylamino)-

The prefix *bi-* is used for (1) "double" molecules, and (2) bridged hydrocarbons.

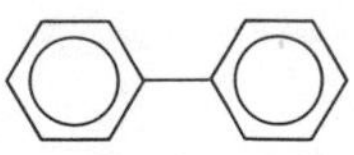

Nomenclature of Organic Compounds

biphenyl
a double molecule

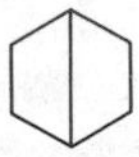

bicyclo[2.2.0]hexane
a bridged hydrocarbon

Order of Prefixes   Prefixes are listed in *alphabetical order* (ethylmethyl-). In alphabetizing, a prefix denoting the number of times a substituent is found (di-, tri-, etc.) is disregarded. Ethyldimethyl- is the correct alphabetical order, even though *d* comes before *e*.

When to Drop a Vowel   In the case of *conjunctive names* (names that are formed by combining two names), vowels are not elided, but are maintained. For example, the *e* in indoleacetic acid is retained (not indolacetic acid).

If there are two successive suffixes, the vowel at the end of the first suffix is dropped (propenoic acid, not propeneoic acid), unless it is followed by a consonant (propanediol, not propandiol).

Nomenclature Priority of Functional Groups   The various functional groups are ranked in priority as to which receives the suffix name and the lowest position number. A list of these priorities is given in Table A8. These are *not* the same priorities that are used for (*E*) and (*Z*) or (*R*) and (*S*).

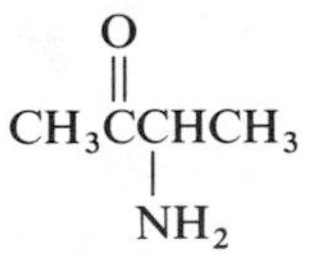

$$CH_3CCHCH_3$$

is 3-amino-2-butanone (not 2-amino-3-butanone)

(structure: CH₃—C(=O)—CH(NH₂)—CH₃)

Table A8.   *Nomenclature Priority*[a]

Structure	Name
—N(CH₃)₃⁺ (as one example)	onium ion
—CO₂H	carboxylic acid
—SO₃H	sulfonic acid
—COX	acid halide
—CONR₂	amide
—CN	nitrile
—CHO	aldehyde
—CO—	ketone
ROH	alcohol
ArOH	phenol
—SH	thiol
—NR₂	amine
—O—O—	peroxide
—MgX (as one example)	organometallic
C=C	alkene
—C≡C—	alkyne
R—, X—, etc.	other substituents

[a] Highest priority is at the top.

The principal functional group is indicated at the end of the name. A name with only one functional ending is preferred. *Example:* $HOCH_2CH_2CO_2H$ is 3-hydroxypropanoic acid. In names that must have two endings, the terminal ending refers to the principal functional group (see Table A8). *Example:* $CH_3CH{=}CHCO_2H$ is 2-butenoic acid.

Numbering of the Parent The parent is numbered so that the principal function receives the lowest number (see preceding section). Greek letters are reserved for trivial names and may not correspond directly to the IUPAC numbers. *Alpha* (α, the first letter of the Greek alphabet) means *on the nearest carbon*, which is often number 2 in the systematic name.

Br
|
CH_3CHCO_2H

2-bromopropanoic acid (IUPAC)
α-bromopropionic acid (trivial)

Numbering of Substituents and Use of Parentheses If two numbering systems are required for complete identification of all atoms in the molecule, primes (') are often used for one of the systems to prevent confusion.

Alkyl substituents are numbered separately from the parent chain, beginning at the point of attachment. In these cases, a prime is not necessary provided that parentheses are used to enclose complex prefixes.

p-(2-bromoethyl)aniline

2-(2-chloropropyl)-1,3,5-hexatriene

Configuration Around a Chiral Carbon A chiral carbon atom with four different groups attached can have either an (*R*) or an (*S*) configuration. For purposes of designating the chiral center as either (*R*) or (*S*), the structure is placed so that the lowest-priority group is in the rear. (See Section 4.1B for determination of priority, which is *not the same* as nomenclature priority.) The direction from the highest-priority group to the second-highest-priority group is then determined. If the direction is *clockwise*, the chiral center is (*R*); if it is *counterclockwise*, then the center is (*S*). If the structure has only one chiral center, (*R*) or (*S*) is used as the first prefix in the name. If the molecule has more than one chiral center, the designation of each chiral center and its position number is enclosed in parentheses in the prefix—e.g., (2*R*,3*R*)-dibromopentane.

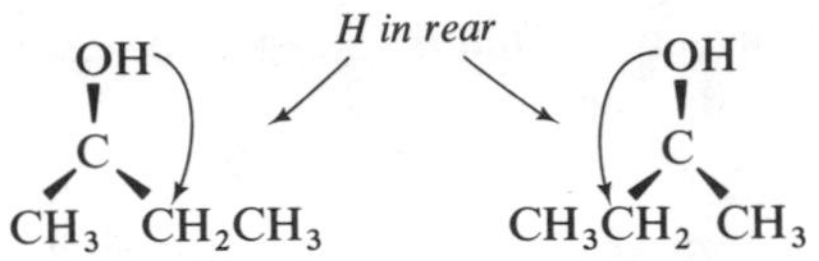

(*R*)-2-butanol   (*S*)-2-butanol

Carboxylic Acids

There are four principal types of names for carboxylic acids: (1) IUPAC; (2) trivial; (3) carboxylic acid; and (4) conjunctive.

IUPAC Names   Except for acids of one to five carbons and some fatty acids, aliphatic monocarboxylic acids are named by the IUPAC system. The longest chain containing the —CO_2H group is chosen as the parent, and the chain is numbered starting with the carbon of the —CO_2H group as position 1. The name is taken from the name of the alkane with the same number of carbons, with the final -*e* replaced by -*oic acid*.

$$CH_3CH_2CH_2CH_2CH_2CO_2H$$

hexanoic acid

Substituents are designated by prefixes. A double bond is designated as a suffix preceding -oic acid.

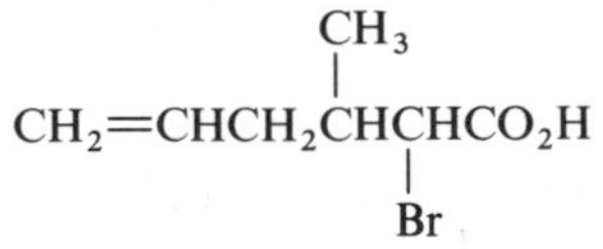

$$CH_2{=}CHCH_2\overset{\overset{\displaystyle CH_3}{|}}{CH}\underset{\underset{\displaystyle Br}{|}}{CH}CO_2H$$

2-bromo-3-methyl-5-hexenoic acid

Trivial Names   Table A9 gives a list of commonly encountered trivial names for carboxylic acids.

Carboxylic Acid Names   A carboxylic acid name is used when a —CO_2H group is attached to a ring. The name is a combination of the name of the ring system with the suffix -*carboxylic acid*. The carboxyl group is considered attached to position 1 of the ring unless the ring system has its own unique numbering system. (The carbon of the —CO_2H group is not numbered, as it is in an IUPAC name.)

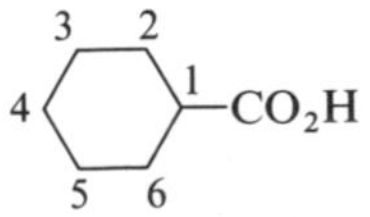

cyclohexanecarboxylic acid 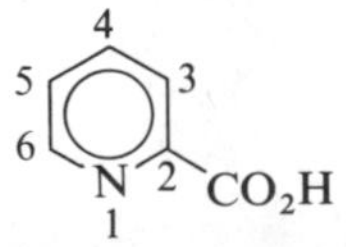   2-pyridinecarboxylic acid

Table A9. *Names of Some Monocarboxylic Acids*

Structure	Name of acid	Structure	Name of acid
Saturated chain:		**Other functionality[b]:**	
HCO_2H	formic	$CH_3COCH_2CO_2H$	acetoacetic
CH_3CO_2H	acetic	$CH_3CH(OH)CO_2H$	lactic
$CH_3CH_2CO_2H$	propionic	CH_3COCO_2H	pyruvic
$CH_3(CH_2)_2CO_2H$	butyric	$CH_3COCH_2CH_2CO_2H$	levulinic
$CH_3(CH_2)_3CO_2H$	valeric		
$CH_3(CH_2)_{10}CO_2H$	lauric	**On rings:**	
$CH_3(CH_2)_{12}CO_2H$	myristic	$C_6H_5CO_2H$	benzoic
$CH_3(CH_2)_{14}CO_2H$	palmitic		
$CH_3(CH_2)_{16}CO_2H$	stearic		

On rings:

$C_6H_5CO_2H$ — benzoic

OH
⌬—CO_2H salicylic

⌬⌬ (naphthalene, positions 1–8) CO_2H 2-naphthoic

(pyridine ring, positions 1–6, N at 1) CO_2H nicotinic

Unsaturated chain[a]:

$CH_2{=}CHCO_2H$	acrylic
$CH_2{=}C(CH_3)CO_2H$	methacrylic
trans-$CH_3CH{=}CHCO_2H$	crotonic

[a] For unsaturated fatty acids, see Table 19.1, page 870.
[b] For α-amino acids, see Table 18.1, page 834.

Conjunctive Names Conjunctive names are combinations of two names: in the following examples, the name of the ring plus the name of the acid.

⬡—CH_2CO_2H (indole ring, positions 2–7, N-H)CH_2CO_2H

cyclohexaneacetic acid   indole-2-acetic acid

Diacids Diacids may be named systematically as *-dioic acids*: for example, $HO_2CCH_2CO_2H$ is propanedioic acid. Trivial names are commonly used. Some of these are listed in Table A10.

Polycarboxylic Acids Polycarboxylic acids of the aliphatic series containing more than two carboxyl groups are named by the carboxylic-acid nomenclature. The longest chain to which the greatest number of carboxyl groups are attached is chosen as the parent. If there is unsaturation, then the double or triple bonds are included in the chain if possible.

③ ② ①
$HO_2CCH_2CHCH_2CO_2H$ is 1,2,3-propanetricarboxylic acid
$|$
CO_2H

Nomenclature of Organic Compounds

Table A10.   *Names of Some Diacids*

Structure	Name of acid
Aliphatic:	
HO_2CCO_2H	oxalic
$HO_2CCH_2CO_2H$	malonic
$HO_2C(CH_2)_2CO_2H$	succinic
$HO_2C(CH_2)_3CO_2H$	glutaric
$HO_2C(CH_2)_4CO_2H$	adipic
$HO_2C(CH_2)_5CO_2H$	pimelic
$HO_2C(CH_2)_6CO_2H$	suberic
$HO_2C(CH_2)_7CO_2H$	azelaic
$HO_2C(CH_2)_8CO_2H$	sebacic
cis-$HO_2CCH{=}CHCO_2H$	maleic
trans-$HO_2CCH{=}CHCO_2H$	fumaric
$HO_2CCH(OH)CH(OH)CO_2H$	tartaric

Aromatic:

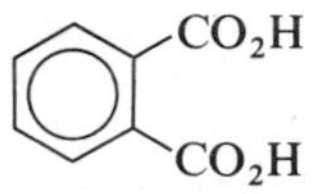

phthalic

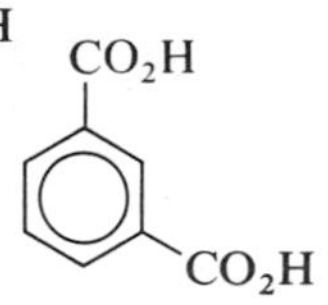

isophthalic

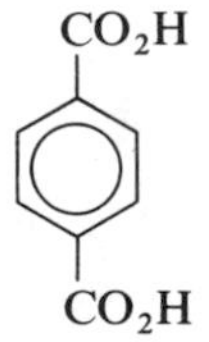

terephthalic

Sulfonic Acids   Sulfonic acids are named by adding the ending *-sulfonic acid* to the name of the rest of the structure.

$$CH_3CH_2SO_3H \qquad C_6H_5SO_3H$$

ethanesulfonic acid   benzenesulfonic acid

Acid Anhydrides

Acid anhydrides are named from the names of the component acid or acids with the word *acid* dropped and the word *anhydride* added. (Either IUPAC or trivial acid names may be used.)

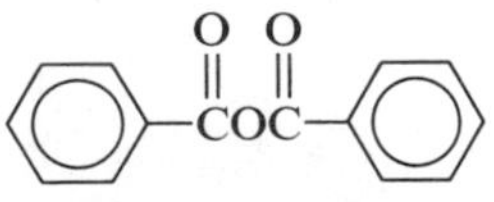

benzoic anhydride   acetic propionic anhydride

Cyclic anhydrides are named from the parent diacid.

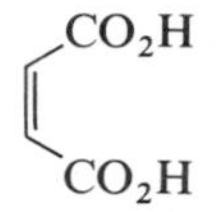

maleic acid 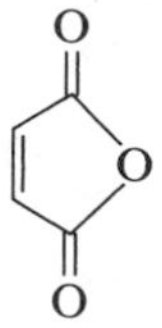   maleic anhydride

Acid Halides

Acid halides are named by changing the ending of the carboxylic acid name from *-ic acid* to *-yl* plus the name of the halide.

acetyl chloride   benzoyl bromide

An ending of *-yl halide* on the name of a *diacid* implies that both carboxyl groups are acid-halide groups.

$ClCCH_2CH_2CCl$ is succinyl chloride

Alcohols

The names of alcohols may be (1) IUPAC; (2) trivial; or, occasionally, (3) conjunctive. *IUPAC names* are taken from the name of the alkane with the final *-e* changed to *-ol*. In the case of polyols, the prefix *di-*, *tri-*, etc. is placed just before *-ol*, with the position numbers placed at the start of the name, if possible.

$CH_3CH_2CH_2CH_2CH_2OH$ HO—⟨ ⟩—OH

1-pentanol   1,4-cyclohexanediol

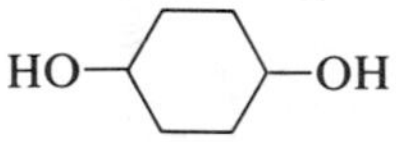

In cases where confusion is possible, the number precedes *-ol*. *Example*: $CH_3CH=CHCH_2OH$ is 2-buten-1-ol.

If higher-priority functionality is present, or in complex molecules, the prefix *hydroxy-* should be used. *Example*: $CH_3CH(OH)CH_2CO_2H$ is 3-hydroxybutanoic acid.

Trivial names are generally composed of the name of the alkyl group plus the word *alcohol*.

$(CH_3)_3COH$ $C_6H_5CH_2OH$

tert-butyl alcohol   benzyl alcohol

Conjunctive names are used principally with structures in which ring systems are attached to an aliphatic alcohol.

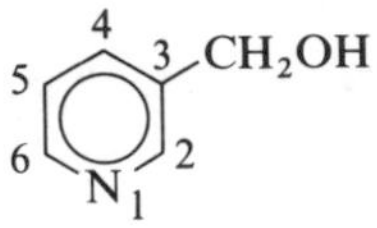

pyridine-3-methanol

Polyols   Structures with two OH groups on adjacent carbons (1,2-diols) are sometimes given trivial *glycol* names: the name of the *alkene* (not the alkane) from which the diol could be formed, plus the word *glycol. Glycerol* and *glycerin* are trivial names for 1,2,3-propanetriol.

$$\underset{\substack{| \\ CH_3CHCH_2OH}}{OH}$$

1,2-propanediol (IUPAC)
propylene glycol (trivial)

$$\underset{\substack{| \\ HOCH_2CHCH_2OH}}{OH}$$

1,2,3-propanetriol (IUPAC)
glycerol (trivial)

Phenols

Phenols are those compounds in which an OH is attached directly to an arene ring. In these cases, phenol (or naphthol, etc.) is considered the parent.

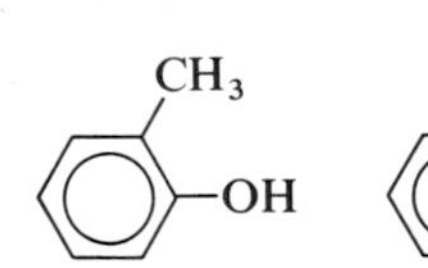

p-nitrophenol

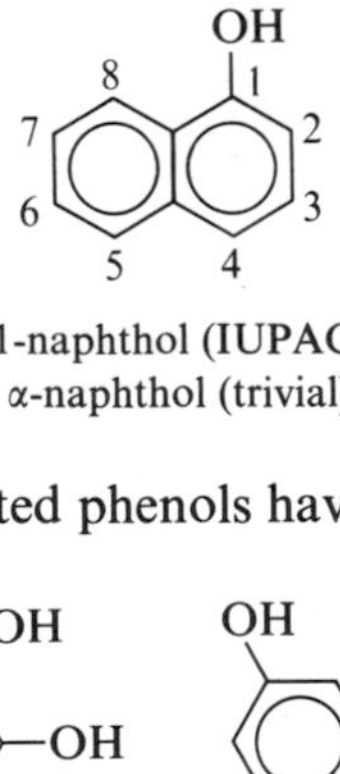

1-naphthol (IUPAC)
α-naphthol (trivial)

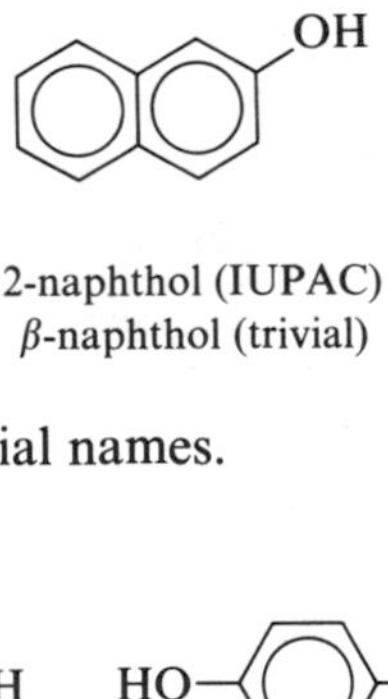

2-naphthol (IUPAC)
β-naphthol (trivial)

Many phenols and substituted phenols have trivial names.

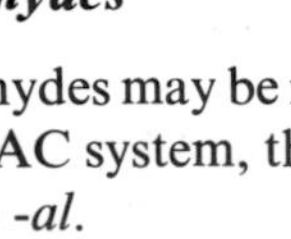

o-cresol

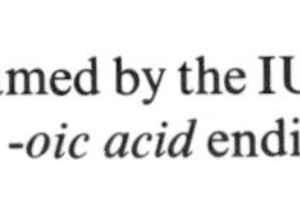

pyrocatechol

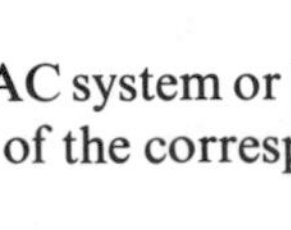

resorcinol

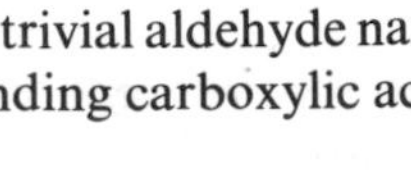

p-hydroquinone

Aldehydes

Aldehydes may be named by the IUPAC system or by trivial aldehyde names. In the IUPAC system, the *-oic acid* ending of the corresponding carboxylic acid is changed to *-al*.

$$CH_3CH_2CH_2CH_2CH_2CHO$$

hexanal

In trivial names, the *-ic* (or *-oic*) *acid* ending is changed to *-aldehyde*.

$$CH_3CHO \qquad C_6H_5CHO \qquad \langle\!\!\!\rangle\!\!-\!CHO$$

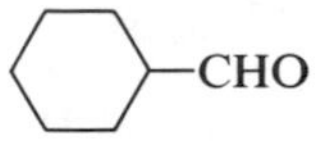

acetaldehyde   benzaldehyde   cyclohexanecarboxaldehyde

Some aldehydes have specific trivial names:

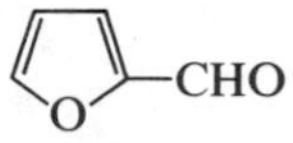

$$\text{(furan ring)}\!\!-\!CHO \qquad HOCH_2CH(OH)CHO$$

2-furaldehyde   glyceraldehyde
or furfural

Amides

In both the IUPAC and trivial systems, an amide is named by dropping the *-ic* (or *-oic*) *acid* ending of the corresponding acid name and adding *-amide*.

$$\overset{\displaystyle O}{\overset{\|}{CH_3(CH_2)_4CNH_2}} \qquad \overset{\displaystyle O}{\overset{\|}{CH_3CNH_2}}$$

hexanamide (IUPAC)   acetamide (trivial)

Substituents on the amide nitrogen are named as prefixes preceded by *N-* or *N,N-*. $C_6H_5CONHCH_3$ is *N*-methylbenzamide, and $C_6H_5CON(CH_3)_2$ is *N,N*-dimethylbenzamide. *N*-Phenylamides have trivial names of *anilides*.

$$\overset{\displaystyle O}{\overset{\|}{CH_3CNHC_6H_5}} \qquad \overset{\displaystyle O}{\overset{\|}{C_6H_5CNHC_6H_5}}$$

acetanilide   benzanilide

Sulfonamides are named by attaching the ending *-sulfonamide* to the name for the rest of the structure. *Example:* $C_6H_5SO_2NH_2$ is benzenesulfonamide.

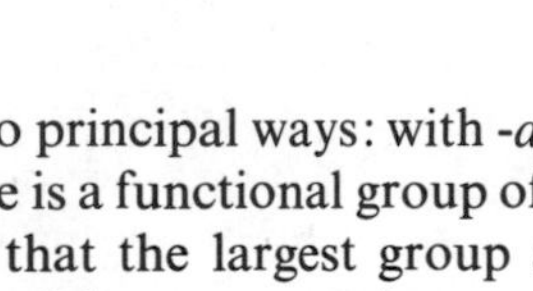

$$H_2N-\overset{3\quad 2}{\underset{5\quad 6}{4\langle\!\!\!\bigcirc\!\!\!\rangle 1}}-SO_2NH_2$$

p-aminobenzenesulfonamide
(sulfanilamide)

Amines

Amines are named in two principal ways: with *-amine* as the ending and with *amino-* as a prefix. Unless there is a functional group of higher priority present, the *-amine* ending is used. Note that the largest group attached to the nitrogen is considered the parent or part of the parent amine.

Ending names: $(CH_3)_2NH$ $CH_3NHCH_2CH_3$

                    dimethylamine   *N*-methylethylamine

                                        larger group

Nomenclature of Organic Compounds

Prefix names:

$$\underset{\text{2-amino-1-propanol}}{\overset{\displaystyle \overset{NH_2}{|}}{CH_3CHCH_2OH}} \qquad \underset{\text{2-(methylamino)-1-propanol}}{\overset{\displaystyle \overset{NHCH_3}{|}}{CH_3CHCH_2OH}}$$

Polyamines may be named as *di-* or *triamines*, etc.

$$\underset{\text{1,2-ethanediamine}}{H_2NCH_2CH_2NH_2}$$

Some arylamines have their own names.

$$\underset{\text{aniline}}{C_6H_5NH_2} \qquad \underset{p\text{-toluidine}}{CH_3-\!\!\!\bigcirc\!\!\!-NH_2}$$

The prefix *aza-* is sometimes used to identify a nitrogen in a chain or ring; see page 943.

Amine Salts   Amine salts are named as *ammonium salts* or (in simple cases) as amine hydrochlorides, acetates, etc.

$$\underset{\substack{\text{trimethylammonium chloride}\\ \text{(trimethylamine hydrochloride)}}}{(CH_3)_3NH^+\ Cl^-} \qquad \underset{\substack{\text{trimethylammonium acetate}\\ \text{(trimethylamine acetate)}}}{(CH_3)_3NH^+\ {}^-O_2CCH_3}$$

Cyclic salts often are named as *-inium salts.*

$$\underset{\substack{\text{anilinium bromide}\\ \text{(aniline hydrobromide)}}}{C_6H_5NH_3{}^+\ Br^-} \qquad \underset{\text{pyridinium acetate}}{\bigcirc\!\!\!\overset{+}{N}H\ {}^-O_2CCH_3}$$

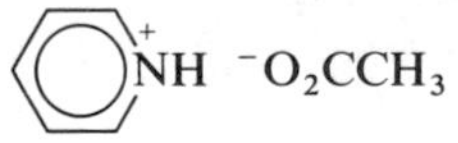

Esters and Salts of Carboxylic Acids

Esters and salts of carboxylic acids are named as two words in both systematic and trivial names. The first word of the name is the name of the substituent on the oxygen. The second word of the name is derived from the name of the parent carboxylic acid with the ending changed from *-ic acid* to *-ate*.

$CH_3(CH_2)_4CO_2CH_3$ methyl hexanoate (IUPAC)

$CH_3CO_2CH_2CH_3$ ethyl acetate (trivial)

$CH_3CH_2CO_2Na$ sodium propanoate (or sodium propionate)

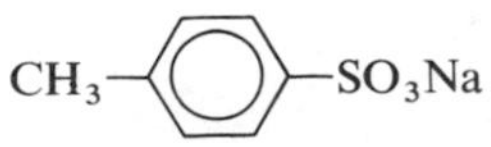

$CH_3-\!\!\!\bigcirc\!\!\!-SO_3Na$ sodium *p*-toluenesulfonate (or sodium tosylate)

Ethers

Ethers are usually named by using the names of attached alkyl or aryl groups followed by the word *ether*. (These are trivial names.)

$$CH_3CH_2OCH_2CH_3$$
diethyl ether

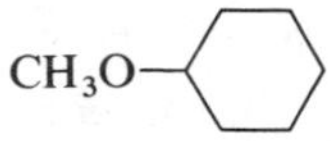

$$CH_3O-⟨\text{cyclohexyl}⟩$$
cyclohexyl methyl ether

In more complex ethers, an *alkoxy-* prefix may be used. (This is the IUPAC preference.)

$$\overset{OCH_3}{\underset{|}{CH_3CH_2CH_2CHCH_2CO_2H}}$$
3-methoxyhexanoic acid

Sometimes the prefix *oxa-* is used; see page 943.

Ketones

In the *systematic* names for ketones, the *-e* of the parent alkane name is dropped and *-one* is added. A prefix number is used if necessary.

$$\overset{O}{\overset{||}{CH_3CCH_2CH_2CH_3}}$$
2-pentanone

$$\overset{O}{\overset{||}{CH_3CCH=CHCH_3}}$$
3-penten-2-one

$$\overset{O\quad\ O}{\overset{||\quad||}{CH_3CCH_2CCH_3}}$$
2,4-pentanedione

In a complex structure, a ketone group may be named in the IUPAC system with the prefix *oxo-*. (The prefix *keto-* is also sometimes encountered.) Contrast the use of oxo- with that of oxa- (an ether).

$$\overset{O}{\overset{||}{CH_3CCH_2CO_2H}}\quad\text{is 3-oxobutanoic acid}$$

In *trivial* names, the alkyl groups attached to the C=O group are named, and the word *ketone* is added. Methyl ethyl ketone ($CH_3COCH_2CH_3$) is a common example. The CH_3CO- group is sometimes called the *aceto-*, or *acetyl*, group, while the C_6H_5CO- group is the *benzo-*, or *benzoyl*, group. Also encountered are *-phenone*, *-naphthone*, or *-acetone* endings, where one of these groups is an attachment to the ketone carbonyl group.

$$\overset{O\quad\ O}{\overset{||\quad||}{CH_3CCH_2CCH_3}}$$
acetoacetone

$$\overset{O}{\overset{||}{CH_3CC_6H_5}}$$
acetophenone

$$\overset{O}{\overset{||}{C_6H_5CC_6H_5}}$$
benzophenone

Some ketones also have specific trivial names: CH_3COCH_3 is called acetone.

Organometallics and Metal Alkoxides

Organometallic compounds, those with C bonded to a metal, are named by the name of the alkyl or aryl groups plus the name of the metal.

$$(CH_3CH_2)_3Al \qquad\qquad C_6H_5MgBr$$

triethylaluminum   phenylmagnesium bromide

Organosilicon or boron compounds are often named as derivatives of the metal hydrides. SiH_4 is silane; $(CH_3)_4Si$ is tetramethylsilane. BH_3 is borane; $(CH_3CH_2)_3B$ is triethylborane.

Sodium or potassium alkoxides are named as salts: the name of the cation plus the name of the alcohol with the *-anol* ending changed to *-oxide*. Salts of phenols are called *phenoxides*. (An alternate ending is *-olate*.)

$$CH_3CH_2ONa \qquad\qquad C_6H_5OK$$

sodium ethoxide   potassium phenoxide
(sodium ethanolate)   (potassium phenolate)

Glossary of Some Prefix Symbols Used in Organic Chemistry

(+)	dextrorotatory
(−)	levorotatory
(±)	racemic
α-	alpha: (1) on the adjacent carbon; (2) refers to configuration of carbon 1 in sugars; (3) refers to configuration of substituents on steroid ring systems
aldo-	aldehyde
allo-	closely related
andro-	relating to male
anhydro-	denoting abstraction of water
antho-	relating to flowers
anthra-	relating to coal or to anthracene
anti-	on opposite faces or sides
β-	beta: (1) opposite to that of α in configuration; (2) second carbon removed from a functional group or a heteroatom
bi-	twice or double
bisnor-	indicating removal of two carbons
chromo-	color or colored
cis-	on the same side of a double bond or ring
cyclo-	cylic
Δ-	double bond
D-	on the right in the Fischer projection (see Section 17.3B)
d-	dextrorotatory
de-	removal of something, such as hydrogen (*dehydro-*) or oxygen (*deoxy-*)
dextro-	to the right, as in dextrorotatory
dl-	racemic
(E)-	on the opposite sides of a double bond
endo-	(1) on the ring and not on a side chain; (2) opposite the bridge side of a ring system:

bridge

exo

endo

	(3) attached as a bridge within a ring, as 1,4-*endo*-methyleneanthracene
epi-	(1) the 1,6-positions of naphthalene; (2) epimeric; (3) a bridge connection on a ring, as 9,10-epidioxyanthracene
erythro-	related in configuration to erythrose
exo-	(1) on a side chain attached to a ring; (2) on the bridge side of a ring system (see *endo*-)
gem-	attached to the same atom
hemi-	one half
hydro-	(1) denotes presence of H; (2) sometimes relating to water
hypo-	indicating a low, lower, or lowest state of oxidation
i-, iso-	(1) methyl branch at the end of the chain; (2) isomeric; (3) occasionally *i*- is used for *inactive*
L-	on the left in the Fischer projection
l-	levorotatory
leuco-	colorless or white
levo-	to the left, as in levorotatory
m-	*meta*-
meso-	(1) with a plane of symmetry and optically inactive; (2) middle position of certain cyclic organic compounds
meta-	(1) 1,3 on benzene; (2) closely related compound, as metaldehyde
n-	*normal*: continuous chain
neo-	one C connected to four other C's
nor-	(1) removal of one or more C's (with H's); (2) structure isomeric to that of root name, as norleucine.
o-	*ortho*-
oligo-	few (units of)
ortho-	1,2 on benzene
p-, *para*-	(1) 1,4 on benzene; (2) polymeric, as paraformaldehyde
per-	saturated with, as in *perhydro*-, or *peroxy*-
peri-	(1) 1,8 on naphthalene; (2) fusion of ring to two or more adjoining rings, as perixanthenoxanthene.
pheno-	relating to phenyl or benzene
poly-	many (units of)
Ψ-, pseudo-	has a resemblance to
pyro-	indicating formation by heat
(*R*)-	clockwise configuration around a chiral carbon
(*R*)(*S*)-	racemic
s-	abbreviation for *secondary*- or *symmetrical*-
(*S*)-	counterclockwise configuration around a chiral carbon
seco-	denoting ring cleavage
sec-	abbreviation for *secondary*-
sym-	symmetrical
syn	on the same face or side
t-, *tert*-	*tertiary*-
threo-	related in configuration to threose
trans-	on opposite sides of a double bond or ring
uns-, *unsym*-	unsymmetrical
v-, *vic*-	vicinal: on adjacent C's
(*Z*)-	on the same side of a double bond

Answers to Problems

The answers to the problems within the textual material are given here. For the answers to the chapter-end problems, see the *Study Guide* that accompanies this text.

Chapter 1

1.1 (a) 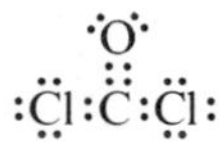 :C̈l:C̈:C̈l: (b)

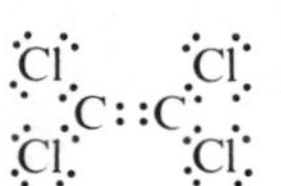

1.2 (a) none; (b) $CH_2 = \overset{+1}{N} = \overset{-1}{N}$; (c)

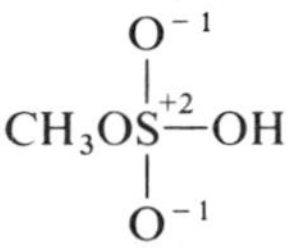

1.3 (a) $(CH_3)_2CHCH_2Cl$; (b) CH_3CHCl_2; (c) $CH_3(CH_2)_3CHClCH_2Cl$;
(d) $(CH_3)_2C=C(CH_3)_2$

1.4 (a) 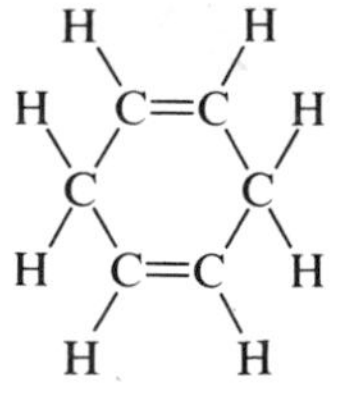 (b) 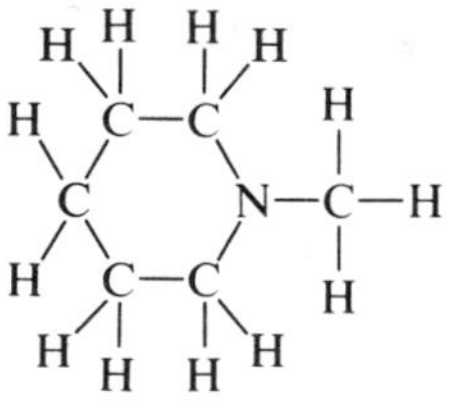 (c)

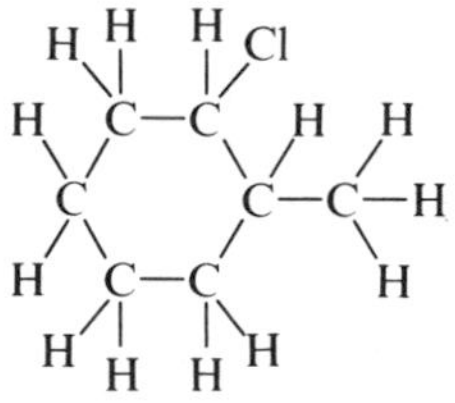

1.5 (a) 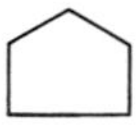 (b) 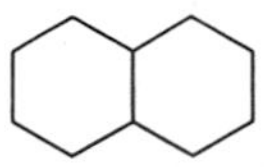 (c) 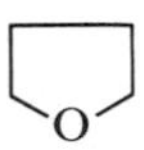 (d) 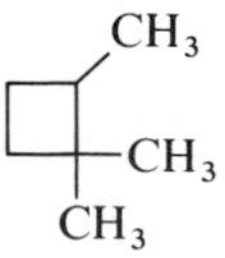 (e)

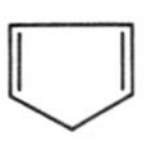

1.6 (a)

1.7 (a) $\overset{\delta+}{C}H_3 - \overset{\delta-}{Br}$, $CH_3 - Br$; (b)

1.8 (a) CH_3OH; (b) CH_3O-H; (c) CH_3Cl

1.9 (a) $CH_3C\equiv N$; (b) $(CH_3)_2C=O$; (c) none; (d)

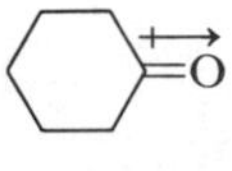

1.10 (a) $CH_3CH_2CH_2NH_2---NH_2CH_2CH_2CH_3$

(b) $CH_3OH---\overset{\overset{\textstyle H}{|}}{O}CH_3$, $CH_3OH---OH_2$, $CH_3O---\overset{\overset{\textstyle H}{|}}{H_2O}$,

$$H_2O---H_2O$$

(c) none   (d) $(CH_3)_2O---H_2O$, H_2O---H_2O

1.11 (a) base;   (b) acid;   (c) base;   (d) acid;   (e) base

1.12 (a) $CH_3CH_2CO_2^- + H_3O^+$ (b) 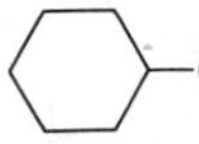 ⟨⟩$-CO_2^- + H_3O^+$

(c) $(CH_3)_2NH_2^+ + OH^-$ (d) 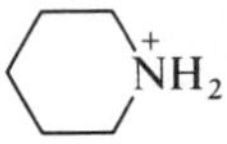 ⟨⟩$\overset{+}{N}H_2 + OH^-$

1.13 (a) < (b) < (c)   *1.14* (c) < (b) < (a)

Chapter 2

2.1 (a)

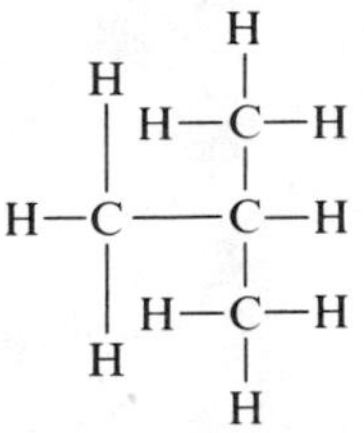

(b)

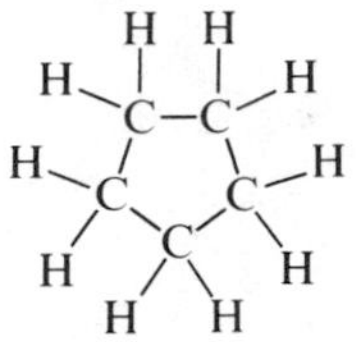

All C—C bonds are sp^3–sp^3 and all C—H bonds are sp^3–s.

2.2 (a)

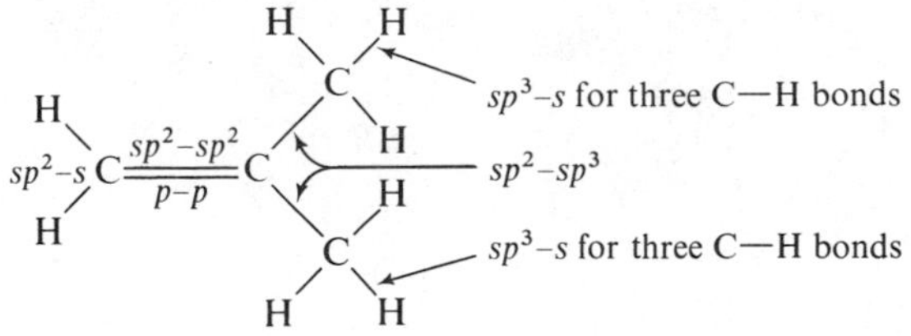

sp^3–s for three C—H bonds

sp^2–sp^3

sp^3–s for three C—H bonds

(b)

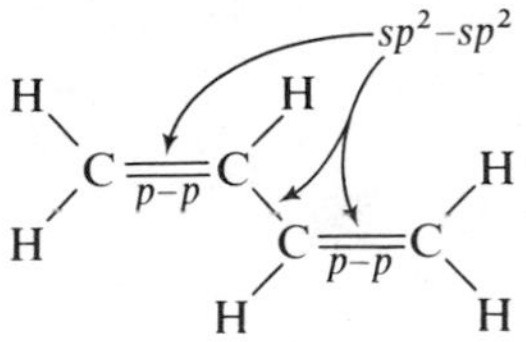

All C—H bonds are sp^2–s.

(c)

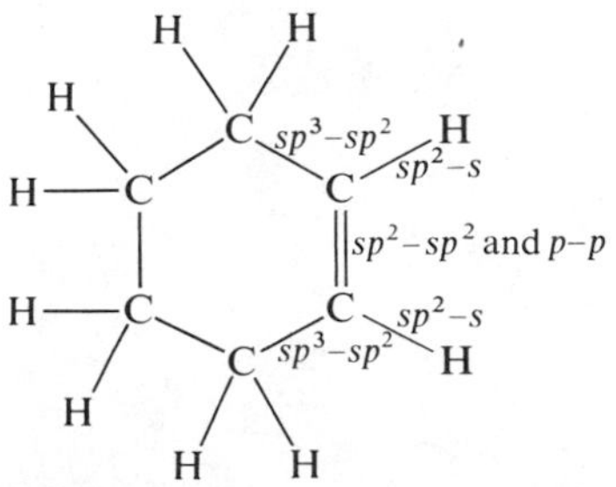

All other C—C bonds are sp^3–sp^3 and all other C—H bonds are sp^3–s.

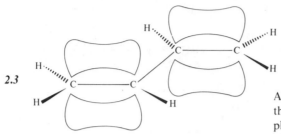

2.3

All C and H atoms are in one plane; the pi bonds are above and below this plane.

2.4

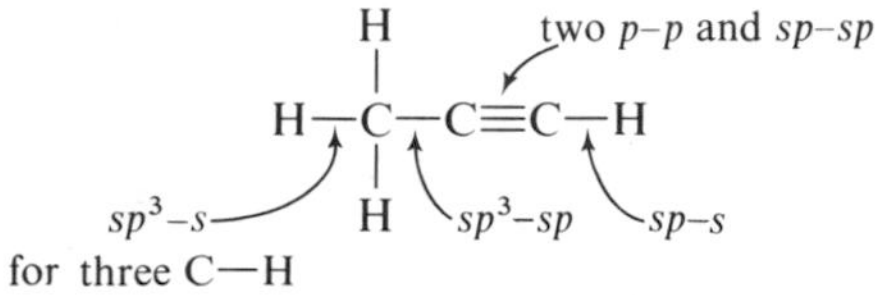

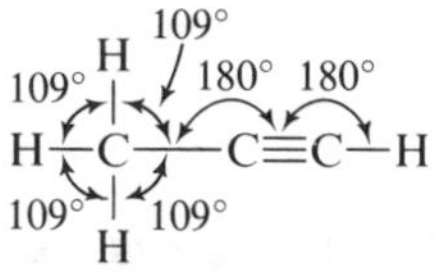

H—C—C≡C—H

sp^3-s for three C—H

two p–p and sp–sp

sp^3-sp $sp-s$

109° 180° 180° 109° 109° 109°

H—C—C≡C—H

2.5 (a) (2), (1); (b) (2), (1); (c) (1), (2), (3)

2.6 (a) CH₂=C HCH₂ CH ; (b) ⬡—NH₂ ; (c)

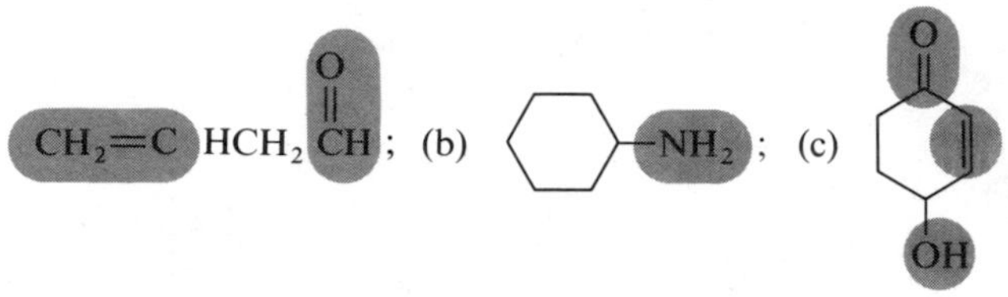

2.7 R—CO₂H

2.8 (a) 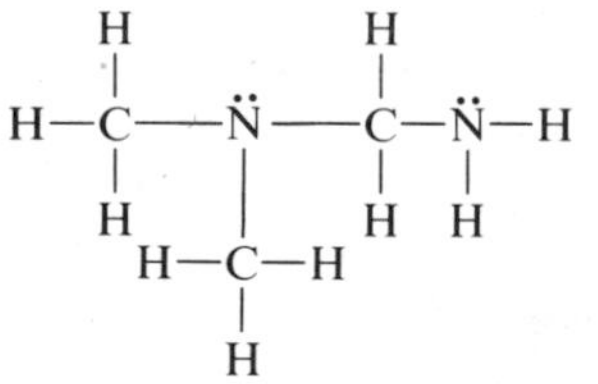 H—C—N—C—N—H

All C—H and N—H bonds are sp^3-s, and all C—N bonds are sp^3-sp^3

(b) 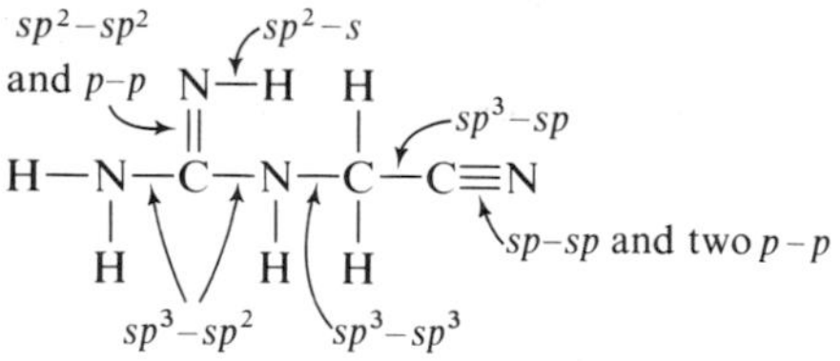 H—N—C—N—C—C≡N

sp^2-sp^2 and p–p
sp^2-s
sp^3-sp
$sp-sp$ and two p–p
sp^3-sp^2
sp^3-sp^3

All unmarked C—H and N—H bonds are sp^3-s.

2.9

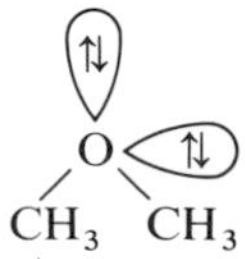

O
CH₃   CH₃

2.10 (a) 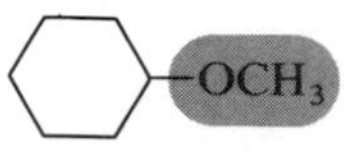 ⬡—OCH₃   or   ⬡—O—CH₃

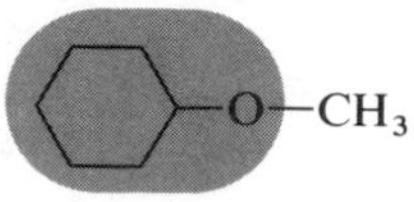

(b)    or

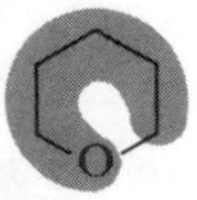

2.11 The following structures are not the only possible answers:

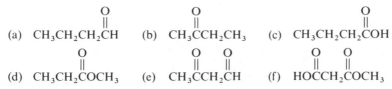

(a) $CH_3CH_2CH_2\overset{\overset{\displaystyle O}{\|}}{C}H$ (b) $CH_3\overset{\overset{\displaystyle O}{\|}}{C}CH_2CH_3$ (c) $CH_3CH_2CH_2\overset{\overset{\displaystyle O}{\|}}{C}OH$

(d) $CH_3CH_2\overset{\overset{\displaystyle O}{\|}}{C}OCH_3$ (e) $CH_3\overset{\overset{\displaystyle O}{\|}}{C}CH_2\overset{\overset{\displaystyle O}{\|}}{C}H$ (f) $HO\overset{\overset{\displaystyle O}{\|}}{C}CH_2\overset{\overset{\displaystyle O}{\|}}{C}CH_3$

2.12 (a), (d), and (f) are esters. (b), (c), and (e) are ethers.

2.13 five

2.14 (a) $CH_3CH=CHCH=CHCH=CHCH_3$
  (b) $CH_2=CHCH_2CH=CHCH=CHCH_3$
  (c) $CH_2=CHCH_2CH=CHCH_2CH=CH_2$

2.15 (a) 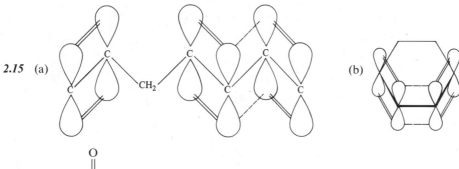 (b)

2.16 $CH_2=CH\overset{\overset{\displaystyle O}{\|}}{C}CH_3$

2.17

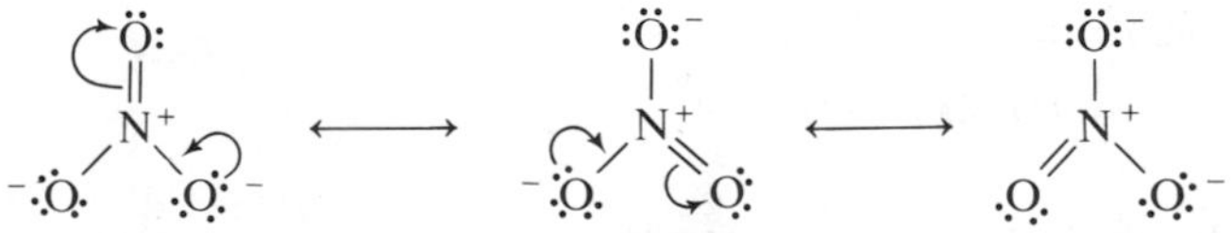

2.18 The right-hand structure is the major contributor because each atom has an octet.

Chapter 3

3.1 (a) $CH_3CH_2\overset{\overset{\displaystyle O}{\|}}{C}CH_2CH_3$; (b) ⬡—$CH_2OH$

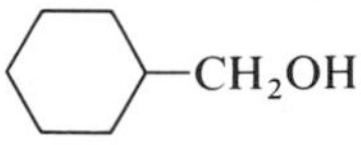

3.2 (a) $CH_3\overset{\overset{\displaystyle O}{\|}}{C}OH$; (b) ⬡—$CH_2OH$; (c) $CH_3CH_2CH_2CH_2\overset{\overset{\displaystyle O}{\|}}{C}H$

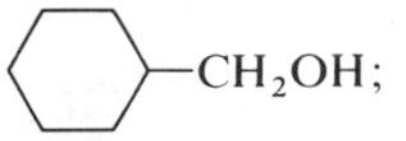

3.3 (a) C_nH_{2n+2} is an open-chain alkane.
  (b) C_nH_{2n} contains either one double bond or one ring.
  (c) C_nH_{2n-2} contains either one triple bond, one double bond plus one ring, two double bonds, or two rings.

3.4 (a) $CH_3CH_2CH_2$—⬡; (b) $(CH_3)_2CHCH_2$—⬡;

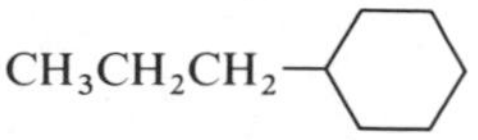

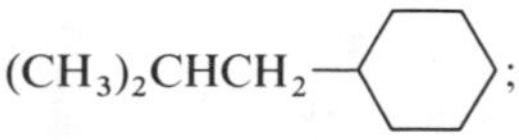

  (c) $CH_3CH_2CH_2\overset{\overset{\displaystyle C(CH_3)_3}{|}}{C}HCH_2CH_2CH_2CH_3$

3.5   (a) Cl_2CHCH_2Cl;   (b) 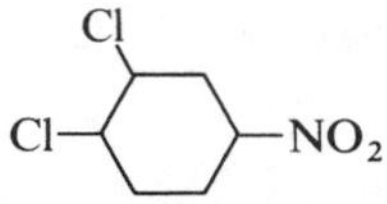   Cl—(ring with Cl top)—NO_2

3.6   (a)   propene;   (b)   cyclohexene;   (c)   1,3-cyclohexadiene

3.7   (a)    (bicyclic structure)   (b) $CH{\equiv}CC{\equiv}CCH_3$

3.8   (a)   2-pentanol;   (b) 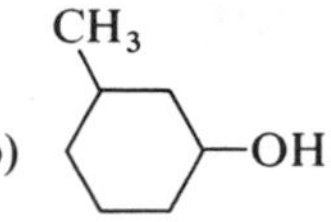   (methylcyclohexanol structure with CH_3 and —OH)

3.9 $CH_3CH_2CH_2\overset{\displaystyle O}{\overset{\|}{C}}H$; $CH_3\overset{\displaystyle O}{\overset{\|}{C}}CH_2CH_3$; $CH_3CH_2CH_2\overset{\displaystyle O}{\overset{\|}{C}}OH$

3.10 $CH_3(CH_2)_4\overset{\displaystyle O}{\overset{\|}{C}}O$—(cyclohexyl)

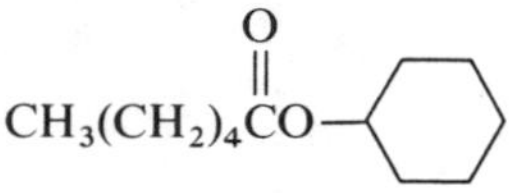

3.11   (a)   5-methyl-2-hexene;   (b)   6-nitro-3-hexanone

Chapter 4

4.1   (E)-2-chloro-1-fluoro-1-butene

4.2   (a)   (E);   (b)   (Z);   (c)   (E);   (d)   (Z)

4.3

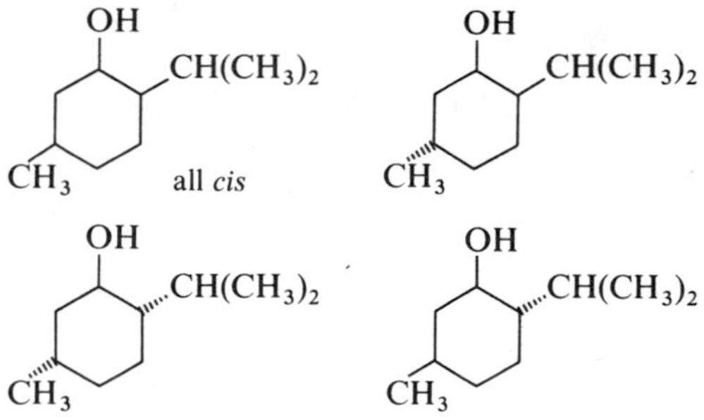

(four cyclohexane ring structures with OH, CH(CH$_3$)$_2$, and CH$_3$ substituents; first labeled "all cis")

4.4   (a) 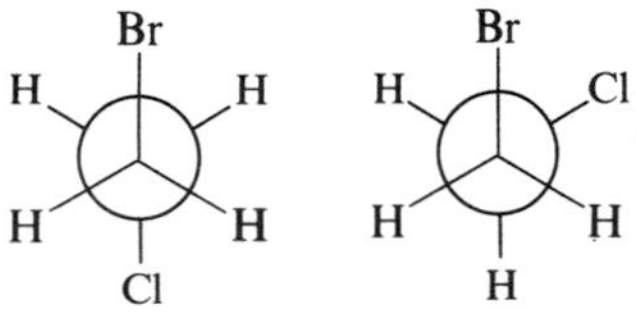   (Newman projections: Br/Cl "anti" and Br/Cl "gauche")   (b) 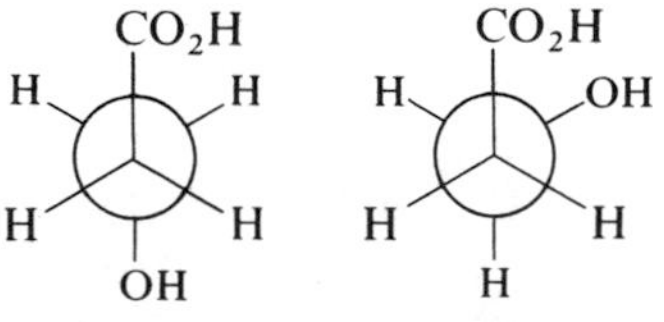   (Newman projections: CO$_2$H/OH "anti" and CO$_2$H/OH "gauche")

anti   *gauche*   *anti*   *gauche*

4.5   (a), (b), (d)

4.6   (a)   *trans e,e*;   (b)   *cis a,e*;   (c)   *trans e,e*;   (d)   no geometric isomers;
      (e)   *trans e,e*;   (f)   *trans a,e*

4.7   (a), (b), (c)   **4.8**   (a), (b), (c)

4.9   (a)   none;   (b) $CH_3CH_2\overset{*}{C}HBr$ (with CH$_3$);   (c) $C_6H_5CH_2\overset{*}{C}HC_6H_5$ (with F)

4.10 (a) 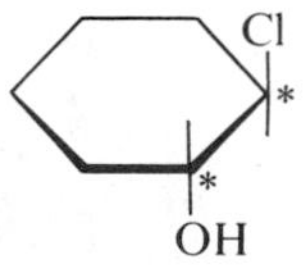 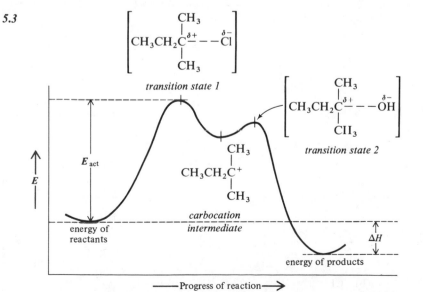 (b) none

4.11 (a) 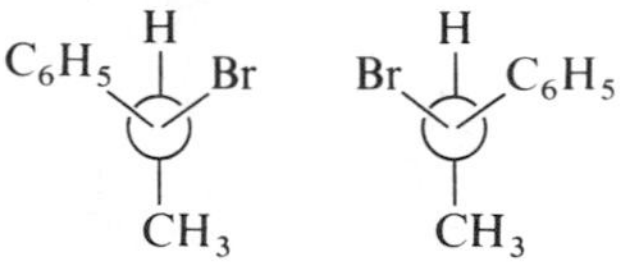 [structures: C₆H₅ and H with Br on CH₃; Br and H with C₆H₅ on CH₃] (b) 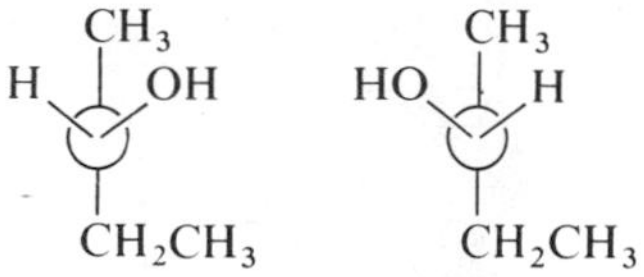 [structures: CH₃ with H and OH on CH₂CH₃; CH₃ with HO and H on CH₂CH₃]

4.12 (a) (R); (b) (S); (c) (R); (d) (S)

4.13 (a) 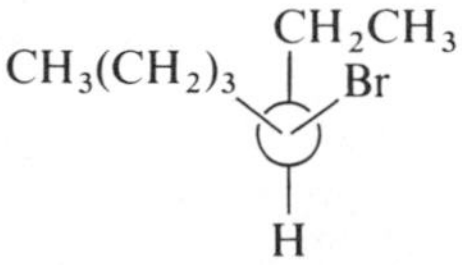 [structure: CH₃(CH₂)₃ and Br on CH₂CH₃ over H] (b) 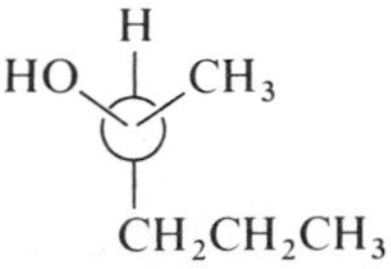 [structure: HO and CH₃ with H over CH₂CH₂CH₃]

4.14 (a) four; (b) two; (c) eight

4.15 [three structures:
first: CH₃ / H, Cl / H, Cl / CH₃ — *meso*
second and third bracketed as *enantiomers*]

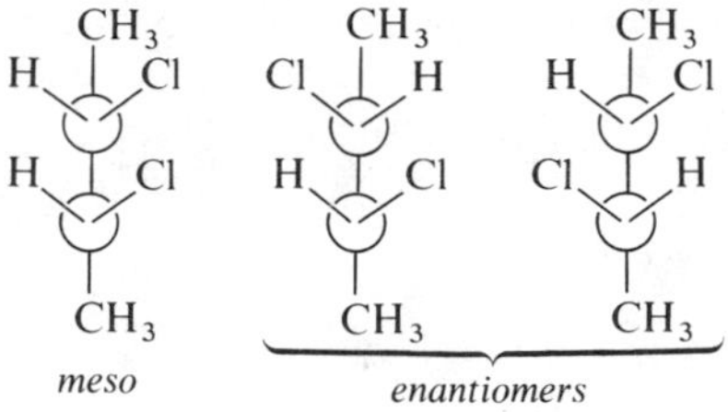

Chapter 5

5.1 (a) *t*-butyl iodide, 2-iodo-2-methylpropane
(b) isopropyl chloride, 2-chloropropane

5.2 (a) $Br_2CHCH_2CH_2CH_3$ (b) $CH_3CHClCH=CH_2$ (c) FCH_2CH_2OH

5.3

$$\left[CH_3CH_2\overset{CH_3}{\underset{CH_3}{\overset{|}{\underset{|}{C}}}}{}^{\delta+} - - - \overset{\delta-}{Cl} \right]$$

transition state 1

$$\left[CH_3CH_2\overset{CH_3}{\underset{CH_3}{\overset{|}{\underset{|}{C}}}}{}^{\delta+} - - - \overset{\delta-}{OH} \right]$$

transition state 2

E_{act}

E

$CH_3CH_2\overset{CH_3}{\underset{CH_3}{\overset{|}{\underset{|}{C}}}}{}^{+}$

carbocation intermediate

energy of reactants

ΔH

energy of products

⟶ Progress of reaction ⟶

5.4   (b), (a), (c)

5.5   (a)   no rearrangement   (b) $(CH_3)_2C\overset{H}{\underset{+}{C}}HCH_2CH_3 \longrightarrow (CH_3)_2\overset{+}{C}CH_2CH_2CH_3$

5.6 $(CH_3)_2CHCHBrCH_2CH_3 + (CH_3)_2CBrCH_2CH_2CH_3$

5.7   (a) 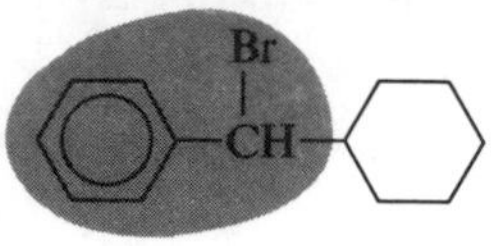   (b)

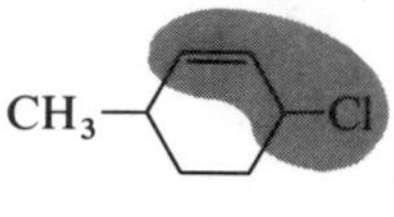

5.8

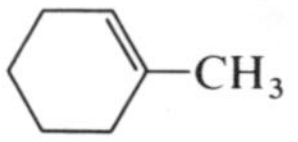

5.9 $(CH_3)_2CHCHBrCH_3 \xrightarrow{-Br^-} [(CH_3)_2CH\overset{+}{C}HCH_3] \longrightarrow$

   $(CH_3)_2C{=}CHCH_3 + (CH_3)_2CHCH{=}CH_2 + [(CH_3)_2\overset{+}{C}CH_2CH_3] \longrightarrow$

   $(CH_3)_2C{=}CHCH_3 + CH_2{=}\overset{\overset{\textstyle CH_3}{|}}{C}CH_2CH_3$

5.10 $\xrightarrow{-HBr}$

(Z)-alkene

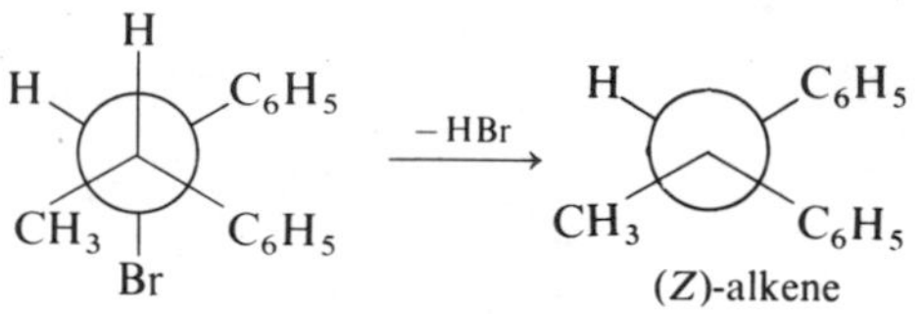

5.11

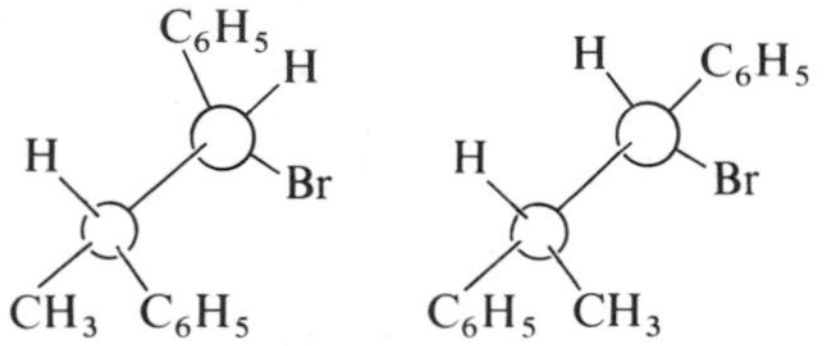

5.12   The enantiomers yield (Z)-1-bromo-1,2-diphenylethene (*trans* phenyls); the *meso* form yields the (E)-isomer (*cis* phenyls).

5.13   (a) $CH_3CH_2CH_2CH{=}CH_2$;   (b) $(CH_3)_2CHCH{=}CH_2$;
   (c)   *trans*-$CH_3CH{=}CHCH_3$

5.14   (a)   *cis*-$CH_3CH{=}CHCH_2CH_2Br \xrightarrow{NaSH}$

   (b) $CH{\equiv}C(CH_2)_4C{\equiv}C(CH_2)_4Br \xrightarrow{NaOCH_2CH_3}$

Chapter 6

6.1   (a) $H:\overset{..}{\underset{..}{O}}\cdot$ (b) $H:\overset{\textstyle H}{\underset{\textstyle H}{C}}:\overset{..}{\underset{..}{O}}\cdot$ (c) $H:\overset{\textstyle H}{\underset{\textstyle H}{C}}:\overset{\textstyle H}{\underset{\textstyle H}{C}}\cdot$

6.2   *initiation:* $Cl_2 \xrightarrow{hv} 2\,Cl\cdot$

propagation: ⬡ + Cl· ⟶ ⬡· + HCl

⬡· + Cl₂ ⟶ ⬡—Cl + Cl·

termination: ⬡· + Cl· ⟶ ⬡—Cl   etc.

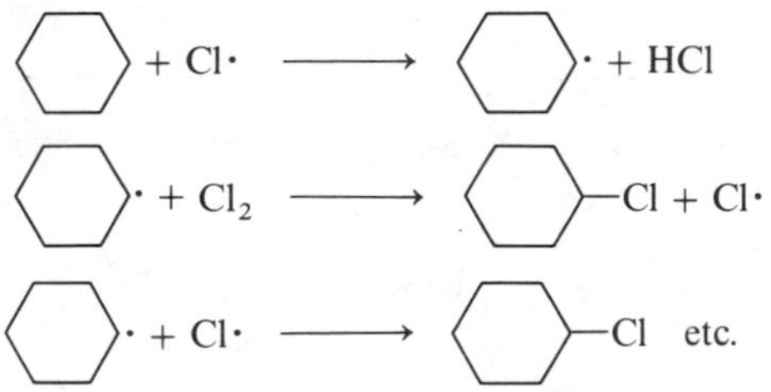

6.3 $CHCl_3 + Cl\cdot \longrightarrow \cdot CCl_3 + HCl$

$\cdot CCl_3 + Cl_2 \longrightarrow CCl_4 + Cl\cdot$

6.4 nine   **6.5** 4.0 moles   **6.6** $CH_3\overset{\cdot}{C}H_2$

sp^3 sp^2

6.7 ⟷

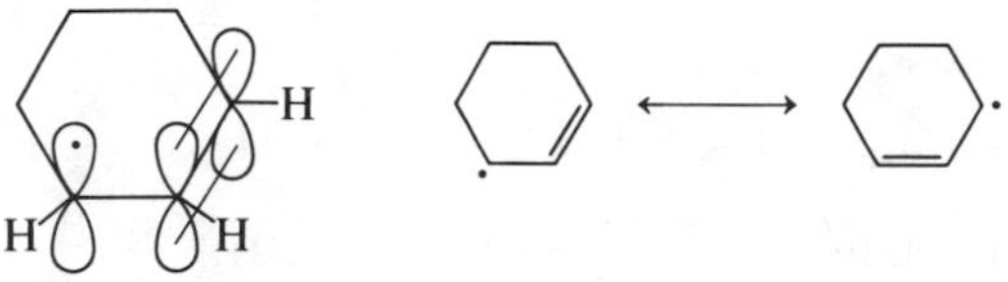

6.8 not racemic,

Cl
|
$CH_3\overset{*}{C}H\overset{*}{C}HCH_2Cl$
|
CH_3

$(R)(S)$ (R)

6.9 9 to 1   **6.10** (b), (c), (a), (d)

6.11 (a) $C_6H_5CHBrCH_2CH_2CH_3$; (b) 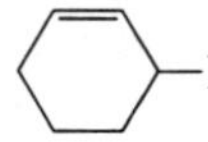 ⬡—Br; (c) $C_6H_5CH{=}CHCH_2Br$

6.12

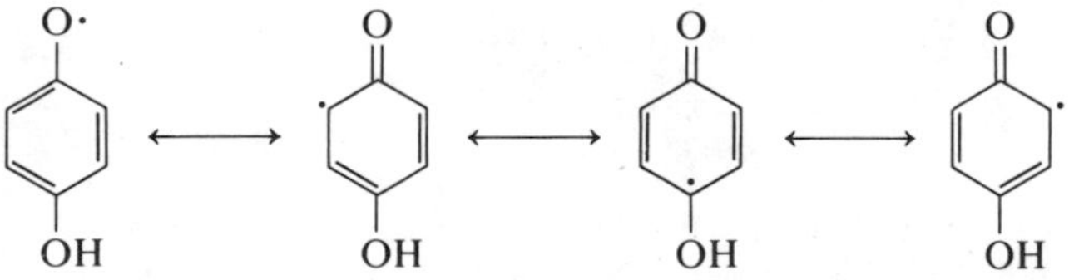

6.13 The reaction is faster because a 3° hydrogen is abstracted more readily than a 2° hydrogen.

2°   3°

$CH_3CH_2O\overset{}{C}H_2CH_3$ $(CH_3)_2\overset{}{C}HO\overset{}{C}H(CH_3)_2$

6.14 (b), (c), (d)

6.15 ⬡—Br $\xrightarrow{Mg}$ ⬡—MgBr $\xrightarrow[\text{(2) } H_2O, H^+]{\text{(1) } CH_3CHO}$ ⬡—CHCH₃ (with OH)

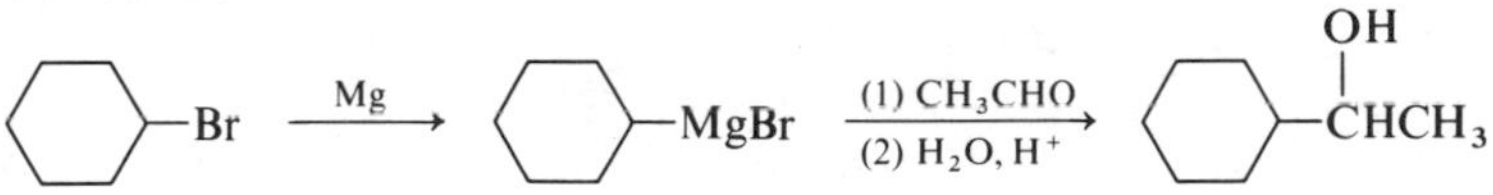

6.16 (a) 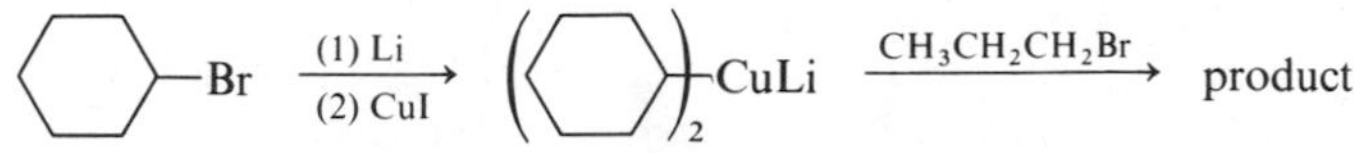 ⬡—Br $\xrightarrow[\text{(2) CuI}]{\text{(1) Li}}$ (⬡)₂CuLi $\xrightarrow{CH_3CH_2CH_2Br}$ product

(b) $(CH_3)_3CBr$ $\xrightarrow[\text{(2) CuI}]{\text{(1) Li}}$ $[(CH_3)_3C]_2CuLi$ $\xrightarrow{CH_3CH_2CH_2Br}$ product

6.17 As fast as the Grignard reagent is formed, it reacts with the alcohol.

$BrMg(CH_2)_4OH \longrightarrow CH_3(CH_2)_3O^-\ ^+MgBr$

6.18 (a), (d)   **6.19** ⬡—Br $\xrightarrow{Mg}$ ⬡—MgBr $\xrightarrow{D_2O}$ product

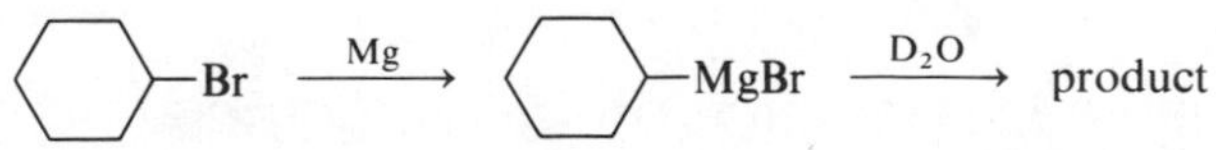

Chapter 7

7.1 (a) 2,4-dimethyl-3-pentanol; (b) 3-methyl-1,2-cyclohexanediol

7.2 (a) $\underset{\underset{OH}{|}}{CH_3}CHC(CH_2CH_3)_2$ (b) $HOCH_2\underset{\underset{CH_3}{|}}{\overset{\overset{CH_3}{|}}{C}}CH_2\overset{\overset{OH}{|}}{C}HCH_2CH_3$

7.3 (a) 3-cyclopenten-1-ol; (b) 4-hydroxy-1-cyclohexanone;
(c) 2-bromo-1-ethanol

7.4 (a) methanol, methyl alcohol; (b) ethanol, ethyl alcohol;
(c) 2-propanol, isopropyl alcohol; (d) 2-methyl-2-propanol, *t*-butyl alcohol;
(e) 2-propen-1-ol, allyl alcohol; (f) phenylmethanol, benzyl alcohol.

7.5 (a) $CH_3CH_2OC_6H_5$; (b) and (c) $CH_3\overset{\overset{OH}{|}}{C}HCH_2CH_3$; (d) $(CH_3)_2\overset{O}{\overbrace{C—CH_2}}$

7.6 (a) $C_6H_5Br \xrightarrow{Mg} C_6H_5MgBr \xrightarrow[\text{(2) }H_2O,\ H^+]{\text{(1) HCHO}} C_6H_5CH_2OH$

(b) $CH_3(CH_2)_3Cl \xrightarrow{OH^-} CH_3(CH_2)_3OH$

(c) $CH_3CH_2Br \xrightarrow{Mg} CH_3CH_2MgBr \xrightarrow[\text{(2) }H_2O,\ H^+]{\text{(1) }C_6H_5CHO} C_6H_5\overset{\overset{OH}{|}}{C}HCH_2CH_3$

7.7 $RCHO \xrightarrow{[H]} RCH_2OH$ (1°) $R\overset{\overset{O}{||}}{C}R \xrightarrow{[H]} R\overset{\overset{OH}{|}}{C}HR$ (2°)

7.8 (a) (naphthalene ring)$-O^-$ $+ CH_3I$; (b) $(CH_3)_2CHO^- + CH_3CH_2Br$

7.9 *trans*

7.10 (a) $HCl + ZnCl_2$, racemization; (b) PCl_3, inversion;
(c) $SOCl_2 + R_3N$, inversion, or $SOCl_2 +$ an ether, retention

7.11 *trans*   **7.12** (a) $(C_6H_5)_2CHCHO$; (b) $(C_6H_5)_2\overset{\overset{O}{||}}{\underset{\underset{CH_3}{|}}{C}}CCH_3$

7.13 (benzene ring with OCH_3, $-OCH_3$, OCH_3) $\xrightarrow[\text{heat}]{3\ HI}$ (benzene ring with OH, $-OH$, OH) $+ 3\ CH_3I \xrightarrow[H_2O]{3\ AgNO_3}$

$3\ CH_3OH + 3\ AgI + 3\ HNO_3$

7.14 (c)   **7.15** (a) and (b), (cyclopentane ring with OH, N, OCH_3)

7.16 (a) $CH_3CH_2CH_2\overset{\overset{OCH_3}{|}}{C}HCH_2OH$; (b) $CH_3CH_2CH_2\overset{\overset{OH}{|}}{C}HCH_2OCH_3$

7.17 (a) $CH_3CH_2CH_2\overset{\overset{\displaystyle O}{\|}}{C}OCH_3$; (b) a naphthalene with $CH_2O\overset{\overset{\displaystyle O}{\|}}{C}CH_3$ substituent

7.18 $2\,HONO \xrightarrow{-NO_2^-} H_2\overset{+}{O}-NO \underset{\longleftarrow}{\overset{-H_2O}{\rightleftharpoons}} \overset{+}{N}O$

$CH_3CH_2OH + \overset{+}{N}O \longrightarrow CH_3CH_2\underset{\underset{\displaystyle H}{|}}{\overset{+}{O}}NO \underset{\longleftarrow}{\overset{-H^+}{\rightleftharpoons}} CH_3CH_2ONO$

7.19 $CH_3CH_2OSO_2O^-\ Na^+$

7.20 (a) $2\,CH_3CH_2CH_2OH + SO_2Cl_2 \xrightarrow{-2HCl} (CH_3CH_2CH_2O)_2SO_2$

(b) $CH_3CH_2CH_2OH + TsCl \xrightarrow{-HCl} CH_3CH_2CH_2OTs$

(c) $(R)\text{-}CH_3\overset{\overset{\displaystyle OH}{|}}{C}H(CH_2)_3CH_3 + TsCl \xrightarrow{-HCl} (R)\text{-}CH_3\overset{\overset{\displaystyle OTs}{|}}{C}H(CH_2)_3CH_3$

7.21 $CH_3\overset{\overset{\displaystyle O}{\|}}{\underset{\underset{\displaystyle O}{\|}}{S}}O^- \longleftrightarrow CH_3\overset{\overset{\displaystyle O^-}{|}}{\underset{\underset{\displaystyle O}{\|}}{S}}=O \longleftrightarrow CH_3\overset{\overset{\displaystyle O}{\|}}{\underset{\underset{\displaystyle O^-}{|}}{S}}=O$

7.22 $(S)\text{-}CH_3\overset{\overset{\displaystyle OH}{|}}{C}H(CH_2)_5CH_3$ **7.23** (b), (a), (c)

7.24 (a) cyclopentane$=O$; (b) $C_6H_5CO_2H$ **7.25** $CH_3\overset{\overset{\displaystyle O}{\|}}{C}H + H\overset{\overset{\displaystyle O}{\|}}{C}CH_2OCH_3$

7.26 $CH_3CH_2OH \xrightarrow{KMnO_4} CH_3CO_2H \xrightarrow[heat]{CH_3CH_2OH,\ H^+} CH_3CO_2CH_2CH_3$

7.27 cyclopentane$-OH \xrightarrow{HBr}$ cyclopentane$-Br \xrightarrow{Mg}$

cyclopentane$-MgBr \xrightarrow[(2)\ H_2O,\ H^+]{(1)\ CH_3CHO}$ cyclopentane$-\overset{\overset{\displaystyle OH}{|}}{C}HCH_3$

7.28 (a) and (b), $C_6H_5O^- + Na^+$

7.29 Phenol undergoes hydrogen bonding, while toluene does not.

7.30 DMSO forms hydrogen bonds with H_2O: $(CH_3)_2S=O---H_2O$

7.31 The anion is resonance-stabilized: $^-CH_2\overset{\overset{\displaystyle \cdot\cdot\overset{\cdot\cdot}{O}}{\|}}{S}CH_3 \longleftrightarrow CH_2=\overset{\overset{\displaystyle :\overset{\cdot\cdot}{O}:^-}{|}}{S}CH_3$

Chapter 8

8.1 (a) $1600\ cm^{-1}$; (b) $200\ nm$; (c) $60{,}004\ Hz$

8.2 (a) $1667\ cm^{-1}$; (b) $12.5\,\mu m$; (c) $1.5\,\mu m$ **8.3** I (d); II (b)

8.4 $CH_3CH_2OCH_2CH_3$ **8.5** I, ester; II, ketone

8.6 (a) two; (b) seven; (c) ten; (d) two   **8.7** (a), (c), (d), (e)

8.8 (a) one; (b) one   **8.9** (a) two; (b) three; (c) four

8.10 Cl—⟨benzene ring⟩—$\overset{\overset{\text{O}}{\|}}{\text{C}}CH_3$

8.11 Two Cl atoms have a greater electron-withdrawing power than one Cl atom.

8.12

triplet, 2.9 ↘   ↙ triplet, 4.3

C$_6$H$_5$CH$_2$CH$_2$O$_2$CCH$_3$

singlet, 7.15 ↗   singlet, 2.0

8.13 I (e); II (d); III (a)

8.14 (CH$_3$)$_2$CHOH   **8.15** C$_6$H$_5$CH$_2$OH   **8.16** CH$_3$CH$_2$CHBrCO$_2$H

Chapter 9

9.1 (a) $\underset{\text{ClCH}_2\text{CH}_2}{\overset{\text{CH}_3}{}}\text{C}=\text{C}\underset{\text{CH}_3}{\overset{\text{CH}_2\text{CH}_3}{}}$ (b) $\underset{\text{H}}{\overset{\text{CH}_2=\text{CH}}{}}\text{C}=\text{C}\underset{\text{H}}{\overset{\text{CH}_3}{}}$

(c) ⟨cyclohexyl⟩—C≡CH (d) C$_6$H$_5$C≡CC$_6$H$_5$

9.2 (a) 2-methyl-1,4-pentadiene; (b) 3,3-dimethyl-1,4-hexadiyne

9.3 B

9.4

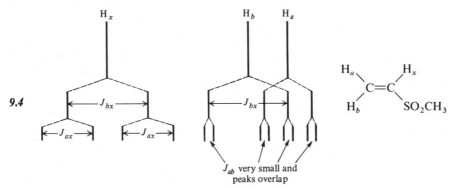

J_{ab} very small and peaks overlap

$\underset{\text{H}_b}{\overset{\text{H}_a}{}}\text{C}=\text{C}\underset{\text{SO}_2\text{CH}_3}{\overset{\text{H}_x}{}}$

9.5 In *p*-chlorostyrene, the chemical shifts are the same for the protons vicinal to the vinyl group and for the protons vicinal to the Cl. However, in styrene, the five aryl protons do not all have the same chemical shift.

9.6 (a) ⟨cyclohexene⟩; (b) and (d), CH$_2$=C(CH$_3$)$_2$; (c) CH$_3$CH=C(CH$_3$)$_2$

9.7 (a) CH$_3$C≡CH $\xrightarrow{\text{Na}}$ CH$_3$C≡C$^-$ Na$^+$ $\xrightarrow{\text{CH}_3\text{CH}_2\text{Br}}$ CH$_3$CH$_2$C≡CCH$_3$

(b) CH$_3$C≡C$^-$ $\xrightarrow{\text{C}_6\text{H}_5\text{CHBrCH}_3}$ C$_6$H$_5$$\overset{\overset{\text{CH}_3}{|}}{\text{C}}$HC≡CCH$_3$

9.8 $CH\equiv CH$ $\xrightarrow[-CH_3CH_3]{CH_3CH_2MgI}$ $CH\equiv CMgI$ $\xrightarrow[\text{(2) } H_2O, H^+]{\text{(1) } CH_3CH_2\overset{\displaystyle O}{\overset{\|}{C}}H}$ $CH_3CH_2\overset{\displaystyle OH}{\underset{|}{C}}HC\equiv CH$

9.9   (a) $CH_3CH_2\overset{+}{C}HCH_3$ $\xrightarrow{Br^-}$ $CH_3CH_2\overset{\displaystyle Br}{\underset{|}{C}}HCH_3$

(c) $(CH_3)_2\overset{+}{C}CH_2CH_3$ $\xrightarrow{Br^-}$ $(CH_3)_2\overset{\displaystyle Br}{\underset{|}{C}}CH_2CH_3$

9.10 $CH_3CH=CH_2$ $\xrightarrow{H^+}$ $[CH_3\overset{+}{C}HCH_3]$ $\xrightarrow{CH_3CH_2OH}$

$CH_3CH_2\overset{+}{O}H$ $\underset{|}{\overset{\displaystyle }{}}$ $\rightleftharpoons^{-H^+}$ $CH_3CH_2OCH(CH_3)_2$
$\quad\quad\quad\quad CH_3\overset{|}{C}HCH_3$

9.11 (a) $CH_3CH_2CCl(CH_3)_2$; (b) $CH_3CH_2\overset{\displaystyle CH_3}{\underset{|}{C}}HCBr(CH_3)_2$

9.12 (a) $(CH_3)_2CHCH_2Br$; (b) $(CH_3)_2CBrCH_3$

9.13 $CH_3CH_2CH=CH_2$ $\xrightarrow{H^+}$ $[CH_3CH_2\overset{+}{C}HCH_3]$ $\xrightarrow{HSO_4^-}$ $CH_3CH_2\overset{\displaystyle OSO_3H}{\underset{|}{C}}HCH_3$

9.14 (a) $CH_3CH_2\overset{\displaystyle OH}{\underset{|}{C}}HCH_3$; (b) $(CH_3)_2\overset{\displaystyle OH}{\underset{|}{C}}CH(CH_3)_2$; (c) $(CH_3)_2\overset{\displaystyle OSO_3H}{\underset{|}{C}}CH_2CH_3$

9.15 (a) $(CH_3)_3CCH=CH_2$ $\xrightarrow[-\,^-O_2CCH_3]{Hg(O_2CCH_3)_2}$ $\left[(CH_3)_3C\overset{\overset{\displaystyle HgO_2CCH_3}{|}}{C}H\overset{+}{-}CH_2\right]$ $\xrightarrow[-H^+]{H_2O}$

$(CH_3)_3C\overset{\overset{\displaystyle HgO_2CCH_3}{|}}{C}H-CH_2$ $\xrightarrow{NaBH_4}$ $(CH_3)_3C\overset{\displaystyle }{C}HCH_3$
$\quad\quad\quad\underset{OH}{\overset{|}{}}$ $\quad\quad\quad\quad\quad\quad\quad\quad\underset{OH}{\overset{|}{}}$

(b) $(CH_3)_3CCH=CH_2 + H_2O$ $\xrightarrow{H^+}$ $(CH_3)_2\overset{\displaystyle OH}{\underset{|}{C}}CH(CH_3)_2$

9.16 (a) $=CH_2 + H_2O$ $\xrightarrow{H^+}$

(b) $=CH_2$ $\xrightarrow{BH_3}$ $-CH_2BH_2$ $\xrightarrow{H_2O_2}$ $-CH_2OH$

(c) $=CH_2 + HBr$ $\xrightarrow{H_2O_2}$ $-CH_2Br$

9.17 (a) $CH_3CHBrCHBrCH_3$; (b) $(CH_3)_2CBrCH_2Br$; (c) $(CH_3)_2CBrCHBrCH_3$

9.18 $-CH_3$ $\xrightarrow[-Br^-]{Br_2}$ $\left[\text{}Br\cdots\overset{+}{-}CH_3\right]$ $\xrightarrow{Br^-}$

9.19 (a)

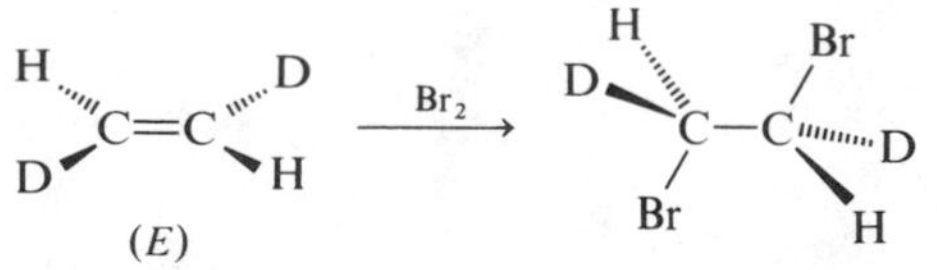

(*E*)   Br$_2$ *meso*

(b)

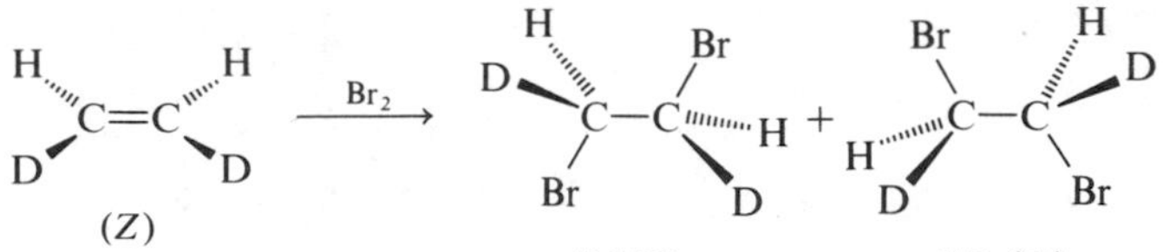

(*Z*)   Br$_2$ (1*S*,2*S*)   (1*R*, 2*R*)

9.20 No, because the intermediate contains Br.

9.21

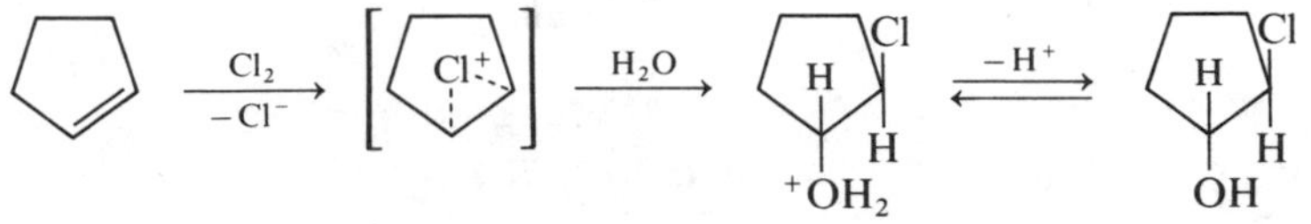

9.22 (a)

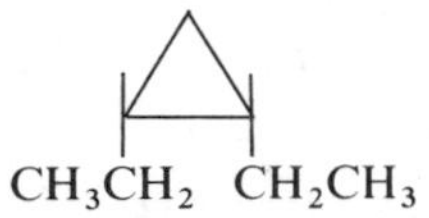

CH$_3$CH$_2$ CH$_2$CH$_3$

(b) and (d):

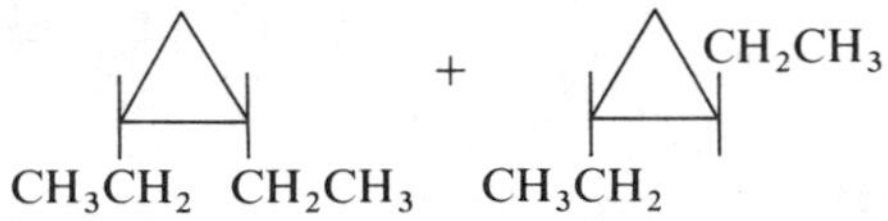

CH$_3$CH$_2$ CH$_2$CH$_3$ +   CH$_3$CH$_2$

(c)

CH$_3$CH$_2$

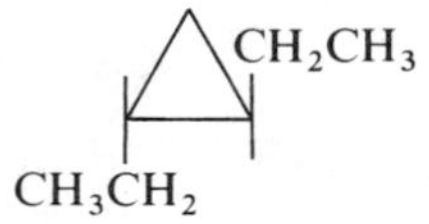

9.23 (a)

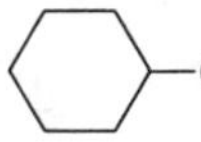

—CH=CH$_2$ + CHBr$_3$ + ⁻OR ⟶ product + ROH + Br⁻

(b)

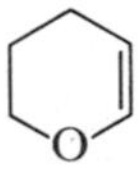

+ CHCl$_3$ + ⁻OR ⟶ product + ROH + Cl⁻

9.24 (a) The difference in energy is greater between *cis*- and *trans*-(CH$_3$)$_3$CCH=CHCH$_2$CH$_3$ because of the greater steric hindrance in the *cis*-isomer. (b) The difference in energy is greater between *cis*- and *trans*-ClCH=CHCl because the *cis*-isomer contains greater dipole–dipole repulsions between the two chlorine atoms.

9.25 (a) CH$_3$CH—C(CH$_3$)$_2$ (b)

OH OH

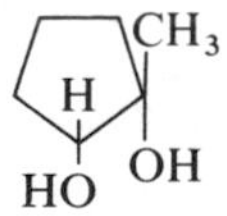

9.26 (a)

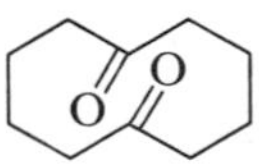

in either case

(b)

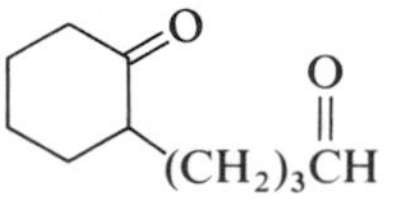

from reductive, 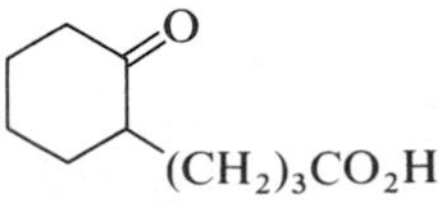 from oxidative

(CH$_2$)$_3$CH   (CH$_2$)$_3$CO$_2$H

(c) OHC—CHO + OHC(CH$_2$)$_4$CHO from reductive

HO$_2$C—CO$_2$H + HO$_2$C(CH$_2$)$_4$CO$_2$H from oxidative

(d) OHC(CH$_2$)$_4$CHO from reductive, HO$_2$C(CH$_2$)$_4$CO$_2$H from oxidative

9.27 $CH_3CHBrCHBrCH_3$; $CH_3CHClCHClCHClCHClCH_3$

9.28 (a) $CH_3CH_2\overset{+}{C}H-CH=CHCH_3 \longleftrightarrow CH_3CH_2CH=CH\overset{+}{C}HCH_3$

(b) $CH_3CH_2CHICH=CHCH_3 + CH_3CH_2CH=CHCHICH_3$

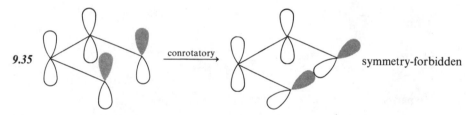

9.29 (a) ... + ... (b) ... + ...

9.30 (a) ... (b) ...

9.31 the *trans*-isomer

9.32 A, $BrCH_2CH=CHCH_2Br$; B, $BrCH_2CHBrCH=CH_2$

9.33 (a) s-*trans*; (b) s-*cis*; (c) s-*trans*; (d) s-*cis*; (e) s-*trans*. (a), (d), and (e) are interconvertible.

9.34 (a)–(d), $4n$; (e) $4n + 2$

9.35 $\xrightarrow{\text{conrotatory}}$ symmetry-forbidden

9.36 (a) *trans*; (b) (3E,7Z)

9.37 (a) [structure with CN] (b) [structure with O]

9.38 [cyclopentadiene structure] + $CH_3CH_2O_2CC\equiv CCO_2CH_2CH_3 \xrightarrow{\text{heat}}$

9.39 $+CF_2CF_2+_x$ **9.40** $CH_2=CHCN$ **9.41** $\left(\begin{array}{c} Cl \\ C=C \\ CH_2 \end{array} \begin{array}{c} CH_2 \\ \\ H \end{array} \right)_x$

Chapter 10

10.1 (a) [benzene]$-CH_2CH_3$ (b) $Br-$[benzene with Br, Br]$-NH_2$ (c) CH_3CH_2-[benzene]$-OH$

(d) [benzene]$-CH_2CH_2OH$ (e) [benzene]$-CH_2Br$

10.2 A, monosubstituted **10.3** A, *p*-iodoanisole; B, *p*-chloroaniline

10.4 not aromatic **10.5** (a), (c)

10.6 $C_6H_6 + R\overset{+}{C}=O \longrightarrow \left[\text{benzene with } \overset{+}{} \text{, H and } \underset{\underset{O}{\|}}{CR}\right] \xrightarrow{-H^+}$ benzene–$\overset{O}{\underset{\|}{C}}$R

$C_6H_6 + R\overset{\overset{O\bar{A}lCl_3}{|}}{\underset{+}{C}}Cl \longrightarrow \left[\text{benzene with } \overset{+}{}, H, O\bar{A}lCl_3, \underset{\underset{R \quad Cl}{|}}{C}\right] \xrightarrow[-HCl]{-AlCl_3}$ benzene–$\overset{O}{\underset{\|}{C}}$R

10.7 (a) $C_6H_5CH_3$ (toluene)

(b) $C_6H_5CH_2CH_2CH_2CH_3$ (*n*-butylbenzene) $+ C_6H_5\overset{\overset{CH_3}{|}}{C}HCH_2CH_3$ (*sec*-butylbenzene)

(c) $C_6H_5\overset{O}{\underset{\|}{C}}CH_2CH(CH_3)_2$ (phenyl isobutyl ketone or 3-methyl-1-phenyl-1-butanone)

10.8 (a) $C_6H_6 + (CH_3)_3CCl \xrightarrow[-HCl]{AlCl_3} C_6H_5C(CH_3)_3$

(b) $C_6H_6 + Cl\overset{O}{\underset{\|}{C}}CH(CH_3)_2 \xrightarrow[-HCl]{AlCl_3} C_6H_5\overset{O}{\underset{\|}{C}}CH(CH_3)_2 \xrightarrow[HCl]{Zn/Hg}$

$C_6H_5CH_2CH(CH_3)_2$

10.9 Two parts *o*-, two parts *m*-, and one part *p*-.

10.10 [resonance structures: benzene rings with H, NO_2, $\ddot{O}H$] $\longleftrightarrow$ $\longleftrightarrow$ $\longleftrightarrow$

[benzene ring with H, NO_2, $\ddot{O}H$]

10.11 The unshared electrons of the nitrogen are delocalized by the carbonyl group and are less available for donation to the ring. Because the amide nitrogen is partially positive, it also exerts a greater electron-withdrawal than an amine nitrogen.

[phenyl–$\dot{N}H$–$\overset{\overset{:\ddot{O}}{\|}}{C}CH_3$] $\longleftrightarrow$ [phenyl–$\overset{+}{N}H$=$\overset{\overset{:\ddot{O}:^-}{|}}{C}CH_3$]

10.12 (a) $(CH_3)_2CH$—⟨benzene⟩—Br + ⟨benzene with $CH(CH_3)_2$⟩—Br

(b) $(CH_3)_2CH$—⟨benzene⟩—OH + ⟨benzene with $CH(CH_3)_2$⟩—OH

(c) 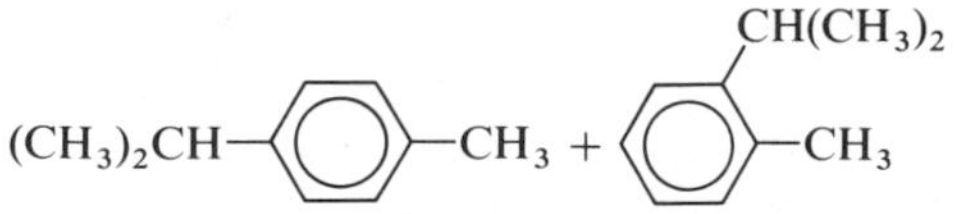 $(CH_3)_2CH$—⬡—CH_3 + ⬡($CH(CH_3)_2$)—CH_3

(d) 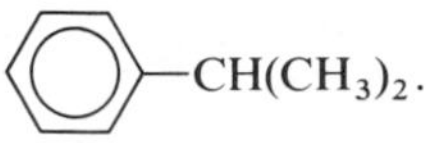 ⬡—$CH(CH_3)_2$.   Relative rates: (b) > (c) > (d) > (a).

10.13 (a) 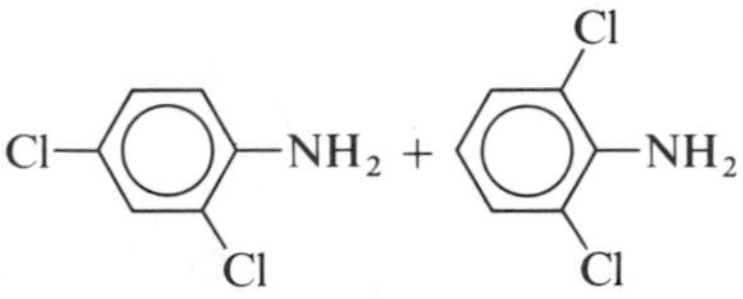 Cl—⬡(Cl)—NH_2 + ⬡(Cl, Cl)—NH_2

(b) 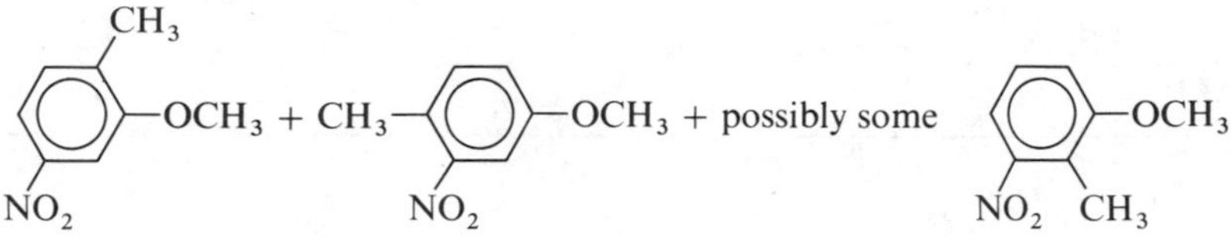 ⬡(CH_3, NO_2)—OCH_3 + CH_3—⬡(NO_2)—OCH_3 + possibly some ⬡(NO_2, CH_3)—OCH_3

(c) 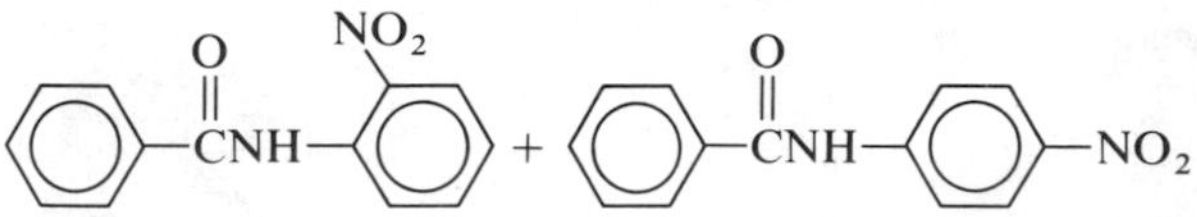 ⬡—$\overset{O}{\overset{||}{C}}NH$—⬡($NO_2$) + ⬡—$\overset{O}{\overset{||}{C}}NH$—⬡—$NO_2$

10.14 (a) 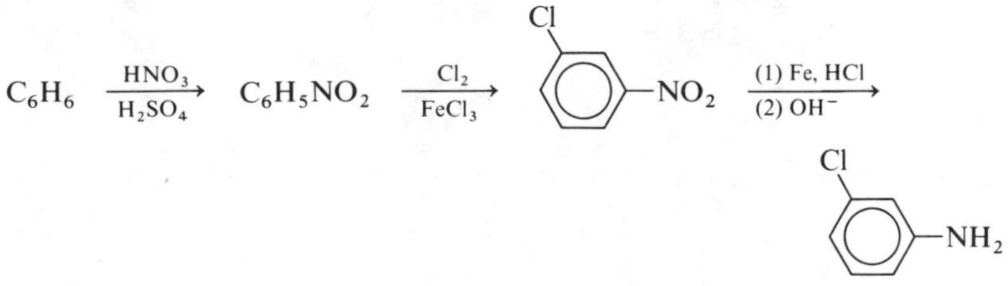 C_6H_6 $\xrightarrow[H_2SO_4]{HNO_3}$ $C_6H_5NO_2$ $\xrightarrow[FeCl_3]{Cl_2}$ ⬡(Cl)—NO_2 $\xrightarrow[(2)\ OH^-]{(1)\ Fe,\ HCl}$ ⬡(Cl)—NH_2

(b) $C_6H_6 + Cl\overset{O}{\overset{||}{C}}(CH_2)_3CH_3$ $\xrightarrow{AlCl_3}$ $C_6H_5\overset{O}{\overset{||}{C}}(CH_2)_3CH_3$ $\xrightarrow[HCl]{Zn/Hg}$ $C_6H_5(CH_2)_4CH_3$

(c) excess $C_6H_6 + ClCH_2CH_2Cl$ $\xrightarrow{AlCl_3}$ $C_6H_5CH_2CH_2C_6H_5$

(d) excess $C_6H_6 + CHCl_3$ $\xrightarrow{AlCl_3}$ $(C_6H_5)_3CH$

10.15 ⬡—$\overset{+}{C}H_2$ ⟷ ⬡=CH_2 ⟷ $+$⬡=CH_2 ⟷ ⬡=CH_2

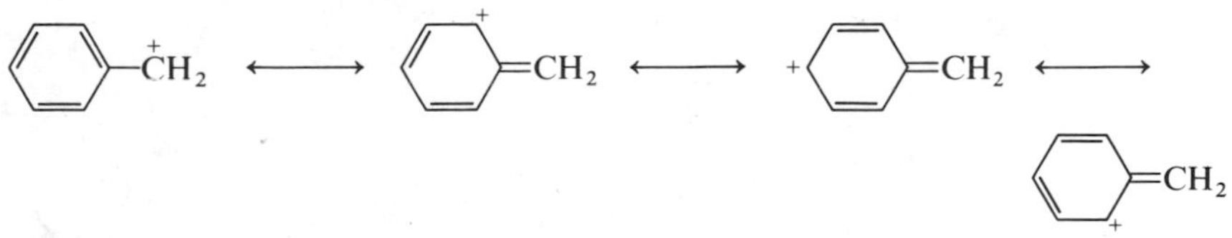

10.16 (a) and (b): ⬡(CO_2H, CO_2H)

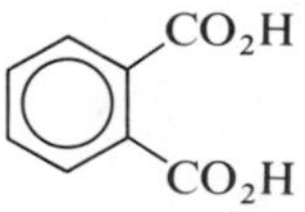

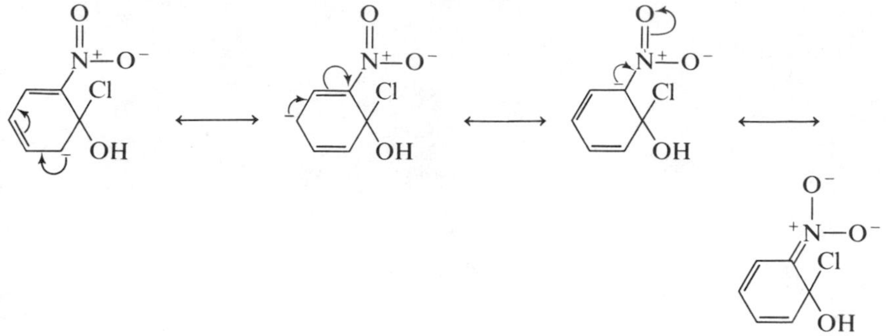

Chapter 11

11.1 (c) **11.2** (c)

11.3 (a) cyclopentanone; (b) 2-pentanone; (c) pentanal;
(d) 2-chlorocyclopentanone.

11.4 (a)

11.5 (a)

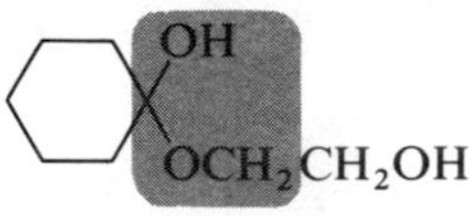

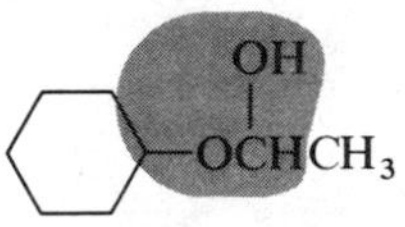

hemiketal   ketal   hemiacetal

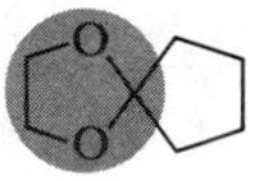

11.6 (a)

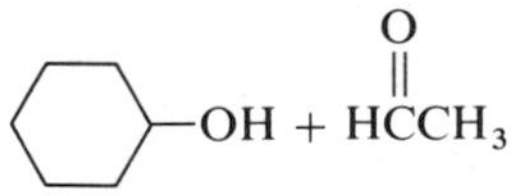

11.7 The hemiacetal carbocation is more stabilized because it is resonance-stabilized.

11.8 (a)

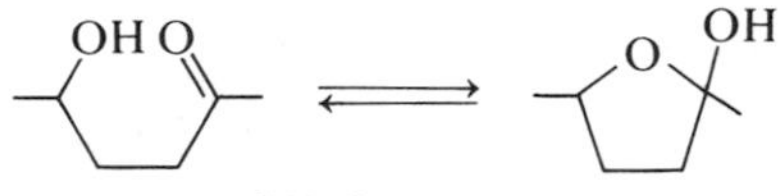

(b) 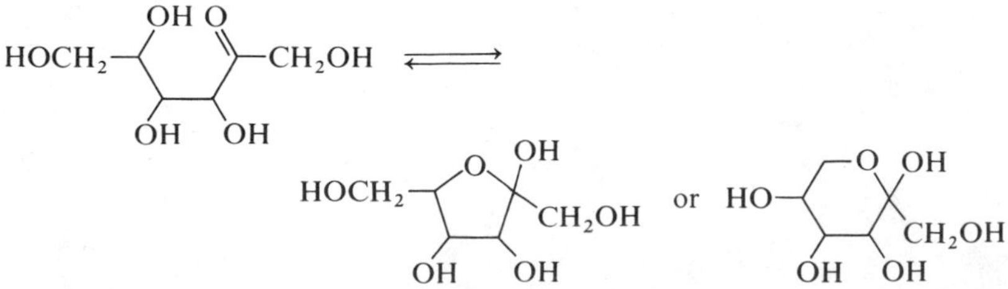 HOCH₂—

11.9 (a), (c), (b)

11.10 CH_3CH_2OH $\xrightarrow[\text{pyridine}]{CrO_3}$ CH_3CHO $\xrightarrow{HCN}$ $CH_3\overset{\overset{\displaystyle OH}{|}}{C}HCN$ $\xrightarrow{H_2O,\ H^+}$

$$CH_3\overset{\overset{\displaystyle OH}{|}}{C}HCO_2H$$

11.11 An arylamine yields a product in which the double bond is in conjugation with the aromatic ring.

11.12 A pair of stereoisomers:

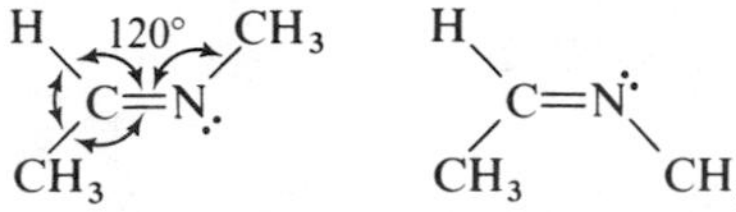

planar with *trans* CH_3 groups   *cis* CH_3 groups

11.13 (a) $\overset{\overset{\displaystyle O}{\|}}{-CH}$ $+\ H_2NCH_2CH_3$ $\xrightarrow{H^+}$ $\rightleftharpoons$

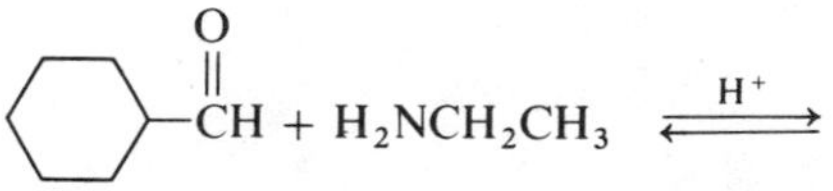

(b) $CH_3-$$-\overset{\overset{\displaystyle O}{\|}}{CH}$ $+\ C_6H_5NH_2$ $\xrightarrow{H^+}$ $\rightleftharpoons$

(c) $(CH_3)_2C{=}O$ $+\ H_2N-$$-CH_3$ $\xrightarrow{H^+}$ $\rightleftharpoons$

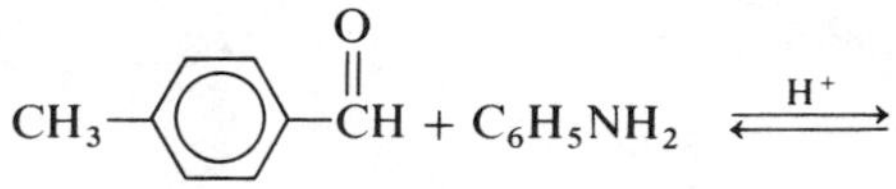

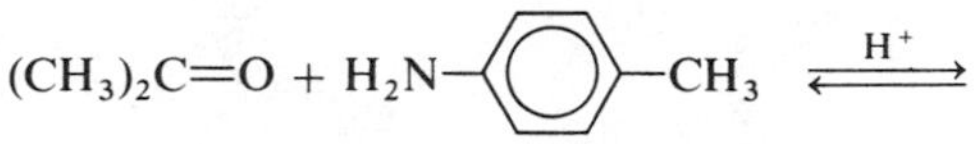

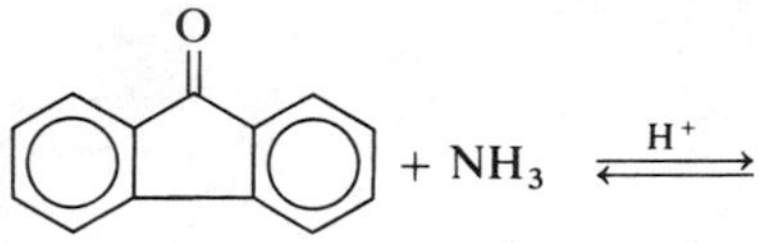

(d) $+\ NH_3$ $\xrightarrow{H^+}$ $\rightleftharpoons$

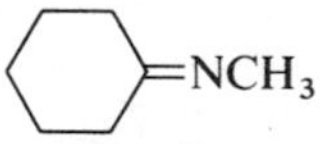

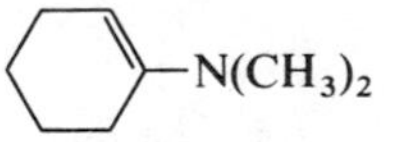

11.14 (a) $={=}NCH_3$ (b) $-N(CH_3)_2$ (c) $-N$

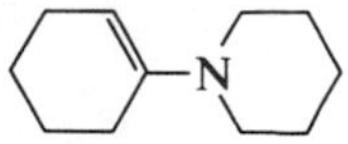

11.15 The observed product is stabilized because the double bond is in conjugation with the aromatic ring.

11.16 (a) $CH_3\overset{\overset{\displaystyle NNHCNH_2}{\overset{\displaystyle \|}{\overset{\displaystyle O}{\|}}}}{C}CH_2CH_3$ (b) $={=}NNH-$$-NO_2$ (c) $C_6H_5\overset{\overset{\displaystyle NNH_2}{\|}}{C}CH_3$

11.17 (a) $={=}O$ $+\ (C_6H_5)_3P{=}CH_2$ $\longrightarrow$ (b) $-CH_3$

11.18 (a) C_6H_5CHO, $CH_3CH_2CH_2Br$ or $C_6H_5CH_2Cl$, CH_3CH_2CHO

(b) $={=}O$, $Br-$

(c) , $BrCH_2CH_2CH_2CH_2Br$ or ,

$$OHCCH_2CH_2CHO$$

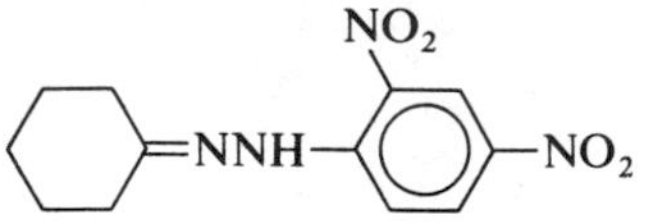

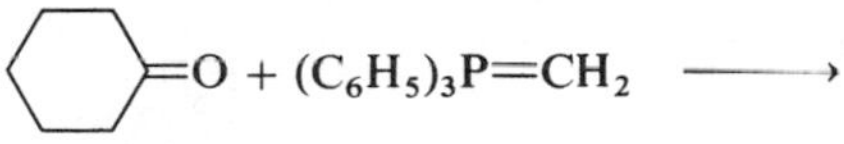

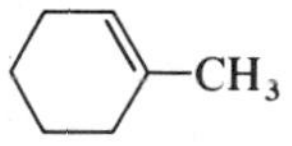

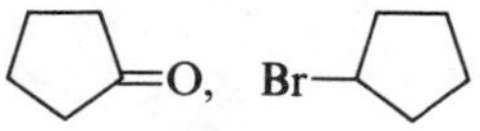

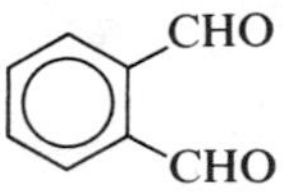

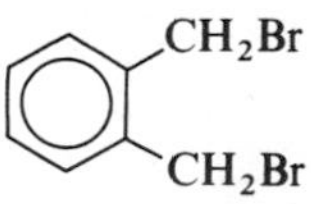

11.19 (a) C_6H_5MgBr; (b) $CH_3CH_2CH_2MgBr$ **11.20** (a), (b), (d)

11.21 $CH_3(CH_2)_4CHO$ $\xrightarrow[\text{(2) } H_2O, H^+]{\text{(1) } CH_3MgI}$

CH_3CHO $\xrightarrow[\text{(2) } H_2O, H^+]{\text{(1) } CH_3(CH_2)_3CH_2MgBr}$ $\longrightarrow$ $CH_3(CH_2)_4\overset{\overset{\displaystyle OH}{|}}{C}HCH_3$

$CH_3(CH_2)_4\overset{\overset{\displaystyle O}{||}}{C}CH_3$ $\xrightarrow[\text{heat, pressure}]{H_2, Ni}$

11.22 (a) CH_3CH_2CHO $\xrightarrow[\text{(2) } H_2O, H^+]{\text{(1) } NaBH_4}$

(b) =O $\xrightarrow[\text{(2) } H_2O, H^+]{\text{(1) } NaBH_4}$ (c) $\overset{\overset{\displaystyle O}{||}}{C}CH_3$ $\xrightarrow[\text{(2) } H_2O, H^+]{\text{(1) } NaBH_4}$

11.23

CH_2OH
|
$HCOH$
|
$HOCH$
|
$HCOH$
|
$HCOH$
|
CH_2OH

11.24 (a) $C_6H_5\overset{\overset{\displaystyle O}{||}}{C}-CH-\overset{\overset{\displaystyle O}{||}}{C}CH_3$ $\longleftrightarrow$ $C_6H_5\overset{\overset{\displaystyle O}{||}}{C}-CH=\overset{\overset{\displaystyle O^-}{|}}{C}CH_3$ $\longleftrightarrow$

$C_6H_5\overset{\overset{\displaystyle O^-}{|}}{C}=CH-\overset{\overset{\displaystyle O}{||}}{C}CH_3$

(b) $CH_3\overset{\overset{\displaystyle O}{||}}{C}-CH-\overset{\overset{\displaystyle O}{||}}{C}CH_3$ $\longleftrightarrow$ $CH_3\overset{\overset{\displaystyle O}{||}}{C}-CH=\overset{\overset{\displaystyle O^-}{|}}{C}CH_3$ $\longleftrightarrow$

$CH_3\overset{\overset{\displaystyle O^-}{|}}{C}=CHC\overset{\overset{\displaystyle O}{||}}{C}CH_3$

11.25 (a) tautomers; (b) resonance structures; (c) tautomers;
(d) resonance structures

11.26 (a) $CH_3\overset{\overset{\displaystyle OH}{|}}{C}=CH\overset{\overset{\displaystyle O}{||}}{C}H$ $\rightleftharpoons$ $CH_3\overset{\overset{\displaystyle O}{||}}{C}CH_2\overset{\overset{\displaystyle O}{||}}{C}H$ $\rightleftharpoons$ $CH_3\overset{\overset{\displaystyle O}{||}}{C}CH=\overset{\overset{\displaystyle OH}{|}}{C}H$

(b) $CH_3\overset{\overset{\displaystyle OH}{|}}{\underset{\underset{\displaystyle CH_3}{|}}{C}}=C\overset{\overset{\displaystyle O}{||}}{C}CH_3$ $\rightleftharpoons$ $CH_3\overset{\overset{\displaystyle O}{||}}{C}\underset{\underset{\displaystyle CH_3}{|}}{C}H\overset{\overset{\displaystyle O}{||}}{C}CH_3$ $\rightleftharpoons$ $CH_3\overset{\overset{\displaystyle O}{||}}{C}\underset{\underset{\displaystyle CH_3}{|}}{C}=\overset{\overset{\displaystyle OH}{|}}{C}CH_3$

(c) $CH_3\overset{\overset{\displaystyle OH}{|}}{C}$ $\rightleftharpoons$ $CH_3\overset{\overset{\displaystyle O}{||}}{C}$ $\rightleftharpoons$ $CH_3\overset{\overset{\displaystyle O}{||}}{C}$

11.27 $CH_2OPO_3H^-$
|
$C-OH$
||
$CHOH$

11.28 Ketone and OH^-, second-order kinetics

11.29 (1)
$$CH_3\overset{\overset{O}{\|}}{C}CH_2Br + OH^- \underset{\longleftarrow}{\overset{-H_2O}{\rightleftharpoons}} CH_3\overset{\overset{O}{\|}}{C}-\overset{-}{C}HBr \longleftrightarrow CH_3\overset{\overset{O^-}{|}}{C}=CHBr$$
stabilized

(2)
$$CH_3\overset{\overset{O}{\|}}{C}\overset{\frown}{C}HBr + Br\overset{\frown}{-}Br \longrightarrow CH_3\overset{\overset{O}{\|}}{C}CHBr_2 + Br^-$$

The anion in step (1) is stabilized by electron withdrawal by the electronegative Br atom.

11.30 (a)
$$CH_3\overset{\overset{+OH}{\|}}{C}CH_3$$

(b) The rates would be the same because neither Br_2 nor I_2 is involved in the rate-determining step.

11.31 (a), (c)

11.32 (a) 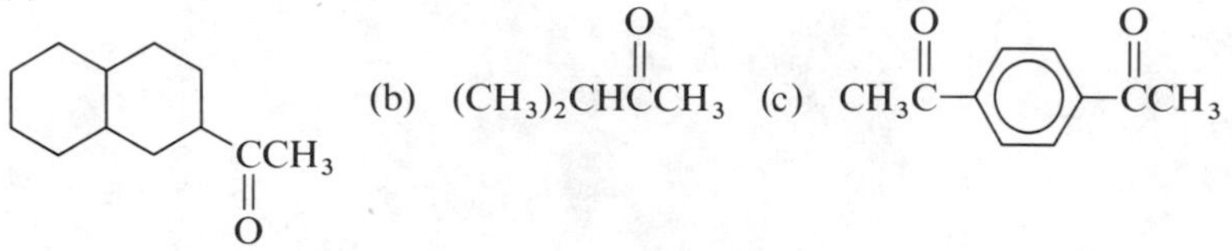 (b) $(CH_3)_2CHCCH_3$ with $\overset{O}{\|}$ (c) CH_3C — ring — CCH_3 with $\overset{O}{\|}$ groups

11.33 (a) 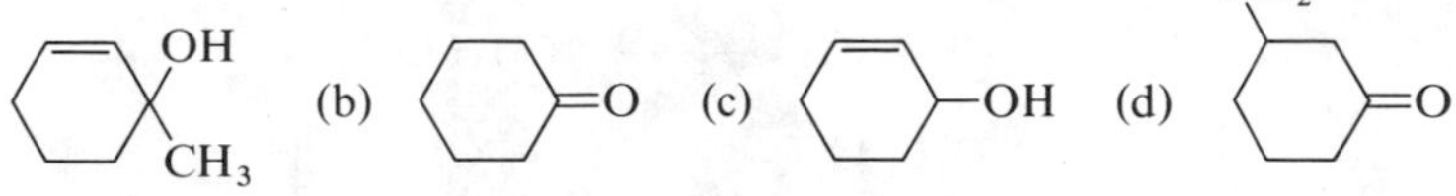 (b) (c) (d)

Chapter 12

12.1 (a) propenoic acid; (b) pentanedioic acid; (c) 2-bromopropanoic acid

12.2 (a) α-bromopropionic acid; (b) β-hydroxypropionic acid

12.3 (a)

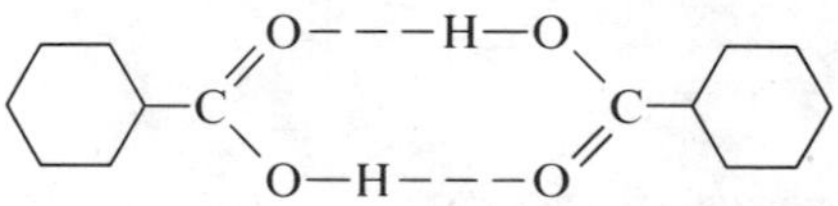

(b) 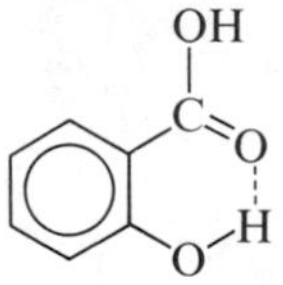 plus hydrogen bonds between molecules of benzoic acid

(c) 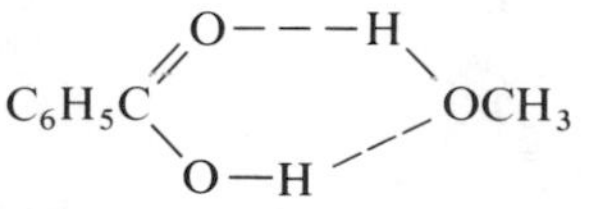 C_6H_5C ... OCH_3 structure plus hydrogen bonds within and between benzoic acid molecules and between methanol molecules.

12.4 (a) $HOCH_2CH_2Cl \xrightarrow{KCN} HOCH_2CH_2CN \xrightarrow{H_2O,\,H^+} HOCH_2CH_2CO_2H$

(b) $(CH_3)_3CCH_2Cl \xrightarrow{Mg} (CH_3)_3CCH_2MgCl \xrightarrow[(2)\,H_2O,\,H^+]{(1)\,CO_2}$

$(CH_3)_3CCH_2CO_2H$

(c) 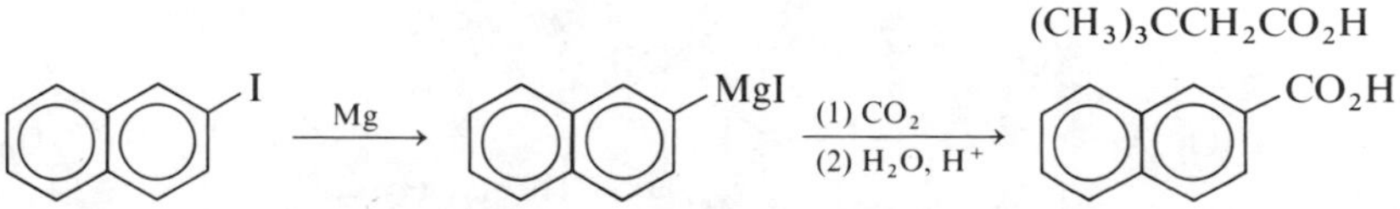 $\xrightarrow{Mg}$ $\xrightarrow[(2)\,H_2O,\,H^+]{(1)\,CO_2}$

(d) $C_6H_5CH_2Br \xrightarrow{KCN} C_6H_5CH_2CN \xrightarrow{H_2O,\,H^+} C_6H_5CH_2CO_2H$

12.5 Dissolve the aldehyde in diethyl ether, extract the ether solution with dilute aqueous NaHCO₃ to remove the acid, and then evaporate the ether to recover the aldehyde.

12.6 Extract with aqueous NaHCO₃, which removes the acid. Extract with aqueous NaOH, which removes the naphthol. The octanol remains in the ether. The acid and phenol may be regenerated by acidification.

12.7 76.5   **12.8** (a) 60.05; (b) 59.5; (c) 76.05

12.9 (a) bromoacetic acid; (b) dibromoacetic acid; (c) 2-iodopropanoic acid

12.10 (a) weaker; (b) 3,5-dinitrobenzoic acid

12.11

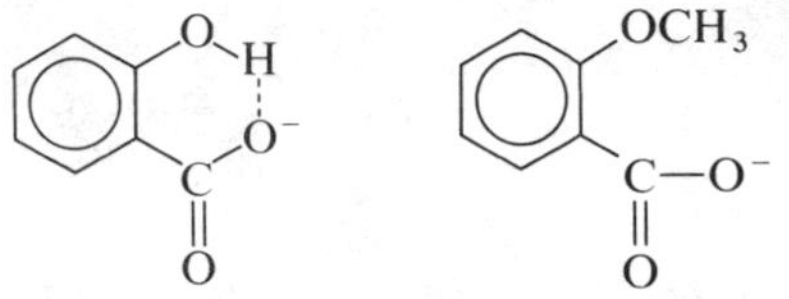

stabilized by   not stabilized by
hydrogen bonding   hydrogen bonding

12.12 (d), (c), (a), (b)

12.13

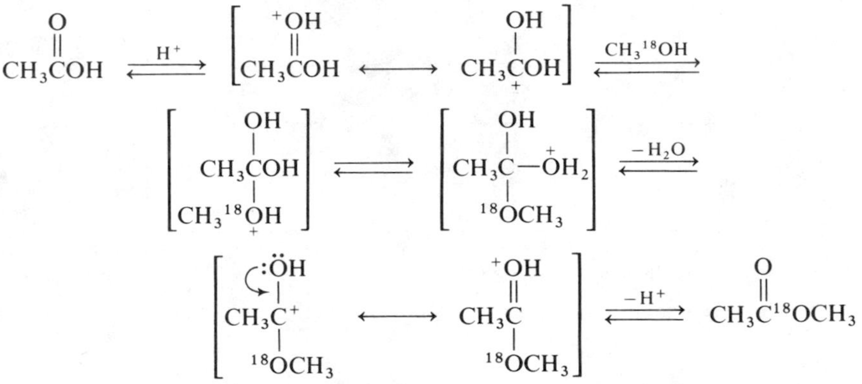

12.14 (a) $CH_3-\langle\rangle-CO_2CH(CH_3)_2$ (b) $CH_3CH_2O_2C-\langle\rangle-CO_2CH_2CH_3$

(c) (R)-$CH_3CO_2\underset{\underset{CH_3}{|}}{C}HCH_2CH_3$

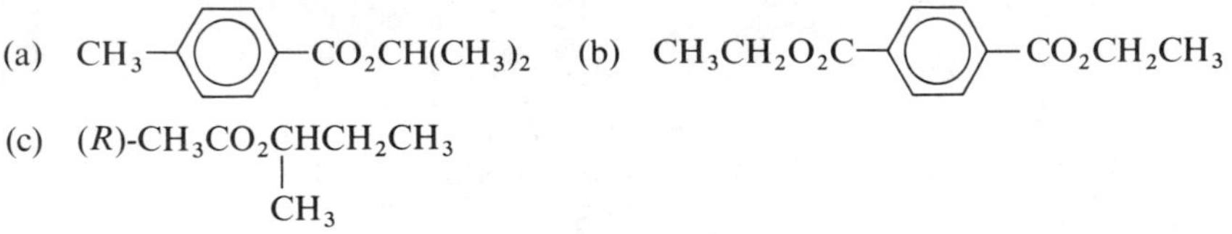

12.15 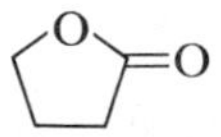   **12.16** (a) 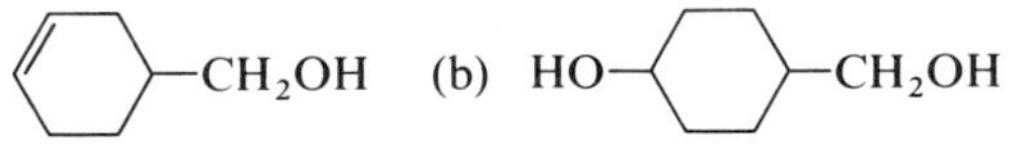   (b)

12.17 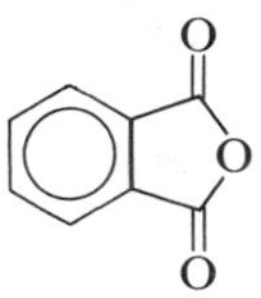   **12.18** $\left[\overset{O}{\overset{||}{C}}(CH_2)_4\overset{O}{\overset{||}{C}}O \right]_x$

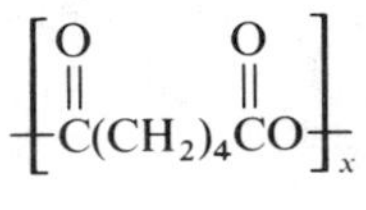

12.19

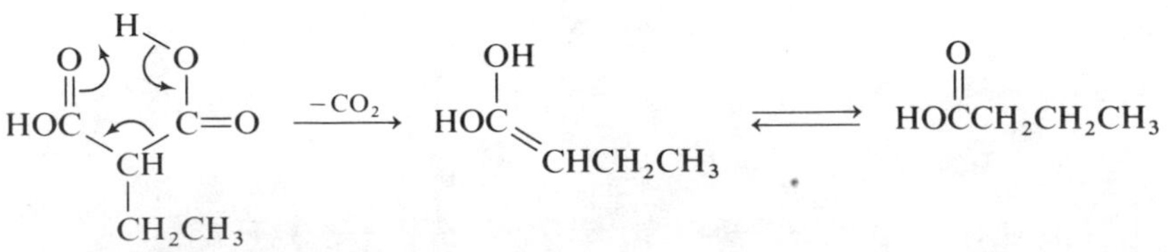

$$\mathbf{12.20} \text{ (a) } CH_3CO_2H \quad \text{(b) } CH_3\overset{\overset{\displaystyle O}{\|}}{C}CH_2CH_3 \quad \text{(c) } CH_3CH_2\overset{\overset{\displaystyle O}{\|}}{C}CH_2CH_2CH_3$$

(d) no reaction

12.21 $CH_3CH_2CH{=}CHCO_2^-\ ^+MgBr + C_6H_6$

13.1 Because of both resonance-stabilization and the inductive effect of the more electro-negative oxygen, the carbonyl carbon is more positive than the vinyl carbon.

13.2 $CH_3O_2CCH_2CN$

13.3 (a) $CH_3CH_2CO_2H + SOCl_2 \longrightarrow CH_3CH_2\overset{\overset{\displaystyle O}{\|}}{C}Cl + HCl + SO_2$

(b) $3\,HO_2C{-}CO_2H + 2\,PCl_3 \longrightarrow 3\,Cl\overset{\overset{\displaystyle O}{\|}}{C}{-}\overset{\overset{\displaystyle O}{\|}}{C}Cl + 2\,H_3PO_3$

(c) $3\,C_6H_5CH_2CO_2H + PCl_3 \longrightarrow 3\,C_6H_5CH_2\overset{\overset{\displaystyle O}{\|}}{C}Cl + H_3PO_3$

(d) $HO_2C{-}\langle\bigcirc\rangle{-}CO_2H + 2\,SOCl_2 \longrightarrow$

$Cl\overset{\overset{\displaystyle O}{\|}}{C}{-}\langle\bigcirc\rangle{-}\overset{\overset{\displaystyle O}{\|}}{C}Cl + 2\,HCl + 2\,SO_2$

13.4 $CH_3CH_2CH_2\overset{\overset{\displaystyle O}{\|}}{C}Cl + OH^- \longrightarrow \left[CH_3CH_2CH_2\overset{\overset{\displaystyle O^-}{|}}{\underset{\underset{\displaystyle OH}{|}}{C}}{-}Cl \right] \xrightarrow{-\,Cl^-}$

$CH_3CH_2CH_2\overset{\overset{\displaystyle O}{\|}}{\underset{\underset{\displaystyle OH}{|}}{C}} \xrightarrow[-\,H^+]{OH^-} CH_3CH_2CH_2CO_2^{-}$

13.5 The chloride ion is not a good enough nucleophile to displace a alkoxide ion.

13.6 $CH_3CH_2CH_2\overset{\overset{\displaystyle O}{\|}}{C}Cl \xrightarrow{C_6H_5OH} \left[CH_3CH_2CH_2\overset{\overset{\displaystyle O^-}{|}}{\underset{\underset{\displaystyle C_6H_5OH}{|}_+}{C}}Cl \right] \xrightarrow{-\,HCl} CH_3CH_2CH_2\overset{\overset{\displaystyle O}{\|}}{C}OC_6H_5$

13.7 $CH_3CO_2^-\ Na^+ + Cl^- + \text{unreacted } CH_3NH_2$

13.8 $C_6H_5\overset{\overset{\displaystyle O}{\|}}{C}Cl + {}^-\overset{\overset{\displaystyle O}{\|}}{O}CCH_3 \longrightarrow \left[C_6H_5\overset{\overset{\displaystyle O^-}{|}}{\underset{\underset{\underset{\displaystyle O}{\|}}{OCCH_3}}{C}}{-}Cl \right] \xrightarrow{-\,Cl^-} C_6H_5\overset{\overset{\displaystyle O}{\|}}{C}O\overset{\overset{\displaystyle O}{\|}}{C}CH_3$

13.9 $C_6H_6 \xrightarrow[\text{AlCl}_3]{\underset{}{\overset{\text{O}}{\overset{\|}{\text{ClCCH(CH}_3)_2}}}} C_6H_5\overset{\text{O}}{\overset{\|}{\text{C}}}CH(CH_3)_2 \xrightarrow[\text{HCl}]{\text{Zn/Hg}} C_6H_5CH_2CH(CH_3)_2$

13.10 (a) $(CH_3)_2CHCl \xrightarrow[\text{(2) CuI}]{\text{(1) Li}} LiCu[CH(CH_3)_2]_2 \xrightarrow{\overset{\text{O}}{\overset{\|}{C_6H_5CCl}}}$

(b) $CH_3I \xrightarrow[\text{(2) CdCl}_2]{\text{(1) Mg}} (CH_3)_2Cd \xrightarrow{}$

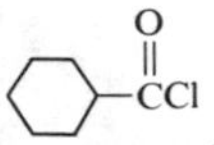

13.11 (a) $(CH_3)_2CClCO_2H$; (b) $C_6H_5CHBrCO_2H$

13.12 (a) pentanoic anhydride; (b) benzoic anhydride;
(c) acetic benzoic anhydride or benzoic ethanoic anhydride

13.13 [benzene ring]$-CO_2H$ with OH $+ (CH_3CO)_2O \longrightarrow$ [benzene ring]$-CO_2H$ with O_2CCH_3 $+ CH_3CO_2H$

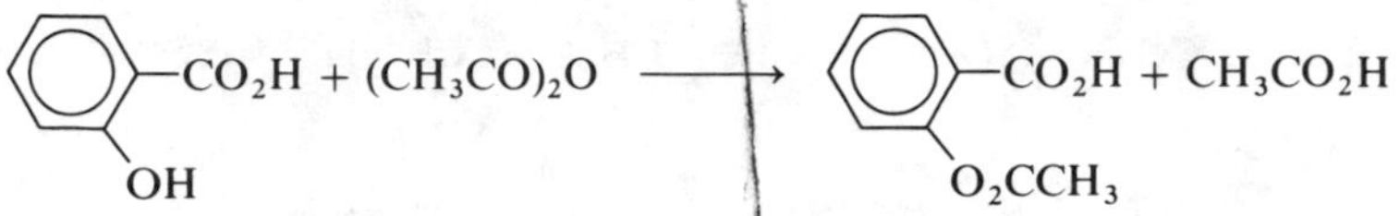

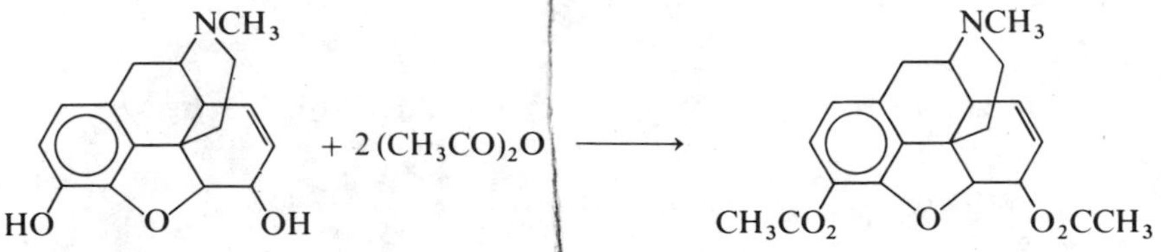

[morphine structure] $+ 2(CH_3CO)_2O \longrightarrow$ [heroin structure]

13.14 [naphthalene with $NHCCH_3$ group] $+ CH_3\overset{\text{O}}{\overset{\|}{C}}O^- \ HN^+$[pyridine ring]

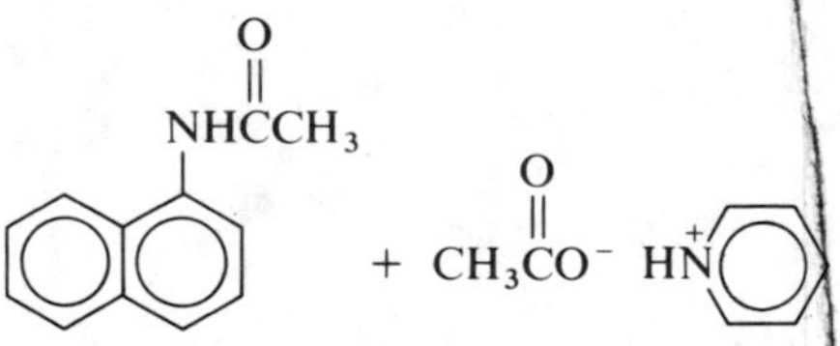

13.15 $C_6H_5CO_2H + CH_3OH \xrightarrow[-\text{H}_2\text{O}]{\text{H}^+, \text{heat}} C_6H_5CO_2CH_3$

$C_6H_5\overset{\text{O}}{\overset{\|}{C}}Cl + CH_3OH \xrightarrow{-\text{HCl}}$

$(C_6H_5CO)_2O + CH_3OH \xrightarrow{-\text{C}_6\text{H}_5\text{CO}_2\text{H}}$

$C_6H_5CO_2^- + CH_3I \xrightarrow{-\text{I}^-}$

$C_6H_5CO_2H + CH_2N_2 \xrightarrow[-\text{N}_2]{\text{ether}}$

13.16 [benzene with CO_2CH_3 and OH] $\xrightarrow[\text{heat}]{\text{H}_2\text{O, H}^+}$ [benzene with CO_2H and OH] $\xrightarrow{(CH_3CO)_2O}$ [benzene with CO_2H and O_2CCH_3]

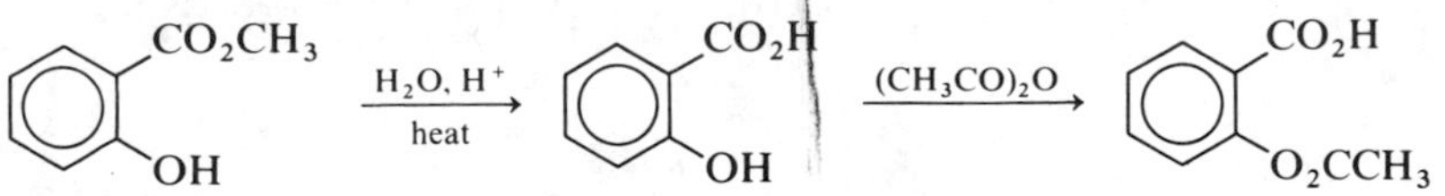

13.17 $CH_3CO_2H + H^{18}OCH_2CH_3$ **13.18** $CH_3CO_2^- + H^{18}OCH_2CH_3$

13.19 (a) $C_6H_5CO_2CH_2CH_3 + OH^- \longrightarrow C_6H_5CO_2^- + HOCH_2CH_3$

(b) 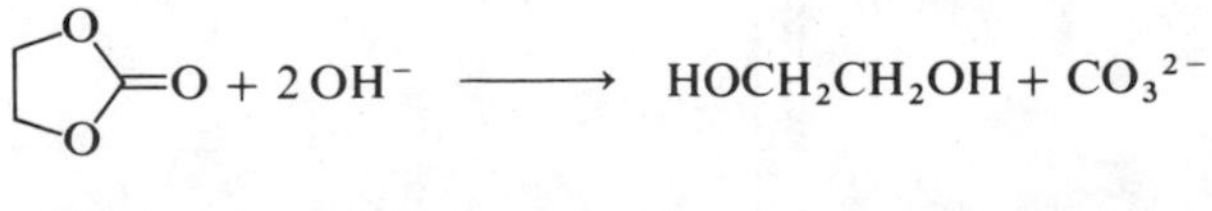 [cyclic carbonate]$=O + 2OH^- \longrightarrow HOCH_2CH_2OH + CO_3^{2-}$

(c) [chroman-2-one structure] + 2 OH⁻ ⟶ [benzene ring with CH₂CH₂CO₂⁻ and O⁻] + H₂O

(d) [quinoxaline structure with N, CH₂CO₂CH₂CH₃, N, OH] + OH⁻ ⟶

[quinoxaline with N, CH₂CO₂⁻, N, OH] + CH₃CH₂OH

13.20 (a)

$$CH_3\overset{O}{\overset{\|}{C}}OCH_2CH_3 \underset{}{\overset{H^+}{\rightleftharpoons}} \left[CH_3\overset{\overset{+}{O}H}{\overset{\|}{C}}OCH_2CH_3 \longleftrightarrow CH_3\overset{OH}{\overset{|}{\underset{+}{C}}}OCH_2CH_3 \right]$$

$$\overset{CH_3OH}{\rightleftharpoons} \left[CH_3\overset{OH}{\underset{\underset{+}{CH_3OH}}{\overset{|}{\underset{|}{C}}}}OCH_2CH_3 \right] \rightleftharpoons \left[CH_3\overset{O\overset{\frown}{\smallfrown}H}{\underset{CH_3O\;\;H}{\overset{|}{\underset{|}{C}}}}OCH_2CH_3 \right]$$

$$\overset{-H^+}{\rightleftharpoons} CH_3\overset{O}{\overset{\|}{C}}OCH_3 + HOCH_2CH_3$$

(b)

$$CH_3\overset{O}{\overset{\|}{C}}OCH_2CH_3 \overset{^-OCH_3}{\rightleftharpoons} \left[CH_3\overset{O^-}{\underset{OCH_3}{\overset{|}{\underset{|}{C}}}}OCH_2CH_3 \right] \rightleftharpoons$$

$$CH_3\overset{O}{\overset{\|}{C}}OCH_3 + {}^-OCH_2CH_3$$

13.21 $CH_3\underset{OH}{\overset{|}{C}}HCO_2H \xrightarrow{SOCl_2} CH_3\underset{Cl}{\overset{|}{C}}H\overset{O}{\overset{\|}{C}}Cl$

13.22 $\underset{CH_2O_2C(CH_2)_{14}CH_3}{\overset{CH_2O_2C(CH_2)_{14}CH_3}{\overset{|}{\underset{|}{C}}HO_2C(CH_2)_{14}CH_3}} \xrightarrow[(2)\,H_2O]{(1)\,LiAlH_4} \underset{CH_2OH}{\overset{CH_2OH}{\overset{|}{\underset{|}{C}}HOH}} + 3\,HOCH_2(CH_2)_{14}CH_3$

13.23 (a) $CH_3CH_2CO_2CH_3 \xrightarrow[(2)\,H_2O,\,H^+]{(1)\,2\,CH_3MgI} CH_3CH_2\underset{}{\overset{OH}{\overset{|}{C}}}(CH_3)_2$

(b) $CH_3CH_2CO_2CH_3 \xrightarrow[(2)\,H_2O,\,H^+]{(1)\,2\,CH_3CH_2MgBr} CH_3CH_2\overset{OH}{\overset{|}{C}}(CH_2CH_3)_2$

13.24 $H\overset{O}{\overset{\|}{C}}OCH_2CH_3 \xrightarrow[(2)\,H_2O,\,H^+]{(1)\,2\,CH_3CH_2MgBr} HOCH(CH_2CH_3)_2$

13.25 [dioxane-dione ring structure with CH₃, O, O, O, CH₃]

13.26 (a) $\xrightarrow{\text{OH}^-}$ $x\,\text{H}_2\text{NCHCO}_2^-$ (b) $\xrightarrow{\text{H}_2\text{O, H}^+}$ $x\,\overset{+}{\text{H}}_3\text{NCHCO}_2\text{H}$
with CH_3 substituent on each.

13.27 (a) [pyridinium ring with CO_2H] $+ \text{NH}_4^+$; (b) [fused ring system with HN, CO_2^-, N–CH_3] $+ \text{HN}(\text{CH}_2\text{CH}_3)_2$;

(c) $^-\text{O}_2\text{C}(\text{CH}_2)_3\text{NHCH}_3$

13.28 (a) $\text{O}=\text{C}\begin{smallmatrix}\nearrow\text{NH}_2\\\searrow\text{NH}_2\end{smallmatrix}$ + $\text{CH}_3\text{CH}_2\text{O}_2\text{C}$, C_6H_5 , C , $\text{CH}_3\text{CH}_2\text{O}_2\text{C}$, CH_2CH_3

(b) $\text{O}=\text{C}\begin{smallmatrix}\nearrow\text{NH}_2\\\searrow\text{NH}_2\end{smallmatrix}$ + $\text{CH}_3\text{CH}_2\text{O}_2\text{C}$, $\text{CH}(\text{CH}_3)\text{CH}_2\text{CH}_2\text{CH}_3$, C , $\text{CH}_3\text{CH}_2\text{O}_2\text{C}$, CH_2CH_3

(c) $\text{O}=\text{C}\begin{smallmatrix}\nearrow\text{NH}_2\\\searrow\text{NH}_2\end{smallmatrix}$ + $\text{CH}_3\text{CH}_2\text{O}_2\text{C}$, $\text{CH}(\text{CH}_3)\text{CH}_2\text{CH}_2\text{CH}_3$, C , $\text{CH}_3\text{CH}_2\text{O}_2\text{C}$, $\text{CH}_2\text{CH}=\text{CH}_2$

13.29 [cyclohexyl]–$\overset{\overset{\text{O}}{\|}}{\underset{\underset{\text{O}}{\|}}{\text{NHS}}}\text{O}^-\ \text{Na}^+$

13.30 (a) $\text{CH}_3(\text{CH}_2)_3\text{CN}$; (b) $\text{CH}_3\text{CH}_2\text{CH}_2\text{CN}$

Chapter 14

14.1 (a), (d)

14.2 (a) $\text{CH}_3\text{CH}_2\text{CHO} + \text{CH}_3\text{CH}_2\text{O}^- \rightleftharpoons \text{CH}_3\overset{-}{\text{C}}\text{HCHO} + \text{CH}_3\text{CH}_2\text{OH}$

(b) $(\text{CH}_3)_2\text{CHCO}_2\text{CH}_2\text{CH}_3 + \text{CH}_3\text{CH}_2\text{O}^- \rightleftharpoons$
$(\text{CH}_3)_2\overset{-}{\text{C}}\text{CO}_2\text{CH}_2\text{CH}_3 + \text{CH}_3\text{CH}_2\text{OH}$

(c) no reaction

(d) $\text{O}_2\text{N}-$[benzene ring with NO_2]$-\text{CH}_2\text{CH}_3 + \text{CH}_3\text{CH}_2\text{O}^- \rightleftharpoons$
$\text{O}_2\text{N}-$[benzene ring with NO_2]$-\overset{-}{\text{C}}\text{HCH}_3 + \text{CH}_3\text{CH}_2\text{OH}$

(e) $\text{CH}_3\text{CH}_2\overset{\overset{\text{O}}{\|}}{\text{C}}\text{CH}_2\text{CO}_2\text{CH}_2\text{CH}_3 + \text{CH}_3\text{CH}_2\text{O}^- \rightleftharpoons$
$\text{CH}_3\text{CH}_2\overset{\overset{\text{O}}{\|}}{\text{C}}\overset{-}{\text{C}}\text{HCO}_2\text{CH}_2\text{CH}_3 + \text{CH}_3\text{CH}_2\text{OH}$

(f) $\text{CH}_2(\text{CO}_2\text{H})_2 + 2\,\text{CH}_3\text{CH}_2\text{O}^- \rightleftharpoons \text{CH}_2(\text{CO}_2^-)_2 + 2\,\text{CH}_3\text{CH}_2\text{OH}$

14.3 Transesterification, as well as enolate formation:

$$CH_2(CO_2C_2H_5)_2 + 2\,CH_3O^- \rightleftharpoons CH_2(CO_2CH_3)_2 + 2\,C_2H_5O^-$$

14.4 (a) $CH_3CH_2CH_2CH(CO_2C_2H_5)_2$ (b) $CH_3CH_2\overset{\overset{\displaystyle CH_3}{|}}{C}(CO_2C_2H_5)_2$

14.5 (a) $CH_3CH_2CH_2CH(CO_2C_2H_5)_2 \xrightarrow[\text{heat}]{H_2O,\ OH^-}$

$$CH_3CH_2CH_2CH(CO_2^-)_2 \xrightarrow{H^+} CH_3CH_2CH_2CH(CO_2H)_2$$

   (b) $(CH_3)_2C(CO_2C_2H_5)_2 \xrightarrow[\substack{\text{heat}\\-CO_2}]{H_2O,\ H^+} (CH_3)_2CHCO_2H$

14.6 $\xrightarrow{-CO_2}$ $\rightleftharpoons$

14.7 $CH_3\overset{\overset{\displaystyle O}{||}}{C}\overset{-}{C}HCO_2C_2H_5\ Na^+$; $CH_3\overset{\overset{\displaystyle O}{||}}{C}\underset{\underset{\displaystyle CH_2CH_2-\bigcirc}{|}}{C}HCO_2C_2H_5$

14.8 (a) $CH_3\overset{\overset{\displaystyle O}{||}}{C}\underset{\underset{\displaystyle CH_3}{|}}{C}HCO_2C_2H_5$ (b) $CH_3\overset{\overset{\displaystyle O}{||}}{C}-\overset{\overset{\displaystyle CH_3}{|}}{\underset{\underset{\displaystyle CH_3}{|}}{C}}CO_2C_2H_5$ (c) $CH_3\overset{\overset{\displaystyle O}{||}}{C}CH(CH_3)_2$

14.9 (a) $CH_2(CO_2C_2H_5)_2 \xrightarrow[\text{(2) } CH_3(CH_2)_3Br]{\text{(1) } NaOC_2H_5}$

$$CH_3(CH_2)_3CH(CO_2C_2H_5)_2 \xrightarrow[\text{(2) } H^+,\ \text{cold}]{\text{(1) } OH^-,\ H_2O,\ \text{heat}}$$

   (b) $CH_2(CO_2C_2H_5)_2 \xrightarrow[\text{(2) } 2\,CH_3I]{\text{(1) } NaOC_2H_5} (CH_3)_2C(CO_2C_2H_5)_2 \xrightarrow[\text{heat}]{H_2O,\ H^+}$

   (c) $CH_3\overset{\overset{\displaystyle O}{||}}{C}CH_2CO_2C_2H_5 \xrightarrow[\text{(2) } CH_3CH_2CH_2Br]{\text{(1) } NaOC_2H_5} CH_3\overset{\overset{\displaystyle O}{||}}{C}\underset{\underset{\displaystyle CH_2CH_2CH_3}{|}}{C}HCO_2C_2H_5 \xrightarrow[\text{(2) } CH_3I]{\text{(1) } NaOC_2H_5}$

$$CH_3\overset{\overset{\displaystyle O}{||}}{C}-\overset{\overset{\displaystyle CH_3}{|}}{\underset{\underset{\displaystyle CH_2CH_2CH_3}{|}}{C}}CO_2C_2H_5 \xrightarrow[\text{heat}]{H_2O,\ H^+}$$

14.10 $CH_2(CO_2C_2H_5)_2 \xrightarrow[\text{(2) } BrCH_2CO_2C_2H_5]{\text{(1) } NaOC_2H_5}$

14.11 (a) $CH_3\overset{O}{\underset{\|}{C}}CH_2\overset{O}{\underset{\|}{C}}CH_3$ $\xrightarrow[\text{(2) }CH_3I]{\text{(1) NaOC}_2H_5}$

(b) $CH_2(CN)_2$ $\xrightarrow[\text{(2) }CH_3CH_2CH_2Br]{\text{(1) NaOC}_2H_5}$

(c) $CH_2(CN)_2$ $\xrightarrow[\text{(2) Br(CH}_2)_4Br]{\text{(1) NaOC}_2H_5}$ $Br(CH_2)_4CH(CN)_2$ $\xrightarrow{\text{NaOC}_2H_5}$

$BrCH_2(CH_2)_3\overset{-}{C}(CN)_2$ $\longrightarrow$

(d) 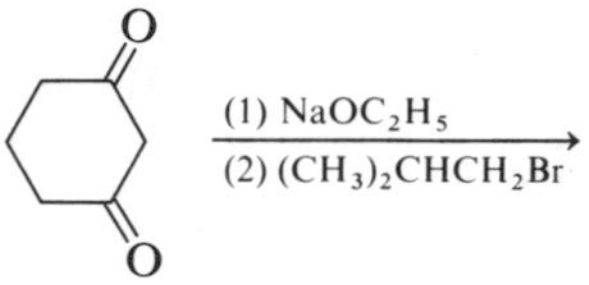 $\xrightarrow[\text{(2) }(CH_3)_2CHCH_2Br]{\text{(1) NaOC}_2H_5}$

14.12

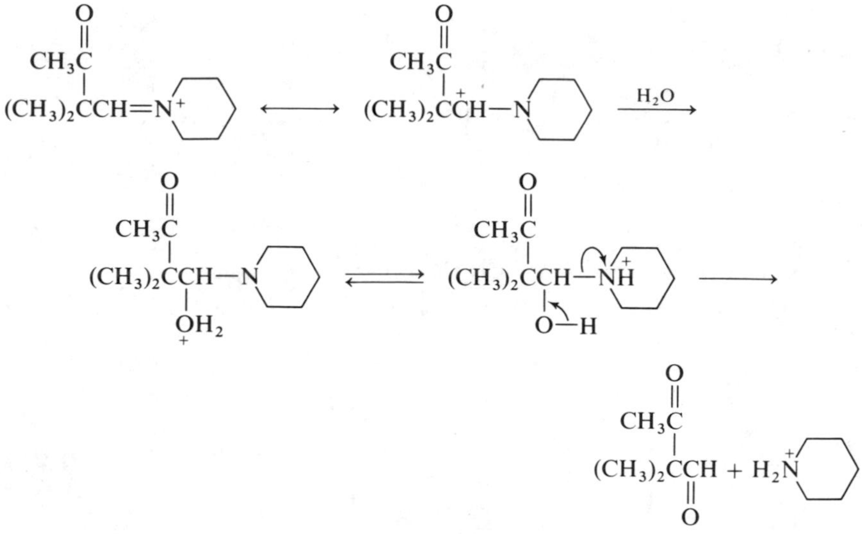

14.13 A cyclic amine has less steric hindrance around the nitrogen than an open-chain amine; therefore, reaction of a cyclic amine with a carbonyl group is more favored.

14.14

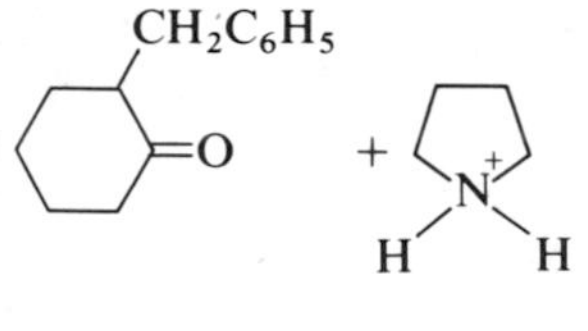

14.15

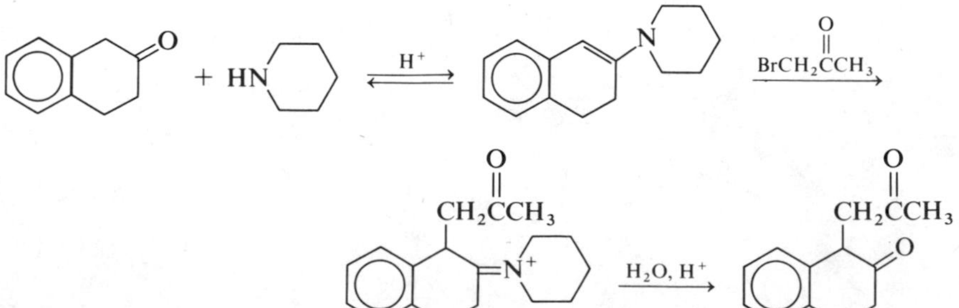

14.16 (c)

14.17 (a) $CH_3CH_2CH_2\overset{\overset{\displaystyle OH}{|}}{CH}-\overset{\overset{\displaystyle O}{\|}}{C}H$ (b) $(CH_3)_2\overset{\overset{\displaystyle OH}{|}}{C}-CH_2\overset{\overset{\displaystyle O}{\|}}{C}CH_3$
$\qquad\qquad\qquad\quad\underset{\underset{\displaystyle CH_2CH_3}{|}}{}$

(c) $(CH_3)_2CHCH_2\overset{\overset{\displaystyle OH}{|}}{C}H\overset{\overset{\displaystyle O}{\|}}{C}H$
$\qquad\qquad\qquad\underset{\underset{\displaystyle CH(CH_3)_2}{|}}{}$

14.18 (a) $C_6H_5CH{=}\overset{}{C}CHO$ (b) $C_6H_5CH{=}\overset{\overset{\displaystyle O}{\|}}{C}CCH_2CH_3$
$\qquad\qquad\quad\underset{\underset{\displaystyle CH_2CH_3}{|}}{}\qquad\qquad\qquad\underset{\underset{\displaystyle CH_3}{|}}{}$

14.19 (a) $C_6H_5CHO + CH_3CH_2CHO \xrightarrow{\;OH^-\;}$

(b) $CH_3\overset{\overset{\displaystyle O}{\|}}{C}(CH_2)_4\overset{\overset{\displaystyle O}{\|}}{C}CH_3 \xrightarrow[\text{(2) } H^+,\,\text{heat}]{\text{(1) } OH^-}$

(c) 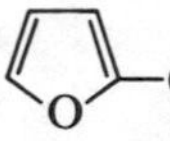 $-CHO + CH_3CHO \xrightarrow{\;OH^-\;}$

(d) $OHC(CH_2)_5CHO \xrightarrow{\;OH^-\;}$

14.20 (a) $(CH_3CH_2)_2C{=}O + \underset{\underset{\displaystyle CO_2C_2H_5}{|}}{CH_2CN} \xrightarrow[\text{heat}]{\overset{\displaystyle NH_4O_2CCH_3}{CH_3CO_2H}}$

(b) 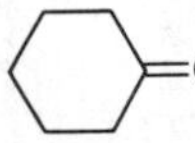 ${=}O + CH_2(CN)_2 \xrightarrow[\text{heat}]{\overset{\displaystyle NH_4O_2CCH_3}{CH_3CO_2H}}$

14.21 (a) $C_6H_5CH_2\overset{\overset{\displaystyle O}{\|}}{C}\overset{}{C}HCO_2C_2H_5;$ (b) $C_6H_5CH_2\overset{\overset{\displaystyle O}{\|}}{C}CH_2C_6H_5$
$\qquad\qquad\qquad\underset{\underset{\displaystyle C_6H_5}{|}}{}$

14.22 (a)

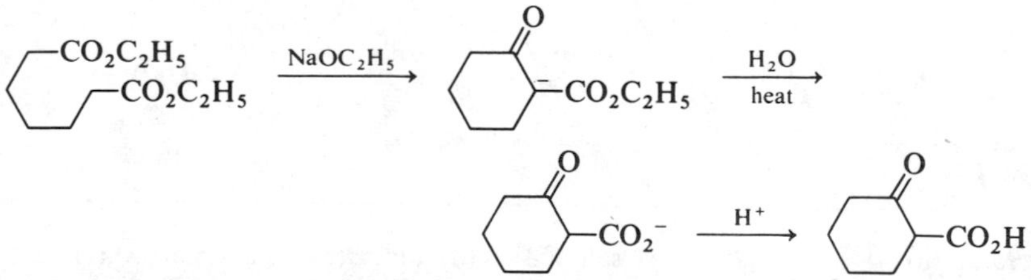

(b)

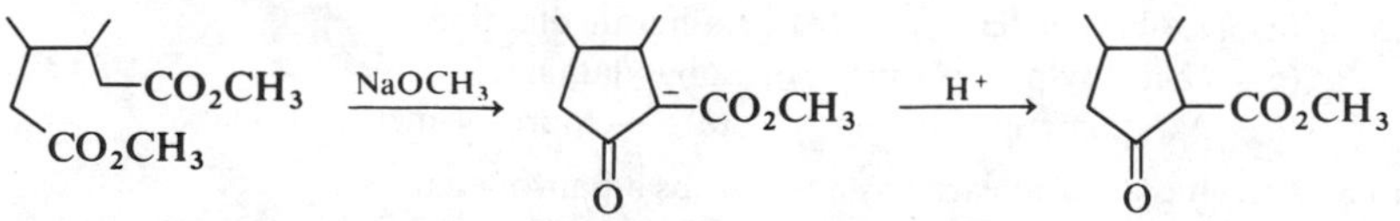

14.23 (a) $C_2H_5O_2\overset{\overset{\displaystyle O}{\|}}{C}CH_2CO_2C_2H_5$ (b)

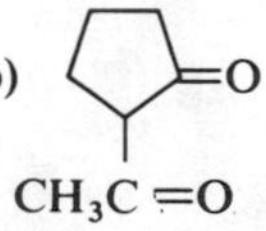

14.24 (a)

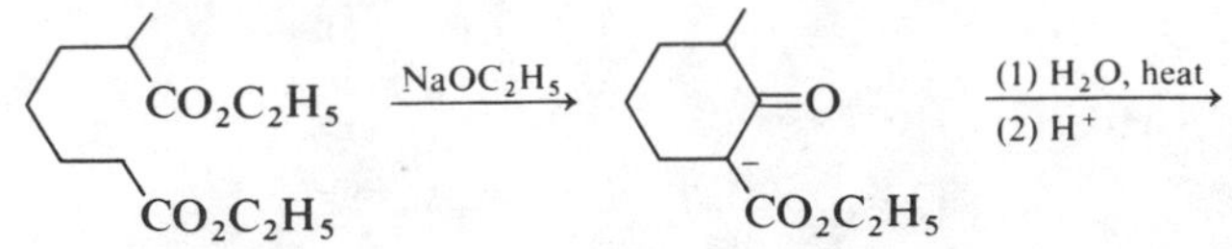

$\xrightarrow{\text{NaOC}_2\text{H}_5}$

$\xrightarrow[\text{(2) H}^+]{\text{(1) H}_2\text{O, heat}}$

(b) $C_6H_5CO_2C_2H_5 + CH_3CO_2C_2H_5 \xrightarrow{\text{NaOC}_2\text{H}_5} C_6H_5\overset{\text{O}}{\overset{\|}{C}}CHCO_2C_2H_5 \xrightarrow[\text{(2) H}^+]{\text{(1) H}_2\text{O, heat}}$

(c) $C_6H_5CO_2C_2H_5 + CH_2(CN)_2 \xrightarrow[\text{(2) H}^+]{\text{(1) NaOC}_2\text{H}_5}$

(d) $(CH_3)_3CCO_2C_2H_5 + CH_3\overset{\text{O}}{\overset{\|}{C}}CH_3 \xrightarrow[\text{(2) H}^+]{\text{(1) NaOC}_2\text{H}_5}$

14.25 $2\,CH_3\overset{\text{O}}{\overset{\|}{C}}SCoA \longrightarrow CH_3\overset{\text{O}}{\overset{\|}{C}}CH_2\overset{\text{O}}{\overset{\|}{C}}SCoA + HSCoA$

$\overset{\uparrow}{acidic}$

14.26

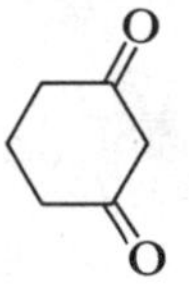

14.27 (a) $CH_3CH(CO_2C_2H_5)_2 + CH_3CH_2CH{=}CHCO_2C_2H_5 \xrightarrow{\text{NaOC}_2\text{H}_5}$

$$CH_2CH_2\underset{\underset{CH_3C(CO_2C_2H_5)_2}{|}}{CH}CH_2CO_2C_2H_5 \xrightarrow[\text{(2) H}^+]{\text{(1) H}_2\text{O, heat}}$$

(b) $CH_2(CO_2C_2H_5)_2 + CH_3CH{=}CHCO_2C_2H_5 \xrightarrow{\text{NaOC}_2\text{H}_5}$

$$CH_3\underset{\underset{^-C(CO_2C_2H_5)_2}{|}}{CH}CH_2CO_2C_2H_5 \xrightarrow[\text{heat}]{\text{H}_2\text{O, H}^+}$$

(c)

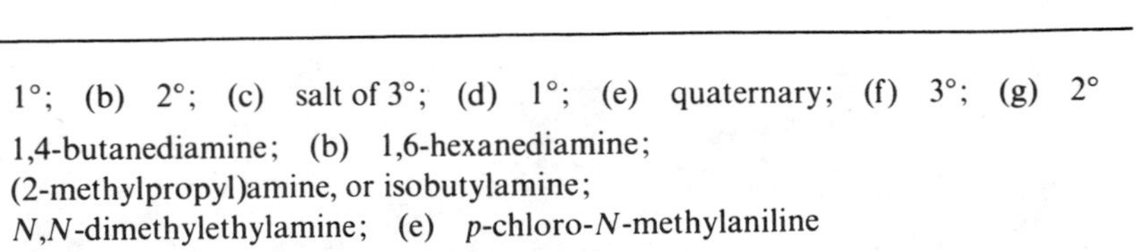

$+ CH_2(CO_2C_2H_5)_2 \xrightarrow{\text{NaOC}_2\text{H}_5}$ $\xrightarrow[\text{heat}]{\text{H}_2\text{O, H}^+}$

Chapter 15

15.1 (a) 1°; (b) 2°; (c) salt of 3°; (d) 1°; (e) quaternary; (f) 3°; (g) 2°

15.2 (a) 1,4-butanediamine; (b) 1,6-hexanediamine;
  (c) (2-methylpropyl)amine, or isobutylamine;
  (d) *N,N*-dimethylethylamine; (e) *p*-chloro-*N*-methylaniline

15.3 (d) has a chiral carbon and exists as a pair of enantiomers.

15.4 (a) $(CH_3)_2NH{-}{-}{-}\underset{H}{N}(CH_3)_2$

  (b) $(CH_3)_2NH{-}{-}{-}\underset{H}{N}(CH_3)_2$, $(CH_3)_2NH{-}{-}{-}OH_2$, $(CH_3)_2\underset{H}{N}{-}{-}{-}H_2O$,

  $H_2O{-}{-}{-}H_2O$

(c) none; (d)

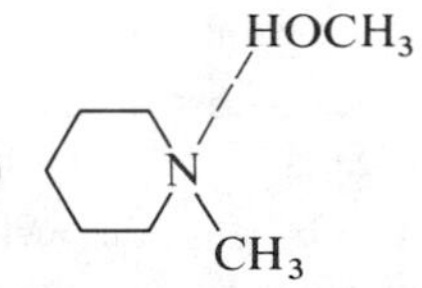

15.5

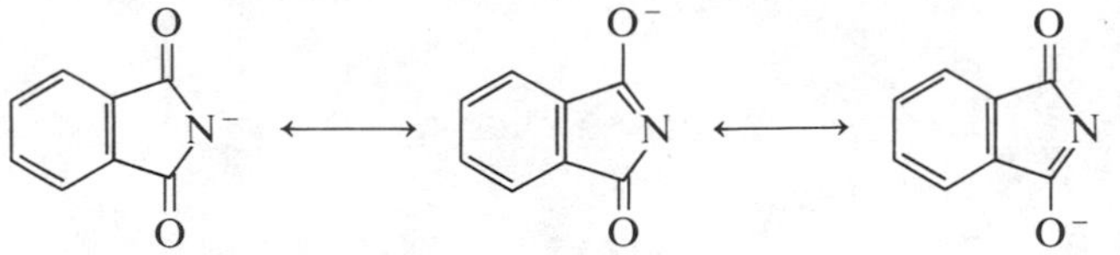

15.6 (a) (1) $CH_3CH_2CH_2Br$, (2) H_2O, OH^-
    (b) (1) $CH_2{=}CHCH_2Cl$, (2) H_2O, OH^-
    (c) (1) $C_6H_5CH_2Cl$, (2) H_2O, OH^-

15.7

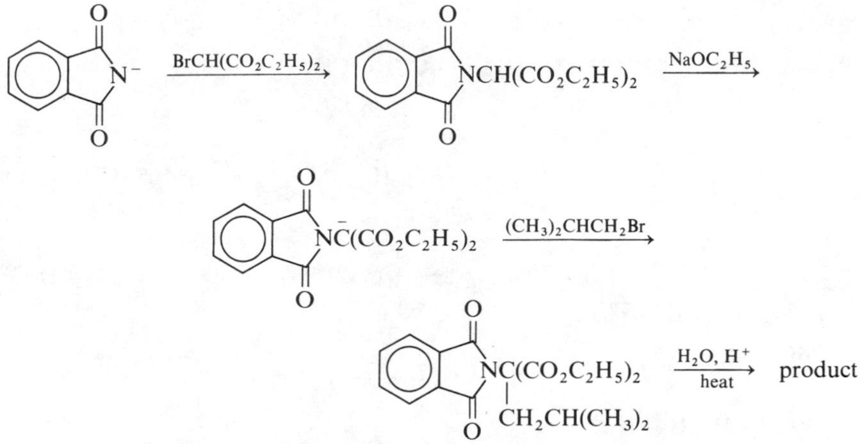

15.8 (a)

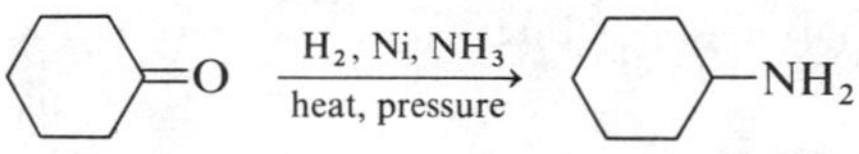

    (b) $BrCH_2CH_2CH{=}CH_2$ $\xrightarrow{KCN}$ $NCCH_2CH_2CH{=}CH_2$ $\xrightarrow[(2)\ H_2O]{(1)\ LiAlH_4}$

    (c) $C_6H_5\overset{O}{\overset{\|}{C}}N(CH_3)_2$ $\xrightarrow[(2)\ H_2O]{(1)\ LiAlH_4}$ $C_6H_5CH_2N(CH_3)_2$

15.9 (a) $CH_3CH_2\overset{O}{\overset{\|}{C}}CH_3$ $\xrightarrow[\text{heat, pressure}]{H_2,\ Ni,\ NH_3}$ $CH_3CH_2\overset{NH_2}{\overset{|}{C}HCH_3}$ ⟵

    (b)

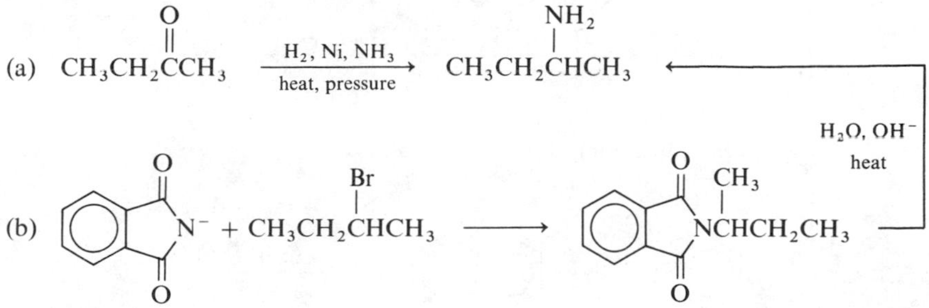

15.10 (a) 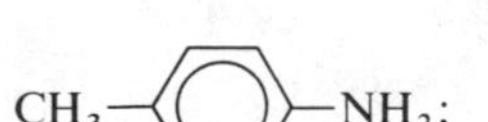 $CH_3{-}\bigcirc{-}NH_2$; (b) $(R)\text{-}C_6H_5CH_2\overset{CH_3}{\overset{|}{C}HNH_2}$;

    (c) $H_2NCH_2CH_2CH_2NH_2$

15.11 (a) methylamine; (b) piperidine; (c) piperazine

15.12 There is no conjugation between the nitrogen of benzylamine and the aromatic ring because the nitrogen is not attached to an sp^2 carbon, but to an sp^3 carbon.

15.13 *p*-Methylaniline is a stronger base than aniline because the methyl group is *electron-releasing*. *p*-Nitroaniline is a weaker base than aniline because the nitro group is *electron-withdrawing*.

15.14
$$\underset{\underset{CH_2CO_2H}{|}}{\overset{\overset{CH_2CO_2H}{|}}{HOCCO_2^{-}}}$$

15.15 $(R)(S)$-CH$_3$CH$_2\overset{\overset{CH_3}{|}}{CH}NH_2$ + $(2R,3S)$-HO$_2$CCH$-\overset{\overset{OH\;\;OH}{|\;\;\;|}}{C}HCO_2$H $\longrightarrow$

$$\underset{(R)}{CH_3CH_2\overset{\overset{CH_3}{|}}{CH}\overset{+}{N}H_3} \quad \underset{(2R,3S)}{{}^{-}O_2CCH-\overset{\overset{OH\;\;OH}{|\;\;\;|}}{C}HCO_2H} + \text{the } (S;2R,3S)\text{-diastereomer}$$

$(R; 2R,3S) \xrightarrow{OH^-} (R)$-CH$_3CH_2\overset{\overset{CH_3}{|}}{CH}NH_2$

$(S; 2R,3S) \xrightarrow{OH^-} (S)$-CH$_3CH_2\overset{\overset{CH_3}{|}}{CH}NH_2$

separate

15.16 CH$_3$CH$_2$CH$_2$CH$_2$NH$_2$

HONO / HCl   HONO / HCl

CH$_3$CH$_2$CH$_2$CH$_2-\overset{+}{N}\equiv$N

$\xrightarrow{-N_2}$ CH$_3$CH$_2$CH$_2$CH$_2$Cl

$\xrightarrow{-N_2}$ CH$_3$CH$_2$CH$_2$CH$_2\overset{+}{O}H_2 \xrightarrow{-H^+}$ CH$_3$CH$_2$CH$_2$CH$_2$OH

Cl$^-$ or H$_2$O

CH$_3$CH$_2\overset{\overset{H}{|}}{C}HCH$_2-\overset{+}{N}\equiv$N

$\xrightarrow{-N_2}$ CH$_3$CH$_2\overset{+}{C}HCH_3$

$\xrightarrow{-H^+}$ CH$_3$CH$=$CHCH$_3$ + CH$_3$CH$_2$CH$=$CH$_2$

$\xrightarrow{Cl^-}$ CH$_3$CH$_2$CHClCH$_3$

$\xrightarrow[-H^+]{H_2O}$ CH$_3$CH$_2\overset{\overset{}{}}{C}HCH_3$
                      $|$
                      OH

15.17 The benzenediazonium ion is resonance-stabilized.

15.18 (a)

NH$_2$ $\xrightarrow[0°]{HONO\;HCl}$ N$_2^+$ Cl$^-$ $\xrightarrow[heat]{CuCN}$

(b) CH$_3-$◯$-$NO$_2$ $\xrightarrow{Fe\;HCl}$ CH$_3-$◯$-$NH$_2$ $\xrightarrow[0°]{HONO\;HCl}$

CH$_3-$◯$-$N$_2^+$ Cl$^-$ $\xrightarrow[heat]{Cu_2Br_2}$

(c) C_6H_6 $\xrightarrow[\text{H}_2\text{SO}_4]{\text{HNO}_3}$ $C_6H_5NO_2$ $\xrightarrow[\text{HCl}]{\text{Fe}}$ $C_6H_5NH_2$ $\xrightarrow[0°]{\substack{\text{HONO}\\ \text{HCl}}}$

$C_6H_5N_2{}^+$ Cl^- $\xrightarrow[\text{(2) CH}_3\text{I}]{\text{(1) NaOH}}$ $C_6H_5OCH_3$ $\xrightarrow{C_6H_5N_2^+ \; Cl^-}$

15.19 (a) $(CH_3)_2CHN(CH_3)_2 + CH_2{=}CH_2 + H_2O$

(b) $C_6H_5CH{=}CH_2 + (CH_3)_2NCH_2CH_3 + H_2O$

15.20 (a)

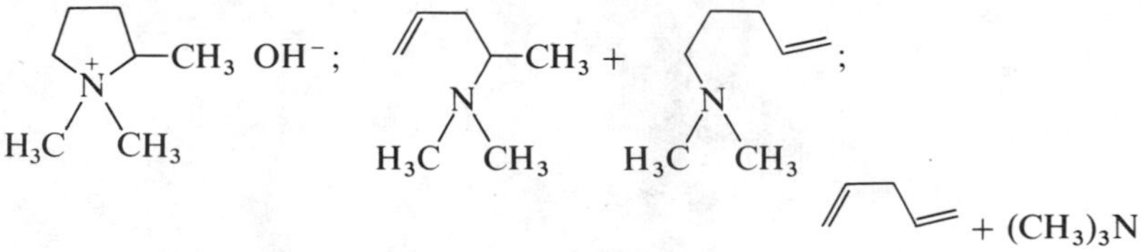

(b)

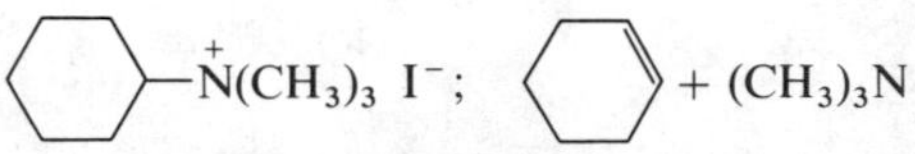

15.21

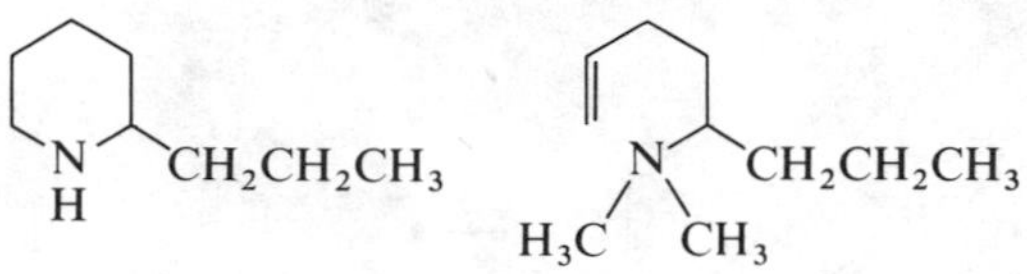

Chapter 16

16.1

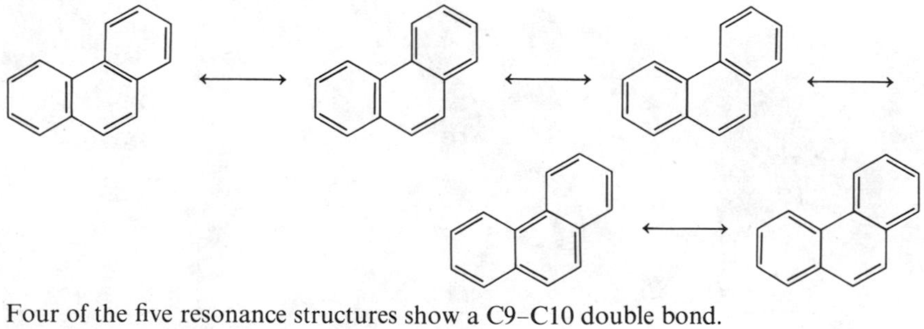

Four of the five resonance structures show a C9–C10 double bond.

16.2 electrophilic attack

16.3 (a)

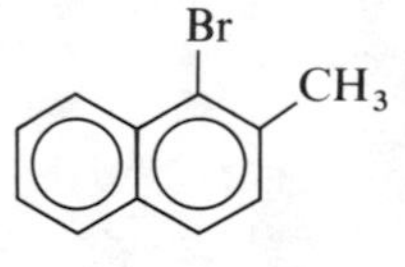

(b)

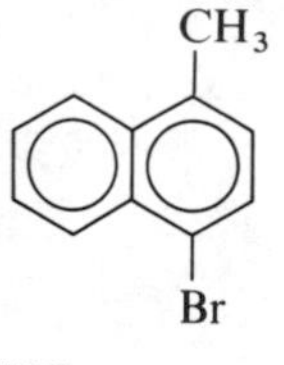

(c)

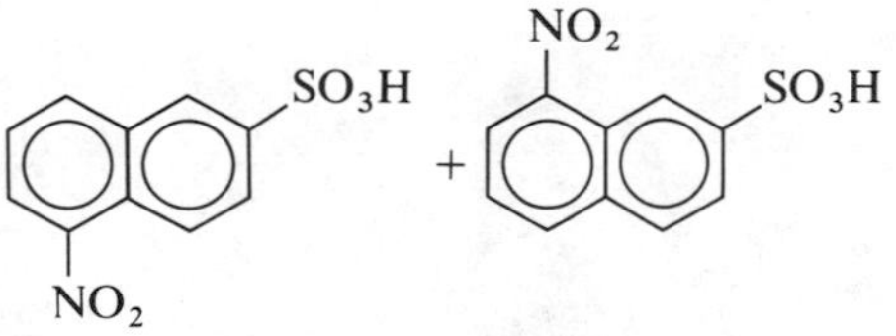

(d)

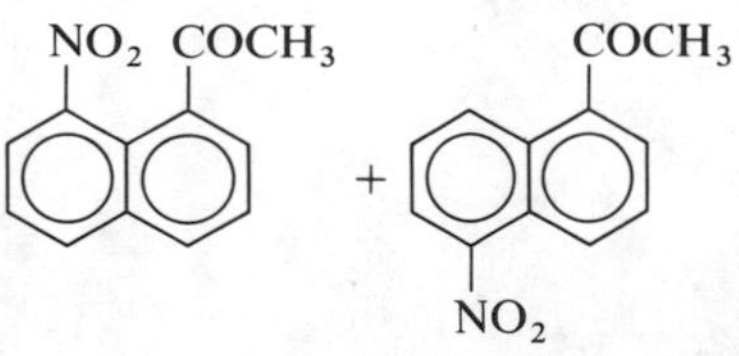

16.4

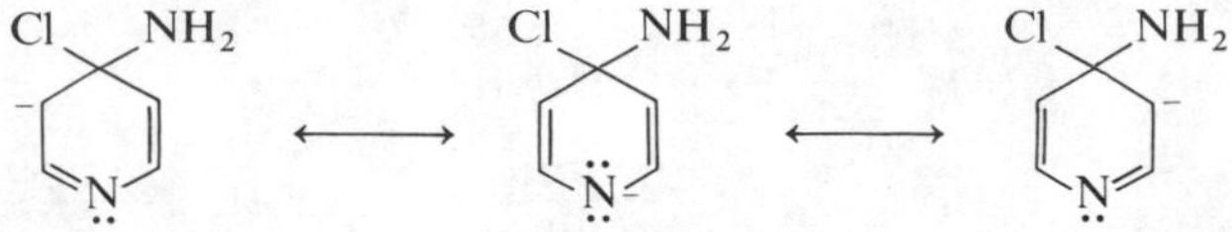

16.5

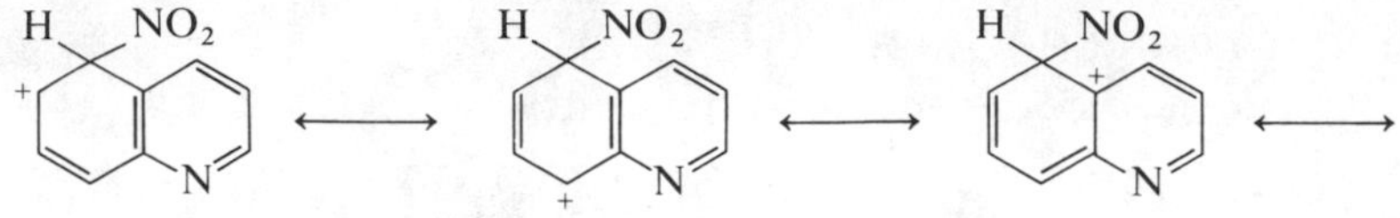

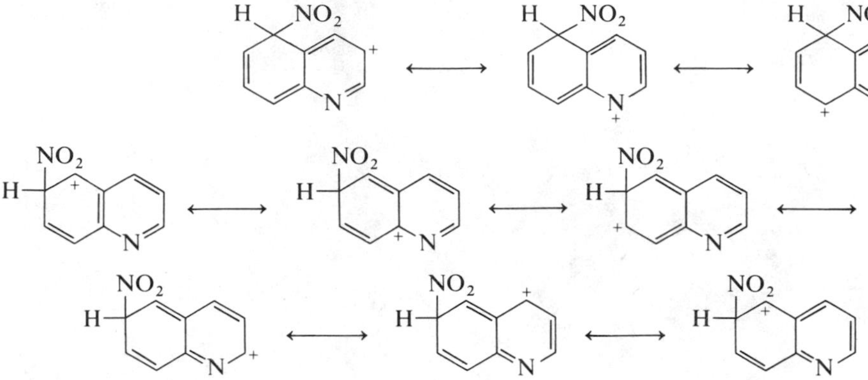

The 5-intermediate has three resonance structures with one aromatic ring, while the 6-intermediate has only two.

16.6

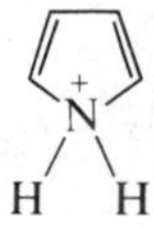

or sp^3 not aromatic

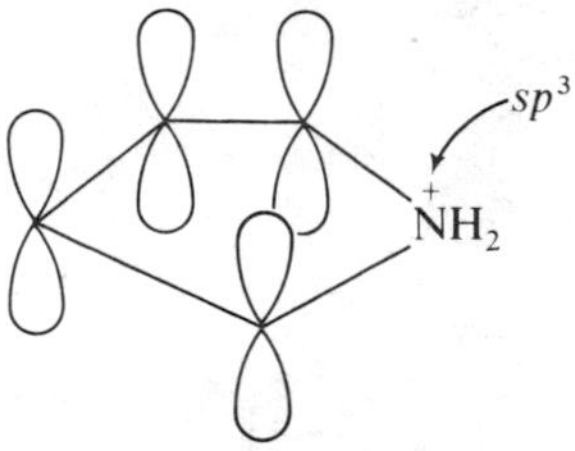

16.7 (a)

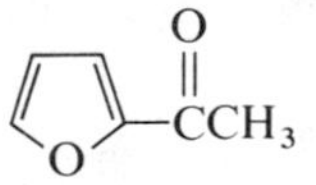

(b)

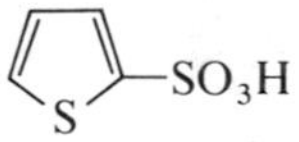

(c)

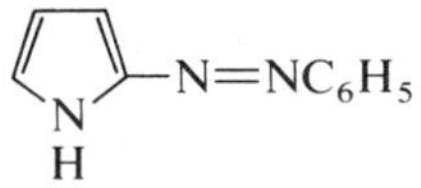

(d)

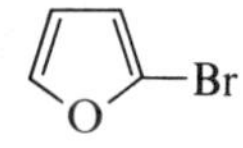

16.8

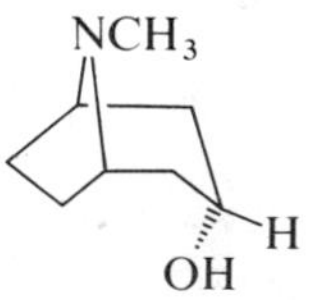

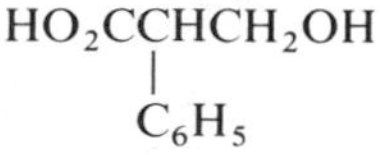

+ HO$_2$CCHCH$_2$OH

          |

          C$_6$H$_5$

tropine   tropic acid

16.9

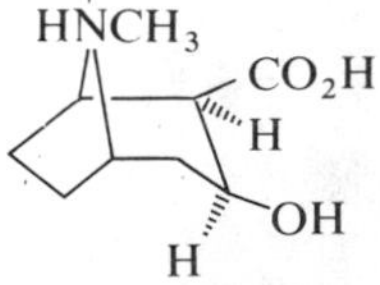

+ CH$_3$OH + C$_6$H$_5$CO$_2$H

16.10 The tertiary amine nitrogen (sp^3) is more basic than the sp^2 nitrogen in the quinoline ring.

16.11

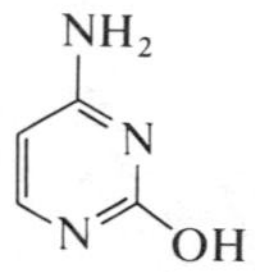

$$
\begin{array}{c}
NH_2 \\
\text{(pyrimidine ring with N, N, OH)}
\end{array}
$$

16.12

$$
O\text{- - -}H_2N
$$
$$
NH\text{- - -}N
$$
$$
\underset{H}{N}\quad O
$$
$$
\text{(purine ring: N, N, N, NH)}
$$

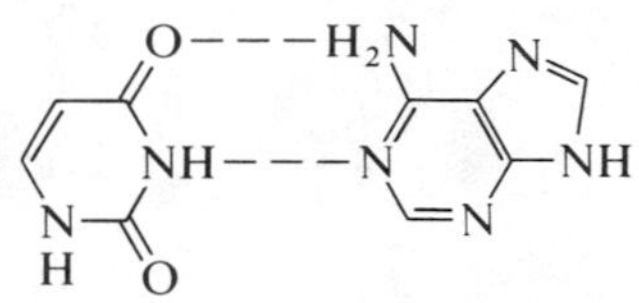

Chapter 17

17.1 (a) aldotetrose; (b) pentulose; (c) aldohexose

17.2 (a) (R) and D; (b) ($3S,4R$) and D

17.3 L-($+$)- and *meso*-tartaric acid

17.4 (a) four; (b) four; (c) three

17.5 (a) 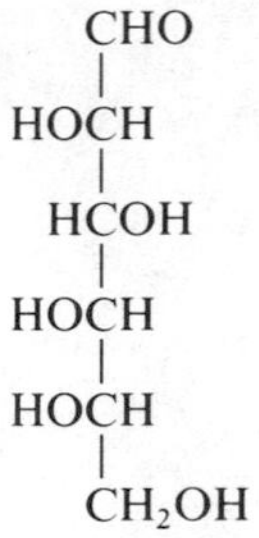
$$
\begin{array}{l}
CHO \\
HOCH \\
HCOH \\
HOCH \\
HOCH \\
CH_2OH
\end{array}
$$
(b) 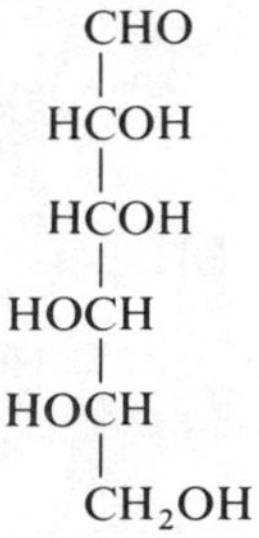
$$
\begin{array}{l}
CHO \\
HCOH \\
HCOH \\
HOCH \\
HOCH \\
CH_2OH
\end{array}
$$

17.6 L-idose

17.7
$$
\begin{array}{l}
CHO \\
CH_2 \\
HCOH \\
HCOH \\
CH_2OH
\end{array}
$$

$$
\begin{array}{l}
HCOH \\
CH_2 \\
HCOH \\
HC \\
CH_2OH
\end{array}\!\!O
\quad + \quad
\begin{array}{l}
HOCH \\
CH_2 \\
HCOH \\
HC \\
CH_2OH
\end{array}\!\!O
$$

$$
\begin{array}{l}
HCOH \\
CH_2 \\
HCOH \\
HCOH \\
CH_2
\end{array}\!\!O
\quad + \quad
\begin{array}{l}
HOCH \\
CH_2 \\
HCOH \\
HCOH \\
CH_2
\end{array}\!\!O
$$

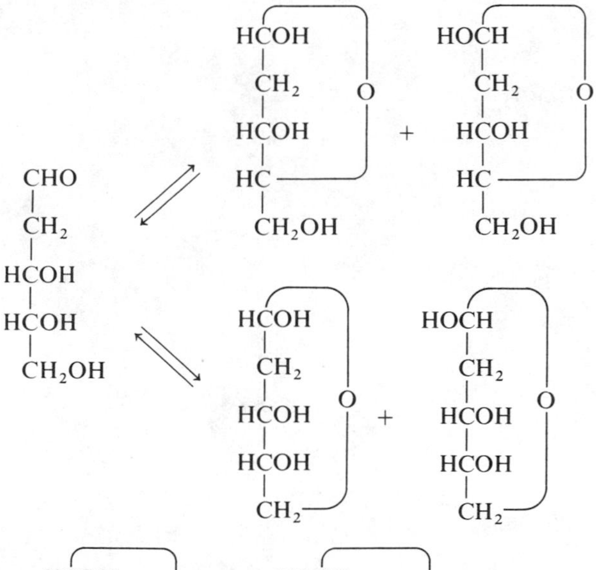

17.8 α:
$$
\begin{array}{l}
HCOH \\
HCOH \\
HCOH \\
HC \\
CH_2OH
\end{array}\!\!O
$$
β:
$$
\begin{array}{l}
HOCH \\
HCOH \\
HCOH \\
HC \\
CH_2OH
\end{array}\!\!O
$$

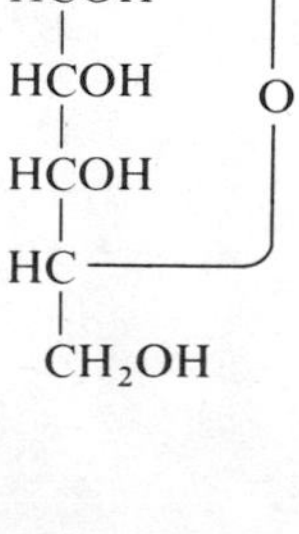

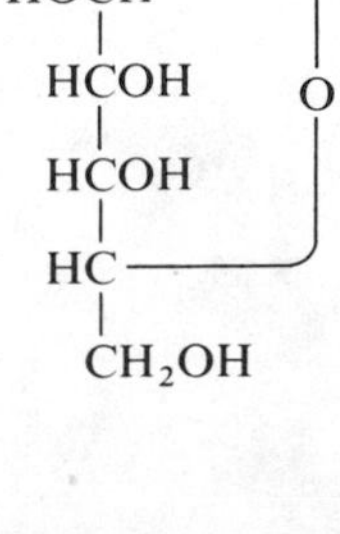

17.9

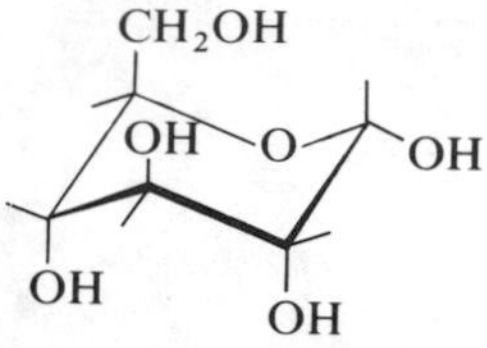

$$CH_2OH$$

(structure: pyranose ring with OH, O, OH, OH, OH substituents)

17.10 α:

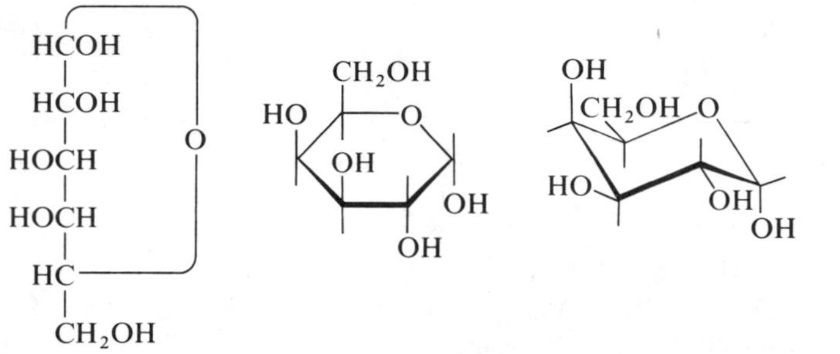

HCOH
HCOH
HOCH
HOCH
HC
CH$_2$OH
(with O bridge)

CH$_2$OH / HO / OH / OH / OH (pyranose)

OH / CH$_2$OH / O / HO / OH / OH (pyranose)

β:

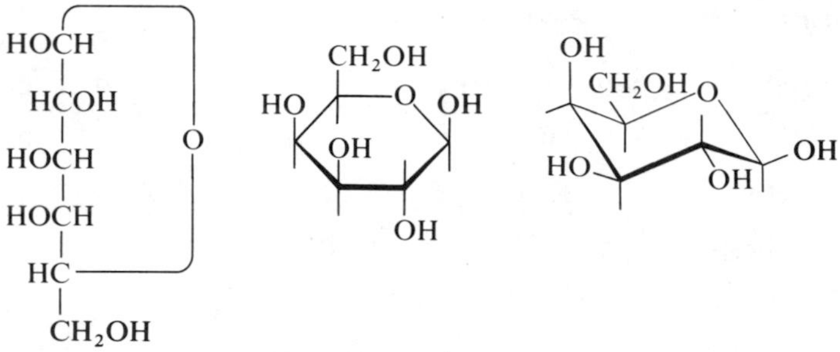

HOCH
HCOH
HOCH
HOCH
HC
CH$_2$OH
(with O bridge)

CH$_2$OH / HO / O / OH / OH / OH (pyranose)

OH / CH$_2$OH / O / HO / OH / OH / OH (pyranose)

17.11 (a)

CO$_2$H
HCOH
CH$_2$OH

(b) 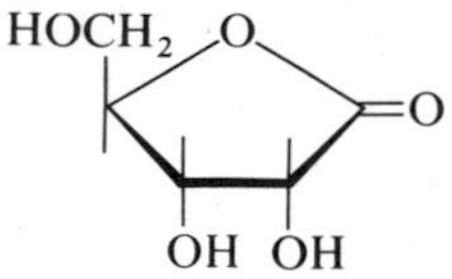 HOCH$_2$ / O / =O / OH OH (furanose lactone)

(c) none

(d) 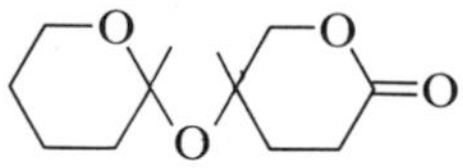 (spiro bicyclic structure with two O ring atoms, one ring bearing =O)

17.12 allose and galactose

17.13 (a)

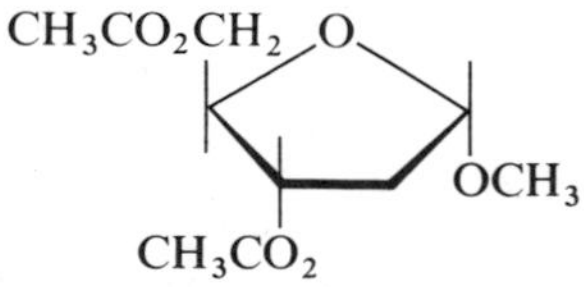

CH$_3$CO$_2$CH$_2$ / O / OCH$_3$ / CH$_3$CO$_2$ (furanose)

(b)

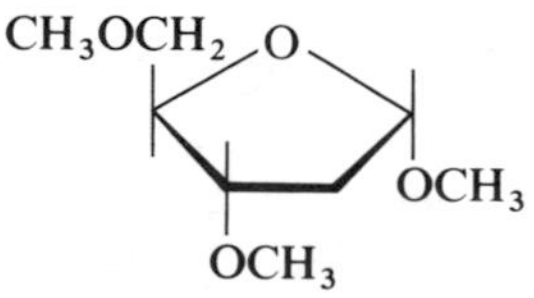

CH$_3$OCH$_2$ / O / OCH$_3$ / OCH$_3$ (furanose)

17.14

CO$_2$H	CO$_2$H	CO$_2$H	CO$_2$H
HCOCH$_3$ +	HCOCH$_3$ +	HCOCH$_3$	+ CH$_2$OCH$_3$
CO$_2$H	CH$_3$OCH	CH$_2$OCH$_3$	
	CO$_2$H		

17.15 α:

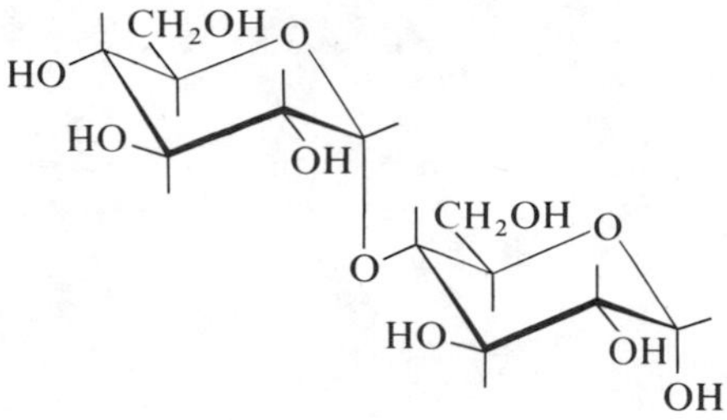

β:

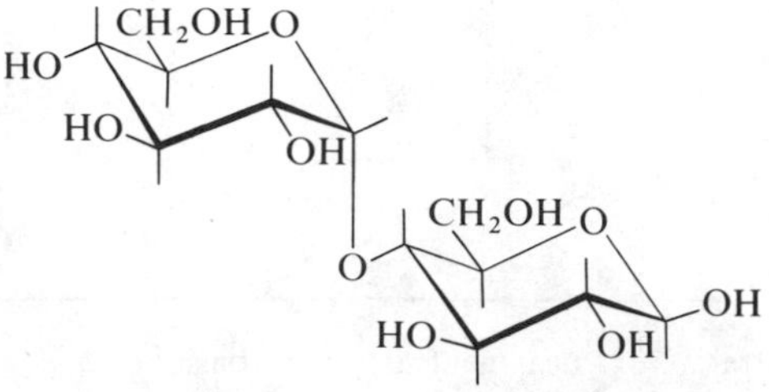

17.16 (a) 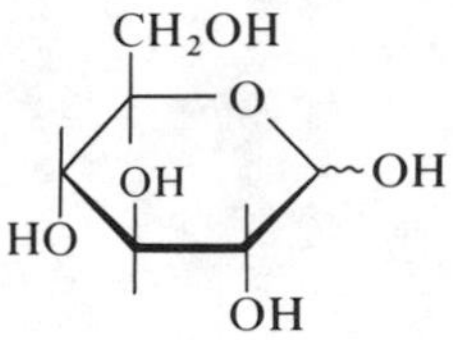 (b)

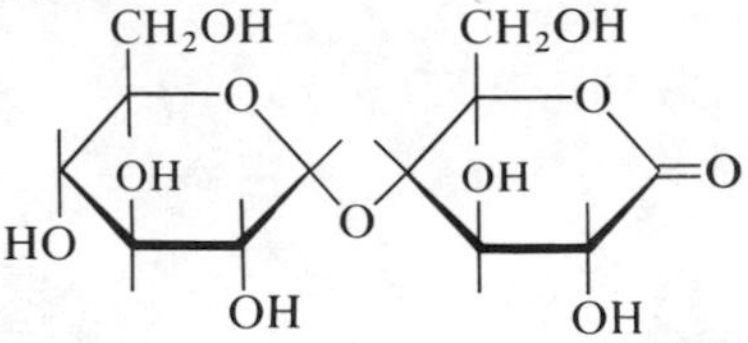

17.17 (a), (b), and (e):

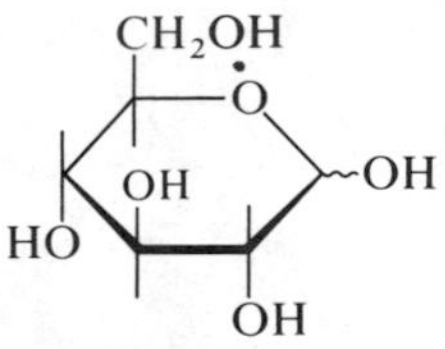

(c) 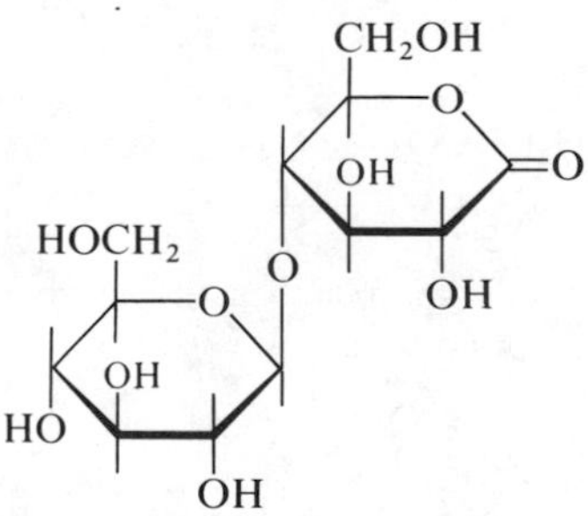 (d)

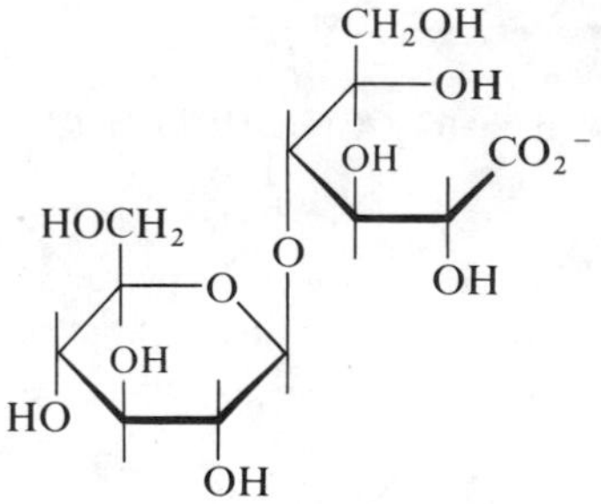

17.18 β-Cellobiose is more stable because each substituent on each ring is equatorial.

17.19 (a) 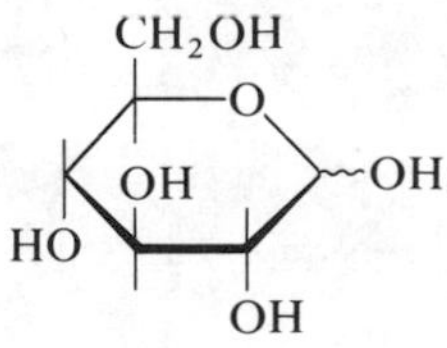 OH; (b) no reaction; (c) no reaction;

(d)

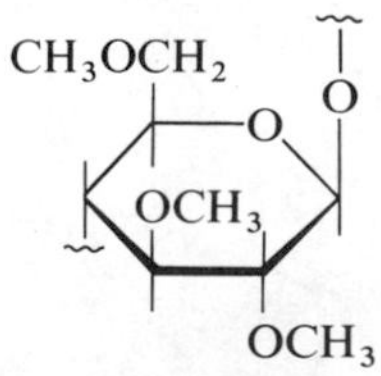

17.20 (a) 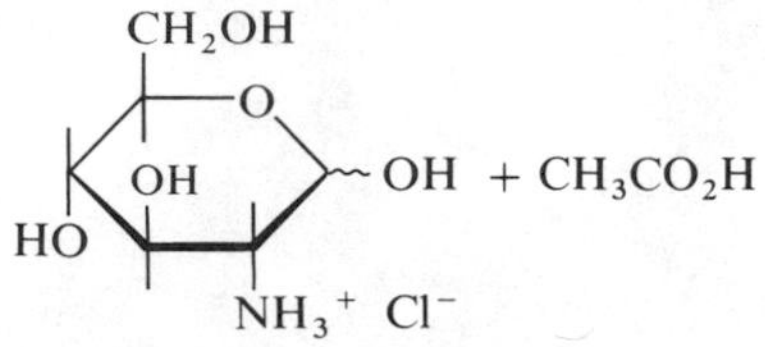 [structure: pyranose ring with CH$_2$OH, OH, HO, OH, NH$_3^+$ Cl$^-$] $+ CH_3CO_2H$

(b) 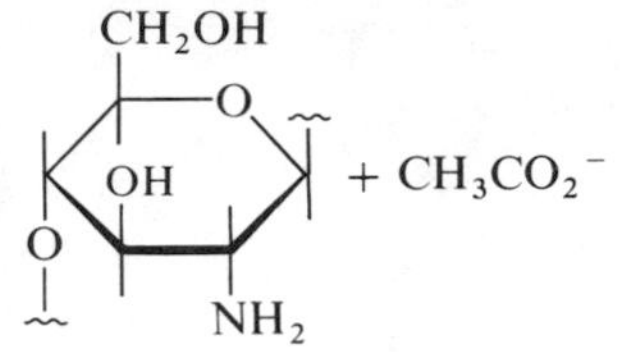 [structure: pyranose ring with CH$_2$OH, OH, O, NH$_2$] $+ CH_3CO_2^-$

Chapter 18

18.1 (a) acidic; (b) near-neutral; (c) near-neutral; (d) basic;
(e) near-neutral

18.2 $HO_2CCH_2CH_2CHCO_2^-$ Na^+
             |
            NH_2

18.3 (a) 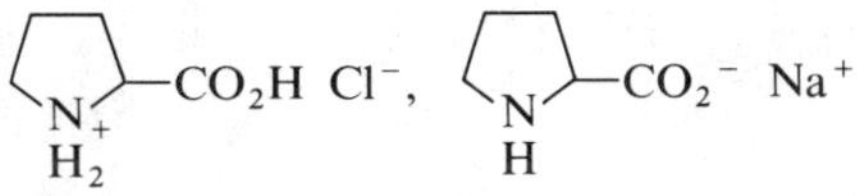 [pyrrolidine ring] $\overset{+}{N}H_2$—CO_2H Cl$^-$, [pyrrolidine ring] $\underset{H}{N}$—CO_2^- Na$^+$

(b) 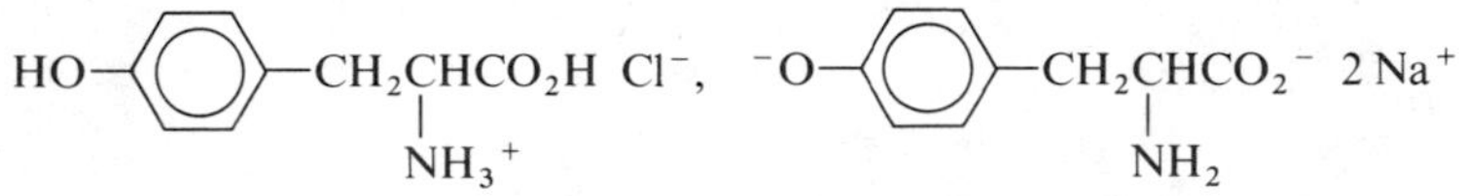 HO—⟨benzene⟩—CH_2CHCO_2H Cl$^-$, ^-O—⟨benzene⟩—$CH_2CHCO_2^-$ 2 Na$^+$
                                   | |
                                 NH_3^+ NH_2

(c) $HOCH_2CHCO_2H$ Cl$^-$, $HOCH_2CHCO_2^-$ Na$^+$
                   | |
                 NH_3^+ NH_2

(d) $HO_2CCH_2CHCO_2H$ Cl$^-$, $^-O_2CCH_2CHCO_2^-$ 2 Na$^+$
                     | |
                   NH_3^+ NH_2

18.4 Like the nitrogen in pyrrole, the nitrogen in tryptophan has no unshared bonding electrons; therefore, tryptophan is a neutral amino acid.

18.5 [series of resonance structures of a bis-indanedione imine anion system]

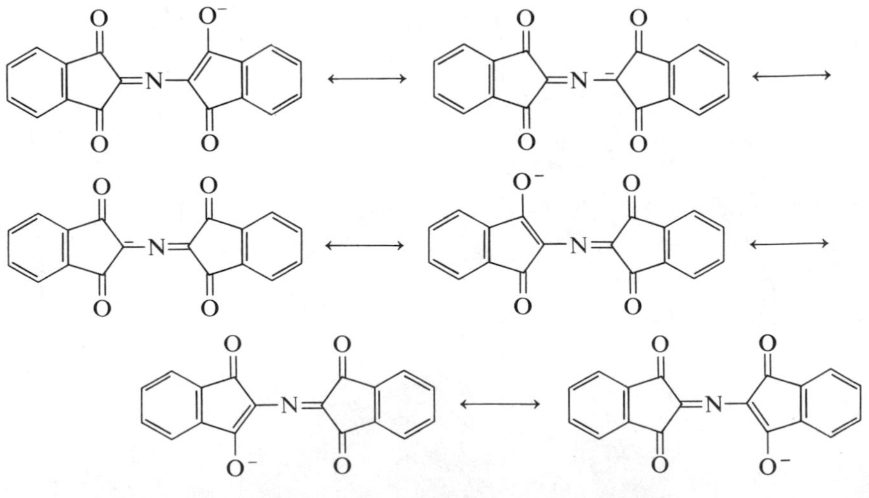

18.6 ala–gly–phe,   ala–phe–gly,   gly–phe–ala,   gly–ala–phe,
phe–ala–gly,   phe–gly–ala

18.7 $C_6H_5CH_2O\overset{O}{\overset{\|}{C}}-NHCH_2\overset{O}{\overset{\|}{C}}-NHCHCO_2H$ (with $CH_2C_6H_5$ substituent) $\xrightarrow{ClCO_2C_2H_5}$

$C_6H_5CH_2O\overset{O}{\overset{\|}{C}}-NHCH_2\overset{O}{\overset{\|}{C}}-NHCH\overset{O}{\overset{\|}{C}}OCO_2C_2H_5$ (with $CH_2C_6H_5$ substituent) $\xrightarrow{CH_3CH(NH_2)CO_2H}$

$C_6H_5CH_2O\overset{O}{\overset{\|}{C}}-NHCH_2\overset{O}{\overset{\|}{C}}-NHCH\overset{O}{\overset{\|}{C}}-NHCHCO_2H$ (with $CH_2C_6H_5$ and CH_3 substituents) $\xrightarrow{H_2,\ Pd}$ gly–phe–ala

18.8 (pyrrolidine ring, NH) $-\overset{O}{\overset{\|}{C}}-NHCHC(=O)-NHCH-\overset{O}{\overset{\|}{C}}NH_2$ (with CH_3 and $CH_2CH(CH_3)_2$ substituents)

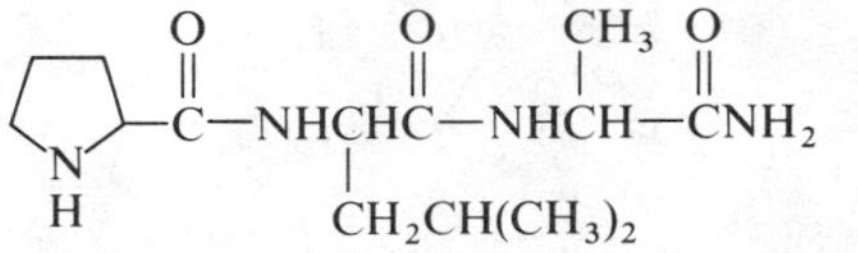

18.9 The enzyme catalyzes: (a) transfer of an acetyl group from one molecule to another;
(b) conversion of phenylalanine to tyrosine by hydroxylation of the benzene ring;
(c) dehydrogenation of an ester or a salt of pyruvic acid.

Chapter 19

19.1
$CH_2O_2C(CH_2)_7CH=CH(CH_2)_7CH_3$
$CHO_2C(CH_2)_7CH=CH(CH_2)_7CH_3$
$CH_2O_2C(CH_2)_7CH=CH(CH_2)_7CH_3$
$\xrightarrow[\text{heat, pressure}]{H_2,\ \text{catalyst}}$

CH_2OH
$CHOH$ $+\ 3\ CH_3(CH_2)_{16}CH_2OH$ $\xrightarrow{H_2SO_4}$ $CH_3(CH_2)_{16}CH_2OSO_3H$
CH_2OH

$\xrightarrow{NaOH}$ $CH_3(CH_2)_{16}CH_2OSO_3Na$

19.2 $CH_3(CH_2)_{12}CH=CHCHCHCH_2OH$ (with OH and NH_2 substituents)

19.3 (a) and (b): (cyclopentanedione with side chain to CO_2H and CO_2H) $+\ HO_2C\overset{O}{\overset{\|}{C}}$ (with chain)

19.4 (cyclohexane structures)

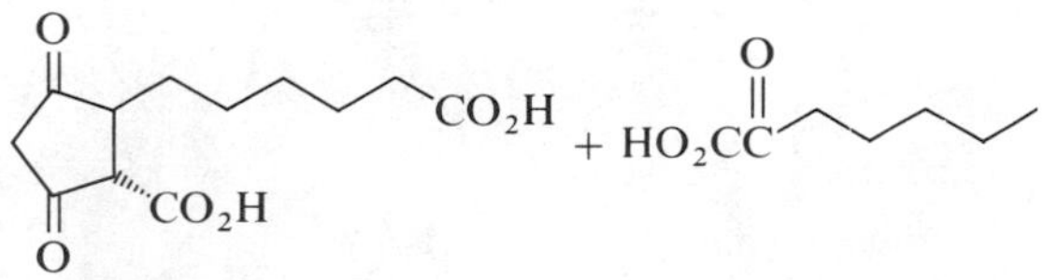

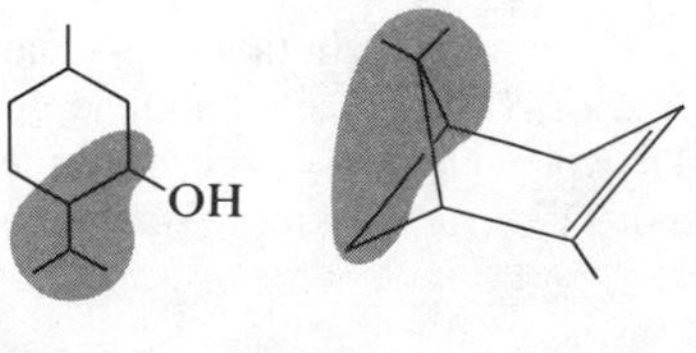

19.5 $CH_3(CH_2)_4\overset{O}{\overset{\|}{C}}CH_3$

19.6 (a)

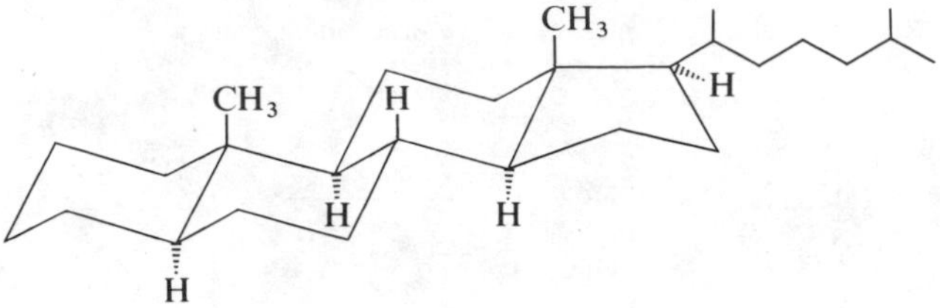

(b)

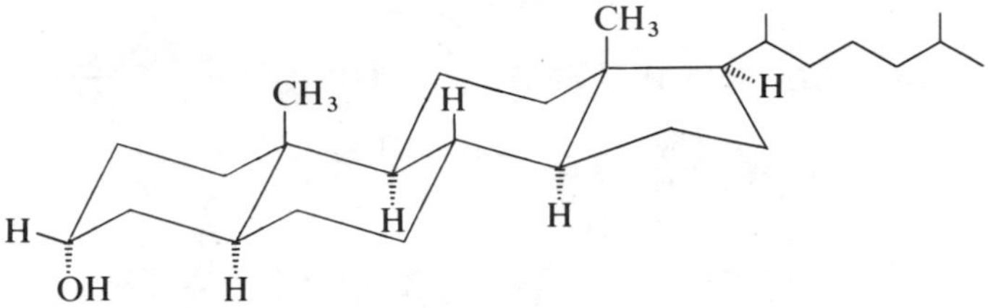

(c)

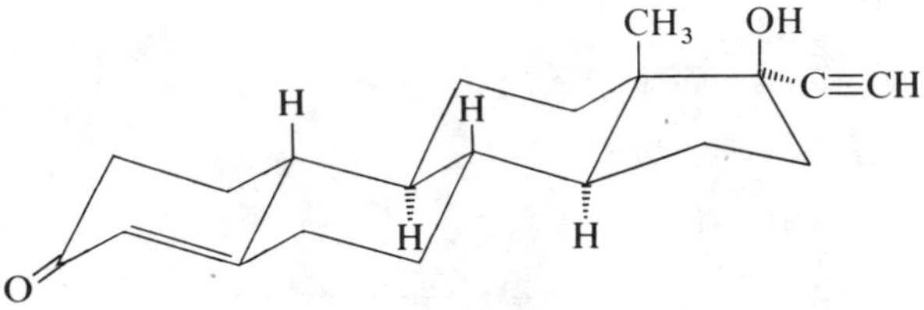

19.7 3β-Cholestanol is more stable because its OH is equatorial.

19.8 A/B, neither; B/C, *trans*; C/D, *trans*.

19.9 The steroid ring system is a large, hydrophobic end, while the glycine portion contains the hydrophilic $-CO_2^-$ Na^+.

Chapter 20

20.1 quinone   **20.2** (c), (b), (a)   **20.3** (b) 446 nm; (c) 416 nm

20.4 The entire ring system of coronene has 24 pi electrons (4*n*, and not 4*n* + 2). Therefore, not all the pi electrons are involved in the aromatic pi cloud. Chemists believe that only the peripheral carbons are part of the aromatic system.

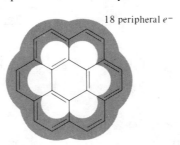

18 peripheral e^-

20.5 $\{-SO_3^-$ – – – $HO-\}$ and also $\{-NH_2$ – – – $O-\}$ and $\{-\underset{H_2}{N}$ – – – $HO-\}$
                                                   H

20.6 A compound that appears violet absorbs at a shorter wavelength (about 570 nm) than one that appears blue-green (about 600 nm), and therefore is the compound with less delocalization. The structure in (b), with only two $-N(CH_3)_2$ groups, has less delocalization and is the violet-colored compound. The structure in (a), therefore, is the blue-green compound.

20.7 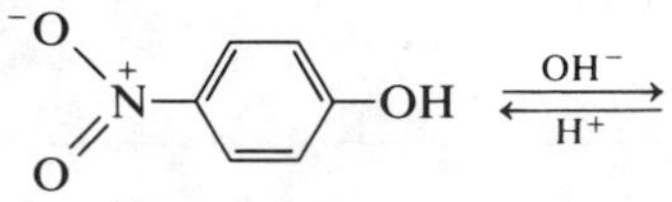

colorless at pH 5

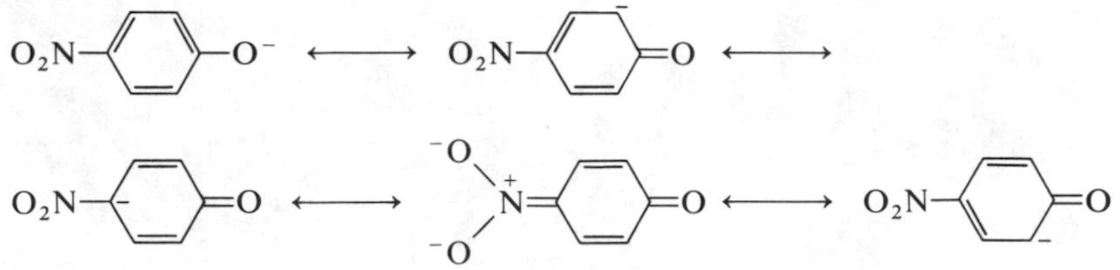

yellow at pH 8

20.8 (a) $[CH_4]^{+\cdot}$, ion-radical; (b) $[CH_3]^+$, cation;
(c) $[CH_2CH_2]^{+\cdot}$, ion-radical; (d) $[CH_2CH_2]^+$, cation

20.9 (a) $[CH_4]^{+\cdot}$; (b) $[CH_3CH_2CH_3]^{+\cdot}$

20.10 (a) 16; (b) 43; (c) 32; (d) 18

20.11 (a) 30; (b) 64; (c) 98; (d) 46; (e) 172

20.12 *B* contains Br, and *C* contains Cl.

20.13 $[CH_3CH_2CH]^{+\cdot}$ or, by rearrangement, $[CH_3CHCH_2]^{+\cdot}$

20.14 (a) $[CH_3CH(CH_3)CH_2CH_2CH_3]^{+\cdot} \longrightarrow [CH_3CH(CH_3)]^+ + [CH_2CH_2CH_3]^+ + [CH_3]^+ + [CH(CH_3)CH_2CH_2CH_3]^+$

(b) $[CH_3C(CH_3)_2CH_3]^{+\cdot} \longrightarrow [(CH_3)_3C]^+ + [CH_3]^+$

$[(CH_3)_3C]^+ \longrightarrow [(CH_3)_2C]^+$

20.15 $CH_3OCH_2CH_2CH_3$ **20.16** (a) 58; (b) 44; (c) 74

Index

Periodic Chart of the Elements

IA	IIA	IIIB	IVB	VB	VIB	VIIB	VIIIB	VIIIB	VIIIB	IB	IIB	IIIA	IVA	VA	VIA	VIIA	VIIIA
1 **H** 1.0080																	2 **He** 4.003
3 **Li** 6.940	4 **Be** 9.013											5 **B** 10.82	6 **C** 12.011	7 **N** 14.008	8 **O** 16.000	9 **F** 19.00	10 **Ne** 20.183
11 **Na** 22.991	12 **Mg** 24.32											13 **Al** 26.98	14 **Si** 28.09	15 **P** 30.975	16 **S** 32.066	17 **Cl** 35.457	18 **Ar** 39.944
19 **K** 39.100	20 **Ca** 40.08	21 **Sc** 44.96	22 **Ti** 47.90	23 **V** 50.95	24 **Cr** 52.01	25 **Mn** 54.94	26 **Fe** 55.85	27 **Co** 58.94	28 **Ni** 58.71	29 **Cu** 63.54	30 **Zn** 65.38	31 **Ga** 69.72	32 **Ge** 72.60	33 **As** 74.91	34 **Se** 78.96	35 **Br** 79.916	36 **Kr** 83.80
37 **Rb** 85.48	38 **Sr** 87.63	39 **Y** 88.92	40 **Zr** 91.22	41 **Nb** 92.91	42 **Mo** 95.95	43 **Tc** (99)	44 **Ru** 101.1	45 **Rh** 102.91	46 **Pd** 106.4	47 **Ag** 107.880	48 **Cd** 112.41	49 **In** 114.82	50 **Sn** 118.70	51 **Sb** 121.87	52 **Te** 127.61	53 **I** 126.91	54 **Xe** 131.30
55 **Cs** 132.91	56 **Ba** 137.36	57 ***La** 138.92	72 **Hf** 178.50	73 **Ta** 180.95	74 **W** 183.86	75 **Re** 186.22	76 **Os** 190.2	77 **Ir** 192.2	78 **Pt** 195.09	79 **Au** 197.0	80 **Hg** 200.61	81 **Tl** 204.39	82 **Pb** 207.21	83 **Bi** 209.00	84 **Po** (210)	85 **At** (210)	86 **Rn** (222)
87 **Fr** (223)	88 **Ra** (226)	89 **†Ac** (227)	104 **Ku** (261)	105 **Ha** (260)													

* Lanthanides

58 **Ce** 140.13	59 **Pr** 140.92	60 **Nd** 144.27	61 **Pm** (147)	62 **Sm** 150.35	63 **Eu** 152.0	64 **Gd** 157.26	65 **Tb** 158.93	66 **Dy** 162.51	67 **Ho** 164.94	68 **Er** 167.27	69 **Tm** 168.94	70 **Yb** 173.04	71 **Lu** 174.99

† Actinides

90 **Th** (232)	91 **Pa** (231)	92 **U** 238.07	93 **Np** (237)	94 **Pu** (242)	95 **Am** (243)	96 **Cm** (247)	97 **Bk** (249)	98 **Cf** (251)	99 **Es** (254)	100 **Fm** (253)	101 **Md** (256)	102 **No** (253)	103 **Lw** (257)